About Pearson

Pearson is the world's learning company, with presence across 70 countries worldwide. Our unique insights and world-class expertise comes from a long history of working closely with renowned teachers, authors and thought leaders, as a result of which, we have emerged as the preferred choice for millions of teachers and learners across the world.

We believe learning opens up opportunities, creates fulfilling careers and hence better lives. We hence collaborate with the best of minds to deliver you class-leading products, spread across the Higher Education and Test Preparation spectrum.

Superior learning experience and improved outcomes are at the heart of everything we do. This product is the result of one such effort.

Your feedback plays a critical role in the evolution of our products and you can contact us - reachus@pearson.com. We look forward to it.

CLASS

9

Trishna's

PEARSON IIT FOUNDATION

Mathematics

Thirteenth Edition

2025

Pearson

Photo Credits

Chapter 1 Opener: Dream01 / Shutterstock
Chapter 2 Opener: Chuhail / Shutterstock
Chapter 3 Opener: jupeart / Shutterstock
Chapter 4 Opener: petrroudny43 / Shutterstock
Chapter 5 Opener: benjaminec / 123RF
Chapter 6 Opener: HL Studios / Pearson Education Ltd
Chapter 7 Opener: Usman Saeed / Shutterstock
Chapter 8 Opener: marekuliasz / Shutterstock
Chapter 9 Opener: Gábor Páll / 123RF
Chapter 10 Opener: amasterphotographer / Shutterstock
Chapter 11 Opener: Radu Bercan / Shutterstock
Chapter 12 Opener: Margarita Vin / Shutterstock
Chapter 13 Opener: Leremy / Shutterstock
Chapter 14 Opener: Darren Whittingham / Shutterstock

ISBN 978-93-6159-574-5

First Impression

Published by Pearson India Education Services Pvt. Ltd, CIN: U72200TN2005PTC057128.
Head Office: 1st Floor, Berger Tower, Plot No. C-001A/2, Sector 16B, Noida - 201 301, Uttar Pradesh, India.
Registered Office: Featherlite, 'The Address' 5th Floor, Survey No 203/10B, 200 Ft MMRD Road, Zamin Pallavaram, Chennai – 600 044.
Website: in.pearson.com, Email: companysecretary.india@pearson.com

Compositor: Saksham Printographics, Delhi
Printed in India: Rahul Print O Pack

Brief Contents

Contents

Preface

"If you have a great ambition, take as big a step as possible in the direction of fulfilling it. The step may only be a tiny one, but trust that it may be the largest one possible for now.".

Mildred McAfee

The *Pearson IIT Foundation* Series has been created keeping in mind the learner's ambition to excel in a competitive examination like IIT-JEE. The series can be used in addition to the books being studied in school to attain that extra edge required to strengthen the concepts and prepare well for future endeavours.

Why Start Early with Pearson Foundation Series

Classes VI to X are the base years of a learner's academic life. In these years learner explore their interests and determine the goals they wish to attain. *Pearson IIT Foundation* series is filled with interactive learning that not only nurtures a learner's interest in science and mathematics but also strengthens their concepts.

The series uses real-life examples and application-based problems to teach theoretical concepts. The objective of this series is to help learners cultivate an analytical mind.

Most of the lessons to be learnt are introduced to the learners in the books for class VI. As they get promoted to higher classes, new topics are added to these lessons. This additive method helps the learners' span their learning over four standards, from VI-X. Thus, learners are not overwhelmed by the introduction of completely new lessons every time they are promoted to a new class.

While their learning is being spanned across five years, so is their ability to resolve doubts for further conceptual clarity. For instance, they can use concepts learnt in class VI to solve questions in class VII. If, in case, they get stuck while answering a question, the learners can infer for themselves that they might be lacking in conceptual clarity. They can then approach their teachers, requesting them to explain the concept once again. This helps the learner to clarify their concepts while revising the lessons previously learnt.

Since classes VI-X are deemed to be a student's formative years, we, at Pearson, aim to provide a foundation level course which serves more than just a standard curriculum.

Here is how it makes a difference to a learner's overall learning...

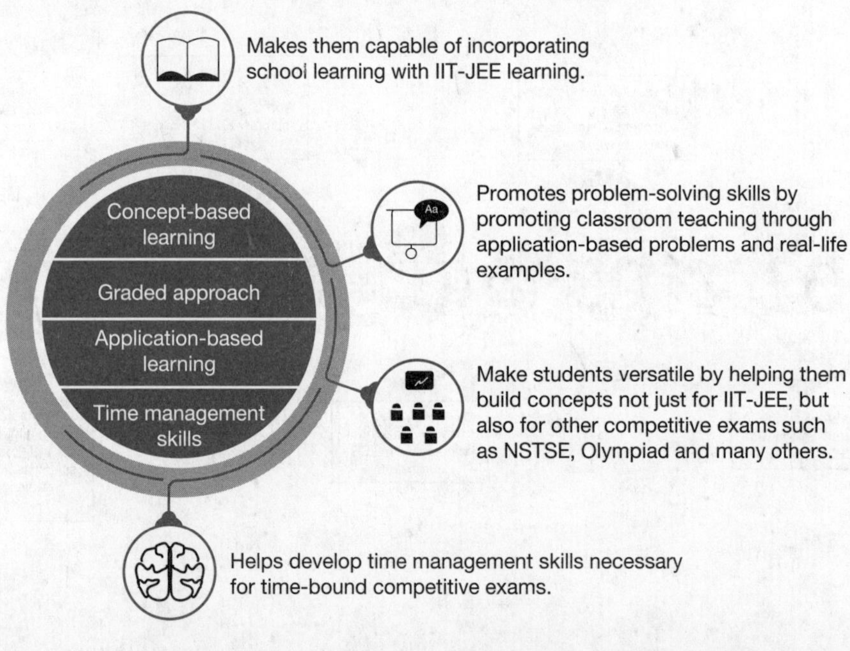

Other Uses of the Series

Instead of limiting themselves to IIT-JEE, a learner can also use this series to prepare for several other competitive examinations such as NSTSE, National and International Olympiads, NEET, BITSAT, etc. This series offers a level of concept learning that empowers learners to handle the challenging nature of questions posed in these examinations. Moreover, this will also allow the learners to have an early insight into their key strengths as well as improvement areas and help them work on themselves.

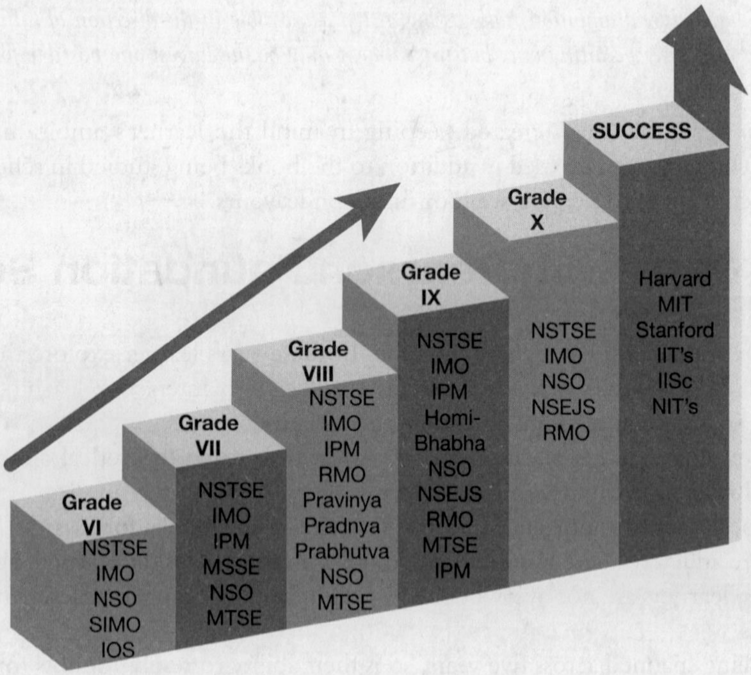

[IMO: International Mathematics Olympiad; NSO: National Science Olympiad, IOS: International Olympiad of Science, NSTSE: National Level Science Talent Search Examination, MTSE: Maharashtra Talent Search Examination, RMO: Regional Mathematical Olympiad, PPP: Pravinya Pradnya Prabhutva, NSEJS: National Standard Examination in Junior Science, IIT: Indian Institute of Technology, IISc: Indian Institute of Science, NIT: National Institute of Technology.]

Highlights of the Series

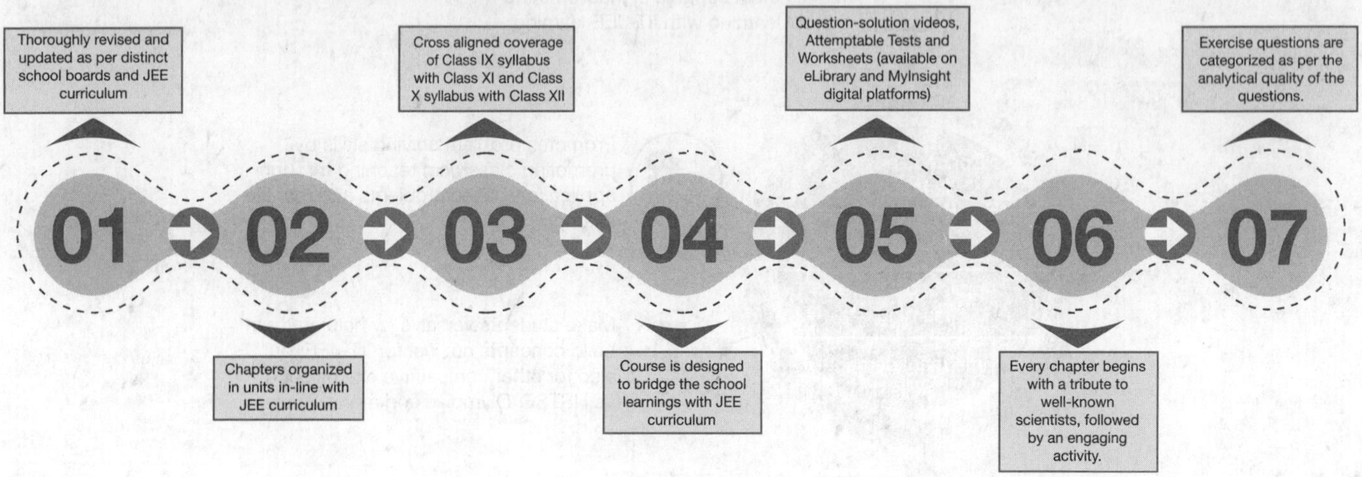

Pearson IIT Foundation series provides a perfect blend of learning through theory and practice questions with a fusion of school and JEE curriculum. It is imperative to note that this series would be as profound as you want it to be. Therefore, to get maximum benefit from this book, were commend following the given study plan.

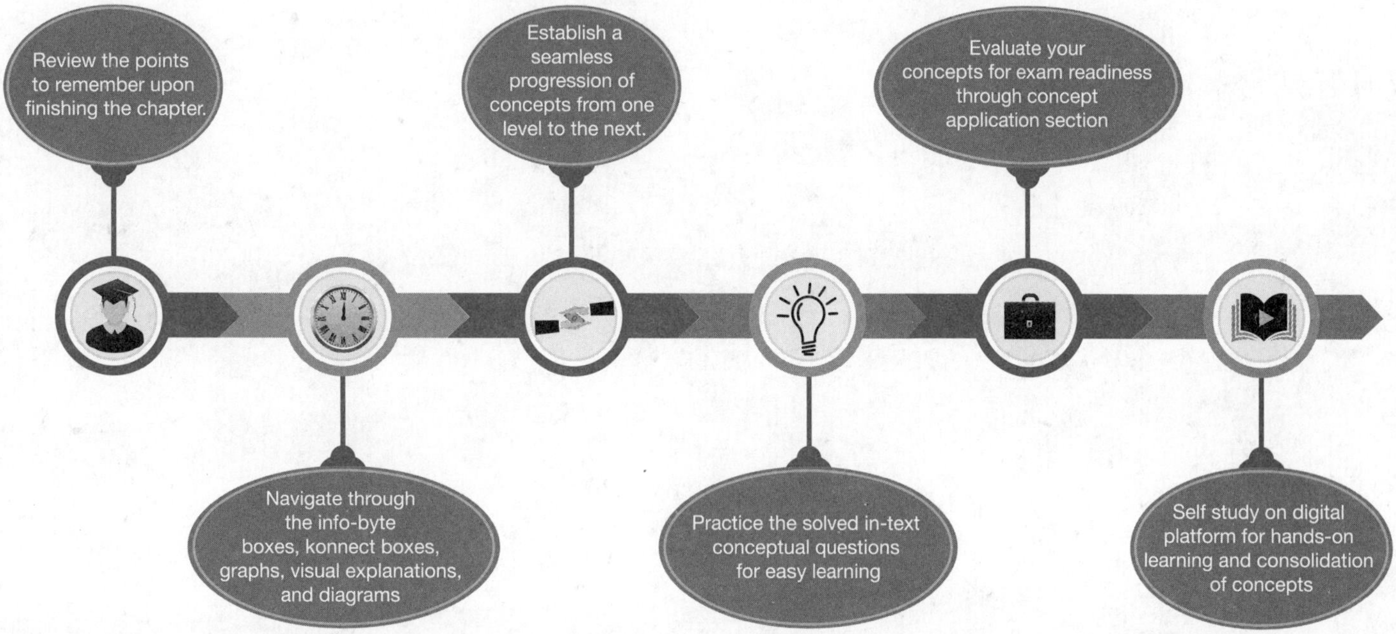

To provide a graded learning approach,the exercise part of each chapter is categorized by using four icons for question tagging. The question categorization helps the learners assess their own problem-solving and analytical skills and motivates them to improve to reach their objectives.

The following icons are used to categorize the questions with specific meanings:

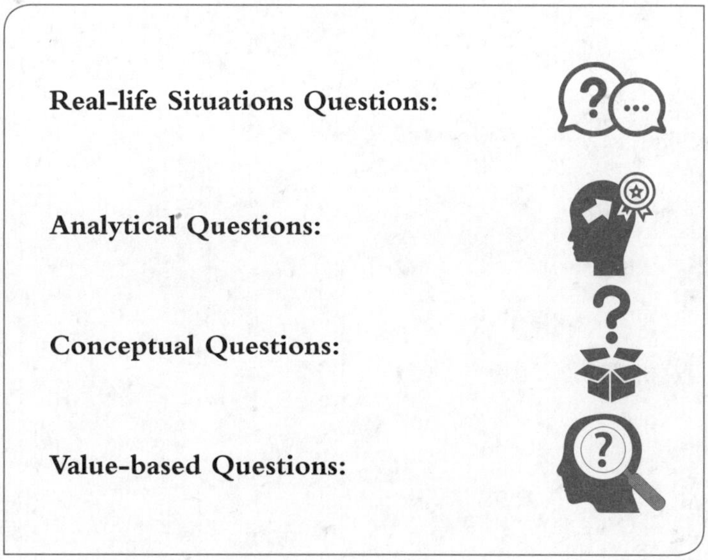

With this refined and well-tuned course from Pearson, students will become more confident when they enter the competitive world for actual IIT-JEE preparation. The effort put in today will transform into a valuable asset, contributing to success in future competitive examinations.

Chapter Insights

Remember

Before beginning this chapter, you should be able to:

- Know the natural numbers, whole numbers, and rational and irrational numbers.
- Apply mathematical operations on numbers.

Remember section will help them to memorize and review the previous learning on a particular topic

Key Ideas

After completing this chapter, you should be able to:

- Review natural numbers, whole numbers, integers, fractional numbers, decimals, rational and irrational numbers and properties

Key points will help the students to identify the essential points in a chapter

Scientific Crypt

A Tribute to Shakuntala Devi

Shakuntala Devi is an Indian mathematician. She was born on 4th November 1939in Bangalore. At the age of six, she demonstrated extraordinary skills of calculating and memorizing large numbers at the University of Mysore. In 1977, she calculated the 23rd root of a 201-digit number mentally. On June 18, 1980, she demonstrated her skills by multiplying two thirteen-digit numbers, given by the computer department of Imperial college in London, in 28 seconds. This particular feat found its way in the Guinness Book of World Records in the year 1995.

She wrote many books on mathematics. Some of her famous books are:

- Mathability: Awaken the Math Genius in your Child
- Puzzles to Puzzle You
- Book of Numbers
- Figuring : The Joy of Numbers
- In the Wonderland of Numbers

FUN TIME

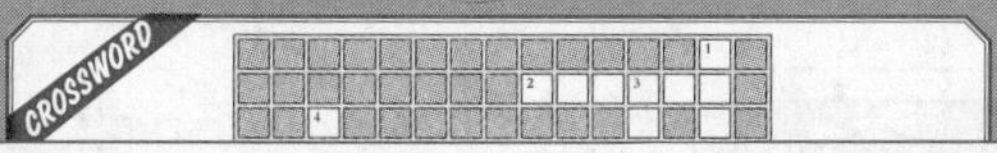

Scientific Crypt provides information about well-known scientists related to the chapter. The engaging activity is also given in the form of a crossword to keep the learners interested.

INTRODUCTION

In this chapter, we shall learn a comprehensive study of numbers including rational and irrational numbers (i.e., real numbers), and properties associated with them, representation of numbers on number line and concepts of HCF and LCM.

Introduction section helps to lay the foundation of the following chapter and leads the way for further learning

Representation of Numbers on the Number Line

We now learn the procedure of representing real numbers on the number line.

Representation of Natural Numbers

Draw a line. Mark a point on it which represents 0 (zero). Now, on the right-hand side of zero (0), mark points at equal intervals of length, as shown below.

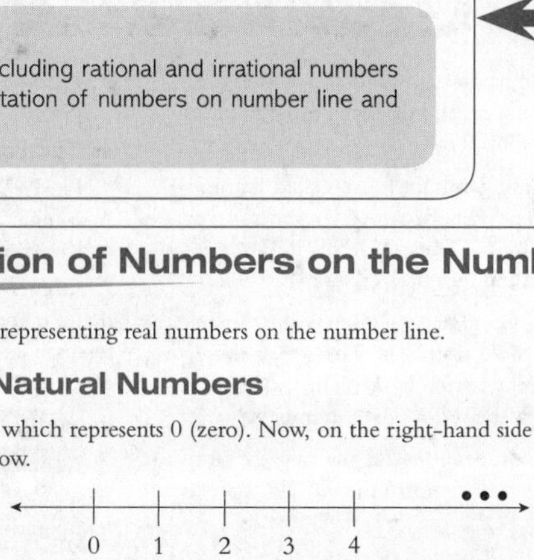

These points represent natural numbers 1, 2, 3…, respectively. The three dots on number line indicate the continuation of these numbers indefinitely.

Representation of Whole Numbers

Concepts are explained in a well-structured and lucid manner

Konnect boxes are some add-on information of related topic

Konnect

HCF of two relative primes is 1, because they do not have any factor in common other than 1.

Example: HCF of 12 and 13 is 1.

Info Bytes!

The real number system is vast. It includes natural numbers, whole numbers, integers, rational numbers, and irrational numbers.

Info bytes are interesting trivia and facts that engage young minds and keep the grey cells ticking!

Examples are given in the form of in-text exercises to reinforce the concepts learnt in a particular chapter

EXAMPLE 1.13 Find the GCD of 72 and 60.

SOLUTION

The set of factors of 72 = {1, 2, 3, 4, 6, 8, 9, 12, 18, 24, 36, 72}

The set of factors of 60 = {1, 2, 3, 4, 5, 6, 10, 12, 15, 20, 30, 60}

The set of common factors for 72 and 60 = {1, 2, 3, 4, 6, 12}

The greatest factor in this set is 12.

∴ The GCD (or) HCF for 72 and 60 is 12.

Illustrative examples solved in a logical and step-wise manner

POINTS TO REMEMBER

✔ Rational and irrational numbers together are called real numbers and the set of real numbers is represented by R.

✔ All the counting numbers are called natural numbers. The set of these numbers are represented by N. Thus, $N = \{1, 2,3, \ldots\}$ is the set of natural numbers.

✔ All counting numbers together with 0 form the set of whole numbers. The set of these numbers is represented by W. Thus, $W = \{0, 1, 2, 3, \ldots\}$ is the set of whole numbers.

✔ All natural numbers, 0, and the negatives of all counting numbers form the set of integers. Thus, $Z = \{\ldots, -3, -2, -1, 0, 1, 2, 3, \ldots\}$ is the set of integers.

✔ Properties of Integers

1. The number that is exactly opposite in sign to an integer m and equidistant from

3. Product of two negative integers is a positive integer.
4. The product of a positive integer and a negative integer is a negative integer.

✔ A number a/b, where a, b are integers, $b \neq 0$, and a is not divisible by b is called a fraction.

✔ A number of the form p/q, where $q \neq 0$, and p and q are integers and p/q are in the lowest terms, i.e., p and q have no common factor other than 1, is called a rational number.

✔ Properties of Rational Numbers

1. *Closure property*: If $x, y \in P$ and $x * y \in P$, then we say P is closed under the operation $*$.
2. Commutative property: If $x, y \in P$ and $x * y = y * x$, then P is commutative under the operation $*$.
3. *Associative property*: If $x * (y * z) = (x * y)$

Points to remember summarises the concepts and topics presented in each chapter

PRACTICE QUESTIONS CLASSROOM WING

Very Short Answer Type Questions

Directions for questions 1 to 14:
Fill in the blanks.

1. The product of two positive integers and eight negative integers is a __________.
2. The greatest common factor of relatively prime numbers is __________.

12. If $x = a^2 . b^3$, where a and b are prime factors of x, then number of factors of x is __________.
13. The units digit of the number 9^{26} is __________.
14. $\frac{\text{Dividend} - \text{Remainder}}{\text{Divisor}} =$ __________

Directions for questions 15 to 18:
…whether the following statements are true or

Short Answer Type Questions

26. How many prime numbers are there between 1 and 50?
27. Which of the following numbers are rational? Also, identify the irrational numbers.
(a) 0 (b) −1
(c) +1 (d) $\frac{3}{2}$

Essay Type Questions

41. Which of the following numbers: 7700, 3080, 5005, 3003; has two pairs of twin primes as their factors?
42. 984x6y is a six-digit number, which is a multiple of 9, and x and y are non-zero digits. Find the minimum

the sam… that 4 a…
43. Fi… siz…

Different typologies of questions have been included in the *Classroom Wing* which help students to develop the problem-solving skill

Competition Wing has been integrated chapter-wise in the exercise part to prepare students for various competitive examinations.

Graded as per complexity: Level 1; Level 2; and Level 3

PRACTICE QUESTIONS CLASSROOM WING

Very Short Answer Type Questions

Directions for questions 1 to 19:
Fill in the blanks.

1. $\sqrt{50.41} + \sqrt{34.81} =$ ______.
2. $\sqrt[3]{-4913} + \sqrt[3]{1728} =$ ______.
3. …

Level 2: Review your Concepts

39. The greatest five digit number exactly divisible by 9 and 13 is ______.
(a) 99,945 (b) 99,918
(c) 99,964 (d) 99,972
40. What is the multiplicative inverse of $a - \frac{1}{a}$?
(a) $a + \frac{1}{a}$ (b) $\frac{1}{a} - a$
(c) $\frac{a}{a-1}$ (d) $\frac{a}{a^2-1}$

47. The GCD … of division … respectively

Level 3: Assess Your Concepts

51. If $\sum_{k=4}^{143} \frac{1}{\sqrt{k} + \sqrt{k+1}} = a - \sqrt{b}$, then a and b, respectivel… are:
(a) 10 and 0 (b) −10 and 4
(c) 10 and 4 (d) −10 and 0
52. The surd $\frac{12}{3+\sqrt{5}+2\sqrt{2}}$, after rationalizing th… denominator becomes:

(B) Which of these surds is the biggest? $\sqrt{34}, 4\sqrt{2}, 2\sqrt{7}, 3\sqrt{5}$?
34. Find the positive square root of the following: $10 + 2\sqrt{6} + \sqrt{60} + 2\sqrt{10}$
35. If both a and b are rational numbers, find the values of a and b in the following equation:
36. Given $\sqrt{2} = 1.414, \sqrt{3} = 1.732, \sqrt{5} = 2.$… the value, correct to three decimals, of th… $\frac{1-\sqrt{3}}{\sqrt{5}-\sqrt{2}}$
37. (A) If $x = 3\sqrt{3} + \sqrt{26}$, find the value of

Essay Type Questions

38. If $x = \frac{1}{7+4\sqrt{3}}$ and $y = \frac{1}{7-4\sqrt{3}}$, find the value of $5x^2 - 7xy - 5y^2$.

62. The GCD of two numbers is 4 and their LCM is 400. How many pairs of values can the numbers assume?
(a) 1 (b) 2
(c) 3 (d) 4
63. The LCM of two numbers is 1024 and one of them is a prime number. Find their GCD.
(a) 3 (b) 2
(c) 5 (d) 7
64. Two groups consisting of 234 boys and 286 girls are to participate in a drill. In how many minimum rows can …

The icons are used for categorisation of the questions in Classroom Wing and Competition Wing

PRACTICE QUESTIONS JEE SPECIAL WING

Multiple-Answer Type Questions

Directions for questions 1 to 5:
Each question has FOUR options (a), (b), (c), and (d). ONE OR MORE THAN ONE of these four option(s) is/are the correct answer(s).

1. A certain sum doubles under simple interest. Which of the following is/are true about the given information?
   (a) Rate is $16\frac{2}{3}$% pa for 6 years.
   (b) Rate is 10% pa for 10 years.
   (c) Rate is $7\frac{1}{7}$% pa for 14 years.
   (d) Rate is 5% pa for 20 years.
2. A certain sum is invested at simple interest for 12 years at 7% pa. The interest for the first three years together is ₹3150. Which of the following is/are true about the
3. A certain sum is invested at compound interest. The interest amounts earned for the first year and for the first two years are ₹4200 and ₹8736 respectively. Which of the following is/are true about the given information?
   (a) The rate of interest will be 10% pa.
   (b) The sum invested will be ₹52,500.
   (c) The rate of interest will be 8% pa.
   (d) The sum invested will be ₹42,000.
4. The value of a piece land appreciates by 15% pa. The present value of the land is ₹50,00,000. Which of the following is/are true about the given information?
   (a) The value of the land after 1 year is ₹57,50,000.
   (b) The value of the land after 2 years is ₹66,12,500.
   (c) The value of the land after 3 years is ₹76,04,375

JEE Special Wing is curated specifically for targeted preparation of JEE examinations.

Hints and Explanations

Classroom Wing

Very Short Answer Type Questions

1. We know,
   - Product of two positive integers is positive i.e. ('+' * '+' = '+')
   - And product of two negative integers is also positive

8. GCD of a and b
   Based on theorem.
9. In the prime factorization method of finding LCM. LCM is given by the product of **the terms containing highest powers** of all the factors.

Hints and Explanations for key questions of classroom wing, competition wing and JEE special wing along with highlights on the common mistakes that students usually make in the examinations

Competition Wing

Level 1: Apply Your Concepts

1. $\sqrt{5}\times\sqrt{125}$
   $= \sqrt{5\times 125}$
   $= \sqrt{625}$
   $= 25$
2. $\frac{\sqrt{20}}{\sqrt{320}}$
   $= \frac{\sqrt{20}}{\sqrt{320}} = \sqrt{\frac{2}{32}} = \sqrt{\frac{1}{16}} =$
3. $\sqrt[3]{6}\times\sqrt[3]{6}\times\sqrt[3]{6}$
   $\sqrt[3]{6\times 6\times 6} = \sqrt[3]{216} = 6$
4. $\sqrt{3} \div 4\sqrt{12}$
   $\frac{\sqrt{3}}{4\sqrt{12}} = \frac{\sqrt{3}}{4\sqrt{4\times 3}} = \frac{1}{8}$
5. $\sqrt{7+\sqrt{48}} = \sqrt{x}+\sqrt{y}$ squarin

16. Convert the base into same number.
17. Substitute the values of p and q.
18. Apply laws of indices.
19. Recall the definitions of similar and dissimilar surds.
20. RF of $a-\sqrt{b}$ is $a+\sqrt{b}$.

JEE Special Wing

Multiple-Answer Type Questions

1. If a and b are rational numbers, then an *RF* of $\sqrt{a}-\sqrt{b}$ is $\sqrt{a}+\sqrt{b}$, since $\left(\sqrt{a}-\sqrt{b}\right)\left(\sqrt{a}+\sqrt{b}\right) = a-b$, which is a rational number.
   The multiples of $\sqrt{a}+\sqrt{b}$ are also *RFs* of $\sqrt{a}-\sqrt{b}$.
   Going by options, $\sqrt{3}+\sqrt{2}$ is a *RF* of $\sqrt{3}-\sqrt{2}$.
   Also, $\sqrt{12}+\sqrt{8} = \sqrt{4\times 3}+\sqrt{4\times 2} = 2(\sqrt{3}+\sqrt{2})$ is an *RF* of $\sqrt{3}-\sqrt{2}$.
   Hence, choice (a) and choice (c) are correct.
2. Given that $2187 \le 3^n < 59049$, where n is an integer.
   We know that: $3^7 = 2187$
   $3^8 = 6561$
   $3^9 = 19683$
   $3^{10} = 59049$
   So, the value of n can be 7, 8, or 9.
   Hence, choice (b), choice (c) and choice (d) are correct.

$= \sqrt{6+2-2\sqrt{6\times 2}}$
$= \sqrt{\left(\sqrt{6}-\sqrt{2}\right)^2} = \sqrt{6}-\sqrt{2}.$
So, $x = 6$ and $y = 2$.
Now, $x-y = 6-2 = 4$.
$\frac{x}{y} = \frac{6}{2} = 3.$
Hence, choice (b) and choice (c) are correct.

Match The Column

Common Solutions for questions 6 to 10:

Given that $A = \frac{1}{5-2\sqrt{6}}$, $B = \frac{1}{5+2\sqrt{6}}$ and $C = -10$.

6. $A+B = \frac{1}{5-2\sqrt{6}}+\frac{1}{5+2\sqrt{6}}$
   $= \frac{5+2\sqrt{6}+5-2\sqrt{6}}{\left(5-2\sqrt{6}\right)\left(5+2\sqrt{6}\right)}$

DW

WORKSHEET
CHAPTER 2: DYNAMICS

Directions for questions from 1 to 5:
Select the correct alternative from the following options.

1. A bullet of mass 100 g moving with a velocity of 100 m s^{-1} is stopped by a plank. If the bullet travels a distance of 10 cm in the plank before it comes to rest, find the average force exerted by the plank.
   (a) 100 N (b) 1000 N
   (c) 2500 N (d) 5000 N
2. Find the power developed by an engine in filling water of 2000 L from a well of depth 20 m in 20 s.
   (a) 6 kW (b) 20 kW

a rough surface, the total work done by the frictional force is zero.

8. The orbital velocity of a satellite is inversely proportional to the radius of the orbit.
9. When a stone is tied to a string and rotated in a circular path, the work done by the tension of the string is zero.
10. A satellite revolving in an orbit closer to the surface of the earth has more speed than one which is moving in an orbit of higher radius.

Directions for questions from 11 to 15:
Answer the following questions.

DW: Downloadable worksheets supplementing textual exercises for hand-on learning

AT

AI Assessments

What is the value of x in the following $(8^x)^3 = (3^x)^2$?

- 4
- 3
- 2
- 0

Questions 1 of 4

Next

AT: Attemptable Tests for assessing understanding of concepts and getting a clear picture of your exam readiness

19. A circle is inscribed in a square of side 7 cm. If we mark a point inside the square at random, then what is the probability that the point does not lie in the interior of the circle?

Video icon: Audio and visual learning to difficult questions for effective learning and retention

CHAPTER 1

Real Numbers

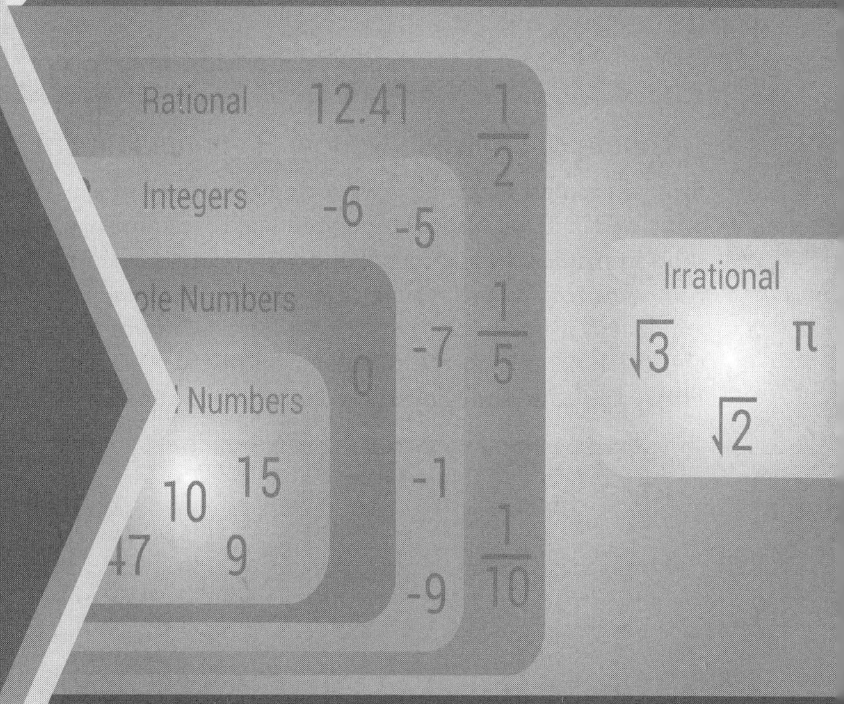

Remember

Before beginning this chapter, you should be able to:

- Represent numbers on number lines
- Obtain LCM and HCF of numbers
- Apply operations on integers, fractions, decimals, rational and irrational numbers

Key Ideas

After completing this chapter, you should be able to:

- Define the numbers and represent them on a number line
- State the properties of numbers
- Understand the basic concepts of radicals and the laws of radicals
- Describe the surd, types and order of the surd, its operations, combination, and conjugations
- Study rationalizing factor (RF) in surds
- Obtain square root of quadratic surds

Scientific Crypt

A Tribute to Srinivasa Iyengar Ramanujan (1887 to 1920)

Srinivasa Iyengar Ramanujan was an Indian mathematician who lived in Tamil Nadu. He demonstrated extraordinary skills in mathematics at school and won many accolades and awards. At the young age of 17, Ramanujan conducted mathematical research on Bernoulli numbers and the Euler-Mascheroni Constant on his own. Once, Hardy arrived at Ramanujan's residence in a car numbered 1729. Hardy commented that the number 1729 seemed to be unattractive. Then Ramanujan replied that it was actually a very interesting number mathematically, being the smallest natural number, which can be expressed as the sum of two perfect cubes in two ways i.e., $1729 = 1000 + 729 = (10)^3 + 9^3$ or $1728 + 1 = (12)^3 + 1^3$.

FUN TIME

CROSSWORD

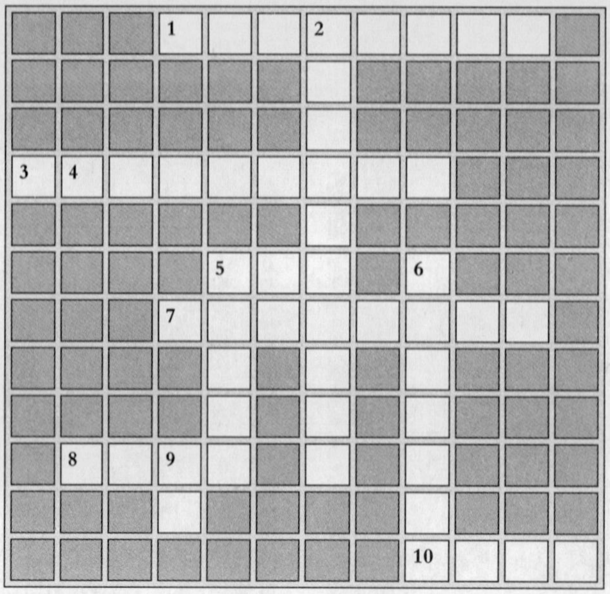

Across

1. The number of rational numbers between two irrational numbers.
3. If each of the product and the sum of two binomial mixed surds is rational, then each surd is said to be
7. A compound surd consisting of two surds.
8. The cube root of 9.
10. A number which is either rational or irrational.

Down

2. The sum of a rational and an irrational.
4. For any non-zero real number a, a to the power zero.
5. The type of the surd, the sum of a rational number and a surd.
6. Surds of different multiples of the same unit surd.
9. If the product of two surds is a rational number, then each surd is said to be

INTRODUCTION

Lets study various types of numbers, laws of indices and then about the surds, types of surds, laws of surds, the four basic operations on surds, their comparison, etc. Basically, a surd is an irrational number. Hence, let us first review the types of numbers and recall the definitions.

Natural Numbers

All counting numbers are natural numbers. If N is the set of natural numbers, then $N = \{1, 2, 3, \ldots\}$

Whole Numbers

Natural numbers including zero represent the set of whole numbers. It is denoted by the symbol W. For example: $W = \{0, 1, 2, 3,\ldots\}$

Integers

The set of integers, $Z = \{\ldots, -3, -2, -1, 0, 1, 2, 3, \ldots\}$

Rational Numbers

Any number that can be expressed in the form $\frac{p}{q}$ (where $q \neq 0$ and p, q are integers) is called a rational number. All integers, all recurring decimals, and all terminating decimals are rational numbers. Any integer can be expressed in the form $\frac{p}{q} (q \neq 0)$.

Example: $\frac{2}{1}, \frac{3}{1}, \frac{4}{1}$, etc.

Any recurring decimal can be expressed in the form $\frac{p}{q} (q \neq 0)$.

Example: $0.333\ldots = \frac{1}{3}$

$0.1666\ldots = \frac{1}{6}$

Any terminating decimal can be expressed in the form $\frac{p}{q} (q \neq 0)$.

Example: $0.5 = \frac{5}{10}$ or $\frac{1}{2}, 0.25 = \frac{25}{100}$ or $\frac{1}{4}$

Info Bytes!

- Zero isn't considered a natural number, but it's essential in the mathematical world.
- The largest natural number ever used in a mathematical proof is called Graham's number, and it's unimaginably huge.

Irrational Numbers

A number that cannot be expressed in the form $\frac{p}{q}$ (where $q \neq 0$), p and q are integers, is an irrational number or any non-terminating and non-recurring decimal is an irrational number.

Example: $\sqrt{2}, \sqrt{3}, \sqrt[3]{5}, \sqrt[4]{25}$ cannot be expressed in the form $\frac{p}{q} (q \neq 0)$, where p and q are integers.

$\therefore$ These numbers are irrational numbers.

Real Numbers

A number that is either rational or irrational is a real number.

Example: -3, $-7/8$, $13/12$, $\sqrt{3}$, $4\sqrt{6}$ ...

Number Line

A straight line on which points are identified with real numbers is called a number line. Successive integers are placed on the number line at regular intervals. The following is an illustration of the number line:

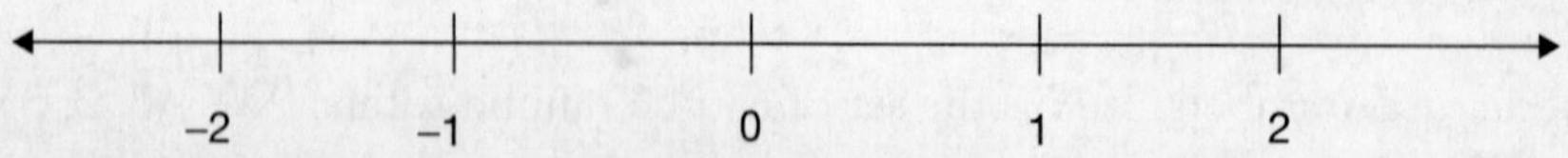

Representation of Numbers on the Number Line

We now learn the procedure of representing real numbers on the number line.

Representation of Natural Numbers

Draw a line. Mark a point on it which represents 0 (zero). Now on the right-hand side of zero (0), mark points at equal intervals of length, as shown below:

These points represent natural numbers 1, 2, 3, ..., respectively. The three dots on the number line indicate the continuation of these numbers indefinitely.

Representation of Whole Numbers

This is similar as above, but with the inclusion of 0 in the number line, it is as follows:

Representation of Integers

Draw a line. Mark a point on it which represents 0 (zero).

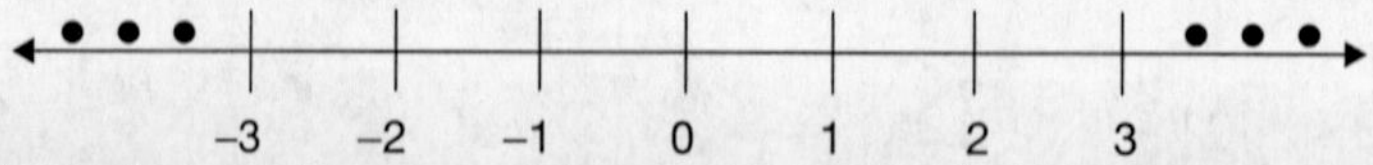

Three dots on either side show the continuation of integers indefinitely on each side.

Representation of Rational Numbers

Rational numbers can be represented by some points on the number line. Draw a line. Mark a point on it which represents 0 (zero).

Set equal distances on both sides of 0. Each point on the division represents an integer as shown below:

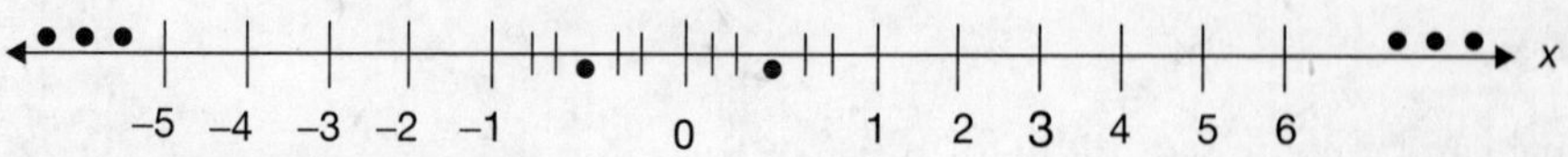

The length between two successive integers is called unit length.

Let us consider a rational number $\frac{2}{7}$.

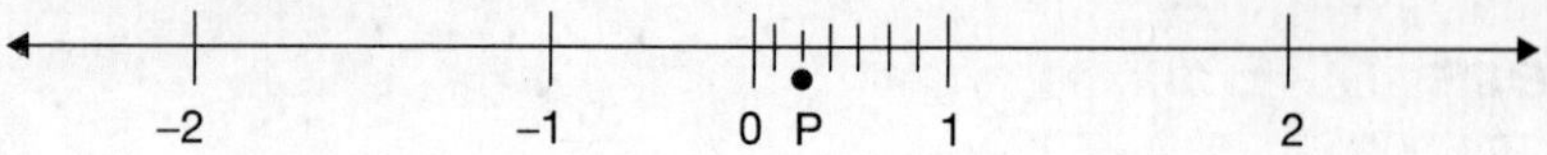

Divide unit length between 0 and 1 into 7 equal parts, and call them sub-divisions. The point at the line indicating the second sub-division from 0 represents $\frac{2}{7}$.

In this, way any rational number can be represented on the number line.

Representation of Irrational Numbers on the Number Line

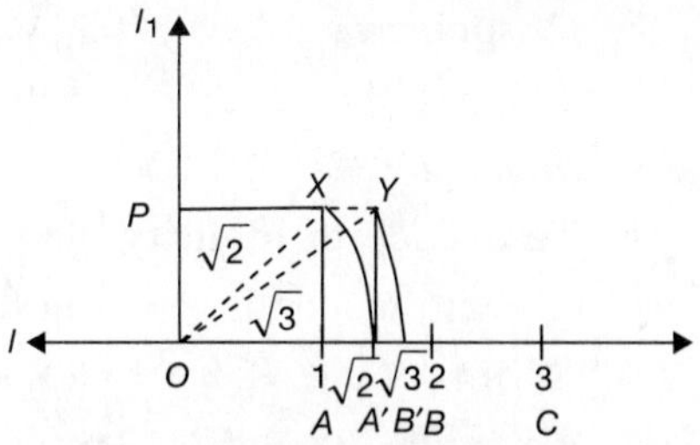

We use the Pythagoras property of a right-angled triangle, according to which, in a right-angled triangle, the square of the hypotenuse is equal to the sum of the squares of other two sides.

Consider the number line l and a perpendicular line l_1 to it. Let $OA = 1$ unit and $OP = 1$ unit. Let $OAXP$ be a square.

$OX = \sqrt{OA^2 + AX^2} = \sqrt{1^2 + 1^2} = \sqrt{2}$

Taking O as the centre and OX as the radius, cut the number line at the point A'.

That is, $OX = OA' = \sqrt{2}$.

Representing $\sqrt{3}$ on the Number Line

Let $OA'YP$ be a rectangle.

$OA' = \sqrt{2}$ units and $A'Y = 1$ unit.

$OY = \sqrt{(\sqrt{2})^2 + (1)^2} = \sqrt{3}$ units.

Taking O as centre and OY as radius, cut the number line with an arc at the point B'. That is, $OB' = \sqrt{3}$ units. In the same way, $\sqrt{5}, \sqrt{6}, \ldots$ can be represented on the number line.

Properties of Real Numbers

Addition

1. **Closure**

   The sum of any two real numbers is also a real number.

   Example: $\frac{1}{2} + 3 = 3\frac{1}{2}$

2. **Commutative**

   If a and b are the real numbers, then $a + b = b + a$.

   Example: $1 + 2 = 2 + 1$.

3. **Associative**

   If a, b, and c are three real numbers, then $(a + b) + c = a + (b + c)$.

   Example: $(1 + 2) + 3 = 1 + (2 + 3)$.

4. **Existence of identity element**

   Zero is the additive identity element for all real numbers. For every real number, there exists a number $0 \in R$ such that $a + 0 = 0 + a = a$.

5. **Existence of inverse element**

   If a is a real number, then there exists a real number $(-a)$ such that $a + (-a) = (-a) + a = 0$.

Konnect

The number line is a visual representation of all real numbers, placed in a specific order.

Multiplication

1. **Closure**

   If a and b are any two real numbers, then $a \times b$ is also a real number.

   Example: $2 \times \sqrt{3} = 2\sqrt{3}$.

2. **Commutative**

   If a and b are real numbers, then $a \times b = b \times a$.

   Example: $3 \times \sqrt{5} = \sqrt{5} \times 3$.

3. **Associative**
   If a, b, and c are real numbers, then $(a \times b) \times c = a \times (b \times c)$.
   Example: $(3\times5)\times\sqrt{3} = 3\times(5\times\sqrt{3})$.
4. **Existence of identity element**
   One is the identity element for all real numbers.
   That is, $\forall\ a \in R,\ a\times1 = 1\times a = a$. ($\forall$ means *for all*)
   Example: $2 \times 1 = 2 = 1 \times 2$.
5. **Existence of inverse element**
   For every non-zero real number, there exists a real number, $\frac{1}{a}$ such that $a\times\frac{1}{a} = \frac{1}{a}\times a = 1$.

Distribution of Multiplication over Addition

If a, b, and c are real numbers, $a \times (b + c) = (a \times b) + (a \times c)$.
Example: $13 \times (10 + 7) = (13 \times 10) + (13 \times 7)$.

Laws of Indices for Real Numbers

1. $a^m \times a^n = a^{m+n}$ (Product of powers)

Examples:

(i) $2^3 \times 2^6 = 2^{3+6} = 2^9$

(ii) $\left(\frac{5}{6}\right)^4 \times \left(\frac{5}{6}\right)^5 = \left(\frac{5}{6}\right)^{4+5} = \left(\frac{5}{6}\right)^9$

(iii) $2^3 \times 2^4 \times 2^5 \times 2^8 = 2^{(3+4+5+8)} = 2^{20}$

(iv) $(\sqrt{7})^3 \times (\sqrt{7})^5 = (\sqrt{7})^{3+5} = (\sqrt{7})^8$

Info Bytes!

$a^{m_1} \times a^{m_2} \times a^{m_3} \times \cdots \times a^{m_n} = a^{m_1 + m_2 + m_3 + \cdots + m_n}$

2. $a^m \div a^n = a^{m-n}$, $a \neq 0$ (Quotient of powers)

Konnect

We now consider what meaning we can assign to a^0. If we want these laws to be true for all values of m and n, i.e., even for $n = m$, by (2), we get $\frac{a^m}{a^m} = a^{m-m}$ or $1 = a^0$. We see that if we define a^0 as 1, this law will be true even for $n = m$. Therefore, we define a^0 as 1, provided $a \neq 0$.

Examples:

(i) $7^8 \div 7^3 = 7^{8-3} = 7^5$

(ii) $\left(\frac{7}{3}\right)^9 \div \left(\frac{7}{3}\right)^5 = \left(\frac{7}{3}\right)^{9-5} = \left(\frac{7}{3}\right)^4$

When $a = 0$, $a^{n-n} = \frac{a^n}{a^n} = \frac{0}{0}$, which is not defined.

$\therefore$ 0^0 is not defined.

We shall now consider, what meaning we can assign to a^n, where n is a negative integer.

We have $a^m \times a^n = a^{m+n}$.

Consider $a^n \times a^{-n} = a^{n+(-n)}$ (if we want the law to be true) $= a^0 = 1$

$\therefore an \times a^{-n} = 1$

$\Rightarrow a^{-n} = \dfrac{1}{a^n}$ and $\dfrac{1}{a^{-n}} = a^n$. If we define a^{-n} as $\dfrac{1}{a^n}$, this law is true even for negative value of n.

Example: $2^{-4} = \dfrac{1}{2^4}, 5^{-1} = \dfrac{1}{5}, a^{-n} = \dfrac{1}{a^n}$ (provided $a \neq 0$).

Konnect

$\left(\dfrac{a}{b}\right)^{-1} = \dfrac{1}{\dfrac{a}{b}} = \dfrac{b}{a}$

3. $(a^m)^n = a^{m \times n}$ (Power of a power)

Examples:

(i) $(5^2)^3 = 5^{2\times3} = 5^6$

(ii) $\left[\left(\dfrac{2}{3}\right)^4\right]^5 = \left(\dfrac{2}{3}\right)^{4\times5} = \left(\dfrac{2}{3}\right)^{20}$

Info Bytes!

$[(a^m)^n]^p = a^{mnp}$.

4. $(ab)^n = a^n \times b^n$ (power in the product)

Examples:

(i) $(20)^5 = (4 \times 5)^5 = 4^5 \times 5^5$.

(ii) $(42)^7 = (2 \times 3 \times 7)^7 = 2^7 \times 3^7 \times 7^7$.

In problems, we may often want to write $a^n \times b^n$ as $(ab)^n$.

Konnect

$(a\,b\,c\,d \ldots z)^n = a^n\, b^n\, c^n\, d^n \ldots z^n$.

Examples:

(i) $8 \times 27 = 2^3 \times 3^3 = (2 \times 3)^3 = 6^3$

(ii) $\dfrac{125}{343} \times \dfrac{729}{8} = \left[\left(\dfrac{5}{7}\right)\left(\dfrac{9}{2}\right)\right]^3 = \left(\dfrac{45}{14}\right)^3$

5. $\left(\dfrac{a}{b}\right)^n = \dfrac{a^n}{b^n}$ (Power in a quotient)

Examples:

(i) $\left(\dfrac{4}{5}\right)^7 = \dfrac{4^7}{5^7}$ **(ii)** $\left(\dfrac{6}{8}\right)^8 = \dfrac{(2^8)(3^8)}{8^8}$

In problems, we may want to write $\dfrac{a^n}{b^n}$ as $\left(\dfrac{a}{b}\right)^n$.

Examples:

(i) $\dfrac{4^8}{5^8} = \left(\dfrac{4}{5}\right)^8$ **(ii)** $\dfrac{\left(\dfrac{2}{3}\right)^5}{\left(\dfrac{9}{8}\right)^5} = \left(\dfrac{\dfrac{2}{3}}{\dfrac{9}{8}}\right)^5 = \left(\dfrac{16}{27}\right)^5$

Konnect

$\left(\dfrac{1}{a}\right)^{-1} = \left(\dfrac{a}{1}\right)^1 = a.$

6. $\left(\dfrac{a}{b}\right)^{-n} = \left(\dfrac{b}{a}\right)^n$

Examples:

(i) $\left(\dfrac{5}{9}\right)^{-3} = \left(\dfrac{9}{5}\right)^3$ **(ii)** $\left(\dfrac{1}{5}\right)^{-1} = \left(\dfrac{5}{1}\right)^1 = 5$

Exponential Equation

1. If $a^m = a^n$, then $m = n$, if $a \neq 0$, $a \neq 1$, and $a \neq -1$.

   Examples:

   (i) If $5^p = 5^3 \Rightarrow p = 3$

   (ii) If $4^p = 256$

   $\because 4^p = 4^4 \Rightarrow p = 4$

2. If $a^n = b^n$, then $a = b$ (when n is odd).

   Examples:

   (i) If $5^7 = p^7$, then $p = 5$.

   (ii) If $(5)^{2n-1} = (3 \times p)^{2n-1}$, then $5 = 3p$ or $p = \frac{5}{3}$.

3. If $a^n = b^n$, $n \neq 0$, then $a = \pm b$ (when n is even).

   Example: $2^4 = x^4 \Rightarrow x = \pm 2$.

Radicals

A radical expression (or simply a radical) is an expression of the type $\sqrt[n]{x}$. The sign '$\sqrt[n]{\ }$' is called the radical sign. The number under this sign, i.e., 'x' is called the radicand and the number in the angular part of the sign, i.e., 'n' is the order of the radical. Currently, we shall deal only with cases where x is a real number. Depending on the values of x, n can have certain corresponding values. Initially, we shall consider only positive integral values of n. But remember that, $\sqrt[n]{x} = x^{1/n}$. Last year, we studied such exponential expressions and we know the values that the index can have for different values of the base. From those results, we get the following results for radicals:

1. If $x > 0$, n can have any real value except zero.
2. If $x = 0$, n can have any positive real value.
3. If $x < 0$, n can have any real value except zero. But, we shall consider only certain rational values. Later, we shall examine what these values are for other values of n, (some rational and all irrational) the radical does not have a real value. We shall study such expressions in higher classes.

Examples:

1. $\sqrt{2}, \sqrt[3]{3}, \sqrt[4]{7}, \sqrt[2]{8}$, are some radicals.
2. $\sqrt{0}, \sqrt[3]{0}$ are also radicals. But $\sqrt[0]{0}$ and $\sqrt[-1]{0}$ are undefined.
3. $\sqrt[3]{-2}, \sqrt[5]{-64}, \sqrt[7]{-128}$ are radicals and $\sqrt[2]{-4}, \sqrt[4]{-16}$ are also radicals, but they are not real numbers. We shall study them only in higher classes.

In all these examples, the value of n, i.e., the order of the radical is a positive integer. But as stated above, it can have other values.

Surds

If a is a positive rational number, which is not the nth power (n is any natural number) of any rational number, then the irrational numbers $\pm\sqrt[n]{a}$ are called simple surds or monomial surds.

Every surd is an irrational root of a rational number but all irrational numbers are not surd such as $\pi \neq \sqrt[n]{a}$ So, the representation of monomial surd on a number line is same as that of irrational numbers.

Examples:

1. $\sqrt{3}$ is a surd and $\sqrt{3}$ is an irrational number.
2. $\sqrt[3]{5}$ is a surd and $\sqrt[3]{5}$ is an irrational number.
3. π is an irrational number, but it is not a surd.
4. $\sqrt[3]{3+\sqrt{2}}$ is an irrational number. It is not a surd, because $3+\sqrt{2}$ is not a rational number.

EXAMPLE 1.1 Which of the following are surds?

(a) $\sqrt{9}$ **(b)** $\sqrt[3]{13}$ **(c)** $\sqrt[4]{25}$ **(d)** $\sqrt[6]{32}$

SOLUTION

(a) $\sqrt{9} = 3$ is not a surd. **(b)** $\sqrt[3]{13}$ is a surd.

(c) $\sqrt[4]{25}$ is a surd. **(d)** $\sqrt[6]{32}$ is a surd.

Types of Surds

Note: All multiples of surds can be expressed as unit surds as $k\sqrt[n]{a} = \sqrt[n]{k^n \cdot a}$.

1. **Unit surds and multiples of surds:** If $\sqrt[n]{a}$ is a surd, it is also referred to as a unit surd. If *k* is a rational number, $k\sqrt[n]{a}$ is a multiple of a surd.
2. **Mixed surds:** If a is a rational number (not equal to 0) and $\sqrt[n]{b}$ is a surd, then $a+\sqrt[n]{b}, a-\sqrt[n]{b}$, are called mixed surds. If $a = 0$, then they are called pure surds.

   Example: $2+\sqrt{3}, 5-\sqrt[3]{6}$ are mixed surds, while $\sqrt{3}, \sqrt[3]{6}$ are pure surds.
3. **Compound surd:** A surd which is the sum or difference of two or more surds is called a compound surd.

   Example: $\sqrt{2}+\sqrt[3]{3}$, $\sqrt{3}+\sqrt[5]{7}-\sqrt[3]{2}$ and $\sqrt{7}+\sqrt{2}-\sqrt{3}$ are compound surds.
4. **Binomial surd:** A compound surd consisting of two surds is called a binomial surd.

   Example: $\sqrt{3}, \sqrt{6}+4\sqrt{5}, \sqrt{8}-\sqrt[3]{7}$.
5. **Similar surds:** If two surds are different multiples of the same surd, they are called similar surds. Otherwise they are called dissimilar surds.

   Example: $2\sqrt{2}, 5\sqrt{2}, 7\sqrt{2}$ are similar surds. $(\sqrt{2}+3\sqrt{3}), (2\sqrt{2}+6\sqrt{3})$ are similar surds and $1+\sqrt{2}, 2+2\sqrt{2}$ are similar surds. $3\sqrt{3}$ and $6\sqrt{5}$ are dissimilar surds.

Equality of Two Mixed Surds of the Form $a + c\sqrt{b}$ and $d + e\sqrt{b}$

Two mixed surds $a+c\sqrt{b}$ and $d+e\sqrt{b}$ are equal, if only their respective rational parts and the irrational parts are equal, i.e., $a = d$ and $c = e$. ç

EXAMPLE 1.2 Identify the following types of surds:

(a) $\sqrt{6}+5\sqrt{3}$ **(b)** $\sqrt{15}+\sqrt{8}-\sqrt{11}$ **(c)** $\sqrt{5}$ **(d)** $5+\sqrt{7}$

SOLUTION

(a) $\sqrt{6}+5\sqrt{3}$. It is the sum of two surds.

$\therefore$ It is a compound surd of two surds, i.e., a binomial surd.

(b) $\sqrt{15}+\sqrt{8}-\sqrt{11}$. It is the combination of three surds.

$\therefore$ It is a compound surd.

(c) $\sqrt{5}$. It is a monomial surd or a simple surd.

(d) $5+\sqrt{7}$. It is the sum of a rational number and a surd.

$\therefore$ It is a mixed surd.

EXAMPLE 1.3 Which of the following surds are similar?

(a) $2\sqrt{5}$ **(b)** $3\sqrt[3]{5}$ **(c)** $4\sqrt{5}$ **(d)** $5\sqrt[4]{5}$

SOLUTION

$2\sqrt{5}$ and $4\sqrt{5}$ are multiples of the same surd, $\sqrt{5}$.

∴ They are similar.

Laws of Radicals

If $a > 0$, $b > 0$ and n is a positive rational number, then

1. $(\sqrt[n]{a})(\sqrt[n]{b}) = \sqrt[n]{ab}$
2. $\dfrac{\sqrt[n]{a}}{\sqrt[n]{b}} = \sqrt[n]{\dfrac{a}{b}}$
3. $\sqrt[m]{\sqrt[n]{a}} = \sqrt[mn]{a} = \sqrt[n]{\sqrt[m]{a}}$
4. $\sqrt[n]{a^p} = a^{p/n}$ and $\sqrt[n]{a^p} = \sqrt[n]{\sqrt[m]{(a^p)^m}}$

The application of laws of radicals are as follows:

1. Convert the multiple of a surd into a unit surd.
2. Convert certain unit surds into multiples of other unit surds.
3. Express surds of different orders as surds of the same order.

EXAMPLE 1.4 Solve: $3\sqrt[4]{3}$ = ______

SOLUTION

$3.\sqrt[4]{3} = \sqrt[4]{3^4} \times \sqrt[4]{3}$

$= \sqrt[4]{3^4 \times 3}$

$= \sqrt[4]{243}$

Order of a Surd

In the surd $\sqrt[n]{a}$, n is called the order of the surd. Thus, the orders of $\sqrt{2}$, $\sqrt[3]{3}$, $\sqrt[4]{5}$ are 2, 3, and 4 respectively.

Comparison of Monomial Surds

If two simple surds are of the same order, then they can easily be compared. If $a < b$, $\sqrt[n]{a} < \sqrt[n]{b}$ for all positive integral values of n.

Konnect

The orders of the radicals $\sqrt[4]{9}$, $\sqrt[6]{16}$, $\sqrt[6]{27}$ are 4, 6, and 6 respectively. We note that $\sqrt[4]{9} = \sqrt[4]{3^2} = 3^{2/4} = \sqrt{3}$ and the order of $\sqrt{3}$ is 2. Thus, the order of a surd is not a property of the surd itself, but of the way in which it is expressed.

Example: $\sqrt[4]{2} < \sqrt[4]{7}$, $\sqrt[3]{3} < \sqrt[3]{5}$, $\sqrt[5]{10} < \sqrt[5]{13}$, etc.

If two simple surds of different orders have to be compared, they have to be expressed as radicals of the same order. Thus, to compare $\sqrt[4]{6}$ and $\sqrt[3]{5}$, we express both as the radicals of 12th (LCM of 3, 4) order.

$$\sqrt[4]{6} = \sqrt[12]{6^3} \text{ and } \sqrt[3]{5} = \sqrt[12]{5^4}$$

$$\text{As } 6^3 < 5^4,\ \sqrt[4]{6} < \sqrt[3]{5}.$$

EXAMPLE 1.5 If $a = \sqrt{7}$, $b = \sqrt[3]{12}$ and $c = \sqrt[4]{25}$, then ________.

SOLUTION

Given, $a = \sqrt{7}$, $b = \sqrt[3]{12}$ and $c = \sqrt[4]{25}$

$a = 7^{\frac{1}{2}}$, $b = 12^{\frac{1}{3}}$ $c = (5^2)^{1/4} = 5^{1/2}$

$a = (7^3)^{\frac{1}{6}}$ $b = ((12)^2)^{\frac{1}{6}}$ $c = (5^3)^{1/6}$

$a = (343)^{1/6}$ $b = (144)^{1/6}$ $c = (125)^{1/6}$ $c < b < a$

Addition and Subtraction of Surds

Addition and subtraction of similar surds can be done using the distributive law,

$$a\sqrt{c} \pm b\sqrt{c} = (a \pm b)\sqrt{c}.$$

EXAMPLE 1.6 Solve: $3\sqrt{12} - 3\sqrt{27} + 2\sqrt{48}$ = ________.

SOLUTION

$3\sqrt{12} - 3\sqrt{27} + 2\sqrt{48} = 3\sqrt{4 \times 3} - 3\sqrt{9 \times 3} + 2\sqrt{16 \times 3}$

$= 6\sqrt{3} - 9\sqrt{3} + 8\sqrt{3}$

$= 5\sqrt{3}$.

Multiplication and Division of Surds

Surds of the same order can be multiplied according to the law, $(\sqrt[n]{x})(\sqrt[n]{y}) = \sqrt[n]{xy}$.

Info Bytes!

When the surds to be multiplied or divided are not of the same order, they have to be necessarily brought into the same order before the operation is performed.

EXAMPLE 1.7 **(a)** $\sqrt{15} \times \sqrt{35}$. **(b)** $2\sqrt{3} \div 3\sqrt{27}$. **(c)** Multiply $\sqrt[3]{3}$ by $\sqrt[4]{2}$. **(d)** Divide $\sqrt[6]{5}$ by $\sqrt[3]{10}$.

SOLUTION

(a) $(\sqrt{15})(\sqrt{35}) = \sqrt{(15)(35)}$

$= \sqrt{(5)(3)(5)(7)} = 5\sqrt{21}$.

(b) $2\sqrt{3} \div 3\sqrt{27} = \dfrac{2\sqrt{3}}{3\sqrt{27}}$

$= \dfrac{2\sqrt{3}}{(3)\sqrt{3^2(3)}} = \dfrac{2\sqrt{3}}{(3)(3)\sqrt{3}} = \dfrac{2}{9}$.

(c) $\sqrt[3]{3} = 3^{1/3}$ and $\sqrt[4]{2} = 2^{1/4}$

The LCM of 3 and 4 is 12.

$\therefore 3^{1/3} = 3^{4/12} = \sqrt[12]{3^4}$

$2^{1/4} = 2^{3/12} = \sqrt[12]{2^3}$

$(\sqrt[3]{3})(\sqrt[4]{2}) = (\sqrt[12]{3^4})(\sqrt[12]{2^3})$

$= \sqrt[12]{(3^4)(2^3)}$

$= \sqrt[12]{(81)(8)} = \sqrt[12]{648}$.

(d) $\sqrt[6]{5} = 5^{1/6}$

$\sqrt[3]{10} = 10^{1/3}$

LCM of 3 and 6 is 6.

$\sqrt[3]{10} = 10^{1/3} = 10^{2/6} = \sqrt[6]{10^2} = \sqrt[6]{100}$

$\therefore \dfrac{\sqrt[6]{5}}{\sqrt[3]{10}} = \dfrac{\sqrt[6]{5}}{\sqrt[6]{100}}$

$= \sqrt[6]{\dfrac{5}{100}} = \sqrt[6]{\dfrac{1}{20}}$.

Rationalizing Factor (RF)

If the product of two surds is a rational number, then each of the two surds is a RF of the other.

1. RF is not unique.
2. If one RF of a surd is known, then the product of this factor and any non-zero rational number is also the RF of the given surd.
3. It is convenient to use the simplest of all RFs of the given surd to convert it to a rational number.

Examples:

1. $(3\sqrt{3})(\sqrt{3}) = (3)(3) = 9$, a rational number.
   $\therefore\ \sqrt{3}$ is a RF of $3\sqrt{3}$.
2. $(\sqrt{3}+\sqrt{2})(\sqrt{3}-\sqrt{2}) = (\sqrt{3})^2 - (\sqrt{2})^2 = 3 - 2 = 1$, a rational number
   $\therefore\ \sqrt{3}-\sqrt{2}$ is a RF of $\sqrt{3}+\sqrt{2}$
   and $\sqrt{3}+\sqrt{2}$ is a RF of $\sqrt{3}-\sqrt{2}$

EXAMPLE 1.8

Find the simplest RF of:
(a) $\sqrt[4]{216}$ and **(b)** $\sqrt[5]{16}$

SOLUTION

(a) $\sqrt[4]{216} = \sqrt[4]{(2^3)(3^3)} = 2^{3/4} \times 3^{3/4}$

So RF is $2^{1/4} \times 3^{1/4} = (2\times 3)^{1/4} = \sqrt[4]{6}$.

$\therefore\ \sqrt[4]{6}$ is the simplest RF of $\sqrt[4]{216}$.

(b) $\sqrt[5]{16} = \sqrt[5]{2^4} = 2^{4/5}$

$\therefore$ RF is $2^{1/5} \Rightarrow (2^{4/5})(2^{1/5}) = 2^{5/5} = 1$.

$\therefore\ \sqrt[5]{2}$ is the simplest RF of $\sqrt[5]{16}$

Konnect

1. $\sqrt[n]{a}$ is a RF of $\sqrt[n]{a^{n-1}}$ and vice-versa.
2. $\sqrt[n]{a^m}$ is a RF of $\sqrt[n]{a^{n-m}}$ and vice-versa.
3. $\sqrt{a}+\sqrt{b}$ is a RF of $\sqrt{a}-\sqrt{b}$ and vice-versa.
4. $\sqrt[3]{a}+\sqrt[3]{b}$ is a RF of $a^{2/3} - a^{1/3}\cdot b^{1/3} - b^{2/3}$ and vice-versa.
5. $\sqrt[3]{a}-\sqrt[3]{b}$ is a RF of $a^{2/3} + a^{1/3}\cdot b^{1/3} + b^{2/3}$ and vice-versa.

EXAMPLE 1.9

Express the following surds with rational denominators:

(a) $\dfrac{2}{\sqrt{14}}$ **(b)** $\dfrac{2\sqrt[3]{3}}{\sqrt[3]{25}}$

SOLUTION

(a) $\dfrac{2}{\sqrt{14}} \times \dfrac{\sqrt{14}}{\sqrt{14}} = \dfrac{2\sqrt{14}}{14} = \dfrac{\sqrt{14}}{7}$.

(b) $\dfrac{2\sqrt[3]{3}}{\sqrt[3]{25}} = \dfrac{2\sqrt[3]{3}}{\sqrt[3]{25}} \times \dfrac{\sqrt[3]{5}}{\sqrt[3]{5}} = \dfrac{2\sqrt[3]{3\times 5}}{\sqrt[3]{5^3}} = \dfrac{2\sqrt[3]{15}}{5}$.

EXAMPLE 1.10

Given that $\sqrt{2} = 1.414$, find the value of $\dfrac{3}{\sqrt{2}}$ up to three decimal places.

SOLUTION

$$\frac{3}{\sqrt{2}} = \frac{3}{\sqrt{2}} \times \frac{\sqrt{2}}{\sqrt{2}}$$
$$= \frac{3\sqrt{2}}{2} = 1.5\sqrt{2}$$
$$= 1.5\,(1.414) = 2.121.$$

Rationalization of Mixed Surds

$a+\sqrt{b}$ is the rationalizing factor of $a-\sqrt{b}$, where a and b are rational.

EXAMPLE 1.11 Rationalize the denominator of $\dfrac{11}{5+\sqrt{3}}$.

SOLUTION

$$\frac{11}{5+\sqrt{3}}=\frac{11}{5+\sqrt{3}}\times\frac{5-\sqrt{3}}{5-\sqrt{3}}$$

$$=\frac{11\left(5-\sqrt{3}\right)}{25-3}=\frac{5-\sqrt{3}}{2}.$$

EXAMPLE 1.12 Which of the following is a rationalizing factor of $\sqrt[3]{25}$ is?

SOLUTION

$\sqrt[3]{25}=\sqrt[3]{5^2}$ Now, $\sqrt[3]{5^2}\times\sqrt[3]{5}=5$.

Rationalizing factor of $\sqrt[3]{25}$ is $\sqrt[3]{5}$.

Conjugate of the Surd of the Form $\sqrt{a}+\sqrt{b}$

Two surds of the form $a+\sqrt{b}$ and $a-\sqrt{b}$, are called conjugate surds. The sum and product of conjugate surds are rational numbers.

EXAMPLE 1.13 Write the conjugate of:

(a) $3+\sqrt{5}$ **(b)** $5+3\sqrt{7}$

SOLUTION

(a) $3-\sqrt{5}$ is the conjugate of $3+\sqrt{5}$, since their sum is 6 (a rational numbers) and their product is 4 (a rational number).

(b) $5-3\sqrt{7}$ is the conjugate of $5+3\sqrt{7}$, since their sum is 10 (a rational number) and their product is 48 (a rational number).

The following formulae are helpful in finding the rationalizing factors of mixed quadratic and cubic surds:

1. $(a+b)(a-b)=a^2-b^2$
2. $(a+b)(a^2-ab+b^2)=a^3+b^3$
3. $(a-b)(a^2+ab+b^2)=a^3-b^3$

EXAMPLE 1.14

(a) Find the RF of $2^{1/3}+2^{-1/3}$

(b) Find the RF of $5^{1/3}-5^{-1/3}$

SOLUTION

(a) $2^{1/3}+2^{-1/3}$

Let $a=2^{1/3}$ and $b=2^{-1/3}$.

$a^3=(2^{1/3})^3=2$

$b^3=(2^{-1/3})^3=2^{-1}=\dfrac{1}{2}$

But $a^3+b^3=(a+b)(a^2-ab+b^2)$

$\therefore a^2-ab+b^2=(2^{1/3})^2-(2^{1/3}\cdot 2^{-1/3})+(2^{-1/3})^2=2^{2/3}-1+2^{-2/3}$

$\therefore$ RF of $2^{1/3}+2^{-1/3}$ is $2^{2/3}-1+2^{-2/3}$.

(b) $5^{1/3}-5^{-1/3}$

We have $a^3-b^3=(a-b)(a^2+ab+b^2)$.

$\therefore$ RF of $5^{1/3}-5^{-1/3}$ is $[5^{1/3}]^2+[5^{1/3}\cdot 5^{-1/3}]+[5^{-1/3}]^2$

$=5^{2/3}+1+5^{-2/3}$.

Comparison of Compound Surds

EXAMPLE 1.15 Among $\sqrt{7}-\sqrt{3}$ and $\sqrt{11}-\sqrt{7}$, which is greater?

SOLUTION

By rationalizing,

$$\sqrt{7}-\sqrt{3}=\frac{(\sqrt{7}-\sqrt{3})(\sqrt{7}+\sqrt{3})}{\sqrt{7}+\sqrt{3}}=\frac{4}{\sqrt{7}+\sqrt{3}}$$

$$\sqrt{11}-\sqrt{7}=\frac{(\sqrt{11}-\sqrt{7})(\sqrt{11}+\sqrt{7})}{\sqrt{11}+\sqrt{7}}=\frac{4}{\sqrt{11}+\sqrt{7}}$$

The numerator of each of the irrational number is 4.

But $\sqrt{11}+\sqrt{7}>\sqrt{7}+\sqrt{3}$

$$\therefore \frac{4}{\sqrt{7}+\sqrt{3}}>\frac{4}{\sqrt{11}+\sqrt{7}}$$

$$\sqrt{7}-\sqrt{3}>\sqrt{11}-\sqrt{7}.$$

EXAMPLE 1.16 If $a=\sqrt{11}-\sqrt{10}$, $b=\sqrt{12}-\sqrt{11}$ and $\sqrt{13}-\sqrt{12}$, then $c=$ ______.

SOLUTION

Given $a=\sqrt{11}-\sqrt{10}$ and $b=\sqrt{12}-\sqrt{11}$.

$$\frac{1}{a}=\frac{1}{\sqrt{11}-\sqrt{10}}\times\frac{\sqrt{11}+\sqrt{10}}{\sqrt{11}+\sqrt{10}}=\frac{\sqrt{11}+\sqrt{10}}{11-10}=\sqrt{11}+\sqrt{10}.$$

$$\frac{1}{b}=\frac{1}{\sqrt{12}-\sqrt{11}}=\frac{1}{\sqrt{12}-\sqrt{11}}\times\frac{\sqrt{12}+\sqrt{11}}{\sqrt{12}+\sqrt{11}}.=\sqrt{12}+\sqrt{11}$$

$$c=\sqrt{13}-\sqrt{12}$$

$$\frac{1}{c}=\frac{1}{\sqrt{13}-\sqrt{12}}$$

$$=\frac{\sqrt{13}+\sqrt{12}}{13-1}$$

$$\therefore \frac{1}{c}>\frac{1}{b}>\frac{1}{a}$$

$$\Rightarrow c<b<a$$

Rationalizing the Numerator

EXAMPLE 1.17 Rationalize the numerator of $\frac{2-\sqrt{3+x}}{x-1}$.

SOLUTION

Rationalizing factor of $2-\sqrt{3+x}$ is $2+\sqrt{3+x}$.

$$\therefore \frac{2-\sqrt{3+x}}{x-1}=\left[\frac{2-\sqrt{3+x}}{x-1}\right]\left[\frac{2+\sqrt{3+x}}{2+\sqrt{3+x}}\right]$$

$$= \frac{(2)^2 - \left(\sqrt{3+x}\right)^2}{(x-1)\left(2+\sqrt{3+x}\right)} = \frac{4-(3+x)}{(x-1)\left(2+\sqrt{3+x}\right)}$$

$$= \frac{1-x}{(x-1)\left(2+\sqrt{3+x}\right)} = \frac{-1}{2+\sqrt{3+x}}.$$

EXAMPLE 1.18 Express $E = \frac{1}{\sqrt{5}+\sqrt{3}-\sqrt{8}}$ with a rational denominator.

SOLUTION

The denominator is a trinomial surd, an expression having all the three terms as surds. We group any two of the three terms, say $\sqrt{5}$ and $\sqrt{3}$.

Thus, $\sqrt{5}+\sqrt{3}-\sqrt{8} = (\sqrt{5}+\sqrt{3})-\sqrt{8}$.

Consider the product,

$$\left[\left(\sqrt{5}+\sqrt{3}\right)-\sqrt{8}\right]\left[\left(\sqrt{5}+\sqrt{3}\right)+\sqrt{8}\right] = \left(\sqrt{5}+\sqrt{3}\right)^2 - \left(\sqrt{8}\right)^2$$

$$= 5+3+2\sqrt{5}\sqrt{3}-8 = 2\sqrt{15}$$

$$\therefore \frac{1}{\sqrt{5}+\sqrt{3}-\sqrt{8}} = \frac{\sqrt{5}+\sqrt{3}+\sqrt{8}}{\left(\sqrt{5}+\sqrt{3}-\sqrt{8}\right)\left(\sqrt{5}+\sqrt{3}+\sqrt{8}\right)}$$

$$= \frac{(\sqrt{5}+\sqrt{3}+\sqrt{8})}{2\sqrt{15}}.$$

Rationalizing the denominator,

$$E = \frac{\sqrt{5}+\sqrt{3}+\sqrt{8}}{2\sqrt{15}}\left(\frac{\sqrt{15}}{\sqrt{15}}\right)$$

$$= \frac{5\sqrt{3}+3\sqrt{5}+2\sqrt{30}}{30}.$$

EXAMPLE 1.19 If both a and b are rational numbers, find the value of a and b in each of the following:

(a) $\frac{3+\sqrt{5}}{3-\sqrt{5}} = a+b\sqrt{5}$ **(b)** $\frac{3+2\sqrt{3}}{5-2\sqrt{3}} = a+b\sqrt{3}$

SOLUTION

(a) $\frac{3+\sqrt{5}}{3-\sqrt{5}}$

$3+\sqrt{5}$ is the RF of $3-\sqrt{5}$.

$$\therefore \frac{3+\sqrt{5}}{3-\sqrt{5}} = \frac{3+\sqrt{5}}{3-\sqrt{5}} \times \frac{3+\sqrt{5}}{3+\sqrt{5}} = \frac{\left(3+\sqrt{5}\right)^2}{(3)^2-\left(\sqrt{5}\right)^2}$$

$$= \frac{9+5+6\sqrt{5}}{9-5} = \frac{14+6\sqrt{5}}{4} = \frac{14}{4}+\frac{6}{4}\sqrt{5} = \frac{7}{2}+\frac{3}{2}\sqrt{5} = a+b\sqrt{5}$$

$$\therefore a = \frac{7}{2} \text{ and } b = \frac{3}{2}.$$

(b) $\frac{3+2\sqrt{3}}{5-2\sqrt{3}}$

$5+2\sqrt{3}$ is the RF of $5-2\sqrt{3}$.

$$\therefore \frac{3+2\sqrt{3}}{5-2\sqrt{3}} = \frac{3+2\sqrt{3}}{5-2\sqrt{3}} \times \frac{5+2\sqrt{3}}{5+2\sqrt{3}} = \frac{15+10\sqrt{3}+12+6\sqrt{3}}{(5)^2-\left(2\sqrt{3}\right)^2}$$

$$= \frac{27+16\sqrt{3}}{25-12} = \frac{27+16\sqrt{3}}{13} = a+b\sqrt{3}$$

$$\Rightarrow a = \frac{27}{13} \text{ and } b = \frac{16}{13}.$$

Square Root of a Quadratic Surd

Consider the real number $a+\sqrt{b}$, where a and b are rational numbers and $\sqrt{b}$ is a surd. Equate the square root of $a+\sqrt{b}$ to $\sqrt{x}+\sqrt{y}$, where x and y are rational numbers, i.e., $\sqrt{a+\sqrt{b}}=\sqrt{x}+\sqrt{y}$.

Squaring both sides, $a+\sqrt{b}=x+y+2\sqrt{xy}$

Equating the rational numbers on the two sides of the above equation, we get,

$$a=x+y \tag{1}$$

and equating the irrational numbers, we get,

$$\sqrt{b}=2\sqrt{xy} \tag{2}$$

By solving (1) and (2), we get the values of x and y.

Similarly, $\sqrt{a-\sqrt{b}}=\sqrt{x}-\sqrt{y}$.

Square Root of a Trinomial Quadratic Surd

Consider the real number $a+\sqrt{b}+\sqrt{c}+\sqrt{d}$, where a is a rational number and $\sqrt{b},\sqrt{c}$ and $\sqrt{d}$ are surds. Let, $\sqrt{a+\sqrt{b}+\sqrt{c}+\sqrt{d}}=\sqrt{x}+\sqrt{y}+\sqrt{z}$.

By squaring both sides, and comparing rational and irrational parts on either sides, we get,

$x+y+z=a$.

$$x=\frac{1}{2}\sqrt{\frac{bd}{c}},\ y=\frac{1}{2}\sqrt{\frac{bc}{d}} \text{ and } z=\frac{1}{2}\sqrt{\frac{cd}{b}}.$$

EXAMPLE 1.20 Solve: $\sqrt{5+2\sqrt{6}}$ = ______.

SOLUTION

$\sqrt{5+2\sqrt{6}} = \sqrt{3+2+2\sqrt{3\times 2}}$

$= \sqrt{\left(\sqrt{3}+\sqrt{2}\right)^2}$

$= \sqrt{3}+\sqrt{2}$

EXAMPLE 1.21 If $x = 2\sqrt{6}+5$, then $x^2-10x-1$ = ______.

SOLUTION

$x = 2\sqrt{6}+5$

$x-5 = 2\sqrt{6}$.

$(x-5)^2 = 24$

$x^2-10x+25-24=0$

$x^2-10x+1=0$

$x^2-10x-1=-2$

POINTS TO REMEMBER

- ✔ A straight line on which points are identified with real numbers is called a number line.
- ✔ A radical expression (or simply a radical) is an expression of the type $\sqrt[n]{x}$.
- ✔ If a is a positive rational number, which is not the nth power (n is any natural number) of any rational number, then the irrational numbers $\pm\sqrt[n]{a}$ are called simple surds or monomial surds.
- ✔ $a^m \times a^n = a^{m+n}$ (Product of powers)
- ✔ $a^m \div a^n = a^{m-n}, a \neq 0$ (Quotient of powers)
- ✔ $((a^m)^n)^p = a^{mnp}$.
- ✔ $(ab)^n = a^n \times b^n$ (power in the product)
- ✔ $(a^m)^n = a^{m\times n}$ (Power of a power)
- ✔ $\left(\frac{a}{b}\right)^n = \frac{a^n}{b^n}$ (Power in a quotient)
- ✔ If $a^m = a^n$, then $m = n$, if $a \neq 0$, $a \neq 1$ and $a \neq -1$.
- ✔ If $a^n = b^n$, then $a = b$ (when n is odd).
- ✔ If $a^n = b^n$, $n \neq 0$, then $a = \pm b$ (when n is even).
- ✔ Surds of the same order can be multiplied according to the law, $(\sqrt[n]{x})(\sqrt[n]{y}) = \sqrt[n]{xy}$.
- ✔ Two surds of the form $a+\sqrt{b}$ and $a-\sqrt{b}$, are called conjugate surds. The sum and product of conjugate surds are rational numbers.

DW

PRACTICE QUESTIONS CLASSROOM WING

Very Short Answer Type Questions

Directions of questions from 1 to 9:

Fill in the blanks.

1. $\left(\sqrt{324+2\sqrt{323}}\right)-\left(\sqrt{324-2\sqrt{323}}\right)$ ________.

2. $\dfrac{9^{3^{6^{0^{8^{7}}}}}-7^{3^{5^{0^{4^{9}}}}}}{(63)^{3^{0^{7}}}+(81)^{5^{0^{7}}}+(49)^{6^{0^{8}}}}=$ ________.

3. The conjugate of $(3\sqrt{2}+6)-(9+2\sqrt{2})$ is ________.

4. If $3^x = 9^y = 27^z = 81$, then $x - y + z =$ ________.

5. Rationalize $\dfrac{6}{3-\sqrt{3}}=$ ________.

6. If $x+\sqrt{5}=4+\sqrt{y}$, then $x + y =$ ________. (where x and y are rational)

7. If the product of two surds is a rational number, then each of the two is a ________ of the other.

8. $(\sqrt[3]{3})^4 =$ ________.

9. RF of $5^{1/3}+5^{-1/3}$ is ________.

Directions of questions from 10 to 12:

State whether the following statements are true or false

10. $\sqrt{6}-\sqrt{7}$ is the conjugate surd of $\sqrt{6}+\sqrt{7}$. (True/False)

11. $\sqrt[3]{3+\sqrt{2}}$ is a surd. (True/False)

12. If $p=2+\sqrt{3}$ and pq is a rational number, then q is a unique surd. (True/False)

Directions of questions from 13 to 24:

Answer the following questions.

13. Express the surd $\dfrac{3}{\sqrt{11}}$ with rational denominator.

14. Find the smallest RF of $\sqrt{28}$.

15. Multiply: $\sqrt[3]{5}$ by $\sqrt[4]{2}$.

16. Which is greater, $\sqrt{2}$ or $\sqrt[3]{3}$?

17. Express the surd $2\sqrt{3}$ as a pure surd.

18. Multiply: $\sqrt{14}$ by $\sqrt{8}$.

19. Express the following in the simplest form:
$\dfrac{\sqrt[3]{81}}{\sqrt[3]{3}}$

20. Express the following in the simplest form:
$\sqrt[3]{625}$

21. Express the following as a pure surd:
$\dfrac{2}{3}\sqrt[3]{16}$

22. Express the surd $\dfrac{\sqrt[3]{5}}{\sqrt[3]{6}}$ with rational denominator.

23. Divide: $\sqrt[6]{144}$ by $\sqrt[6]{4}$.

24. Express the following in the simplest form:
$\sqrt[3]{\sqrt{15625}}$

Short Answer Type Questions

25. If $x = 7 + \sqrt{3}$ and xy is a rational number, then y can be ________.

26. $\dfrac{3}{\sqrt{3}+1}+\dfrac{3}{\sqrt{5}+\sqrt{3}}+\dfrac{3}{\sqrt{7}+\sqrt{5}}+\dots\dots\dots+\dfrac{3}{\sqrt{25}+\sqrt{23}}=$ ________.

27. (A) Simplify: $2\sqrt{12}-3\sqrt{32}+2\sqrt{48}$.

(B) If $x^4 - 1 = 2400$ and $y^5 + 1 = 3126$, then find the value of xy, where both x and y are positive integers.

28. If $x=c\sqrt{b}+4$, find $x+\dfrac{1}{x}$.

29. $2\sqrt{125}-5\sqrt{5}+3\sqrt{3125}=$ ________.

30. If $x=\sqrt{2}-\sqrt{3}$, then $x+\dfrac{1}{x}=$ ________.

31. Which of the two expressions, $\sqrt{11}-\sqrt{10}$ and $\sqrt{12}-\sqrt{11}$ is greater?

32. Simplify the following:
$\dfrac{5\sqrt{5}}{\sqrt{11}+\sqrt{6}}-\dfrac{3\sqrt{3}}{\sqrt{6}+\sqrt{3}}-\dfrac{3\sqrt{2}}{\sqrt{15}+3\sqrt{2}}$

33. (A) Arrange the following surds in an ascending order of magnitude:

$\sqrt[3]{4}, \sqrt[4]{5}, \sqrt{8}$

(B) Which of these surds is the biggest?

$\sqrt{34}, 4\sqrt{2}, 2\sqrt{7}, 3\sqrt{5}$?

34. Find the positive square root of the following:

$10 + 2\sqrt{6} + \sqrt{60} + 2\sqrt{10}$

35. If both a and b are rational numbers, find the values of a and b in the following equation:

$$\frac{2+3\sqrt{5}}{4+5\sqrt{5}} = a + b\sqrt{5}$$

36. Given $\sqrt{2} = 1.414, \sqrt{3} = 1.732, \sqrt{5} = 2.236$, find the value, correct to three decimals, of the following:

$$\frac{1-\sqrt{3}}{\sqrt{5}-\sqrt{2}}$$

37. (A) If $x = 3\sqrt{3} + \sqrt{26}$, find the value of $\frac{1}{2}\left(x + \frac{1}{x}\right)$.

(B) Find the value of $\frac{4^{3x-2}}{2^{x+3}} \times \frac{3^{x+4}}{(27)^{3-x}}$, when $x = 2$.

Essay Type Questions

38. If $x = \frac{1}{7+4\sqrt{3}}$ and $y = \frac{1}{7-4\sqrt{3}}$, find the value of $5x^2 - 7xy - 5y^2$.

39. $\frac{1}{\sqrt{1}+\sqrt{3}} + \frac{1}{\sqrt{3}+\sqrt{5}} + \ldots\ldots\ldots \frac{1}{\sqrt{79}+\sqrt{81}} =$ ________.

40. If $\frac{2^x}{1+2^x} = \frac{1}{3}$, then $\frac{8^x}{1-8^x} =$ ________.

41. Simplify: (i) $\sqrt{7+2\sqrt{10}} + \sqrt{7-2\sqrt{10}}$

(ii) $\sqrt{11+2\sqrt{3}+2\sqrt{7}+2\sqrt{21}}$

42. Simplify: $\frac{3}{\sqrt{19-2\sqrt{88}}} - \frac{8}{\sqrt{14+2\sqrt{33}}}$.

PRACTICE QUESTIONS COMPETITION WING

Level 1: Apply Your Concepts

Directions of questions from 1 to 5:
Evaluate.

1. $\sqrt{5} \times \sqrt{125} =$ ______.
2. $\dfrac{\sqrt{20}}{\sqrt{320}} =$ ______.
3. $\sqrt[3]{6} \times \sqrt[3]{6} \times \sqrt[3]{6} =$ ______.
4. $\sqrt{3} \div 4\sqrt{12} =$ ______.
5. $\sqrt{7+\sqrt{48}} =$ ______.

Directions of questions from 6 to 65:
Select the correct alternative from the given choices.

6. Which of the following fractions lie between $\frac{1}{5}$ and $\frac{1}{4}$?

A. $\frac{7}{33}$ B. $\frac{4}{11}$

C. $\frac{13}{57}$ D. $\frac{7}{17}$

(a) A and B (b) A and C
(c) B, C, and D (d) A, B, and D

7. What is the value of 4^{2x-2}, if $(16)^{2x+3} = (64)^{x+3}$?
(a) 64 (b) 256
(c) 32 (d) 512

8. Which of the following pairs have two equal values? (where $x \in R$) ______.
(a) $9^{x/2}, 24^{x/3}$ (b) $(256)^{4/x}, (4^3)^{4/x}$
(c) $(343)^{x/3}, (7^4)^{x/12}$ (d) $(36^2)^{2/7}, (6^3)^{2/7}$

9. The expression $\left(\sqrt{5}-\sqrt{3}\right)\left(\sqrt{7}-\sqrt{2}\right)$ when simplified becomes a:
(a) Simple surd. (b) Mixed surd.
(c) Compound surd. (d) Binomial surd.

10. If m and n are positive integers, then for a positive number a, $\left\{\sqrt[m]{\left(\sqrt[n]{a}\right)}\right\}^{mn} =$ ______.
(a) a^{mn} (b) a
(c) $a^{m/n}$ (d) 1

11. If $2^{-m} \times \frac{1}{2^m} = \frac{1}{4}$, then $\frac{1}{14}\left[(4^m)^{1/2} + \left(\frac{1}{5^m}\right)^{-1}\right] =$ ______
(a) $\frac{1}{2}$ (b) 2
(c) 4 (d) $\frac{-1}{4}$

12. If $6^x = 30$, then $6^{x-1} + 6^{x+1} =$ ______
(a) 30 (b) 150
(c) 185 (d) 900

13. $2[(16-15)^{-1} + 25\,(13-8)^{-2}]^{-1} + (1024)^0 =$ ______.
(a) 2 (b) 3
(c) 1 (d) 5

14. If $x = 2$ and $y = 4$, then $\left(\frac{x}{y}\right)^{x-y} + \left(\frac{y}{x}\right)^{y-x} =$ ______.
(a) 4 (b) 8
(c) 12 (d) 2

15. In which of the following pairs of surds are the given two surds similar?
(a) $\sqrt{5}, 7\sqrt{5}$ (b) $\sqrt[3]{7}, \sqrt[2]{7}$
(c) $\sqrt{7}, \sqrt{28}$ (d) Both (a) and (c)

16. Which of the following is the greatest?
(a) 7^2 (b) $(49)^{3/2}$
(c) $\left(\frac{1}{343}\right)^{-1/3}$ (d) $(2401)^{-1/4}$

17. If $p = 3$ and $q = 2$, then $(3p - 4q)^{q-p} \div (4p - 3q)^{2q-p}$ = ______.
(a) 1 (b) 6
(c) $\frac{1}{6}$ (d) $\frac{2}{3}$

18. $\left[\dfrac{(32)^{0.2} + (81)^{0.25}}{(256)^{0.5} - (121)^{0.5}}\right] =$ ______.

(a) 2 (b) 5
(c) 1 (d) 11

19. If $\sqrt{m} = \sqrt{a} + \sqrt{c}$ and $\sqrt{m}$, $\sqrt{a}$, and $\sqrt{c}$ are three surds, then
(a) $\sqrt{m}$ is dissimilar to $\sqrt{a}$ and $\sqrt{c}$.
(b) $\sqrt{a}$ and $\sqrt{c}$ are similar to $\sqrt{m}$.
(c) Only $\sqrt{a}$ is similar to $\sqrt{m}$.
(d) None of these

20. The surd obtained after rationalizing the numerator of $\dfrac{4-\sqrt{25-a}}{a-9}$ is equal to:
(a) $\dfrac{a-9}{4-\sqrt{25-a}}$
(b) $\dfrac{1}{4-\sqrt{25-a}}$
(c) $\dfrac{1}{(a-9)(4+\sqrt{25-a})}$
(d) $\dfrac{1}{4+\sqrt{25-a}}$

21. If $\sqrt{13-x\sqrt{10}} = \sqrt{8}+\sqrt{5}$, then what is the value of x?
(a) −5 (b) −6
(c) −4 (d) −2

22. If the surds $\sqrt[4]{4}, \sqrt[6]{5}, \sqrt[8]{6}$, and $\sqrt[12]{8}$ are arranged in ascending order from left to right, then the third surd from the left is:
(a) $\sqrt[12]{8}$ (b) $\sqrt[4]{4}$
(c) $\sqrt[8]{6}$ (d) $\sqrt[6]{5}$

23. $\sqrt{11\sqrt{11\sqrt{11\ldots}}}$
(a) $\sqrt[16]{11^5}$ (b) $\sqrt[16]{11}$
(c) $\sqrt[16]{11^{14}}$ (d) $\sqrt[16]{11^{15}}$

24. If $\dfrac{5-\sqrt{3}}{2+\sqrt{3}} = x + y\sqrt{3}$, then (x, y) is:
(a) (13, −7) (b) (−13, 7)
(c) (−13, −7) (d) (13, 7)

25. The simplified form of $\sqrt{125}+\sqrt{125}-\sqrt{845}$ is:
(a) $\sqrt{15}$ (b) $2\sqrt{5}$
(c) $-3\sqrt{5}$ (d) $-2\sqrt{5}$

26. Which of the following statements is true?
I. If x is a conjugate surd of y, then x can be a RF of y.
II. If x is a RF of y, then x need not be the conjugate of y.
(a) Only I (b) Only II
(c) Both I and II (d) Neither I nor II

27. If $\dfrac{3^{5x}\times(81)^2\times 6561}{3^{2x}} = 3^7$, then $x =$ ________
(a) 3 (b) −3
(c) $\dfrac{1}{3}$ (d) $\dfrac{-1}{3}$

28. If $\sqrt{2^n} = 1024$, then $3^{\left(\frac{n}{4}-4\right)} =$ ________.
(a) 3 (b) −3
(c) 27 (d) 81

29. If $\left[\left\{\left(\dfrac{1}{7^2}\right)^{-2}\right\}^{-1/3}\right]^{1/4} = 7^m$, then $m =$ ________.
(a) $\dfrac{-1}{3}$ (b) $\dfrac{1}{4}$
(c) −3 (d) 2

Level 2: Review Your Concepts

30. $\left[\left\{\left(\dfrac{1}{x^{a^2-b^2}}\right)^{\frac{1}{a-b}}\right\}^{a+b}\right]^{\frac{1}{(a+b)^2}} =$ ________.
(a) x^2 (b) $\dfrac{1}{x}$
(c) 7^3 (d) $\dfrac{1}{x^2}$

31. If $\dfrac{2^{m+n}}{2^{m-n}} = 16$ and $a = 2^{\frac{1}{10}}$, then $\dfrac{(a^{2m+n-p})^2}{(a^{m-2n+2p})^{-1}} =$ ________.
(a) 2 (b) $\dfrac{1}{4}$

(c) 9 (d) $\frac{1}{8}$

32. Simplify

$$\left[(p^{-1}+q^{-1})(p^{-1}-q^{-1})\div\left(\frac{1}{p^{-1}}-\frac{1}{q^{-1}}\right)\left(\frac{1}{p^{-1}}+\frac{1}{q^{-1}}\right)\right](pq)^2.$$

(a) $(pq)^2$ (b) -1
(c) $-(pq)^{-2}$ (d) 1

33. If $x=\frac{2}{\sqrt{10}-\sqrt{8}}$, $y=\frac{2}{\sqrt{10}+2\sqrt{2}}$, then $(x-y)^2=$

(a) $4\sqrt{2}$ (b) 32
(c) $8\sqrt{2}$ (d) 64

34. If $a=\sqrt{6}-\sqrt{3}$, $b=\sqrt{3}-\sqrt{2}$ and $c=\sqrt{2}-\sqrt{6}$, then find the value of $a^3+b^3+c^3-2abc$.

(a) $3\sqrt{2}-5\sqrt{3}-\sqrt{6}$
(b) $3\sqrt{2}-5\sqrt{3}-\sqrt{6}$
(c) $3\sqrt{2}-4\sqrt{3}+\sqrt{6}$
(d) $3\sqrt{2}+4\sqrt{3}+\sqrt{6}$

35. $\sqrt{\frac{81}{64}\sqrt{\frac{81}{64}\sqrt{\frac{81}{64}\sqrt{\frac{81}{64}}}}}\cdots\infty=$

(a) $\frac{81}{64}$ (b) $\frac{9}{8}$
(c) $\frac{3}{2}$ (d) $\frac{3}{2\sqrt{2}}$

36. If $a^p=b^q=c^r=abc$, then $pqr=$ ________.

(a) p^2q+q^2r (b) $pq+qr+pr$
(c) $(pq+qr+rp)^2$ (d) $pq(qr+rp)$

37. The value of $\left[(23+2^2)^{2/3}+(140-29)^{1/2}\right]^2$ is ________.

(a) 196 (b) 289
(c) 324 (d) 400

38. If $x=\sqrt{6}+\sqrt{5}$, then $x^2+\frac{1}{x^2}-2=$

(a) $2\sqrt{6}$ (b) $2\sqrt{5}$
(c) 24 (d) 20

39. Simplify

$$\frac{1}{\sqrt{19-\sqrt{360}}}-\frac{1}{\sqrt{21-\sqrt{440}}}+\frac{2}{\sqrt{20+\sqrt{396}}}=$$

________.

(a) 1 (b) 2
(c) 0 (d) None of these

40. If $a=\sqrt{17}-\sqrt{16}$ and $b=\sqrt{16}-\sqrt{15}$, then:

(a) $a<b$ (b) $a>b$
(c) $a=b$ (d) None of these

41. $\left(\sqrt[6]{15-2\sqrt{56}}\right)\cdot\left(\sqrt[3]{\sqrt{7}+2\sqrt{2}}\right)=$ ________.

(a) 0 (b) 1
(c) -1 (d) 2

42. $\sqrt{\sqrt{63}+\sqrt{56}}=$

(a) $\sqrt[4]{7}(\sqrt{3}+\sqrt{5})$ (b) $\sqrt[4]{7}(\sqrt{3}+1)$
(c) $\sqrt[4]{7}(\sqrt{3}+\sqrt{5})$ (d) $\sqrt[4]{7}(\sqrt{2}+1)$

43. If $\frac{\sqrt{7}+2\sqrt{3}}{2\sqrt{7}-\sqrt{5}}=\frac{c+\sqrt{p}+\sqrt{q}+\sqrt{r}}{23}$ $(p<q<r)$, where p, q, r are rational numbers, then $q+r-p=$

(a) 361 (b) 302
(c) 418 (d) 426

44. The following are the steps involved in finding the value of $x-y$ from $\frac{\sqrt{8}-\sqrt{5}}{\sqrt{8}+\sqrt{5}}=x-y\sqrt{40}$. Arrange them in sequential order.

(A) $\frac{13-2\sqrt{40}}{8-5}=x-y\sqrt{40}$

(B) $\frac{(\sqrt{8})^2+(\sqrt{5})^2-2(\sqrt{8})(\sqrt{5})}{(\sqrt{8})^2-(\sqrt{5})^2}=x-y\sqrt{40}$

(C) $x-y=\frac{11}{3}$

(D) $x=\frac{13}{3}$ and $y=\frac{2}{3}$

(E) $\frac{(\sqrt{8}-\sqrt{5})(\sqrt{8}-\sqrt{5})}{(\sqrt{8}+\sqrt{5})(\sqrt{8}-\sqrt{5})}=x-y\sqrt{40}$

(a) EABDC (b) EBADC
(c) ABDEC (d) DEBAC

45. The following are the steps involved in finding the smallest among $\sqrt{3}, \sqrt[3]{4}$, and $\sqrt[6]{15}$. Arrange them in sequential order.

(A) $\therefore \sqrt[6]{15}$ is the smallest.

(B) $\therefore 3^{1/2} = 3^{3/6}, 4^{1/3} = 4^{2/6}, 15^{1/6} = 15^{1/6}$

(C) The LCM of the denominators of the exponents is 6.

(D) $\sqrt{3} = 3^{1/2}, \sqrt[3]{4} = 4^{1/3}, \sqrt[6]{15} = 15^{1/6}$

(E) $\therefore \sqrt{3} = \sqrt[6]{27}, \sqrt[3]{4} = \sqrt[6]{16}, \sqrt[6]{15} = \sqrt[6]{15}$

(a) DCABE (b) DABEB
(c) DCBEA (d) DBCAE

46. If $y = 3 - \sqrt{8}$, then $\left(y - \frac{1}{y}\right)^2 =$ ______.

(a) 9 (b) 81
(c) 4 (d) 32

47. If $x = \frac{1}{\sqrt{3}+2}$, then $\left(x + \frac{1}{x}\right)^2 =$ ______.

(a) 16 (b) 3
(c) 12 (d) 6

48. If $\sqrt[x]{3} \times \sqrt[y]{5} = 10125$, then $12xy =$ ______.

(a) 1 (b) $\frac{1}{3}$
(c) 2 (d) $\frac{1}{2}$

49. If $x = \frac{1}{5+2\sqrt{6}}$, then $x^2 - 10x + 1 =$ ______.

(a) 1 (b) −1
(c) 0 (d) 10

50. If $x = \frac{2}{\sqrt{3}-\sqrt{5}}$ and $y = \frac{2}{\sqrt{3}+\sqrt{5}}$, then $x + y =$ ______.

(a) 3 (b) $4\sqrt{3}$ (c) $-2\sqrt{3}$ (d) 6

Level 3: Assess Your Concepts

51. If $\sum_{k=4}^{143} \frac{1}{\sqrt{k}+\sqrt{k+1}} = a - \sqrt{b}$, then a and b, respectively, are:

(a) 10 and 0 (b) −10 and 4
(c) 10 and 4 (d) −10 and 0

52. The surd $\frac{12}{3+\sqrt{5}+2\sqrt{2}}$, after rationalizing the denominator becomes:

(a) $\sqrt{5} - \sqrt{2} + \sqrt{10} + 1$

(b) $\sqrt{5} + \sqrt{10} + \sqrt{2} + 1$

(c) $\sqrt{10} + \sqrt{2} + \sqrt{5} + 1$

(d) $\sqrt{5} - \sqrt{10} - \sqrt{2} - 1$

53. If $A^{1/A} = B^{1/B} = C^{1/C}$, $A^{BC} + B^{AC} + C^{AB} = 729$. Which of the following equals $A^{1/A}$?

(a) $\sqrt[ABC]{81}$ (b) $\sqrt{2}$
(c) $\sqrt[ABC]{27}$ (d) $\sqrt[ABC]{9}$

54. If $x = \frac{1}{2-\sqrt{3}}$, the value of $x^3 - 2x^2 - 7x + 10$ is equal to:

(a) $2+\sqrt{3}$ (b) 10
(c) $7+2\sqrt{3}$ (d) 8

55. If $x = 1 + 5^{1/3} + 5^{2/3}$, then find the value of $x^3 - 3x^2 - 12x + 6$.

(a) 22 (b) 20
(c) 16 (d) 14

56. $\frac{4}{\sqrt{10-2\sqrt{21}}} =$ ______.

(a) $\frac{1}{4}(\sqrt{7}+\sqrt{3})$ (b) $\frac{1}{4}(\sqrt{7}-\sqrt{3})$
(c) $\sqrt{7}+\sqrt{3}$ (d) $\sqrt{7}-\sqrt{3}$

57. If $y = 3^{1/3} + 3$, then $y^3 - 9y^2 + 27y =$ ______.

(a) 27 (b) −27
(c) −30 (d) 30

58. $\frac{1}{\sqrt{8+2+\sqrt{15}}}$ ______.

(a) $\frac{1}{2}(\sqrt{5}+\sqrt{3})$ (b) $\frac{1}{2}(\sqrt{5}-\sqrt{3})$
(c) $\frac{1}{2}(\sqrt{5}+1)$ (d) $\frac{1}{2}(\sqrt{5}-1)$

59. If $x = 2^{1/3} - 2$, then $x^3 + 6x^2 + 12x =$ ______.

(a) 6 (b) −6
(c) 8 (d) −8

60. $\dfrac{3}{\sqrt{19 - 2\sqrt{88}}} - \dfrac{8}{\sqrt{14 + 2\sqrt{33}}} =$ ______.

(a) $\sqrt{19 + 2\sqrt{33}}$ (b) $\sqrt{14 - 2\sqrt{88}}$
(c) $\sqrt{11 + 2\sqrt{24}}$ (d) $\sqrt{11 - 2\sqrt{55}}$

61. $\sqrt{\sqrt[x]{2^x \sqrt[x^2]{3^{x^3} \sqrt[x^3]{6^{x^6} \sqrt[x^4]{9^{x^{10}}}}}}} =$

(a) 18 (b) 54
(c) 24 (d) 36

62. $\sqrt{7 + 2\sqrt{6}} + \sqrt{7 - 2\sqrt{6}} =$ ______.

(a) 14 (b) $\sqrt{6}$
(c) $2\sqrt{6}$ (d) 7

63. $\sqrt{3^2 \sqrt{9^2 \sqrt{(81)^2 \sqrt{16^{16}}}}} =$ ______.

(a) 6×2^4 (b) $3^3 \times 2$
(c) $6^3 \times 2^3$ (d) $6^3 \times 2$

64. $\sqrt[6]{15 - 2\sqrt{56}}\,\sqrt[3]{\sqrt{7} + 2\sqrt{2}} =$ ______.

(a) 0 (b) $\sqrt{2}$
(c) 1 (d) $\sqrt[6]{2}$

65. If $p = 7 - 4\sqrt{3}$, then $\dfrac{p^2 + 1}{7p} =$ ______.

(a) 2 (b) 1
(c) 7 (d) $\sqrt{3}$

AT

PRACTICE QUESTIONS JEE SPECIAL WING

Multiple-Answer Type Questions

Directions for questions 1 to 5:
Each question has FOUR options (a), (b), (c), and (d). ONE OR MORE THAN ONE of these four option(s) is/are the correct answer(s).

1. Which of the following is/are RF/RFs of $\sqrt{3}-\sqrt{2}$?
   (a) $\sqrt{3}+\sqrt{2}$ (b) $\sqrt{3}-\sqrt{2}$
   (c) $\sqrt{12}+\sqrt{8}$ (d) $\sqrt{12}-\sqrt{8}$

2. If $2187 \le 3^n < 59049$, where n is an integer, which of the following can be the value of n?
   (a) 6 (b) 7
   (c) 8 (d) 9

3. If $x^y = 4096$, where x and y are positive integers, then which of the following can be the value of xy.
   (a) 24 (b) 32
   (c) 48 (d) 128

4. Which of the following lies between 0.12 and 0.14?
   (a) $\frac{12}{90}$ (b) $\frac{12}{99}$
   (c) $\frac{11}{90}$ (d) $\frac{13}{99}$

5. $\sqrt{8-4\sqrt{3}} = \sqrt{x}-\sqrt{y}$, then which of the following is/are true?
   (a) $x-y=-4$ (b) $x-y=4$
   (c) $\frac{x}{y}=3$ (d) $\frac{x}{y}=\frac{1}{3}$

Match The Column

Directions for questions 6 to 10:
Read the paragraph given below and answer the questions.

$$A=\frac{1}{5-2\sqrt{6}}$$

$$B=\frac{1}{5+2\sqrt{6}}$$

$C=-10.$

Column A	Column B
6. $A+B$	(a) -30
7. $A\times B$	(b) -12
8. $(A-B)^2$	(c) 1
9. $\frac{1}{A^2}+\frac{1}{B^2}$	(d) 10
10. $A^3+B^3+C^3$	(e) 96
	(f) 98
	(g) 100

Comprehension-Based Questions

Directions for questions 11 to 15:
Read the paragraph given below and answer the questions.
In the diagram $ABCD$ and $APQR$ are two rectangular fields. QR and CD are produced to meet at point N. QP and CB are produced to meet at point M. $BR \perp PD$. An ant is at A. It found food particles at C, M, Q and N. The ant is very hungry and is confused in finding the shortest path among AC, AM, AQ and AN, to get to the food. Please help the ant in finding the shortest path from A to reach its food.

Also given that $AB=\sqrt{28}+\sqrt{36}$ m.

$BC=\sqrt{18}+\sqrt{10}$ m.

$AP=\sqrt{24}+\sqrt{39}$ m.

$PQ=\sqrt{12}+\sqrt{15}$ m.

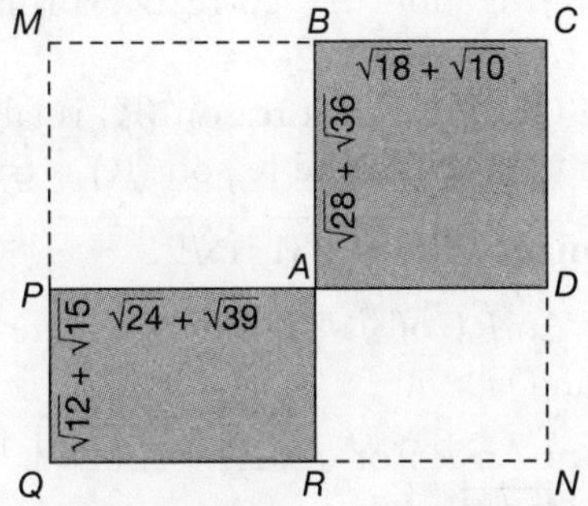

11. If the ant travels in the path AC, what is the distance travelled by the ant (in metres)??

(a) $\sqrt{127+24\sqrt{7}+12\sqrt{26}}$ (b) $\sqrt{92+24\sqrt{7}+12\sqrt{5}}$

(c) $\sqrt{127+12\sqrt{7}+24\sqrt{13}}$ (d) $\sqrt{92+12\sqrt{7}+24\sqrt{5}}$

12. If the ant travels in the path AM, what is the distance travelled by the ant (in metres)?

(a) $\sqrt{127+24\sqrt{7}+12\sqrt{26}}$ (b) $\sqrt{55+12\sqrt{10}}$

(c) $\sqrt{127+12\sqrt{7}+24\sqrt{13}}$ (d) $\sqrt{55+24\sqrt{5}}$

13. If the ant travels in the path AQ, what is the distance travelled by the ant (in metres)?

(a) $\sqrt{55+12\sqrt{10}}$ (b) $\sqrt{60+12\sqrt{26}+12\sqrt{5}}$

(c) $\sqrt{90+12\sqrt{26}+12\sqrt{5}}$ (d) $\sqrt{55+24\sqrt{5}}$

14. If the ant travels in the path AN, what is the distance travelled by the ant (in metres)?

(a) $\sqrt{55+24\sqrt{5}}$ (b) $\sqrt{92+12\sqrt{7}+12\sqrt{10}}$

(c) $\sqrt{92+12\sqrt{7}+24\sqrt{5}}$ (d) $\sqrt{55+12\sqrt{10}}$

15. What is the length of the shortest path (in metres)?

(a) $\sqrt{127+24\sqrt{7}+12\sqrt{26}}$ (b) $\sqrt{90+12\sqrt{26}+12\sqrt{5}}$

(c) $\sqrt{92+24\sqrt{7}+12\sqrt{5}}$ (d) $\sqrt{55+24\sqrt{5}}$

Directions for questions 16 to 20:
Read the options given below and answer the questions.

$P=\sqrt{29}+\sqrt{37}$

$Q=\sqrt{31}+\sqrt{35}$

$R=\sqrt{27}+\sqrt{39}$

$S=\sqrt{32}+\sqrt{34}$

$T=\sqrt{40}+\sqrt{26}$

16. The greatest among P, Q, R, and T?

(a) P (b) Q

(c) R (d) T

17. The smallest among P, R, S, and T?

(a) P (b) R

(c) S (d) T

18. The value of $\frac{6}{(S+Q)(S-Q)}$ is ____.

(a) $\sqrt{1040}-\sqrt{1037}$

(b) $\sqrt{1088}+\sqrt{1085}$

(c) $\sqrt{1073}-\sqrt{1070}$

(d) $\sqrt{1056}-\sqrt{1053}$

19. Which of the following is true?

(a) $S>P>T$ (b) $Q>S>R$

(c) $S>R>Q$ (d) $Q>R>P$

20. Which of the following is true?

(a) $\frac{1}{Q}<\frac{1}{R}<\frac{1}{P}$ (b) $\frac{1}{Q}<\frac{1}{S}<\frac{1}{R}$

(c) $\frac{1}{S}<\frac{1}{P}<\frac{1}{T}$ (d) $\frac{1}{S}<\frac{1}{R}<\frac{1}{Q}$

Assertion and Reason Type Questions

Directions for questions 21 to 25:
Read the options given below and answer the questions.

(a) Both assertion (A) and reason (R) are true, and the reason (R) is the correct explanation of the assertion (A).
(b) Both assertion (A) and reason (R) are true, and the reason (R) is not the correct explanation of the assertion (A).
(c) Assertion (A) is true, but reason (R) is false.
(d) Assertion (A) is false, and reason (R) is true.

21. **Assertion:** An RF of $\sqrt[6]{81}$ is $\sqrt[6]{9}$.

Reason: An RF of $\sqrt[m]{a^n}$ is $\sqrt[m]{a^{m-n}}$, where a is a rational number and $m>n$.

22. **Assertion:** An RF of $\sqrt{2027}-\sqrt{2026}$ is $\sqrt{2027}+\sqrt{2026}$.

Reason: An RF of $\sqrt[m]{a}-\sqrt[m]{b}$ is $\sqrt[m]{a}+\sqrt[m]{b}$.

23. **Assertion:** The conjugate $\sqrt{20}-28$ is $\sqrt{20}+28$.

Reason: Two surds are conjugate to each other, when their sum is a rational number, and their product is also a rational number.

24. **Assertion:** Every rational number can be expressed as terminating decimal or non-terminating recurring decimal.

Reason: An irrational number cannot be expressed as $\frac{p}{q}$ form where p and q are coprimes.

25. **Assertion:** $1^0\times2^0\times3^0\times4^0\times\ldots\times100^0=1$.

Reason: Any number raised to the power of zero is one.

ANSWER KEYS

Crossword

Across

1. Infinite 3. Conjugate 7. Binomial 8. Surd 10. Real

Down

2. Irrational 4. One 5. Mixed 6. Similar 9. RF

Classroom Wing

Very Short Answer Type Questions

1. 2 2. 2 3. $-\sqrt{2}-3$ 4. $\frac{10}{3}$ 5. $3+\sqrt{3}$

6. 9 7. Rationalizing factor 8. $3\times\sqrt[3]{3}$

9. $5^{2/3}-1+5^{-2/3}$ 10. True 11. False 12. False 13. $\frac{3\sqrt{11}}{11}$

14. $2\sqrt{7}$ 15. $\sqrt[12]{5000}$ 16. $\sqrt[3]{3}$ 17. $\sqrt{12}$ 18. $4\sqrt{7}$

19. 3 20. $5\sqrt[3]{5}$ 21. $\sqrt[3]{\frac{128}{27}}$ 22. $\frac{\sqrt[3]{180}}{6}$ 23. $\sqrt[6]{36}$

24. 5

Short Answer Type Questions

25. 46 26. 6 27. (A) $12\sqrt{3}-12\sqrt{2}$ (B) 35

28. $\frac{(c^2b+8c\sqrt{b}+17)}{(c\sqrt{b}+4)}$ 29. $80\sqrt{5}$ 30. $-2\sqrt{3}$ 31. $\sqrt{11}-\sqrt{10}$

32. $\sqrt{55}-3\sqrt{2}-3$ 33. (A) $\sqrt[4]{5},\sqrt[3]{4},\sqrt{8}$ (B) $3\sqrt{5}$ 34. $\sqrt{2}+\sqrt{3}+\sqrt{5}$

35. $a=\frac{67}{109}, b=\frac{-2}{109}$ 36. -0.891 37. (A) $3\sqrt{3}$ (B) 216

Essay Type Questions

38. $-7(1+80\sqrt{3})$ 39. 4 40. $\frac{1}{7}$

41. (i) $2\sqrt{5}$, (ii) $1+\sqrt{3}+\sqrt{7}$ 42. $\sqrt{8}+\sqrt{3}$

Competition Wing

Level 1: Apply Your Concepts

1. 25 2. $\frac{1}{4}$ 3. 6 4. $\frac{1}{8}$ 5. $2+\sqrt{3}$

6. (b) 7. (b) 8. (a) 9. (c) 10. (b)

11. (a)	12. (c)	13. (a)	14. (b)	15. (d)
16. (b)	17. (c)	18. (c)	19. (b)	20. (d)
21. (c)	22. (d)	23. (d)	24. (a)	25. (c)
26. (c)	27. (b)	28. (b)	29. (a)	

Level 2: Review Your Concepts

30. (b)	31. (a)	32. (b)	33. (b)	34. (c)
35. (a)	36. (b)	37. (d)	38. (d)	39. (c)
40. (a)	41. (b)	42. (d)	43. (a)	44. (b)
45. (c)	46. (d)	47. (a)	48. (a)	49. (c)
50. (c)				

Level 3: Assess Your Concepts

51. (a)	52. (b)	53. (b)	54. (d)	55. (a)
56. (c)	57. (d)	58. (b)	59. (b)	60. (c)
61. (a)	62. (c)	63. (d)	64. (c)	65. (a)

JEE Special Wing

Multiple-Answer Type Questions

1. (a, c)	2. (b, c, d)	3. (a, b, c, d)	4. (a, b, c, d)	5. (b, c)

Match The Column

6. (d)	7. (c)	8. (e)	9. (f)	10. (a)

Comprehension-Based Questions

11. (b)	12. (a)	13. (c)	14. (a)	15. (d)
16. (b)	17. (d)	18. (b)	19. (a)	20. (c)

Assertion and Reason Type Questions

21. (a)	22. (c)	23. (d)	24. (b)	25. (c)

Hints and Explanations

Classroom Wing

Very Short Answer Type Questions

1. $\sqrt{324+2\sqrt{323}}=\sqrt{\left(\sqrt{323}+1\right)^2}=\sqrt{323}+1$

$\sqrt{324-2\sqrt{323}}=\sqrt{\left(\sqrt{323}-1\right)^2}=\sqrt{323}-1$

Required value $=\sqrt{323}+1-\left(\sqrt{323}-1\right)$

$=\sqrt{323}+1-\sqrt{323}+1=2$

2. $\dfrac{9^{3^{6^{0^{8^{7}}}}}-7^{3^{5^{0^{4^{9}}}}}}{(63)^{3^{0^{7}}}+(81)^{5^{0^{7}}}+(49)^{6^{0^{8}}}}$

$=\dfrac{9^{3^1}-7^{3^1}}{(63)^1+(81)^1+(79)^1}$

$=\dfrac{9^3-7^3}{9(7)+9^2+7^2}$

$=\dfrac{(9-7)(9^2+9(7)+7^2)}{9^2+9(7)+7^2}$

$=9-7=2$

3. $(3\sqrt{2}+6)-(9+2\sqrt{2})=\sqrt{2}-3$

Choice (2) follows, $\left(\sqrt{2}-3\right)\left(-\sqrt{2}-\sqrt{3}\right)=-(2-9)=7$

$\sqrt{2}-3-\sqrt{2}-3=-6$

$-\sqrt{2}-3$ is a conjugate of the given surd.

4. $3^x = 9^y = 27^z = 81$

$3^x = 81$ $\quad$ $9^y = 81$ $\quad$ $27^z = 81$

$x = 4$ $\quad$ $y = 2$ $\quad$ $3^{3z} = 3^4$

$z = \dfrac{4}{3}$

$x - y + z = 4 - 2 + \dfrac{4}{3} = \dfrac{10}{3}$.

5. $\dfrac{6}{3-\sqrt{3}}=\dfrac{6}{3-\sqrt{3}}\times\dfrac{3+\sqrt{3}}{3+\sqrt{3}}$

$=\dfrac{6\left(3+\sqrt{3}\right)}{9-3}=3+\sqrt{3}.$

6. If x and y are rational,

i.e., the given equation is equal.

Therefore, $x = 4$ and $y = 5$

Hence, $x + y = 9$

7. If the product of two surds is a rational number, then each of the two is a RF of the other.

8. $\left((3)^{\frac{1}{3}}\right)^4=(3)^{\frac{4}{3}}=(3)^{\frac{1}{3}}(3)^{\frac{3}{3}}=3\sqrt[3]{3}$

9. Rationalizing factor of $5^{\frac{1}{3}}+5^{\frac{-1}{3}}$ is $a^3 + b^3 = (a + b)(a^2 - ab + b^2)$

$\therefore$ RF of $5^{\frac{1}{3}}+5^{\frac{-1}{3}}$ is $\left[5^{\frac{1}{3}}\right]^2-\left[5^{\frac{1}{3}}.5^{\frac{-1}{3}}\right]+\left[5^{\frac{-1}{3}}\right]^2$

$=5^{\frac{2}{3}}-1+5^{\frac{-2}{3}}$

10. $\sqrt{6}-\sqrt{7}$ is the conjugate surd of $\sqrt{6}+\sqrt{7}$.

11. False.

12. False

There can be many values of q for which pq is rational.

13. Divide and multiply by $\sqrt{11}$.

$\dfrac{3\times\sqrt{11}}{\sqrt{11}\times\sqrt{11}}=\dfrac{3\sqrt{11}}{\sqrt{11\times11}}=\dfrac{3\sqrt{11}}{11}$

14. $\sqrt{28}=\sqrt{7\times4}=2\sqrt{7}$

15. $(5)^{\frac{1}{3}}\times(2)^{\frac{1}{4}}=(5)^{\frac{4}{12}}\times(2)^{\frac{3}{12}}=\sqrt[12]{5^4}\times\sqrt[12]{2^3}$

$=\sqrt[12]{5^4\times2^3}=\sqrt[12]{625\times8}=\sqrt[12]{5000}$

16. $\sqrt{2}=1.414$

$\sqrt[3]{3}=1.4422$

$\therefore$ $\sqrt[3]{3}$ is greater.

17. $2\sqrt{3}=\sqrt{2^2\times3}=\sqrt{4\times3}=\sqrt{12}$

18. $\sqrt{14}\times\sqrt{8}=\sqrt{14\times8}=\sqrt{112}$

$=\sqrt{16\times7}=4\sqrt{7}$

19. $\dfrac{\sqrt[3]{81}}{\sqrt[3]{3}}=\sqrt[3]{\dfrac{81}{3}}=\sqrt[3]{27}=3$

20. $\sqrt[3]{625} = \sqrt[3]{125 \times 5} = \sqrt[3]{5^3 \times 5} = 5\sqrt[3]{5}$

21. $\sqrt[3]{\left(\frac{2}{3}\right)^3 16} = \sqrt[3]{\frac{8}{27} \times 16} = \sqrt[3]{\frac{128}{27}}$

22. Multiply and divide by $\left(\sqrt[3]{6}\right)^2$

$\sqrt[3]{\frac{5}{6}} \times \frac{\left(\sqrt[3]{6}\right)^2}{\left(\sqrt[3]{6}\right)^2} = \frac{\sqrt[3]{5}}{\sqrt[3]{6}} \times \frac{\sqrt[3]{36}}{\sqrt[3]{36}} = \frac{\sqrt[3]{180}}{6}$

23. $\sqrt[6]{\frac{144}{4}} = \sqrt[6]{36}$

24. $\sqrt{15625} = 125$

$\sqrt[3]{125} = 5$

Short Answer Type Question

25. Going by the options, $x = 7 + \sqrt{3}$, $y = 7 - \sqrt{3}$

$xy = (7 + \sqrt{3})(7 - \sqrt{3})$

$= 49 - 3 = 46$ is a rational number

26. $\frac{3\left(\sqrt{3}-1\right)}{2} + \frac{3\left(\sqrt{5}-\sqrt{3}\right)}{2} + \frac{3\left(\sqrt{7}-\sqrt{5}\right)}{2} + \ldots\ldots + \frac{3\left(\sqrt{25}-\sqrt{23}\right)}{2}$

$= \frac{3}{2}\left[\sqrt{3} - 1 + \sqrt{5} - \sqrt{3} + \sqrt{7} - \sqrt{5} + \ldots. + \sqrt{25} - \sqrt{23}\right]$

$= \frac{3}{2}\left[-1 + \sqrt{25}\right] = \frac{3}{2}[4] = 6$

27. (A) $2\sqrt{4 \times 3} - 3\sqrt{8 \times 4} + 2\sqrt{3 \times 16}$

$4\sqrt{3} - 12\sqrt{2} + 8\sqrt{3}$

$12\sqrt{3} - 12\sqrt{2}$

(B) Given, $x^4 - 1 = 2400$

$x^4 = 2401$

$x^4 = 7^4$

$\Rightarrow x = 7$ ($\because x$ is positive)

$y^5 + 1 = 3126$

$y^5 = 3125$

$y^5 = 5^5$

$y = 5$

$\therefore\ xy = 7 \times 5 = 35.$

28. We are given that, $x = c\sqrt{b} + 4$.

It is required to find the value of $x + \frac{1}{x}$

As we have, $x = c\sqrt{b} + 4$

Then, $\frac{1}{x} = \frac{1}{(c\sqrt{b} + 4)}$

Thus, we get,

$x + \frac{1}{x} = (c\sqrt{b} + 4) + \frac{1}{(c\sqrt{b} + 4)}$

i.e. $x + \frac{1}{x} = \frac{(c\sqrt{b} + 4)^2 + 1}{c\sqrt{b} + 4}$

i.e. $x + \frac{1}{x} = \frac{c^2 b + 16 + 8c\sqrt{b} + 1}{c\sqrt{b} + 4}$

i.e. $x + \frac{1}{x} = \frac{c^2 b + 8c\sqrt{b} + 17}{c\sqrt{b} + 4}$

Hence, the value of $x + \frac{1}{x} = \frac{c^2 b + 8c\sqrt{b} + 17}{c\sqrt{b} + 4}$.

29. $2\sqrt{125} - 5\sqrt{5} + 3\sqrt{3125}$

$= 2\sqrt{25 \times 5} - 5\sqrt{5} + 3\sqrt{625 \times 5}$

$= 10\sqrt{5} - 5\sqrt{5} + 75\sqrt{5}$

$= 80\sqrt{5}.$

30. Given, $x = \sqrt{2} - \sqrt{3}$

$\frac{1}{x} = \frac{1}{\sqrt{2} - \sqrt{3}} \times \frac{\sqrt{2} + \sqrt{3}}{\sqrt{2} + \sqrt{3}}$

$= \frac{\sqrt{2} + \sqrt{3}}{2 - 3}$

$= -\sqrt{2} - \sqrt{3}$

$X + \frac{1}{x} = \sqrt{2} - \sqrt{3} + \left(-\sqrt{2} - \sqrt{3}\right)$

$= \sqrt{2} - \sqrt{3} - \sqrt{2} - \sqrt{3}$

$= -2\sqrt{3}.$

31. $\sqrt{11} - \sqrt{10} = 3.3166 - 3.1622 = 0.154$

$\sqrt{12} - \sqrt{11} = 3.4641 - 3.3166 = 0.147$

$\sqrt{11} - \sqrt{10}$ is greater.

32. $\frac{5\sqrt{5}}{\sqrt{11} + \sqrt{6}} \times \frac{\sqrt{11} - \sqrt{6}}{\sqrt{11} - \sqrt{6}} - \frac{3\sqrt{2}}{\sqrt{6} + \sqrt{3}} \times \frac{\sqrt{6} - \sqrt{3}}{\sqrt{6} - \sqrt{3}}$

$- \frac{3\sqrt{2}}{\sqrt{15} + 3\sqrt{2}} \times \frac{\sqrt{15} - 3\sqrt{2}}{\sqrt{15} - 3\sqrt{2}}$

$\frac{5\sqrt{5}(\sqrt{11} - \sqrt{6})}{11 - 6} - \frac{3\sqrt{3}(\sqrt{6} - \sqrt{3})}{6 - 3} - \frac{3\sqrt{2}(\sqrt{15} - 3\sqrt{2})}{15 - 18}$

$$\sqrt{5}(\sqrt{11}-\sqrt{6})-\sqrt{3}(\sqrt{6}-\sqrt{3})+\sqrt{2}(\sqrt{15}-3\sqrt{2})$$
$$=\sqrt{55}-3\sqrt{2}-3$$

33. (A) Order of the given irrational number is different. So, first we need to convert them into same order.

Order of the given irrational number is 3, 4, 2, respectively, and LCM of 3, 4, 2 is 12.

So, we need to convert them into order of 12.

Now,

$$\sqrt[3]{4}=\left(\sqrt[12]{(4)\frac{1}{3}}\right)^{12}=\sqrt[12]{(4)\frac{12}{3}}=\sqrt[12]{4^4}=\sqrt[12]{256}$$

$$\sqrt[4]{5}=\left(\sqrt[12]{(5)\frac{1}{4}}\right)^{12}=\sqrt[12]{(5)\frac{12}{4}}=\sqrt[12]{5^3}=\sqrt[12]{125}$$

$$\sqrt{8}=\left(\sqrt[12]{(8)\frac{1}{2}}\right)^{12}=\sqrt[12]{(8)\frac{12}{2}}=\sqrt[12]{(8)^6}=\sqrt[12]{262,144}$$

Hence, correct ascending order is $\sqrt[4]{5}, \sqrt[3]{4}, \sqrt{8}$.

(B) $\sqrt{34}$; $4\sqrt{2}=\sqrt{4^2\times 2}=\sqrt{32}$

$2\sqrt{7}=\sqrt{2^2\times 7}=\sqrt{28}$

$3\sqrt{5}=\sqrt{3^2\times 5}=\sqrt{45}$

$\therefore$ $3\sqrt{5}$ is the biggest

34. $10+2\sqrt{6}+\sqrt{60}+2\sqrt{10}=a+\sqrt{x}+\sqrt{y}+\sqrt{z}$

$a=10,\ b=24,\ c=60,\ d=40$

$$x=\frac{1}{2}\sqrt{\frac{bd}{c}}=\frac{1}{2}\sqrt{\frac{24\times 40}{60}}=2$$

$$y=\frac{1}{2}\sqrt{\frac{bc}{d}}=\frac{1}{2}\sqrt{\frac{24\times 60}{40}}=3$$

$$z=\frac{1}{2}\sqrt{\frac{cd}{b}}=\frac{1}{2}\sqrt{\frac{60\times 40}{24}}=5$$

$$\sqrt{x}+\sqrt{y}+\sqrt{z}=\sqrt{2}+\sqrt{3}+\sqrt{5}$$

35. $\dfrac{2+3\sqrt{5}}{4+5\sqrt{5}}\times\dfrac{4-5\sqrt{5}}{4-5\sqrt{5}}$

$$\frac{(2+3\sqrt{5})(4-5\sqrt{5})}{16-125}=\frac{8-10\sqrt{5}+12\sqrt{5}-75}{-109}$$
$$=\frac{2\sqrt{5}-67}{-109}$$

$$\frac{2\sqrt{5}-67}{-109}=a+b\sqrt{5}$$

$$a=\frac{67}{109}\quad b=\frac{-2}{109}$$

36. Given $\sqrt{2}=1.414, \sqrt{3}=1.732, \sqrt{5}=2.236$

$$=\frac{1-1.732}{2.236-1.414}=\frac{-0.732}{0.822}=-0.891$$

37. (A) If $x=3\sqrt{3}-\sqrt{26}$,

$$\frac{1}{2}\left(3\sqrt{3}+\sqrt{13}\sqrt{2}+\frac{1}{3\sqrt{3}+\sqrt{13}\sqrt{2}}\right)$$
$$=\frac{1}{2}\left(3\sqrt{3}+\sqrt{13}\sqrt{2}+\frac{(3\sqrt{3}-\sqrt{13}\sqrt{12})}{27-26}\right)$$
$$=\frac{1}{2}\left(\frac{6\sqrt{3}}{1}\right)=3\sqrt{3}$$

(B) $$\frac{(2^2)^{(3x-2)}}{2^{x+3}}\times\frac{3^{x+4}}{(3^3)^{3-x}}$$
$$=\frac{2^{6x-4}\times 3^{x+4}}{2^{x+3}\times 3^{9-3x}}$$
$$=2^{6x-4-x-3}\times 3^{x+4-9+3x}$$
$$=2^{5x-7}\times 3^{4x-5}$$
$$=2^{10-7}\times 3^{8-5}(\text{given } x=2)$$
$$=2^3\times 3^3$$
$$=8\times 27$$
$$=216$$

Essay Type Questions

38. If $x=\dfrac{1}{7+4\sqrt{3}}, y=\dfrac{1}{7-4\sqrt{3}}$

$$x^2=\frac{1}{(7+4\sqrt{3})^2}=\frac{1}{49+48+56\sqrt{3}}=\frac{1}{97+56\sqrt{3}}$$

$$y^2=\frac{1}{(7+4\sqrt{3})^2}=\frac{1}{49+48+56\sqrt{3}}=\frac{1}{97+56\sqrt{3}}$$

$$xy=\frac{1}{7+4\sqrt{3}}\times\frac{1}{7-4\sqrt{3}}=\frac{1}{7^2-(4\sqrt{3})^2}$$
$$=\frac{1}{49-48}=1$$

$$5x^2-7xy-5y^2=\frac{5}{97+56\sqrt{3}}-7(1)-\frac{5}{97-56\sqrt{3}}$$
$$=-7+\frac{5(97-56\sqrt{3})-5(97+56\sqrt{3})}{(97)^2-(56\sqrt{3})2}$$

$$= -7 + \frac{-280\sqrt{3} - 280\sqrt{3}}{9409 - 9408}$$

$$= -7 - 560\sqrt{3} = -7\left(1 + 80\sqrt{3}\right)$$

39. $\frac{1}{1+\sqrt{3}} = \frac{1}{1+\sqrt{3}} \times \frac{1-\sqrt{3}}{1-\sqrt{3}} = \frac{1-\sqrt{3}}{-2}$

$\frac{1}{\sqrt{3}+\sqrt{5}} = \frac{1}{\sqrt{3}+\sqrt{5}} \times \frac{\sqrt{3}-\sqrt{5}}{\sqrt{3}-\sqrt{5}} = \frac{\sqrt{3}-\sqrt{5}}{-2}$

$\vdots \qquad \vdots$

Now, $\frac{1}{\sqrt{79}+\sqrt{81}} = \frac{1}{\sqrt{79}+\sqrt{81}} \times \frac{\sqrt{79}-\sqrt{81}}{\sqrt{79}-\sqrt{81}}$

$$= \frac{\sqrt{79}-\sqrt{81}}{-2}$$

$$= \frac{1}{1+\sqrt{3}} + \frac{1}{\sqrt{3}+\sqrt{5}} + ... \frac{1}{\sqrt{79}+\sqrt{81}}$$

$$\frac{1-\sqrt{3}}{-2} + \frac{\sqrt{3}-\sqrt{5}}{-2} + ... \frac{\sqrt{79}-\sqrt{81}}{-2}$$

$$= \frac{1-\sqrt{3}+\sqrt{3}-\sqrt{5}+.....+\sqrt{79}-\sqrt{81}}{-2}$$

$$= \frac{1-9}{-2} = \frac{-8}{-2} = 4$$

40. $\frac{2^x}{1+2^x} = \frac{1}{3}$

$3.2^x = 1 + 2^x$

$3.2^x - 2^x = 1 \Rightarrow 2.2^x = 1$

$\Rightarrow 2^{x+1} = 2^0 \Rightarrow x + 1 = 0 \Rightarrow x = -1$

$$\frac{8^x}{1-8^x} = \frac{8^{-1}}{1-8^{-1}} = \frac{\frac{1}{8}}{1-\frac{1}{8}} = \frac{\frac{1}{8}}{\frac{7}{8}}$$

$$= \frac{1}{7}$$

41. (i) $\sqrt{7+2\sqrt{10}} + \sqrt{7-2\sqrt{10}}$

$$= \sqrt{5+2+2\sqrt{5}.\sqrt{2}} + \sqrt{5+2-2\sqrt{5}.\sqrt{2}}$$

$$= \sqrt{\left(\sqrt{5}\right)^2 + \left(\sqrt{2}\right)^2 + 2\sqrt{5}.\sqrt{2}} + \sqrt{\left(\sqrt{5}\right)^2 + \left(\sqrt{2}\right)^2 - 2\sqrt{5}.\sqrt{2}}$$

$$= \sqrt{\left(\sqrt{5}+\sqrt{2}\right)^2} + \sqrt{\left(\sqrt{5}-\sqrt{2}\right)^2}$$

$$= \sqrt{5} + \sqrt{2} + \sqrt{5} - \sqrt{2} = 2\sqrt{5}.$$

(ii) $\sqrt{11+2\sqrt{3}+2\sqrt{7}+2\sqrt{21}}$

$$= \sqrt{1+3+7+2\sqrt{3\times 1}+2\sqrt{7\times 1}+2\sqrt{3\times 7}}$$

$$= \sqrt{\left(\sqrt{1}+\sqrt{3}+\sqrt{7}\right)^2}$$

$$= 1 + \sqrt{3} + \sqrt{7}$$

42. $\frac{3}{\sqrt{19-2\sqrt{88}}} - \frac{8}{\sqrt{14+2\sqrt{33}}}$

$$= \frac{3}{\sqrt{11}-\sqrt{8}} - \frac{8}{\sqrt{11}+\sqrt{3}}$$

$$= \frac{3\left(\sqrt{11}+\sqrt{8}\right)}{11-8} - \frac{8\left(\sqrt{11}-\sqrt{3}\right)}{11-3}$$

$$= \sqrt{11} + \sqrt{8} - \sqrt{11} + \sqrt{3}$$

$$= \sqrt{8} + \sqrt{3}.$$

Competition Wing

Level 1: Apply Your Concepts

1. $\sqrt{5}\times\sqrt{125}$

$= \sqrt{5\times125}$

$= \sqrt{625}$

$= 25$

2. $\frac{\sqrt{20}}{\sqrt{320}}$

$= \frac{\sqrt{20}}{\sqrt{320}} = \sqrt{\frac{2}{32}} = \sqrt{\frac{1}{16}} = \frac{1}{4}$

3. $\sqrt[3]{6}\times\sqrt[3]{6}\times\sqrt[3]{6}$

$\sqrt[3]{6\times6\times6} = \sqrt[3]{216} = 6$

4. $\sqrt{3}\div4\sqrt{12}$

$\frac{\sqrt{3}}{4\sqrt{12}} = \frac{\sqrt{3}}{4\sqrt{4\times3}} = \frac{1}{8}$

5. $\sqrt{7+\sqrt{48}} = \sqrt{x}+\sqrt{y}$ squaring on both sides

$7+\sqrt{48} = x+y+2\sqrt{xy}$

$\Rightarrow\ x+y=7$

$\sqrt{xy} = 2\sqrt{3}$

$xy = 12$

$x = 4,\ y = 3$

$\sqrt{x}+\sqrt{y}$

$2+\sqrt{3}$

6. Convert them into decimal form.
7. Simplify the bases which makes the powers equal.
8. Simplify the numbers given in options.
9. Find the product and recall the types of surds.
10. Recall the laws of radicals.
11. $2^{-2m} = 2^{-2}$ which gives $m = 1$.
12. Given, $6^x = 30$

$6^{x-1} = \frac{6^x}{6} = \frac{30}{6} = 5; 6^{x+1} = (6^x)6 = (30)6 = 180.$

$\therefore 6^{x-1}+6^{x+1} = 5+180 = 185.$

13. Simplify the expression.
14. Substitute the values of x and y.
15. Recall the definition of similar surds.
16. Convert the base into same number.
17. Substitute the values of p and q.
18. Apply laws of indices.
19. Recall the definitions of similar and dissimilar surds.
20. RF of $a-\sqrt{b}$ is $a+\sqrt{b}$.
21. Taking squares on both the sides.
22. Convert the surds into similar surds.
23. $\sqrt{a\sqrt{a\sqrt{a\ldots}}}$ n terms $= a^{\frac{2^n-1}{2^n}}$.
24. Rationalize the denominator of $\frac{(5-\sqrt{3})}{(2+\sqrt{3})}$.
25. Factorize each rational part in the compound surd.
26. Recall the definitions of RF and conjugate.
27. Apply laws of indices.
28. $2^n = (2^{10})^2$ which gives n = 20
29. Apply laws of indices.

Level 2: Review Your Concepts

30. (i) $(a^m)^n = a^{mn}$.

(ii) Use $\left((a^m)^n\right)^s = a^{mns}$.

31. (i) Apply laws of indices

(ii) $\frac{2^{m+n}}{2^{m-n}} = 16\ \Rightarrow\ 2^{2m} = 2^4$. Find the value of m and apply in the given expression.

32. (i) $\frac{1}{a^{-m}} = a^m$ and $a^{-m} = \frac{1}{a^m}$.

(ii) $p^{-1}+q^{-1} = \frac{1}{p}+\frac{1}{q}$ and $\frac{1}{p^{-1}}+\frac{1}{q^{-1}} = p+q$.

33. (i) Rationalize the denominators of x and y

(ii) Rationalize the denominators of both x and y.

34. (i) If $a+b+c=0$, then $a^3+b^3+c^3 = 3abc$.

(ii) If $a+b+c=0$, then $a^3+b^3+c^3-3abc = 0$.

(iii) $a^3+b^3+c^3-2abc = abc$.

35. (i) Let the given expression be y and square on both sides.

(ii) Let $y = \sqrt{\frac{81}{64}\sqrt{\frac{81}{64}\sqrt{\frac{81}{64}}}}\ldots\infty$

(iii) $y^2 = \frac{81}{64}\sqrt{\frac{81}{64}\sqrt{\frac{81}{64}}}\ldots\infty$

$\Rightarrow y^2 = \frac{81}{64}y.$

36. (i) Assume each of the power as k, then find pqr.

(ii) Using, $a^p = b^q = c^r = abc$, find the values of a, b and c in terms of (abc).

(iii) Multiply the obtained a, b, and c values and compare the exponents.

37. (i) Simplify the numbers in the brackets first and then write into exponential forms.

(ii) $23+2^2 = 27 = 3^3$; $140-19$

$= 121 = 11^2.$

38. (i) Rationalize the denominator of $\frac{1}{x}$.

(ii) $x = \sqrt{6}+\sqrt{5} \Rightarrow \frac{1}{x} = \sqrt{6}-\sqrt{5}$.

(iii) $\left(x^2+\frac{1}{x^2}-2\right) = \left(x-\frac{1}{x}\right)^2.$

39. (i) Express every denominator in the form $\sqrt{a}-\sqrt{b}$ or $\sqrt{a}+\sqrt{b}$ by finding the square root and rationalize them.

(ii) Simplify the surds in each denominator and then rationalize.

40. (i) If $a > b$, then $\frac{1}{a} < \frac{1}{b}$.

(ii) Rationalize the numerators of given surds and then compare.

41. (i) Use '$\sqrt[6]{x} = \sqrt[3]{\sqrt{x}}$' and simplify by finding the square root wherever necessary.

(ii) $\sqrt[6]{x} = \sqrt[3]{\sqrt[2]{x}}$

(iii) $\sqrt[3]{x+y}\,.\sqrt[3]{x-y} = \sqrt[3]{(x^2-y^2)}.$

42. (i) Bring a possible term out of the root.

(ii) $\sqrt{\sqrt{63}+\sqrt{56}} = \sqrt[4]{7}\sqrt{\sqrt{9}+\sqrt{8}}$

(iii) Let $\sqrt{3+2\sqrt{2}} = \sqrt{x}+\sqrt{y}$.

43. (i) Rationalize the denominator of the equation and compare with RHS.

44. EBADC is the required sequential order.

45. DCBEA is the required sequential order.

46. Given that, $y = 3-\sqrt{8}$

$$\frac{1}{y} = \frac{1}{3-\sqrt{8}} = \frac{3+\sqrt{8}}{(3-\sqrt{8})(3+\sqrt{8})}$$

$$= \frac{3+\sqrt{8}}{9-8} = 3+\sqrt{8}.$$

$$\text{Now, } \left(y-\frac{1}{y}\right)^2 = (3-\sqrt{8}-3-\sqrt{8})^2$$

$$= (-2\sqrt{8})^2 = 32.$$

47. Given that $x = \frac{1}{\sqrt{3}+2}$

$$\Rightarrow x = \frac{2-\sqrt{3}}{(2+\sqrt{3})(2-\sqrt{3})}$$

$$\Rightarrow x = \frac{2-\sqrt{3}}{4-3} \Rightarrow x = 2-\sqrt{3}.$$

$$\text{And } \frac{1}{x} = \sqrt{3}+2$$

$$\text{Now } \left(x+\frac{1}{x}\right)^2 = (2-\sqrt{3}+\sqrt{3}+2)^2$$

$$= (4)^2 = 16.$$

48. $\sqrt[x]{3} \times \sqrt[y]{5} = 10125$

$$3^{1/x}\cdot 51^{1/y} = 3^4 \times 5^3$$

$$\Rightarrow \frac{1}{x} = 4,\ \frac{1}{y} = 3 \Rightarrow 4x = 1,\ 3y = 1$$

$$\Rightarrow 12xy = 1.$$

49. $x = \frac{1}{5+2\sqrt{6}}$

$$x = \frac{5-2\sqrt{6}}{25-24} \Rightarrow x = 5-2\sqrt{6}$$

$$\frac{1}{x} = 5+2\sqrt{6} \Rightarrow x+\frac{1}{x} = 10$$

$$x^2+1 = 10x \Rightarrow x^2-10x+1 = 0.$$

50. $x = \frac{2}{\sqrt{3}-\sqrt{5}},\ y = \frac{2}{\sqrt{3}+\sqrt{5}}$

$$x+y = \frac{2}{\sqrt{3}-\sqrt{5}} + \frac{2}{\sqrt{3}+\sqrt{5}}$$

$$= \frac{2\sqrt{3}+2\sqrt{5}+2\sqrt{3}-2\sqrt{5}}{3-5} = \frac{4\sqrt{3}}{-2}$$

$$(x+y) = -2\sqrt{3}.$$

Level 3: Assess Your Concepts

51. (i) Substitute the values of k and rationalize every term of LHS.

(ii) $\sum_{k=4}^{143} \frac{1}{\sqrt{k}+\sqrt{k+1}}$

$$= \frac{1}{\sqrt{5}+\sqrt{4}} + \frac{1}{\sqrt{6}+\sqrt{5}} + \cdots + \frac{1}{\sqrt{144}+\sqrt{143}}.$$

(iii) Rationalize the denominator of each term and simplify.

52. (i) Rationalize the denominator two times.

(ii) RF of denominator is $(3+\sqrt{5}-2\sqrt{2})$.

(iii) Rationalize the denominator twice and simplify.

56. $\frac{4}{\sqrt{10-2\sqrt{21}}} = \frac{4}{\sqrt{(\sqrt{7})^2+(\sqrt{3})^2-2\sqrt{7\times 3}}}$

$$= \frac{4}{\sqrt{(\sqrt{7}-\sqrt{3})^2}} = \frac{4}{\sqrt{7}-\sqrt{3}}$$

$$= \frac{4(\sqrt{7}+\sqrt{3})}{(\sqrt{7}-\sqrt{3})(\sqrt{7}+\sqrt{3})}$$

$$= \frac{4(\sqrt{7}+\sqrt{3})}{4} = \sqrt{7}+\sqrt{3}.$$

57. Given, $y = 3^{1/3}+3$

$\Rightarrow y-3 = 3^{1/3}$

Taking the cubes on both sides

$\Rightarrow (y-3)^3 = (3^{1/3})^3$

$\Rightarrow y^3 - 9y^2 + 27y - 27 = 3$

$\Rightarrow y^3 - 9y^2 + 27y = 30.$

58. $\frac{1}{\sqrt{8+2\sqrt{15}}} = \frac{1}{\sqrt{(\sqrt{5})^2+(\sqrt{3})^2+2\sqrt{5\times 3}}} = \frac{1}{\sqrt{5}+\sqrt{3}}$

$$= \frac{\sqrt{5}-\sqrt{3}}{(\sqrt{5}+\sqrt{3})(\sqrt{5}-\sqrt{3})} = \frac{1}{2}(\sqrt{5}-\sqrt{3}).$$

59. Given $x = 2^{1/3}-2$

$\Rightarrow x+2 = 2^{1/3}$

Taking the cubes of the terms on both the sides,

$\Rightarrow (x+2)^3 = (2^{1/3})^3$

$\Rightarrow x^3 + 6x^2 + 12x + 8 = 2$

$\Rightarrow x^3 + 6x^2 + 12x = -6.$

60. $\frac{3}{\sqrt{19-2\sqrt{88}}} - \frac{8}{\sqrt{14+2\sqrt{33}}}$

$$= \frac{3}{\sqrt{11}-\sqrt{8}} - \frac{8}{\sqrt{11}+\sqrt{3}}$$

$$= \frac{3(\sqrt{11}+\sqrt{8})}{11-8} - \frac{8(\sqrt{11}-\sqrt{3})}{11-3}$$

$$= \sqrt{11}+\sqrt{8}-\sqrt{11}+\sqrt{3}$$

$$= \sqrt{8}+\sqrt{3} = \sqrt{11+2\sqrt{24}}.$$

61. $\sqrt{\sqrt[x]{2^x \sqrt[x^2]{3^{x^3} \sqrt[x^3]{6^{x^6} \sqrt[x^4]{9^{x^{10}}}}}}}$

$$= \sqrt{2^{x/x} \cdot 3^{x^3/x^3} \cdot 6^{x^6/x^6} \cdot 9^{x^{10}/x^{10}}} = 18.$$

62. $\sqrt{7+2\sqrt{6}} + \sqrt{7-2\sqrt{6}}$

$$= \sqrt{6+1+2\sqrt{6}} + \sqrt{6+1-2\sqrt{6}}$$

$$= \sqrt{6}+1+\sqrt{6}-1 = 2\sqrt{6}.$$

63. $\sqrt{3^2\sqrt{9^2\sqrt{(81)^2\sqrt{16^{16}}}}}$

$$= (3^2)^{1/2} \times (9^2)^{1/4} \times \left[(81)^2\right]^{1/8} \times \left[(16)^{16}\right]^{1/16}$$

$$= 3\times 3\times 3\times 16 = 6^3 \times 2.$$

64. $(\sqrt[6]{15-2\sqrt{56}})(\sqrt[3]{\sqrt{7}+2\sqrt{2}})$

$$\sqrt[3]{\sqrt{15-2\sqrt{56}}}\ \sqrt[3]{\sqrt{7}+2\sqrt{2}}$$

$$= \sqrt[3]{\sqrt{8}-\sqrt{7}}\ \sqrt[3]{\sqrt{7}+\sqrt{8}} = \sqrt[3]{8-7} = 1.$$

65. $p = 7-4\sqrt{3}$

$$\frac{1}{p} = \frac{1}{7-4\sqrt{3}} = \frac{7+4\sqrt{3}}{49-48}$$

$$\therefore \frac{1}{p} = 7+4\sqrt{3}$$

$$p + \frac{1}{p} = \frac{p^2+1}{p} = 7-4\sqrt{3}+7+4\sqrt{3} = 14$$

$$\Rightarrow \frac{p^2+1}{7p} = \frac{14}{7} = 2.$$

JEE Special Wing

Multiple-Answer Type Questions

1. If a and b are rational numbers, then an *RF* of $\sqrt{a}-\sqrt{b}$ is $\sqrt{a}+\sqrt{b}$, since $\left(\sqrt{a}-\sqrt{b}\right)\left(\sqrt{a}+\sqrt{b}\right)=a-b$, which is a rational number.

   The multiples of $\sqrt{a}+\sqrt{b}$ are also *RFs* of $\sqrt{a}-\sqrt{b}$.

   Going by options, $\sqrt{3}+\sqrt{2}$ is a *RF* of $\sqrt{3}-\sqrt{2}$.

   Also, $\sqrt{12}+\sqrt{8}=\sqrt{4\times3}+\sqrt{4\times2}=2(\sqrt{3}+\sqrt{2})$ is an *RF* of $\sqrt{3}-\sqrt{2}$.

   Hence, choice (a) and choice (c) are correct.

2. Given that $2187 \le 3^n < 59049$, where n is an integer.

   We know that: $3^7 = 2187$

   $3^8 = 6561$

   $3^9 = 19683$

   $3^{10} = 59049$

   So, the value of n can be 7, 8, or 9.

   Hence, choice (b), choice (c) and choice (d) are correct.

3. Given that $x^y = 4096$, where x and y are positive integers.

   $\Rightarrow x^y = 2^{12} \Rightarrow xy = 2\times12 = 24.$

   $\Rightarrow x^y = 4^6 \Rightarrow xy = 4\times6 = 24.$

   $\Rightarrow x^y = 8^4 \Rightarrow xy = 8\times4 = 32.$

   $\Rightarrow x^y = 16^3 \Rightarrow xy = 16\times3 = 48.$

   $\Rightarrow x^y = 64^2 \Rightarrow xy = 64\times2 = 128.$

   $\Rightarrow x^y = 4096^1 \Rightarrow xy = 4096\times1 = 4096.$

   Hence, choice (a), choice (b), choice (c), and choice (d) are correct.

4. Going by options:

   Choice (a): $\dfrac{12}{90}=\dfrac{13-1}{90}=0.1\bar{3}=0.1333\ldots$

   Choice (b): $\dfrac{12}{99}=\dfrac{12-0}{99}=0.\overline{12}=0.121212\ldots$

   Choice (c): $\dfrac{11}{90}=\dfrac{12-1}{90}=0.1\bar{2}=0.1222\ldots$

   Choice (d): $\dfrac{13}{99}=\dfrac{13-0}{99}=0.\overline{13}=0.131313\ldots$

   So, $0.12 < 0.\overline{12} < 0.1\bar{2} < 0.\overline{13} < 0.1\bar{3} < 0.14$

   Hence, choice (a), choice (b), choice (c), and choice (d) are follows.

5. $\sqrt{x}-\sqrt{y}=\sqrt{8-4\sqrt{3}}$

   $=\sqrt{8-2\sqrt{12}}$

   $=\sqrt{6+2-2\sqrt{6\times2}}$

   $=\sqrt{\left(\sqrt{6}-\sqrt{2}\right)^2}=\sqrt{6}-\sqrt{2}.$

   So, $x = 6$ and $y = 2$.

   Now, $x - y = 6 - 2 = 4$.

   $\dfrac{x}{y}=\dfrac{6}{2}=3.$

   Hence, choice (b) and choice (c) are correct.

Match The Column

Common Solutions for questions 6 to 10:

Given that $A=\dfrac{1}{5-2\sqrt{6}}$, $B=\dfrac{1}{5+2\sqrt{6}}$ and $C=-10$.

6. $A+B=\dfrac{1}{5-2\sqrt{6}}+\dfrac{1}{5+2\sqrt{6}}$

   $=\dfrac{5+2\sqrt{6}+5-2\sqrt{6}}{\left(5-2\sqrt{6}\right)\left(5+2\sqrt{6}\right)}$

   $=\dfrac{10}{5^2-\left(2\sqrt{6}\right)^2}$

   $=\dfrac{10}{25-24}=10.$

   Hence, the correct option is (d).

7. $A\times B=\dfrac{1}{5-2\sqrt{6}}\times\dfrac{1}{5+2\sqrt{6}}$

   $=\dfrac{1}{5^2-\left(2\sqrt{6}\right)^2}$

   $=\dfrac{1}{25-24}=1.$

   Hence, the correct option is (c).

8. $A-B=\dfrac{1}{5-2\sqrt{6}}-\dfrac{1}{5+2\sqrt{6}}$

   $=\dfrac{5+2\sqrt{6}-5+2\sqrt{6}}{\left(5-2\sqrt{6}\right)\left(5+2\sqrt{6}\right)}$

   $=\dfrac{4\sqrt{6}}{5^2-\left(2\sqrt{6}\right)^2}$

   $=\dfrac{4\sqrt{6}}{25-24}=4\sqrt{6}.$

   Now $\left(A-B\right)^2=\left(4\sqrt{6}\right)^2=96.$

   Hence, the correct option is (e).

9. $\frac{1}{A^2} = \left(5 - 2\sqrt{6}\right)^2 = 25 + 24 - 20\sqrt{6} = 49 - 20\sqrt{6}.$

$\frac{1}{B^2} = \left(5 + 2\sqrt{6}\right)^2 = 25 + 24 + 20\sqrt{6} = 49 + 20\sqrt{6}.$

$\frac{1}{A^2} + \frac{1}{B^2} = 49 - 20\sqrt{6} + 49 + 20\sqrt{6} = 98.$

Hence, the correct option is (f).

10. $A + B + C = (A + B) + C$

$= 10 + (-10) = 0.$

As $A + B + C = 0$, $A^3 + B^3 + C^3 = 3ABC.$

Now $A^3 + B^3 + C^3 = 3(A \times B) \times C$

$= 3(1) \times (-10) = -30.$

Hence, the correct option is (a).

Comprehension-Based Questions

Common Solutions for questions 11 to 15:

In the diagram *ABCD* and *APQR* are two rectangular fields. *QR* and *CD* are produced to meet at point *N*. *QP* and *CB* are produced to meet at point *M*. *ADNR* and *PABM* are also rectangles.

Also, $AB = CD = PM = \sqrt{28} + \sqrt{36}$ m.

$BC = AD = RN = \sqrt{18} + \sqrt{10}$ m.

$AP = BM = RQ = \sqrt{24} + \sqrt{39}$ m.

$PQ = AR = DN = \sqrt{12} + \sqrt{15}$ m.

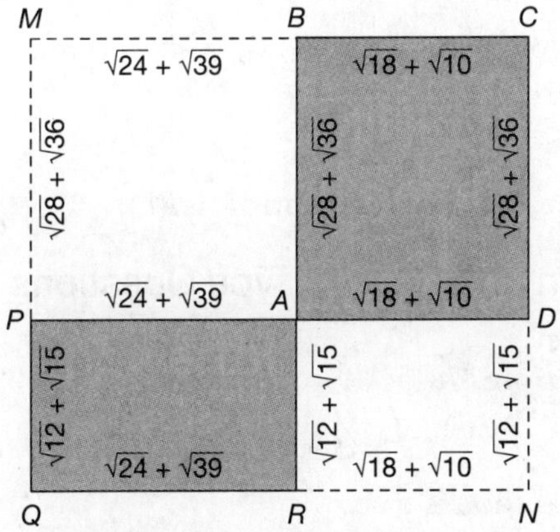

11. In rectangle *ABCD*, $AC = \sqrt{AB^2 + BC^2}$.

(By Pythagoras theorem)

$AC = \sqrt{\left(\sqrt{28} + \sqrt{36}\right)^2 + \left(\sqrt{18} + \sqrt{10}\right)^2}.$

$AC =$

$\sqrt{\left(28 + 36 + 2 \times \sqrt{28} \times \sqrt{36}\right) + \left(18 + 10 + 2 \times \sqrt{18} \times \sqrt{10}\right)}$

$AC = \sqrt{\left(64 + 2 \times 2\sqrt{7} \times 6\right) + \left(28 + 2 \times \sqrt{180}\right)}$

$AC = \sqrt{\left(64 + 24\sqrt{7}\right) + \left(28 + 2 \times 6\sqrt{5}\right)}$

$AC = \sqrt{\left(64 + 24\sqrt{7}\right) + \left(28 + 12\sqrt{5}\right)}$

$AC = \sqrt{92 + 24\sqrt{7} + 12\sqrt{5}}$ m.

Hence, the correct option is (b).

12. In rectangle *ABMP*, $AM = \sqrt{AP^2 + PM^2}$.

(By Pythagoras theorem)

$AM = \sqrt{\left(\sqrt{24} + \sqrt{39}\right)^2 + \left(\sqrt{28} + \sqrt{36}\right)^2}.$

$AM =$

$\sqrt{\left(24 + 39 + 2 \times \sqrt{24} \times \sqrt{39}\right) + \left(28 + 36 + 2 \times \sqrt{28} \times \sqrt{36}\right)}$

$AM =$

$\sqrt{\left(63 + 2 \times \sqrt{2 \times 12 \times 3 \times 13}\right) + \left(28 + 36 + 2 \times \sqrt{4 \times 7} \times \sqrt{36}\right)}$

$AM = \sqrt{\left(63 + 2 \times 6\sqrt{26}\right) + \left(64 + 24\sqrt{7}\right)}$

$AM = \sqrt{\left(63 + 12\sqrt{26}\right) + \left(64 + 24\sqrt{7}\right)}$

$AM = \sqrt{127 + 24\sqrt{7} + 12\sqrt{26}}$ m.

Hence, the correct option is (a).

13. In rectangle *APQR*, $AQ = \sqrt{AP^2 + PQ^2}$.

(By Pythagoras theorem)

$AQ = \sqrt{\left(\sqrt{24} + \sqrt{39}\right)^2 + \left(\sqrt{12} + \sqrt{15}\right)^2}.$

$AQ =$

$\sqrt{\left(24 + 39 + 2 \times \sqrt{24} \times \sqrt{39}\right) + \left(12 + 15 + 2 \times \sqrt{12} \times \sqrt{15}\right)}$

$AQ =$

$\sqrt{\left(63 + 2 \times \sqrt{2 \times 12 \times 3 \times 13}\right) + \left(12 + 15 + 2 \times \sqrt{180}\right)}$

$AQ = \sqrt{\left(63 + 2 \times 6\sqrt{26}\right) + \left(27 + 2 \times 6\sqrt{5}\right)}$

$AQ = \sqrt{\left(63 + 12\sqrt{26}\right) + \left(27 + 12\sqrt{5}\right)}$

$AQ = \sqrt{90 + 12\sqrt{26} + +12\sqrt{5}}$ m.

Hence, the correct option is (c).

14. In rectangle *ADNR*, $AN = \sqrt{AR^2 + AD^2}$.

(By Pythagoras theorem)

$AN = \sqrt{\left(\sqrt{12} + \sqrt{15}\right)^2 + \left(\sqrt{18} + \sqrt{10}\right)^2}.$

$AN =$

$\sqrt{\left(12 + 15 + 2 \times \sqrt{12} \times \sqrt{15}\right) + \left(18 + 10 + 2 \times \sqrt{18} \times \sqrt{10}\right)}$

$AN = \sqrt{\left(12 + 15 + 2 \times \sqrt{180}\right) + \left(28 + 2 \times \sqrt{180}\right)}$

$AN=\sqrt{\left(27+2\times6\sqrt{5}\right)+\left(28+2\times6\sqrt{5}\right)}$

$AN=\sqrt{\left(27+12\sqrt{5}\right)+\left(28+12\sqrt{5}\right)}$

$AN=\sqrt{55+24\sqrt{5}}$ m.

Hence, the correct option is (a).

15. We know $AC=\sqrt{92+24\sqrt{7}+12\sqrt{5}}\ m$

$AM=\sqrt{127+24\sqrt{7}+12\sqrt{26}}\ m$

$AQ=\sqrt{90+12\sqrt{26}++12\sqrt{5}}\ m$

$AN=\sqrt{55+24\sqrt{5}}\ m$

Clearly, the length of the shortest path is $\sqrt{55+24\sqrt{5}}$ m.

Hence, the correct option is (d).

Common Solutions for questions 16 to 20:

Given that $P=\sqrt{29}+\sqrt{37}$

$Q=\sqrt{31}+\sqrt{35}$

$R=\sqrt{27}+\sqrt{39}$

$S=\sqrt{32}+\sqrt{34}$

$T=\sqrt{40}+\sqrt{26}$

$P^2=\left(\sqrt{29}+\sqrt{37}\right)^2=29+37+2\times\sqrt{29}\times\sqrt{37}$

$\Rightarrow P^2=66+2\sqrt{1073}$

$Q^2=\left(\sqrt{31}+\sqrt{35}\right)^2=31+35+2\times\sqrt{31}\times\sqrt{35}$

$\Rightarrow Q^2=66+2\sqrt{1085}$

$R^2=\left(\sqrt{27}+\sqrt{39}\right)^2=27+39+2\times\sqrt{27}\times\sqrt{39}$

$\Rightarrow R^2=66+2\sqrt{1053}$

$S^2=\left(\sqrt{32}+\sqrt{34}\right)^2=32+34+2\times\sqrt{32}\times\sqrt{34}$

$\Rightarrow S^2=66+2\sqrt{1088}$

$T^2=\left(\sqrt{40}+\sqrt{26}\right)^2=40+26+2\times\sqrt{40}\times\sqrt{26}$

$\Rightarrow T^2=66+2\sqrt{1040}$

Clearly $S^2>Q^2>P^2>R^2>T^2$

$\Rightarrow S>Q>P>R>T$ (1)

(Since P, Q, R, S, and T are positive numbers)

$\Rightarrow \frac{1}{S}<\frac{1}{Q}<\frac{1}{P}<\frac{1}{R}<\frac{1}{T}$ (2)

16. The greatest number among P, Q, R, and T is Q.

Hence, the correct option is (b).

17. The smallest among P, R, S, and T is T.

Hence, the correct option is (d).

18. $\frac{6}{(S+Q)(S-Q)}=\frac{6}{S^2-Q^2}$

$=\frac{6}{\left(66+2\sqrt{1088}\right)-\left(66+2\sqrt{1085}\right)}$

$=\frac{6}{2\left(\sqrt{1088}-\sqrt{1085}\right)}$

$=\frac{3\left(\sqrt{1088}+\sqrt{1085}\right)}{\left(\sqrt{1088}-\sqrt{1085}\right)\left(\sqrt{1088}+\sqrt{1085}\right)}$

$=\frac{3\left(\sqrt{1088}+\sqrt{1085}\right)}{\left(\sqrt{1088}^2-\sqrt{1085}^2\right)}$

$=\frac{3\left(\sqrt{1088}+\sqrt{1085}\right)}{(1088-1085)}$

$=\sqrt{1088}+\sqrt{1085}$

Hence, the correct option is (b).

19. We know that $S>Q>P>R>T$ (From (1))

$\Rightarrow S>P>T$ is true.

Hence, the correct option is (a).

20. We know that $\frac{1}{S}<\frac{1}{Q}<\frac{1}{P}<\frac{1}{R}<\frac{1}{T}$ (From (1))

$\Rightarrow \frac{1}{S}<\frac{1}{P}<\frac{1}{T}$ is true.

Hence, the correct option is (c).

Assertion and Reason Type Questions

21. Assertion: $\sqrt[6]{81}\times\sqrt[6]{9}=\sqrt[6]{81\times9}$

$=\sqrt[6]{3^4\times3^2}=\sqrt[6]{3^6}=3$ is a rational number.

So, Assertion is true.

Reason: $\sqrt[m]{a^n}\times\sqrt[m]{a^{m-n}}=\sqrt[m]{a^n\times a^{m-n}}$

$=\sqrt[m]{a^{n+m-n}}=\sqrt[m]{a^m}=a$ is a rational number.

Reason is true and is the correct explanation to Assertion.

Hence, the correct option is (a).

22. Assertion: $\left(\sqrt{2027}-\sqrt{2026}\right)\left(\sqrt{2027}+\sqrt{2026}\right)$

$=\sqrt{2027}^2-\sqrt{2026}^2$

$=2027-2026=1.$

A RF of $\sqrt{2027}-\sqrt{2026}$ is $\sqrt{2027}+\sqrt{2026}$.

So, Assertion is true.

Reason: A *RF* of $\sqrt[m]{a}-\sqrt[m]{b}$ is $\sqrt[m]{a}+\sqrt[m]{b}$, when *m* is 2.

So, Reason is false.

Hence, the correct option is (c).

23. **Assertion:** $\left(\sqrt{20}-28\right)\left(\sqrt{20}+28\right)=\sqrt{20}^{2}-(28)^{2}$

$=20-784=-764.$

$\left(\sqrt{20}+28\right)+\left(\sqrt{20}-28\right)=2\sqrt{20}$, which is not a rational number.

So, $\sqrt{20}+28$ is not a conjugate of $\sqrt{20}-28$.

Reason: Two surds are conjugate to each other, when their sum is a rational number, and their product is also a rational number.

Reason is true.

Hence, the correct option is (d).

24. **Assertion:** Every rational number can be expressed as terminating decimal or non-terminating recurring decimal.

So, Assertion is true.

Reason: An irrational number cannot be expressed as $\frac{p}{q}$ form where *p* and *q* are coprime.

Reason is true and not the correct explanation to Assertion.

Hence, the correct option is (b).

25. **Assertion:** We know that $1^0=2^0=3^0=4^0=\ldots$

$=100^0=1.$

$1^0\times2^0\times3^0\times4^0\times\ldots\times100^0=1\times1\times1\times1\times\ldots\times1=1.$

So, Assertion is true.

Reason: Any non-zero number raised to the power of zero is one.

So, Reason is false.

Hence, the correct option is (c).

CHAPTER 2

Ratio, Proportion and Variation

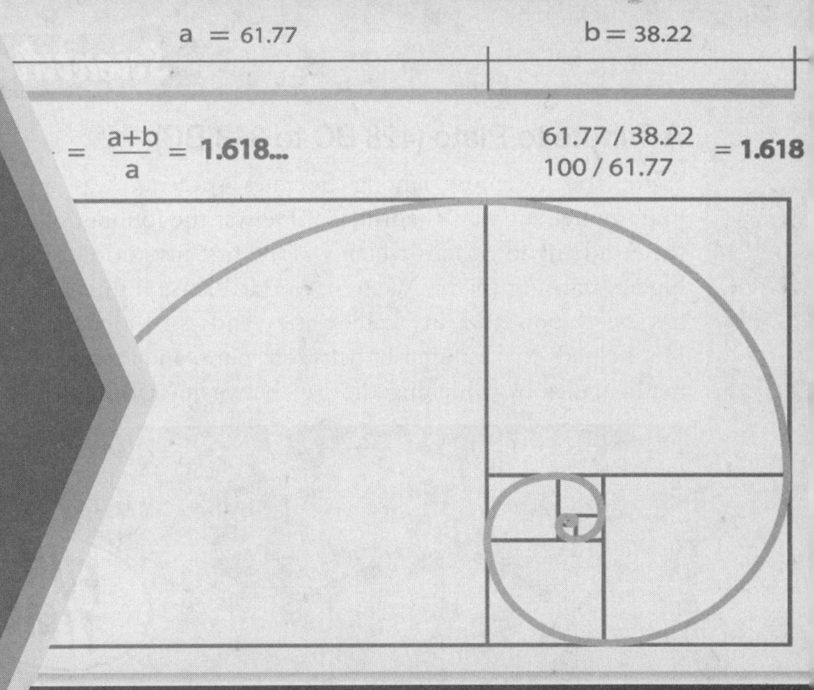

Remember

Before beginning this chapter, you should be able to:

- Calculate the ratio of quantities given
- Understand the concepts of proportion and variation
- Apply unitary method in solving problems

Key Ideas

After completing this chapter, you should be able to:

- Learn about ratios and related terms
- Know the properties and types of ratios
- Study about proportion and variations
- Know properties and types of a proportion

Scientific Crypt

A Tribute to Plato (428 BC to 348 BC)

Plato, the foremost among Socrates students was a philosopher and a mathematician. He was the founder of the Academy in Athens which was the first institution of higher learning in the Western world. Plato's influence has been powerful in mathematics and the sciences. He helped to distinguish between pure and applied mathematics by widening the gap between 'arithmetic' (number theory) and 'Logistic' (arithmetic). He regarded logistics as appropriate for the businessman and the man of war who 'must learn the art of numbers or he will not know how to array his troops,' while arithmetic was appropriate for the philosopher because 'he has to rise out of the sea of change and lay hold of true being'.

FUN TIME

CROSSWORD

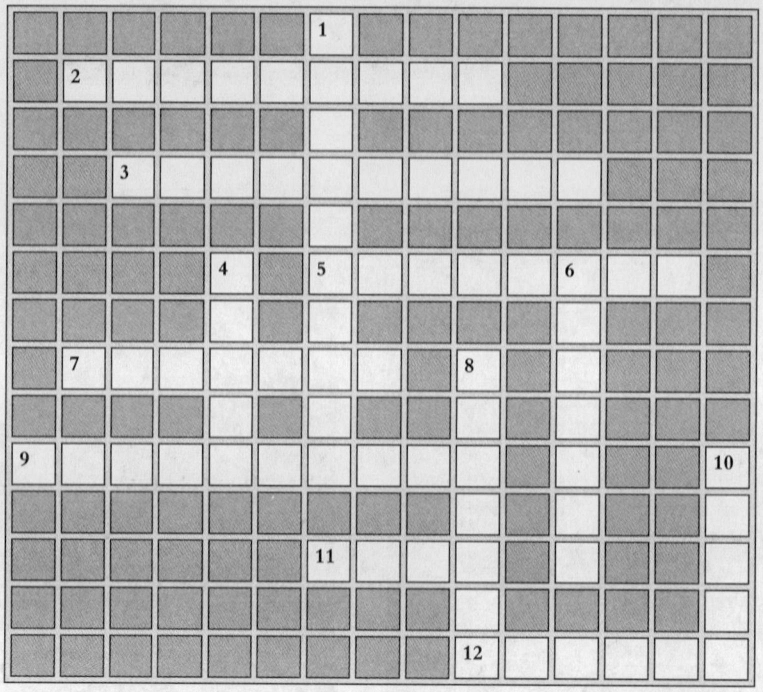

Across

2. The proportion in which the second and third terms are equal.
3. The second term of a ratio.
5. The ratio 1 : 1 is called as
7. It is the third proportional of 4 and 8.
9. The equality of ratios.
11. It is the mean proportional between 2 and 8.
12. The variation involved between the distance travelled and the time taken at constant speed.

Down

1. The first term of a ratio.
4. The comparison by division.
6. The variation involved between the number of persons required and the number of days taken to complete a certain work.
8. The simplest form of 1000 : 10.
10. The fourth proportion of 3, 4, 6.

INTRODUCTION

In this chapter, we discuss ratio, proportion and their properties. *A ratio is the comparison or simplified form of two quantities of the same kind. This relation indicates how many times one quantity is equal to the other; or in other words, ratio is a number, which expresses one quantity as a fraction of the other. E.g. Ratio of 3 to 4 is 3 : 4.* Proportion is represented by the symbol '=' or '::'

If the ratio $a : b$ is equal to the ratio $c : d$, then a, b, c, d are said to be in proportion. Using symbols, we write as $a : b = c : d$ or $a : b :: c : d$

Ratio

The value obtained when two similar quantities are compared by dividing one quantity with the other is called ratio. The ratio of two quantities is that value which gives us how many times one quantity is of the other. Only quantities of the same kind, i.e., the quantities with the same units can be compared.

Terms of a Ratio

For a given ratio $a : b$, we say that a is the **first term** or **antecedent** and b is the **second term** or **consequent**.

In the ratio 3 : 4, 3 is the antecedent while 4 is the consequent.

Properties of a Ratio

The value of a ratio remains the same if both the terms of the ratio are multiplied or divided by the same non-zero quantity. If a, b, and m are non-zero real numbers:

1. $\frac{a}{b} = \frac{ma}{mb} \Rightarrow a : b = am : bm$

2. $\frac{a}{b} = \frac{\frac{a}{m}}{\frac{b}{m}} \Rightarrow a : b = \frac{a}{m} : \frac{b}{m}$

Konnect

1. The ratio of a and b is written as $a : b$ and is measured by the fraction $\frac{a}{b}$.
   Example: The ratio of 5 and 8 is written as 5 : 8 and measured by the fraction $\frac{5}{8}$.
2. If two quantities are in the ratio $a : b$, then the first and the second quantities will be $\frac{a}{a+b}$ times and $\frac{b}{a+b}$ times the sum of the two quantities, respectively.
   Example: If $x : y = 3 : 5$, then $x = \frac{3}{8}(x + y)$ and $y = \frac{5}{8}(x + y)$.
3. The ratio of two quantities can be found, only when both the quantities are of the same kind.
   Example: Ratio between 1 meter and 5 seconds cannot be found, as the quantities given are not of the same kind.
4. A ratio is an abstract quantity and a ratio does not have any units.
   Example: The ratio of 30 seconds and one minute is 30 seconds : 60 seconds or 1 : 2.

Simplest Form of a Ratio

The ratio of two or more quantities is said to be in the simplest form, if the highest common factor (HCF) of the quantities is 1. If the HCF of the quantities is not 1, then each quantity of the ratio is divided by the HCF to convert the ratio into its simplest form.

For example, suppose there are three numbers 6, 9, and 12. The HCF of the numbers is 3. Dividing each of 6, 9, and 12 by 3, the results obtained are 2, 3, and 4. The ratio of 6, 9, and 12 in the simplest form is 2 : 3 : 4.

EXAMPLE 2.1 Express 81 : 93 in its simplest form.

SOLUTION

The HCF of 81 and 93 is 3.

We divide each term by 3.

Then, $81:93 = \frac{81}{3}:\frac{93}{3} = 27:31$

∴ The ratio 81 : 93 in its simplest form is 27 : 31.

Comparison of Ratios

Two ratios $a : b$ and $c : d$ can be compared in the following way: If $\frac{a}{b} > \frac{c}{d}$, then $a : b > c : d$.

EXAMPLE 2.2 Compare the ratios 4 : 5 and 18 : 25.

SOLUTION

$4:5 = \frac{4}{5} = 0.8$

$18:25 = \frac{18}{25} = 0.72$

As, 0.8 > 0.72,

∴ 4 : 5 > 18 : 25.

Alternate method:

Ratios can also be compared by reducing them to equivalent fractions of a common denominator.

$4:5 = \frac{4}{5}$ and $18:25 = \frac{18}{25}$

$\frac{4}{5} = \frac{4\times5}{5\times5} = \frac{20}{25}$

As, $\frac{20}{25} > \frac{18}{25}; \frac{4}{5} > \frac{18}{25}$

∴ 4 : 5 > 18 : 25.

Types of Ratios

1. A ratio $a : b$, where $a > b$, is called a ratio of **greater inequality**. For a ratio of greater inequality, if a positive quantity is added to both terms, then the obtained ratio is lesser than $a : b$. In other words, if a positive quantity x is added to the two terms in the ratio $a : b$ (where $a > b$), then $a + x : b + x < a : b$.

   Example: The ratio 4 : 3 is a ratio of greater inequality, because the antecedent (4) is greater than the consequent (3). It can be seen that for the ratio $4:3, \frac{4+1}{3+1} < \frac{4}{3}$.

2. A ratio $a : b$, where $a < b$, is called a ratio of **lesser inequality**. For a ratio of lesser inequality, if a positive quantity is added to both terms, the obtained ratio is greater than $a : b$. In other words, if a positive quantity x is added to the two terms of the ratio $a : b$ (where $a < b$), then $(a + x) : (b + x) > a : b$.

Example: The ratio 3 : 4 is a ratio of lesser inequality, because the antecedent 3 is less than the consequent (4). It can be seen that for the ratio $3:4, \frac{3+1}{4+1} > \frac{3}{4}$.

3. A ratio $a : b$, where $a = b$, is called a ratio of equality. If a positive quantity is added to both the terms, the value of the ratio remains unchanged. In other words, if a positive quantity x is added to two terms in the ratio $a : b$, then $(a + x) : (b + x) = a : b$.
4. The duplicate ratio of $a : b$ is $a^2 : b^2$.
5. The sub-duplicate ratio of $a : b$ is $\sqrt{a} : \sqrt{b}$.
6. The triplicate ratio of $a : b$ is $a^3 : b^3$.
7. The sub-triplicate ratio of $a : b$ is $\sqrt[3]{a} : \sqrt[3]{b}$.
8. The inverse ratio of $a : b$ is $b : a$.
9. The compound ratio of two ratios $a : b$ and $c : d$ is $ac : bd$.

Konnect

If three quantities a, b, and c are in the ratio 1 : 2 : 3, we write a : b : c = 1 : 2 : 3. It follows that a : b = 1 : 2, a : c = 1 : 3, and b : c = 2 : 3. The ratio of two quantities can be found similarly when there are more than 3 quantities given and the ratio of all quantities is known.

EXAMPLE 2.3

Divide ₹5000 in the ratio of 2 : 3.

SOLUTION

We have to divide ₹5000 in the ratio 2 : 3

$\Rightarrow$ 5 parts = ₹5000

$\Rightarrow$ 2 parts = $\frac{2}{5} \times 5000$ = ₹2000

$\Rightarrow$ 3 parts = s × 5000 = ₹3000

The required amounts are ₹2000 and ₹3000.

EXAMPLE 2.4

Divide ₹780 among three friends P, Q, and R in the ratio $\frac{1}{4}:\frac{1}{3}:\frac{1}{2}$.

SOLUTION

Given ratio is $\frac{1}{4}:\frac{1}{3}:\frac{1}{2}$.

The LCM of the denominators is 12.

$$\Rightarrow \frac{1}{4}:\frac{1}{3}:\frac{1}{2} = \frac{1}{4}\times 12 : \frac{1}{3}\times 12 : \frac{1}{2}\times 12 = 3:4:6$$

The sum of the terms of the ratio = (3 + 4 + 6) = 13.

P's share = ₹$\left(780 \times \frac{3}{13}\right)$ = ₹180.

$\therefore$ Q's share = ₹$\left(780 \times \frac{4}{13}\right)$ = ₹240

and, R's share = ₹$\left(780 \times \frac{6}{13}\right)$ = ₹360.

EXAMPLE 2.5

If A : B = 1 : 2, B : C = 3 : 2 and C : D = 3 : 4, then find A : D.

SOLUTION

$A : B = 3 : 6, B : C = 6 : 4, C : D = 4 : 4 \times \frac{4}{3}$

$A : B : C : D = 3 : 6 : 4 : \frac{16}{3}$

$\Rightarrow A : D = 3 : \frac{16}{3}$

$\therefore$ A : D = 9 : 16

OR

Alternate method:

$$A:D = \frac{A}{D} = \frac{A}{B}\times\frac{B}{C}\times\frac{C}{D} = \frac{1}{2}\times\frac{3}{2}\times\frac{3}{4} = \frac{9}{16} = 9:16$$

EXAMPLE 2.6

If $B = 3A$ and $A = 4C$, then find $B : C$.

SOLUTION

$B = 3A = 3(4C) = 12C$

$\Rightarrow B = 12C$

$\Rightarrow \frac{B}{C} = \frac{12}{1}$

$\therefore B : C = 12 : 1.$

EXAMPLE 2.7

In a bag there are coins in the denominations ₹1, ₹2, and ₹5 in the ratio 3 : 5 : 7, respectively. If the total value of the coins in the bag is ₹144, find the number of coins in each denomination and also the total value of ₹2 coins.

SOLUTION

Let the number of coins of denominations of ₹1, ₹2, and ₹5 be $3x$, $5x$, and $7x$, respectively. The total value of the coins in the bag = ₹$[3x + 5x(2) + 7x(5)]$ = ₹$(3x + 10x + 35x)$ = ₹$48x$.

Given, the total amount in the bag = ₹144

$\Rightarrow 48x = 144$

$\Rightarrow x = 3.$

The number of ₹1 coins in the bag = $3x = 9$.

$\therefore$ The number of ₹2 coins in the bag = $5x = 5(3) = 15$

The number of ₹5 coins in the bag = $7x = 21$.

$\therefore$ The total value of ₹2 coins in the bag = ₹15 × 2 = ₹30.

EXAMPLE 2.8

The ratio of marks obtained by Amal, Bimal, and Komal in an examination is 12 : 8 : 15. Find the marks obtained by Bimal and Komal, if Amal scored 15 marks less than that of Komal.

SOLUTION

Let the marks scored by Amal, Bimal, and Komal be $12x$, $8x$, and $15x$, respectively.

Given that Amal scored 15 marks less than that of Komal.

$\Rightarrow 12x = 15x - 15$

$\Rightarrow 3x = 15$

$\Rightarrow x = 5.$

$\therefore$ Marks scored by Bimal = $8x = 8(5) = 40$.

Marks scored by Komal = $15x = 15(5) = 75$.

EXAMPLE 2.9

If $\frac{4}{5} = \frac{12}{15} = \frac{16+12x}{5y+30}$ where $x, y \in$ N, then the value of $x + y$ can be ______.

SOLUTION

We know that $\frac{a}{b} = \frac{c}{b} = \frac{ax \pm cy}{bx \pm dy}$

Given $\frac{4}{5} = \frac{12}{15} = \frac{16+12x}{5y+30} = \frac{4\times4+12x}{5\times y+15\times2}$

$\therefore x = 4, y = 2$

$x + y = 4 + 2 = 6.$

EXAMPLE 2.10 If $\frac{a}{b}=\frac{c}{d}=\frac{e}{f}$, then prove that each of these ratio's is equal to $\left(\frac{4a^2+3c^2-7e^2}{4b^2+3d^2-7f^2}\right)^{1/2}$.

SOLUTION

Let $\frac{a}{b}=\frac{c}{d}=\frac{e}{f}=k.$

$\Rightarrow a = kb;\ c = kd;\ e = kf.$

Now, $\left(\frac{4a^2+3c^2-7e^2}{(4b^2+3d^2-7f^2)}\right)^{1/2} = \left(\frac{(4(kb)^2+3(kd)^2-7(kf)^2)}{4b^2+3d^2-7f^2}\right)^{1/2}$

$= \left[\frac{k^2(4b^2+3d^2-7f^2)}{(4b^2+3d^2-7f^2)}\right]^{1/2} = k.$

Proportion

The equality of two ratios is called proportion.

Konnect

If $a : b = c : d$, then a, b, c, and d are said to be in proportion and the same can be represented as $a : b :: c : d$. It is read as "***a* is to *b* as *c* is to *d*.**"

Properties of Proportion

1. a, b, c, and d are, respectively, known as the first, second, third, and the fourth proportional.
2. The first and the fourth terms are called extremes while the second and the third terms are called means.
3. Product of extremes = Product of means
4. The fourth term can also be referred to as the fourth proportional of a, b, and c.
5. If $a : b = c : d$, i.e., $\frac{a}{b}=\frac{c}{d}$, then the given proportion can be written as $b : a :: d : c$, i.e., $\frac{b}{a}=\frac{d}{c}$, by taking the reciprocals of terms on both sides. This relationship is known as **invertendo**.
6. If $a : b :: c : d$, then multiplying both sides of the proportion by $\frac{b}{c}$, we get $a : c = b : d$. This relationship is known as **alternendo**.
7. Adding 1 to both sides of the proportion $a : b :: c : d$, we get $\frac{a}{b}+1=\frac{c}{d}+1$
$$\Rightarrow \frac{a+b}{b}=\frac{c+d}{d} \quad (1)$$
That is, $(a + b) : b = (c + d) : d$
This relationship is known as **componendo**.
8. Subtracting 1 from both sides of the proportion $a : b :: c : d$, we get,
$$\frac{a}{b}-1=\frac{c}{d}-1 \Rightarrow \frac{a-b}{b}=\frac{c-d}{d} \quad (2)$$
$$(a-b) : b = (c-d) : d$$
This relationship is known as **dividendo**.
9. Dividing the Eq. (1) by Eq. (2), we get,
$$\frac{\frac{a+b}{b}}{\frac{a-b}{b}}=\frac{\frac{c+d}{d}}{\frac{c-d}{d}}$$
$$\Rightarrow (a+b) : (a-b) = (c+d) : (c-d)$$
This relationship is known as **componendo and dividendo**.

10. If $\frac{a}{b} = \frac{c}{d} = \frac{e}{f}$ and l, m, and n are any three non-zero numbers, then $\frac{a}{b} = \frac{c}{d} = \frac{e}{f} = \frac{la + mc + ne}{lb + md + nf}$.

Continued Proportion

Three quantities a, b, and c are said to be in continued proportion if $a : b :: b : c$.
If $a : b :: b : c$, then c is called the third proportional of a and b.

Mean Proportional of a and c

If $a : b :: b : c$, then b is called the mean proportional of a and c.
We have already learnt that,
Product of means = Product of extremes.

$\Rightarrow b \times b = a \times c$

$\Rightarrow b^2 = ac$

$\Rightarrow b = \pm\sqrt{ac}$

$\therefore$ The mean proportional of a and c is $\sqrt{ac}$.

Info Bytes!

- In nature, the concept of continued proportion can be observed in the arrangement of leaves in some plants, ensuring that each leaf gets maximum sunlight.
- The Fibonacci sequence, related to the golden ratio, exemplifies continued proportion in its growth. It's found everywhere from art to nature, including the pattern of leaves, flowers, and fruits.

Variation

Two type of quantities exists: one is Constant and other is Variable. Variables changes with the change in other parameters. The change in variable parameters is called Variation.

Types of Variations

Direct Variation

If two quantities are related to each other such that an increase (or decrease) in the first quantity results in a corresponding proportionate increase (or decrease) in the second quantity, then the two quantities are said to vary directly with each other.

Example: At constant speed, distance covered varies directly as time.

This is expressed as, distance travelled $\propto$ time.

Indirect Variation

If two quantities are related to each other such that an increase (or decrease) in the first quantity results in a corresponding proportionate decrease (or increase) in the second quantity, then the two quantities are said to vary inversely with each other.

Example: Number of men working together to complete a job is inversely proportional to the time taken by them to finish the job. When the number of men increases, the time taken to finish the same job decreases.

$\therefore$ The number of men (n) working together to complete a job is inversely proportional to the time taken (t) by them to finish it.

This is expressed as, $n \propto \frac{1}{t}$.

Joint Variation

When a change in a quantity depends on the changes in two or more quantities, it is said to vary jointly with those quantities.

When a quantity A varies directly as B, when C is constant and varies directly as C, when B is constant, then A varies directly as the product of B and C.

It is represented as $A \propto B$ (C is constant) and $A \propto C$ (B is constant)

$\Rightarrow A \propto BC$ or $A = k \cdot BC$, where k is a constant.

When a quantity A varies directly as B, when C is constant and varies inversely as C, when B is constant, then A varies as $\frac{B}{C}$.

It is represented as $A \propto B$ (C is constant) and $A \propto \frac{1}{C}$ (B is constant).

$\Rightarrow A \propto \frac{B}{C}$ or $A = k\frac{B}{C}$, where k is a constant.

When a quantity A varies inversely as B, when C is constant and varies inversely as C, when B is constant, then A varies inversely as BC.

It is represented as $A \propto \frac{1}{B}$ (C is constant) and $A \propto \frac{1}{C}$ (B is constant).

$\Rightarrow A \propto \frac{1}{BC}$ or $A = k \cdot \frac{1}{BC}$, where k is a constant.

Info Bytes!

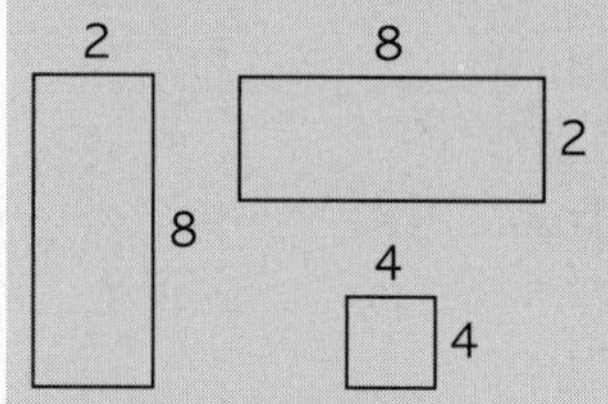

Inverse Variation:

$x \times y$ = Constant remain same. Here area remains same such as $2 \times 8 = 8 \times 2 = 4 \times 4$

EXAMPLE 2.11 If $\frac{x+3y}{x-3y} = \frac{8}{5}$, then find the value of $x : y$.

SOLUTION

$\frac{x+3y}{x-3y} = \frac{8}{5}$

$5(x + 3y) = 8(x - 3y)$

$8x - 5x = 15y + 24y$

$3x = 39y$

$x : y = 13 : 1$

EXAMPLE 2.12 Verify whether 6, 7, 12, and 14 are in proportion or not.

SOLUTION

Ratio between 6 and 7 = 6 : 7.

Ratio between 12 and 14 $= 12:14 = \frac{12}{14} = \frac{6}{7} = 6:7$.

$\Rightarrow 6 : 7 = 12 : 14$ or $6 : 7 :: 12 : 14$.

Hence, the numbers 6, 7, 12, and 14 are in proportion.

EXAMPLE 2.13 Find the fourth proportional to the numbers 8, 10, and 12.

SOLUTION

Let x be the fourth proportional to 8, 10, and 12.

$\Rightarrow 8 : 10 :: 12 : x$.

Product of means = Product of extremes

$10 \times 12 = 8 \times x$

$x = \frac{10 \times 12}{8} = 15$.

$\therefore$ The fourth proportional to 8, 10, and 12 is 15.

EXAMPLE 2.14 If the mean proportion of 81 and k is 27, then what is the value of k?

SOLUTION

If $a{:}b{:}c$ are in proportion then mean proportion is b.

$b = \sqrt{ac}$

Now, $27 = \sqrt{81 \times k}$

$27^2 = 81\,k$

$k = \dfrac{27 \times 27}{81}$

$\therefore k = 9.$

EXAMPLE 2.15 If 4 taps can fill a tank in 10 hours, then in how many hours can 6 taps fill the same tank?

SOLUTION

Assume that 6 taps can do the same work in x hours. As more taps require less hours to do the same work, number of taps vary inversely as the number of hours.

$\therefore$ (Inverse ratio of number of taps) :: (Ratio of number of hours)

$\Rightarrow 6 : 4 :: 10 : x$

$\Rightarrow \dfrac{6}{4} = \dfrac{10}{x}$

$\Rightarrow x = \dfrac{40}{6} = 6\dfrac{2}{3}$ hours.

$\therefore$ Six taps can fill the tank in $6\dfrac{2}{3}$ hours.

EXAMPLE 2.16 In a family, the consumption of power is 120 units for 18 days. Find how many units of power are consumed in 30 days.

SOLUTION

Let the consumption of power in 30 days be x units

The more the period of time, the more is the consumption of power. Hence, the consumption of power varies directly as the number of days.

$\therefore$ (Ratio of number of days) :: (Ratio of consumption of power)

$\Rightarrow 18 : 30 :: 120 : x$

Product of means = Product of extremes

$\Rightarrow 30 \times 120 = 18 \times x \Rightarrow x = \dfrac{30 \times 120}{18} = 200$ units.

$\therefore$ The consumption of power for 30 days is 200 units.

EXAMPLE 2.17 If $(2a + 7b) : (2a - 7b) :: (2c + 7d) : (2c - 7d)$, then $a : b =$ ______.

SOLUTION

Given,

$(2a + 7b) : (2a - 7b) = (2c + 7d) : (2c - 7d)$

$\Rightarrow \dfrac{2a+7b}{2a-7b} = \dfrac{2c+7d}{2c-7d}$

Applying componendo and dividendo on both sides

$$\frac{2(a+7b)+(2a-7b)}{(2a+7b)-(2a-7b)} = \frac{(2c+7d)+(2c-7d)}{(2c+7d)-(2c-7d)}$$

$\Rightarrow \dfrac{2a+7b+2a-7b}{2a+7b-2a+7b} = \dfrac{2c+7d+2c-7d}{2c+7d-2c+7d}$

$\Rightarrow \dfrac{4a}{14b} = \dfrac{4c}{14d}$

$\Rightarrow a : b = c : d$

EXAMPLE 2.18 If $\frac{3k+4l+6m+7n}{3k+4l-6m-7n}=\frac{3k-4l+6m-7n}{3k-4l-6m+7n}$, then show that k, $2m$, $4l$, and $7n$ are in proportion.

SOLUTION

Given, $\frac{3k+4l+6m+7n}{3k+4l-6m-7n}=\frac{3k-4l+6m-7n}{3k-4l-6m+7n}$

$\Rightarrow \frac{(3k+4l)+(6m+7n)}{(3k+4l)-(6m+7n)}=\frac{(3k-4l)+(6m-7n)}{(3k-4l)-(6m-7n)}$

$\Rightarrow \frac{3k+4l}{6m+7n}=\frac{3k-4l}{6m-7n} \Rightarrow \frac{3k+4l}{3k-4l}=\frac{6m+7n}{6m-7n}$

$\Rightarrow \frac{3k}{4l}=\frac{6m}{7n} \Rightarrow \frac{k}{4l}=\frac{2m}{7n}$

$\Rightarrow \frac{k}{2m}=\frac{4l}{7n}$

$\therefore$ k, $2m$, $4l$, and $7n$ are in proportion.

EXAMPLE 2.19 If a, b, c, and d are in proportion, then show that $\frac{a^3+3ab^2}{3a^2b+b^3}=\frac{c^3+3cd^2}{3c^2d+d^3}$.

SOLUTION

Given a, b, c, and d are in proportion,

$\Rightarrow \frac{a}{b}=\frac{c}{d}$

Applying componendo and dividendo,

$\Rightarrow \frac{a+b}{a-b}=\frac{c+d}{c-d}$

Cubing on both sides, we have,

$\Rightarrow \frac{(a+b)^3}{(a-b)^3}=\left[\frac{c+d}{c-d}\right]^3$

$\Rightarrow \frac{a^3+3a^2b+3ab^2+b^3}{a^3-3a^2b+3ab^2-b^3}=\frac{c^3+3c^2d+3cd^2+d^3}{c^3-3c^2d+3cd^2-d^3}$

$\frac{(a^3+3ab^2)+(3a^2b+b^3)}{(a^3+3ab^2)-(3a^2b+b^3)}=\frac{(c^3+3cd^2)+(3c^2d+d^3)}{(c^3+3cd^2)-(3c^2d+d^3)}$

$\Rightarrow \frac{a^3+3ab^2}{3a^2b+b^3}=\frac{c^3+3cd^2}{3c^2d+d^3}$

EXAMPLE 2.20 Four men, each working 6 hours per day, can build a wall in 9 days. How long will 6 men, each working 3 hours per day, take to finish the same work?

SOLUTION

Clearly, $M \propto \frac{1}{D}$ and $M \propto \frac{1}{H}$.

$\Rightarrow MDH =$ Constant.

$\Rightarrow M_1D_1H_1 = M_2D_2H_2$

$\Rightarrow 4 \times 9 \times 6 = 6 \times D_2 \times 3$

$\Rightarrow D_2 = 12.$

$\therefore$ Six men each working 3 hours per day can finish the job in 12 days.

EXAMPLE 2.21 The area of a circle varies with the square of its radius. The area of a circle having radius 3 cm is C cm^2. Find the area of the circle having radius 9 cm.

SOLUTION

Let the area of the circle be denoted by C and its radius be denoted by r.

$$C \propto r^2 \Rightarrow \frac{C_1}{C_2} = \frac{r_1^2}{r_2^2}.$$

Taking $r_1 = 3$ cm, $r_2 = 9$ cm, and $C_1 = C$ cm^2,

$$C_2 = C_1\left(\frac{r_2^2}{r_1^2}\right) = C\left(\frac{9}{3}\right)^2 = 9C \text{ cm}^2.$$

EXAMPLE 2.22 The pressure of a gas varies directly as the temperature when volume is kept constant and varies inversely as the volume when temperature is kept constant. The gas occupies volume of 400 ml when the temperature is 160 K and the pressure is 640 Pa. What is the temperature of gas whose volume and pressure are 200 ml and 320 Pa, respectively?

SOLUTION

Given $P \propto T$ and $P \propto \frac{1}{V}$.

$$\Rightarrow P \propto \frac{T}{V} \Rightarrow PV \propto T$$

$$\Rightarrow \frac{PV}{T} = \text{Constant}$$

$$\Rightarrow \frac{P_1V_1}{T_1} = \frac{P_2V_2}{T_2}$$

$$\Rightarrow \frac{640 \times 400}{160} = \frac{320 \times 200}{T_2} \Rightarrow T_2 = \frac{160}{4} = 40 \text{ K}.$$

EXAMPLE 2.23 A garrison of 700 men is provisioned for 30 days at the rate of $2\frac{1}{2}$ kg per day per man. If 100 men had left the garrison, then the provisions would have lasted for x days at the rate of $3\frac{1}{2}$ kg per day per man. Find the value of x. Choose the correct answer from the following options:

(a) 18 **(b)** 20 **(c)** 25 **(d)** 15

SOLUTION

In both cases, the provisions are the same.

$$700 \times 30 \times 2\frac{1}{2}$$

$$= (700 - 100) \times x \times 3\frac{1}{2}.$$

$$\Rightarrow 700 \times 30 \times \frac{5}{2} = 600 \times x \times \frac{7}{2}$$

$$\therefore x = 25.$$

EXAMPLE 2.24 Three positive numbers are in the ratio 1 : 3 : 5. The sum of their squares is 875. Find the sum of the numbers. Choose the correct answer from the following options:

(a) 45 **(b)** 90 **(c)** 75 **(d)** 150

SOLUTION

Given that the ratio of the three numbers is 1 : 3 : 5.

Let the numbers be x, $3x$, and $5x$.

And also given,

$x^2 + (3x)^2 + (5x)^2 = 875$

$\Rightarrow 35x^2 = 875$

$\Rightarrow x^2 = 25$

$\Rightarrow x = 5$ (the numbers are positive)

$\therefore$ The required sum $= x + 3x + 5x = 9x = 9(5) = 45$.

EXAMPLE 2.25 Two positive numbers x and y satisfy the condition $4x^2 + 25y^2 = 20xy$. Find the value of $x : y$.

(a) 5 : 2 **(b)** 2 : 5 **(c)** 3 : 2 **(d)** 2 : 3

SOLUTION

Given,

$4x^2 + 25y^2 = 20xy$

$\Rightarrow (2x - 5y)^2 = 0 \Rightarrow 2x - 5y = 0$

$\Rightarrow \frac{x}{y} = \frac{5}{2} \Rightarrow x : y = 5 : 2.$

EXAMPLE 2.26 There are four numbers e, f, g and h, where f is one-fifth of e, g is one-third of f and h is half of g. Then, $h : e =$ ______.

SOLUTION

Given, $f = \frac{1}{5} \times e \Rightarrow \frac{f}{e} = \frac{1}{5}; g = \frac{1}{3} \times f \Rightarrow \frac{g}{f} = \frac{1}{3}; h = \frac{1}{2} \times g \Rightarrow \frac{h}{g} = \frac{1}{2}$

Thus $h : e = \frac{h}{e} = \frac{f}{e} \times \frac{g}{f} \times \frac{h}{g} = \frac{1}{5} \times \frac{1}{3} \times \frac{1}{2} = \frac{1}{30} = 1 : 30.$

EXAMPLE 2.27 If we divide ₹35,600 among three persons X, Y and Z in the ratio $\frac{2}{5} : \frac{2}{3} : \frac{2}{12}$, find the difference between the shares of Z and X.

SOLUTION

Let the shares of X, Y and Z be ₹a, ₹b and ₹c rupees respectively.

Given, $a : b : c = \frac{2}{5} : \frac{2}{3} : \frac{2}{12}$

The L.C.M. of the denominators is 60.

Therefore $a : b : c = \frac{2}{5} \times 60 : \frac{2}{3} \times 60 : \frac{5}{12} \times 60 = 24 : 40 : 25$

The difference between the shares of Z and X = $₹35600 \times \frac{25 - 24}{(24 + 40 + 25)} = 400.$

POINTS TO REMEMBER

- For a given ratio $a : b$, we say that a is the first term or antecedent and b is the second term or consequent.
- A ratio $a : b$, where $a > b$, is called a ratio of greater inequality.
- A ratio $a : b$, where $a < b$, is called a ratio of lesser inequality.
- The equality of two ratios is called proportion.
- The first and the fourth terms are called extremes while the second and the third terms are called means.
- Product of extremes = Product of means
- The mean proportional of a and c is $\sqrt{ac}$.

DW

PRACTICE QUESTIONS CLASSROOM WING

Very Short Answer Type Questions

Directions of questions from 1 to 6:
Fill in the blanks.

1. The inverse ratio of $\frac{1}{8}$: 4 is ______.
2. The triplicate ratio of 8 : 15 is ________.
3. The compound ratio of $p : r$ and $r : q$ is ______.
4. If P and Q^2 are in direct proportion. If Q doubles then P becomes ______.
5. If $a : b$ is 17 : 6 and $b : c$ is 3 : 2, then $a : b : c$ is ______.
6. When $a = 3, 5, 8, 10, \ldots$, $b = 9, 15, 24, 30, \ldots$, then a and b are in ______.

Directions of questions from 7 and 8:
State whether the following statements are true or false

7. The numbers 4, 7, 8, and 14 are in proportion. (True/False)
8. The mean proportional between 4 and 8 is 6. (True/False)

Directions of questions from 9 to 21:
Answer the following questions.

9. Express the ratio 1.5 litres : 250 ml in the lowest terms.
10. A^2 is inversely proportional to B. If A = 4, then B = 16. If A = 8, then B = ______.
11. A varies inversely as the square of B and A is 1, when B is 3. What is the value of B, when A is 3?
12. Express the ratio $\frac{3}{5} : \frac{7}{9}$ in the lowest terms.
13. If $x : y = 5 : 6$ and $y : z = 3 : 7$, then find $x : z$.
14. If $a : b = 2 : 3$, then find $(3a - b) : (2a + 3b)$.
15. Two numbers are in the ratio 3 : 4. When 7 is added to each, the ratio becomes 4 : 5. Find the numbers.
16. What is the compounded ratio of $6\frac{1}{2} : 8\frac{2}{3}$ and $3\frac{3}{4} : 5\frac{1}{3}$?
17. Find the fourth proportional of 4, 9, and 12.
18. Write a ratio equal to 7 : 9 in which antecedent is 63.
19. If $(3a + 2b) : (5a + 7b) = 1 : 2$, then find $a : b$.
20. A certain sum of money is distributed among A, B and C in the ratio of $\frac{1}{2} : \frac{1}{3} : \frac{1}{4}$ and B gets ₹120. Find the shares of A and C.
21. What number must be subtracted from each of the numbers 32, 38, 17, and 20, so that the terms formed will be in proportion?

Short Answer Type Questions

22. The number of boys and girls in a class are in the ratio of 3 : 4. Find the strength of the class if there are 10 more girls than there are boys.
23. The numbers A, $A + 2$, $A + 12$, and $A + 22$ are in proportion. Find A.
24. If $\frac{a^3 + 2ab^2}{2a^2b + b^3} = \frac{123}{136}$, then find the value of $a : b$.
25. P, Q, and R have to share 52 apples among themselves such that P gets thrice as many apples as Q gets and Q gets thrice as many as R gets. Find the number of apples R must get.
26. The ratio of the present ages of a father and his son is 3 : 1. The sum of their ages after five years is 58. Find the ratio of their ages 3 years ago.
27. The ratio of the present ages of Raju and his wife is 5 : 4. Which of the following cannot be the ratio of their ages 20 years hence?
    (a) 11 : 10 (b) 6 : 5
    (c) 23 : 20 (d) 13 : 10
28. The ratio of the present ages of Swarupa and her daughter is 7 : 3. When Swarupa was 26 years old, her daughter was 6 years old. Find the present age of Swarupa. (in years)
29. Solve: $\frac{\sqrt{10+3x} + \sqrt{10-3x}}{\sqrt{10+3x} - \sqrt{10-3x}} = 3$.
30. Find $\frac{x+2p}{x-2p} + \frac{x+2q}{x-2q}$, when $x = \frac{4pq}{p+q}$.

31. The volume of a sphere (V) varies directly as the cube of its radius. The volume of the sphere of radius 3 cm is 36π cm^3. What is the volume of a sphere of radius 15 cm?

32. The ratio of the tens digit and the units digit of a two-digit number is 1 : 2. How many two-digit numbers satisfy this condition?

33. The ratio of the monthly earnings of A and B is 3 : 2. The ratio of the monthly expenditures of A and B is 4 : 3. A saves ₹300 each month. Which of the following cannot be the monthly savings of B?(in ₹)

(a) 180 (b) 195
(c) 165 (d) 205

34. If $\dfrac{2p+5q}{2r+5s} = \dfrac{4p-3q}{4r-3s}$, then find the relation between p, q, r, and s.

Essay Type Questions

35. There are two boxes, red and white in color. The ratio of the number of chocolates in the white box to the number of biscuits in the red box is 3 : 2 and the ratio of the number of biscuits in the white box to the number of chocolates in the red box is 3 : 4. If the ratio of the total number of chocolates and biscuits in the white box to the total number of chocolates and biscuits in the red box is 15 : 16. Find the ratio of the total number of chocolates to the total number of biscuits in the two boxes.

36. A father distributed ₹12250 among his four sons A, B, C, and D, such that $\dfrac{\text{A's share}}{\text{B's share}} = \dfrac{\text{B's share}}{\text{C's share}} = \dfrac{\text{C's share}}{\text{D's share}} = \dfrac{3}{4}$. Then find the share of C.

37. Some amount is to be divided between X and Y in the ratio of 3 : 4. But due to wrong calculation, it was found that X got one-seventh of the total amount more than his expected share. Find the share of Y, when X got an amount of ₹480.

38. The value of a precious stone is directly proportional to the square of its weight. If such a stone of worth ₹81000 is broken into three pieces whose weights are in the ratio 3 : 4 : 2, then find the loss incurred due to breakage of the stone.

39. If $\dfrac{a+b}{c} = \dfrac{b+c}{a} = \dfrac{a+c}{b}$, find the value(s) of each of the fractions.

PRACTICE QUESTIONS COMPETITION WING

Level 1: Apply Your Concepts

Directions of questions from 1 to 4:
Fill in the blanks.

1. The result obtained after applying componendo to $b : (a - b) :: d : (c - d)$ is ______.

2. The simplest form of 57 : 72 is ______.

3. If $X = 3Y = 4Z$, then $X : Y : Z =$ ______.

4. The greater ratio between two ratios 4 : 9 and 5 : 8 is ________.

Directions of questions from 5 to 60:
Select the correct alternative from the given choices.

5. What is the compound ratio of 15 : 6 and 9 : 5?
(a) 27 : 5 (b) 75 : 54
(c) 9 : 2 (d) 8 : 3

6. P and Q have some coins with them. The ratio of the numbers of coins with P and Q is 7 : 8. Q has 5 more coins than P has. Find the number of coins with Q.
(a) 72 (b) 40
(c) 48 (d) 80

7. If $a : b = c : d$, then which of the following is/are false?
(A) $\frac{b}{a} = \frac{d}{c}$ (B) $\frac{a+b}{a-b} = \frac{c+d}{c-d}$
(C) $\frac{a+b}{b} = \frac{c+d}{d}$ (D) $\frac{a+c}{b+d} = \frac{c}{d}$
(a) D only (b) B, C, and D only
(c) C only (d) None of these

8. If $qr : pr : pq = 1 : 4 : 7$, then find $\frac{p}{qr} : \frac{q}{pr}$.
(a) 4 : 1 (b) 1 : 4
(c) 1 : 16 (d) 16 : 1

9. What number must be added to each term of the ratio 9 : 11, so that it becomes 4 : 5.
(a) 1 (b) 2
(c) –2 (d) –1

10. A purse contains ₹50, ₹10, and ₹5 notes in the ratio 6 : 3 : 7 and the total amount in the purse is ₹730. Find the number of ₹5 notes in the purse.
(a) 7 (b) 14
(c) 21 (d) 28

11. If $p : q : r : s = 3 : 4 : 7 : 8$ and $p + s = 55$, then find $q + r$.
(a) 33 (b) 55
(c) 44 (d) 66

12. A metal X is 15 times as dense as metal Z and a metal Y is 8 times as dense as metal Z. In what ratio should these two metals be mixed to get an alloy which is 13 times as dense as metal Z?
(a) 2 : 5 (b) 2 : 3
(c) 3 : 2 (d) 5 : 2

13. What must be added to each of the numbers 3, 7, 8, and 16 so that the resulting numbers are in proportion?
(a) 4 (b) 3
(c) 2 (d) 1

14. The cost of 570 bags of rice is ₹17,100. Find the number of bags of rice which can be bought for ₹19,200.
(a) 720 (b) 800
(c) 640 (d) 600

15. Seven friends planned a tea party. The expenses per boy in rupees is numerically 1 less than the number of girls and the expenses per girl in rupees is numerically 1 less than the number of boys. If the ratio of the total expenses of the boys and the girls is 8 : 9, then what is the expenditure of each boy?
(a) ₹2 (b) ₹3
(c) ₹1 (d) ₹4

16. If a, b, and c are in continued proportion, then $a^2 : b^2$ is–
(a) $a^2 : c^2$ (b) $a : b$
(c) $a : c$ (d) $b : c$

17. A wall is divided into three parts. If one part, which is $\frac{1}{4}^{th}$ of the wall, is painted, then which of the following could be the parts left unpainted?
(a) $\frac{1}{4}$ and $\frac{1}{3}$ (b) $\frac{1}{6}$ and $\frac{1}{8}$
(c) $\frac{1}{3}$ and $\frac{5}{12}$ (d) $\frac{1}{12}$ and $\frac{1}{6}$

18. The velocity of a freely falling body when it strikes the ground is directly proportional to the square of the time taken by it to strike the ground. It takes 5 seconds to strike the ground, with a velocity of 10 m/sec. If it strikes the ground with the velocity of 40 m/sec, then for how long would it have travelled?
(a) 7.5 sec (b) 2.5 sec
(c) 10 sec (d) 20 sec

19. The ratio of the number of students in two classrooms, C_1 and C_2, is 2 : 3. It is observed that after shifting ten students from C_1 to C_2, the ratio is 3 : 7. Further, how many students have to be shifted from C_2 to C_1 for the new ratio to become 9 : 11?
(a) 10 (b) 15
(c) 20 (d) 8

20. Rakesh attended a party, where a lady asked him his age. He said that ten years ago, the sum of his and his daughter's ages was 40 years, and the ratio of his present age to that of his daughter is 7 : 3. What is the present age of Rakesh in years?
(a) 42 (b) 28
(c) 25 (d) 30

21. The mean proportional between two numbers is 56. If the third proportional of the same two numbers is 448, then find the sum of the two numbers.
(a) 180 (b) 440
(c) 240 (d) 140

22. The speed at which a person runs is directly proportional to the blood pressure in his body. If the speed of a person is 2 m/sec his blood pressure would be 120 units. Find the blood pressure in units of a person running at 8.5 m/sec.
(a) 510 (b) 425
(c) 340 (d) 5950

23. A father wants to divide ₹22,515 among his four sons P, Q, R, and S such that $\frac{\text{P's share}}{\text{Q's share}} = \frac{\text{Q's share}}{\text{R's share}} = \frac{\text{R's share}}{\text{S's share}} = \frac{1}{2}$. Find the share of Q.
(a) ₹1507 (b) ₹3002
(c) ₹6004 (d) ₹12,008

24. If 40 men can complete a job in 6 days, then find the number of days taken by 60 men to complete it.
(a) 3 (b) 10
(c) 12 (d) 4

25. The cost of a precious stone varies as the cube of its weight. The stone broke into 3 pieces whose weights are in the ratio 1 : 2 : 3. As a result, its cost reduces. If the cost of the unbroken stone is ₹96,336, then find the loss incurred due to breakage.
(a) ₹80,280 (b) ₹16,056
(c) ₹40,140 (d) ₹8028

26. A diamond falls and breaks into pieces whose weights are in the ratio 2 : 3 : 5. The value of the diamond is directly proportional to the square of its weight. Find the loss incurred, if the actual cost of the diamond is ₹96,000. (in ₹)
(a) 36,480 (b) 59,520
(c) 72,960 (d) None of these

27. In a monthly unit test, the marks scored by Bunny and Sunny are in the ratio of 10 : 7 and those scored by Bharat and Sunny are in the ratio of 8 : 9. If Bharat scores 112 marks, then find the marks scored by Bunny.
(a) 170 (b) 190
(c) 200 (d) 180

28. If $\frac{x^3 + 4xy^2}{4x^2y + y^3} = \frac{15}{16}$, then find $x : y$.
(a) 2 : 3 (b) 3 : 2
(c) 4 : 3 (d) 3 : 4

29. The ratio of the tens digit and the units digit of a two digits number is 2 : 3. How many possible values can it assume?
(a) 3 (b) 4
(c) 2 (d) 5

30. The least integer which when subtracted from the antecedent and added to the consequent of the ratio 9 : 8 gives a ratio less than the ratio 15 : 26 is
(a) 2 (b) 3
(c) 4 (d) 1

31. Ram wanted to distribute a certain amount between his two children Lava and Kusha in the ratio 5 : 7. But it was found that due to incorrect calculations Lava got one-sixth of the total amount more than what he should get. Find the share of Kusha, in rupees, if Lava got ₹560 in all.
(a) 300 (b) 350
(c) 400 (d) 450

32. A bag contains one rupee, 50 paise and 25 paise coins. The ratio of the number of 1 rupee coins to that of 50 paise coins is 5 : 9 and the ratio of the number of

50 paise coins to that of 25 paise coins is 2 : 1. Find the value of the 50 paise coins in the bag if the total value of the coins in the bag is ₹425.

(a) ₹254 (b) ₹180
(c) ₹78 (d) Cannot be determined

Level 2: Review Your Concepts

33. Seven years ago the ratio of the ages of P and Q (in years) was 7 : 6. Which of the following cannot be the ratio of their ages 6 years from now?
(a) 13 : 11 (b) 15 : 14
(c) 13 : 12 (d) 16 : 15

34. The ratio of the monthly incomes of Ram and Shyam is 3 : 4 and the ratio of their monthly expenditures is 4 : 5. If Shyam saves ₹400 per month, which of the following cannot be the savings of Ram? (In ₹/month)
(a) 290 (b) 280
(c) 270 (d) 310

35. The ratio of the present ages of Anand and Bala is 8 : 3. When Anand was 30 years old, Bala was 5 years old. Find the present age of Bala. (In years)
(a) 10 (b) 12
(c) 15 (d) 20

36. There are three sections A, B, and C in class VIII of a school. The ratio of the number of students in A, B, and C is 2 : 3 : 4. The section which has neither the maximum number of students nor the minimum number of students has a strength of 30. Find the total strength of the three sections.
(a) 63 (b) 81
(c) 72 (d) 90

37. In a solution of 45 litres of milk and water, 40% is water. How many litres of milk must be added to become the ratio of milk and water 5 : 3?
(a) 8 (b) 3
(c) 7 (d) 6

38. Find the triplicate ratio of $(2y - x) : (2x - y)$, if $x : y = 4 : 3$.
(a) 64 : 125 (b) 27 : 64
(c) 8 : 125 (d) 27 : 125

39. A varies directly with x^2. If $x = 2$ or 4, then $A = 20$. Find A if $x = 8$.
(a) 48 (b) 120
(c) 64 (d) 320

40. The force applied on a stationary body varies directly with the acceleration with which it starts to move. If a force of 10 N is applied on a stationary body, it starts to move with an acceleration of 2 m/sec^2. Find the force (in N) to be applied on the body at which it starts to move with an acceleration of 4 m/sec^2.
(a) 30 (b) 20
(c) 40 (d) 50

41. Ninety coins are to be distributed among P, Q, and R such that P gets twice as many coins as Q gets and Q gets thrice as many coins as R gets. Find the number of coins R gets.
(a) 6 (b) 3
(c) 10 (d) 9

42. P varies inversely with $\sqrt{y}$. If $y = 2$, then $P = 40$. If $P = 20$, then find y.
(a) $\sqrt{8}$ (b) 8
(c) 4 (d) $\sqrt{2}$

43. The monthly electricity bill raised by the municipal corporation consists of two parts-a fixed charge for providing the service and a variable charge which is directly proportional to the number of watts of power consumed. An amount of ₹500 is charged for consuming 125 watts in a particular month. The ratio of the amount charged for 400 watts to that of 500 watts is 21 : 25. How much is the fixed charge per month?
(a) ₹125 (b) ₹200
(c) ₹250 (d) ₹500

44. A solution of 30 litres of milk and water, has 70% milk. How many litres of water must be added so that the volumes of milk and water will be in the ratio 3 : 2?
(a) 6 (b) 3
(c) 5 (d) 4

45. If $\dfrac{a+b}{xa+yb} = \dfrac{b+c}{xb+yc} = \dfrac{c+a}{xc+ya}$ where $x + y \neq 0$ and $a + b + c \neq 0$, then each of these ratios is equal to:
(a) 1 (b) $\dfrac{1}{x+y}$
(c) $\dfrac{2}{x+y}$ (d) $\dfrac{2}{a+b}$

46. The ratio of sugar and other ingredients in the biscuits of three bakeries—Monginis, Karachi, and Baker's Inn are 5 : 4, 13 : 12, and 29 : 24 respectively. The biscuits of which bakery are the sweetest?
(a) Monginis
(b) Karachi
(c) Baker's inn
(d) All the three types of biscuits are equally sweet.

47. ₹x is divided among three persons Mr Vaayu, Mr Jala, and Mr Agni in the ratio 3 : 4 : 7. If the share of Mr Jala is ₹5600, then find the value of x.
(a) 15,400 (b) 16,800
(c) 18,200 (d) 19,600

48. The ratio of the monthly incomes of Mr Anand and Mr Milind is 9 : 10 and the ratio of their monthly savings is 9 : 10. If the monthly expenditure of Mr Milind is ₹15,000, then find the monthly expenditure of Mr Anand (in ₹).
(a) ₹12,000 (b) ₹9000
(c) ₹8500 (d) ₹13,500

49. What must be added to both the terms of $x : y$, so that the resultant ratio is inverse of the given ratio ($x \neq y$)?
(a) $y - x$ (b) $x - y$
(c) $-(x + y)$ (d) $x + y$

Level 3: Assess Your Concepts

50. Nine friends had a tea party. All boys took only coffee and all girls took only tea. The cost per cup of coffee in rupees is numerically 2 less than the number of girls and the cost per cup of tea in rupees is numerically 2 less than the number of boys. If the ratio of the total expenses of the boys and the girls is 5 : 6, then what is the cost of each coffee? (In ₹)
(a) 2 (b) 5
(c) 7 (d) 3

51. If $x : y = 3 : 5$, find the duplicate ratio of $(3x + y) : (5x - y)$.
(a) 49 : 25 (b) 25 : 9
(c) 36 : 25 (d) 49 : 36

52. There are some students in an auditorium, some of them are dressed in white and the others are dressed in blue. The ratio of the number of boys dressed in white to the number of girls dressed in blue is 4 : 3 and the ratio of the total number of girls dressed in white to the number of boys dressed in blue is 4 : 5. The ratio of the total number of boys and girls dressed in white to the total number of boys and girls dressed in blue is 12 : 13. Find the ratio of the total number of boys to that of girls in the auditorium.
(a) 13 : 15 (b) 19 : 17
(c) 14 : 11 (d) Cannot be determined

53. Eleven friends had a tea party. All boys took only coffee and all girls took only tea. The cost per cup of coffee in rupees is numerically one more than the number of girls and the cost per cup of tea in rupees is numerically equal to the number of boys. If the ratio of the total expenses of the boys and the girls is 7 : 6, then what is the cost of each coffee? (In ₹)
(a) 4 (b) 5
(c) 6 (d) 7

54. The ratio of the present ages of Mrs. Anoukika and Mrs. Mythili is 5 : 6. After 6 years, Mrs. Anoukika would reach the present age of Mrs. Mythili. Find the sum of their present ages (in years).
(a) 66 (b) 44
(c) 33 (d) 15

55. The incomes of A and B are in the ratio 4 : 3. The expenditures of A and B are in the ratio 5 : 2. If B saves ₹3000, then which of the following cannot be the savings of A?
(a) ₹1500 (b) ₹2500
(c) ₹3500 (d) ₹4500

56. If $a + b$ varies directly with $a - b$, then which of the following vary directly?
(a) a and b (b) $a^2 + b^2$ and $a^2 - b^2$
(c) Both (a) and (b) (d) None of these

57. If 20 men take 15 days to complete a certain amount of work working at 10 hours per day, then how many more men are required to complete twice the previous work in 10 days working at 12 hours a day?
(a) 10 (b) 20
(c) 30 (d) 40

58. The ratio of the amounts with Mr Umar and Mr Gumar is 3 : 4. If Mr Gumar gives ₹5 to Mr Umar, then the ratio of the amounts with Umar and Gumar is 4 : 3. Mr Umar gives ₹5 to Mr Gumar. Find the ratio of the amounts with them.

(a) 3 : 5 (b) 2 : 5
(c) 4 : 5 (d) 1 : 5

59. If $\frac{x^3 + 3xy^2}{y^3 + 3x^2y} = \frac{62}{63}$, then find the value of $x : y$.

(a) 2:3 (b) 2:5
(c) 3:4 (d) 3:2

60. The value of a precious stone varies directly with square of its weight. The stone broken into three pieces whose weights are in the ratio 2: 3: 4. The loss incurred due to breakage is ₹104000. Find the value of the stone.

(a) ₹142000 (b) ₹165000
(c) ₹162000 (d) ₹100000

AT

PRACTICE QUESTIONS JEE SPECIAL WING

Multiple-Answer Type Questions

Directions for questions 1 to 10:

Each question has FOUR options (a), (b), (c), and (d). ONE OR MORE THAN ONE of these four option(s) is/are the correct answer(s).

1. In a school, the number of boys, girls, and teachers are in the ratio 17 : 19 : 2. Which of the following can be the total number of students and teachers in the school?

(a) 456 (b) 874
(c) 1444 (d) 1710

2. If 5, $x+2$, $x+5$ and 8 are in proportion, then which of the following can be the value of x?

(a) −10 (b) −8
(c) 3 (d) 5

3. If $\frac{p+q}{r+s}=\frac{q+r}{p+s}=\frac{r+s}{p+q}=\frac{s+p}{q+r}$, then which of the following can be the value of $\frac{r+s}{p+q}$?

(a) −1 (b) 0
(c) 1 (d) 2

4. Ten men can complete a piece of work in 15 days working 8 hours a day. Which of the following is/are correct with respect to the given data?

(a) If we appoint 10 more people and work for 10 hours per day, the work will be completed in 6 days.
(b) If we appoint 4 people fewer to complete the work in 20 days, they need to work for 10 hours per day.
(c) If we appoint 5 more people and work for 8 hours per day, then the two units of work will be completed in 16 days.
(d) If we appoint 2 people fewer and work for 12 hours per day, then the three units of work will be completed in 37.5 days.

5. The income of Krupa is 40% more than the income of Apoorva. The ratio of the savings of Apporva and Krupa is 7 : 9. Which of the following cannot be the ratio of their expenditures?

(a) 5 : 7 (b) 7 : 9
(c) 9 : 11 (d) 11 : 13

6. In a garden, there are different types of tress. The ratio of the number of Oak trees and that of Alder trees is 11 : 12. The ratio of the number of Alder trees and that of Birch trees is 15 : 16. Which of the following can be the total number of Oak, Alder and Birch trees in the garden?

(a) 108 (b) 179
(c) 216 (d) 358

7. Kinetic energy of an object varies directly with the square of its speed when mass of the object is kept constant and varies directly with mass of the object when its speed is kept constant. An object of mass 4 kg and moving with a speed of 2 m/s has a kinetic energy of 8 joules. Which of the following is/are correct with respect to the given data?

(a) An object of mass 6 kg and moving with a speed of 3 m/s has a kinetic energy of 18 joules.
(b) An object of mass 8 kg and moving with a speed of 5 m/s has a kinetic energy of 100 joules.
(c) An object of mass 10 kg and moving with a speed of 7 m/s has a kinetic energy of 245 joules.
(b) An object of mass 12 kg and moving with a speed of 11 m/s has a kinetic energy of 726 joules.

8. If $a:b=b:c=c:d=d:e=2:3$, which of the following is/are true?

(a) $a:e=16:81$
(b) $b:d:a=12:27:8$
(c) $(c-b):(a+e)=12:43$
(d) $(a+c+e):(b+d+a)=133:94$

9. Adhvik grows apple and banana plants in his farmhouse. The number of apple plants and the number of banana plants are represented by x and y respectively. Each apple plant produces 200 apples, and each banana plant produces 450 bananas.

If $\frac{x^3+3xy^2}{3x^2y+y^3}=\frac{76}{49}$, then which of the following represents the total number of apples and bananas for all the plants in the farmhouse?

(a) 1250 (b) 2500
(c) 3750 (d) 5500

10. For a given ratio 1 : 8, which of the following is true?
(a) The sub-duplicate ratio is $1:2\sqrt{2}$
(b) The sub-triplicate ratio is 1 : 2
(c) The duplicate ratio is 1 : 64
(d) The triplicate ratio is 1 : 512

Match The Column

Directions for questions 11 to 15:
Read the paragraph given below and answer the questions.
A precious stone of worth ₹2,70,00,000 is broken into five pieces. The value of each stone varies directly with cube of its weight. The weights of the pieces are in the ratio 1 : 2 : 3 : 4 : 5 and the pieces are named as Amethyst, Emerald, Garnet, Opal, and Ruby respectively.

Match the items in column A with the values in column B.

Column A	Column B
11. The value of Opal	(a) ₹2,80,000
12. The difference of the values of Ruby and Opal	(b) ₹4,88,000
13. The sum of the values of Emerald and Garnet	(c) ₹5,12,000
14. The difference of the values of Ruby and the sum of the values of Amethyst, Emerald, and Garnet	(d) ₹6,44,000
15. The loss incurred due to breakage	(e) ₹7,12,000
	(f) ₹25,20,000
	(g) ₹2,52,00,000

Comprehension-Based Questions

Directions for questions 16 to 20:
Read the paragraph given below and answer the questions.
A garrison of 1200 soldiers has sufficient food-stock for 180 days when the rate of consumption is 1500 grams per day per soldier.

16. If 200 soldiers leave the garrison, for how many days is the food-stock sufficient?
(a) 200 (b) 210
(c) 216 (d) 224

17. If 300 soldiers join the garrison, how many grams of food per day must each soldier consume so that the food-stock is sufficient for the same 180 days?
(a) 1200 (b) 1250
(c) 1300 (d) 1350

18. If each soldier consumes 300 grams more per day, for how many days is the food-stock sufficient?
(a) 160 (b) 150
(c) 120 (d) 100

19. If after 30 days 200 soldiers leave the garrison and 500 soldiers join the garrison, for how many more days is the food-stock sufficient?
(a) 144 (b) 136
(c) 120 (d) 100

20. After 80 days, if 800 soldiers join the garrison and each soldier consumes 500 grams less per day, for a total of how many days is the food-stock sufficient?
(a) 90 (b) 120
(c) 150 (d) 170

Assertion and Reason Type Questions

Directions for questions 21 to 25:
Read the options given below and answer the questions.

(a) Both assertion (A) and reason (R) are true, and reason (R) is the correct explanation of the assertion.
(b) Both assertion (A) and reason (R) are true, and reason (R) is not the correct explanation of the assertion.
(c) Assertion (A) is true, but reason (R) is false.
(d) Assertion (A) is false, and reason (R) is true.

21. **Assertion:** The duplicate ratio of 1 : 2 is 1 : 4.
Reason: The duplicate ratio of $a : b$ is $a : 2b$.

22. **Assertion:** If $a : b = 2 : 3$, then the value of $\frac{a^2 + ab}{a^2 - b}$ cannot be determined.

Reason: If $a : b$ is known, then the value of $\frac{a^2 + ab}{a^2 - b}$ cannot be determined since the degrees of the terms of the numerator and the denominator are different.

23. **Assertion:** The ratio of the incomes of Anan and Buvan is 2 : 3. If the ratio of the expenditures of Anan and Buvan is 2 : 3, then the ratio of savings of Anan and Buvan is also 2 : 3.

    Reason: For any two persons, if the ratio of their incomes is equal to the ratio of their expenditures, then the ratio of their savings is also equal to the ratio of their incomes.

24. **Assertion:** The mean proportional of 5 and 125 is 25.

    Reason: If a, b, and c are in proportion, then c is the third proportion to a and b.

25. **Assertion:** The compound ratio of 2 : 3 and 5 : 7 is 14 : 15.

    Reason: If two ratios are equal, then the product of extremes is equal to the product of means.

ANSWER KEYS

Crossword

Across

2. Continued 3. Consequent 5. Equality 7. Sixteen 9. Proportion
11. Four 12. Direct

Down

1. Antecedent 4. Ratio 6. Inverse 8. Hundred 10. Eight

Classroom Wing

Very Short Answer Type Questions

1. 32 : 1 2. 512 : 3375 3. $p : q$ 4. 4 times 5. 17 : 6 : 4
6. direct proportion 7. True 8. False 9. 6 : 1 10. 4
11. $\sqrt{3}$ 12. 27 : 35 13. 5 : 14 14. 3 : 13 15. 21 and 28
16. 135 : 256 17. 27 18. 63 : 81 19. 3 : 1 20. ₹90, ₹180
21. 2

Short Answer Type Questions

22. 70 23. 3 24. 3 : 4 25. 4 26. 11 : 3
27. 13 : 10 28. 35 29. 2 30. 2 31. 4500π cm^3
32. 4 33. 205 34. $ps = qr$

Essay Type Questions

35. 18 : 13 36. ₹3360 37. ₹480 38. ₹52000 39. 2 or–1

Competition Wing

Level 1: Apply Your Concepts

1. $\frac{a}{a-b} = \frac{c}{c-d}$ 2. 19 : 24 3. 12 : 4 : 3 4. 5 : 8 5. (c)
6. (b) 7. (d) 8. (d) 9. (d) 10. (b)
11. (b) 12. (d) 13. (c) 14. (c) 15. (a)
16. (c) 17. (c) 18. (c) 19. (b) 20. (a)
21. (d) 22. (a) 23. (b) 24. (d) 25. (a)
26. (b) 27. (d) 28. (b) 29. (a) 30. (b)
31. (c) 32. (b)

Level 2: Review Your Concepts

33. (a) 34. (d) 35. (c) 36. (d) 37. (b)
38. (c) 39. (d) 40. (b) 41. (d) 42. (c)

43. (c)	44. (c)	45. (c)	46. (a)	47. (d)
48. (d)	49. (c)			

Level 3: Assess Your Concepts

50. (a)	51. (a)	52. (c)	53. (d)	54. (a)
55. (d)	56. (c)	57. (c)	58. (b)	59. (a)
60. (c)				

JEE Special Wing

Multiple-Answer Type Questions

1. (a, b, c, d)	2. (a, c)	3. (a, c)	4. (a, b, d)	5. (a, b)
6. (b, d)	7. (b, c, d)	8. (a, b, d)	9. (a, b, c)	10. (a, b, c, d)

Match The Column

11. (c)	12. (b)	13. (a)	14. (e)	15. (g)

Comprehension-Based Questions

16. (c)	17. (a)	18. (b)	19. (c)	20. (d)

Assertion and Reason Type Questions

21. (c)	22. (a)	23. (a)	24. (b)	25. (d)

Hints and Explanations

Classroom Wing

Very Short Answer Type Questions

1. Inverse ratio $\frac{1}{8}:4$

   $a : b$ $\quad 4:\frac{1}{8}$

   $b : a$ <inverse ratio> $\quad$ multiply by 8

   32 : 1

2. Triplicate ratio of $a : b = a^3 : b^3$

   $\Rightarrow$ Triplicate ratio of $8 : 15 = 8^3 : 15^3 = 512 : 3375$.

3. Compound ratio $= p:r::r:q$

   $= p:q$

4. If P and Q^2 are in direct proportion. If Q doubles the P becomes:

   $P \alpha Q^2$ $\quad P : Q^2$

   If a doubles, $2(Q^2)$ i.e., $Q^2 \times Q^2$ $\quad P : (2Q)^2$

   P will be 4 times $\quad P : 4Q^2$

5. $a:b = 17:6$ and $b:c = 3:2$

   Multiplying each term of the ratio 3 : 2 by 2

   $b : c = 3 \times 2 : 2 \times 2 = 6 : 4$

   $\therefore a:b:c = 17 : 6 : 4$

6. $a = 3, 5, 8, 10$

   $b = 9, 15, 24, 30$

   $b = 3a$

   Direct proportion

7. 4, 7, 8, 14 are in proportion

   $8 : 14 = 4 : 7$

   $\therefore$ 4, 7, 8, 14 are in proportion

   $4 : 7 :: 8 : 14$

8. The mean proportion between 4 and 8 is 6

   Mean proportional $= \sqrt{4 \times 8} = \sqrt{32}$ = false

9. 1.5 lts : 250 ml

   1000 ml = 1lt

   1500 ml : 250 ml

   6 ml : 1 ml

10. $A^2 \propto \frac{1}{B}$

    $A^2B = k$(constant)

    $A_1^2B_1 = A_2^2 B_2$

    $(4)^2 (16) = (8)^2 \times (B_2)^2$

    $B_2 = 4$

11. $A \propto \frac{1}{B^2} \Rightarrow A = \frac{k}{B^2}$: k = constant of proportionality

    given, $A = 1$ when $B = 3$

    $\Rightarrow 1 = \frac{k}{3^2}$

    $\Rightarrow k = 9$

    Now, when $A = 3$

    $3 = \frac{k}{B^2}$

    $3 = \frac{9}{B^2}$

    $B^2 = 3$

    $\therefore B = \sqrt{3}$

12. $\frac{3}{5}:\frac{7}{9}$

    cross multiplication

    $9 \times 3 : 7 \times 5$

    27 : 35

13. $x : y = 5 : 6$ and $y : z = 3 : 7$, $x : z = ?$

    $x : y = 5 : 6$ $\quad x : y : z = 15 : 18 : 42$

    $y : z = 3 : 7$ $\quad x : z = 15 : 42$

    $= 5 : 14$

14. $a : b = 2 : 3$, $(3a - b) : (2a + 3b)$

    $\frac{a}{b} = \frac{2}{3}$ $\quad \frac{(3a-b)}{(2a+3b)} = \frac{\left(3 \times \frac{2b}{3} - b\right)}{\left(2 \times \frac{2b}{3} + 3b\right)} = \frac{b}{\frac{4b}{3} + 3b}$

    $a = \frac{2b}{3}$ $\quad \frac{3b}{4b + 9b} = \frac{3b}{13b}$ $\quad 3 : 13$

15. $x : y$

    $3x : 4y$

    $x + 7 : y + 7$

4 : 5

$\frac{x}{y} = \frac{3}{4}$ $\qquad \frac{x+7}{y+7} = \frac{4}{5}$

$4x = 3y$ $\qquad 5x + 35 = 4y + 28$

$4x - 3y = 0 \quad (1) \qquad 5x - 4y = -7 \quad (2)$

on solving,

$$\begin{array}{r} 4x - 3y = 0 \\ 5x - 9y = -7 \\ (-) \ (+) \ (-) \\ \hline 20x - 15y = 0 \\ 20x - 16y = 28 \\ (-) \ (+) \ (-) \\ \hline y = 28 \\ x = 21 \end{array}$$

Hence, numbers are 21, 28.

16. $6\frac{1}{2} : 8\frac{2}{3}$ and $3\frac{3}{4} : 5\frac{1}{3}$ compounded ratio?

$a : b$ and $c : d$ is $ac : bd$

$$\frac{6\frac{1}{2} \times 5\frac{1}{3}}{8\frac{2}{3} \times 3\frac{3}{4}} = \frac{\frac{13}{2} \times \frac{16}{3}}{\frac{34}{3} \times \frac{15}{4}}$$

135 : 256

17. 4, 9 and 12

$4 : 9 = 12 : x$

$\frac{4}{9} = \frac{12}{x}$

$4x = 12 \times 9$

$x = \frac{12 \times 9}{4} = 3 \times 9 = 27$

18. 7 : 9

Multiply both by 9

$7 \times 9 : 9 \times 9$

63 : 81

19. $(3a + 2b) : (5a + 7b) = 1 : 2,\ a : b = ?$

$\frac{3a + 2b}{5a + 7b} = \frac{1}{2}$

$6a + 4b = 5a + 7b$

$a = 3b$

$\frac{a}{b} = \frac{3}{1} \qquad (1) \times 5$

$3 : 1 \qquad (2) \times 4$

20. $A : B : C \qquad B = ₹\ 120$

$\frac{1}{2} : \frac{1}{3} : \frac{1}{4}$

LCM = 24 $\quad 12 : 8 : 6 \frac{120}{4} =$ ₹ 30 (one part)

6 : 4 : 3

$6 \times 30 =$ ₹ 180

$3 \times 30 =$ ₹ 90

21. 32, 38, 17, 20

Subtraction by 2 makes it all divisible by 3

30, 36, 15, 18

10 : 12 :: 5 : 6

Short Answer Type Questions

22. Boys : Girls

3 : 4

$4x = 3x + 10$

$x = 10$

$30 + 40 = 70$

23. $A : A + 2 :: A + 12 : A + 22$

$$\frac{A}{A+2} = \frac{A+12}{A+22}$$

$$A^2 + 22A = A^2 + 2A + 12A + 24$$

$$22A - 14A = 24$$

$$8A = 24$$

$$A = 3$$

24. $\frac{a^3 + 2ab^2}{2a^2b + b^3} = \frac{123}{136}$

$136\,(a^3 + 2ab^2) = 123\,(2a^2b + b^3)$

$a\,(a^2 + 2b^2) = b\,(2a^2 + b^2)$

$\frac{a}{b} = \frac{2a^2 + b^2}{a^2 + 2b^2} \times \frac{123}{136}$

$\frac{a}{b} = \frac{3}{4}$

25. $P : Q : R$

$P : Q = 3x : x$

$Q : R = 3x : x$

$P : Q : R = 9x^2 : 3x^2 : x^2$

$= 9 : 3 : 1$

$\frac{1}{13}(52) = 4$

26. Father : Son

$3x : 1x$

$4x + 10 = 58$

$4x = 48$

$x = 12$

Son's present age = 12 years

Father's age = 36 years.

The required ratio = (36 – 3)/(12 – 3)

$\Rightarrow \frac{33}{9} = \frac{11}{3}$

27. $H : W$

$5x : 4x$

$\frac{5x+20}{4x+20} = \frac{13}{10}$

$50x + 200 = 52x + 260$

$-60 = 2x$

Age cannot negative

13 : 10

28. $M : D$ Mother is 20 years older than daughter

7 : 3

$3x + 20 = 7x$

$20 = 4x$ Swaroopa's present age = 35 years

$x = 5$ Daughter present age = 15 years

$7x = 35$

$3x = 15$

29. $$\frac{\sqrt{10+3x}+\sqrt{10-3x}}{\sqrt{10+3x}-\sqrt{10-3x}} = 3$$

$$\frac{\sqrt{10+3x}+\sqrt{10-3x}}{\sqrt{10+3x}-\sqrt{10-3x}} \times \frac{\sqrt{10+3x}+\sqrt{10-3x}}{\sqrt{10+3x}+\sqrt{10-3x}} = 3$$

$$\frac{\left(\sqrt{10+3x}+\sqrt{10-3x}\right)^2}{(10+3x)-(10-3x)} = 3$$

$$\left(\sqrt{10+3x}+\sqrt{10-3x}\right)^2 = 18x$$

$\Rightarrow 10 + 3x + 10 - 3x + 2\sqrt{(10+3x)(10-3x)} = 18x$

$\Rightarrow 10 + \sqrt{100-9x^2} = 9x$

$\Rightarrow \sqrt{100-9x^2} = 9x - 10$

$\Rightarrow 90x^2 = 180x$

$\Rightarrow x = 2$

30. $$\frac{x+2p}{x-2p} + \frac{x+2q}{x-2q} = ?, \quad x = \frac{4pq}{p+q}$$

$$\frac{\frac{4pq}{p+q}+2p}{\frac{4pq}{p+q}-2p} + \frac{\frac{4pq}{p+q}+2q}{\frac{4pq}{p+q}-2q}$$

$$= \frac{\frac{4pq+2p^2+2pq}{p+q}}{\frac{4pq-2pq-2p^2}{p+q}} + \frac{\frac{4pq+2pq+2q^2}{p+q}}{\frac{4pq-2pq-2q^2}{p+q}}$$

$$= \frac{6pq+2p^2}{2pq-2p^2} + \frac{6pq+2q^2}{2pq-2q^2} \Rightarrow \frac{3pq+p^2}{pq-p^2} + \frac{3pq+q^2}{pq-q^2}$$

$$\frac{x^2 - 2qx + 2px - 4pq + x^2 + 2qx - 2px - 4pq}{(x-2p)(x-2q)}$$

$$\frac{2x^2-8pq}{(x-2p)(x-2q)} = \frac{2(x^2-4pq)}{x^2-2xq-2px-4pq}$$

$$= \frac{2(x^2-4pq)}{(x^2-4pq)} = 2$$

31. $V \propto (r)^3$

if $r = 3$ cm if $r = 15$ cm

$V = 36\,\pi$ cm^3 $V = 4500\,\pi$ cm^3

Volume = $\frac{4}{3}\pi r^3$

32. $T : U$

1 : 2 $\left.\begin{matrix}12\\24\\36\\48\end{matrix}\right\} = 4$

33. $A : B$

Income 3 : 2 $\frac{A}{B} = \frac{3}{2}$ $2A = 3B$

Expense 4 : 3 $A = 3x$, $B = 2x$ $A = 4y$, $B = 3y$

$3x - 4y = 300$

$2x - 3y = ?$ $600 + 8y - 9y = 615$

$2\left(\frac{300+4y}{3}\right) - 3y$ $-y = 15$

$\frac{2}{3}(300+4y) - 3y = 205 \therefore$ 205 as the answer cannot be negative

34. $$\frac{2p+5q}{2r+5s} = \frac{4p-3q}{4r-3s}$$

$8pr - 6ps + 20qr - 15qs = 8pr + 20ps - 6qr - 15qs$

$20qr + 6qr = 20ps + 6ps$

$26qr = 26ps$

$qr = ps$

Essay Type Questions

35. White : Red

$3C : 2B$

$3B : 4C$

Total $15C : 16B$

$3C + 3B = 15C + x$

$2B + 4C = 16B + y$

$(-) \quad (-) \quad (-) \quad (-)$

$B - C = 15C - 16B + x - y$

$18B - 13C = x - y$

$x - y = B - C$

$18 : 13$

36. ₹ 12250

$\frac{a}{b} = \frac{b}{c} = \frac{c}{d} = \frac{3}{4}$

$a : b = 3 : 4 \quad a = \frac{3}{4}b \quad c = \frac{3}{4}d$

$b : c = 3 : 4 \qquad b = \frac{3}{4}c \qquad a : b : c = b : c : d$

$c : d = 3 : 4$

$a : b : c : d = 9 : 12 : 12 : 16$

Hence, C's shares $= \frac{12}{49} \times 12250 = 3360$

37. $\frac{x}{y} = \frac{3}{4}$ Total amount $= a$

$x = \frac{1}{7}a + \frac{3a}{7}$

$480 = \frac{1}{7}a + \frac{3a}{7}$

$480 = \frac{4a}{7}$

$\frac{480 \times 7}{4} = a$

$a = 840$

Hence, y's share $= 4 \times \frac{840}{7} = 480$

38. $V = k W^2$

Let the weight of broken pieces be $3x$, $4x$ and $2x$.

Total weight $= 9x$.

Therefore $V = k(9x)^2$

$81000 = k\, 81x^2$

$1000 = kx^2$

The total value of the broken pieces $= v_1 + v_2 + v_3$

$= k(3x)^2 + k(4x)^2 + k(2x)^2$

$= k(29x^2)$

$= 29kx^2$

$= 29 \times 1000$

$=$ ₹29000

Therefore the loss due to breakage $=$(₹81000 – ₹29000)

$=$ ₹52000.

39. Given that $\frac{a+b}{c} = \frac{b+c}{a} = \frac{a+c}{b}$.

$\frac{a+b}{c} = \frac{b+c}{a} = \frac{a+c}{b} = \frac{(a+b)+(b+c)+(a+c)}{c+a+b}$.

$= \frac{2(a+b+c)}{a+b+c}$.

$= 2$ (When $a+b+c \neq 0$)

When $a+b+c = 0$, $a+b = -c$.

$\frac{a+b}{c} = -1$.

$\therefore$ The value of each fraction is 2 or -1.

Competition Wing

Level 1: Apply Your Concepts

1. $b : (a - b) :: d : (c - d)$

$\not{b}(c-d) \cdot d(\not{a} - \not{b}) \dfrac{b}{a \cdot b} + 1 - \dfrac{d}{c \cdot d} + 1$ (add 1 on both sides)

$\dfrac{b + a - b}{a - b} = \dfrac{d + c - d}{c - d}$

$\dfrac{a}{a - b} = \dfrac{c}{c - d}$

2. The simplest form of 57 : 72 is
57 : 72
divided by 3
19 : 24

3. $x = 3y = 4z$ $\quad x : y : z$

$y = \dfrac{1}{3}x$ $\quad \dfrac{12}{12}x : \dfrac{1}{3}x \times \dfrac{4}{4} : \dfrac{1}{4}x \times \dfrac{1}{3}$

$z = \dfrac{1}{4}x$ $\quad \dfrac{12x}{12} : \dfrac{4x}{12} : \dfrac{3x}{12}$

$12 : 4 : 3$

4. 4 : 9 and 5 : 8

$\dfrac{4}{9} = 0.44 \quad \dfrac{5}{8} = 0.625$

5. The compound ratio of 15 : 6 and 9 : 5

$15 \times 9 : 6 \times 5 = 135 : 30$

$= 9 : 2.$

6. Let P = $7x$ and Q = $8x$. The difference in the number of coins with P and Q is 5.

7. If $a : b = c : d$
(A), (B), (C) and (D) are all correct.
Choice (d) follows.

8. Simplify the required ratio.

9. Assume 'x' as the number to be added and apply Product of extremes = Product of means.

10. Let the number of notes be $6x$, $3x$, and $7x$.

11. Let p, q, r, and s be $3x$, $4x$, $7x$, and $8x$.

12. (i) Let the required ratio be x : 1.

(ii) Let the density of metal z be k.

∴ Density of metal $x = 15k$

Density of metal $y = 8k$.

(iii) Let required ratio be m : 1.

(iv) $(15k)m + (8k)1 = (m + 1)(13k)$.

Solve this equation to get m.

13. Let the number added be x and use. Product of extremes = Product of means.

14. Use the unitary method.

15. (i) Consider the expenses of boys and girls as x and y respectively and proceed.

(ii)

	Number of Boys	Number of Girls
	b	g
Expense per student	$b - 1$	$g - 1$

(iii) $\dfrac{bg - b}{gb - g} = \dfrac{8}{9}$.

(iv) Solve $b + g = 7$ and the above equation and get $(g - 1)$ in rupees.

16. (i) If a, b, and c are in continued proportion, then $b^2 = ac$.

(ii) Substitute $b^2 = ac$ in $a^2 : b^2$.

17. Given, the wall is divided into three parts.

One part is $\dfrac{1}{4}$

The sum of other two parts should be

$1 - \dfrac{1}{4} = \dfrac{4 - 1}{4} = \dfrac{3}{4}$

$\therefore \dfrac{1}{3} + \dfrac{5}{12} = \dfrac{4 + 5}{12} = \dfrac{9}{12} = \dfrac{3}{4}$.

18. (i) $\dfrac{V_1}{V_2} = \dfrac{t_1^2}{t_2^2}$. (Apply the concept of variation).

(ii) Given that $\dfrac{V}{t^2} = k$ (where k is constant).

(iii) $\dfrac{V_1}{t_1^2} = \dfrac{V_2}{t_2^2}$.

19. (i) Consider the number of students in C_1 and C_2 as $2x$ and $3x$, respectively.

(ii) Let the number of students in the two classes C_1 and C_2 be $2x$ and $3x$, respectively.

(iii) Given $(2x - 10) : (3x + 10) = 3 : 7$.
Find x from this equation.

(iv) Let y be the number of students to be shifted from C_2 to C_1.

(v) Substitute value of x in $(2x - 10 + y) : (3x + 10 - y) = 9 : 11$ and find y.

20. (i) Frame the linear equations and solve them.

(ii) The sum of present ages of Rakesh and his daughter is (40 + 20) years.

(iii) Divide 60 in the ratio 7 : 3.

21. (i) If $b^2 = ac$, then b is the mean proportional and c is the third proportional.

(ii) Let the two numbers be a and b.

(iii) $ab = (56)^2$.

(iv) $b^2 = 448a$.

22. (i) $\frac{S_1}{S_2} = \frac{BP_1}{BP_2}$. (Apply the concept of variation).

$\Rightarrow \frac{2}{8.5} = \frac{120}{BP_2}$

$\therefore BP_2 = 510$

23. (i) Find the ratio of P : Q : R : S and proceed.

(ii) Given P : Q = Q : R = R : S = 1 : 2, find P : Q : R : S.

(iii) R's share

$= \frac{\text{term corresponding to R}}{\text{Sum of the terms of the ratio}} \times 22{,}515.$

24. Use the unitary method.

25. (i) Let the weights of the three pieces be x, $2x$ and $3x$ and their costs be C_1, C_2, and C_3, respectively.

(ii) $\frac{C_1}{x^3} = \frac{C_2}{(2x)^3} = \frac{C_3}{(3x)^3} = \frac{96{,}336}{(6x)^3}$.

(iii) Find C_1, C_2 and C_3 and then $96{,}336 - (C_1 + C_2 + C_3)$.

26. Let the weights of the three pieces be $2x$, $3x$ and $5x$ and their costs be v_1, v_2, and v_3 respectively.

$v_1 = 4x^2k$, $v_2 = 9x^2k$, $v_3 = 25x^2k$,

$96{,}000 = 100x^2k$

$x^2k = 960$

$v_1 + v_2 + v_3 = 38x^2k$

$= 38 \times 960 = 36{,}480$,

$\therefore$ loss = 96,000 − 36,480 = ₹59,520.

27. (i) Find the ratio marks of Bunny, Sunny, and Bharat.

(ii) Marks scored by sunny $= \left(\frac{9}{8}\right)$ (marks scored by Bharat).

(iii) Marks scored by Bunny $= \left(\frac{10}{7}\right)$ (marks scored by Sunny).

28. Divide both the numerator and the denominator by y^3.

29. Let the number be $10a + b$. Given $\frac{a}{b} = \frac{2}{3}$.

30. (i) Let the required number be x.

(ii) $\frac{9-x}{8+x} < \frac{15}{26}$.

(iii) Solve the inequation to get least integer value of x.

31. (i) Frame the linear equation and solve it.

(ii) Let the actual shares of Lava and Kusha be ₹$5x$ and ₹$7x$, respectively.

(iii) As the amount is $(5x + 7x)$, one sixth of total amount = $2x$.

(iv) The amount is divided in the ratio $(5x + 2x) : (7x - 2x)$.

32. (i) Find the ratio of number of 1 rupee, 50 paise, and 25 paise coins.

(ii) The ratio of number of one rupee coins, number of 50 paise coins, and number 25 paise coins is (5 × 2) : (9 × 2) : (1 × 9), i.e., 10 : 18 : 9.

(iii) Let the number of one rupee coins, 50 paise coins and 25 paise coins be $10x$, $18x$, and $9x$, respectively.

(iv) Given $(10x) + (18x)\frac{1}{2} + (9x)\frac{1}{4} = 425$,

Find $\left(\frac{18x}{2}\right)$, i.e., $9x$.

Level 2: Review Your Concepts

34. Let the monthly incomes of Ram and Shyam be $3x$ and $4x$ and their expenditures be $4y$ and $5y$.

35. Let Anand's age k years ago, be 30 years.

36. Let the number of students in A, B, and C be $2x$, $3x$ and $4x$.

40. Apply the concept of variation.

43. (i) Let x be the fixed charge and y be the variable charge.

(ii) Given data can be expressed as $x + 100y$.

$= 300 \cdot \frac{x + 300y}{x + 400y} = \frac{5}{6}$.

(iii) Solve the above two equations and get the value of x.

45. (i) Each ratio $= \frac{\text{Sum of all the antecedents}}{\text{Sum of all the consequents}}$.

(ii) Each fraction is equal to the ratio of sum of the numerators and the sum of the denominators of all the equivalent fractions.

46.

Name of the Bakery	Ratio of Sugar and Other Ingredients
Monginis	5 : 4 = 30 : 24
Karachi	13 : 12 = 26 : 24
Bakers Inn	29 : 24

From the above table, when the other ingredients are 24 units, their sugar quantities are 30 units, 26 units and 29 units.

∴ Monginis biscuits are the sweetest.

47. Given that the ratio of shares of Mr Vaayu, Mr Jala and Mr Agni is 3 : 4 : 7.

Share of Mr Jala = ₹5600.

∴ The total sum (in ₹) $= \frac{(3+4+7)}{4} = (5600)$

$\Rightarrow (14)(1400) \Rightarrow$ ₹19,600.

48. Let the incomes of Mr Anand and Milind be $9x$ and $10x$, and their savings be $9y$ and $10y$.

∴ The ratio of expenditures of Mr Anand and Mr Milind $= \frac{9x-9y}{10x-10y}$

$= \frac{9(x-y)}{10(x-y)} = \frac{9}{10}.$

Given that the expenditure of Mr Milind is ₹15,000.

∴ The expenditure of Mr Anand (in ₹) $= \frac{9}{10}(15{,}000) = 13{,}500.$

49. Let $\frac{x+k}{y+k} = \frac{y}{x} \Rightarrow x^2 + kx = y^2 + ky$

$\Rightarrow k(x-y) = y^2 - x^2 \Rightarrow k = -(y+x).$

Level 3: Assess Your Concepts

50. (i) Number of boys be 'b' and number of girls be 'g'.

(ii) Expenses of each boy $= g - 2$
expenses of each girl $= b - 2$

(iii) Solve $b + g = 9$ in the above equation and get $(g - 2)$ in rupees.

52. (i) Frame the linear equations and solve them.

(ii) Given data can be expressed as
the number of boys dressed in white $= 4p$
the number of girls dressed in blue $= 3p$
the number of girls dressed in white $= 4q$
the number of boys dressed in blue $= 5q$.

(iii) From the above data:

$\frac{4p+4q}{3p+5q} = \frac{12}{13}$, find $\left(\frac{p}{q}\right)$ from this equation.

(iv) Required ratio is $(4p + 5q) : (3p + 4q)$,

i.e., $4\left(\frac{p}{q}\right)+5 : 3\left(\frac{p}{q}\right)+4.$

53. (i) Let the number of boys be 'b' and number of girls be 'g'.

(ii) Expenses of each boy $= g + 1$,
expenses of each girl $= b + 1$.

(iii) $\frac{b(g+1)}{g(b)} = \frac{7}{6}.$

(iv) Solve $b + g = 11$ and the above equation and get $(g + 1)$ in ₹.

54. Let the ages of Mrs. Anoukika and Mrs. Mythili be $5x$ years and $6x$ years.

From the given data.

$5x + 6 = 6x \Rightarrow x = 6$

∴ The sum of their present ages $= 5x + 6x = 11x = 11(6) = 66$ years.

55.

	A	B
Income	4x	3x
Expenditure	5y	2y
Savings	4x – 5y	3x – 2y

Given, $3x - 2y = 3000 \Rightarrow x = 1000 + \frac{2y}{3}$

Now, saving of A $= 4x - 5y = 4\left(1000 + \frac{2y}{3}\right)$

$-5y \Rightarrow 4000 + \frac{8y}{3} - 5y \Rightarrow 4000 - \frac{7y}{3}.$

∴ The saving of A cannot be more than ₹4000.

56. Given that $a + b$ vary directly with $a - b$.

$\frac{a+b}{a-b} = k$ (constant)

Applying componendo–dividendo theorem,

$\frac{a}{b} = \frac{k+1}{k-1}$ as k is constant, $\frac{k+1}{k-1}$ is also a constant.

∴ a and b vary directly.

Let $\frac{k+1}{k-1}$ be p

$\Rightarrow \frac{a}{b} = p \Rightarrow \frac{a^2}{b^2} = p^2.$

By applying componendo–dividendo theorem,

$$\frac{a^2+b^2}{a^2-b^2}=\frac{p^2+1}{p^2-1}.$$

As p is a constant, $\frac{p^2+1}{p^2-1}$ is also a consonant.

$\therefore$ a^2+b^2 and a^2-b^2 vary directly.

57. Let the required number of men be x.

We have, $\frac{M_1D_1H_1}{W_1}=\frac{M_2D_2H_2}{W_2}$

$$\frac{(20)(15)(10)}{1}=\frac{(20+x)(10)(12)}{2}$$

$\Rightarrow 20+x=50 \Rightarrow x=30.$

58. Let the amounts with Mr Umar and Mr Gumar be ₹$3x$ and ₹$4x$, respectively.

Given, $\frac{3x+5}{4x-5}=\frac{4}{3}$

$\Rightarrow 9x+15=16x-20$

$\Rightarrow x=5.$

$\therefore$ The amounts with Mr Umar and Mr Gumar are ₹15 and ₹20, respectively.

The required ratio $=\frac{15-5}{20+5}=\frac{10}{25}=\frac{2}{5}.$

Ratio of the amount with them is 2 : 5.

59. Given $\frac{x^3+3xy^2}{y^3+3x^2y}=\frac{62}{63}.$

Applying Componendo–Dividendo rule,

$$\frac{x^3+3xy^2+y^3+3x^2y}{x^3+3xy^2-\left(y^3+3x^2y\right)}=\frac{62+63}{62-63}$$

$\Rightarrow (x+y)^3$

$$\Rightarrow \frac{(x+y)^3}{(x-y)^3}=\frac{5^3}{(-1)^3}$$

$$\Rightarrow \frac{x+y}{x-y}=\frac{5}{-1}$$

$\Rightarrow 5x-5y=-x-y$

$\Rightarrow 6x=4y$

$\Rightarrow x:y=2:3$

60. The value (V) varies directly with square of weight (W)

$V \propto W^2 \Rightarrow \frac{V}{W}=$ constant.

Let the weight of the pieces be $2k$, $3k$, $4k$.

$\therefore$ The weight of the actual piece $=(2k+3k+4k)=9k.$

The value of the stone varies directly with square of its weight.

$$\Rightarrow \frac{V_1}{4k^2}=\frac{V_2}{9k^2}=\frac{V_3}{16k^2}=\frac{V_4}{81k^2}=x \text{ (constant)}.$$

$$\Rightarrow \frac{V_1}{9k^2}=\frac{V_2}{16k^2}=\frac{V_3}{25k^2}=\frac{V_4}{144k^2}=c \text{ (say)}$$

$\Rightarrow V_1+V_2+V_3=(29k^2)c$

$\Rightarrow V_4=(81k^2)\,c$

$\Rightarrow$ Given that $V_4-(V_1+V_2+V_3)=$ ₹104000

$\Rightarrow (52k^2)c=$ ₹104000

$\Rightarrow k^2c=$ ₹2000

$\therefore$ The value of the stone $=81k^2c$

$=$ ₹162000.

JEE Special Wing

Multiple-Answer Type Questions

1. The ratio of the number of boys, girls, and teachers = 17 : 19 : 2.

   The sum of the terms of the ratio = 17 + 19 + 2 = 38.

   So, the total number of students and teachers in the school is a multiple of 38.

   (a) $456 = 38 \times 12$

   (b) $874 = 38 \times 23$

   (c) $1444 = 38 \times 38$

   (d) $1710 = 38 \times 45$

   Hence, choice (a, b, c, d) are correct.

2. Given that 5, $x + 2$, $x + 5$ and 8 are in proportion.

   $(x+2)(x+5)=5\times 8$

   (Since, the product of means = the product of extremes)

   $x^2+7x+10=40$

   $x^2+7x-30=0$

   $x^2+10x-3x-30=0$

   $x(x+10)-3(x+10)=0$

   $(x+10)(x-3)=0$

   $x+10=0$ (or) $x-3=0$

   $x=-10$ (or) $x=3$

   Hence, choice (a and c) are correct.

3. Given that $\frac{p+q}{r+s}=\frac{q+r}{p+s}=\frac{r+s}{p+q}=\frac{s+p}{q+r}$.

   $\frac{p+q}{r+s}=\frac{q+r}{p+s}=\frac{r+s}{p+q}=\frac{s+p}{q+r}=k$ (say)

   $\Rightarrow p+q=k(r+s)$

   $\Rightarrow q+r=k(p+s)$

   $\Rightarrow r+s=k(p+q)$

   $\Rightarrow p+s=k(q+r)$

   Adding the above four equations we get:

   $p+q+q+r+r+s+p+s=k(r+s+p+s+p+q+q+r)$

   $\Rightarrow 2(p+q+r+s)=2k(p+q+r+s)$

   $\Rightarrow k=\frac{2(p+q+r+s)}{2(p+q+r+s)}$

   $\Rightarrow k=\frac{p+q+r+s}{p+q+r+s}$

   Case 1: If $p+q+r+s\neq 0, k=1.$

   $\Rightarrow \frac{r+s}{p+q}=1$

   Case 2: If $p+q+r+s=0, r+s=-(p+q).$

   $\Rightarrow \frac{r+s}{p+q}=-1.$

   Hence, choice (a and c) are correct.

4. Given that ten men can complete a piece of work in 15 days working 8 hours a day.

   We have MDH = constant and also $\frac{\text{MDH}}{\text{W}}$ = constant.

   Now $\text{MDH}=10\times 15\times 8=1200$ which is a constant proportionality.

   If we assume that the number of units of work is 1, $\frac{\text{MDH}}{\text{W}}=\frac{1200}{1}=1200$ which is a constant proportionality.

   Choice (a): $M = 10 + 10 = 20$, $D = 6$, and $H = 10$.

   Now $\text{MDH}=20\times 6\times 10=1200.$

   Choice (b): $M = 10 - 4 = 6$, $D = 20$, and $H = 10$.

   Now $\text{MDH}=6\times 20\times 10=1200.$

   Choice (c): $M=10+5=15$, $D=6$, $H=8$, and $W=2$.

   Now $\frac{\text{MDH}}{\text{W}}=\frac{15\times 16\times 8}{2}=960.$

   Choice (d): $M = 10 - 2 = 8$, $D = 37.5$, $H = 12$, and $W = 3$.

   Now $\frac{\text{MDH}}{\text{W}}=\frac{8\times 37.5\times 12}{3}=1200.$

   Hence, choice (a, b, d) are correct.

5. The ratio of the incomes of Apporva and Krupa is 100% : 140% = 5 : 7.

   Let the incomes of Apporva and Krupa be $5x$ and $7x$ respectively.

   The ratio of the savings of Apporva and Krupa is 7 : 9.

   Let the savings of Apporva and Krupa be $7y$ and $9y$ respectively.

   Now, the expenditures of Apporva and Krupa are $5x-7y$ and $7x-9y$ respectively.

   Going by options:

   Choice (a): $\frac{5x-7y}{7x-9y}=\frac{5}{7}$

   $\Rightarrow 35x-49y=35x-45y$

   $\Rightarrow -49y=-45y$ which is false.

   So, 5 : 7 cannot be the ratio of the expenditures Apporva and Krupa.

   Choice (b): $\frac{5x-7y}{7x-9y}=\frac{7}{9}$

   $\Rightarrow 45x-63y=49x-63y$

$\Rightarrow 45x = 49x$ which is false.

So, 7 : 9 cannot be the ratio of the expenditures Apporva and Krupa.

Choice (c): $\dfrac{5x-7y}{7x-9y} = \dfrac{9}{11}$

$\Rightarrow 55x - 77y = 63x - 81y$

$\Rightarrow 8x = 4y$

$\Rightarrow x : y = 1 : 2.$

So, 9 : 11 can be the ratio of the expenditures of Apporva and Krupa.

Choice (d): $\dfrac{5x-7y}{7x-9y} = \dfrac{11}{13}$

$\Rightarrow 65x - 91y = 77x - 99y$

$\Rightarrow 12x = 8y$

$\Rightarrow x : y = 2 : 3.$

So, 11 : 13 can be the ratio of the expenditures of Apporva and Krupa.

Hence, choice (a) and choice (b) follow.

6. The ratio of the number of Oak trees and that of Alder trees is 11 : 12.

The ratio of the number of Alder trees and that of Birch trees is 15 : 16.

In two ratios, the number of Alder trees is represented by the numbers 12 and 15.

The LCM of 12 and 15 is 60.

The ratio of the number of Oak trees and that of Alder trees = 11 : 12 = (11 × 5): (12 × 5)

= 55 : 60

The ratio of the number of Alder trees and that of Birch trees = 15 : 16 =.(15 × 4) : (16 × 4)

= 60 : 64.

Now, the ratio of the number of Oak, Alder and Birch trees in the garden = 55 : 60 : 64.

The sum of the terms of the ratio = 55 + 60 + 64

= 179.

So, the total number of Oak, Alder and Birch trees in the garden is a multiple of 179.

Hence, choice (b) and choice (d) follow.

7. Kinetic energy (KE) of an object varies directly with the square of its speed (v) when mass of the object is kept constant and varies directly with mass (m) of the object when its speed is kept constant.

$\Rightarrow \text{KE} \propto v^2$ and $\text{KE} \propto m$

$\Rightarrow \dfrac{\text{KE}}{mv^2} = \text{constant}.$

Given that KE = 8 joules, $v = 2$ m/s, and $m = 4$ kg.

Now, $\dfrac{\text{KE}}{mv^2} = \dfrac{8}{4\times 2^2} = \dfrac{1}{2}.$

Choice (a): Given that $v = 3$ m/s, $m = 6$ kg, KE = ?

We have $\dfrac{\text{KE}}{mv^2} = \dfrac{1}{2}.$

$\Rightarrow \dfrac{\text{KE}}{6\times 3^2} = \dfrac{1}{2}$

$\Rightarrow \dfrac{\text{KE}}{54} = \dfrac{1}{2}$

$\Rightarrow$ KE = 27 joules.

So, choice (a) is not correct.

Choice (b): Given that $v = 5$ m/s, $m = 8$ kg, KE = ?

We have $\dfrac{KE}{mv^2} = \dfrac{1}{2}.$

$\Rightarrow \dfrac{KE}{8\times 5^2} = \dfrac{1}{2}$

$\Rightarrow \dfrac{KE}{200} = \dfrac{1}{2}$

$\Rightarrow KE = 100$ joules.

So, choice (b) is correct.

Choice (c): Given that $v = 7$ m/s, $m = 10$ kg, KE = ?

We have $\dfrac{KE}{mv^2} = \dfrac{1}{2}.$

$\Rightarrow \dfrac{KE}{10\times 7^2} = \dfrac{1}{2}$

$\Rightarrow \dfrac{KE}{490} = \dfrac{1}{2}$

$\Rightarrow KE = 245$ joules.

So, choice (c) is correct.

Choice (d): Given that $v = 11$ m/s, $m = 12$ kg, KE = ?

We have $\dfrac{KE}{mv^2} = \dfrac{1}{2}.$

$\Rightarrow \dfrac{KE}{12\times (11)^2} = \dfrac{1}{2}$

$\Rightarrow \dfrac{KE}{1452} = \dfrac{1}{2}$

$\Rightarrow KE = 726$ joules.

So, choice (d) is correct.

Hence, choice (b, c, d) are correct.

8. $a : b = b : c = c : d = d : e = 2 : 3.$

$\dfrac{a}{b}\times\dfrac{b}{c}\times\dfrac{c}{d}\times\dfrac{d}{e} = \dfrac{2}{3}\times\dfrac{2}{3}\times\dfrac{2}{3}\times\dfrac{2}{3}$

$\Rightarrow \dfrac{a}{e} = \dfrac{16}{81}$

Now $a:b=2:3=(2\times 8):(3\times 8)=16:24$.

$b:c=(2\times 12):(3\times 12)=24:36$.

$c:d=(2\times 18):(3\times 18)=36:54$.

$d:e=(2\times 27):(3\times 27)=54:81$.

$\Rightarrow a:b:c:d:e=16:24:36:54:81$

$\Rightarrow a:e=16:81$

$b:d:a=24:54:16=12:27:8$

$(c-b):(a+e)=(36-24):(16+81)=12:97$

$(a+c+e):(b+d+a)=(16+36+81):(24+54+16)$
$=133:94$

Hence, choice (a, b, d) are correct.

9. The number of apple plants and the number of banana plants are represented by x and y respectively. Each apple plant produces 200 apples, and each banana plant produces 450 bananas.

Also, $\dfrac{x^3+3xy^2}{3x^2y+y^3}=\dfrac{76}{49}$

$\Rightarrow \dfrac{x^3+3xy^2+3x^2y+y^3}{x^3+3xy^2-3x^2y-y^3}=\dfrac{76+49}{76-49}$

(By Componendo-dividend rule)

$\Rightarrow \dfrac{(x+y)^3}{(x-y)^3}=\dfrac{125}{27}$

$\Rightarrow \dfrac{(x+y)^3}{(x-y)^3}=\dfrac{5^3}{3^3}$

$\Rightarrow \dfrac{x+y}{x-y}=\dfrac{5}{3}$

$\Rightarrow \dfrac{x+y}{x-y}=\dfrac{4+1}{4-1}$

$\Rightarrow \dfrac{x}{y}=\dfrac{4}{1}$

Let x be $4k$ and y be k.

Total number of apples $=4k\times 200=800k$.

Total number of bananas $=k\times 400=450k$.

Therefore, the total number of apples and bananas for all the plants $=800k+450k$

$=1250k$.

Hence, choice (a), choice (b), and choice (c) follow.

10. The sub-duplicate ratio of $a:b$ is $\sqrt{a}:\sqrt{b}$.

The sub-triplicate ratio of $a:b$ is $\sqrt[3]{a}:\sqrt[3]{b}$.

The duplicate ratio of $a:b$ is $a^2:b^2$.

The triplicate ratio of $a:b$ is $a^3:b^3$.

(a) The sub-duplicate ratio of $1:8=\sqrt{1}:\sqrt{8}=1:2\sqrt{2}$.

(b) The sub-triplicate ratio of $1:8=\sqrt[3]{1}:\sqrt[3]{8}=1:2$.

(c) The duplicate ratio of $1:8=1^2:8^2=1:64$.

(d) The triplicate ratio of $1:8=1^3:8^3=1:512$.

So, the above statements are true:

Hence, choice (a, b, c, d) are correct.

Match The Column

Common Solutions for questions 11 to 15:

The worth of the precious stone $(V)=₹2{,}70{,}00{,}000$.

The stone is broken into five pieces.

The weights of the pieces are in the ratio 1 : 2 : 3 : 4 : 5 and the pieces are named as Amethyst, Emerald, Garnet, Opal, and Ruby respectively.

Let the weights of Amethyst, Emerald, Garnet, Opal, and Ruby be x, $2x$, $3x$, $4x$, and $5x$ respectively.

Let the values of Amethyst, Emerald, Garnet, Opal, and Ruby be V_1, V_2, V_3, V_4, and V_5 respectively.

The weight of the stone $=x+2x+3x+4x+5x=15x$.

The value of each stone varies directly with cube of its weight.

$V\propto w^3$

$\Rightarrow \dfrac{V}{w^3}=$ constant.

$\Rightarrow \dfrac{V}{(15x)^3}=\dfrac{V_1}{(x)^3}=\dfrac{V_2}{(2x)^3}=\dfrac{V_3}{(3x)^3}=\dfrac{V_4}{(4x)^3}=\dfrac{V_5}{(5x)^3}$

$\Rightarrow \dfrac{V}{3375x^3}=\dfrac{V_1}{x^3}=\dfrac{V_2}{8x^3}=\dfrac{V_3}{27x^3}=\dfrac{V_4}{64x^3}=\dfrac{V_5}{125x^3}$

$\Rightarrow \dfrac{V}{3375}=V_1=\dfrac{V_2}{8}=\dfrac{V_3}{27}=\dfrac{V_4}{64}=\dfrac{V_5}{125}$

11. We know $\dfrac{V}{3375}=\dfrac{V_4}{64}$.

$\Rightarrow \dfrac{₹2{,}70{,}00{,}000}{3375}=\dfrac{V_4}{64}$

$\Rightarrow V_4=₹8{,}000\times 64=₹5{,}12{,}000$.

Hence, the value of Opal $(V_4)=₹5{,}12{,}000$.

Hence, the correct option is (c).

12. We know $\dfrac{V}{3375}=\dfrac{V_5}{125}$.

$\Rightarrow \dfrac{₹2{,}70{,}00{,}000}{3375}=\dfrac{V_5}{125}$

$\Rightarrow V_5=₹8{,}000\times 125=₹10{,}00{,}000$.

The value of Ruby (V_5) = ₹10,00,000.
Hence, the difference of the values of Ruby and Opal
= ₹10,00,000 – ₹5,12,000
= ₹4,88,000.

Hence, the correct option is (b).

13. We know $\frac{V}{3375} = \frac{V_2}{8}$.

$\Rightarrow \frac{₹2,70,00,000}{3375} = \frac{V_2}{8}$

$\Rightarrow V_2 = ₹8,000 \times 8 = ₹64,000$.

The value of Emarald (V_2) = ₹64,000.

Also, $\frac{V}{3375} = \frac{V_3}{27}$.

$\Rightarrow \frac{₹2,70,00,000}{3375} = \frac{V_3}{27}$

$\Rightarrow V_3 = ₹8,000 \times 27 = ₹2,16,000$.

The value of Garnet (V_3) = ₹2,16,000.
Hence, the sum of the values of Emerald and Garnet = ₹64,000 + ₹2,16,000
= ₹2,80,000.

Hence, the correct option is (a).

14. The value of Ruby (V_5) = ₹10,00,000.

The value of Emarald (V_2) = ₹64,000.

The value of Garnet (V_3) = ₹2,16,000.

Also, $\frac{V}{3375} = V_1$.

$\Rightarrow \frac{₹2,70,00,000}{3375} = V_1$

$\Rightarrow V_1 = ₹8,000$.

The value of Amethyst (V_1) = ₹8,000.
Hence, the difference of the values of Ruby and the sum of the values of Amethyst, Emerald, and Garnet
= ₹10,00,000 – (₹8,000 + ₹64,000 + ₹2,16,000)
= ₹10,00,000 – ₹2,88,000
= ₹7,12,000.

Hence, the correct option is (e).

15. The loss incurred due to breakage = The value of the stone – The total value of the pieces
= ₹2,70,00,000 – (₹8,000 + ₹64,000 + ₹2,16,000 + ₹5,12,000 + ₹10,00,000)
= ₹2,70,00,000 – ₹18,00,000 = ₹2,52,00,000.

Hence, the correct option is (g).

Comprehension-Based Questions

Solutions for questions 16 to 20:
Let the number of soldiers be n, number of days be d and the consumption of food per soldier per day be g grams.

The stock of the food is ***ndg*** which is a constant.

A garrison of 1200 soldiers has sufficient food-stock for 180 days when the rate of consumption is 1500 grams per day per soldier.

The stock of the food is 1200 × 180 × 1500 which is a constant.

$\Rightarrow ndg = 1200 \times 180 \times 1500$

16. Given that n = 1200 – 200 = 1000, g = 1500 and d = ?

We have $ndg = 1200 \times 180 \times 1500$.

$1000 \times d \times 1500 = 1200 \times 180 \times 1500$

$d = \frac{1200 \times 180 \times 1500}{1000 \times 1500} = 216$ days.

Hence, the correct option is (c).

17. Given that n = 1200 + 300 = 1500, d = 180 and g = ?

We have $ndg = 1200 \times 180 \times 1500$.

$1500 \times 180 \times g = 1200 \times 180 \times 1500$

$g = \frac{1200 \times 180 \times 1500}{1500 \times 180} = 1200$ grams.

Hence, the correct option is (a).

18. Given that n = 1200, g = 1500 + 300 = 1800 and d = ?

We have $ndg = 1200 \times 180 \times 1500$.

$1200 \times d \times 1800 = 1200 \times 180 \times 1500$

$d = \frac{1200 \times 180 \times 1500}{1200 \times 1800} = 150$ days.

Hence, the correct option is (b).

19. After 30 days, the food-stock is sufficient for 150 days.

Now, $ndg = 1200 \times 150 \times 1500$

Given that n = 1200 – 200 + 500 = 1500, g = 1500 and d = ?

$1500 \times d \times 1500 = 1200 \times 150 \times 1500$

$d = \frac{1200 \times 150 \times 1500}{1500 \times 1500} = 120$ days.

Hence, the correct option is (c).

20. After 80 days, the food-stock is sufficient for 100 days.

Now, $ndg = 1200 \times 100 \times 1500$

Given that n = 1200 + 800 = 2000, g = 1500 – 500 = 1000 and d = ?

$2000 \times d \times 1000 = 1200 \times 100 \times 1500$

$d = \frac{1200 \times 100 \times 1500}{2000 \times 1000} = 90$ days.

Total number of days = 80 + 90 = 170.

Hence, the correct option is (d).

Assertion and Reason Type Questions

Solutions for questions 21 to 25:

21. **Assertion:** The duplicate ratio of $1 : 2 = 1^2 : 2^2 = 1 : 4$.

    So, Assertion is true.

    Assertion: The duplicate ratio of $a : b$ is $a^2 : b^2$.

    So, Reason is false.

    Hence, the correct option is (c).

22. **Assertion:** Given that $a : b = 2 : 3$.

    Let $a = 2k$ and $b = 3k$.

    $$\frac{a^2 + ab}{a^2 - b} = \frac{(2k)^2 + (2k)(3k)}{(2k)^2 - 3k}$$

    $$= \frac{4k^2 + 6k^2}{4k^2 - 3k}$$

    $$= \frac{10k^2}{(4k - 3)k} = \frac{10k}{4k - 3}.$$

    Hence, the value of $\frac{a^2 + ab}{a^2 - b}$ cannot be determined.

    So, Assertion is true.

    Reason: If $a : b$ is known, then the value of $\frac{a^2 + ab}{a^2 - b}$ cannot be determined since the degrees of the terms of the numerator and the denominator are different.

    So, Reason is true and is the correct explanation of Assertion.

    Choice (a)

23. **Assertion:** The ratio of the incomes of Anan and Buvan is 2 : 3. If the ratio of the expenditures of Anan and Buvan is 2 : 3, then the ratio of savings of Anan and Buvan is also 2 : 3.

    Let the incomes of Anan and Buvan be $2x$ and $3x$.

    Let the expenditures of Anan and Buvan be $2y$ and $3y$.

    The ratio of savings of Anan and Buvan = $(2x - 2y)$: $(3x - 3y)$

    $= 2(x - y): 3(x - y) = 2 : 3$.

    So, Assertion is true.

    Reason: For any two persons, if the ratio of their incomes is equal to the ratio of their expenditures, then the ratio of their savings is also equal to the ratio of their incomes.

    So, Reason is true and is the correct explanation of Assertion.

    Choice (a)

24. **Assertion:** The mean proportional of 5 and 125

    $= \sqrt{5 \times 125} = \sqrt{625} = 25$.

    So, Assertion is true.

    Reason: If a, b, and c are in proportion, then c is the third proportion to a and b. So, Reason is true but not the correct explanation of Assertion.

    Choice (b)

25. **Assertion:** The compound ratio of 2 : 3 and 5 : 7 is $2 \times 5 : 3 \times 7 = 10 : 21$.

    So, Assertion is false.

    Reason: If two ratios are equal, then the product of extremes is equal to the product of means.

    So, Assertion is true.

    Hence, the correct option is (d).

CHAPTER

3

Percentages, Profit and Loss, Discount and Partnership

Remember

Before beginning this chapter, you should be able to:

- Understand the concepts of percentage.
- Know the terms profit and loss in mathematics.
- Understand the concepts of discount and partnership.

Key Ideas

After completing this chapter, you should be able to:

- Calculate percentage of absolute values given.
- Express percentage as fraction and fraction as percentage and decimal.
- Solve numerical problems on percentage.
- Make comparison of different percentages in a given problem.
- Understand terms, like selling price, cost price, profit and loss.
- Know about partnership and its types.

Scientific Crypt

A Tribute to Shakuntala Devi (1929-2013)

Shakuntala Devi is an Indian mathematician. She was born on 4th November 1939 in Bangalore. At the age of six, she demonstrated extraordinary skills of calculating and memorizing large numbers at the University of Mysore. In 1977, she calculated the 23rd root of a 201-digit number mentally. On June 18, 1980, she demonstrated her skills by multiplying two thirteen-digit numbers, given by the computer department of Imperial College in London, in 28 seconds. This particular feat found its way into the Guinness Book of World Records in the year 1995.

She wrote many books on mathematics. Some of her famous books are:

- Mathability: Awaken the Math Genius in Your Child
- Puzzles to Puzzle You
- Book of Numbers
- Figuring: The Joy of Numbers
- In the Wonderland of Numbers

FUN TIME

CROSSWORD

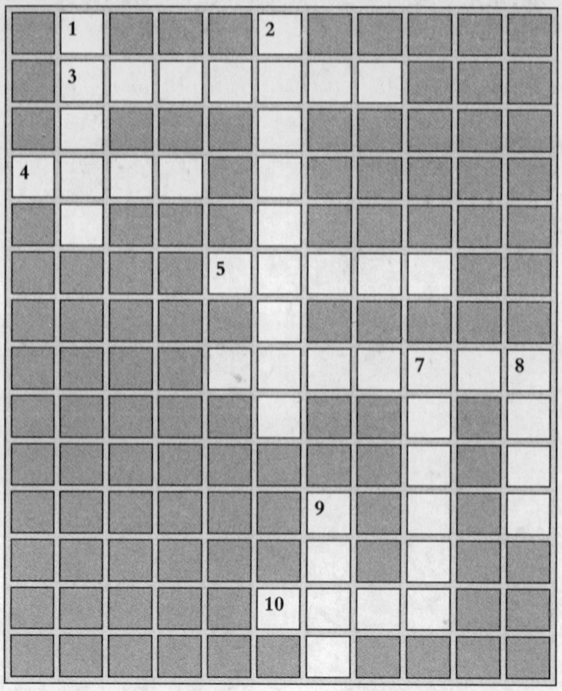

Across

3. If x% of 10 + 10% of x = 20, then x is
4. The difference between compound interest and simple interest for the first year.
5. What percentage of 50 is 25?
6. The total amount of money required to start a business.
10. 1/20 as a percentage.

Down

1. 300% as a fraction
2. The original sum borrowed
7. 10% of 20% of 30% of 2000
8. SP − CP < 0
9. The partners divide it in the ratio of their investments.

INTRODUCTION

We will study the concepts of percentage and their wider applications in day-to-day life situations. In order to solve problems in chapters, like profit and loss, simple interest, compound interest, it is essential to have a thorough understanding of this topic.

Percentage

In mathematics, 'per cent' means 'for every hundred'. The result of any division in which the divisor is 100, is a percentage. The divisor, that is, 100 is denoted by a special symbol '%', read as per cent.

Example: $\frac{10}{100} = 10\%$, $\frac{25}{100} = 25\%$

$\frac{x}{100} = x\%$

Since any ratio is also a division, each ratio can also be expressed as a percentage.

Example: The ratio $\frac{1}{2}$ can be converted into a percentage value:

$$\frac{1}{2} = \frac{1 \times 50}{2 \times 50} = \frac{50}{100} = 50\%.$$

Expressing *x*% as a Fraction

Any percentage can be expressed as a decimal fraction by dividing the percentage figure by 100.

Example: $37\% = \frac{37}{100} = 0.37$

$$75\% = 75 \text{ out of } 100 = \frac{75}{100} = \frac{3}{4} \text{ or } 0.75.$$

Expressing a Fraction *a*/*b* as a Decimal and as a Percentage

Any fraction can be expressed as a decimal (i.e., terminating or non-terminating, but recurring), and any decimal fraction can be converted to percentage by multiplying it with 100.

$$\frac{1}{2} = 0.5 = 50\%,\ \frac{1}{4} = 0.25 = 25\%,\ \frac{1}{5} = 0.2 = 20\%,\ \frac{1}{3} = 0.33\ldots = 33.33\%.$$

EXAMPLE 3.1 Express 36% as a fraction.

SOLUTION

$36\% = \frac{36}{100} = \frac{9}{25}$

$\therefore$ 36% as a fraction is $\frac{9}{25}$.

EXAMPLE 3.2 Express 64% as a decimal.

SOLUTION

$64\% = \frac{64}{100} = 0.64$ $\therefore$ 64% as a decimal is 0.64.

EXAMPLE 3.3 Express $\frac{3}{20}$ as per cent.

SOLUTION

$\frac{3}{20} = \left(\frac{3}{20} \times 100\right)\% = 15\%$ $\therefore$ $\frac{3}{20}$ as per cent is 15%.

EXAMPLE 3.4 Find 36% of 30.

SOLUTION

36% of 30 $= \frac{36}{100} \times 30 = 10.8$ $\therefore$ 36% of 30 is 10.8.

Percentage: A Relative Value

When you score 18 marks out of 20 marks in your maths unit test, then it is an absolute value. Let us say that you have scored 90% in the maths unit test; it is understood that you obtained 90 marks out of 100 marks. However, if the maximum marks for the unit test is 50, then the marks you obtained are 90% of 50, or $\frac{90}{100} \times 50 = 45$.

Hence, the actual score depends upon the maximum marks of the unit test. It varies with the maximum marks. For example, if the maximum marks are 60, then 90% of 60 = 54. If the maximum marks are 70, then 90% of 70 = 63. As the maximum marks vary, your marks also vary. Hence, percentage is a relative or comparative value. That means, in relation to the total marks, or when compared with the total marks, you score 90% marks.

Comparison of Percentages

Let us say that in your class 30% of the students are girls, and in Class IX 40% of the students are girls. Can you say that the number of girls in your class is less than the number of girls in Class IX? The answer depends on the total number of students in each class. If there are 50 students in your class, the number of girls in your class $= \frac{30}{100} \times 50 = 15$.

If there are 30 students in Class IX, then the number of girls in Class IX $= \frac{40}{100} \times 30 = 12$. Although the percentage of girls in your class is less than the percentage of girls in Class IX, the number of girls in your class may be more than that of Class IX.

However, you can say that the percentage of girls in your class is more than the percentage of girls in Class IX. But the number of girls in the two classes cannot be compared, if the total number of students in each class is not known.

However, when you say that the percentage of girls in your class is less than the percentage of girls in Class IX, you can specify that it is less by 10 percentage points (i.e., 40% – 30% = 10% points).

Percentage points is the difference between two percentage values. It is not equal to either percentage increase or percentage decrease.

When two absolute values are given, different percentage values can be calculated involving the two values. Let one value be greater than the other. The percentage values involved are:

1. One value as a percentage of the other.

EXAMPLE 3.5 x is what per cent of y?

SOLUTION

Let $x = k\%$ of y

$$x = \frac{k}{100} \text{ of } y$$

$$\Rightarrow k = \frac{x}{y} \times 100.$$

EXAMPLE 3.6 y is what percentage of x?

SOLUTION

Let $y = p\%$ of x

$$\Rightarrow p = \frac{y}{x} \times 100.$$

EXAMPLE 3.7 What percent of 3.6 km is 360 metres?

SOLUTION

We know that 1 km = 1000 metres.

$\Rightarrow$ 3.6 km = 3.6 × 1000 = 3600 metres

$$\therefore \text{ The required percentage } = \left(\frac{360}{3600} \times 100\right)\% = 10\%.$$

EXAMPLE 3.8 If ($2x\%$ of y) + ($x\%$ of $3y$) = 12.5% of ($x + y$), then what is the value of $\frac{1}{x} + \frac{1}{y}$?

SOLUTION

Given, ($2x\%$ of y) + (x % of $3y$) = 12.5% of ($x + y$)

$$\frac{2xy}{100} + \frac{3xy}{100} = \frac{125}{1000}(x+y)$$

$$\frac{5xy}{100} = \frac{125}{1000}(x+y)$$

$$\Rightarrow \frac{x+y}{xy} = \frac{5}{125} \times \frac{1000}{100}$$

$$\Rightarrow \frac{1}{y} + \frac{1}{x} = \frac{2}{5}.$$

2. By what per cent is the greater quantity more than the smaller?

$$\text{Percentage more} = \frac{\text{Greater} - \text{Smaller}}{\text{Smaller}} \times 100\%$$

EXAMPLE 3.9 By what per cent is the sum of ₹100 more than the sum of ₹90?

SOLUTION

$$\frac{(100-90)}{90}(100)\% = 11\frac{1}{9}\%$$

That is, the sum of ₹100 is more than ₹90 by $11\frac{1}{9}\%$.

EXAMPLE 3.10 If Anil's salary is 20% less than Raju's salary, then by what per cent is Raju's salary more than that of Anil?

SOLUTION

Let Raju's salary be ₹100.

Anil's salary is 20% less than Raju's salary.

$\Rightarrow$ Salary of Anil = 80% of 100 = ₹80.

Raju's salary is ₹20 more than that of Anil's.

$\Rightarrow$ Now, the required percentage $= \frac{20}{80}(100)\% = 25\%$

$\therefore$ Raju's salary is 25% more than Anil's salary.

3. By what per cent is the smaller quantity less than the greater?

$$\text{Percentage less} = \frac{\text{Greater} - \text{Smaller}}{\text{Greater}} \times 100\%.$$

EXAMPLE 3.11 If A gets 50% more than B, then by what percentage does B get less than A?

SOLUTION

Share of A	Share of B
150	100

Required percentage $= \left(\frac{150-100}{150}\right) \times 100\% = 33\frac{1}{3}\%$

EXAMPLE 3.12 In an examination, Mohit secured 60% of the maximum marks which is 45 marks more than the pass marks. If the pass mark is 45%, then find the maximum marks in the examination.

SOLUTION

Marks secured by Mohit = 60%

Pass marks = 45%

Difference between the marks obtained and pass marks = (60 – 45)% = 15%

Given that Mohit obtained 45 marks more than the pass marks.

Let the maximum marks be x.

$\Rightarrow 15\%$ of $x = 45$

$$\Rightarrow x = \frac{45 \times 100}{15} = 300$$

$\therefore$ The maximum marks in the examination = 300.

EXAMPLE 3.13 If the cost price of an article increased by 60% then by what percentage should it be decreased to bring it back to its original price?

SOLUTION

Let cost price of an article = ₹100

$\therefore$ The value of the article after increase of 60% = ₹160

$$\text{Required percentage} = \frac{160 - 100}{160} \times 100 = \frac{60}{160} \times 100 = \frac{300}{8} = 37\frac{1}{2}\%$$

EXAMPLE 3.14 In an office, 60% of the employees are female. 30% of the female employees have children, and 20% of the male employees have children. What percentage of the employees has children? Choose the correct answer from the following options:

(a) 28% (b) 26% (c) 30% (d) 32%

SOLUTION

(i) Let the total number of employees in the office be $100x$.

(ii) Given, the number of female employees as 60% of $100x$. Then, male employees will be 40% of $100x$.

(iii) Find the number of male employees and female employees who have children.

(iv) $\text{Required percentage} = \frac{\text{Number of employees who have children}}{\text{Total number of employees}} \times 100.$

Profit and Loss

In our everyday life and in the business world, we encounter transactions involving sales and purchases. Every time such a transaction occurs, it may be observed that there is a seller and a buyer involved.

The seller sells some things/goods for a certain amount paid by the buyer. The seller eventually makes some profit or loss in the transaction. This chapter deals with various aspects relating to such transactions of sales and purchases.

Cost Price (CP)

The price at which an article is purchased is called its cost price.

Info Bytes!

Percentage of profit/loss is always calculated on the cost price of an article.

Selling Price (SP)

The price at which an article is sold is called its selling price.

Profit

If the selling price of an article is greater than its cost price, we say that there is profit or gain.

$$\text{Profit} = \text{selling price} - \text{cost price}$$

When SP > CP

1. Profit = SP – CP
2. SP = CP + Profit
3. CP = SP – Profit
4. % Profit $= \frac{\text{Profit}}{\text{CP}}(100)\%$
5. Profit = % Profit (CP)
6. When CP and Profit Percentage are given, $\text{SP} = (\text{CP})\left(\frac{100 + \text{Profit } \%}{100}\right)$
7. When SP and Profit Percentage are given, $\text{CP} = \frac{100\ (\text{SP})}{100 + \text{Profit } \%}$

Konnect

- The concept of profit and loss has been around since ancient civilizations. The ancient Mesopotamians had detailed business records indicating profits from their trade expeditions.
- A company's highest selling product isn't always its most profitable. Sometimes, lesser-known products have better profit margins.

Loss

If the selling price of an article is less than its cost price, we say that there is a loss.

Loss = cost price – selling price.

When SP < CP:

1. Loss = CP – SP
2. SP = CP – Loss
3. CP = Loss + SP
4. Loss Percentage $= \frac{\text{Loss}}{\text{CP}} \times 100\%$
5. Loss = Loss Percentage × CP
6. When CP and Loss Percentage are given, $\text{SP} = \text{CP}\left(\frac{100 - \text{Loss Percentage}}{100}\right)$
7. When SP and Loss Percentage are given, $\text{CP} = \frac{\text{SP}\,(100)}{(100 - \text{Loss Percentage})}$

Overheads

All the expenditure incurred on transportation, repairs, etc., (if any) are categorized as overheads. These overheads are always included in the CP of the article.

Konnect

When there are two articles having the same cost price and, if one article is sold at a% profit and the other is sold at the same loss per cent, then effectively neither profit nor loss is made. If there are two articles having the same selling price and, one is sold at x% profit and the other is sold at x% loss, effectively, there is always a loss and the loss percentage is $\left(\frac{x}{10}\right)^2$ %.

EXAMPLE 3.15 A shopkeeper bought a cycle for ₹1200 and sold it for ₹1500. Find his profit or loss percentage.

SOLUTION

Cost price of the cycle = ₹1200

Selling price of the cycle = ₹1500

SP > CP ⇒ There is a gain.

⇒ Gain = SP – CP = 1500 – 1200 = ₹300

$$\therefore \text{Gain Percentage} = \frac{\text{Gain}}{\text{CP}}(100)\% = \frac{300}{1200}(100)\% = 25\%$$

∴ The shopkeeper makes a profit of 25%.

EXAMPLE 3.16 Rakesh purchased a TV for ₹5000. He paid ₹250 for its transportation. If he sold the TV for ₹5075, then find his profit or loss percentage.

SOLUTION

Price at which the TV was bought = ₹5000

Overheads in the form of transportation = ₹250

∴ The total cost price of the TV = (5000 + 250) = ₹5250

Selling price of the TV = ₹5075

SP < CP ⇒ There is a loss.

The amount of loss = CP – SP = 5250 – 5075 = ₹175.

$$\therefore \text{Loss percentage} = \frac{\text{Loss}}{\text{CP}}(100)\% = \frac{175}{5250}(100)\% = \frac{10}{3}\% = 3.33\%.$$

∴ Rakesh incurred a loss of 3.33%.

EXAMPLE 3.17 By selling 24 pens, Kranthi lost an amount equal to the CP of 3 pens. Find his loss percentage.

SOLUTION

Let us assume that cost price of each pen is ₹1.

⇒ CP of 24 pens = ₹24

Loss = CP of 3 pens = 3 × 1 = ₹3

$$\Rightarrow \text{Loss Percentage} = \left(\frac{\text{Loss}}{\text{CP}} \times 100\right)\%$$

$$= \frac{3}{24} \times 100\% = 12.5\%$$

∴ Kranthi's loss is 12.5%.

EXAMPLE 3.18 Naresh sold two books for ₹600 each, thereby gaining 20% on one book and losing 20% on the other book. Find his overall loss or gain percent.

SOLUTION

Selling price of the first book = ₹600; Profit = 20%.

$$\Rightarrow \text{CP} = \frac{100\ \text{SP}}{(100 + \text{Profit Percentage})} = \frac{(100)(600)}{100 + 20} = ₹500$$

The selling price of the second book = ₹600; Loss = 20%

$$\Rightarrow CP = \frac{100 \times SP}{(100 - \text{Loss Percentage})} = \frac{100 \times 600}{100 - 20} = ₹750$$

So, the total cost price of the books = ₹500 + ₹750 = ₹1250.

The total selling price of the books = 2 × 600 = ₹1200.

As the total selling price of the books < the total cost price of the books, there is a loss. Loss= CP – SP = ₹1250 – ₹1200 = ₹50.

$$\Rightarrow \text{Loss Percentage} = \frac{\text{Loss}}{CP}(100)\%$$

$$= \left(\frac{50}{1250}\right)100\% = 4\%$$

∴ Naresh's loss is 4%.

EXAMPLE 3.19 By selling a ball for ₹39, a shopkeeper gains 30%. At what price should he sell it to gain 40%?

SOLUTION

The selling price of the ball = ₹39; Gain = 30%.

$$\Rightarrow CP = \left(\frac{100 \times SP}{100 + \text{Gain Percentage}}\right) = \frac{100 \times 39}{100 + 30} = ₹30$$

Now, CP = ₹30 and gain required = 40%, then

$$\Rightarrow SP = \frac{CP(100 + \text{Gain Percentage})}{100}$$

$$= ₹\frac{(30)(140)}{100} = ₹42.$$

∴ To gain 40%, the shopkeeper has to sell it for ₹42.

EXAMPLE 3.20 A merchant marked his product at 50% above the cost price and then allowed 50% discount before selling it. The selling price of the product was ₹225. What is the profit that he made/incurred out of this? Choose the correct answer from the following options:

(a) profit of ₹37.50 (b) profit of ₹75

(c) loss of ₹75 (d) loss of ₹37.50

SOLUTION

Let the cost price of the product be ₹100x.

∴ Marked price = ₹(100x + 50x)

= ₹150x

$$\text{Discount} = \frac{50}{100}(₹150x) = ₹75x$$

Selling price = ₹75x

Given, $75x = 225$

$x = 3$

$75x < 100x$

∴ A loss was incurred.

Loss incurred = ₹25x = ₹75.

EXAMPLE 3.21 The cost price and the marked price of a watch are ₹200 and ₹300. It was sold at a discount of y%. The profit percentage was $\frac{3}{2}y$%. Find the value of y from the following options:

(a) $16\frac{2}{3}$ (b) 25 (c) $33\frac{1}{3}$ (d) 20

SOLUTION

Selling price $= ₹300\left(1-\frac{y}{100}\right) = ₹(300-3y)$

Selling price = ₹200 $\left(1+\frac{\frac{3}{2}y}{100}\right) = ₹(200+3y)$

(∵ '+' applies in case of a profit and '–' applies in case of a loss)

$300 - 3y = 200 + 3y$

$100 = 6y$

$\therefore\ y = 16\frac{2}{3}.$

Partnership

The total amount of money required to start a business is called its **capital**. It is not always possible for a single person to invest huge amount of money. So, two or more persons come together and start business jointly. Such a business is called **partnership**. The people who jointly runs the business are called **partners**. The money invested by the partners in the business is called **investment**.

Types of Partnership

1. In general partnership, the period of investment is the same and the partners divide profit or loss in the ratio of their investments.
2. In compound partnership, the investments and the periods of investment differ. Then their investments reduce to investments per month or year and the profit or loss is divided in the ratio of these converted investments.

EXAMPLE 3.22 Satish and Kranthi started a business with capitals of ₹12,000 and ₹18,000, respectively. The business made a profit of ₹3500. Find the share of Kranthi and Satish in the profit at the end of the year.

SOLUTION

Investment made by Satish = ₹12,000

Investment made by Kranthi = ₹18,000

Ratio of the investments of Satish and Kranthi = 12,000 : 18,000 = 2 : 3.

As the period of investment is the same, profit is to be divided in the ratio of their investments.

⇒ Ratio in which the profit is divided = 2 : 3

Profit = ₹3500

∴ Satish's share in the profit $= \frac{3500 \times 2}{5} = ₹1400.$

Kranthi's share in the profit $= \frac{3500 \times 3}{5} = ₹2100.$

EXAMPLE 3.23 Rakesh set up a factory with a capital of ₹90,000. Ramesh joined him later with an investment of ₹50,000. The total profit earned at the end of the year was ₹68,000. Find when Ramesh joined Rakesh as the partner, if Rakesh's share in the profit is ₹48,000.

SOLUTION

Investment of Rakesh = ₹90,000.

Investment period of Rakesh = 12 months.

Investment of Ramesh = ₹50,000.

Let investment period of Ramesh be 'x' months.

⇒ Ratio of their investments = $90{,}000 \times 12 : 50{,}000 \times x = 108 : 5x$.

Total profit at the end of the year = ₹68,000.

Share of Rakesh in the profit = ₹48,000.

⇒ Share of Ramesh in the profit = ₹(68,000 − 48,000) = ₹20,000.

⇒ Ratio of their profits = 48000 : 20000 = 12 : 5

Ratio of investments = Ratio of profits

⇒ $108 : 5x = 12 : 5$

⇒ $\frac{108}{5x} = \frac{12}{5}$

⇒ $x = 9$

⇒ Investment period of Ramesh = 9 months.

∴ Ramesh joined Rakesh as a partner after (12 − 9) months from the commencement of the business, i.e., he joined after 3 months.

EXAMPLE 3.24 Naresh, Gopi, and Sarath started a business with initial investments of ₹10,000, ₹20,000, and ₹20,000, respectively. After 6 months, Gopi withdrew an amount of ₹5000 from his investment. After 3 more months, Sarath brought in ₹10,000. If at the end of the year, the total amount of profit earned is ₹36,000, then find the share of each partner.

SOLUTION

(a) Investment of Naresh = ₹10,000
  Period of investment = 12 months
  ⇒ Total investment made by Naresh = ₹(12 × 10,000) (1)

(b) Investment of Gopi = ₹20,000
  Period of investment = 6 months
  Amount withdrawn = ₹5000
  ⇒ Investment for the remaining 6 months = ₹(20,000 − 5000) = ₹15,000
  ⇒ Total investment made by Gopi = ₹(6 × 20,000 + 6 × 15,000) (2)
  Investment of Sarath = ₹20,000
  Period of investment = (6 + 3) = 9 months
  Additional investment = ₹10,000
  ⇒ Investment for the remaining 3 months = ₹(20,000 + 10,000) = ₹30,000
  ⇒ Total investment made by Sarath = ₹(9 × 20,000 + 3 × 30,000)

From Eqs. (1), (2) and (3), we find the ratio of investments of Naresh, Gopi, and Sarath as (3) (12 × 10,000) : (6 × 20,000 + 6 × 15,000) : (9 × 20,000 + 3 × 30,000) = 12 : 21 : 27 = 4 : 7 : 9.

Total profit at the end of the year = ₹36,000.

Total profit is divided in the ratio of their investments.

∴ Naresh's share in the profit = $\frac{4}{20} \times 36{,}000$ = ₹7200

Gopi's share in the profit $= \frac{7}{20} \times 36{,}000 = ₹12{,}600$

Sarath's share in the profit $= \frac{9}{20} \times 36{,}000 = ₹16{,}200$

EXAMPLE 3.25 In a business, P, Q, R, and S are four partners. P's investment is twice R's investment, Q's investment is $\frac{1}{4}$ of S's investment, and P and Q invested equally. If the total profit at the end of the year is ₹13,000, then find the sum of the shares of P and R in the profit.

(a) ₹10,000 (b) ₹3000 (c) ₹4000 (d) ₹5000

SOLUTION

(i) Using the given data, find the ratio of the investments of P, Q, R, and S.
(ii) Let the investment of A and B be ₹x each.
(iii) Now, find the investments of C and D in terms of x.
(iv) Ratio of shares of profits is equal to the ratio of their investments.

POINTS TO REMEMBER

✔ Percentage points is the difference between two percentage values. It is not equal to either percentage increase or percentage decrease

✔ By what per cent is the greater quantity more than the smaller?

$$\text{Percentage more} = \frac{\text{Greater} - \text{Smaller}}{\text{Smaller}} \times 100\%$$

✔ By what per cent is the smaller quantity less than the greater?

✔ $$\text{Percentage less} = \frac{\text{Greater} - \text{Smaller}}{\text{Greater}} \times 100\%.$$

✔ Percentage change can be defined as

$$\frac{\text{Final value} - \text{Initial value}}{\text{Initial value}} \times 100.$$

✔ When SP > CP

When CP and Loss Percentage are given, SP = $\text{CP}\left(\frac{100 - \text{Loss Percentage}}{100}\right)$

When SP and Loss Percentage are given,

$$\text{CP} = \frac{\text{SP}(100)}{(100 - \text{Loss Percentage})}$$

✔ When SP < CP:

When CP and Loss Percentage are given, SP = CP $\left(\frac{100 - \text{Loss Percentage}}{100}\right)$

When SP and Loss Percentage are given,

$$\text{CP} = \frac{\text{SP}(100)}{(100 - \text{Loss Percentage})}$$

✔ The total amount of money required to start a business is called its capital.

✔ Two or more persons come together and start business jointly. Such a business is called partnership. The people who jointly runs the business are called partners. The money invested by the partners in the business is called investment.

PRACTICE QUESTIONS CLASSROOM WING

Very Short Answer Type Questions

Directions of questions from 1 to 12:
Fill in the blanks.

1. The ratio of incomes of Akshay and Aravind is $4 : 3\frac{2}{3}$. Income of Aravind is less than that of Akshay by ________%.

2. If the cost price of an article is ₹64 and its selling price is ₹80, then profit percentage is ________.

3. If cost price is ₹100, marked price is 200% above the cost price, and discount offered is 50%, then profit per cent is _______.

4. If Nityananda scored 25% more than Advaita, then Advaita scored _______ % less than Nityananda.

5. A number becomes 63 after it is reduced by 12.5%. The original number is _______.

6. If Krishna and Balaram share profits in the ratio 3 : 5 at the end of the year, then the share of Krishna in the total investment of ₹16,000 crores is ₹ _______.

7. An article is marked up by 100%. If a discount of ₹12 on it is equal to 10%, then the cost price of the article is _______.

8. An increase in the side of a square by 20% results in _______ % increase in its area.

9. Ram and Lakshman started a business by investing ₹30 lakhs and ₹48 lakhs, respectively. The ratio in which they share the profits is ________.

10. The cost price of a machine is $66\frac{2}{3}\%$ of its selling price, then profit per cent is _______.

11. If 30% of 40% of x = 60% of 12.5% of 96, then x is ________.

12. Every year there is a 30% hike in Rama's salary. If his present salary is ₹2000, then his salary after two years will be ₹ _______.

Directions of questions from 13 to 22:
Answer the following questions.

13. Koutons, an apparel showroom, offers two successive discounts of 50% and 20%. What is the single equivalent discount percentage?

14. If $2a = 3b$, $b = \frac{3}{4}c$, and $c = 0.8d$, then find by what per cent is a less/more than d.

15. If the cost price is obtained by multiplying the selling price by $\frac{7}{8}$, then find the profit percentage.

16. This year, the number of children in a colony is three times that of the previous year. What is the percentage increase in the number of children in the colony?

17. When calculated on selling price, profit is found to be 25%, find the actual profit percent.

18. If Nanda sold an article at ₹40 and earned 100% profit, then what should be the selling price to earn a profit of 300%?

19. When the selling price is ₹80, there is a loss of 20%. Find the selling price to earn 40% profit.

20. In a class, 40% of students are girls. Of the total number of boys, 50% failed in an exam. What per cent of the boys passed in the exam?

21. Santan sells a diamond at a loss of 10%. If he had sold it at a profit of 5% he would have earned ₹37.5 lakhs more. What is the cost price of the diamond?

22. A person sells $33\frac{1}{3}\%$ of his property at 20% loss. At what profit per cent should he sell the remaining property to earn 20% profit on the whole?

Short Answer Type Questions

23. The selling price and the marked price of an article are ₹132x and ₹165x, respectively. If the article is marked 65% above the cost price and a discount of ₹198 is given, then find the profit on the article.

24. In an election, there were only two contestants. The democrats secured 35% valid votes more than the republicans. If 6% of votes were invalid, then what percentage of the total votes polled was in favour of the democrats?

25. By selling an article at $\frac{1}{4}$ of its actual selling price, a trader incurs a loss of 50%. What will be the profit per cent if the trader sells the article at its actual selling price?

26. An electric room heater is sold at $880, after a reduction of 12% in its price. What was the original price, in dollars, before the reduction?

27. A dishonest trader declares to sell his goods at cost price, but gives only 960 gms for every 1 kg. Find the error percentage.

28. Noel and Mathew save 20% and 30% of their income. If their expenditures are equal and Mathew's income is $5600, then find Noel's savings (in dollars).

29. In an election, there were only two candidates, A and B. A secured 60% valid votes more than B, and 9% of the total votes were invalid. What percentage of the total votes was in favor of A?

30. A trader suffered a loss of 15% by selling an article. Had he sold it for ₹100 more, he would have made a profit of 5%. Find the article's cost price.

31. The price of a commodity is decreased by 25%. By what percentage must its consumption increase so that the consumption on it remains unchanged?

32. Find the single discount equivalent to successive discounts of 25% and 20%.

33. Ajay marked an article at 60% above its cost price. Find the maximum percentage of discount he can offer and still avoid incurring a loss.

34. Find the single discount equivalent to successive discounts of 20% and 10%.

35. Profit percentage is numerically equal to the cost price of an article on selling it for ₹31.25. Find the cost price.

Essay Type Questions

36. Three merchants A, B, and C marked three identical articles each at ₹2000. A sold his article after two successive discounts of 30% each. B sold his article after successive discounts of 40% and 20%. C sold his article after successive discounts of 50% and 10%. Find the highest selling price.

37. In a business, A, B, C, and D are the four partners. A's investment is thrice C's investment, B's investment is $\frac{1}{3}$ of D's investment. A and B invested equally. The total profit at the end of the year is ₹16,000. Find the sum of the shares of A and C in the profit.

38. Amar, Bhuvan, and Chetan have some marbles with them. Bhuvan has 20% more marbles than Amar, and Chetan has 10% less marbles than Bhuvan. If the total number of marbles with them is 328, then find the number of marbles with Bhuvan.

39. In a business, Gita and Sita invested in the ratio of 4 : 5. At the end of the year, they earned a profit of ₹72,000. If Sita's salary is included, the ratio of their earning is 1 : 2. Find the salary of Sita.

40. Mr. P and Mr. Q started a business. The ratio of their investments is 2 : 3. Mr. R joined the business with an investment of ₹40,000 after 4 months. They shared the profit at the end of the year in the ratio 18 : 27 : 4. Find the investments of P and Q respectively.

PRACTICE QUESTIONS COMPETITION WING

Level 1: Apply Your Concepts

Directions of questions from 1 to 5:
Fill in the blanks.

1. 26% of 640 is ________.
2. If X is 20% more than Y, then ________ per cent of Y is X.
3. The value of 99% of 1500 + 45% of 360 + 55.99% of 3600 is ________.
4. If $\frac{1}{4}$ is 25%, then $\frac{9}{16}$ is ________.
5. If 13% of a number is 28, then 26.52% of the same number is ________.

Directions of questions from 6 to 59:
Select the correct alternative from the given choices.

6. The population of a city increases by 20% at the end of every year. During which of the following years, the population would be doubled?
(a) Second (b) Third
(c) Fourth (d) Fifth

7. If 20% of a and 40% of b is 230, and 40% of a and 20% of b is 190, then b is what percentage more or less than a?
(a) 80% (b) 60%
(c) 50% (d) 40%

8. In a test, Arun scored 20% and failed by 10 marks. Bala scored 40% in the same test and obtained 10 marks more than the pass marks. Find the maximum marks.
(a) 100 (b) 300
(c) 400 (d) 200

9. On an occasion, 40% of the young men wear grey hats, 60% of the remaining young men wear black hats. What percentage of the young men wears neither grey hats nor black hats? (No young man wears both grey hat and black hat)
(a) 12% (b) 18%
(c) 24% (d) 25%

10. If a number x is increased by 20% and then reduced by 20, it results in 160. Instead, if the number x is reduced by 20% and increased by 20, then what will be the result?
(a) 140 (b) 144
(c) 148 (d) 152

11. The price of an article is increased by 25%. By what percentage must its consumption decrease so that the expenditure on it remains unchanged?
(a) 25% (b) 20%
(c) $33\frac{1}{3}$% (d) 10%

12. If the cost price of 15 articles is equal to the selling price of 20 articles, find the profit or loss percentage.
(a) 25% profit (b) 20% profit
(c) 33.33% loss (d) 25% loss

13. The profit made in selling 25 m of a cloth equals the selling price of 5 m of that cloth. Find the profit percentage.
(a) 25% (b) 20%
(c) $33\frac{1}{3}$% (d) 15%

14. Ajay sold two motorbikes for ₹40,000 each. He sold one at 20% profit and the other at 20% loss. Find the profit or loss percentage in the whole transaction.
(a) 2% profit (b) 3% loss
(c) 4% loss (d) No profit, no loss

15. A sold an article to B at 30% loss, B sold it to C at 20% profit and C sold it to D at 10% profit. If D bought it for ₹924, then the cost price for A. (in ₹)
(a) 1200 (b) 1050
(c) 900 (d) 1000

16. Raja spent $0.5x$% of his monthly salary on rent. He spent x% of the remaining salary on food, $2x$% of the remaining salary on transport, and $4x$% of the remaining salary on various bills. If these expenditures are denoted by R, F, T, and S, respectively, and if x is 20, then find the ascending order of these expenditures.
(a) R, S, F, T (b) R, F, T, S
(c) R, T, F, S (d) R, F, S, T

17. In a certain season, the Indian cricket team had a 40% success rate in the first 80 matches it played. What is the minimum number of additional matches it must play so that it has a 60% success rate for the season?
(a) 30 (b) 40
(c) 45 (d) 35

18.

Year	Percentage of First-Generation Immigrants in US	Population of US (in Millions)
1990	3%	8*k*
2000	3.2%	9*k*

If x denotes the percentage increase in the number of first-generation immigrants from 1990–2000, and y denotes the percentage increase in the total population of US from 1990–2000, which of the following is equal to $(x - y)$?

(a) 12.5% (b) 12.2%
(c) 9.6% (d) 7.5%

19. Trader A gives a single discount of 30% and trader B gives two successive discounts of 20% and 10% on an identical article. If the discount given by A is ₹600 more than the discount given by B, find the marked price of the article.

(a) ₹1500 (b) ₹3000
(c) ₹30,000 (d) ₹600

20. X sells an article to Y at 15% profit. Y sells it to Z at 10% profit. What is X's cost price, if Y makes a profit of ₹23?

(a) ₹230 (b) ₹200
(c) ₹150 (d) ₹180

21. When a discount of 10% is given on the marked price of an article, the gain of the trader is 20%. What will be the profit percent, if a discount of 13% is given?

(a) 12% (b) 16%
(c) 20% (d) 24%

22.

Year	Percentage of the First-Generation Immigrants in UK	The Population of UK (in Millions)
1995	2%	6*x*
2005	2.4%	8*x*

If p denotes the percentage increase in the number of the first generation immigrants from 1995–2005, and q denotes the percentage increase in the total UK population from 1995–2005, find $p - q$.

(a) $13\frac{1}{3}\%$ (b) $26\frac{2}{3}\%$
(c) $33\frac{1}{3}\%$ (d) $46\frac{2}{3}\%$

23. A shopkeeper marks the price of an article 50% above the cost price and declares a discount of 20%. If profit earned is ₹30, then find the marked price.

(a) ₹150 (b) ₹180
(c) ₹225 (d) ₹250

24. In a business, P, Q, and R are three partners. Thrice P's investment is equal to twice Q's investment and R's investment is equal to twice P's investment. Q's period of investment is $\frac{4}{3}$ times P's period of investment and is twice R's period of investment. If the total profit at the end of the year is ₹52,000, find the sum of the shares of P and Q in the profit. (in ₹)

(a) 32,000 (b) 36,000
(c) 40,000 (d) 28,000

25. Ratan spends 70% of his income. His income increases by 25%, and his expenditure also increased by 25%. Find the percentage increase in his savings.

(a) 25 (b) 30
(c) 10 (d) No change

26. Mahesh sold an article for ₹39 and obtained profit percentage which is numerically equal to its cost price (in rupees). Find the cost price of the article.

(a) ₹28 (b) ₹32
(c) ₹30 (d) ₹35

27. The selling price of an article after giving three successive discounts is ₹7560. If the marked price is ₹15,000, then which of the following can be the successive discounts?

(a) 8, 16, 24 (b) 5, 10, 15
(c) 10, 20, 30 (d) 15, 30, 45

28. A trader marks his product 30% above his cost price, and then offers a 30% discount. Find his cost price if he incurs a loss of ₹900. (in ₹)

(a) 12,000 (b) 10,000
(c) 9000 (d) 8000

Level 2: Review Your Concepts

29. Three merchants, P, Q, and R marked three identical articles each at ₹4000, respectively. P sold his article after two successive discounts of 40% each. Q sold it after successive discounts of 50% and 30%. R sold it after successive discounts of 60% and 20%. Find the least selling price. (in ₹)

(a) 1320 (b) 1280
(c) 1440 (d) 1200

30. A shopkeeper marks the cost of two identical articles, one 100% above the cost price and the other 50% above the cost price. If a discount of 20% is allowed on each of them, then find the overall profit percentage.
(a) 10% (b) 20%
(c) 30% (d) 40%

31. The profit made in selling 5 m of a cloth equals the cost price of 2 m of that cloth. Find the profit percentage.
(a) 30% (b) 40%
(c) $33\frac{1}{3}\%$ (d) 45%

32. The price of an article is increased by 20%. By what percentage must its consumption be reduced so that the expenditure on it reduces by 10%?
(a) 20% (b) 30%
(c) 25% (d) 15%

33.

Name of the class	A	B
Number of girls	24	36
Number of girls as a percentage of total number of students	60	80

As per the information given in the above table, approximately by what percentage is the total number of students in class A is less than those in class B?
(a) 9% (b) 10%
(c) 11% (d) 13%

34. A person bought two articles for ₹1800. He sold the first article at a profit of 25% and the second at a loss of 20%. On the whole there is neither loss nor gain. Find the cost price of the second article.
(a) ₹800 (b) ₹1000
(c) ₹900 (d) ₹1200

35. The ratio of the marked price and the cost price of an article is 5 : 3. If a loss of $2a$% is obtained after giving a discount of $4a$%, then find a.
(a) $14\frac{6}{7}$ (b) $12\frac{3}{7}$
(c) $13\frac{2}{7}$ (d) $14\frac{2}{7}$

36. Three persons X, Y, and Z started a business with investments in the ratio of 3 : 2 : 4. The ratio of their periods of investments is 5 : 6 : 7. The difference in the shares of profits of X and Z is what percentage of the share of profit of Y at the end of the year? (Approximately)
(a) 120% (b) 108.33%
(c) 115.25% (d) 125.66%

37. Ajay invested ₹m for 7 months and ₹n for the remaining period. Sohail invested ₹n for the first 9 months and ₹m for the remaining period. If at the end of the year, they share profits equally, then what is the relation between m and n?
(a) $m = n + 1$ (b) $m - n = 2$
(c) $m = n$ (d) $m + n = 2$

38. A dishonest shopkeeper sells his items at cost price. But, for every kg he gives 200 gm less. His profit percentage is _______.
(a) 20% (b) 25%
(c) 30% (d) 15%

39. Preetam bought two mobile phones for ₹4800. He sold the first mobile phone at a loss of 15%, and the second at a profit of 25%. On the whole, there was neither loss nor gain. The cost price of the second mobile phone is _______.
(a) ₹1800 (b) ₹3000
(c) ₹1200 (d) ₹2400

40. The selling price of a TV, after giving two successive discounts, is ₹15,840. If the marked price is ₹20,000, then which of the following could be the successive discounts given on the marked price of the TV?
(a) 10, 15 (b) 12, 15
(c) 10, 12 (d) 15, 18

41. Ramapada has just enough money to purchase either 30 pens or 50 pencils. He decides to spend only 80% of his money and buys 10 pens. At the maximum, how many pencils can he buy with the remaining money that he has?
(a) 23 (b) 24
(c) 25 (d) 26

42. A trader claims to sell his goods at cost price. But, he gives only 900 g for every kg. Find his profit percentage.
(a) $11\frac{1}{9}\%$ (b) $9\frac{1}{11}\%$
(c) 10% (d) $12\frac{2}{3}\%$

43. Amish sold an article at two-thirds of the marked price and suffered a loss of $16\frac{2}{3}\%$. Find the percentage of profit, if he sold the article at the marked price.

(a) 20% (b) 25%
(c) $16\frac{2}{3}\%$ (d) $33\frac{1}{3}\%$

44. Raman suffered a loss of 10% by selling an article. Had he sold it by ₹180 more, he would have made a profit of 2%. Find his cost price (in ₹).
(a) 1350 (b) 1800
(c) 1650 (d) 1500

45. Anil bought certain number of books at the rate of 12 books for ₹18 and sold them at the rate of 18 books for ₹30. Find his profit/loss percentage.
(a) $9\frac{1}{11}\%$ (b) 10%
(c) $11\frac{1}{9}\%$ (d) $12\frac{1}{2}\%$

46. In an election, there were only two contestants P and Q. 14% of the total votes polled were invalid. The number of valid votes secured by P was 15% more than that secured by Q. What percentage of the total votes was cast in favour of Q?
(a) 48% (b) 37.5%
(c) 40% (d) 31.5%

Level 3: Assess Your Concepts

47. Bindu goes to a shop to buy a gift costing ₹1500. On her request, the shopkeeper allows two successive discounts of $x\%$ and $y\%$. ($x < y$). Bindu buys the gift for ₹1188 including sales tax of 10%. Which of the following could be the discount rates offered by the shopkeeper?
(a) 15%, 20% (b) 20%, 25%
(c) 20%, 30% (d) 10%, 20%

48. In the year 2001, the population in a village is x. Every year, the population increases by 10%. In which year, for the first time, will the population of the village be at least 50% more than that of year 2001?
(a) 2005 (b) 2006
(c) 2004 (d) 2007

49. In a family, a person saves 30% of his income. If his salary is increased by 20% and savings are decreased by 20%, then find the percentage increase in the expenditure.
(a) $34\frac{1}{4}\%$ (b) $37\frac{1}{7}\%$
(c) $41\frac{1}{7}\%$ (d) $43\frac{1}{3}\%$

50. A person spends 25% of his salary on house rent, 20% of the remaining salary on clothes, $16\frac{2}{3}\%$ of the remaining on petrol and 30% of the remaining on food. If after incurring the above expenditure his savings are ₹147, then find his salary.
(a) ₹480 (b) ₹300
(c) ₹350 (d) ₹420

51. In an office, 30% of the employees are unmarried; 20% of these employees are post-graduates. The number of married employees in the office who are post-graduates is $3\frac{1}{2}$ times that of the unmarried employees who are post-graduates. What percentage of the married employees are post-graduates?
(a) 36% (b) 32%
(c) 30% (d) 27%

52. Amar, Bhavan, and Chetan divide a certain amount among themselves. The average of the amounts with them is ₹1180. Amar's share is $33\frac{1}{3}\%$ more than that of Bhavan's and $16\frac{2}{3}\%$ less than that of Chetan's. Find Amar's share. (in ₹)
(a) 1050 (b) 1200
(c) 1350 (d) 1500

53. In a certain season, the Indian cricket team had won 30% of the first 60 matches it had played. Find the minimum possible number of additional matches it should play to achieve a success rate of 44% in that season.
(a) 20 (b) 15
(c) 25 (d) 30

54. X and Y are two natural numbers. The sum of thrice of X and twice of Y is 230. If $3X$ increases by 40% and $2Y$ increases by 30%, then their sum will increase by 84. If X decreases by 40% and Y decreases by 30%, then their sum will be ______.
(a) 58 (b) 66
(c) 52 (d) 46

55. Giri sold two books. The selling price of a book equals the cost price of the second book. He sold the first book at 10% profit and the second book at 10% loss. Find the overall profit/loss percentage.

(a) $\frac{5}{21}$% profit (b) $\frac{5}{21}$% loss

(c) $\frac{10}{21}$% profit (d) $\frac{10}{21}$% loss

56. P sold an article at 20% profit to Q. Q sold it at 10% profit to R. The profit made by Q was ₹24 less than the profit made by P. Find the cost price of the article for P. (in ₹)

(a) 250 (b) 300

(c) 360 (d) 200

57. In a class, 45% of the students drink pulpy orange and 90% of the remaining students drink Maaza. No student drinks both Maaza and pulpy orange. Find the percentage of students in the class who drink neither Maaza nor pulpy orange.

(a) 4.5% (b) 6.5%

(c) 7.5% (d) 5.5%

58. A, B and C are three friends have some chocolates with them. 40% of chocolates with A is equal to 50% of chocolates with B. Three times the number of chocolates with C is equal to the total number of chocolates with A and B together. If all the three of them together have 72 chocolates, then find what percent of the number of chocolates with C is the number of chocolates with A?

(a) $166\frac{2}{3}$% (b) 166%

(c) 100/6 % (d) None

59. Mr. Prem Ratan deposits 12% of the total sale amount to a charitable trust shop. One day he sold all the articles at 25% profit after giving a 20% discount. If the amount contributed to charity was ₹28800 and the number of articles is 12, then find the marked price of each article and also find net profit % after the donation. (All articles are identical).

(a) 28000, 50% (b) 20000, 40%

(c) 25000, 10% (d) None

AT

PRACTICE QUESTIONS JEE SPECIAL WING

Multiple-Answer Type Questions

Directions for questions 1 to 5:

Each question has FOUR options (a), (b), (c), and (d). ONE OR MORE THAN ONE of these four option(s) is/are the correct answer(s).

1. A manufacturer marks his goods, which costs him ₹100, at ₹150 whose cost price is ₹100. He allows a d % discount. Which of the following can be the value of d such that the manufacturer avoids loss?

   (a) $16\frac{2}{3}\%$ (b) 25%

   (c) $33\frac{1}{3}\%$ (d) 50%

2. Which of the following successive discounts is not equal to a single discount of 40%?

   (a) 25% and 20% (b) 25% and 15%

   (c) 20% and 20% (d) $33\frac{1}{3}\%$ and 10%

3. In which of the following cases, is there 4% increase in the price of the item?

   (a) The price of sugar is increased by 30% and then decreased by 20%.

   (b) The price of oil is increased by 25% and then decreased by $16\frac{4}{5}\%$.

   (c) The price of Jowar is increased by 20% and then decreased by $13\frac{1}{3}\%$.

   (d) The price of petrol is increased by 10% and then decreased by $5\frac{5}{11}\%$.

4. A shop keeper sells a book and a pen at ₹99 each. She gains 10% on selling the book and incurs a 10% loss on selling the pen. Which of the following is/are true for the whole transaction?

   (a) There is no profit and no loss.

   (b) There is a loss of 1%.

   (c) There is a profit of ₹1.

   (d) There is a loss of ₹2.

5. A and B started a business. In which of the following cases will A and B share the profits equally at the end of the year?

   (a) Each of them invested ₹25,00,000 and for 12 months.

   (b) A invested ₹90,00,000 for 8 months and B invested ₹80,00,000 for 9 months.

   (c) A invested ₹44,00,000 for 9 months and B invested ₹33,00,000 for 12 months.

   (d) A invested ₹25,00,000 for 12 months and B invested ₹37,50,000 for 8 months.

Match The Column

Directions for questions 6 to 10:

Read the paragraph given below and answer the questions.

A trader has five types of articles of different prices. She marked each article at 80% above the cost price. The cost prices are as follows:

Article	Cost Price (In ₹)
P	40
Q	50
R	75
S	100
T	125

Column A (Article: Discount%)	Column B (Profit)
6. P: 25%	(a) 5
7. Q: 30%	(b) 6
8. R: 40%	(c) 10
9. S: 35%	(d) 12
10. T : 40%	(e) 13
	(f) 14
	(g) 17

Comprehension-Based Questions

Directions for questions 11 to 15:

Read the paragraph given below and answer the questions.

Deva donates sugar worth ₹600 to a temple every month. The price of the sugar per kg (in ₹) is $33\frac{1}{3}\%$ less than the quantity of kg of sugar (in kg) that he could purchase.

11. If the price of sugar increases by 20%, then how many kg of sugar can he purchase for the same amount?

(a) 20 (b) 22
(c) 24 (d) 25

12. If the price of sugar decreases by 25%, then the quantity of sugar (in kg) that he can purchase for the same amount would increase by?

(a) $16\frac{2}{3}\%$ (b) 25%
(c) $33\frac{1}{3}\%$ (d) 40%

13. If both the price of sugar and the quantity of sugar (in kg) donated increases by 10%, then how much more would he have to spend?

(a) 127 (b) 126
(c) 125 (d) 124

14. If the price of sugar increases by 10% and the quantity of sugar (in kg) donated decreases by 10%, then what is the percentage increase or decrease in the amount he would spend?

(a) 1% increase (b) 2% increase
(c) 1% decrease (d) 2% decrease

15. If he wants to increase the amount spends on donating sugar by 50%, how many more kg of sugar will he donate?

(a) 10 (b) 12
(c) 15 (d) 18

Directions for questions 16 to 20:

Read the paragraph given below and answer the questions.

We are all aware that there is a huge demand for consumer durables during festive seasons. Most of the shops offer massive discounts during these periods. Some of the consumers purchase the goods irrespective of their requirement owing to the huge discounts. It is a business strategy of the shop owners to clear their stock and increase their sales.

During a festive sale, a company outlet sold ACs, Fridges, Dishwashers, and Washing Machines. The company sold at least one item of each category. The other details of these items are given below.

Item	Successive Discounts	SP Per Unit (in ₹)	Profit%
AC	20% + 30%	56,000	12
Fridge	25% + 25%	56,250	12.5
Washing Machine	10% + 40%	54,000	20
Dishwasher	15% + 35%	55,250	10.5

16. What is the total marked price of an AC and a washing machine?

(a) ₹2,00,000 (b) ₹1,80,000
(c) ₹1,75,000 (d) ₹1,50,000

17. What is the difference in the cost prices of a fridge and a dishwasher?

(a) ₹10,000 (b) ₹1000
(c) ₹100 (d) ₹0

18. By what % is each fridge marked above its cost price?

(a) 200% (b) 100%
(c) 50% (d) 25%

19. What is the discount % offered on each washing machine?

(a) 50% (b) 48%
(c) 46% (d) 44%

20. A customer wants to purchase one item from each category and bargains for a 5% additional discount on each item. If the shop keeper allows the same, what will be his profit % on selling the four items to the customer? (Approximated to the nearest integer)

(a) 6 (b) 7
(c) 8 (d) 9

Assertion and Reason Type Questions

Directions for questions 21 to 23:

Read the options given below and answer the questions.

(a) Both assertion (A) and reason (R) are true, and the reason (R) is the correct explanation of the assertion (A).
(b) Both assertion (A) and reason (R) are true, and the reason (R) is not the correct explanation of the assertion (A).
(c) Assertion (A) is true, but reason (R) is false.
(d) Assertion (A) is false, and reason (R) is true.

21. **Assertion:** If the SP and the MP of an article are ₹80 and ₹100 respectively, then the percentage discount offered is 20%.

    Reason: The percentage of discount is given by $\frac{\text{Discount}}{\text{MP}} \times 100\%$.

22. **Assertion:** If A is 20% more than B and B is 30% more than C, then A is 156% of C.

    Reason: If A is x% more than B and B is y% more than C, then A is $\frac{(100+x)\%\times(100+y)\%}{100\%}$ of C.

23. **Assertion:** A started a business with ₹1,50,00,000. After two months B joins A with the investment of ₹2,00,00,000. At the end of one year, they share the profits in the ratio 9 : 10.

    Reason: If in a business A invests ₹x for a months and B invests ₹y for b months, then they will share the profits in the ratio $by : ax$.

ANSWER KEYS

Crossword

Across

3. Hundred
4. Zero
5. Fifty
6. Capital
10. Five

Down

1. Three
2. Principal
7. Twelve
8. Loss
9. Gain

Classroom Wing

Very Short Answer Type Questions

1. 4.34%
2. 25%
3. 50%
4. 20% less
5. 72
6. ₹6000 crores
7. ₹60
8. 44%
9. 5 : 8
10. 50%
11. 60
12. ₹3380
13. 60%
14. 10% less
15. $14\frac{2}{7}\%$
16. 200%
17. $33\frac{1}{3}\%$
18. ₹80
19. ₹140
20. 30%
21. 250 lakhs
22. $x = 40\%$

Short Answer Type Questions

23. 192
24. 64.5
25. 100%
26. 1000
27. 4%
28. ₹980
29. 75.5
30. 500
31. $33\frac{1}{3}\%$
32. 40%
33. 37.5%
34. 28%
35. 25%

Essay Type Questions

36. 980
37. 4000
38. 120
39. ₹24,000
40. ₹120000, ₹180000

Competition Wing

Level 1: Apply Your Concepts

1. 166.4
2. 120%
3. 3662.64
4. 56.25%
5. 57.12
6. (c)
7. (a)
8. (a)
9. (c)
10. (a)
11. (b)
12. (d)
13. (a)
14. (c)
15. (d)
16. (b)
17. (b)
18. (d)
19. (c)
20. (b)
21. (b)
22. (b)
23. (c)
24. (b)
25. (a)
26. (c)
27. (c)
28. (b)

Level 2: Review Your Concepts

29. (b)
30. (d)
31. (b)
32. (c)
33. (c)
34. (b)
35. (d)
36. (b)
37. (c)
38. (b)
39. (a)
40. (c)
41. (a)
42. (a)
43. (b)
44. (d)
45. (c)
46. (c)

Level 3: Assess Your Concepts

47. (d)	48. (b)	49. (b)	50. (d)	51. (c)
52. (b)	53. (b)	54. (a)	55. (d)	56. (b)
57. (d)	58. (a)	59. (c)		

JEE Special Wing

Multiple-Answer Type Questions

1. (a, b, c)	2. (b, c)	3. (a, b, c, d)	4. (b, d)	5. (a, b, c, d)

Match The Column

6. (f)	7. (e)	8. (b)	9. (g)	10. (c)

Comprehension-Based Questions

11. (d)	12. (c)	13. (b)	14. (a)	15. (c)
16. (a)	17. (d)	18. (b)	19. (c)	20. (c)

Assertion and Reason Type Questions

21. (a)	22. (c)	23. (c)

Hints and Explanations

Classroom Wing

Very Short Answer Type Questions

1. $4:3\frac{2}{3} = 4:\frac{11}{3} = 12:11$

$11x + 12x = 100$

$23x = 100$

$x = \frac{100}{23}$

$\frac{1200}{23} - \frac{1110}{23} = \frac{100}{23} = 4.34\%$

2. $\frac{\text{profit}}{\text{CP}} \times 100 \Rightarrow \frac{16}{64} \times 100 = 25\%$

3. $\frac{200}{100} \times 100 = 200$

$CP = 200 + 100$

$CP = 300$

CP after discount of 50% = 150

Profit = 50

Profit % = $\frac{50}{100} \times 100 = 50\%$

4. % of Advaita = A

$\frac{125}{100} \times A = N$

$A = \frac{100}{125} \times N \times 100$

$A = 80\%$ of N

So, Advaita scored 100 – 80 = 20% less

5. 87.5 % of $x = 63$

$x = \frac{100 \times 63}{87.5}$

$x = 72$

6. $3x + 5x = 16000$ Cr

$x = 2000$ Cr

Krisha Discount is 3×2000 Cr

= 6000 Cr

7. If 10 % of $x = 12$

$x = \frac{1200}{10} = ₹\ 120 - SP$

$CP = 50\%$ of $SP = \frac{50}{100} \times 120 = 60$

8. Let side of square be x

Area = x^2

On increasing 20% of side,

Area = $(1.2\ x)^2$

Area = $1.44\ x^2$

Increase in area = $0.44\ x^2$

% increase in area = 44 %

That is 44% increase in case

9. Ram : Lakhman

30:48

5:8

10. $P = 66\frac{2}{3} - 33\frac{1}{3}$

$P = 33\frac{1}{3}$

$P = \frac{33\frac{1}{3}}{66\frac{2}{3}} \times 100$

$= \frac{1}{2} \times 100 = 50\%$

11. $\frac{\cancel{30}}{\cancel{100}} \times \frac{40}{\cancel{100}} \times x = \frac{\overset{2}{\cancel{60}}}{\cancel{100}} \times \frac{12.5}{\cancel{100}} \times 96$

$x = \frac{2 \times 12.5}{40} \times 96$

$x = \frac{25}{40} \times 96$

$x = 60$

12. Year 1 end

30% of 2000 = 600

Year 2 end

30% of 2600 = 780

2600 + 780 = 3380

13. 50% of $x = 0.5\ x$

$0.2 \times 0.5\ x = 0.10\ x$

total discount on x is 0.6

So, 60% is the equivalent discount

14. $2a = 3b,\ b = \frac{3}{4}c,\ c = 0.8d$

$a = 1.5b$

$a = 1.5\left(\frac{3}{4} \times 0.8d\right)$

$a = 0.9d$

a is 10% less than d

15. $CP = \frac{7}{8}\text{SP}$

$\text{Profit} = \frac{8\text{CP} - 7\text{CP}}{7} = \frac{\text{CP}}{7}$

$\text{Profit} = \frac{\frac{\text{CP}}{7}}{\text{CP}} \times 100 = \frac{100}{7} = 14.28$

$= 14\frac{2}{7}\%$

16. Children in previous year be x

This year children are $3x$

$\text{Increase} = \frac{3x - x}{x} \times 100 = \frac{2x}{x} \times 100$

$= 200\%$

17. $P = \frac{25}{100} \times \text{SP}$

$\frac{25}{100} \times \text{SP=CP-SP}$

$\text{CP=}\frac{125SP}{100}$

$\text{SP} = \frac{100\text{CP}}{125}$

$P = \frac{125\text{CP} - 100\text{CP}}{125} = \frac{25}{125}\text{CP}$

$= \frac{1}{5}(P)$

$P\% = \frac{\frac{1}{5}\cancel{CP}}{\cancel{CP}} \times 100 = 20\%$

Cost be $= 33\frac{1}{3}\%$

18. $SP = 40$

Profit is 100 %

$CP = 20$

for 300% profit

$SP = CP + 300\%\ CP$

$= 20 + 60$

$=$ ₹ 80

19. 80% of $CP = 80$

$CP = 100$

140% of $CP = \frac{140}{100} \times 100 = 140$

The price should be 140

20. Let class strength be x

60 % of x are Boys

50 % passed (60% of x)

30 % of total passed who were Boys

21. $\left(\frac{105}{100} \times x\right) - \left(\frac{90}{100} \times x\right) = 37.5\ \text{lakh}$

$\frac{15x}{100} = 37.5$

$x = \frac{3750}{15} = 250\ \text{lakh}$

22. Let full property be x

$\frac{80}{100} \times \left(\frac{33\frac{1}{3}}{100} \times x\right) =$ **20%** loss

For profit of 20%

Book a profit on next $33\frac{1}{3}\%$ of profit 20%

Next $33\frac{1}{3}\%$ Book a profit of 20%

So total sell the best of property on 40% profit to gain profit of 20%

Short Answer Type Question

23. Discount $= 165x - 132x$

$= 33x$

165% of $CP = 165x$

$198 = 33x$

$x = \frac{198}{33}$

165 % of CP $= \frac{165 \times 198}{33}$

$$CP = \frac{100 \times \cancel{165} \times \overset{6}{\cancel{198}}}{\cancel{33} \times \cancel{165}}$$

$CP = 600$

$SP = 132 \times \frac{198}{33}$

$= 132 \times 6$

$SP = 792$

Profit $= 792 - 600 = 192$

24. Total valid votes are

$100\% - 6\% = 94\%$

Let democrats secure D% valid votes and republicans secure R% valid votes

$\therefore D + R = 94$ (i)

$D - R = 35$ (ii)

$2D = 129$

$D = \frac{129}{2} = 64.5\%$

$R = 64.5\% - 35\% = 29.5\%$

Hence, Democrats secure 64.5% valid votes.

25. $ASP = x$, $SP = \frac{x}{4}$

$\frac{50}{100} \times CP = \frac{x}{4}$

$CP = \frac{100x}{200} = \frac{x}{2}$

$P = ASP - CP = x - \frac{x}{2} = \frac{x}{2}$

$P\% = \frac{\frac{x}{2}}{\frac{x}{2}} \times 100 = 100\%$

26. $\frac{88}{100} \times x = 880$

$x = \frac{\overset{10}{\cancel{880}} \times 100}{\cancel{88}}$

$x = 1000$

27. Error percentage $= \frac{1000 - 960}{1000} \times 100$

$= \frac{40}{1000} \times 100 = 4\%$

28.

	Savings	Expenduture
N	20%	80%
M	30%	70%

$70\ \% \times 5600 = 80\ \%$ of x

$\frac{7\cancel{0}}{\cancel{100}} \times \overset{700}{\cancel{5600}} \times \frac{\cancel{100}}{\cancel{80}} = x$

$x = 4900$

20% of 4900

$\frac{20}{1\cancel{00}} \times 49\cancel{00} =$ ₹980 is savings

29. Total valid votes are $100\% - 9\% = 91\%$

Therefore, $A + B = 91$ (i)

$A - B = 60$ (ii)

$2A = 151$

$A = 75.5\%$

$B = 15.5\%$

Hence, A secure 75.5% of valid votes.

30. Orchid price be x

We sold it for y

$\frac{85}{100} \times x = y$

$\frac{105}{100} \times x = y + 100$

$\frac{105}{100} \times x = \frac{85}{100} \times x + 100$

$\frac{20}{100} x = 100$

$x = 500$

31. Increase in consumption $=$

$\left(\frac{\%\ \text{price decrease}}{100 - \%\ \text{price decr.}}\right) \times 100$

$= \left(\frac{25}{100 - 25}\right) \times 100$

$= \frac{25}{75} \times 100$

$= \frac{1}{3} \times 100 = 33.3$

32. Discount 1 = $\frac{25}{100}(x)$

Price after 1st discount = $\frac{3}{4}(x)$

Discount 2 = $\frac{20}{100} \times \frac{3}{4}(x)$

$= \frac{3}{20}(x)$

effective discount $= \frac{25x}{100} + \frac{15x}{100}$

$= \frac{40x}{100} = 40\%$

33. Let article CP be "100"

He marked it for 160

$\frac{60}{160} \times 100 = 37.5$

So he can give Maximum discount of 37.5%

34. 20% of $x \rightarrow$ discount 1

$\left(\frac{20x}{100}\right)$

80% of $x \rightarrow$ after discount 1 price

$10\left(\frac{80}{100}x\right) \rightarrow$ discount 2

$\left(\frac{1}{10} \times \frac{8}{10}\right)x$

Equivalent Discount $= \frac{20x}{100} + \frac{8x}{100}$

$= \frac{28x}{100} = 28\ \%$

35. Profit% $= \frac{\text{Profit}}{\text{CP}} \times 100$

$P\% = \frac{\text{SP} - \text{CP}}{\text{CP}} \times 100$

$x = \frac{31.25 - x}{x} \times 100$

$x^2 + 100x - 3125 = 0$

$x^2 + 125 - 25x - 3125 = 0$

$x(x + 125) - 125(x + 125)$

$x = -125$ or 25

Cost Be -125

So $x = 25\%$

Essay Type Questions

36. 70% of 2000 (30% is discounted)

Discount 1 = (70 × 20)

Discount 2 = $\frac{70}{100}(70 \times 20)$

A's SP = 980

60% of 2000 (40% discount)

$= \frac{60}{100} \times 2000 = 1200$

$= \frac{80}{100}(1200)$ (20% discount)

B's SP = 80 × 12 = 960

C's SP = (discount 1) = 50% (2000)

= 1000

(discount 2) = 90 % (1000)

= 900

So A's SP is highest = 980

37. $A = 3C$

$3B = D$

$A = B$

$\Rightarrow 3C = \frac{D}{3}$

Investment is done in Ratio

3 : 3 : 1 : 9

$A : B : C : D$

$3x + 3x + 1x + 9x = 1600$

$16x = 16000$

$x = 1000$

$C + A = 4000$

C share is 1000 and A's share is 3000

38. Let Amar has x number of marbles.

$\Rightarrow$ Bhuvan has $x + x \times \frac{20}{100} = \frac{6x}{5}$ marbles

$\Rightarrow$ Chetan has $\frac{6x}{5} - \frac{6x}{5} \times \frac{10}{100} = \frac{27x}{25}$ marbles

$\therefore x + \frac{6x}{5} + \frac{27x}{25} = 328$

$\Rightarrow \frac{25x + 30x + 27x}{25} = 328$

$\Rightarrow 82x = 328 \times 25$

$\Rightarrow x = 4 \times 25 = 100$

Hence, Bhuvan has $\frac{6 \times 100}{5} = 120$ marbles.

39. Gita and Sita invested in 4 : 5

Let Gita invested = $4x$

$\Rightarrow$ Sita invested = $5x$

Their earning will be in the same ratio.

$\Rightarrow$ Let Gita earned = $4y$

Sita earned = $5y$

Total earning = $9y = 72000$ *Rs*

$\Rightarrow y = 8000$ *Rs*

$\Rightarrow$ Gita earned = 32000 *Rs*

Sita earned = 40000 *Rs*

Let salary of Sita = p

$\Rightarrow$ Total earning of Sita = $p + 40000$

$$\Rightarrow = \frac{32000}{p+40000} = \frac{1}{2}$$

$\Rightarrow 64000 = p + 40000$

$\Rightarrow p = 24000$ *Rs*

$\Rightarrow$ Salary of Sita = 24000 *Rs*

40. Let the investments of P and Q be $2x$ and $3x$.

Ratio of profits: $(2x)12 : (3x)12 : 8(40000) = 18 : 27 : 4$

$$\Rightarrow \frac{(3x)12}{8(40000)} = \frac{27}{4}$$

$\Rightarrow 3x = 180000$

$$\Rightarrow 2x = (180000)\left(\frac{2}{3}\right) = 120000$$

$\therefore$ P's investment = ₹120000

Q's investment = ₹180000

Competition Wing

Level 1: Apply Your Concepts

1. $\frac{26}{100}\times 640 = 166.4$

2. X is 20% more than Y

   Y is 120% of X

3. $\frac{99}{100}\times 1500 \times \frac{45}{100}\times 360 + \frac{55.99}{100}\times 3600$

   $= 99\times 15 + 4.5\times 36\times 55.99\times 36$

   $= 3662.64$

4. $\frac{1}{4}$ is 25%, $\frac{9}{16}\times 100 = 56.25$

5. 13% of $x = 28$

   $x = \frac{2800}{13}$

   26.52% of $x = 57.119 \approx 57.12$

6. Use the formula, $A = P\left(1+\frac{r}{100}\right)^n$.

7. 20% a + 40% b = 230.

   40% a + 20% b = 190. Find a and b.

8. Difference in the percentages = Difference in the marks.

9. (i) Let the total number of young men be 100.
   (ii) Let the number of young men who attend the party be $100x$.
   (iii) Find number of young men who wear grey hats, and also find that of who wear black hats.

10. Find x from the first statement.

11. Let the initial price be ₹100 and initial consumption be 100 units.

12. (i) Find SP and CP of 20 articles by taking CP of 1 article = ₹x.
    (ii) As the CP of 15 articles is equal to the SP of 20 articles, trader suffers loss.
    (iii) Let C = 15 and S = 20. Loss % $= \left(\frac{S-C}{S}\right)\times 100.$

13. (i) Let SP of 1 m of cloth be ₹x.
    (ii) Let SP of 25 m of a cloth be ₹$25x$.
    ∴ Profit = ₹$5x$.
    (iii) Now find the CP, and then the profit %.

14. (i) Whenever SP is same and % of loss = % of profit = x%, there is always loss, and loss% $= \frac{x^2}{100}$.
    (ii) In the given conditions, trader suffer loss.
    (iii) Loss percentage $= \frac{(\text{Profit \% or loss \%})^2}{100}$

15. (i) Let CP of A be ₹100.
    (ii) Let CP for A be ₹x.
    (iii) $x\left(\frac{70}{100}\right)\left(\frac{120}{100}\right)\left(\frac{110}{100}\right) = 924.$

16. (i) Let Raja's monthly salary be ₹100.
    (ii) Let the salary of Raja be ₹$100x$.
    (iii) R = 10% of ₹$100x$ = ₹$10x$.
    (iv) Similarly, find F, T, and S, and then compare.

17. (i) Find the number of matches won out of 80 matches. Minimum number of additional matches is equal to the number of matches to be won.
    (ii) First, find the number of matches won out of 80 matches played.
    That is, $\frac{40}{100}\times 80 = 32.$
    (iii) To get minimum number of matches to be played, it has to win all the additional matches.
    (iv) Let the required number of matches = x.
    $\Rightarrow \frac{(32+x)}{(8+x)}\times 100 = 60.$

18. (i) Find x and y using the given information.
    (ii) First, find population of the first-generation immigrants in 1990 and 2000, i.e., 3% of $8k$ and 3.2% of $9k$.
    (iii) Then find percentage increase (x).
    (iv) $y = \frac{1k}{8k}(100)$, and then find $(x - y)$.

19. (i) Let MP of A be ₹100, then find the difference in the discount given by A and B.
    (ii) Let the MP be ₹x.
    (iii) Successive discounts 20% and 10% is equivalent to a single discount of 28%.
    (iv) Now, 30% of x − 28% of x = ₹600.

20. (i) Let CP of x be ₹100, then find SP of x.
    (ii) Let CP for X be ₹$100x$.
    (iii) Find CP and SP for Y. Then find profit earned by Y (in x) and compare it with ₹23.
    (iv) CP of Y = SP of X.

21. Assume the cost price be ₹100.
    $m\left(\frac{90}{100}\right) = 120.$

22. (i) Find p and q using the given information.
(ii) First, find the population of the first generation immigrants in 1995 and 2005, i.e., 2% of $6x$ and 2.4% of $8x$.
(iii) Then find percentage increase (q).
(iv) $P = \frac{2x}{6x}(100)$, and then find $(p - q)$.

23. Assume the cost price be ₹100, then marked price is ₹150.

24. (i) Find the ratio of investments and the ratio of time periods.
(ii) Let P's investment be ₹x.
(iii) Now, find investments of Q and R in terms of x with the given data.
(iv) Let the time period of investment of R be y months.
(v) Now, find time periods of investment of P and Q.
(vi) Ratio of shares of profits is equal to the ratio of product of investments and investment periods.

28. (i) Let CP of the product be ₹100, then find MP and SP.
(ii) Let the CP be ₹$100x$.
(iii) MP = $130x$ and SP = 70% of $130x$.
(iv) CP – SP = 900, find x.

Level 2: Review Your Concepts

29. (i) Find the discounts given by P, Q, and R.
(ii) Find the SP for P, Q, and R by using the following formulae.

$$SP = \frac{(100 - d)}{100} MP \text{ (OR)}$$

$$SP = \frac{(100 - d_1)}{100}\frac{(100 - d_2)}{100} MP$$

(iii) Compare the SP's.

30. Marked price of the first article = ₹200.
Marked price of the second article = ₹150.

31. (i) Let CP of 1 m cloth be ₹x.
(ii) Let the CP of 5 m of a cloth be ₹$5x$.
(iii) So, profit = ₹$2x$.
(iv) Now, find the profit percentage.

32. (i) Let the initial price and initial consumption be ₹100 and 100 units, respectively.
(ii) (Consumption) (Price of an article) = Total expenditure.
(iii) Let consumption be 100 articles and rate be ₹100.
(iv) Given, rate = ₹80 and total expenditure = ₹9000. Find the consumption by using the formula which is mentioned in (i).
(v) Find the percentage decrease in the consumption.

33. (i) Find the total number of students in class A and class B.
(ii) Total number of students in class $A = \left(\frac{24}{60}\right) \times 100.$
(iii) Similarly, find the total number of students in class B.
(iv) Find the difference between the total number of students in both the sections, and then find percentage difference with respect to the total number of students in class B.

41. Assume that Ramapada have ₹150, then find the CP of pen and pencil.

42. Let the cost price be ₹$1000x$/kg.

The selling price of 900 g = The cost price of 1000 g.

∴ The selling price of 900 g = ₹$1000x$.

The cost price of 900 g = $\frac{900}{1000}$ (₹$1000x$) = ₹$900x$

Profit in selling 900 g = ₹$100x$.

$$\text{Profit \%} = \frac{100x}{900x}(100\%) = 11\frac{1}{9}\%.$$

43. Let the marked price of the article be ₹$100x$.

$$\therefore \text{Selling price} = \frac{2}{3} \times (₹100x) = ₹\frac{200}{3}x \quad (1)$$

Let the cost price be ₹$100y$.

$$\text{Loss} = \frac{16\frac{2}{3}}{100} \times (₹100y) = ₹\frac{100y}{6}$$

$$\Rightarrow \text{Selling price} = ₹100y - ₹\frac{100y}{6}$$

$$= \frac{₹500y}{6} \quad (2)$$

$$\frac{500y}{6} = \frac{200x}{3} \text{ (from Eqs. (1) and (2))} y = \frac{4}{5}x$$

$$\therefore \text{Cost price} = 100\left(\frac{4x}{5}\right) = ₹80x$$

If he sold the article at marked price.

$$\therefore \text{Profit percentage} = \frac{100x - 80x}{80x} \times (100\%) = 25\%.$$

44. Let his cost price be ₹$100x$.
Actual SP = 90% of $(100x)$

Considered SP = 102% of $(100x)$

102% of $(100x)$ = 90% of $(100x)$ + 180

12% of $(100x)$ = 180

$\therefore 100x = \frac{180}{12}(100) = 1500$

$\therefore$ Cost price = ₹1500.

45. While calculating the profit/loss percentage, we must consider equal number of books being bought and sold.

The cost price of each book $= ₹\frac{18}{12} = ₹\frac{3}{2}$.

The selling price of each book $= ₹\frac{30}{18} = ₹\frac{5}{3}$.

As $\frac{3}{2} < \frac{5}{3}$, a profit is made.

$$\text{Profit \%} = \frac{\frac{5}{3} - \frac{3}{2}}{\frac{3}{2}x} \times (100\%)$$

$$= \frac{\frac{1}{6}}{\frac{3}{2}} \times (100\%) = 11\frac{1}{9}\%.$$

46. Let the total number of votes casted be $100x$.

The number of invalid votes $= \frac{14}{100}(100x) = 14x$.

The number of valid votes $= 100x - 14x = 86x$.

Let the number of votes secured by Q be q.

Number of votes secured by $P = q$.

$$\left(1 + \frac{15}{100}\right) = \frac{23}{20}q \Rightarrow \frac{23}{20}q + q = 86x$$

$$\frac{43}{20}q = 86x \Rightarrow q = 40x$$

$\therefore$ The required percentage $= \frac{40x}{100x}(100\%) = 40\%$.

Level 3: Assess Your Concepts

48. Let the population of the village in the year 2001 be 100 and proceed.

49. Assume the income of the person to be ₹100 and proceed.

50. Assume that the salary of the person to be ₹100 and follow the data given in the problem.

51. Let the total number of employees be $100x$. The number of unmarried employees $= \frac{30}{100}(100x) = 30x$.

The number of unmarried post-graduates $= \frac{20}{100}(30x) = 6x$.

The number of married post-graduates $= \left(3\frac{1}{2}\right)(6x) = 21x$.

The number of married employees $= 100x - 30x = 70x$.

The required percentage $= \frac{21x}{70x}(100)\% = 30\%$.

52. Let the amounts with Amar, Bhavan and Chetan be ₹a, ₹b, and ₹c, respectively.

$$\frac{a+b+c}{3} = 1180$$

$$a+b+c = 3540$$

$$a = b\left(1 + \frac{33\frac{1}{3}}{100}\right) = c\left(1 - \frac{16\frac{2}{3}}{100}\right)$$

$$a = \frac{4}{3}b = \frac{5}{6}c$$

$$b = \frac{3}{4}a \text{ and } c = \frac{6}{5}a$$

$$a+b+c = \frac{59}{20}a$$

$$\frac{59}{20}a = 3540 \text{ (given)}$$

$$\frac{a}{20} = 60$$

$$a = 1200.$$

a = ₹1200.

53. Let the number of matches played be $60 + x$. This is minimum when x is minimum.

As the target was achieved for the minimum value of x, all the x matches must have been won.

Let the minimum $(x) = y$.

$\therefore$ The total number of matches won $= \frac{30}{100}(60) + y = 18 + y$

$$\frac{18+y}{60+y} \times (100)\% = 44\%$$

$$1800 + 100y = 2640 + 44y$$

$$56y = 840$$

$$y = 15$$

54. $3X + 2Y = 230$ (1)

If $3X$ increases by 40% and $2X$ increases by 30%, total

increase $= \frac{40}{100}(3X) + \frac{30}{100}(2Y)$

$\therefore \frac{40}{100}(3X) + \frac{30}{100}(2Y) = 84$

$1.2X + 0.6Y = 84$

Dividing both sides by 0.6, $2X + Y = 140$

$\therefore Y = 140 - 2X$ (2)

$\therefore 2Y = 280 - 4X$

$(1) \Rightarrow 2Y = 230 - 3X$

$\therefore 280 - 4X = 230 - 3X$

$50 = X$

$(2) \Rightarrow Y = 40$

The required sum $= X\left(1 - \frac{40}{100}\right) + Y\left(1 - \frac{30}{100}\right)$

$= (50)(0.6) + (40)$

$(0.7) = 58.$

55. Let the cost price of the first book be ₹$100x$.

The profit made on it $= \frac{10}{100}$(₹$100x$) = ₹$10x$

Its selling price = ₹$110x$

The cost price of the second book = ₹$110x$

The loss suffered on it $= \frac{10}{100}$(₹$111x$) = ₹$11x$

Its selling price = ₹$99x$

Total cost price = ₹$210x$

Total selling price = ₹$209x$

As $210x > 209x$, on overall loss is made.

Overall loss = ₹x

$\therefore$ Overall loss percentage $= \frac{x}{210x} \times (100)\% = \frac{10}{21}\%.$

56. Let the cost price for P be ₹$100x$.

P's profit $= \frac{20}{100}$(₹$100x$) = ₹$20x$

The selling price for P = ₹$120x$

The cost price for Q = The selling price for P = ₹$120x$

Q's profit $= \frac{10}{100}$(₹$120x$) = ₹$12x$

Given, $12x = 20x - 24$

$\Rightarrow 3 = x \Rightarrow 100x =$ ₹300.

57. Let the strength of the class be $100x$.

The number of students who drink pulpy orange

$= \frac{45}{100}(100x) = 45x.$

The number of students who drink Maaza

$= \frac{90}{100}(100x - 45x)$

$= \frac{9}{10}(55x) = 49.5x$

No student drinks both Maaza and pulpy orange.

The number of students of the class who drink neither Maaza nor pulpy orange

$= 100x - 94.5x = 5.5x$

The required percentage $= \frac{5.5x}{100x}(100)\% = 5.5\%.$

58. $40\%\ A = 50\%\ B$

$4A = 5B$ (1)

$3C = A + B$ (2)

$A + B + C = 72$ (3)

$3C + C = 72$ (from (2) and (3))

$4C = 72$

$C = 18$ (4)

$\therefore A + B + 18 = 72$

$A + B = 54$

$5A + 5B = 270$

$5A + 4A = 270$

$9A = 270$

$A = 30$

$\therefore$ The required % $= \frac{30}{18} \times 100\% = \frac{1000}{6}\% = 166\frac{2}{3}\%$

$\therefore 166\frac{2}{3}\%$ of the chocolates with C is the number of chocolates with A.

59. Let the marked price of each article be ₹x.

Discount allowed = 20% of x.

Total sale price = $12 \times 80\%\ (x)$

12% of $[12 \times 80\%\ (x)] = 28800$

$x = \frac{28800 \times 100 \times 100}{12 \times 12 \times 80}$

$x = \frac{200 \times 100 \times 100}{80}$

$x = 25000$

$\therefore$ Marked price of each article = ₹25000

Selling price of each article = 80% of ₹25000

$= 8 \times ₹2500 = ₹20000$

Profit% on each article is 25% of *CP*.

$\therefore$ 125% of $CP = ₹20000$

$\frac{5}{4} \times CP = ₹20000$

$CP = ₹16000$

$\therefore$ Profit on each article = $SP - CP$

$= ₹\,(20000 - 16000) = ₹4000$

$\therefore$ Net profit on each article after charity

$= 4000 - \frac{28800}{12} = ₹1600$

$\therefore$ Profit % $= \frac{1600}{16000} \times 100\% = 10\%$

JEE Special Wing

Multiple-Answer Type Questions

1. CP = ₹100 and MP = ₹150.

The maximum discount that can be offered to avoid loss = ₹150 – ₹100 = ₹50.

$$\text{Maximum discount \%} = \frac{\text{Max. Dicsount}}{\text{MP}} \times 100\%$$

$$= \frac{₹50}{₹150} \times 100\%$$

$$= \frac{1}{3} \times 100\% = 33\frac{1}{3}\%.$$

So, the manufacturer can allow a discount up to $33\frac{1}{3}\%$ to avoid loss.

Hence, choice (a, b, c) are correct.

2. Let the marked price be ₹100.

Going by options:

(a) **Successive discounts:** 25% and 20%

Selling Price = (100 – 25) % of (100 – 20) % of ₹100

$$= \frac{75}{100} \times \frac{80}{100} \times ₹100 = ₹60.$$

Discount = MP – SP = ₹100 – ₹60 = ₹40.

Discount % = 40%

(b) **Successive discounts:** 25% and 15%

Selling Price = (100 – 25) % of (100 – 15)% of ₹100

$$= \frac{75}{100} \times \frac{85}{100} \times ₹100 = ₹63.75.$$

Discount = MP – SP = ₹100 – ₹63.75 = ₹36.25.

Discount % = 36.25%

(c) **Successive discounts:** 20% and 20%

Selling Price = (100 – 20)% of (100 – 20)% of ₹100

$$= \frac{80}{100} \times \frac{80}{100} \times ₹100 = ₹64.$$

Discount = MP – SP = ₹100 – ₹64 = ₹36.

Discount % = 36%

(d) **Successive discounts:** $33\frac{1}{3}\%$ and 10%

Selling Price = $(100 - 33\frac{1}{3})\%$ of (100 – 10)% of ₹100

$$= \frac{66\frac{2}{3}}{100} \times \frac{90}{100} \times ₹100$$

$$= \frac{200}{3 \times 100} \times \frac{90}{100} \times ₹100 = ₹60.$$

Discount = MP – SP = ₹100 – ₹60 = ₹40.

Discount % = 40%

Hence, choice (b and c) are correct.

3. Let the initial price be ₹100.

Percentage increase = 4%.

Final Price = (100 + 4) % of ₹100 = ₹104.

Going by options:

(a) **The price of sugar is increased by 30% and then decreased by 20%.**

The final price of sugar = (100 + 30)% of (100 – 20)% of ₹100

$$= \frac{130}{100} \times \frac{80}{100} \times ₹100 = ₹104.$$

(b) **The price of oil is increased by 25% and then decreased by $16\frac{4}{5}\%$.**

The final price of oil = (100 + 25)% of $(100 - 16\frac{4}{5})\%$ of ₹100

$$= \frac{125}{100} \times \frac{83\frac{1}{5}}{100} \times ₹100$$

$$= \frac{125}{100} \times \frac{416}{5 \times 100} \times ₹100 = ₹104.$$

(c) **The price of Jowar is increased by 20% and then decreased by $13\frac{1}{3}\%$.**

The final price of jowar = (100 + 20) % of $(100 - 13\frac{1}{3})\%$ of ₹100

$$= \frac{120}{100} \times \frac{86\frac{2}{3}}{100} \times ₹100$$

$$= \frac{120}{100} \times \frac{260}{3 \times 100} \times ₹100 = ₹104.$$

(d) **The price of petrol is increased by 10% and then decreased by $5\frac{5}{11}\%$.**

The final price of petrol = (100 + 10) % of $(100 - 5\frac{5}{11})\%$ of ₹100

$$= \frac{110}{100} \times \frac{94\frac{6}{11}}{100} \times ₹100$$

$$= \frac{110}{100} \times \frac{1040}{11 \times 100} \times ₹100 = ₹104.$$

Hence, choice (a, b, c, d) are correct.

4. The SP a book = The SP of pen = ₹99.

Profit % on selling the book = 10%.

Loss % on selling the pen = 10%.

$$\text{The CP of the book} = \frac{100}{100+10} \times ₹99$$

$$= \frac{100}{110} \times ₹99 = ₹90.$$

$$\text{The CP of the pen} = \frac{100}{100-10} \times ₹99$$

$$= \frac{100}{90} \times ₹99 = ₹110.$$

Total CP = ₹90 + ₹110 = ₹200.

Total SP = ₹99 + ₹99 = ₹198.

As SP < CP, there is a loss.

Loss = CP – SP = ₹200 – ₹198 = ₹2.

$$\text{Loss \%} = \frac{\text{Loss}}{\text{Total CP}} \times 100\%$$

$$= \frac{₹2}{₹200} \times 100\% = 1\%.$$

Hence, choice (b and d) are correct.

5. We know that the ratio of profits = the ratio of investments.

Going by options:

(a) **Each of them invested ₹25,00,000 and for 12 months:**

The ratio of profits = the ratio of investments

= (₹25,00,000 × 12) : (₹25,00,000 × 12) = 1 : 1.

So, *A* and *B* share the profit equally.

(b) ***A* invested ₹90,00,000 for 8 months and *B* invested ₹80,00,000 for 9 months:**

The ratio of profits = the ratio of investments

= (₹90,00,000 × 8) : (₹80,00,000 × 9) = 1 : 1.

So, *A* and *B* share the profit equally.

(c) ***A* invested ₹44,00,000 for 9 months and *B* invested ₹33,00,000 for 12 months:**

The ratio of profits = the ratio of investments

= (₹44,00,000 × 9) : (₹33,00,000 × 12)

= (44× 9) : (33× 12)

= (4 × 3) : (3 × 4) = 1 : 1.

So, *A* and *B* share the profit equally.

(d) ***A* invested ₹25,00,000 for 12 months and *B* invested ₹37,50,000 for 8 months:**

The that the ratio of profits = the ratio of investments

= (₹25,00,000 × 12) : (₹37,50,000 × 8)

= (250 × 12) : (375 × 8)

= (2 × 3) : (3 × 2) = 1 : 1.

So, *A* and *B* share the profit equally.

Hence, choice (a, b, c, d) are correct.

Match The Column

Common Solutions for questions 6 to 10:

Article	Cost Price (In ₹)	Market Price (In ₹)	Discount%	Selling Price (In ₹)	Profit = SP – CP (In ₹)
P	40	180% of 40 = 72	25%	75% of 72 = 54	54 – 40 = 14
Q	50	180% of 50 = 90	30%	70% of 90 = 63	63 – 50 = 13
R	75	180% of 75 = 135	40%	60% of 135 = 81	81 – 75 = 6
S	100	180% of 100 = 180	35%	65% of 180 = 117	117 – 100 = 17
T	125	180% of 125 = 225	40%	60% of 225 = 135	135 – 125 = 10

6. The profit earned on selling the article *P* = ₹14.

Hence, the correct option is (f).

7. The profit earned on selling the article *Q* = ₹13.

Hence, the correct option is (e).

8. The profit earned on selling the article *R* = ₹6.

Hence, the correct option is (b).

9. The profit earned on selling the article *S* = ₹17.

Hence, the correct option is (g).

10. The profit earned on selling the article T = ₹10.

Hence, the correct option is (c).

Comprehension-Based Questions

Common Solutions for questions 11 to 15:

The total cost of sugar = ₹600.

Given that the price of the sugar (in ₹) is $33\frac{1}{3}\%$ less than the number of kg of sugar that he could purchase.

Let the number of kg of sugar that he could purchase be x.

The price of the sugar per kg (in ₹) = $x - 33\frac{1}{3}\%$ of x.

$= 66\frac{2}{3}\%$ of $x = \frac{2x}{3}$.

Now $x \times \frac{2x}{3} = 600$

$x^2 = 900$

$x = 30$.

Therefore, the number of kg of sugar that he could purchase = 30.

The price of sugar per kg = $\frac{2x}{3}$ = ₹20.

11. The price of sugar increases by 20%.

The new price per kg = 120% of ₹20 = $\frac{120}{100} \times$ ₹20 = ₹24.

The quantity of sugar (in kg) that he can purchase for ₹600 = $\frac{₹600}{₹24} = 25$.

Hence, the correct option is (d).

12. The price of sugar decreases by 25%.

The new price per kg = 75% of ₹20 = $\frac{75}{100} \times$ ₹20 = ₹15.

The quantity of sugar (in kg) that he can purchase for ₹600 = $\frac{₹600}{₹15} = 40$.

Increase in the quantity of sugar (in kg) = 40 – 30 = 10.

Percentage increase $= \frac{10}{30} \times 100\%$

$= \frac{1}{3} \times 100\% = 33\frac{1}{3}\%$.

Hence, the correct option is (c).

13. Both the price of sugar and the consumption of sugar increase by 10%.

The new price per kg = 110% of ₹20 = $\frac{110}{100} \times$ ₹20 = ₹22.

The new quantity of sugar = 110% of ₹30 = $\frac{110}{100} \times 30$ = 33.

The amount required = 33 × ₹22 = ₹726.

The extra amount required = ₹726 – ₹600 = ₹126.

Hence, the correct option is (b).

14. The price of sugar increases by 10% and the consumption of sugar decreases by 10%.

The new price per kg = 110% of ₹20 = $\frac{110}{100} \times$ ₹20 = ₹22.

The new quantity of sugar = 90% of ₹30 = $\frac{90}{100} \times 30$ = 27.

The amount required = 27 × ₹22 = ₹594.

Change in amount = ₹600 – ₹594 = ₹6.

Percentage decrease = $\frac{₹6}{₹600} \times 100\% = 1\%$.

Hence, the correct option is (a).

15. Deva wants to increase the donation amount by 50%.

The new amount = 150% of ₹600 = $\frac{150}{100} \times$ ₹600 = ₹900.

The quantity of sugar (in kg) that he can purchase for ₹900 = $\frac{₹900}{₹20} = 45$.

Increase in the quantity of sugar (in kg) = 45 – 30 = 15.

Hence, the correct option is (c).

Common Solutions for questions 16 to 20:

(i)

Item	Successive Discounts	SP Per Unit (in ₹)	Profit%
AC	20% + 30%	56,000	12

SP of each AC = 80% of 70% of MP.

₹56,000 = $\frac{80}{100} \times \frac{70}{100} \times$ MP

MP of each AC = ₹1,00,000.

SP of each AC = 112% of CP.

₹56,000 = $\frac{112}{100} \times$ CP

CP of each AC = ₹50,000.

(ii)

Item	Successive Discounts	SP Per Unit (in ₹)	Profit%
Fridge	25% + 25%	56,250	12.5

SP of each fridge = 75% of 75% of MP.

$$₹56,250 = \frac{75}{100} \times \frac{75}{100} \times MP$$

MP of each fridge = ₹1,00,000.

SP of each fridge = 112.5% of CP.

$$₹56,250 = \frac{112.5}{100} \times CP$$

CP of each fridge = ₹50,000.

(iii)

Item	Successive Discounts	SP Per Unit (in ₹)	Profit%
Washing Machine	10% + 40%	54,000	20

SP of each washing machine = 90% of 60% of MP.

$$₹54,000 = \frac{80}{100} \times \frac{70}{100} \times MP$$

MP of each washing machine = ₹1,00,000.

SP of each washing machine = 120% of MP.

$$₹54,000 = \frac{120}{100} \times CP$$

CP of each washing machine = ₹45,000.

(iv)

Item	Successive Discounts	SP Per Unit (in ₹)	Profit%
Dishwash Machine	15% + 35%	55,250	10.5

SP of each dishwasher = 85% of 65% of MP.

$$₹55,250 = \frac{85}{100} \times \frac{65}{100} \times MP$$

MP of each dishwasher = ₹1,00,000.

SP of each dishwasher = 110.5% of CP.

$$₹55,250 = \frac{110.5}{100} \times CP$$

CP of each dishwasher = ₹50,000.

16. The total marked prices of an AC and a washing machine = ₹1,00,000 + ₹1,00,000

= ₹2,00,000.

Hence, the correct option is (a).

17. The difference of the cost prices of a fridge and a dishwasher

= ₹50,000 – ₹50,000 = ₹0.

Hence, the correct option is (d).

18. CP of each fridge = ₹50,000.

MP of each fridge = ₹1,00,000.

Therefore, each fridge is marked above its cost price by 100%.

Hence, the correct option is (b).

19. MP of each washing machine = ₹1,00,000.

SP of each washing machine = ₹54,000.

Discount = MP – SP

= ₹1,00,000 – ₹54,000 = ₹46,000.

$$\text{Percentage of discount} = \frac{\text{Discount}}{\text{MP}} \times 100\%$$

$$= \frac{₹46,000}{₹1,00,000} \times 100\% = 46\%.$$

Hence, the correct option is (c).

20. The total CP of the four items = ₹50,000 + ₹50,000 + ₹45,000 + ₹50,000 = ₹1,95,000.

The total actual SP of four items

= ₹56,000 + ₹56,250 + ₹54,000 + ₹55,250

= ₹2,21,500.

The total SP after allowing 5% more discount = 95% of ₹2,21,500

$$= \frac{95}{100} \times ₹2,21,500 = ₹2,10,425.$$

Profit = SP – CP

= ₹2,10,425 – ₹1,95,000 = ₹15,425.

$$\text{Profit\%} = \frac{\text{Profit}}{\text{CP}} \times 100\%$$

$$= \frac{₹15,425}{₹1,95,000} \times 100\%$$

$$= \frac{15425}{1950}\%$$

$$= \frac{3085}{390}\%$$

$$= \frac{617}{78}\%$$

= 8% (Approximated to the nearest integer)

Hence, the correct option is (c).

Assertion and Reason Type Questions

Solutions for questions 21 to 23:

21. Assertion: Given That SP = ₹80 and MP = ₹100.

Discount = MP – SP = ₹20.

$$\text{Percentage of discount} = \frac{\text{Discount}}{\text{MP}} \times 100\%$$

$$= \frac{₹20}{₹100} \times 100\% = 20\%.$$

So, Assertion is true.

Reason: The percentage of discount is given by $\frac{\text{Discount}}{\text{MP}} \times 100\%$.

Reason is true and is the correct explanation Assertion.

Hence, the correct option is (a).

22. **Assertion:** Given that A is 20% more than B and B is 30% more than C, then A is 156% of C.

Let C be 100.

$B = 30\%$ more than $C = 130\%$ more than $C = 130\% \times 100 = 130$.

$A = 20\%$ more than $B = 120\%$ more than $B = 120\% \times 130 = \frac{120}{00} \times 130 = 156$.

So, Assertion is true.

Reason: If A is $x\%$ more than B and B is $y\%$ more than C, then A is $(100+x)\% \times (100+y)\%$ of C.

So, Reason is false.

Hence, the correct option is (c).

23. **Assertion:** A started a business with ₹1,50,00,000. After two months B joins A with the investment of ₹2,00,00,000.

At the end of one year, the ratio of their profits $= (₹1,50,00,000 \times 12) : (₹2,00,00,000 \times 10) = 9:10$.

Reason: If in a business a invests ₹ x for a months and B invests ₹y for b months, then they will share the profits in the ratio $by : ax$.

At the end of one year, the ratio of their profits $= (₹x \times a) : (₹y \times \text{b}) = ax : by$.

So, Reason is false.

Hence, the correct option is (c).

CHAPTER

4

Simple Interest and Compound Interest

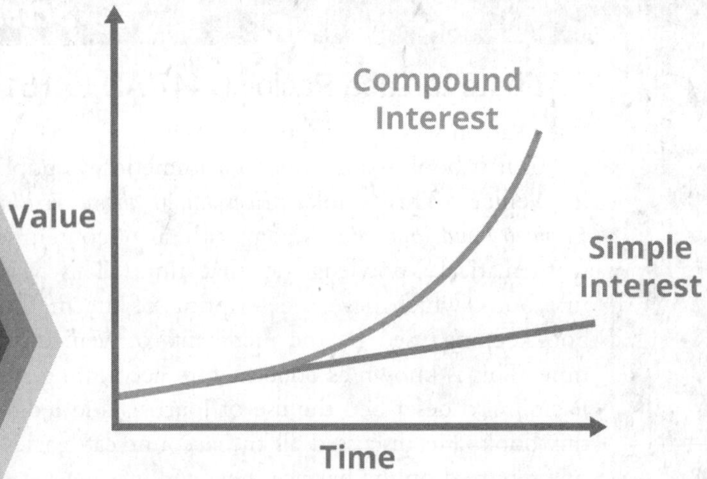

Remember

Before beginning this chapter, you should be able to:

- Calculate percentage
- Understand interest rates and time period
- Compute formulae for simple interest

Key Ideas

After completing this chapter, you should be able to:

- Review the concept of simple interest and solve word problems on it
- Learn practical applications of simple and compound interest
- Understand functions of compound interest and calculate compound interest
- Know about compounding more than a year

Scientific Crypt

A Tribute to Luca Pacioli (1447 AD to 1517 AD)

Luca Pacioli was born in Tuscany, Italy.

His first book – a treatise on arithmetic was published in Venice. This book, *'Everything about Arithmetic, Geometry and Proportion'* was a synthesis of contemporary mathematical knowledge at that time. This was the first book which gave a description of the method of bookkeeping used by the merchants of Venice at that time. This is known as double-entry accounting system. Pacioli also described the use of journals and ledgers in this book. He discussed all the account categories that one reported on the balance sheet and income statement of a business organisation. His methods are still followed. He is known as 'the father of Accounting', for his valuable contribution to the field.

In his book, *'De various quantitatis'*, he dealt with mathematical problems, puzzles and tricks.

He wrote about mathematical and artistic proportion, especially the mathematics of the golden ratio and its application in architecture, in his book, 'De divine proportions' The divine proportion. Among his students was Leonardo Da Vinci.

FUN TIME

CROSSWORD

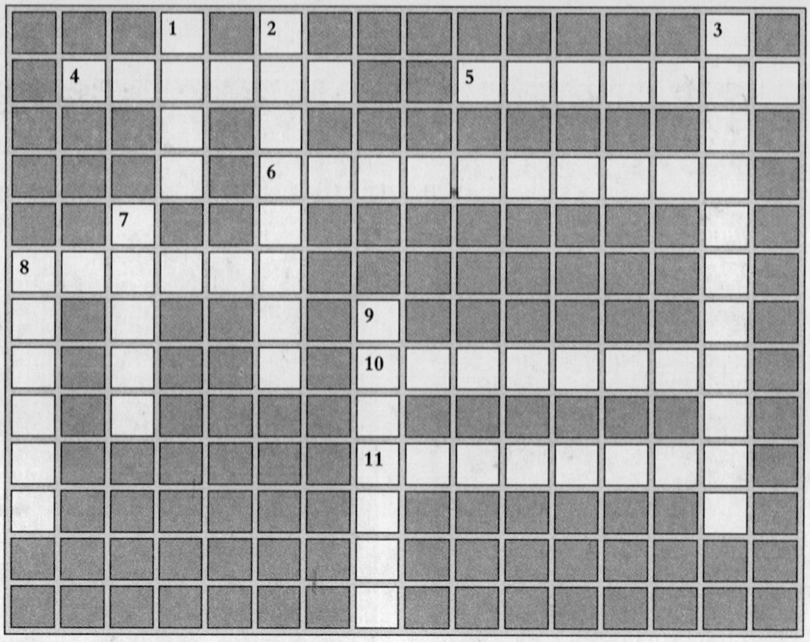

Across

4. CP < SP
5. For every hundred
6. The money arranged and used for setting up a company.
8. The bank on whom the cheque is drawn.
10. A person who pays income tax
11. Extra money paid to the lender by the borrower.

Down

1. CP > SP
2. Annual profit distributed among the shareholders.
3. The small amounts we pay in instalment scheme.
7. The party to whom the amount on the cheque is payable.
8. The account holder who writes the cheques.
9. Total money required to start a business.

INTRODUCTION

In this chapter, Simple interest is based on the principal amount of a loan or deposit, while compound interest is based on the principal amount and the interest that accumulates on it in every period. Since simple interest is calculated only on the principal amount of a loan or deposit, it's easier to determine than compound interest.

Simple Interest

Interest is paid to the lender by the borrower for using money for a specified period of time. Various terms and their general representations are as follows:

1. **Principal:** The original sum borrowed and denoted by P (expressed in rupees).
2. **Time:** The time for which money is borrowed. It is denoted by N (N is expressed in number of periods, which is normally one year).
3. **Rate:** The rate at which interest is calculated on the original sum. It is denoted by R (calculated per 100 per year).
4. **Amount:** The sum of principal and interest. It is denoted by A.

When interest is calculated every year (or every time period) on the original principal, i.e., the sum at the beginning of the first year, such interest is called **simple interest**. Here, year after year, even though the interest gets accumulated and is due to the lender, this accumulated interest is not taken into account for the purpose of calculating interest for the later years.

Simple interest $= \dfrac{PNR}{100}$; where P, N and R are explained above.

Total amount, $A = P + \dfrac{PNR}{100} = P\left(1 + \dfrac{NR}{100}\right)$.

Info Bytes!

In Simple Interest, amount is calculated by adding the variables with principal -> Arithmetic Progression

Compound Interest

In compound interest, the interest is added to the principal at the end of each period to arrive at the new principal for the next period.

In other words, the amount at the end of the first year (or period) will become the principal for the second year (or period); the amount at the end of the second year (or period) becomes the principal for the third year (or period), and so on.

If P denotes the principal at the beginning of period 1, then

P at the beginning of year $2 = P\left(1 + \dfrac{r}{100}\right) = PR$.

P at the beginning of year $3 = P\left(1 + \dfrac{r}{100}\right)^2 = PR^2$.

P at the beginning of year $(n+1) = P\left(1 + \dfrac{r}{100}\right)^n = PR^n$; where $R = \left\{1 + \left(\dfrac{r}{100}\right)\right\}$.

Hence, the amount after n years (or periods) $= PR^n = A$.

Interest $= I = A - P = P[R^n - 1]$.

Info Bytes!

In Compound Interest, amount is calculated by multiplying the variables with principal -> Geometric Progression

EXAMPLE 4.1 Find the simple interest on a sum of ₹1000 at an interest rate of 6% per annum, for a period of 6 years.

SOLUTION

The formula for simple interest is $I = \frac{PNR}{100}$; where principal P = ₹1000; rate of interest R = 6%, and number of years N = 6.

$SI = \frac{1000 \times 6 \times 6}{100} = ₹360.$

EXAMPLE 4.2 A sum becomes four times itself in 5 years at simple interest. In how many years will the same sum become sixteen times itself at the same rate.

SOLUTION

Given, $A = 4P$.

We know that $A = P + I$

$4p = P + I$

$3P = I$

$S.I = \frac{PTR}{100}$

$3P = \frac{P \times 5 \times R}{100}$

$\Rightarrow \frac{300}{5} = R$

Given, the same sum becomes sixteen times itself.

i.e, $A = 16P$

$A = P + I$

$16\,P = P + I$

$\Rightarrow I = 15P$

$S.I = \frac{P \times T \times R}{100}$

$15P = \frac{P \times T \times R}{100} \times \frac{300}{5}$

T = 25 years.

The following table gives an example of how simple interest and compound interest operate, i.e., how the principal is for various years under simple interest and compound interest. A principal at the beginning of 1st year, of ₹100 and a rate of 10% per annum are considered. The details are worked out for three years and shown below:

(All figures pertaining to principal, interest and amount are in rupees)

	Under Simple Interest				Under Compound Interest			
Year	Principal at the Begining of the Year (₹)	Interest for the Year (₹)	Interest till the End of the Year (₹)	Amount at the End of the Year (₹)	Principal at the Begining of the Year (₹)	Interest for the Year (₹)	Interest till the End of the Year (₹)	Amount at the End of the Year (₹)
1	100	10	10	110	100	10	10	110
2	100	10	20	120	110	11	21	121
3	100	10	30	130	121	12.1	33.1	133.1

As we observe in the table:

In case of simple interest,

- The principal remains same every year.
- The interest for any year is same as that for any other year.

In case of compound interest,

- The amount at the end of a year is the principal for the next year.
- The interest for different years is not the same.

The compound interest for the first year (where compounding is done every year) is the same as simple interest for one year.

EXAMPLE 4.3 Mr. Reddy wants to borrow ₹9000 at 10% simple interest and lend the same amount at compound interest at same rate of interest for two years. What would be his income in the above transaction?

SOLUTION

Let P = ₹90000

R = 10%

T = 2 years

$$\text{Difference} = P\left(\frac{R}{100}\right)^2 = ₹9000\left[\frac{10}{100}\right]^2 = ₹90.$$

EXAMPLE 4.4 A certain sum lent for a period of $2\frac{1}{2}$ years under simple interest at 9% per annum earned an interest of ₹234. From the following options, find the sum that was lent.

(a) ₹960 **(b)** ₹1040 **(c)** ₹1246 **(d)** ₹1146

SOLUTION

$$\frac{PNR}{100} = 1$$

$$\frac{P \times \frac{5}{2} \times 9}{100} = 234$$

$$\Rightarrow \frac{P \times 45}{200} = 234$$

$$\Rightarrow P = \frac{234 \times 200}{45}$$

$$\therefore P = ₹1040.$$

Compounding More Than Once a Year

We just looked at calculating amount and interest when compounding is done once in a year. But, compounding can also be done for multiple times in a year. For example, interest can be added to the principal in every six months or every four months, and so on.

If interest is added to the principal in every six months, we say that compounding is done twice a year. If interest is added to the principal in every four months, we say that compounding is done thrice a year. If interest is added to the principal in every three months, we say that compounding is done four times a year.

The formula that we have discussed above for calculating the amount will essentially be the same,

That is, Amount $= P\left(1+\frac{r}{100}\right)^n$, but the rate ($r$) will not be for one year but for the time period over which compounding is done and the power to which the term inside the bracket is raised (n in the above case) will not be the number of years, but the number of years multiplied by the number of times compounding is done per year (this product is referred to as the total number of time periods).

For example, if a sum of ₹10,000 is lent at the rate of 10% per annum and compounding is done in every four months (thrice a year), then the amount for two years will be equal to:

$$10,000\left(1+\frac{10}{3}\times\frac{1}{100}\right)^{2\times 3}$$

Here, the dividing factor of 3 in the rate and the multiplying factor of 3 in the exponent (multiplying the number of years)—both shown by arrow marks—are nothing, but the number of times compounding is done in a year.

If compounding is done k times a year (i.e., once in every $\frac{12}{k}$ months), at the rate of r% per annum, then in n years the principal (P) will amount to $= P\left(1+\frac{r}{k\times 100}\right)^{kn}$.

When compounding is done more than once a year, the rate of interest given in the problem is called nominal rate of interest.

We can also calculate the rate of interest which will yield simple interest in one year equal to the interest obtained under the compound interest at the given nominal rate of interest. The rate of interest so calculated is called effective rate of interest.

The following points helpful in solving problems should also be noted.

The difference between compound interest and simple interest on a certain sum for two years is equal to the interest calculated for one year on one year's simple interest.

In mathematical terms, the difference between compound interest and simple interest for two years will be equal to $P(r/100)^2$, which can be written as $P(r/100)\ (r/100)$. In this, $P\left(\frac{r}{100}\right)$ is the simple interest for one year. When this is again multiplied by $r/100$, it gives interest for one year on $Pr/100$, i.e., interest for one year on one year's simple interest.

The difference between the compound interest for k years and the compound interest for $(k + 1)$ years is the interest for one year on the amount at the end of kth year.

This can also be expressed as follows:

The difference between the amount for k years and the amount for $(k + 1)$ years under compound interest is the interest for one year on the amount at the end of the kth year.

The difference between the compound interest for the kth year and the compound interest for the $(k + 1)$th year is equal to the interest for one year on the compound interest for the kth year.

EXAMPLE 4.5 The value of a machine depreciates at the rate of 7.5% p.a. every year. What was the value of the machine two years ago, if it's present value is ₹1711.25?

SOLUTION

Given, $P\left(1-\frac{r}{100}\right)^n = 1711.25$

$$P\left(1-\frac{7.5}{100}\right)^2 = 1711.25$$

$$P\left(1-\frac{7.5}{100}\right)^2 = \frac{1711.25}{100}$$

$$P\left(\frac{925}{1000}\right)\left(\frac{925}{1000}\right) = \frac{171125}{100}$$

$$P = \frac{171125\times 1000\times 1000}{925\times 925\times 100}$$

$P =$ ₹2000.

EXAMPLE 4.6 A sum becomes twice itself at compound interest in six years. In how many years will the same become sixteen times itself?

SOLUTION

A sum becomes doubled itself at compound interest in six years.

Given, A = 2P

$$P\left(1+\frac{r}{100}\right)^n = A$$

$$P\left(1+\frac{r}{100}\right)^6 = 2P$$

$$\left(1+\frac{r}{100}\right)^6 = 2$$

$$\left(\left(1+\frac{r}{100}\right)^6\right)^4 = (2)^4$$

$$\left(1+\frac{r}{100}\right)^{24} = 16 \Rightarrow P\left(1+\frac{r}{100}\right)^{24} = 16P$$

∴ In 24 years the sum will become sixteen times itself.

EXAMPLE 4.7

The difference between simple interest and compound interest on ₹40000 at the end of two years is ₹400. The rate of interest is same in both the cases. What is the rate of interest?

SOLUTION

$$CI - SI = P\left(\frac{R}{100}\right)^2$$

$$400 = 40000\left(\frac{R}{100}\right)^2$$

$$R^2 = 100$$

$$\Rightarrow R = 10.$$

EXAMPLE 4.8

The population of certain type of bacteria grows at 4%, 5%, and 8% during first, second and third years, respectively. Find the population of the bacteria after 3 years, if the present population is 100,000.

SOLUTION

$$A = P\left(1+\frac{r_1}{100}\right)\left(1+\frac{r_2}{100}\right)\left(1+\frac{r_3}{100}\right)$$

$$A = 100{,}000\left(1+\frac{4}{100}\right)\left(1+\frac{5}{100}\right)\left(1+\frac{8}{100}\right)$$

$$A = 100{,}000\left[\frac{26}{25}\right]\left(\frac{21}{20}\right)\left(\frac{27}{25}\right) \Rightarrow A = 117{,}936.$$

∴ The population of the bacteria after 3 years is 117,936.

EXAMPLE 4.9

A man borrowed ₹10,000 at 12% per annum, interest compounded quarterly. Find the amount that he has to pay after 9 months.

SOLUTION

$P = ₹10{,}000$

Rate = 12% per annum

Rate $= \frac{12}{4}$% per quarter

Time period = 9 months

$$\therefore\ n = \frac{9}{3} = 3$$

$$A = 10{,}000\left(1+\frac{3}{100}\right)^3$$

$$= 10{,}000 \times \frac{103}{100} \times \frac{103}{100} \times \frac{103}{100} = ₹10{,}927.27.$$

EXAMPLE 4.10

Find the compound interest on ₹50,000 for 3 years, compounded annually, and the rate of interest being 10%, 12%, and 15% for the three successive years, respectively.

SOLUTION

$$A = P\left(1+\frac{r_1}{100}\right)\left(1+\frac{r_2}{100}\right)\left(1+\frac{r_3}{100}\right)$$

$$A = 50{,}000\left(1+\frac{10}{100}\right)\left(1+\frac{12}{100}\right)\left(1+\frac{15}{100}\right)$$

$$A = 50{,}000\left(\frac{11}{10}\right)\left(\frac{112}{100}\right)\left(\frac{115}{100}\right)$$

$A = ₹70,840.$

$\therefore$ CI $= A - P =$ ₹20,840.

EXAMPLE 4.11

Two persons P and Q lent certain amounts at the same rate of interest for 2 years and 3 years, respectively, under compound interest. If their final amounts are in the ratio of 3 : 5, Q's amount at the end of the first year being ₹8500 and P earned an interest of ₹510 for the first year, then find the ratio of their principals.

(a) 33 : 50 **(b)** 27 : 47 **(c)** 35 : 61 **(d)** 22 : 51

SOLUTION

P_1, P_2 are the principals of P and Q.

$$\frac{P_1\left(1+\frac{R}{100}\right)^2}{P_2\left(1+\frac{R}{100}\right)^3} = \frac{3}{5}$$

$$\Rightarrow \frac{P_1}{P_2\left(1+\frac{R}{100}\right)} = \frac{3}{5} \Rightarrow \frac{P_1}{8500} = \frac{3}{5}$$

$$\Rightarrow \quad P_1 = 5100.$$

$$\frac{P_1 \times 1 \times R}{100} = 510$$

$$\Rightarrow \frac{5100 \times R}{100} = 510$$

$$R = 10\%$$

$$\Rightarrow P_2\left(1+\frac{R}{100}\right) = 8500.$$

$$\Rightarrow P_2\left(1+\frac{10}{100}\right) = 8500 \Rightarrow P_2 \times \frac{11}{10} = 8500$$

$$\Rightarrow P_2 = 8500 \times \frac{10}{11}.$$

$$\therefore P_1 : P_2 = 5100 : 8500 \times \frac{10}{11}$$

$$= 3 : \frac{50}{11} = 33 : 50.$$

EXAMPLE 4.12

The difference between simple interest and compound interest on a sum of ₹20,000 for two years is ₹112.50. What is the annual rate of interest? Choose the correct answer from the following options:

(a) 6% **(b)** 7.5% **(c)** 8.5% **(d)** 8%

SOLUTION

The difference between simple interest and compound interest on a sum (x) $= x\left(\frac{r}{100}\right)^2$.

Therefore, $20{,}000\left(\frac{r}{100}\right)^2 = 112.5$

$$\left(\frac{r}{100}\right)^2 = \frac{112.5}{20{,}000} \Rightarrow \left(\frac{r}{100}\right)^2 = 0.005625 \Rightarrow \left(\frac{r}{100}\right) = 0.075$$

$$\therefore r = 7.5\%$$

EXAMPLE 4.13 Ravi borrowed ₹15,000 at the rate of 15% per annum for 2 years under simple interest. As he could not repay the loan after two years, the moneylender increased the rate of interest to 20% per annum for the further period. If Ravi wants to repay the entire amount at the end of a total period of 3 years and 4 months, then how much he has to pay (in ₹)?

(a) 24,500 **(b)** 24,000 **(c)** 23,500 **(d)** 23,000

SOLUTION

Case 1: For the first two years

$P = 15{,}000$, $R = 15\%$, $T = 2$

$$I = \frac{15{,}000 \times 15 \times 2}{100} = ₹4500.$$

Case 2: For the remaining time period

$P = 15{,}000$, $R = 20\%$, $T = 16$ months

$$\Rightarrow I = \frac{15{,}000 \times 20 \times \frac{16}{12}}{100} \quad \Rightarrow I = \frac{15{,}000 \times 20 \times 16}{1200} = ₹4000.$$

∴ Total amount that Ravi has to pay =15,000 + 4500 + 4000 = ₹23,500.

POINTS TO REMEMBER

- ✔ The sum at the beginning of the first year, such interest is called simple interest.
- ✔ Simple Interest $= \frac{PNR}{100}$; where P, N and R are principal, time and rate of interest respectively.
- ✔ Total amount, $A = P + \frac{PNR}{100} = P\left(1 + \frac{NR}{100}\right)$.
- ✔ In compound interest, the interest is added to the principal at the end of each period to arrive at the new principal for the next period.
- ✔ P at the beginning of year $(n + 1)$ = $P\left(1 + \frac{r}{100}\right)^n = PR^n$; where $R = \left\{1 + \left(\frac{r}{100}\right)\right\}$.
- ✔ The amount after n years (or periods) $= PR^n = A$.
- ✔ Interest = I = A − P = $P[R^n - 1]$.
- ✔ If compounding is done k times a year (i.e., once in every $\frac{12}{k}$ months), at the rate of r% per annum, then in n years the principal (P) will amount to $= P\left(1 + \frac{r}{k \times 100}\right)^{kn}$.
- ✔ The difference between the amount for k years and the amount for $(k + 1)$ years under compound interest is the interest for one year on the amount at the end of the kth year.
- ✔ The difference between the compound interest for the kth year and the compound interest for the $(k + 1)$th year is equal to the interest for one year on the compound interest for the kth year.

PRACTICE QUESTIONS CLASSROOM WING

Very Short Answer Type Questions

Directions of questions from 1 to 3:
State whether the following statements are true or false

1. The difference between the compound interest for the $(p + 1)$th year and compound interest for $(p + 2)$th year is equal to the interest for one year on the compound interest for the $(p + 1)$th year. (True/False)
2. Compound interest for one year on ₹500 calculated half yearly at 20% per annum is ₹100. (True/False)
3. The difference between the compound interest and the simple interest on a certain sum for 2 years is equal to the interest calculated for 1 year on one year's simple interest. (True/False)

Directions of questions from 4 to 22:
Answer the following questions.

4. Bank P provides loan at 10% per annum simple interest, and bank Q provides loan at 20% per annum simple interest. Vinay borrowed ₹1000 for 2 years from bank P, Kumar borrowed ₹1000 for 2 years from bank Q. How much extra interest does Kumar have to pay?
5. Find the compound interest on ₹5000 at 10% per annum for 1 year, interest compounded annually?
6. A certain sum doubles in 3 years under simple interest. In how many years will the sum become 5 times itself?
7. If a certain sum becomes 3 times itself in 4 years at compound interest, in how many years will the sum become 81 times itself at the same rate of interest?
8. Farheen borrowed a sum of ₹18,000 at the rate of 20% per annum, interest compounded semi-annually. Find the amount and compound interest for a period of $1\frac{1}{2}$ years.
9. Find the rate of simple interest per annum, if the sum borrowed becomes 3 times itself in 12 years.
10. Find the simple interest on ₹5600 at 20% per annum from May 22 to November 5 of the same year.
11. If ₹6000 becomes ₹6720 in 2 years at simple interest, how much does a sum of ₹10,000 become in 5 years at the same rate of simple interest?
12. The compound interest for 2 years and simple interest for 1 year on a certain sum at certain rate of interest are ₹3780 and ₹1800, respectively. Find the principal amount and interest rate.
13. The compound interest on a certain sum at a certain rate of interest for the 2nd year is ₹720, and for the 3rd year is ₹864. Find the principal and rate of interest.
14. The compound interest on ₹1000 is ₹331 for 3 years at certain rate of interest. What is the rate of interest?
15. If ₹6000 is lent at 10% per annum, interest being compounded annually, then what is the interest for the 3rd year?
16. What sum would amount to ₹17,280 in 3 years, at an interest of 20% per annum rate, interest compounded annually?
17. Shyam borrowed ₹18,000 at 15% per annum at compound interest compounded annually. He repaid ₹10,700 at the end of the 1st year. What is the amount he should pay at the end of 2nd year to completely disburse the loan?
18. Rajesh borrows ₹50,000 at simple interest, but the rate of interest is not constant for the entire period. For the first three years it is 10% per annum, for the next two years it is 5% per annum and for next three years it is 8% per annum. He repaid the entire amount after 8 years. How much he have to repay to clear the debt?
19. Janardhan deposited a certain sum of money in fixed deposit account at k% per annum interest being compounded annually. If the amount of interest accrued for the 3rd and the 4th years is ₹5000 and ₹6250, respectively, what is the total interest accrued for the first two years?
20. The difference between compound interest at 10% per annum and simple interest at 8% per annum on a certain sum for 3 years is ₹910. Find the sum.
21. Find the simple interest on ₹3750 at $5\frac{1}{2}$% per annum for the period beginning 3rd February 2007 to 29th June 2007.
22. A sum at $12\frac{1}{2}$% per annum amounts to ₹8723 in 5 years at simple interest. Find the sum.

Short Answer Type Questions

23. The population of a town increases at the rate of 5% every year. Find the population of the town in the year 2008, if it's population in 2005 was 200,000.

24. Suman borrowed ₹8000 from Mahesh at 20% per annum at simple interest. After 3 years when Suman wanted to clear the debt, Mahesh insisted to pay the amount at compound interest. How much more Suman have to pay?

25. Jahangir borrowed ₹80,000 at the rate of 7% per annum at compound interest, interest being compounded annually. How much should he repay at the end of the first year, so that by repaying ₹48,792 at the end of second year he can clear the loan?

26. Sunil borrowed a certain sum from a moneylender under compound interest, interest being annually. If the interest for the 2nd year is 2 times the interest for the first year, then what is the rate of interest?

27. The compound interest is earned on a sum of money at a rate of 8% per annum for the first year and 10% per annum for the second year. Find the single equivalent rate of interest on the sum for the two years.

28. Akhil invested ₹8000 in a bank, which pays compound interest, compounded semi-annually. He receives ₹9261 after 18 months from the bank. Find the rate of interest per annum.

29. A moneylender found that a fall in the annual rate of simple interest from 7% to 6% resulted in his amount of income being reduced by ₹212.50. Find his capital. (in ₹)

30. A sum doubles itself in 4 years at simple interest. How many times will it amount in 8 years at the same rate of simple interest?

31. Mahesh deposited ₹5000 in Syndicate Bank for 6 months. If the bank pays compound interest at 12% per annum, reckoned quarterly, find the interest received by him.

32. The difference between SI and CI (compounded annually) on a sum of ₹64,000 for 2 years is ₹1000. What is the rate of interest per annum?

33. A sum of ₹150 is borrowed at simple interest at 4% per annum for the first month, 8% per annum for the second month, 12% per annum for the third month, and so on. What is the total amount of interest to be paid at the end of 6 months?

34. The difference between the CI and SI on a sum of ₹7200 for two years is ₹72. Find the rate of interest per annum.

35. Roja invested ₹6000 in a bank, which paid compound interest, interest being compounded semi-annually. She received ₹10,368 after 18 months from the bank. Find the rate of interest. (per annum)

36. A sum of ₹40 is borrowed at simple interest. It is borrowed at 2% per annum for the first month, 4% per annum for the second month, 6% per annum for the third month, and so on. What is the total interest to be paid at the end of 6 months? (in ₹)

Essay Type Questions

37. A certain sum of money at simple interest increases by 50% in 5 years. What will be the compound interest, compounded annually on ₹13,000 for 3 years at the same rate?

38. A sum of ₹100,000 amounts to ₹171,600 in 3 years under compound interest, interest being compounded annually. It is lent at 10% per annum for the first year, 20% per annum for the second year and x% per annum for the third year. Find x.

39. Two persons each lent ₹2000 at simple interest for 2 years. The difference between the simple interests received by them is ₹20. Find the difference between the rates of interest.

40. P and Q borrowed ₹600 each for a period of 3 years. P paid simple interest at 25% per annum while Q paid compound interest at 20% per annum, interest being compounded annually. Who paid more interest and by how much?

41. What is the ratio of compound interest accrued on a certain sum in two years at 20% per annum to the compound interest accrued on the same amount in three years at 10% per annum?

PRACTICE QUESTIONS COMPETITION WING

Level 1: Apply Your Concepts

Directions of questions from 1 to 5:
Fill in the blanks

1. Simple interest on a sum of ₹10,000 for 3 years at the rate of 20% per annum is ______.
2. ______ time will a sum become three times itself at 20% per annum, at simple interest.
3. A certain sum becomes 16 times in 4 years at compound interest, compounded annually. The rate of interest is ______.
4. If compounding is done p times a year, at the rate of 5% per annum for n years, the principal x will amount to ______.
5. A certain sum amounts to ₹73,255 in 3 years, and ₹84,525 in 5 years at simple interest. The sum is ______.

Directions of questions from 6 to 59:
Select the correct alternative from the given choices.

6. A sum of money at simple interest amounts to ₹800 in 2 years and to ₹1200 in 6 years. The sum is ______.
   (a) ₹600 (b) ₹1000
   (c) ₹400 (d) ₹500
7. A certain sum of money becomes ₹2100 in 4 years and ₹2550 in 7 years. Find the rate of simple interest per annum.
   (a) 10% (b) 8%
   (c) 12% (d) 15%
8. There are three amounts a, b, and c, such that b is the simple interest on c and c is the simple interest on a. Which of the following must always be true?
   (a) $a^2 = bc$ (b) $b^2 = ac$
   (c) $c^2 = ab$ (d) $a^2 + b^2 = c^2$
9. If the compound interest on a certain sum at 8% per annum, interest compounded annually for 2 years is ₹2496, then find the simple interest on the same amount at the same rate and for the same period.
   (a) ₹2300 (b) ₹2450
   (c) ₹2400 (d) ₹2375
10. A sum of ₹22000 is divided into three parts such that the corresponding interests earned after 1 year at 2%, per annum, 4 years at 2% per annum and 16 years at 1% per annum simple interest are equal. Find the least of the sums which was lent. (in ₹)
   (a) 1000 (b) 2000
   (c) 5000 (d) 4000
11. A sum of ₹1750 is lent out at simple interest into two parts, the smaller part being lent at 7% per annum and the larger part at 5% per annum. If the total amount of interest in one year is ₹98, then find the part which was lent at 5% per annum.
   (a) ₹525 (b) ₹975
   (c) ₹1225 (d) ₹1350
12. A sum of money invested at compound interest doubles itself in six years. In how many years will it become 64 times itself at the same rate of compound interest?
   (a) 30 (b) 36
   (c) 42 (d) 48
13. Two equal sums are lent at simple interest. The first sum is recovered in 3 years and the second sum in 6 years. The rate of interest per annum on the first sum is 2% more than that of the second sum. Find the total sum lent if the amount in each case is ₹560.
   (a) ₹530 (b) ₹500
   (c) ₹1480 (d) ₹1000
14. A sum was borrowed at simple interest at R% per annum for 2 years. If it had been borrowed at $(R + 5)$% per annum, it would have become ₹200 more. Find the sum (in ₹).
   (a) 2500 (b) 2000
   (c) 3000 (d) 1500
15. The ratio of the interest accrued on a sum, when invested at simple interest for 2 years and the interest accrued on it, if it is invested at compound interest, interest being compounded annually for 3 years at the same rate of interest is 50 : 91. Find the rate of interest (per annum).
   (a) 10% (b) 15%
   (c) 25% (d) 20%
16. Two equal sums were lent at the same time at simple interest rates of 6% and 4% per annum. The first sum was recovered 2 years earlier than the second sum, and the amount in each case was ₹930. What was the sum lent?
   (a) ₹820 (b) ₹780
   (c) ₹690 (d) ₹750

17. A person invested three different amounts at 3%, 5% and 6% per annum at simple interest. At the end of the year, he received the same interest in each case. If the person's net investment is ₹4200, then the money invested at 5% is ______.
(a) ₹2000 (b) ₹1000
(c) ₹1500 (d) ₹1200

18. A sum of ₹3000 is lent out in two parts. The smaller part is lent at 10% per annum and the larger part is lent at 20% per annum. If the total interest in a year is ₹500, then find the sum lent at 10% per annum (in ₹).
(a) 800 (b) 1000
(c) 1200 (d) 900

19. The integral number of years in which a sum of money at 25% per annum under compound interest will become more than twice itself is at least.
(a) 3 (b) 2
(c) 4 (d) 1

20. Find the least integral number of years in which a sum at 20% per annum compound interest will be more than double.
(a) 4 (b) 5
(c) 3 (d) 6

21. A sum is split into two equal parts. One of the parts is lent at simple interest at 20% per annum for 6 years. The other part is lent at 40% per annum simple interest for 2 years. The difference in the interests is ₹72. Find the total sum (in ₹).
(a) 180 (b) 360
(c) 240 (d) 270

22. A sum is split into five equal parts. Each part is lent at annual rates of simple interests of 8%, 7%, 5%, 3%, and 2%. They are lent for 1 year, 2 years, 3 years, 4 years, and 5 years. On how many parts is the simple interest at least 25% of the total interest?
(a) 1 (b) 2
(c) 3 (d) 4

23. A sum of ₹2500 is split into two parts, one part being lent at simple interest and the other part being lent at compound interest, interest being compounded annually. At the end of two years, the total amount of interest earned on the sum is ₹201. Find the sum lent at simple interest, if both the parts are lent at an interest rate of 4% per annum.
(a) ₹1250 (b) ₹1625
(c) ₹1875 (d) ₹1500

24. A sum is split into five equal parts. They are lent at annual rates of simple interests of 1%, 2%, 3%, 10%, and 5%. They are lent for 6 years, 4 years, 3 years, 1 year and 1 year, respectively. The simple interest on how many parts is at least 20% of the total interest?
(a) 1 (b) 2
(c) 3 (d) 4

25. Sreedhar borrowed ₹3500 at 6% per annum for 3 years under simple interest. But, after one year he was asked to pay compound interest for the remaining two years on the sum borrowed initially. How much additional interest Sreedhar has to pay?
(a) ₹10 (b) ₹14.50
(c) ₹12.60 (d) ₹12

26. Ajay borrowed ₹4000 at 10% per annum for 4 years under simple interest. But, after 2 years he was asked to pay compound interest for the remaining 2 years on the initially borrowed amount. How much Ajay have to pay additionally if interest was compounded annually? (in₹)
(a) 40 (b) 20
(c) 80 (d) 160

27. A sum of ₹10,500 is divided into two parts *X* and *Y*, such that the interest calculated on *X* for 4 years is equal to the interest on *Y* for 6 years. If the rates of interest on *X* and *Y* are 8% and 4%, respectively, then find the larger part between *X* and *Y*.
(a) ₹5000 (b) ₹6000
(c) ₹6500 (d) ₹7000

28. A sum of ₹62,000 is divided into three parts such that the corresponding interests earned for 3 years, 5 years and 6 years are equal. If the rates of simple interest are 5% per annum, 4% per annum and 3% per annum, then what is the greatest of the sums that were lent?
(a) ₹18,000 (b) ₹22,000
(c) ₹24,000 (d) ₹26,000

29. The difference between the compound interest on a sum of ₹4000, interest being compounded annually and the simple interest on it for two years is ₹250. Find the rate of interest (per annum).
(a) 15% (b) 10%
(c) 25% (d) 20%

30. A sum of ₹4000 is split into two parts. One part is lent at simple interest and the other at compound interest, interest being compounded annually. At the end of two years, the total amount of interest earned is ₹1720. Find the sum lent at simple interest, if each part is lent at 20% per annum (in ₹).
(a) 1200 (b) 1000
(c) 800 (d) 1500

Level 2: Review Your Concepts

31. A sum of ₹1500 amounts to ₹1680 in 3 years at simple interest. If the interest rate is increased by 2%, it would amount to ______.
(a) ₹1770 (b) ₹1815
(c) ₹1590 (d) ₹1850

32. A sum of money doubles itself in 3 years. At same rate of simple interest, for a period of 9 years, how many times will the sum become?
(a) 4 (b) 6
(c) 8 (d) 9

33. Due to a fall in the annual rate of interest from 6% to 5%, a person's yearly income reduces by ₹245.25. His capital is ______.
(a) ₹24,525 (b) ₹24,600
(c) ₹23,675 (d) ₹24,000

34. The cost of a television is ₹15625. Its value depreciates at the rate of 8% per annum. Calculate the total depreciation in its value at the end of 3 years.
(a) ₹3458 (b) ₹3748
(c) ₹3548 (d) ₹3845

35. The value of an ornament decreases every year at the rate of 5% over that of the previous year. If its value at the end of 2 years is ₹9025, then what was its original value at the beginning of these two years?
(a) ₹12,000 (b) ₹11,000
(c) ₹10,000 (d) ₹13,000

36. A certain sum of money triples itself in 6 years at compound interest. In how many years will it become 27 times at the same rate of compound interest?
(a) 27 (b) 30
(c) 24 (d) 18

37. A sum of ₹24,000 is divided into two parts P_1 and P_2, such that the simple interest calculated on P_1 for 3 years and on P_2 for 4 years are equal. If the rates of interest on P_1 and P_2 are 4% and 5%, respectively, then find the smaller of the parts P_1 and P_2.
(a) ₹10,000 (b) ₹12,000
(c) ₹8000 (d) ₹9000

38. A certain sum of money amounts to ₹4200 in 3 years and to ₹6000 in 6 years at simple interest. Find the rate of interest.
(a) $12\frac{1}{2}\%$ (b) 20%
(c) 25% (d) 30%

39. A sum of money becomes four times itself in 5 years at a certain rate of interest, compounded annually. In how many years will it become 16 times itself at the same rate of interest?
(a) 20 (b) 16
(c) 12 (d) 10

40. The difference between simple interest and compound interest on a sum of ₹40,000 for two years is ₹900. What is the annual rate of interest?
(a) 20% (b) 10%
(c) 12% (d) 15%

41. The difference between the compound interest (compounded annually) and simple interest, for two years on the same sum at the amount rate of interest is ₹370. Find the rate of interest if the simple interest on the amount at the same rate of interest for 1 year is ₹3700.
(a) 10% (b) 12%
(c) 16% (d) 15%

42. A certain sum amounts to ₹13,310 after 3 years and to ₹16,105.10 after 5 years under compound interest. Find the sum borrowed, if the interest is compounded annually (in ₹).
(a) 12,000 (b) 8,000
(c) 10,000 (d) 16,000

43. A certain sum amounts to ₹77,000 in 5 years and to ₹68,200 in 3 years, under simple interest. If the rate of interest is increased by 2%, then in how many years will it double itself?
(a) 8 (b) 9
(c) 10 (d) 12

44. Find the compound interest on ₹40,000 at 12% per annum for a period of 2 years. (in ₹)
(a) 10,176 (b) 8000
(c) 9176 (d) 10,000

45. A person borrowed a certain sum at 25% per annum compound interest (compounded annually) and paid ₹10,000 at the end of 4 years. Find the sum borrowed.
(a) ₹4096 (b) ₹5000
(c) ₹5016 (d) ₹4960

46. Find the amount on the sum of ₹15,625 for 18 months under compound interest, compounded half yearly at the rate of 16% per annum.
(a) ₹19,683 (b) ₹19,625
(c) ₹20,504 (d) ₹19,625

Level 3: Assess Your Concepts

47. Rakesh borrowed ₹42,000 from Rajnikant at 6% per annum simple interest. He lent the same sum to Kishore at 10% per annum compound interest, compounded annually, for 2 years. Find the amount earned by Rakesh in the transaction.
(a) ₹3614 (b) ₹3550
(c) ₹3610 (d) ₹3780

48. A certain sum amounts to ₹7935 in 2 years and ₹9125.25 in 3 years, under compound interest. Find the sum borrowed if interest is compounded annually (in ₹).
(a) 6000 (b) 7500
(c) 8000 (d) 10,000

49. Ravi lent Ramu a certain sum of money at the rate of $2\frac{1}{2}\%$ per annum, interest compounded annually. After two years, Ramu paid a sum of ₹2560 to Ravi. What amount of money did Ramu borrow from Ravi?
(a) ₹2036.64 (b) ₹2236.64
(c) ₹2436.64 (d) ₹2636.64

50. In how many years will a sum of ₹25,600, interest compounded quarterly, at the rate of 25% per annum, amount to ₹28,900?
(a) 1 (b) $\frac{1}{2}$
(c) 2 (d) 4

51. The value of an old bike decreases every year at the rate of 4% over that of the previous year. If its value at the end of three years is ₹13824, then find its present value.
(a) ₹15,625 (b) ₹14,525
(c) ₹16,625 (d) ₹15,425

52. At compound interest of 8%, 10%, and 12% for three consecutive years, the interest earned in the 3rd year is ₹891. Find the principal amount (in ₹).
(a) 6250 (b) 6050
(c) 6200 (d) 6225

53. A certain amount of money doubles in 4 years under compound interest. In how many additional years will it become 4 times of the principal amount under the same conditions.
(a) 8 (b) 4
(c) 12 (d) 16

54. A sum of money was lent in two parts which were in the ratio of 2 : 3 for 2 years and 3 years, respectively, both at the rate of 10% per annum at simple interest. If the difference between the interest earned is ₹6000, then find the total sum that was lent.
(a) ₹24,000 (b) ₹36,000
(c) ₹60,000 (d) ₹84,000

55. Find the amount on ₹9900 at 20% per annum for 2 years at compound interest (compounded annually).
(a) ₹12,946 (b) ₹13,548
(c) ₹14,256 (d) ₹15,678

56. Find the amount when ₹9999 is lent at simple interest for 3 years and 4 months at 10% per annum (in ₹).
(a) 13,332 (b) 12,332
(c) 12,232 (d) 13,333

57. The compound interest on a certain sum for 2 years is ₹882, whereas the simple interest on it is ₹840. Find the rate of interest.
(a) 10% (b) 12%
(c) 8% (d) 15%

58. A shop keeper purchased an article for ₹25000 on 17th Feb 2015. He marked the article 40% above the cost price. He could sell the article on 14th Dec 2015 by allowing a discount of 25%. Find the rate of interest yielded for the shop keeper under simple interest.
(a) 6.08% (b) 6%
(c) 6.8% (d) None

59. Ajay took a loan of ₹75000 from a bank at the rate of 12% p.a. and lent this money for 18% p.a. to Mr. Vijay. If the interest is calculated half yearly in both the cases, find the amount (approx.) earned by Mr. Ajay in $1\frac{1}{2}$ years.
(a) 7800 (b) 7000
(c) 7801 (d) None

AT

PRACTICE QUESTIONS JEE SPECIAL WING

Multiple-Answer Type Questions

Directions for questions 1 to 5:
Each question has FOUR options (a), (b), (c), and (d). ONE OR MORE THAN ONE of these four option(s) is/are the correct answer(s).

1. A certain sum doubles under simple interest. Which of the following is/are true about the given information?
   (a) Rate is $16\frac{2}{3}$% pa for 6 years.
   (b) Rate is 10% pa for 10 years.
   (c) Rate is $7\frac{1}{7}$% pa for 14 years.
   (d) Rate is 5% pa for 20 years.

2. A certain sum is invested at simple interest for 12 years at 7% pa. The interest for the first three years together is ₹3150. Which of the following is/are true about the given information?
   (a) The interest for the 11th and 12th years together is ₹2100.
   (b) The interest for the 4th, 5th, 6th, 7th and 8th years together is ₹5250.
   (c) The interest for the 9th year is ₹1150.
   (d) The interest for any four years is ₹4300.

3. A certain sum is invested at compound interest. The interest amounts earned for the first year and for the first two years are ₹4200 and ₹8736 respectively. Which of the following is/are true about the given information?
   (a) The rate of interest will be 10% pa.
   (b) The sum invested will be ₹52,500.
   (c) The rate of interest will be 8% pa.
   (d) The sum invested will be ₹42,000.

4. The value of a piece land appreciates by 15% pa. The present value of the land is ₹50,00,000. Which of the following is/are true about the given information?
   (a) The value of the land after 1 year is ₹57,50,000.
   (b) The value of the land after 2 years is ₹66,12,500.
   (c) The value of the land after 3 years is ₹76,04,375
   (d) The value of the land after 4 years is ₹87,50,625.

5. The value of a car depreciates by 10% pa. The value of the car one year ago was ₹9,00,000. Which of the following is/are true about the given information?
   (a) The present value of the car is ₹8,10,000.
   (b) The value of the car after 1 year will be ₹7,29,000.
   (c) The value of the car after 2 years will be ₹6,65,100.
   (d) The value of the car after 3 years will be ₹5,90,490.

Match The Column

Directions for questions 6 to 10:
Read the paragraph given below and answer the questions.
A person invested different amounts in different banks which pay compound interest compounding annually. He invested the amounts for two years.

Bank	Investment (In ₹)
P	4,60,000
Q	5,00,000
R	6,00,000
S	7,00,000
T	8,00,000

If he had invested the same amounts for the same period at same rates of interests, what would be the difference between the compound interests and the corresponding simple interests?

Match the values in Column A with those in Column B.

Column A (Bank: Rate of Interest pa)	Column B (CI – SI) (In ₹)
6. P: 8%	(a) 2957.5
7. Q: 7.5%	(b) 2944
8. R: 7%	(c) 2940
9. S: 6.5%	(d) 2925
10. T: 6%	(e) 2895
	(f) 2880
	(g) 2812.5

Assertion and Reason Type Questions

Directions for questions 11 to 15:
Read the paragraph given below and answer the questions.

(a) Both assertion (A) and reason (R) are true, and reason (R) is the correct explanation of the assertion.
(b) Both assertion (A) and reason (R) are true, and reason (R) is not the correct explanation of the assertion.
(c) Assertion (A) is true, but reason (R) is false.
(d) Assertion (A) is false, and reason (R) is true.

11. Assertion: A certain sum doubles in 20 years at 10% per annum, under simple interest.
Reason: Interest is the difference of the amount and principal. Also, interest $= \frac{\text{PTR}}{100}$.

12. Assertion: If a certain sum becomes ₹12,100 in one year at 10% pa under compound interest, then the same sum becomes ₹13,310 in two years at the same rate of interest.
Reason: Under compound interest, the amount is given by $A = P\left(1+\frac{R}{100}\right)^n$.

13. Assertion: On a certain sum and at a certain rate of interest pa for 1 year, the interest compounded half yearly is more than the interest compounded annually.
Reason: The compound interest is given by $A = P\left(1+\frac{R}{100}\right)^n$.

14. Assertion: If a certain sum triples in 6 years under compound interest, then the same sum at the same rate of interest becomes 27 times in 18 years.
Reason: Under compound interest, the amount is given by $A = P\left(1+\frac{R}{100}\right)^n$.

15. Assertion: Amith wants to borrow a certain amount from a money lender for three years. For the money lender, the compound interest is more beneficial when compared to the simple interest at the same rate of interest. Assuming both principal and interest are being paid at the end of three years.
Reason: The simple interest $= \frac{\text{PTR}}{100}$.

Comprehension-Based Questions

Directions for questions 16 to 20:
Read the options given below and answer the questions.
Kaushik took a loan of ₹2,00,000 for four years at compound interest, compounded annually. The rates of interests for the first, second, third and fourth year are x%, 6%, 8% and 10% respectively. The sum amounts to ₹2,10,000 in a year.

16. What is the value of x?
(a) 4 (b) 4.5
(c) 5 (d) 5.5

17. If the same sum is borrowed at x% p.a. for the entire period, what is the interest (approx.) paid by Kaushik?
(a) ₹40,000 (b) ₹41,205
(c) ₹42,500 (d) ₹43,101

18. If Kaushik pays ₹97,600 at the end of two years, what is the amount to be paid by Kaushik at the end of the fourth year?
(a) ₹1,36,000 (b) ₹1,45,625
(c) ₹1,48,500 (d) ₹1,52,000

19. If Kaushik pays ₹1,10,000 at the end of one year and the moneylender demands that he pay the remaining amount at the end of the fourth year at 10% pa, then what will be the interest paid by Kaushik for four years?
(a) ₹47,500 (b) ₹43,100
(c) ₹36,500 (d) ₹33,100

20. If Kaushik pays only interest at the end of each year, then what is the total interest paid by him?
(a) ₹58,000 (b) ₹45,000
(c) ₹40,000 (d) ₹33,000

ANSWER KEYS

Crossword

Across

4. Profit 5. Per cent 6. Investment 8. Drawee 10. Assessee
11. Interest

Down

1. Loss 2. Dividend 3. Instalments 7. Payee 8. Drawer
9. Capital

Classroom Wing

Very Short Answer Type Questions

1. True 2. False 3. False 4. ₹200 5. ₹500
6. 12 7. 16 years 8. ₹23,958, ₹5958 9. $16\frac{2}{3}$% per annum
10. ₹512.40 11. ₹13,000
12. $r = 10\%$ per annum
    Principal = ₹18,000
13. $r = 20\%$
    Principal = ₹3000
14. 10% per annum 15. ₹726 16. ₹10,000 17. ₹11,500 18. ₹82,000
19. ₹7200 20. ₹10,000 21. ₹82.50 22. ₹5,368

Short Answer Type Questions

23. 231,525 24. ₹1024 25. ₹40,000 26. 100% 27. 8.9%
28. 10% 29. 21250 30. 3 31. ₹304.50 32. $12\frac{1}{2}$%
33. ₹10.50 34. 10% 35. 40% 36. 1.40

Essay Type Questions

37. ₹4303 38. ₹30 39. 0.5%
40. P paid an additional amount of interest of ₹13.20 than Q 41. $\frac{440}{331}$

Competition Wing

Level 1: Apply Your Concepts

1. ₹6000 2. 10 years 3. 100% per annum 4. $x\left(1+\frac{5}{100p}\right)^{pn}$
5. ₹56,350 6. (a) 7. (a) 8. (c) 9. (c)
10. (b) 11. (c) 12. (b) 13. (d) 14. (b)
15. (d) 16. (d) 17. (d) 18. (b) 19. (c)
20. (a) 21. (b) 22. (a) 23. (c) 24. (c)
25. (c) 26. (a) 27. (b) 28. (c) 29. (c)
30. (b)

Level 2: Review Your Concepts

31. (a)	32. (a)	33. (a)	34. (a)	35. (c)
36. (d)	37. (d)	38. (c)	39. (d)	40. (d)
41. (a)	42. (c)	43. (c)	44. (a)	45. (a)
46. (a)				

Level 3: Assess Your Concepts

47. (d)	48. (a)	49. (c)	50. (b)	51. (a)
52. (a)	53. (a)	54. (c)	55. (c)	56. (a)
57. (a)	58. (a)	59. (c)		

JEE Special Wing

Multiple-Answer Type Questions

1. (a, b, c, d)	2. (a, b)	3. (b, c)	4. (a, b, c)	5. (a, b, d)

Match The Column

6. (b)	7. (g)	8. (c)	9. (a)	10. (f)

Assertion and Reason Type Questions

11. (d)	12. (a)	13. (c)	14. (a)	15. (b)

Comprehension-Based Questions

16. (c)	17. (d)	18. (c)	19. (b)	20. (a)

Hints and Explanations

Classroom Wing

Very Short Answer Type Questions

1. True

2. $P = ₹\ 500$
$r = 20\%$
$n = 2$
$t = 1$
$A = ₹\ 100$
$$A = P\left(1 + \frac{r}{100}\right)^n$$
$$= 500\left(1 + \frac{20}{200}\right)^{2\times1}$$
$$= 500\left(1 + \frac{1}{10}\right)^2$$
$$= 500\left(\frac{11}{10}\right)^2$$
$$= 500 \times \frac{121}{100}$$
$$= 605$$
CI = A – P = 605 – 500 = 105

3. The difference between the CI and SI on a certain sum for 2 years $= \frac{PR^2}{(100)^2}$
SI for 1 year $= \frac{PR}{100}$
Hence, not equal.

4. $P = ₹\ 1000$
$T = 2$ years
$R =$ 10% (Bank P) 20% (Bank Q)
$$SI = \frac{PTR}{100}$$
$$= \frac{1000 \times 2 \times 10}{100}$$
$$= 200$$
$$SI = \frac{1000 \times 2 \times 20}{100} = 400$$
400 – 200 = ₹ 200

5. $P = ₹\ 5000$
$R = 10\%$
$n = 1$
$T = 1$
$$A = 5000\left(1 + \frac{10}{100}\right)^1$$
$$= 5000 \times 1.1$$
$$= 5500$$
CI = A – P = 5550 – 5000 = 500

6. $$SI = \frac{PTR}{100}$$
$$A = SI + P$$
$$2P = \frac{P \times 3 \times R}{100} + P$$
$$P = \frac{3PR}{100}$$
$$R = 33.3\%$$
$$5P = \frac{P \times T \times 33.3}{100} + P$$
$$4P = PT\ (0.333)$$
$$T \simeq 12$$
$\therefore$ 12 Years

7. $$3P = P\left(1 + \frac{r}{100}\right)^4$$
$$3 = \left(1 + \frac{r}{100}\right)^4$$
$$81P = P\left(1 + \frac{r}{100}\right)^n$$
$$81 = \left(1 + \frac{r}{100}\right)^n$$
Comparing both equation
$n = 16$ years

8. $P = ₹18000$
$R = 20\%$
$n = 4$
$t = 1.5$ years = 18 months

$$A = 18000\left(1+\frac{20}{100\times 4}\right)^{4\times 1.5}$$

$$= 18000\left(1+\frac{1}{20}\right)^{6}$$

$$= 23958$$

CI = A – P = 23958 – 18000 = ₹5958

9. $A = SI + P$

$$3P = \frac{P\times 12\times R}{100} + P$$

$$2P = \frac{PR\times 12}{100}$$

$$\frac{2\times 100}{12} = R$$

$R = 16.667\%$

$R = 16\frac{2}{3}\%$

10. $SI = \frac{PTR}{100}$

$T = 167$ days

$$= \frac{5600\times 20\times \frac{167}{365}}{100}$$

$SI =$ ₹512.40

11. $720 = \frac{6000\times 2\times R}{100}$

$720 = 120 \times R$

$R = 6\%$

$$SI = \frac{10000\times 5\times 6}{100}$$

= ₹3000

Total sum = 10000+3000=13000

12. $\Rightarrow 3780 + P = P\left(1+\frac{180000}{P\times 100}\right)^2$

$$\Rightarrow 3780 + P = P\left(1+\frac{1800}{P}\right)^2$$

$$\Rightarrow 3780 + P = P\left(\frac{P+1800}{P}\right)^2$$

$$\Rightarrow 3780 + P = \frac{(P+1800)^2}{P}$$

$$\Rightarrow 3780P + \cancel{P^2} = \cancel{P^2} + 3240000 + 3600P$$

$$\Rightarrow 3780P - 3600P = 3240000$$

$$\Rightarrow 180P = 3240000$$

$\Rightarrow P =$ ₹18,000

$$\Rightarrow P = \frac{18.0000}{18000} = 10\%$$

Hence, $r = 10\%$, Principal = 18,000

13. Compound interest for 2nd year = 720

Compound interest for 3rd year 864

$$\text{Compound interest} = P\left(1+\frac{r}{100}\right)^n - P$$

Solving for $n = 2$ and $n = 3$.

On equating both equations,

$P = 3000$

Putting value of P in formula,

$r = 20\%$

14. $I = 331$

$P = 1000$

$T = 3$

$$1331 = 1000\left(1+\frac{R}{100}\right)^3$$

$$\sqrt[3]{\frac{1331}{1000}} = \left(1+\frac{R}{100}\right)$$

$$\frac{11}{10} = 1+\frac{R}{100}$$

$(0.1)\ 100 = R$

$R = 10\%$

15. $P = 6000$

$R = 10\%$

$T = 3$

$$A = 6000\left(1+\frac{10}{100}\right)^3$$

$$= 6000\left(1+\frac{1}{10}\right)$$

= ₹6600 (end of 1st year)

$$A = 6600\left(1+\frac{1}{10}\right)$$

= ₹ 7260 (end of 2nd year)

$$A = 7260\left(1+\frac{1}{10}\right)$$

= ₹7986 (end of 3rd year)

interest for 3rd year = ₹7986 – 7260 = ₹726

16. $A = P\left(1+\frac{20}{100}\right)^T$

$17280 = P\left(1+\frac{20}{100}\right)^3$

$17280 = P\,(1.728)$

$P = ₹10000$

17. $P = ₹18000$

$R = 15\%$

$A = 18000\left(1+\frac{15}{100}\right)$

$= ₹20700$

He paid ₹ 10700

$A = 10000\left(1+\frac{15}{100}\right) = 11500$

18. $P = ₹\ 50000$

$SI = \frac{PTR}{100}$

$= \frac{50000\times 3\times 10}{100}$

$= ₹15000$

$SI = \frac{50000\times 2\times 5}{100} = ₹\ 5000$

$SI = \frac{50000\times 3\times 8}{100} = ₹\ 12000$

Total amount to be paid after 8 yr = 82000

19. Let interest on 1st year = x

2nd year = y

$I = K\%$

$x = P\left[\left(1+\frac{K}{100}\right)-1\right]$

$= \frac{PK}{100}$ (1)

$y = (P+x)\left(1+\frac{K}{100}-1\right)$

$= (P+x)\frac{K}{100}$ (2)

$\Rightarrow x+y = \frac{PK}{100}+(P+x)\frac{K}{100}$

$= \frac{PK}{100}+\left(P+\frac{PK}{100}\right)\frac{K}{100}$

Similarly

$\Rightarrow 5000 = (P+x+y)\left(1+\frac{K}{100}-1\right)$

$= (P+x+y)\left(\frac{K}{100}\right)$ (3)

$6250 = (P+x+y+5000)\left(1+\frac{K}{100}-1\right)$

$= (P+x+y+5000)\frac{K}{100}$ (4)

on solving (4) – (3),

$1250 = (P+x+y+5000)\frac{K}{100}-(P+x+y)\left(\frac{K}{100}\right)$

$\Rightarrow 1250 = \frac{5000K}{100}$

$\Rightarrow K = \frac{1250\times 100}{5000} = 25\%$

$\Rightarrow x+y = \frac{P}{4}+\left(P+\frac{P}{4}\right).\frac{1}{4} = \frac{P}{4}+\frac{5P}{16} = \frac{9P}{16}$

Put the value of K and $(x+y)$ in (3).

$\therefore 5000 = \left(P+\frac{9P}{16}\right).\left(\frac{K}{4}\right)$

$\Rightarrow 5000 = \frac{25P}{64}$

$\Rightarrow P = \frac{5000\times 64}{25} = 12800$

Hence, $x+y = \frac{12800\times 25}{100}+\left(12800+12800\times\frac{25}{100}\right)\times\frac{25}{100}$

$= 3200+(16000)\times\frac{1}{4}$

$= 3200+4000$

$= 7200$

20. $P\left(1+\frac{10}{100}\right)^3 - P - \frac{P\times 3\times 8}{100} = 910$

$P\,(1.331) - P - P\,(0.24) = 910$

$P\,(0.91) = 910$

$P = 10000$

21. $P = 3750$

$R = 5.5\%$

$T = \frac{146}{365}$ yrs

$$SI = \frac{3750 \times 5.5 \times \frac{146}{365}}{100}$$

$= ₹\ 82.50$

22. $A = ₹8723$

$R = 12.5\%$

$T = 5$ yrs

$$SI = \frac{PTR}{100}$$

$$8723 - P = \frac{PTR}{100}$$

$$8723 - P = \frac{P \times 5 \times 12.5}{100}$$

$(1.625)\ P = 8723$

$P = ₹\ 5368$

Short Answer Type Question

23. $P = 200000$

$T = 3$ years

$R = 5\%$

$$A = 200000\left(1+\frac{5}{100}\right)^3$$

$= 200000\ (1.05)^3$

$= 231525$

24. $P = ₹\ 8000$

$T = 3$ years

$R = 20\%$

$$SI = \frac{8000 \times 3 \times 20}{100} = 4800$$

$$A = 8000\left(1+\frac{20}{100}\right)^3 = 13824$$

Interest $= 13824 - 8000 = 5824$

He has to pay $5824 - 4800 = ₹\ 1024$ extra.

25. $P = ₹\ 80000$

$R = 7\%$

$$A = 80000\left(1+\frac{7}{100}\right)$$

$= \mathbf{85600}$

$$48792 = P\left(1+\frac{7}{100}\right)$$

$P = 45600$

$85600 - 45600 = 40000$

26. CI after 1 year $= P\left[\left(1+\frac{r}{100}\right)-1\right] = \frac{PY}{100}$

A after 1 year $= P + CI = P + \frac{Pr}{100}$

CI for second year $= \left(P+\frac{Pr}{100}\right)P\left[\left(1+\frac{r}{100}\right)-1\right]$

$$= \left(P+\frac{Pr}{100}\right)\cdot\left(\frac{r}{100}\right)$$

According to question, $2\left(\frac{Pr}{100}\right) = \left(P+\frac{Pr}{100}\right)\cdot\frac{r}{100}$

$$\Rightarrow 2P = P + \frac{Pr}{100}$$

$$\Rightarrow P = \frac{Pr}{100}$$

$\Rightarrow r = 100\%$

27. Total amount after 2 year

$$= P\left(1+\frac{8}{100}\right)\left(1+\frac{10}{100}\right)$$

$$= P\left(\frac{108}{100}\right)\left(\frac{11}{10}\right)$$

$\therefore$ Total CI after 2 year $= A - P = \frac{1188P}{1000} - P$

$$CI = \frac{188P}{1000}$$

$$\Rightarrow P\left[\left(1+\frac{r}{100}\right)^2 - 1\right] = \frac{188P}{1000}$$

$$\Rightarrow \left(1+\frac{r}{100}\right)^2 = \frac{1188}{1000}$$

$$\Rightarrow 1+\frac{r}{100} = 1.089$$

$$\Rightarrow \frac{r}{100} = 0.89$$

$\Rightarrow r = 8.9\%$

28. $₹\ 8000 = P$

$n = 2$

$T = 18$ months

$A = ₹\ 9261$

$$9261 = 8000\left(1+\frac{R}{100\times 2}\right)^{1.5\times 2}$$

$$1.158 = \left(1+\frac{R}{200}\right)^3$$

$$1.05 = 1+\frac{R}{200}$$

$R \simeq 10\%$

29. $SI = \frac{PTR}{100}$

$$\frac{P\times 7}{100} - \frac{P\times 6}{100} = 212.50$$

$$\frac{P}{100}(1) = 212.50$$

$P = 212.50 \times 100$

$P = ₹\ 21250$

30. $A - P = \frac{PTR}{100}$

$$2P - P = \frac{P\times 4\times R}{100}$$

$$P = \frac{P\times 4\times R}{100}$$

$$\frac{100}{4} = R$$

$R = 25\%$

$$A - P = \frac{P\times 8\times 25}{100}$$

$x\,P - P = 2P$

$x\,P = 3P$

Hence, 3 times $x = 3$

31. $P = ₹\ 5000$

$R = 12\%$

$T = 6$ months

$n = 4$

$$R = \frac{12}{4} = 3\%$$

$$n = \frac{6}{3} = 2$$

$$A = 5000\left(1+\frac{3}{100}\right)^2$$

$A = 5000\ (1.03)^2$

$A = 5304.5$

Interest = 304.5

32. $CI - SI = 1000$

$$\Rightarrow 64000\left[\left(1+\frac{R}{100}\right)^2 - 1\right] - \frac{64000\times 2\times R}{100} = 1000$$

$$\Rightarrow 64000\left[\frac{(100+R)^2}{10000} - 1\right] - 1280R = 1000$$

$$\Rightarrow 64000\left(\frac{10000+R^2+200R-10000}{10000}\right) - 1280R = 1000$$

$$\Rightarrow \frac{64000}{10000}(R^2+200R) - 1280R = 1000$$

$$\Rightarrow 64R^2 + 12800R - 12800R = 10000$$

$$\Rightarrow 64R^2 = 10000$$

$$\Rightarrow R^2 = \frac{10000}{64}$$

$$\Rightarrow R = \frac{100}{8} = 12.5\% = 12\frac{1}{2}\%$$

33. $SI = \frac{PTR}{12}$

$$= \frac{150\times\frac{1}{12}\times 4}{100} \quad (1^{st}\ \text{month})$$

$= ₹\ 0.5$

$$= \frac{150\times\frac{1}{12}\times 8}{100} \quad (2^{nd}\ \text{month})$$

$= ₹\ 1$

$$= \frac{150\times\frac{1}{12}\times 12}{100} \quad (3^{rd}\ \text{month})$$

$= ₹\ 1.5$

$$= \frac{150\times\frac{1}{12}\times 16}{100} \quad (4^{th}\ \text{month})$$

$= ₹\ 2$

$$= \frac{150\times\frac{1}{12}\times 20}{100} \quad (5^{th}\ \text{month})$$

$= ₹\ 2.5$

$$= \frac{150\times\frac{1}{12}\times 24}{100} = 3 \quad (6^{th}\ \text{month})$$

Total I = ₹ 10.5

34. $CI - SI = 72$

$$\Rightarrow 7200\left[\left(1+\frac{R}{100}\right)^2 - 1\right] - \frac{7200 \times R \times 2}{100} = 72$$

$$\Rightarrow 7200\left[\frac{(100+R)^2}{10000} - 1\right] - 144R = 72$$

$$\Rightarrow 7200\left(\frac{10000 + R^2 + 200R - 10000}{10000}\right) - 144R = 72$$

$$\Rightarrow \frac{7200}{10000}(R^2 + 200R) - 144R = 72$$

$$\Rightarrow 72R^2 + 14400R - 14400R = 7200$$

$$\Rightarrow 72R^2 = 7200$$

$$\Rightarrow R^2 = 100$$

$$\Rightarrow R = 10\%$$

35. $P = ₹\ 6000$

$A = 10368$

$T = 18$ months

$n = 2$

$$A = P\left(1+\frac{R}{100n}\right)^{nt}$$

$$nt = 2 \times 1.5 = 3$$

$$10368 = 6000\left(1+\frac{R/2}{100}\right)^3$$

$R = 40\%$

36. $P = 40$

$$SI = \frac{PTR}{100}$$

$$= \frac{40 \times \frac{1}{12} \times 2}{100} = 0.066$$

$$= \frac{40 \times \frac{1}{12} \times 4}{100} = 0.133$$

$$= \frac{40 \times \frac{1}{12} \times 6}{100} = 0.2$$

$$= \frac{40 \times \frac{1}{12} \times 8}{100} = 0.26$$

$$= \frac{40 \times \frac{1}{12} \times 10}{100} = 0.33$$

$$= \frac{40 \times \frac{1}{12} \times 12}{100} = 0.4$$

Total interest $\simeq 1.40$

Essay Type Questions

37. $\frac{P}{2} = \frac{PTR}{100}$ ⟨increases by 50%⟩

$$\frac{100}{2} = 5 \times R$$

10% = R

$$A = P\left(1+\frac{R}{100}\right)^T$$

$$= 13000\left(1+\frac{10}{100}\right)^3$$

$A = 17303$

Interest $= 17303 - 13000 = ₹\ 4303$

38. $P = ₹\ 100000$

$$171600 = 100000\left(1+\frac{10}{100}\right)\left(1+\frac{20}{100}\right)\left(1+\frac{x}{100}\right)$$

$$1.716 = (1.1)(1.2)\left(1+\frac{x}{100}\right)$$

$$\frac{1.716}{1.32} = 1 + \frac{x}{100}$$

$$0.3 = \frac{x}{100}$$

$x = 30\%$

39. $SI = \frac{PTR}{100}$

$$\frac{2000 \times 2 \times R_1}{100} - \frac{2000 \times 2 \times R_2}{100} = 20$$

$$\frac{4000}{100}(R_1 - R_2) = 20$$

$$R_1 - R_2 = \frac{20}{40}$$

$$R_1 - R_2 = 0.5\%$$

40. P

$$SI = \frac{600 \times 3 \times 25}{100}$$

$= ₹\ 450$

Q

$$A = 600\left(1+\frac{20}{100}\right)^3$$

$A = 1036.8$

$\text{I} = 436.8$

P paid extra interest of ₹ 13.2

$$\frac{\frac{36-25}{25}}{\frac{1331-100}{1000}} = \frac{11}{25}\times\frac{1000}{331} = \frac{11\times 40}{331}$$

$$= \frac{440}{331}$$

41. $CI = P\left[\left(1+\frac{R}{100}\right)^t - 1\right]$

$$\text{Therefore, ratio} = \frac{P\left[\left(1+\frac{20}{100}\right)^2 - 1\right]}{P\left[\left(1+\frac{10}{100}\right)^3 - 1\right]} = \frac{\left(-\frac{6}{5}\right)^2 - 1}{\left(\frac{11}{10}\right)^3 - 1}$$

Competition Wing

Level 1: Apply Your Concepts

1. $P = ₹\ 10000$

   $T = 3$ years

   $R = 20\%$

   $$SI = \frac{10000 \times 3 \times 20}{100} = ₹\ 6000$$

2. $A = SI + P$

   $$3P = \frac{P \times T \times 20}{100} + P$$

   $$2P = \frac{PT}{5}$$

   10 years $= T$

3. $$A = P\left(1+\frac{r}{100}\right)^t$$

   $$16P = P\left(1+\frac{r}{100}\right)^4$$

   $$\sqrt[4]{16} = 1+\frac{r}{100}$$

   $$2 = 1+\frac{r}{100}$$

   $1 \times 100 = r$

   $r = 100\%$ pa

4. $$A = P\left(1+\frac{r}{100}\right)^{nt}$$

   $n = p$

   $r = 5$

   $t = n$

   $P = x$

   $$x\left(1+\frac{5}{100p}\right)^{pn}$$

5. $$SI = \frac{PIR}{100}$$

   $A = SI + P$

   $$73255 = \frac{P \times 3 \times R}{100} + P$$

   $$84525 = \frac{P \times 5 \times R}{100} + P$$

   Solving two equations,

   $$84525 = \frac{P \times 5 \times R}{100} + P$$

   $$73255 = \frac{P \times 3 \times R}{100} + P$$

   (–) (–) (–)

   $$11270 = \frac{2PR}{100}$$

   $PR = 563500$

   $$73255 = \frac{563500 \times 3}{100} + P$$

   $P = 56350$

6. (i) Interest for 4 years $= ₹(1200 - 800) = ₹400$.
   (ii) Interest for 2 years $= ₹200$.
   (iii) Sum $= 800 -$ Interest for 2 years.

7. (i) Interest for 3 years $= ₹2550 - ₹2100 = 450$.
   (ii) Interest for 4 years $= ₹600$.
   (iii) Sum $= 2100 -$ Interest for 4 years.

8. (i) Let rate of interest be $r\%$ and time period be t years.
   (ii) $b = \frac{c \times r \times t}{100}$ and $c = \frac{a \times r \times t}{100}$.
   (iii) Using the above, find the relation among a, b and c.

9. (i) Find the principal from the given data and proceed.
   (ii) Let the sum be $₹P$.
   (iii) $\text{CP} = P\left[\left(1+\frac{R}{100}\right)^n - 1\right]$, find P by substituting R, n and CP values.
   (iv) Now, find SI on P at same rate for same period.

10. (i) Find the interests in each case and equate them.
    (ii) Let the sums lent be $₹x$, $₹y$ and $₹22{,}000 - (x + y)$.
    (iii) $$\frac{x \times 2}{100} = \frac{y \times 2 \times 4}{100} = \frac{[22{,}000 - (x+y)] \times 1 \times 6}{100}.$$
    (iv) Solve the above equation and find the least of the sums.

11. (i) Let, $₹P$ be lent at 7% and $₹(1750 - P)$ be lent at 5%.
    (ii) Take $\frac{P \times 7 \times 1}{100} + \frac{(1750 - P) \times 5 \times 1}{100} = 98$.
    (iii) Use the above information to find P and $(1750 - P)$.

12. (i) ₹P becomes ₹$2P$ in 6 years.

(ii) $2P = P\left(1+\frac{R}{100}\right)^6$, find $\left(1+\frac{R}{100}\right)$ value.

(iii) Now, $64P = P\left(1+\frac{R}{100}\right)^n$ and substitute $\left(1+\frac{R}{100}\right)$ value to find n.

13. (i) Let the rate of interest on the second sum be $R\%$.

(ii) Let the sum be ₹P in each case and rate of interest on second sum be $r\%$ per annum.

(iii) Take $P\left[1+\frac{(r+2)3}{100}\right] = P\left[1+\frac{r\times 6}{100}\right] = 560.$

Find P and then $2P$.

14. (i) Find the difference between the simple interests and proceed.

(ii) Let the sum be ₹P.

(iii) Take $\frac{P\times(R+5)\times 2}{100} - \frac{P\times R\times 2}{100} = 200$, solve for P.

15. (i) Find the ratio of SI for 2 years and CI for 3 years and equate it to the given ratio.

(ii) $\left(\frac{P\times r\times 2}{100}\right) \div P\left[\left(1+\frac{r}{100}\right)^3 - 1\right] = 50:91.$

(iii) Solve the above and find r.

16. (i) Let the time period for the sum lent at 6% be T years.

(ii) Let the sum be ₹P in each case and second sum recovered in x years.

(iii) $P\left[1+\frac{6(x-2)}{100}\right] = P\left[1+\frac{4(x)}{100}\right] = 930$. Find x.

(iv) Using the above information, find P.

17. (i) Take the sum invested at 3% rate of interest to be x and that at 5% rate of interest to be y and that at 6% be ₹$4200 - (x + y)$.

(ii) $\frac{x\times 3}{100} = \frac{y\times 5}{100} = \frac{[4200-(x+y)]\times 6}{100}.$

(iii) Solve the above and find y.

18. (i) Let the two parts be ₹x and ₹$(300 - x)$, respectively.

(ii) In $\frac{x\times 10}{100} + \frac{(300-x)20}{100} = 500$, find x.

19. (i) Let the sum be ₹P.

(ii) $P\left(1+\frac{20}{100}\right)^n > 2P$, solve the inequality for n.

20. (i) Let the sum be ₹P.

(ii) $P\left(1+\frac{20}{100}\right)^n > 2P$, solve the inequality for n.

21. (i) Find the interests in each case and then equate their difference to the given value.

(ii) Let the total sum be ₹$2x$.

(iii) $\frac{x\times 20\times 6}{100} - \frac{x\times 40\times 2}{100} = 72.$

(iv) Solve for x and find $2x$.

22. (i) Let the total sum be ₹$5x$.

(ii) 25% of $5x$ = ₹$\frac{5x}{4}$.

(iii) Find the interest on each sum of ₹x using given data, and check which is greater than $\frac{5x}{4}$.

23. (i) Let the sum lent at CI be x and the sum lent at SI be $(2500 - x)$.

(ii) $\frac{(2500-x)4\times 2}{100} + x\left[\left(1+\frac{4}{100}\right)^2 - 1\right] = 201.$

(iii) Solve for x.

24. (i) Let the total sum be ₹$5x$.

(ii) Find the interest on each part.

(iii) Find the sum of the interest of 5 parts. Check which is greater than 20% of the sum of interests.

25. (i) Find the SI for 1 year and CI for the last two years.

(ii) Find SI and CI as per the given data.

(iii) Find the difference between CI and SI.

26. (i) Find SI on ₹4000 at 10% per annum for 4 years.

(ii) Find sum of SI on ₹4000 at 10% per annum for 2 years and CI on 4000 at 10% per annum for 2 years.

(iii) Find the difference of the above two.

27. (i) Find SI_1 at 8% and SI_2 at 4% and equalize them.

(ii) Solve the equation to find larger share

28. (i) Let the sums lent be ₹x, ₹y and ₹$22,000 - (x + y)$.

(ii) $\frac{x\times 3\times 5}{100} = \frac{y\times 5\times 4}{100} = \frac{[22,000-(x+y)]6\times 3}{100}.$

(iii) Solve the above equation and find the least of the sums.

29. (i) Let the rate of interest be r%.v

(ii) $4000\left[\left(1+\frac{r}{100}\right)^2-1\right]-\frac{4000\times r\times 2}{100}=250.$

(iii) Solve the above to find r.

30. (i) Let ₹x be lent at simple interest and ₹$(4000-x)$ at compound interest.

(ii) $\frac{x\times 20\times 2}{100}+(4000-x)\left[\left(1+\frac{20}{100}\right)^2-1\right]=1720,$

solve for x.

Level 2: Review Your Concepts

31. Find the interest for 1 year and the rate of interest.

32. Assume that ₹P becomes ₹$2P$ in 3 years and proceed.

33. Apply the formula for finding the simple interest.

34. Use depreciation concept or let $A=P\left(1-\frac{r}{100}\right)^n$, when $n=3$.

44. $P=$ ₹40,000, $R=12\%$, $n=2$.

$$CI=P\left[\left(1+\frac{R}{100}\right)^n-1\right]$$

$$=P\left[\left(1+\frac{12}{100}\right)^2-1\right]$$

$$=40{,}000\left[\left(\frac{28}{25}\right)^2-1\right]$$

$$=40{,}000\left[\frac{28^2-25^2}{(25)^2}\right]$$

$$=40{,}000\frac{(28+25)(28-25)}{25\times 25}$$

$$=64\times 53\times 3=₹10{,}176.$$

45. Let the sum borrowed be ₹P.

$R=25\%$ per annum

$n=4$

$A=10{,}000$

$$A=P\left(1+\frac{R}{100}\right)^n$$

$$10{,}000=P\left(1+\frac{25}{100}\right)^4$$

$$\Rightarrow 10{,}000=P\left(1+\frac{1}{4}\right)^4$$

$$\Rightarrow 10{,}000=P\left(\frac{5}{4}\right)^4$$

$$\Rightarrow P=\frac{4\times 4\times 4\times 4}{5\times 5\times 5\times 5}\times 10{,}000$$

$$\Rightarrow P=₹4096.$$

46. $A=P\left(1+\frac{R}{100}\right)^n$

$$R=\frac{16}{2}=8\%$$

$$\Rightarrow A=15{,}625\left[1+\frac{8}{100}\right]^3$$

$$\Rightarrow A=15{,}625\left(1+\frac{2}{25}\right)^3$$

$$\Rightarrow A=15{,}625\left(\frac{27}{25}\right)^3$$

$$\Rightarrow A=15{,}625\left(\frac{27\times 27\times 27}{25\times 25\times 25}\right)$$

$$A=₹19{,}683.$$

Level 3: Assess Your Concepts

49. $A=P\left(1+\frac{R}{100}\right)^N$

$A=$ ₹2560, $R=2\frac{1}{2}\%$, $n=2$ years, find P.

50. Use formula for amount and then use laws of indices.

$28{,}900=25{,}600\left(1+\frac{25}{400}\right)^n$, n is the number of quarters.

51. Let P be the original value.

$$P\left(1-\frac{4}{100}\right)^3=13{,}824$$

$$\Rightarrow P\left(1-\frac{1}{25}\right)^3=13{,}824$$

$$\Rightarrow P\left(\frac{25-1}{25}\right)=13{,}824$$

$$\Rightarrow P\left(\frac{24\times 24\times 24}{25\times 25\times 25}\right)=13{,}824$$

$$\Rightarrow P=25\times 25\times 25=₹15{,}625.$$

52. 1st year's interest = 8%

Principal = P

$$I_1 = \frac{P \times 1 \times 8}{100} = \frac{2P}{25}.$$

2nd year:

$$R = 10\%, \text{ Principal } = P + \frac{2P}{25} = \frac{27P}{25}$$

$$I_2 = \frac{\frac{27P}{25} \times 10}{100} \Rightarrow I_2 = \frac{27P}{250}.$$

3rd year:

R = 12%

$$\text{Principal } = \frac{27P}{25} + \frac{27P}{250} = \frac{297P}{250}$$

$$I_3 = \frac{\frac{297P}{250} \times 12}{100} \Rightarrow \frac{297P \times 3}{6250}$$

$$I_3 = \frac{891P}{6250}.$$

Given that interest earned in the 3rd year = ₹891.

$$\therefore I_3 = \frac{891P}{6250} = 891$$

$\Rightarrow P =$ ₹6250.

53. Time period = 4 years

Principal = P

Amount = $2P$

$$2P = P\left(1 + \frac{R}{100}\right)^4$$

$$2 = \left(1 + \frac{R}{100}\right)^4$$

$$\Rightarrow 2^{1/4} = \left(1 + \frac{R}{100}\right)$$

Let the amount becomes $4P$ in 'n' years.

$$4P = P\left(1 + \frac{R}{100}\right)^n \Rightarrow 4 = \left(2^{\frac{1}{4}}\right)^n$$

$$4 = 2^{n/4}$$

$$2^2 = 2^{n/4} \qquad \Rightarrow \frac{n}{4} = 2$$

$n = 8$ years.

54. Let the two parts be $2P$ and $3P$

$$\frac{(3P) \times 3 \times 10}{100} - \frac{(2P) \times 2 \times 10}{100} = 6000$$

$$\frac{90P - 40P}{100} = 6000$$

$$\frac{50P}{100} = 6000 \Rightarrow 5P = ₹60,000.$$

55. Amount after two years $= P\left(1 + \frac{R}{100}\right)^2$

$$= 9900\left(1 + \frac{20}{100}\right)^2$$

$$= 9900\left(\frac{36}{25}\right) = 396 \times 36 = ₹14,256$$

56. $P =$ ₹9999

R = 10%

T = 3 years and 4 months

$= 3 \text{ years} + \frac{4}{12} \text{ years}$

$= 3\frac{1}{3} \text{ years} = \frac{10}{3} \text{ years}.$

$$A = P + \frac{PTR}{100}$$

$$A = 9999 + \frac{9999 \times \frac{10}{3} \times 10}{100}$$

= 9999 + 3333 = ₹13,332

57. $SI_1 = SI_2 = \frac{840}{2} = 420.$

Difference between compound interest and simple interest for 2 years is the interest on the first year's simple interest.

$882 - 840 = R\%(420)$

$$42 = \frac{R}{100}(420)$$

$\Rightarrow R = 10\%.$

58. $P =$ ₹25000

Marked price = 140% ₹25000 = ₹35000.

Time period is 17th Feb 2015 to 14th Dec 2015

Time = (12 + 31 + 30 + 31 + 30 + 31 + 31 + 30 + 31 + 30 + 13) = 300 days

Discount = 25% on MP

$\Rightarrow SP = 75\%\ MP$

$= \frac{3}{4} \times ₹35000 = 3 \times ₹8750 = ₹26250$

Profit earned = $SP - CP$ = ₹26250 – ₹25000 = ₹1,250

I = ₹1,250

$T = \frac{300}{365}$

R =?

$I = \frac{PTR}{100}$

$1250 = \frac{25000 \times 300 \times R}{365 \times 100}$

$\frac{1250 \times 36500}{25000 \times 300} = R \Rightarrow \frac{5 \times 365}{300} = R$

$R \sim 6.08$

Rate ~ 6.08%

59. R = 12% p.a. and 18% p.a.

Half yearly R = 6% and 9%

$$\text{Required difference} = P\left[\left(1+\frac{R_2}{100}\right)^2 - P\left(1+\frac{R_1}{100}\right)^3\right]$$

$$= 75000\left[\left(1+\frac{9}{100}\right)^3 - \left(1+\frac{6}{100}\right)^3\right]$$

$$= 75000\left[\left(\frac{109}{100}\right)^3 - \left(\frac{106}{100}\right)^3\right]$$

$$= \frac{75000}{100 \times 100 \times 100}\left[(109)^3 - (106)^3\right]$$

$$= \frac{3}{40}(109 - 106)\ [(109)^2 + 109 \times 106 + (106)^2]$$

$$= \frac{3}{40} \times 3\ [11881 + 11554 + 11236]$$

$$= \frac{9}{40}[34671]$$

$$= \frac{312039}{40}$$

= ₹7800.975

Mr. Ajay earned ₹ 7801 (approx.).

JEE Special Wing

Multiple-Answer Type Questions

1. Given that a certain sum doubles under simple interest.

Let the principal be P.

Amount (A) = $2P$.

Interest (I) = $2P - P = P$.

We know $I = \frac{PTR}{100}$

$P = \frac{PTR}{100}$

$TR = 100$.

Going by options:

(a) Rate is $16\frac{2}{3}\%$ pa for 6 years:

$TR = 6 \times 16\frac{2}{3} = 6 \times \frac{50}{3} = 100$.

(b) Rate is 10% pa for 10 years:

$TR = 10 \times 10 = 100$.

(c) Rate is $7\frac{1}{7}\%$ pa for 14 years.

$TR = 14 \times 7\frac{1}{7} = 14 \times \frac{50}{7} = 100$.

(d) Rate is 5% pa for 20 years.

$TR = 20 \times 5 = 100$.

Hence, choice (a, b, c, d) are correct.

2. Given that a certain sum is invested at simple interest for12 years at 7% pa.

The interest for the first three years is ₹3150.

We know that the simple interest is same for all the years.

Hence, the interest for one year = $\frac{₹3150}{3}$ = ₹1050.

The interest for two years = ₹1050 × 2 = ₹2100.

The interest for four years = ₹1050 × 4 = ₹4200.

The interest for five years = ₹1050 × 5 = ₹5250.

Hence, choice (a and b) are correct.

3. Given that: The CI for 1 year = ₹4200.

The CI for 2 years = ₹8736.

The CI for the 2nd year = ₹8736 – ₹4200 = ₹4536.

The difference between the interests for the first year and the second year

= ₹4536 – ₹4200 = ₹336.

We can understand that the ₹336 is the interest on the first year i.e., on ₹4200.

The rate of interest per annum = $\frac{₹336}{₹4200} \times 100\% = 8\%$.

We know interest = $\frac{PTR}{100}$

$₹4200 = \frac{P \times 1 \times 8}{100}$

$₹525 = \frac{P}{100}$

P = ₹52,500

Hence, choice (b and c) are correct.

4. Given that the present value of the land (P) is ₹50,00,000.

The rate of appreciation = 15%.

We know $A = P\left(1 + \frac{R}{100}\right)^n$.

(a) The value of the land after 1 year

$= ₹50,00,000\left(1 + \frac{15}{100}\right)^1$.

$= ₹50,00,000 \times 1.15 = ₹57,50,000$.

(b) The value of the land after 2 years

$= ₹50,00,000\left(1 + \frac{15}{100}\right)^2$.

$= ₹50,00,000 \times (1.15)^2 = ₹66,12,500$.

(c) The value of the land after 3 years

$= ₹50,00,000\left(1 + \frac{15}{100}\right)^3$.

$= ₹50,00,000 \times (1.15)^3 = ₹76,04,375$.

(d) The value of the land after 4 years

$= ₹50,00,000\left(1 + \frac{15}{100}\right)^4$.

$= ₹50,00,000 \times (1.15)^4 = ₹87,45,031.25$.

Hence, choice (a, b, c) are correct.

5. Given that the value of the car one year ago was ₹9,00,000.

The rate of depreciation = 10%.

We know $A = P\left(1 - \frac{R}{100}\right)^n$

(a) The present value of the car $= ₹9,00,000\left(1 - \frac{10}{100}\right)^1$.

$= ₹9,00,000 \times 0.9 = ₹8,10,000$.

(b) The value of the car after 1 year

$= ₹8,10,000\left(1-\frac{10}{100}\right)^1.$

$= ₹8,10,000 \times 0.9 = ₹7,29,000.$

(c) The value of the car after 2 years

$= ₹7,29,000\left(1-\frac{10}{100}\right)^1.$

$= ₹7,29,000 \times 0.9 = ₹6,56,100.$

(d) The value of the car after 3 years

$= ₹6,56,100\left(1-\frac{10}{100}\right)^1.$

$= ₹6,56,100 \times 0.9 = ₹5,90,490.$

Hence, choice (a, b, d) are correct.

Match The Column

Common Solutions for questions 6 to 10:

Bank	Investment (In ₹)	Time Period (In Years)	Rate of Interest (pa)
P	4,60,000	2	8%
Q	5,00,000	2	7.5%
R	6,00,000	2	7%
S	7,00,000	2	6.5%
T	8,00,000	2	6%

We have $CI - SI = P\left(\frac{R}{100}\right)^2$

6. $CI - SI = 4,60,000\left(\frac{8}{100}\right)^2 = ₹2944.$

Hence, the correct option is (b).

7. $CI - SI = 5,00,000\left(\frac{7.5}{100}\right)^2 = ₹2812.5.$

Hence, the correct option is (g).

8. $CI - SI = 6,00,000\left(\frac{7}{100}\right)^2 = ₹2940.$

Hence, the correct option is (c).

9. $CI - SI = 7,00,000\left(\frac{6.5}{100}\right)^2 = ₹2957.5.$

Hence, the correct option is (a).

10. $CI - SI = 8,00,000\left(\frac{6}{100}\right)^2 = ₹2880.$

Hence, the correct option is (f).

Assertion and Reason Type Questions

Common Solutions for questions 11 to 15:

11. **Assertion:** A certain sum doubles in 20 years at 10% per annum under simple interest. We know simple interest $= \frac{PTR}{100}$

$= \frac{P \times 20 \times 10}{100} = 2P.$

Amount $= P + 2P = 3P.$

So, Assertion is false.

Reason: Interest is the difference of amount and principal. Also, interest $= \frac{PTR}{100}$.

Reason is true.

Hence, the correct option is (d).

12. **Assertion:** Given that $P\left(1+\frac{10}{100}\right)^1 = ₹12,100.$

Now $P\left(1+\frac{10}{100}\right)^2 = P\left(1+\frac{10}{100}\right)^1 \times \left(1+\frac{10}{100}\right)^1$

$= ₹12,100 \times \frac{11}{10} = ₹13,310.$

So, Assertion is true.

Reason: Under compound interest the amount is given by $A = P\left(1+\frac{R}{100}\right)^n$.

So, Reason is true and is the correct explanation to Assertion.

Hence, the correct option is (a).

13. **Assertion:** On a certain sum and certain rate of interest pa for 1 year, the interest compounded half yearly is more than the interest compounded annually.

Assertion is true.

Reason: The compound interest is given by $A = P\left(1+\frac{R}{100}\right)^n$, because it is the formula to find the amount under compound interest.

So, Reason is false.

Hence, the correct option is (c).

14. **Assertion:** Given that $P\left(1+\frac{R}{100}\right)^6 = 3P.$

$\Rightarrow \left(1+\frac{R}{100}\right)^6 = 3$

Now $P\left(1+\frac{R}{100}\right)^{18} = P\left(1+\frac{R}{100}\right)^{6\times3}$

$= P\left[\left(1+\frac{R}{100}\right)^{6}\right]^{3}$

$= P[3]^3 = 27P.$

So, Assertion is true.

Reason: Under compound interest the amount is given by $A = P\left(1+\frac{R}{100}\right)^{n}$.

So, Reason is true and is the correct explanation to Assertion.

Hence, the correct option is (a).

15. **Assertion:** For money lenders, compound interest is more beneficial when compared to simple interest at same rate of interest.

Assertion is true.

Reason: The simple interest $= \frac{PTR}{100}$.

Reason is true, but the not correct explanation to Assertion.

Hence, the correct option is (b).

Comprehension-Based Questions

Common Solutions for questions 16 to 20:

$P =$ ₹2,00,000

The rates of interests for the first, second, third and fourth year are x%, 6%, 8% and 10% respectively.

$A =$ ₹2,10,000 in a year.

We have $A = P\left(1+\frac{R}{100}\right)^{n}$

$\Rightarrow 2,10,000 = 2,00,000\left(1+\frac{x}{100}\right)^{1}$

$\Rightarrow 1+\frac{x}{100} = \frac{21}{20}$

$\Rightarrow \frac{x}{100} = \frac{1}{20}$

$\Rightarrow x = 5$

The rate of interest for the first year = 5%.

16. $x = 5$.

Hence, the correct option is (c).

17. $P =$ ₹2,00,000

$R = x = 5$

$n = 4$

We have $A = P\left(1+\frac{R}{100}\right)^{n}$

$\Rightarrow$ A = ₹2,00,000$\left(1+\frac{5}{100}\right)^{4}$

$\Rightarrow$ A = ₹2,00,000$(1.05)^4$

$\Rightarrow A =$ ₹2,43,101 (Approx.)

CI = $A - P$

= ₹2,43,101 – ₹2,00,000 = ₹43,101.

Hence, the correct option is (d).

18. $P =$ ₹2,00,000

Rates for the first two years are 5% and 6% respectively.

$n = 2$

We have $A = P\left(1+\frac{R_1}{100}\right)\left(1+\frac{R_2}{100}\right)$

$\Rightarrow$ A = ₹2,00,000$\left(1+\frac{5}{100}\right)\left(1+\frac{6}{100}\right)$

$\Rightarrow$ A = ₹2,00,000$(1.05)(1.06)$

$\Rightarrow A =$ ₹2,22,600

The money paid by Kaushik at the end of two years = ₹97,600.

The remaining sum = ₹2,22,600 – ₹97,600 = ₹1,25,000.

Now, $P =$ ₹1,25,000

Rates for the next two years are 8% and 10% respectively.

$n = 2$

We have $A = P\left(1+\frac{R_{31}}{100}\right)\left(1+\frac{R_4}{100}\right)$

$\Rightarrow$ A = ₹1,25,000$\left(1+\frac{8}{100}\right)\left(1+\frac{10}{100}\right)$

$\Rightarrow$ A = ₹1,25,000$(1.08)(1.1)$

$\Rightarrow A =$ ₹1,48,500.

Hence, the correct option is (c).

19. $P =$ ₹2,00,000

Rates for the first year is 5%.

$n = 1$

We have $A = P\left(1+\frac{R}{100}\right)^{n}$

$\Rightarrow$ A = ₹2,00,000$\left(1+\frac{5}{100}\right)^{1}$

$\Rightarrow$ A = ₹2,00,000(1.05)

$\Rightarrow A =$ ₹2,10,000

The money paid by Kaushik at the end of one year = ₹1,10,000.

The remaining sum = ₹2,10,000 – ₹1,10,000 = ₹1,00,000.

Now, $P = ₹1,00,000$

Rates for the next three years is 10% p.a.

$n = 3$

We have $A = P\left(1+\frac{R}{100}\right)^n$

$\Rightarrow A = ₹1,00,000\left(1+\frac{10}{100}\right)^3$

$\Rightarrow A = ₹1,00,000(1.1)^3$

$\Rightarrow A = ₹1,33,100.$

The total interest for four years

= (₹2,10,000 – ₹2,00,000) + (₹1,33,100 – ₹1,00,000)

= ₹43,100.

Hence, the correct option is (b).

20. $P = ₹2,00,000$

The rates of interests for the first, second, third and fourth year are 5%, 6%, 8% and 10% respectively.

As he pays interest at the end of each year, the principal remains the same.

We have $A = P\left(1+\frac{R}{100}\right)^n$

(i) Amount at the end of the first year,

$A = ₹2,00,000\left(1+\frac{5}{100}\right)^1$

$\Rightarrow A = ₹2,00,000(1.05)$

$\Rightarrow A = ₹2,10,000$

Interest for the first year = ₹2,10,000 – ₹2,00,000
= ₹10,000.

(ii) Amount at the end of the second year,

$A = ₹2,00,000\left(1+\frac{6}{100}\right)^1$

$\Rightarrow A = ₹2,00,000(1.06)$

$\Rightarrow A = ₹2,12,000$

Interest for the first year = ₹2,12,000 – ₹2,00,000
= ₹12,000.

(iii) Amount at the end of the third year,

$A = ₹2,00,000\left(1+\frac{8}{100}\right)^1$

$\Rightarrow A = ₹2,00,000(1.08)$

$\Rightarrow A = ₹2,16,000$

Interest for the first year = ₹2,16,000 – ₹2,00,000
= ₹16,000.

(iv) Amount at the end of the first year,

$A = ₹2,00,000\left(1+\frac{10}{100}\right)^1$

$\Rightarrow A = ₹2,00,000(1.1)$

$\Rightarrow A = ₹2,20,000$

Interest for the first year = ₹2,22,000 – ₹2,00,000
= ₹22,000.

Hence, total interest for the four years

= ₹(10,000 + ₹12,000 + 16,000 + 20,000)

= ₹58,000.

Hence, the correct option is (a).

[illegible]

[illegible]

[illegible]

= [illegible]

Now, [illegible] = ₹1,00,000

[illegible]

[illegible]

The compound interest [illegible]

[illegible]

[illegible]

[illegible]

= [illegible]

CHAPTER

5

Polynomials and Square Roots of Algebraic Expressions

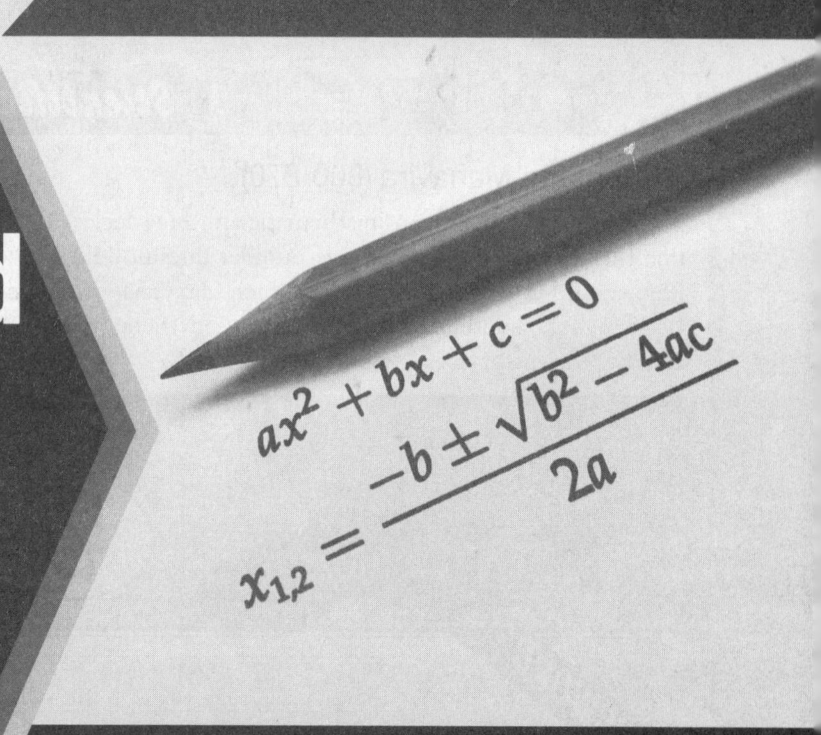

Remember

Before beginning this chapter, you should be able to:

- Apply basic operations on polynomials.
- Solve basic factorization of polynomials.

Key Ideas

After completing this chapter, you should be able to:

- State the types of polynomials and operations on polynomials.
- Find the factorization of polynomials and obtain HCF and LCM of polynomials.
- Understand different methods for finding square roots of algebraic expressions.
- Learn about homogeneous, symmetric and cyclic expressions.

Scientific Crypt

A Tribute to Mahavira (800-870)

Mahavira was an Indian mathematician. He declared that the square root of a negative number does not exist. He worked on the subjects on which Aryabhata and Brahmagupta contended, but he expressed them more clearly. Also, he gave the following result.

$$1^2 + 2^2 + 3^2 + \ldots\ldots + n^2 = \frac{n(n+1)(2n+1)}{6}$$

He was the author of 'Ganit Saar Sangraha'. This book is on Numerical Mathematics

FUN TIME

CROSSWORD

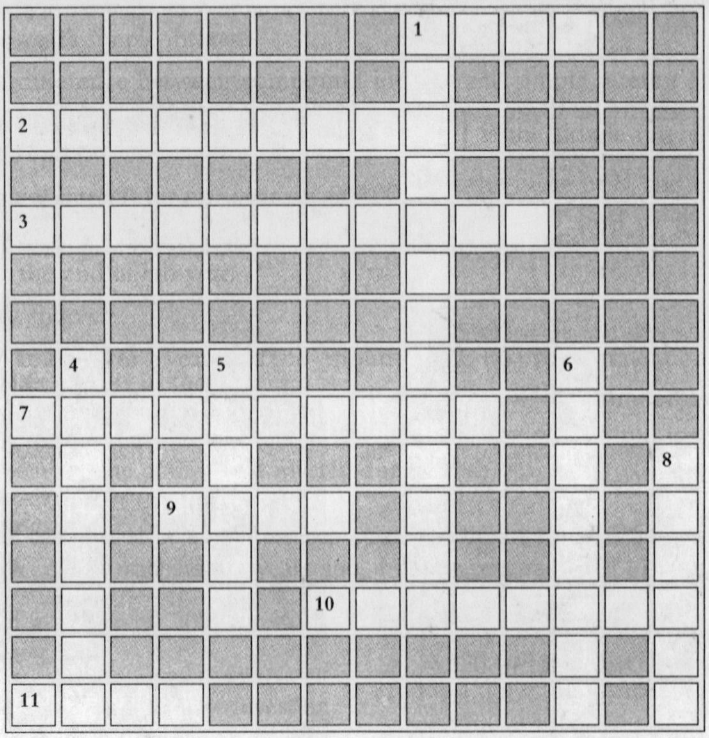

Across

1. The degree of bi-quadratic polynomial.
2. An expression $f(x, y)$, where $f(x, y) = f(y, x)$.
3. An algebraic expression, in which the degrees of all terms are equal.
7. An algebraic expression, in which the exponents of variables are whole numbers.
9. Terms having the same literal coefficients.
10. The square root of a trinomial, which is a perfect square.
11. The degree of a non-zero constant polynomial.

Down

1. Expressing a given polynomial as a product of two or more polynomials.
4. A homogeneous expression, which contains all possible terms in it.
5. Terms having different literal coefficients.
6. The square root of a monomial which is a perfect square.
8. An expression $f(x, y, z)$, where $f(x, y, z) = f(y, z, x)$.

INTRODUCTION

Before learning the meaning and scope of polynomials, the terms like, constants, variables, algebraic expressions etc., have to be understood.

Constant

A number having a fixed numerical value is called a **constant**.

Example: 7, $\frac{1}{2}$, 4.7, 16.5, etc.

> **Info Bytes!**
>
> A constant is a value that does not change. In equations, while variables can represent any number, constants remain the same. For instance, in the equation $y = 5x + 7$, while x can vary, the number 7 is constant.

Variable

A number which can take various numerical values is known as a **variable**.

Example: x, y, z, a, b, c, etc.

A variable raised to any non-zero real number is also a variable.

Example: x^5, $y^{10/3}$, $z^{0.9}$, etc.

A number which is the product of a constant and a variable is also a variable.

Example: $8x^3$, $-7x^5$, $4x^{10}$, etc.

A combination of two or more variables separated by a (+) ve sign or a (–) ve sign is also a variable.

Example: $x^2 - y^3 + z$, $x^3 - y^3$, etc.

Algebraic Expression

A combination of constants and variables connected by +, –, × and ÷ signs is known as an **algebraic expression**.

Example: $8x + 7$, $11x^2 - 13x$, $5x^5 + 8x^2y$, etc.

Terms

The parts of an algebraic expression separated by + or – signs are called the **terms** of the expression.

Example: In the expression $3x + 4y - 7$, we call $3x$, $4y$ and -7 as terms.

Coefficient of a Term

Consider the term $8x^2$. In this case, 8 is called the numerical coefficient and x^2 is said to be the literal coefficient.

In case of $9xy$, we have the numerical coefficient as 9 and the literal coefficient as xy.

Like Terms

Terms having the same literal coefficients are called **like terms**.

Examples:

1. $15x^2$, $-19x^2$ and $35x^2$ are all like terms.
2. $8x^2y$, $5x^2y$ and $-7x^2y$ are all like terms.

Unlike Terms

Terms having different literal coefficients are called **unlike terms.**

Example: $5x^2$, $-10x$ and $15x^3$ are unlike terms.

Polynomial

An algebraic expression in which the variables involved have only non-negative integral powers is called a **polynomial**.

Example: $5x^2 - 8x + 7$, $3x^3 + 5x^2 - 9$, $3y^2 - 5y + z$, etc.

The expression $3x^5 - 8x + \frac{4}{x} + 11\,x^{5/2}$ is not a polynomial. Since the exponents of x are negative integers and fractions.

A polynomial with one variable is known as a polynomial in that variable.

Example: $5x^4 + 7x^3 + 3x - 9$ is a polynomial in the variable x.

$3y^3 + y^2 + y$ is a polynomial in the variable y.

$4x^2y^2 + 3xy^2 - 7xy$ is a polynomial in variables x and y.

Degree of a Polynomial in One Variable

The highest index of the variable in a polynomial of one variable is called the **degree of the polynomial.**

Examples:

1. $11x^3 - 7x^2 + 5x + 2$ is a polynomial of degree 3.
2. $15x^6 - 8x + 7$ is a polynomial of degree 6.

Types of Polynomials with Respect to Degree

1. **Linear polynomial:** A polynomial of degree one is called a linear polynomial.

   Example: $11x - 5$, $10y + 7$ and $13z + 4$ are polynomials of degree one and hence they can be called as linear polynomials.
2. **Quadratic polynomial:** A polynomial of degree two is called a quadratic polynomial.

   Example: $5x^2 - 8x + 3$ and $13y^2 - 8y + 3$ are polynomials of degree two and hence can be called as quadratic polynomials.
3. **Cubic polynomial:** A polynomial of degree three is called a cubic polynomial.

   Example: $5x^3 + 6x^2 + 7x + 8$ and $4y^3 - 9y^2 + 3$ are polynomials of degree three and hence can be called as cubic polynomials.
4. **Biquadratic polynomial:** A polynomial of degree four is called a biquadratic polynomial.

   Example: $3x^4 - x^3 + 7x^2 - 2x + 1$ and $5x^4 - 2x + 7$ are polynomials of degree four and hence can be called as biquadratic polynomials.
5. **Constant polynomial:** A polynomial having only one term which is a non-zero constant is called a constant polynomial. Degree of a constant polynomial is 0.

   Example: 10, -11 are constant polynomials.

   Note: The degree of zero is not defined.

Types of Polynomials with Respect to Number of Terms

1. **Monomial:** An expression containing only one term is called a monomial.

   Example: $8x$, $-11x^2y$, $-15x^2y^3z^2$, etc.
2. **Binomial:** An expression containing two terms is called a binomial.

   Example: $3x - 8y$, $4xy - 5x$, $9x + 5x^2$, etc.

3. **Trinomial:** An expression containing three terms is called a trinomial.
   Example: $5x - 2y + 3z$, $x^2 + 2xy - 5z$, etc.

Polynomial Operations

Addition of Polynomials

The sum of two or more polynomials can be obtained by arranging the terms and then adding the like terms.

EXAMPLE 5.1 Add $7x^2 - 8x + 5$, $3x^2 - 8x + 5$ and $-6x^2 + 15x - 5$.

SOLUTION

$$\begin{array}{rrr} 7x^2 - & 8x & +5 \\ 3x^2 - & 8x & +5 \\ -6x^2 + & 15x & -5 \\ \hline 4x^2 - & x & +5 \\ \hline \end{array}$$

$\therefore$ The required sum is $4x^2 - x + 5$.

Subtraction of Polynomials

The difference of two polynomials can be obtained by arranging the terms and subtracting the like terms.

EXAMPLE 5.2 Subtract $11x^3 - 7x^2 + 10x$ from $16x^3 + 4x^2 - 11x$.

SOLUTION

$$\begin{array}{rrr} 16x^3 + & 4x^2 - & 11x \\ 11x^3 - & 7x^2 + & 10x \\ - & + & - \\ \hline 5x^3 + & 11x^2 - & 21x \\ \hline \end{array}$$

$\therefore$ The required difference is $5x^3 + 11x^2 - 21x$.

Multiplication of Polynomials

The result of multiplication of two polynomials is obtained by multiplying each term of the polynomial by each term of the other polynomial and then taking the algebraic sum of these products.

EXAMPLE 5.3 Multiply $(5x^2 - 8x + 7)$ with $(2x - 5)$.

SOLUTION

$$\begin{array}{l} 5x^2 - 8x + 7 \\ 2x - 5 \\ \hline 10x^3 - 16x^2 + 14x \\ \qquad\quad - 25x^2 + 40x - 35 \\ \hline 10x^3 - 41x^2 + 54x - 35 \\ \hline \end{array}$$

$\therefore$ The required product is $10x^3 - 41x^2 + 54x - 35$.

This is true for all real values of x. Such equations are called algebraic identities.

Division of Polynomial by a Monomial

To divide a polynomial by a monomial, we need to divide each term of the polynomial by the monomial.

EXAMPLE 5.4 Divide $18x^4 - 15x^3 + 24x^2 + 9x$ by $3x$.

SOLUTION

$$\frac{18x^4 - 15x^3 + 24x^2 + 9x}{3x}$$

$$= \frac{18x^4}{3x} - \frac{15x^3}{3x} + \frac{24x^2}{3x} + \frac{9x}{3x}$$

$$= 6x^3 - 5x^2 + 8x + 3$$

$\therefore$ The required result is $6x^3 - 5x^2 + 8x + 3$.

Division of Polynomial by a Polynomial

Factor Method

In this method, we factorize the polynomial to be divided so that one or more of the factors is equal to the polynomial by which we wish to divide.

EXAMPLE 5.5 Divide $4x^2 + 7x - 15$ by $x + 3$.

SOLUTION

$4x^2 + 7x - 15 = 4x^2 + 12x - 5x - 15$

$4x(x + 3) - 5(x + 3) = (4x - 5)(x + 3)$

$$\therefore \frac{4x^2 + 7x - 15}{x + 3} = \frac{(4x - 5)(x + 3)}{x + 3} = 4x - 5.$$

Long Division Method

Step 1: First arrange the terms of the dividend and the divisor in the descending order of their degrees.

Step 2: Now the first term of the quotient is obtained by dividing the first term of the dividend by the first term of the divisor.

Step 3: Then multiply all the terms of the divisor by the first term of the quotient and subtract the result from the dividend.

Step 4: Consider the remainder as new dividend and proceed as before.

Step 5: Repeat this process till we obtain a remainder which is either 0 or a polynomial of degree less than that of the divisor.

Info Bytes!

The factor method for division of polynomials is used only when the remainder is zero.

EXAMPLE 5.6 Divide $2x^3 + 9x^2 + 4x - 15$ by $2x + 5$.

SOLUTION

$$
\begin{array}{l}
2x + 5\ )\ 2x^3 + 9x^2 + 4x - 15\ (x^2 + 2x - 3 \\
\qquad\quad 2x^3 + 5x^2 \\
\qquad\quad (-)\quad (-) \\
\hline
\qquad\qquad 4x^2 + 4x \\
\qquad\qquad 4x^2 + 10x \\
\qquad\qquad (-)\quad (-) \\
\hline
\qquad\qquad\qquad -6x - 15 \\
\qquad\qquad\qquad -6x - 15 \\
\qquad\qquad\qquad (+)\quad (+) \\
\hline
\qquad\qquad\qquad\quad 0 \\
\hline
\end{array}
$$

$$\therefore \frac{(2x^3 + 9x^2 + 4x - 15)}{(2x + 5)} = x^2 + 2x - 3.$$

Horner's Method of Synthetic Division

Let us understand the division with the help of the following example.

EXAMPLE 5.7 Divide $27x^3 - 81x^2 + 45x + 23$ by $(x - 2)$.

SOLUTION

	27	−81	45	23	
$x = 2$	0	54	−54	−18	
	27	−27	−9	5	remainder

coefficients of quotient

Step 1: We first write the coefficients of the dividend arranging them in descending powers of x with zero as the coefficient for missing power of x.

Step 2: To divide by $x - 2$, we write $x = 2$.

Step 3: Bring down the leading coefficient of the dividend, multiply by 2 and add the second coefficient which results −27.

Step 4: Now multiply −27 by 2 and add this to the third coefficient to get −9.

Step 5: This process is continued until the final sum.

Step 6: Thus, we get the quotient as $27x^2 - 27x - 9$ and the remainder as 5.

Factorization

Factorization is expressing a given polynomial as a product of two or more polynomials.

Example: $x^3 - 15x^2 = x^2(x - 15)$

$\Rightarrow x^2$ and $x - 15$ are the factors of $x^3 - 15x^2$.

1. **Factorization of polynomials of the form $x^2 - y^2$.**

   $x^2 - y^2 = (x + y)(x - y)$

   $\Rightarrow x + y$ and $x - y$ are the factors of $x^2 - y^2$.

EXAMPLE 5.8 Factorize: $(5x + 4y)^2 - (5x - 4y)^2$

SOLUTION

We know that $(a + b)^2 - (a - b)^2 = 4ab$

$(5x + 4y)^2 - (5x - 4y)^2$

$= 4(5x)(4y)$

2. **Factorization of polynomials by grouping of terms:** In this method, we group the terms of the polynomials in such a way that we get a common factor out of them.

EXAMPLE 5.9 (a) Factorize $a^2 - (b - 8)a - 8b$
(b) Factorize $4x^3 - 10y^3 - 8x^2y + 5xy^2$

SOLUTION

(a) $\Rightarrow a^2 - (b - 8)a - 8b$

$= a^2 - ab + 8a - 8b$

$= a(a - b) + 8(a - b)$

$= (a + 8)(a - b)$

$\therefore a^2 - (b - 8)a - 8b = (a + 8)(a - b)$.

(b) $4x^3 - 8x^2y + 5xy^2 - 10y^3$

$= 4x^2(x - 2y) + 5y^2(x - 2y)$

$= (4x^2 + 5y^2)(x - 2y)$.

3. **Factorization of a trinomial that is a perfect square. A trinomial of the form $x^2 \pm 2xy + y^2$ is equivalent to $(x \pm y)^2$. This identity can be used to factorize perfect square trinomials.**

EXAMPLE 5.10 Factorize: $x^2 + 2x - \frac{2}{x} + \frac{1}{x^2} - 1$

SOLUTION

$$x^2 + 2x - \frac{2}{x} + \frac{1}{x^2} - 1 = \left(x^2 + \frac{1}{x^2}\right) + 2\left(x - \frac{1}{x}\right) - 1$$

$$= \left(x^2 + \frac{1}{x^2} - 2\right) + 2\left(x - \frac{1}{x}\right) + 1$$

$$= \left(x - \frac{1}{x}\right)^2 + 2\left(x - \frac{1}{x}\right) + 1^2$$

$$= \left(x - \frac{1}{x} + 1\right)^2$$

4. **Factorization of a polynomial of the form $x^2 + (a + b)x + ab$:** As we have already seen, $(x + a)(x + b) = x^2 + (a + b)x + ab$

$\therefore x^2 + (a + b)x + ab$ can be factorized as $(x + a)(x + b)$.

EXAMPLE 5.11 (a) Factorize $x^2 + 25x + 144$
(b) Factorize $x^2 - 8x + 15$
(c) Factorize $x^2 - 5x - 14$

SOLUTION

(a) Here, the constant term is 144 = (16 × 9) and the coefficient of x is 25 = (16 + 9)

$\therefore x^2 + 25x + 144$
$= x^2 + 16x + 9x + 144$
$= x(x + 16) + 9(x + 16)$
$= (x + 16)(x + 9).$

(b) Here, the constant term is 15 = (−5)(−3) and the coefficient of x is −8 = −5 − 3.

$\Rightarrow x^2 - 8x + 15$
$= x^2 - 5x - 3x + 15$
$= x(x - 5) - 3(x - 5)$
$= (x - 3)(x - 5)$
$\therefore x^2 - 8x + 15 = (x - 3)(x - 5).$

(c) Constant term is −14 = (−7)(2)
Coefficient of x is −5 = −7 + 2

$\Rightarrow x^2 - 5x - 14$
$= x^2 - 7x + 2x - 14$
$= x(x - 7) + 2(x - 7)$
$= (x + 2)(x - 7).$
$\therefore x^2 - 5x - 14 = (x + 2)(x - 7).$

5. Factorization of polynomials of the form $ax^2 + bx + c$.

Step 1: Take the product of the constant term and the coefficient of x^2, i.e., ac.

Step 2: Now this product ac is to split into two factors m and n such that $m + n$ is equal to the coefficient of x, i.e., b.

Step 3: Then we pair one of them, say mx, with ax^2 and the other nx, with c and factorize.

EXAMPLE 5.12 (a) Factorize $6x^2 + 19x + 15$
(b) Factorize $7 - 17x - 12x^2$

SOLUTION

(a) Here, 6 × 15 = 90 = 10 × 9 and 10 + 9 = 19

$\therefore 6x^2 + 19x + 15$
$= 6x^2 + 10x + 9x + 15$
$= 2x(3x + 5) + 3(3x + 5)$
$= (2x + 3)(3x + 5).$

(b) Here, (7)(−12) = −84 = (−21)(4) and
−17 = −21 + 4

$= 7 - 17x - 12x^2$
$= 7 - 21x + 4x - 12x^2$
$= 7(1 - 3x) + 4x(1 - 3x) = (1 - 3x)(7 + 4x).$

6. Factorization of expressions of the form $x^3 + y^3$ and $x^3 - y^3$.

$x^3 + y^3 = (x + y)(x^2 - xy + y^2)$
$\Rightarrow x^3 + y^3$ has factors $(x + y)$ and $(x^2 - xy + y^2)$
$x^3 - y^3 = (x - y)(x^2 + xy + y^2)$
$\Rightarrow x^3 - y^3$ has factors $(x - y)$ and $(x^2 + xy + y^2)$.

EXAMPLE 5.13 Solve: $8x^3 + y^3 =$ ______.

SOLUTION

$8x^3 + y^3 = (2x)^3 + y^3$
$= (2x + y)((2x)^2 + y^2 - (2x)(y))$
$= (2x + y)(4x^2 + y^2 - 2xy).$
$= 80xy.$

7. Factorization of expressions of the form $x^3 + y^3 + z^3$ when $x + y + z = 0$.

(Given $x + y + z = 0$)

As $x + y + z = 0$, $z = -(x + y)$

$$x^3 + y^3 + z^3 = x^3 + y^3 + \{-(x + y)\}^3$$
$$= x^3 + y^3 - (x + y)^3$$
$$= x^3 + y^3 - \{x^3 + y^3 + 3xy(x + y)\}$$
$$= -3xy(x + y)$$
$$= -3xy(-z) \ \{\text{Since } x + y = -z\}$$
$$= 3xyz$$

$\therefore$ If $x + y + z = 0$, then $x^3 + y^3 + z^3 = 3xyz$.

Konnect

Factorization is like breaking down a puzzle into its individual pieces. Mathematicians have been using this technique for millennia to simplify complex problems.

HCF of Given Polynomials

For two given polynomials, $f(x)$ and $g(x)$, $r(x)$ can be taken as the highest common factor, if:

1. $r(x)$ is a common factor of $f(x)$ and $g(x)$ and
2. Every common factor of $f(x)$ and $g(x)$ is also a factor of $r(x)$.

Highest common factor is generally referred to as HCF.

Method for Finding HCF of the Given Polynomials

Step 1: Express each polynomial as a product of powers of irreducible factors which also requires the numerical factors to be expressed as the product of the powers of primes.

Step 2: If there is no common factor then HCF is 1 and if there are common irreducible factors, we find the least exponent of these irreducible factors in the factorized form of the given polynomials.

Step 3: Raise the common irreducible factors to the smallest or the least exponents found in step 2 and take their product to get the HCF.

EXAMPLE 5.14 If the HCF of x^3y^2 and x^ay^b is x^3y^2, then the minimum value of $a + b$ is ________.

SOLUTION

The HCF of x^3y^2 and x^ay^b

$= x^3y^2$

$\Rightarrow a \geq 3$ and $b \geq 2$

The minimum value of $a + b = 3 + 2 = 5$.

LCM of the Given Polynomials

Least Common Multiple or the Lowest Common Multiple is the product of all the factors (taken once) of the polynomials given with their highest exponents respectively.

Method to Calculate LCM of the Given Polynomials

Step 1: First express each polynomial as a product of powers of irreducible factors.

Step 2: Consider all the irreducible factors (only once) occurring in the given polynomials. For each of these factors, consider the greatest exponent in the factorized form of the given polynomials.

Step 3: Now raise each irreducible factor to the greatest exponent and multiply them to get the LCM.

EXAMPLE 5.15 If the LCM of $x^9 y^a$ and $x^b y^6$ is $x^{10}y^{10}$, then $a + b =$ ________.

SOLUTION

The LCM of $x^9 y^a$ and $x^b y^6$

$= x^{10}y^{10}$

$\Rightarrow a = 10$ and $b = 10$

$\Rightarrow a + b = 20.$

Relation between the HCF, the LCM, and the Product of Polynomials

If $f(x)$ and $g(x)$ are two polynomials, then we have the relation,

$$(\text{HCF of } f(x) \text{ and } g(x)) \times (\text{LCM of } f(x) \text{ and } g(x)) = \pm(f(x) \times g(x)).$$

Example: Let $f(x) = (x + 5)^2(x - 7)(x + 8)$ and

$g(x) = (x + 5)(x - 7)^2(x - 8)$ be two polynomials.

The common factors with the least exponents are $x + 5$ and $x - 7$.

$$\therefore \quad \text{HCF} = (x + 5)\ (x - 7)$$

All the factors (taken only once) with the highest exponents are $(x + 5)^2$, $(x - 7)^2$, $(x - 8)$ and $(x + 8)$.

$$\Rightarrow \quad \text{LCM} = (x + 5)^2(x - 7)^2(x - 8)\ (x + 8)$$

Now $f(x) \cdot g(x) = (x + 5)^2(x - 7)(x + 8)(x + 5)(x - 7)^2(x - 8)$

$= (x + 5)^3(x - 7)^3(x + 8)(x - 8)$

$$\text{LCM} \times \text{HCF} = (x + 5)^2(x - 7)^2(x - 8)(x + 8) \times (x + 5)(x - 7) = (x + 5)^3(x - 7)^3(x - 8)\ (x + 8)$$

Thus, we say

(LCM of two polynomials) × (HCF of two polynomials) = Product of the two polynomials.

Concept of Square Roots

If x is any variable, then x^2 is called the square of the variable and for x^2, x is called the square root.

Square root of x^2 can be denoted as $\pm\sqrt{x^2} \cdot x$ and $-x$ can both be considered as the square roots of x^2 because $(x) \cdot (x) = x^2$ and $(-x)(-x) = x^2$.

In this study, we restrict the square root of x^2 to x, i.e., positive value of x.

Square Root of Monomials

The square root of a monomial can be directly calculated by finding the square roots of the numerical coefficient and that of the literal coefficients and then multiplying them.

EXAMPLE 5.16 Find the square root of $1296b^4$.

SOLUTION

Now, the given monomial is $1296b^4$.

Square root of

$1296b^4 = \sqrt{1296b^4} = \sqrt{1296} \times \sqrt{b^4}$

$= \sqrt{(36)^2} \times \sqrt{(b^2)} = 36 \times b^2 \Rightarrow \sqrt{1296b^4} = 36b^2.$

EXAMPLE 5.17 Find the square root of $\frac{81b^2a^4}{36x^2y^6}$.

SOLUTION

Square root of $\frac{81b^2a^4}{36x^2y^6} = \sqrt{\frac{81b^2a^4}{36x^2y^6}}$

$$= \sqrt{\frac{81b^2a^4}{36x^2y^6}}$$

$$= \frac{\sqrt{81} \times \sqrt{b^2a^4}}{\sqrt{36} \times \sqrt{x^2y^6}}$$

$$= \frac{\sqrt{9^2} \times \sqrt{(ba^2)^2}}{\sqrt{6^2} \times \sqrt{(xy^3)^2}}$$

$$= \frac{9ba^2}{6xy^3} = \frac{3ba^2}{2xy^3}$$

$\Rightarrow$ Square root of $\frac{81b^2a^4}{36x^2y^6} = \frac{3ba^2}{2xy^3}$.

Methods of Finding the Square Roots of Algebraic Expressions Other Than Monomials

We have four methods to find the square root of an algebraic expression which is not a monomial. They are:

1. Method of inspection (using algebraic identities).
2. Method of factorization
3. Method of division
4. Method of undetermined coefficients

Method of Inspection

In this method, the square root of the given algebraic expression is found by using relevant basic algebraic identities after proper inspection.

EXAMPLE 5.18 Find the square root of $x^2 + 12xy + 36y^2$.

SOLUTION

$x^2 + 12xy + 36y^2 = (x)^2 + 2(x)(6y) + (6y)^2$

We know that $a^2 + 2ab + b^2 = (a + b)^2$

Now,

$$\sqrt{x^2 + 12xy + 36y^2} = \sqrt{(x)^2 + 2(x)(6y) + (6y)^2}$$

$$= \sqrt{(x + 6y)^2} = (x + 6y)$$

$\therefore \sqrt{x^2 + 12xy + 36y^2} = x + 6y$.

EXAMPLE 5.19 Find the square root of $a^2x^2 - 2ayx^2 + x^2y^2$.

SOLUTION

$a^2x^2 - 2ayx^2 + x^2y^2 = x^2(a^2 - 2ay + y^2)$

We know that $a^2 - 2ab + b^2 = (a - b)^2$

Now,

$$\sqrt{a^2x^2 - 2ayx^2 + x^2y^2} = \sqrt{x^2(a^2 - 2ay + y^2)} = \sqrt{x^2(a-y)^2}$$

$$= \sqrt{[x(a-y)]^2} = x(a-y)$$

$$\Rightarrow \sqrt{a^2x^2 - 2ayx^2 + x^2y^2} = x(a-y).$$

Method of Factorization

EXAMPLE 5.20 The square root of $x^2 + 2x + 3 + \frac{2}{x} + \frac{1}{x^2}$ is ________.

SOLUTION

$$x^2 + 2x + 3 + \frac{2}{x} + \frac{1}{x^2}$$

$$= (x)^2 + \left(\frac{1}{x}\right)^2 + 1^2 + 2(x)\left(\frac{1}{x}\right) + 2\left(\frac{1}{x}\right)(1) + 2(x)(1)$$

$$= \left(x + \frac{1}{x} + 1\right)^2$$

$$\therefore \sqrt{x^2 + 2x + 3 + \frac{2}{x} + \frac{1}{x^2}}$$

$$= x + \frac{1}{x} + 1.$$

Method of Division

We discuss the method of division to find the square root of an algebraic expression using the following example.

EXAMPLE 5.21 Find the square root of $x^2 - 18x + 81$.

SOLUTION

	$x - 9$
x	$x^2 - 18x + 81$
	x^2
$2x - 9$	$-18x + 81$
	$-18x + 81$
	0

$$\therefore \sqrt{x^2 - 18x + 81} = x - 9.$$

Step 1: First the given expression is arranged in the descending powers of x.

Step 2: Then the square root of the first term in the expression is calculated. In the above problem, first term is x^2 whose square root is x. This is now the first term of the square root of the expression.

Step 3: Then the square of x, i.e., x^2 is written below the first term of the expression and subtracted. The difference is zero. Then the next two terms in the expression $-18x + 81$ are brought down as the dividend for the next step. Double the first term of the square root and put it down as the first term of the next divisor, i.e., $2(x) = 2x$ is to be written as the first term of the next divisor. Now the first term $-18x$ of the dividend $-18x + 81$ is to be divided by the first term $2x$ (of the new divisor). Here we get -9 which is the second term of the square root of the given expression and the second term of the new divisor.

Step 4: Thus, the new divisor becomes $2x - 9$. Multiply $(2x - 9)$ by (-9) and the product $-18x + 81$ is to be brought down under the second dividend $-18x + 81$ and subtracted where we get 0.

Step 5: Thus, $x - 9$ is the square root of the given expression $x^2 - 18x + 81$.

EXAMPLE 5.22 Find the square root of $4x^6 - 12x^5 + 9x^4 + 8x^3 - 12x^2 + 4$.

SOLUTION

Follow the steps indicated in the previous example.

$$\begin{array}{l|l}
 & 2x^3 - 3x^2 + 2 \\
\hline
2x^3 & 4x^6 - 12x^5 + 9x^4 + 8x^3 - 12x^2 + 4 \\
 & 4x^6 \\
 & - \\
\hline
4x^3 - 3x^2 & \quad -12x^5 + 9x^4 \\
 & \quad -12x^5 + 9x^4 \\
 & \quad + \qquad - \\
\hline
4x^3 - 6x^2 + 2 & \qquad\qquad 8x^3 - 12x^2 + 4 \\
 & \qquad\qquad 8x^3 - 12x^2 + 4 \\
 & \qquad\qquad + \qquad\quad - \\
\hline
 & \qquad\qquad\qquad 0
\end{array}$$

$\therefore \sqrt{4x^6 - 12x^5 + 9x^4 + 8x^3 - 12x^2 + 4} = 2x^3 - 3x^2 + 2.$

Method of Undetermined Coefficients

The method of undetermined coefficients to find the square root of an algebraic expression is explained in the following examples.

EXAMPLE 5.23

(a) Find the square root of $x^4 + 4x^3 + 10x^2 + 12x + 9$.

(b) Find the square root of $4x^4 - 4x^3 + 5x^2 - 2x + 1$.

SOLUTION

(a) The degree of the given expression is 4, its square root will hence be an expression of degree 2. Let us assume the square root to be $ax^2 + bx + c$.

$\Rightarrow x^4 + 4x^3 + 10x^2 + 12x + 9 = (ax^2 + bx + c)^2$

We know that $(p + q + r)^2 = p^2 + q^2 + r^2 + 2pq + 2qr + 2rp$

Here, $p = ax^2$, $q = bx$, $r = c$

$\Rightarrow x^4 + 4x^3 + 10x^2 + 12x + 9$

$= (ax^2)^2 + (bx)^2 + c^2 + 2(ax^2)(bx) + 2(bx)(c) + 2(c)(ax^2)$

$\Rightarrow x^4 + 4x^3 + 10x^2 + 12x + 9 = a^2x^4 + b^2x^2 + 2abx^3 + 2cax^2 + 2bcx + c^2$

Now equating the like terms on either sides of the equality sign, we have,

$x^4 = a^2x^4$

$\Rightarrow a^2 = 1 \Rightarrow a = 1$

$4x^3 = 2abx^3 \Rightarrow 2ab = 4$

$\Rightarrow ab = 2$, but $a = 1 \Rightarrow b = 2$

$b^2 + 2ca = 10 \Rightarrow 2^2 + 2c = 10$

$\Rightarrow 2c = 6 \Rightarrow c = 3$

$\therefore$ The square root of the given expression is $ax^2 + bx + c$, i.e., $x^2 + 2x + 3$.

(b) The degree of the given expression is 4, its square root will hence be an expression in degree 2.

Let $\sqrt{4x^4 - 4x^3 + 5x^2 - 2x + 1} = ax^2 + bx + c$

$\Rightarrow (4x^4 - 4x^3 + 5x^2 - 2x + 1) = (ax^2 + bx + c)^2$

$\Rightarrow 4x^4 - 4x^3 + 5x^2 - 2x + 1$

$= (ax^2)^2 + (bx)^2 + c^2 + 2(ax^2)(bx) + 2(bx)(c) + 2(c)(ax^2)$

$\Rightarrow 4x^4 - 4x^3 + 5x^2 - 2x + 1 = a^2x^4 + 2abx^3 + (b^2 + 2ac)x^2 + 2bcx + c^2$

Now equating the like terms on either sides of the equation, we have,

$4x^4 = a^2x^4 \Rightarrow a^2 = 4 \Rightarrow a = 2$

$c^2 = 1 \Rightarrow c = 1$

$2bcx = -2x \Rightarrow 2bc = -2 \Rightarrow bc = -1$

$\Rightarrow b = \frac{-1}{c} \Rightarrow b = -1 \; (\because c = 1)$

$\therefore$ The square root of the given expression is $ax^2 + bx + c$, i.e., $2x^2 - x + 1$.

Rational Integral Function of x

A polynomial in x, the exponents in powers of x are non-negative integers and the coefficients of the various powers of x are integers.

Example: $11x^2 - 8x + 3$, $4x^2 - 5x + 1$, $8x^5 - 7x^3 + 8x^2 + 4x + 5$, etc.

Remainder Theorem

$q(x)$ is a rational integral function of x.

If $q(x)$ is divided by $x - a$, then the remainder is $q(a)$.

Info Bytes!

If $q(x)$ is divided by $ax - b$, then the remainder is $q\left(\frac{b}{a}\right)$.

EXAMPLE 5.24 The remainder obtained when $x^4 + 3x^2 - 2x - 10$ is divided by $x + 2$ is ________.

SOLUTION

Let $f(x) = x^4 + 3x^2 - 2x - 10$ and divisor $= x + 2$

Remainder $= f(-2)$

$= (-2)^4 + 3(-2)^2 - 2(-2) - 10$

$= 16 + 12 + 4 - 10$

$= 22.$

EXAMPLE 5.25 Find the remainder when $x^2 - 8x + 6$ is divided by $2x - 1$.

SOLUTION

Let $q(x) = x^2 - 8x + 6$

$\therefore$ Remainder $= q\left(\frac{1}{2}\right)$

i.e., $q\left(\frac{1}{2}\right)=\left(\frac{1}{2}\right)^2-8\left(\frac{1}{2}\right)+6$

$=\frac{1}{4}-4+6=\frac{1}{4}+2$

$\therefore q\left(\frac{1}{2}\right)=\frac{9}{4}$.

Factor Theorem

$q(x)$ is a rational integral function of x and if $q(\alpha) = 0$, then $x - \alpha$ is the factor of $q(x)$.

EXAMPLE 5.26

(a) Is $x - 2$ a factor of $x^3 + x^2 - 4x - 4$?
(b) Find the value of m, if $x + 2$ is a factor of $x^3 - 4x^2 + 3x - 5m$.
(c) Factorize $x^3 - 2x^2 - 5x + 6$.
(d) Factorize $x^4 - x^3 - 11x^2 + 9x + 18$.

SOLUTION

(a) Let $q(x) = x^3 + x^2 - 4x - 4$

$q(2) = 8 + 4 - 8 - 4 = 0$

$\therefore x - 2$ is a factor of $q(x)$.

(b) Let $q(x) = x^3 - 4x^2 + 3x - 5m$.

Given $x + 2$ is a factor of $q(x)$.

$\therefore q(-2) = 0$

$\Rightarrow (-2)^3 - 4(-2)^2 + 3(-2) - 5m = 0$

$-8 - 16 - 6 - 5m = 0$

$-5m = 30$

$m = -6$.

(c) Let $f(x) = x^3 - 2x^2 - 5x + 6$

Step 1: First we find one of the factors of $f(x)$ by substituting the value of x as ± 1, ± 2 and so on till the remainder is zero.

Here,

$f(1) = (1)^3 - 2(1)^2 - 5(1) + 6$

$= 1 - 2 - 5 + 6$

$f(1) = 0$

$\therefore x - 1$ is a factor of $f(x)$.

Step 2: To find the other two factors, we use synthetic division.

$x = 1$	1	−2	−5	6
	0	1	−1	−6
	1	−1	−6	0

$\therefore$ The other two factors are $x^2 - x - 6$, i.e., $(x - 3)(x + 2)$.

$\therefore$ The factorization of the given expression is $(x - 1)(x - 3)(x + 2)$.

(d) Let $f(x) = x^4 - x^3 - 11x^2 + 9x + 18$

$f(-1) = (-1)^4 - (-1)^3 - 11(-1)^2 + 9(-1) + 18$

$= 1 + 1 - 11 - 9 + 18 = 20 - 20 = 0$

$\therefore x + 1$ is a factor of $f(x)$.

Now,

$f(2) = (2)^4 - 2^3 - 11(2)^2 + 9(2) + 18$

$= 16 - 8 - 44 + 18 + 18 = 52 - 52 = 0$

$\therefore x - 2$ is a factor of $f(x)$.

$x = -1$	1	−1	−11	9	18
	0	−1	2	9	−18
$x = 2$	1	−2	−9	18	0
	0	2	0	−18	
	1	0	−9	0	

∴ The other two factors of $f(x)$ are $(x + 3)$ and $(x - 3)$.

Hence, the factorization of the given expression, is $(x + 1)(x - 2)(x - 3)(x + 3)$.

POINTS TO REMEMBER

- ✔ A number having a fixed numerical value is called a constant.
- ✔ A number which can take various numerical values is known as a variable.
- ✔ A combination of constants and variables connected by +, −, × and ÷ signs is known as an algebraic expression.
- ✔ Terms having the same literal coefficients are called like terms.
- ✔ Terms having different literal coefficients are called unlike terms.
- ✔ An algebraic expression in which the variables involved have only non-negative integral powers is called a polynomial.
- ✔ The highest index of the variable in a polynomial of one variable is called the degree of the polynomial.
- ✔ A polynomial in x, the exponents in powers of x are non-negative integers and the coefficients of the various powers of x are integers.
- ✔ $q(x)$ is a rational integral function of x. If $q(x)$ is divided by $x - a$, then the remainder is $q(a)$. It is called Remainder theorem.
- ✔ $q(x)$ is a rational integral function of x and if $q(\alpha) = 0$, then $x - \alpha$ is the factor of $q(x)$. It is called Factor Theorem.
- ✔ An algebraic expression in which, the degree of all the terms is equal is a homogeneous expression.

PRACTICE QUESTIONS CLASSROOM WING

Very Short Answer Type Questions

Directions of questions from 1 to 12:
Fill in the blanks.

1. The LCM of $\sqrt{2}x, \sqrt{8}x^7y^2$ is _____.
2. The HCF of $44a^3$ and $66b^pa^4$ is $22a^3$, then p can be _____.
3. If the degree of two polynomials $f(x)$ and $g(x)$ are 15 and 10, then the degree of $(f(x).g(x))$ is _________.
4. The remainder obtained when $2x^5 - 3x^3 + x^2 - 18$ is divided by $x - 2$ is ________.
5. The remainder obtained when $80x^3 + 55x^2 + 20x + 172$ is divided by $x + 2$ is _____.
6. **Simplify:** $n^4 - 4 =$ _____.
7. If $f(x - 2) = 2x^2 + 4x + 9$, then the remainder when $f(x)$ is divided by $(x + 4)$ is ________.
8. Let $f(x) = (3x^2 + 2x - 1)(x^2 - 2x + 4)$, then the product of the coefficients of x^3 and x^3 is _______.
9. The LCM of $48x^by^az^5$ and $72x^cy^bz^a$ is $144x^4y^6z^6$, then find the minimum value of $a + b + c$.
10. The factors of $a^3 + b^3 + c^3 - 3abc$ are _____.
11. The HCF of $(a^2 + 1)(a + 11)$ and $(a^2 + 1)^2\ (a + 11)^2$ is _____.
12. The value of $81^3 - 100^3 + 19^3$ is _____.

Directions of questions from 13 to 23:
Answer the following questions.

13. If $x - 1$ is a factor of $x^2 - bx + 8$, then the value of b is _____.
14. Find the LCM and HCF of the polynomials $15x^2y^3z$, $3x^3yz^2$.
15. Find the remainder when x^{15} is divided by $x - 2$.
16. Find the remainder if $x^5 - 3x^3 + 5x + 1$ is divided by $2x - 1$.
17. Factorize $a^5b - ab^5$.
18. The degree of a polynomial A is 7 and that of polynomial AB is 56, then find the degree of polynomial B.
19. If $A = x^3$, $B = 4x^2 + x - 1$, then find AB.
20. Factorize $m^7 + m^4$.
21. Factorize $\frac{1}{6}a^2 - a + \frac{4}{3}$.
22. If $3x^2 + 8ax + 3$ is a perfect square, then find the value of a.
23. If $A = 4x^3 - 8x^2$, $B = 7x^3 - 5x + 3$ and $C = 3x^3 + x - 11$, then find $(A + C) - B$.

Short Answer Type Questions

24. If the HCF of the polynomials $(x^2 - 1)^{2018}\ (x - 2)^a$ and $(x - 1)^{2019}\ (x - 2)^{2018}$ is $(x - 1)^b\ (x - 2)^{1009}$, then the LCM of a and b is _______.
25. If $2018x^{2018} - 2017x^{2017} + \ldots\ldots\ldots\ldots + 2x^2 - x + k$ is divided by $x - 1$, the remainder is 1, then k is _______.
26. If $A = 4x^3 - 8x^2$, $B = 7x^3 - 5x + 3$ and $C = 3x^3 + x - 11$, then find $2A - 3B + 4C$.
27. If $A = x^3$, $B = 4x^2 + x - 1$, $C = x + 1$, then find $(A - B)(A - C)$.
28. Find the quotient and remainder when $x^4 + 4x^3 - 31x^2 - 94x + 120$ is divided by $x^2 + 3x - 4$.
29. Factorize $a^3 + \frac{3ax}{8} + \frac{x^3}{64} - \frac{1}{8}$.
30. Find the LCM and HCF of the following polynomials. $36(x + 2)^2\ (x - 1)^3\ (x + 3)^5$, $45(x + 2)^5\ (x - 1)^2\ (x + 3)^5$ and $63(x - 1)^5\ (x + 2)^5\ (x + 3)^4$.
31. The LCM of the polynomials $(x^2 + x - 2)\ (x^2 + x - a)$ and $(x^2 + x - b)(x^2 + 5x + a)$ is $(x - 1)\ (x + 2)^2\ (x + 3)$, then find the values of a and b.
32. Find the remainder when x^{23} is divided by $x^2 - 3x + 2$.
33. If $lmx^2 + mnx + ln$ is a perfect square then prove that, $4l^2 = mn$.
34. Find the value of

$$\sqrt{(a+b+c)^2 + (a+b-c)^2 + 2(c^2 - a^2 - b^2 - 2ab)}.$$

35. If $\sqrt{\frac{125a^6b^4c^2}{5a^4b^2}} = x$, then find $\frac{x^2}{abc}$.

36. Find the square root of $(x^2 + 6x + 8)(x^2 + 5x + 6)(x^2 + 7x + 12)$.

Essay Type Questions

37. The square root of $x^4 + 6x^2 + 4x + 9 + \frac{12}{x} + \frac{4}{x^2}$ is ________.

38. $P(x) = x^4 - 2x^3 + 3x^2 - mx + n$ leaves the remainders 5 and 19 when divided by $(x - 1)$ and $(x + 1)$ respectively. The remainder when $P(x)$ is divided by $(x - 2)$ is ______.

39. Find the square root of $16x^6 - 24x^5 + 25x^4 - 20x^3 + 10x^2 - 4x + 1$ by the method of division.

40. Find the quadratic polynomial when divided by x, $x - 1$ and $x - 2$ leaves remainders 1, 2, and 9, respectively.

41. Find the factors of $a^2(b + c) + b^2(c + a) + c^2(a + b) - 2b^2c$.

PRACTICE QUESTIONS COMPETITION WING

Level 1: Apply Your Concepts

Directions of questions from 1 to 4:
Fill in the blanks.

1. $11x^2 - 88x^3 + 14x^4$ is called a _____ polynomial.
2. The degree of the polynomial $7x^3y^{10}z^2$ is _____.
3. If $a + b + c = 0$, then $a^3 + b^3 + c^3 =$ _____.
4. Factors of $x^6 - y^6$ is _____.

Directions of questions from 5 to 61:
Select the correct alternative from the given choices.

5. The following are the steps involved in factorizing $x^4 + x^2 + 1$. Arrange them in sequential order.
   (A) $(x^2 + 1)^2 - x^2$
   (B) $x^4 + x^2 + 1 = x^4 + 2x^2 + 1 - x^2$
   (C) $(x^2 + 1 + x)(x^2 + 1 - x)$
   (D) $(x^2)^2 + 2(x^2)(1) + 1^2 - x^2$
   (a) DBCA (b) DBAC
   (c) BDAC (d) BDCA

6. If $f(x, y) = 5x^5 - 3y^5 + 2x^3y^a - 7x^by$ is a homogeneous expression, then $a - b =$ _____.
   (a) –4 (b) –2
   (c) 2 (d) 4

7. The remainder when $x^3 - 3x^2 + 5x - 1$ is divided by $x + 1$ is _____.
   (a) –8 (b) –12
   (c) –10 (d) –9

8. Which of the following is a homogeneous expression?
   (a) $4x^2 - 5xy + 5x^2y + 10y^2$
   (b) $5x + 10y + 100$
   (c) $14x^3 + 15x^2y + 16y^2x + 24y^3$
   (d) $x^2 + y^2 + x + y + 1$

9. $\Sigma x(y^3 - z^3) =$ _____.
   (a) $(x - y)(y - z)(z - x)(x + y + z)$
   (b) $(x - y)(y - z)(x - z)(x - y - z)$
   (c) $(x + y)(y + z)(z + x)(x + y + z)$
   (d) $(x + y)(y + z)(z + z)(z - y - z)$

10. The remainder when $f(x) = 4x^3 - 3x^2 + 2x - 1$ is divided by $2x + 1$ is _____.
    (a) 1 (b) $\frac{-3}{4}$
    (c) $\frac{-13}{4}$ (d) $\frac{-7}{4}$

11. The HCF of the polynomials $12a^3b^4c^2$, $18a^4b^3c^3$ and $24a^6b^2c^4$ is _____.
    (a) $12a^3b^2c^2$ (b) $6a^6b^4c^4$
    (c) $6a^3b^2c^2$ (d) $48a^6b^4c^4$

12. If $x + 1$ is a factor of $x^2 + 8x + a$, then the value of a is _____.
    (a) 5 (b) 6
    (c) 7 (d) 8

13. Which of the following is not a polynomial?
    (a) $x^2 + \sqrt{2017}$ (b) $x^2 + x + \frac{1}{2}$
    (c) $x^2 + \sqrt{x} + 2018$ (d) All of these.

14. If the expression $ax^3 + 2x^2y - bxy^2 - 2y^3$ is symmetric, then $(a, b) =$
    (a) (2, 2) (b) (–2, 2)
    (c) (–2, –2) (d) (2, –2)

15. The square root of $y^2 + \frac{1}{y^2} + 2$ is
    (a) $y + \frac{1}{y}$ (b) $y - \frac{1}{y}$
    (c) $y^2 + \frac{1}{y^2}$ (d) $y^2 - \frac{1}{y^2}$

16. The product of the polynomials $2x^3 - 3x^2 + 6$ and $x^2 - x$ is _____.
    (a) $2x^6 - 5x^4 + 3x^3 + 6x^2 - 6x$
    (b) $2x^5 - x^4 + 3x^3 - 6x^2 + 6x$
    (c) $2x^5 - 5x^4 + 3x^3 + 6x^2 - 6x$
    (d) None of these

17. The HCF of $x^by^cz^5$ and $x^ay^bz^4$ is $x^2y^2z^c$,, then find the minimum value of $a + b + c$.
    (a) 6 (b) 7
    (c) 8 (d) 9

18. If $P = 3x^3 - 5x + 9$, $Q = 4x^3 + 5x^2 - 11$ and $R = 5x^3 + 4x^2 - 3x + 7$, then $P - 2Q + R$ is:
    (a) $2(3x^2 + 4x - 19)$ (b) $-6x^2 - 5x + 38$
    (c) $-2(3x^2 + 4x + 19)$ (d) $-2(3x^2 + 4x - 19)$

19. If $g(x) = 3a^x + 7a^2b - 13ab^2 + 9b^y$ is a homogeneous expression in terms of a and b, then the values of x and y, respectively, are ______.
(a) 2, 2 (b) 2, 1
(c) 3, 2 (d) 3, 3

20. The polynomial $11a^2 - 12\sqrt{2}\,a + 2$ on factorization gives
(a) $(11a+\sqrt{2})(a-\sqrt{2})$ (b) $(a-\sqrt{2})(11a-\sqrt{2})$
(c) $(a+11)(a+\sqrt{2})$ (d) $(11a-\sqrt{2})(a+\sqrt{2})$

21. If $x^n + 1$ is divisible by $x + 1$, n must be:
(a) Any natural number (b) An odd natural number
(c) An even natural number (d) None of these

22. What is the first degree expression to be subtracted from $x^6 + 8x^4 + 2x^3 + 16x^2 + 4x + 5$ in order to make it a perfect square?
(a) $-4x - 4$ (b) $4x + 4$
(c) $4x - 4$ (d) $-4x + 4$

23. Find the square root of $\dfrac{m^{n^2} n^{m^2} a^{(m+n)}}{(m+n)^{(m+n)^2}}$.
(a) $m^n n^m a^{\frac{m+n}{2}}$ (b) $\dfrac{m^{\frac{n^2}{2}} n^{\frac{m^2}{2}} a^{\frac{m+n}{2}}}{(m+n)^{\frac{(m+n)^2}{2}}}$
(c) $\dfrac{m^n n^m a^{\sqrt{m+n}}}{(m+n)^{(m+n)}}$ (d) None of these

24. What is the first-degree expression to be added to $16x^6 + 8x^4 - 2x^3 + x^2 + 2x + 1$ in order to make it a perfect square?
(a) $\frac{5}{2}x + \frac{15}{16}$ (b) $-\frac{5}{2}x - \frac{15}{16}$
(c) $-\frac{5}{2}x + \frac{15}{16}$ (d) $+\frac{2}{2}x - \frac{15}{16}$

25. Factorize the polynomial $8x^3 - \dfrac{1}{64}$.
(a) $\left(2x - \frac{1}{4}\right)\left(4x^2 - \frac{x}{2} + \frac{1}{16}\right)$
(b) $\left(2x - \frac{1}{8}\right)\left(4x^2 + \frac{x}{2} - 16\right)$
(c) $\left(2x - \frac{1}{4}\right)\left(4x^2 + \frac{1}{16} + \frac{x}{2}\right)$
(d) $\left(2x - \frac{1}{4}\right)\left(4x^2 + \frac{x}{2} - 16\right)$

26. The LCM and HCF of two monomials is $60x^4y^5a^6b^6$ and $5x^2y^3$, respectively. If one of the two monomials is $15x^4y^3a^6$, then the other monomial is:
(a) $12x^2y^3a^6b^6$ (b) $20x^4y^5b^6$
(c) $20x^2y^5b^6$ (d) $15x^2y^5b^6$

27. Which of the following is a factor of the polynomial $f(x) = 2x^3 - 5x^2 + x + 2$?
(a) $x + 1$ (b) $x + 2$
(c) $2x + 1$ (d) $2x - 1$

28. If $3x - 1$ is a factor of the polynomial $81x^3 - 45x^2 + 3a - 6$, then a is ______.
(a) $\frac{8}{3}$ (b) $\frac{-7}{3}$
(c) $\frac{-10}{3}$ (d) $\frac{11}{3}$

29. The square root of $x^{m^2-n^2} \cdot x^{n^2+2mn} \cdot x^{n^2}$ is:
(a) x^{m+n} (b) $x^{(m+n)^2}$
(c) $x^{(m+n)/2}$ (d) $x^{\frac{1}{2}(m+n)^2}$

30. $x^{831} + y^{831}$ is always divisible by:
(a) $x - y$ (b) $x^2 + y^2$
(c) $x + y$ (d) None of these

31. If $(x + 1)(x + 2)(x + 3)(x + k) + 1$ is a perfect square, then the value of k is:
(a) 4 (b) 5
(c) 6 (d) 7

Level 2: Review Your Concepts

32. If $x + \dfrac{1}{x} = 4$, then find $x^3 + \left(\dfrac{1}{x}\right)^3$.
The following are the steps involved in solving the above problem. Arrange them in a sequential order.
(A) $x^3 + \left(\frac{1}{x}\right)^3 = 52$
(B) $x^3 + \left(\frac{1}{x}\right)^3 + (3)(4) = 64$
(C) $\left(x + \frac{1}{x}\right)^3 = 64$
(D) $x^3 + \left(\frac{1}{x}\right)^3 + 3\left(x + \frac{1}{x}\right) = 64$

(a) CBAD (b) CDBA
(c) DCAB (d) CDAB

33. Which of the following is a polynomial?

(a) $x^2 + x\sqrt{x}$ (b) $x^2 + \frac{7}{6}y^2 - 9$
(c) $y^{-1/2} + 3x + 2$ (d) $\sqrt{2x} + \sqrt{3}$

34. If $x^n - y^n$ is divisible by $(x - y)$, then n is ______.
(a) even (b) odd
(c) any natural number (d) Cannot say

35. $(2x + 3y)^2 + (2x - 3y)^2 =$ ________.
(a) $8x^2 + 18y^2$ (b) $4x^2 + 9y^2$
(c) $12xy$ (d) $24xy$

36. If $f(x + 3) = x^2 - 2x + 8$, then the remainder, when $f(x)$ is divisible by $(x - 2)$ is ________.
(a) 9 (b) 11
(c) 13 (d) 15

37. The polynomial $6y^4 - 19y^3 - 23y^2 + 10y + 8$ on factorization gives:
(a) $(y + 1)(y - 4)(3y + 2)(2y + 1)$
(b) $(y + 1)(y - 4)(3y - 2)(2y - 1)$
(c) $(y + 1)(y - 4)(3y - 2)(2y + 1)$
(d) $(y + 1)(y - 4)(3y + 2)(2y - 1)$

38. If the LCM of the polynomials $(y - 3)^a(2y + 1)^b(y + 13)^7$ and $(y - 3)^4(2y + 1)^9(y + 13)^c$ is $(y - 3)^6(2y + 1)^{10}(y + 13)^7$, then the least value of $a + b + c$ is:
(a) 23 (b) 3
(d) 10 (d) 16

39. The LCM of the polynomials $195(x + 3)^2(x - 2)(x + 1)^2$ and $221(x + 1)^3(x + 3)(x + 4)$ is ______.
(a) $221(x + 3)^2 (x + 1)^2(x - 2)(x - 14)$
(b) $13(x + 3)(x + 1)^2$
(c) $3315 (x + 3)^2 (x + 1)^3(x - 2)(x + 4)$
(d) None of these

40. For what value of k the HCF of $x^2 + x + (5k - 1)$ and $x^2 - 6x + (3k + 11)$ is $(x - 2)$?
(a) 2 (b) 2
(c) −2 (d) −1

41. The HCF of the polynomials $9(x + a)^p(x - b)^q (x + c)^r$ and $12(x + a)^{p+3}(x - b)^{q-3}(x + c)^{r+2}$ is $3(x + a)^6(x - b)^6(x + c)^6$, then the value of $p + q - r$ is:
(a) 21 (b) 9
(c) 15 (d) 6

42. The remainders obtained when the polynomial $x^3 + x^2 - 9x - 9$ divided by x, $x + 1$, and $x + 2$, respectively, are ______.
(a) −9, 0, −15 (b) −9, −16, 5
(c) 0, 0, 5 (d) −9, 0, 5

43. Find the value of

$$\frac{(a+b)^2}{(b-c)(c-a)} + \frac{(b+c)^2}{(a-b)(c-a)} + \frac{(c+a)^2}{(a-b)(b-c)}.$$

(a) −1 (b) 0
(c) 1 (d) 2

44. Find the square root of the expression

$$\frac{1}{xyz}(x^2 + y^2 + z^2) + 2\left(\frac{1}{x} + \frac{1}{y} + \frac{1}{z}\right).$$

(a) $\frac{x + y + z}{xyz}$ (b) $\sqrt{\frac{yz}{x}} + \sqrt{\frac{zx}{y}} + \sqrt{\frac{xy}{z}}$
(c) $\sqrt{x} + \sqrt{y} + \sqrt{z}$ (d) $\sqrt{\frac{x}{yz}} + \sqrt{\frac{y}{xz}} + \sqrt{\frac{z}{xy}}$

45. Factorize the expression $9x^4 + \frac{1}{x^4} + 2$.

(a) $\left(3x^2 - \frac{1}{x^2} + 2\right)\left(3x^2 + \frac{1}{x^2} + 2\right)$
(b) $\left(3x^2 - \frac{1}{x^2} - 2\right)\left(3x^2 + \frac{1}{x^2} + 2\right)$
(c) $\left(3x^2 - \frac{1}{x^2} + 2\right)\left(3x^2 - \frac{1}{x^2} + 2\right)$
(d) $\left(3x^2 + \frac{1}{x^2} + 2\right)\left(3x^2 + \frac{1}{x^2} - 2\right)$

46. The following are the steps involved in factorizing $64x^6 - y^6$. Arrange them in sequential order.
(A) $\{(2x)^3 + y^3\}\ \{(2x)^3 - y^3\}$
(B) $(8x^3)^2 - (y^3)^2$
(C) $(8x^3 + y^3)(8x^3 - y^3)$
(D) $(2x + y)(4x^2 - 2xy + y^2)(2x - y)(4x^2 + 2xy + y^2)$
(a) BADC (b) BDAC
(c) BCAD (d) BACD

47. If $a + b + c = 0$, show that $a^3 + b^3 + c^3 = 3abc$.
The following are the steps involved in showing the above result. Arrange them in sequential order.
(A) $a^3 + b^3 + 3ab(-c) = -c^3$
(B) $(a + b)^3 = (-c)^3$

(C) $a + b + c = 0 \Rightarrow a + b = -c$
(D) $a^3 + b^3 + 3ab(a + b) = -c^3$
(E) $a^3 + b^3 + c^3 = 3abc$

(a) ABDCE (b) BCDAE
(c) CBDAE (d) CADBE

48. The polynomial $5x^5 - 3x^3 + 2x^2 - k$ gives a remainder 1, when divided by $x + 1$. Find the value of k.
(a) 5 (b) −1
(c) 2 (d) 1

49. If $x + \frac{1}{x} = 3$, then $\sqrt{x} + \sqrt{\frac{1}{x}}$ can be ______.
(a) $\sqrt{3}$ (b) $\sqrt{5}$
(c) $\sqrt{7}$ (d) $\sqrt{2}$

50. If f and g are two polynomials of degrees 3 and 4, respectively, then what is the degree of $f - g$?
(a) 1 (b) 3
(c) 4 (d) Cannot be determined

51. Find the square root of $\frac{x^2}{9} + \frac{9}{4x^2} - \frac{x}{3} - \frac{3}{2x} + \frac{5}{4}$.
(a) $\frac{2x}{3} + \frac{3}{2x} - \frac{1}{2}$ (b) $\frac{x}{3} - \frac{3}{2x} + 1$
(c) $\frac{3}{x} + \frac{2}{3x} - \frac{1}{2}$ (d) $\frac{x}{3} + \frac{3}{2x} - \frac{1}{2}$

52. The square root of $(xy + xz - yz)^2 - 4xyz(x - y)$ is ______.
(a) $xy + yz - 2xyz$ (b) $(x + y - 2xy)$
(c) $(xy + 3 - y)$ (d) $(xy + yz - zx)$

Level 3: Assess Your Concepts

53. If $\sqrt{4x^4 + 12x^3 + 25x^2 + 24x + 16} = ax^2 + bx + c$, then which of the following is true?
(a) $2b = a - c$
(b) $2a = b + c$
(c) $2b = a + c$
(d) $2b = c - a$

54. Find the square root of the algebraic expression which is the average of the following expressions: $x^2 + \frac{1}{x^2}, -2\left(x - \frac{1}{x}\right)$ and -1.
(a) $\frac{x}{\sqrt{3}} - \frac{1}{\sqrt{3}} + \frac{1}{x}$ (b) $\frac{x}{\sqrt{3}} + 1 + x$
(c) $\frac{1}{\sqrt{3}}\left(x - 1 - \frac{1}{x}\right)$ (d) None of these

55. If the each of algebraic expressions $lx^2 + mx + n$, $mx^2 + nx + l$ and $nx^2 + lx + m$ are prefect squares, then $\frac{l + m}{n} =$ ______.
(a) −4 (b) 6
(c) −8 (d) None of these

56. Which of the following is to be added to make $x^6 - 6x^4 + 4x^3 + 8x^2 - 10x + 3$ a perfect square?
(a) $(x - 1)^2$ (b) $(x - 2)^2$
(c) $(2x - 3)^2$ (d) $(2x + 1)^2$

57. Find the square root of $\frac{a^2}{4} + \frac{1}{a^2} - \frac{1}{a} + \frac{a}{2} - \frac{3}{4}$.
(a) $\frac{a}{2} - \frac{1}{a} + \frac{1}{2}$ (b) $\frac{a}{2} + \frac{2}{a} - 1$
(c) $\frac{a}{2} + \frac{1}{a} - \frac{1}{2}$ (d) $\frac{a}{2} - \frac{2}{a} - \frac{1}{2}$

58. $\frac{(x + y)^3 + (x - y)^3}{2} - y(3x^2 + y^2) =$ ______.
(a) $x^3 - y^3$ (b) $(x - y)^3$
(c) $2x^3 - 3x^2y$ (d) $x^3 - 6xy^2$

59. Find the square root of $(4a + 5b + 5c)^2 - (5a + 4b + 4c)^2 + 9a^2$.
(a) $\sqrt{3}\,(b + c)$ (b) $3(b + c - a)$
(c) $3(b + c)$ (d) $3(b + c - a)$

60. $\frac{(a - b)^3 - (a + b)^3}{2} + a(a^2 + 3b^2) =$ ______.
(a) $a^3 - b^3$ (b) $(a + b)^3$
(c) $a^3 + b^3$ (d) $(a - b)^3$

61. The square root of $(3a + 2b + 3c)^2 - (2a + 3b + 2c)^2 + 5b^2$ is
(a) $\sqrt{5}(a + b + c)$ (b) $\sqrt{5}(a + b)$
(c) $\sqrt{5}(a + c)$ (d) $\sqrt{5}(a + c - b)$

AT

PRACTICE QUESTIONS JEE SPECIAL WING

Multiple-Answer Type Questions

Directions for questions 1 to 9:
Each question has FOUR options (a), (b), (c), and (d). ONE OR MORE THAN ONE of these four option(s) is/are the correct answer(s).

1. A and B are two polynomials of degree 10 each. Which of the following can be the degree of polynomial $A - B$?

(a) 2 (b) 3
(c) 5 (d) 7

2. Which of the following are trinomials?

(a) $(3x^2 - 5yz^2)(3x^2 - 5yz^2)$
(b) $(3x^2 + 5yz^2)(3x^2 - 5yz^2)$
(c) $(3x^2 + 5yz^2)(3x^2 + 5yz^2)$
(d) $(3x^2 + 5yz^2)(3x^2 - 5yz^2)(9x^4 + 25y^2z^4)$

3. A, B and $\frac{A}{B}$ are three polynomials. If the degree of polynomial $\frac{A}{B}$ is 4, then which of the following can be true?

(a) The degree of A is 12 and the degree of B is 3.
(b) The degree of A is 8 and the degree of B is 2.
(c) The degree of A is 6 and the degree of B is 2.
(d) The degree of A is 4 and the degree of B is 0.

4. The LCM of $(3x + 2y^4)^n$ and $(3x + 2y^4)^{10}$ is $(3x + 2y^4)^n$. Which of the following can be the value of n?

(a) 5 (b) 10
(c) 50 (d) 100

5. The HCF of $(x+3y)^2(2x-y)^n$ and $(x+3y)^m(2x-y)^3$ is $(x+3y)^m(2x-y)^n$. Which of the following can be the value of $m+n$?

(a) 2 (b) 3
(c) 4 (d) 5

6. If the square of a polynomial A is $y^4 - 2y^3 + 3y^2 - 2y + 1$, then which of the following can be A?

(a) $y^2 - y + 1$ (b) $y^2 + y - 1$
(c) $y^2 - y - 1$ (d) $-y^2 + y - 1$

7. Given that $f(y) = y^4 + 2y^3 + y^2 + y + 1$. Which of the following can be the degree of one of the factors of $f(y)$?

(a) 0 (b) 1
(c) 2 (d) 3

8. Which of the following is/are factor(s) of $x^6 - y^6$?

(a) $x^4 + x^2y^2 + y^4$ (b) $x^3 + 2x^2y + 2xy^2 + y^3$
(c) $x^4 - x^2y^2 + y^4$ (d) $x^3 - 2x^2y + 2xy^2 - y^3$

9. Which of the following are factor(s) of $x^4 - 17x^2 + 16$?

(a) $x - 1$ (b) $x - 2$
(c) $x - 4$ (d) $x + 4$

Match The Column

Directions for questions 10 to 15:
Read the paragraph given below and answer the questions.
Polynomials are used in various fields. Some of them are as follows:

- Financial Planning
- Construction
- Expense Budgeting
- Gravitational Acceleration
- Trajectory of Projectiles
- Voltage Difference

In the following table, column-A consists of polynomials and column-B consists of some of the factors of the polynomials. Match the values in Column A with those in Column B.

Column A (Polynomial	Column B (Factor)
10. $x^3+x^2-17x+15$	(a) $x+5$
11. $x^3+3x^2-22x-24$	(b) $x+3$
12. $x^3+3x^2-28x-60$	(c) $x+2$
13. $x^3-15x^2+66x-80$	(d) $x+1$
14. $x^3+4x^2-17x-60$	(e) $x-1$
15. $x^4-5x^3+5x^2+5x-6$	(f) $x-2$
	(g) $x-3$
	(h) $x-4$
	(i) $x-5$

Comprehension-Based Questions

Directions for questions 16 to 20:

Read the paragraph given below and answer the questions.

A polynomial can be shown on the coordinate plane. We can represent a polynomial in the form of a graph. Graph can be a point, straight lines, or curved lines. Anvesh, an enthusiastic student, gave a polynomial for given graph. The polynomial is as follows:

$f(x-3)=x^3-6x^2+14x-8.$

Answer the following questions based on the polynomial given by Anvesh.

16. What is the remainder when $f(x)$ is divided by $(x-3)$?

(a) 62 (b) 76
(c) 84 (d) 98

17. What is the remainder when $f(x)$ is divided by $(x+2)$?

(a) 1 (b) 2
(c) 3 (d) 4

18. What is the remainder when $f(x-4)$ is divided by $(x-1)$?

(a) −6 (b) −8
(c) −10 (d) −12

19. What is the remainder when $f(x-2)$ is divided by $(x-2)$?

(a) 3 (b) 37
(c) 7 (d) 33

20. Find the polynomial $f(x-1)$.

(a) x^3+4x^2+2x+4 (b) x^3+8x^2+2x+4
(c) x^3+4x+4 (d) x^3+2x+4

Assertion and Reason Type Questions

Directions for questions 21 to 25:

Read the options given below and answer the questions.

(a) Both assertion (A) and reason (R) are true, and the reason (R) is the correct explanation of the assertion (A).

(b) Both assertion (A) and reason (R) are true, and the reason (R) is not the correct explanation of the assertion (A).

(c) Assertion (A) is true, but reason (R) is false.

(d) Assertion (A) is false, and reason (R) is true.

21. Assertion: If $f(x)=5x^7+6x^6-7x^5+8x^4-5x^3-6x^2+7x-8$, then $x-1$ is a factor of $f(x)$.

Reason: If the sum of the numerical coefficients of a polynomial is zero, then $x-1$ is a factor of the polynomial.

22. Assertion: If $f(x)=5x^7-6x^6-7x^5-8x^4-5x^3+6x^2+7x+18$, then $x+1$ is a factor of $f(x)$.

Reason: If the sum of the numerical coefficients of even powers of variables is equal to the sum of the numerical coefficients of odd powers of variables of a polynomial, then $x+1$ is a factor of the polynomial.

23. **Assertion:** The factors of $x^2 - 7x + 10$ are $x - 2$ and $x - 5$.
Reason: The maximum possible number of factors of a quadratic polynomial is two.

24. **Assertion:** If the LCM of two linear polynomials is $x^2 - 1$, then their HCF is 1.
Reason: The HCF of $x^2 - y^2$ and $x + y$ is 1.

25. **Assertion:** If n is a positive even number, then the square root of $\left(4x^2 + 17x - 12\right)^n$ is $\left(4x^2 + 17x - 12\right)^{\frac{n}{2}}$.
Reason: The square of $x^2 + y^2$ is $x^4 + 2x^2y^2 + y^4$.

ANSWER KEYS

Crossword

Across

1. Four 2. Symmetric 3. Homogeneous 7. Polynomial 9. Like
10. Binomial 11. Zero

Down

1. Factorization 4. Complete 5. Unlike 6. Monomial 8. Cyclic

Classroom Wing

Very Short Answer Type Questions

1. $\sqrt{8}x^7y^2$ 2. any real number 3. 25 4. 26 5. –288
6. $(n^2+2)(n+\sqrt{2})(n-\sqrt{2})$ 7. 9 8. –28 9. 10
10. $(a + b + c)(a^2 + b^2 + c^2 - ab - bc - ca)$ 11. $(a^2 + 1)(a + 11)$ 12. –461700 13. 9
14. The LCM of given polynomials $= 3 \times 5 \times x^3 \times y^3 \times z^3 = 15x^3y^3z^3$
The HCF of given polynomials $= 3x^2yz^2$
15. $f(2) = 2^{15}$ 16. $f\left(\frac{1}{2}\right)=\frac{101}{32}$ 17. $ab(a^2 + b^2)(a + b)(a - b)$ 18. 49
19. $4x^5 + x^4 - x^3$ 20. $m^4(m + 1)(m^2 - m + 1)$ 21. $\frac{1}{6}(a-2)(a-4)$
22. 2018 23. $-8x^2 + 6x - 14$

Short Answer Type Questions

24. 1, 1 25. –1008 26. $-x^3 - 16x^2 + 19x - 53$
27. $x^6 - 4x^5 - 2x^4 + 4x^3 + 5x^2 - 1$ 28. $x^2 + x - 30, 0$
29. $\left(a+\frac{x}{4}-\frac{1}{2}\right)\left(a^2+\frac{x^2}{16}+\frac{1}{4}-\frac{ax}{4}+\frac{x}{8}+\frac{a}{2}\right)$
30. HCF $= 9(x + 2)^2(x - 1)^2(x + 3)^4$, LCM $= 1260\ (x + 2)^5(x - 1)^5(x + 3)^5$
31. $a = 6, b = 2$ 32. $(2^{23} - 1)x + (2 - 2^{23})$ 34. $2c$
35. $25abc$ 36. $(x + 2)(x + 3)(x + 4)$

Essay Type Questions

37. $x^2+\frac{2}{x}+3$ 38. 10
39. $4x^3 - 3x^2 + 2x - 1$ 40. $3x^2 - 2x + 1$
41. $ab(a + b) + ac(a + c) + bc(c - b)$

Competition Wing

Level 1: Apply Your Concepts

1. biquadratic
2. 15
3. $a^3 + b^3 + c^3 = 3abc$
4. $(x - y)(x + y)(x^2 + y^2 - xy)(x^2 + y^2 + xy)$
5. (c)
6. (b)
7. (c)
8. (c)
9. (a)
10. (c)
11. (c)
12. (c)
13. (b)
14. (c)
15. (a)
16. (c)
17. (d)
18. (d)
19. (d)
20. (b)
21. (b)
22. (d)
23. (b)
24. (b)
25. (c)
26. (c)
27. (c)
28. (a)
29. (d)
30. (c)
31. (a)

Level 2: Review Your Concepts

32. (b)
33. (b)
34. (c)
35. (a)
36. (d)
37. (b)
38. (d)
39. (c)
40. (d)
41. (b)
42. (d)
43. (a)
44. (d)
45. (d)
46. (c)
47. (c)
48. (b)
49. (b)
50. (c)
51. (d)
52. (d)

Level 3: Assess Your Concepts

53. (c)
54. (c)
55. (a)
56. (a)
57. (a)
58. (b)
59. (c)
60. (d)
61. (c)

JEE Special Wing

Multiple-Answer Type Questions

1. (a, b, c, d)
2. (a, c)
3. (c, d)
4. (b, c, d)
5. (a, b, c, d)
6. (a, d)
7. (a, b, d)
8. (a, b, d)
9. (a, c, d)

Match The Column

10. (a, e, g)
11. (d, h)
12. (c, i)
13. (f, i)
14. (b, h)
15. (d, e, f, g)

Comprehension-Based Questions

16. (b)
17. (a)
18. (c)
19. (c)
20. (d)

Assertion and Reason Type Questions

21. (a)
22. (d)
23. (b)
24. (c)
25. (b)

Hints and Explanations

Classroom Wing

Very Short Answer Type Questions

1. The LCM of $\sqrt{2}x$, $\sqrt{8}x^7y^2$ is

$\sqrt{8}\cdot\sqrt{2}=\sqrt{8}$

$x^7\cdot x=x^7$

$y^0\cdot y^2=y^2$

$\sqrt{8}x^7y^2$

2. The HCF of $44a^3$ and $66b^pa^4$ is $22a^3$, then p can be any real number as one of the expression does not have the variable 'b' value of p can be any real number.

3. Degree of $f(x).\,g(x)$ = Degree of $f(x)$ + Degree of $g(x)$ $= 15 + 10 = 25$.

4. Let $f(x) = 2x^5 - 3x^3 + x^2 - 18$ and divisor $= x - 2$

Remainder $= f(2)$

$= 2(2)^5 - 3(2)^3 + (2)^2 - 18$

$= 64 - 24 + 4 - 18$

$= 68 - 42$

$= 26$.

5. Remainder theorem $\rightarrow q(x)$ divided by $x - a$, then remainder is $q(a)$

$q(x) = 80x^3 + 55x^2 + 20x + 172$

$q(-2) = 80(-2)^3 + 55\,(-2)^2 + 20(-2) + 172$

$= 80(-8) + 55\,(4) + (-40) + 172$

$= -288$

6. $n^4 - 4 = (n^2)^2 - 2^2$

$= (n^2 + 2)\,(n^2 - 2)$

$= \left(n^2+2\right)\left(n+\sqrt{2}\right)\left(n-\sqrt{2}\right)$

7. Given, $f(x - 2) = 2x^2 + 4x + 9$

The remainder, when $f(x)$ is divided by $x + 4$ is $f(-4)$.

Put $x = -2$

$\Rightarrow f(-2-2) = 2(-2)^2 + 4(-2) + 9$

$\Rightarrow f(-4) = 8 - 8 + 9 = 9$.

8. $f(x) = (3x^2 + 2x - 1)(x^2 - 2x + 4)$

$= 3x^4 - 6x^3 + 12x^2 + 2x^3 - 4x^2 + 8x - x^2 + 2x - 4$

$= 3x^4 - 4x^3 + 7x^2 + 10x - 4$

The product of coefficients of x^3 and $x^2 = (-4)\,(7)$

$= -28$

9. Given, LCM of $4x^b\,y^a\,z^5$ and $72x^c\,y^b\,z^a$ is $144x^4y^6z^6$

The possible values of $a = 6$, $b \le 4$, $c = 4$

$\min(a + b + c) = 6 + 0 + 4 = 10$

10. $a^3 + b^3 + c^3 = (a + b + c)\,(a^2 + b^2 + c^2 - ab - bc - ca) + 3abc$

$a^3 + b^3 + c^3 - 3abc = (a + b + c)\,(a^2 + b^2 + c^2 - ab - bc - ca)$

11. $(a^2 + 1)(a + 11)$ is the highest common factor

12. $(a + b)^3 = a^3 + b^3 + 3ab(a + b)$

$81^3 = (80 + 1)^3$

$= 80^3 + 1^3 + 3 \times 80 \times 1(80 + 1)$

$= 531441$

$100^3 = (90 + 10)^3$

$= 90^3 + 10^3 + 3 \times 90 \times 10(90 + 10)$

$= 1000000$

$19^3 = 20^3 - 1^3 - 3 \times 20 \times 1(20 - 1) = 6859$

$81^3 - 100^3 + 19^3 = -461700$

13. Let $f(x) = x^2 - bx + 8$ and a factor is $(x - 1)$

$\Rightarrow f(1) = 0$

$\Rightarrow (1)^2 - b(1) + 8 = 0$

$\Rightarrow g - b = 0$

$\Rightarrow b = 9$.

14. LCM $= 5 \times 3 \times x^3 \times y^3 \times z^2 = 15\,x^3y^3z^2$

HCF $= 3 \times x^2 \times y \times z = 3x^2yz$

LCM $= 15\,x^3y^3z^2$

HCF $= 3x^2yz$

15. $q(x) = x^{15}$

$q(2) = 2^{15}$

16. $q(x) = x^5 - 3x^3 + 5x + 1$

$$q\left(\frac{1}{2}\right)=\left(\frac{1}{2}\right)^5-3\left(\frac{1}{2}\right)^3+5\left(\frac{1}{2}\right)+1$$

$$q\left(\frac{1}{2}\right)=\frac{1}{32}-\frac{3}{8}+\frac{5}{2}+1=\frac{1-12+80+32}{32}$$

$$=\left(\frac{101}{32}\right)$$

17. $ab\,(a^4 - b^4)$

$ab\,[(a^2)^2 - (b^2)^2] = ab\,[(a^2 - b^2)\,(a^2 + b^2)]$

$= ab\,[(a + b)\,(a - b)\,(a^2 + b^2)]$

$= ab\,(a^2 + b^2)\,(a + b)\,(a - b)$

18. Degree of product of two polynomial is:

deg (AB) = deg (A) + deg (B)

$\therefore$ deg (B) = deg (AB) – deg (A) = 56 – 7 = 49

19. $AB = x^3\,(4x^2 + x - 1)$

$= 4x^5 + x^4 - x^3$

20. $m^7 + m^4$

$m^4\,(m^3 + 1)$

$m^4\,(m + 1)\,(m^2 - m + 1)$

21. $\frac{1}{6}(a^2 - 6a + 8) = \frac{1}{6}(a^2 - 4a - 2a + 8)$

$= \frac{1}{6}(a(a-4) - 2(a-4))$

$= \frac{1}{6}[(a-2)(a-4)]$

22. $(x^2 - 1)^{2018}\,(x - 2)^a = (x + 1)^{2018}\,(x - 1)^{2018}\,(x - 2)^a$

$(x - 1)^{2019}\,(x - 2)^{2018} = (x - 1)^{2019}\,(x - 2)^{2018}$

HCF = $(x - 1)^b\,(x - 2)^{1009}$

$\therefore a = 1009,\ b = 2018$

$\therefore$ The LCM of 1009 and 2018 = 2018.

23. $(A + C) = 4x^3 - 8x^2 + 3x^3 + x - 11$

$\Rightarrow 7x^3 - 8x^2 + x - 11$

$(A + C) - B = 7x^3 - 8x^2 + x - 11 - 7x^3 + 5x - 3$

$\Rightarrow -8x^2 + 6x - 14$

Short Answer Type Question

24. HCF = $a^2 - 1 = (a + 1)\,(a - 1)$

$\therefore$ $(a + 1)$ must be in the first expression also

$\therefore m = 1$

$\therefore$ $(a - 1)$ must be in 2nd and 3rd expression

$\therefore n = 1$

$m = 1$ and $n = 1$

25. Let $P(x) = 2018x^{2018} - 2017x^{2017} + \ldots\ldots\ldots 2x^2 - x + k$

Since $P(x)$ is divided by $x - 1$, the remainder is 1.

$\therefore P(1) = 1.$

$2018(1)^{2018} - 2017(1)^{2017} + \ldots\ldots\ldots + 2(1)^2 - 1 + k = 1$

$2018 - 2017 + \ldots\ldots\ldots 2 - 1 + k = 1$

$1009 + k = 1$

$k = -1008.$

26. $2(4x^3 - 8x^2) - 3(7x^3 - 5x + 3) + 4(3x^3 + x - 11)$

$8x^3 - 16x^2 - 21x^3 + 15x - 9 + 12x^3 + 4x - 44$

$-x^3 - 16x^2 + 19x - 53$

27. $(x^3 - 4x^2 - x + 1)\,(x^3 - x - 1)$

$(x^6 - x^4 - \cancel{x^3} - 4x^5 + 4x^3 + 4x^2 - x^4 + x^2 + x +$

$\cancel{x^3} - x - 1)$

$(x^6 - 4x^5 - 2x^4 + 4x^3 + 5x^2 - 1)$

28. $x^2 + 3x - 4\,\big)\ x^4 + 4x^3 - 31x^2 - 94x + 120\ \big(\ x^2 + x - 30$

$x^4 + 3x^3 - 4x^2$

(–) (–) (+)

$x^3 - 27x^2 - 94x$

$x^3 + 3x^2 - 4x$

(–) (–) (+)

$-30x^2 - 90x + 120$

$-30x^2 - 90x + 120$

(+) (+) (–)

0 0 0

Hence, the answer is $x^2 + x - 30$, 0

29. $a^3 + \frac{3ax}{8} + \frac{x^3}{64} - \frac{1}{8}$

add and subtract $\left(\frac{3ax}{4}\left(a + \frac{x}{4}\right)\right)$

$= a^3 + \frac{3ax}{4}\left(a + \frac{x}{4}\right) + \frac{x^3}{64} - \frac{1}{8} + \frac{3ax}{8} - \frac{3ax}{4}\left(a + \frac{x}{4}\right)$

$= \left(a + \frac{x}{4}\right)^3 - \left(\frac{1}{2}\right)^3 - \frac{3ax}{4}\left(a + \frac{x}{4} - \frac{1}{2}\right)$

$= \left(a + \frac{x}{4} - \frac{1}{2}\right)\left(\left(a + \frac{x}{4}\right)^2 + \left(\frac{1}{2}\right)^2 + \frac{1}{2}\left(a + \frac{x}{4}\right)\right)$

$- \frac{3ax}{4}\left(a + \frac{x}{4} - \frac{1}{2}\right)$

$= \left(a + \frac{x}{4} - \frac{1}{2}\right)\left(a^2 + \frac{x^2}{16} + \frac{1}{4} + \frac{a}{2} + \frac{x}{8} - \frac{3ax}{4} + \frac{2ax}{4}\right)$

$= \left(a + \frac{x}{4} - \frac{1}{2}\right)\left(a^2 + \frac{x^2}{16} + \frac{1}{4} + \frac{a}{2} + \frac{x}{8} - \frac{ax}{4}\right)$

30. $36\,(x + 2)^2\,(x - 1)^3\,(x + 3)^5$,

$45\,(x + 2)^5\,(x - 1)^2\,(x + 3)^5$ and

$63\,(x - 1)^2\,(x + 2)^5\,(x + 3)^4$

HCF = (36, 9) = 9

$[(x+2)^2, (x+2)^2, (x+2)^5] = (x+2)^2$

$[(x-1)^5, (x-1)^3, (x-1)^2] = (x-1)^2$

$[(x+3)^4, (x+3)^5, (x+3)^5] = (x+3)^4$

HCF = $9(x+2)^2(x-1)^2(x+3)^4$

LCM = [36, 45, 63] = 1260

$[(x+2)^2, (x+2)^2, (x+2)^5] = (x+2)^5$

$[(x-1)^3, (x-1)^2, (x-1)^5] = (x-1)^5$

$[(x+3)^5, (x+3)^5, (x+3)^4] = (x+3)^5$

LCM = $1260(x+2)^5(x-1)^5(x+3)^5$

31. $(x^2+x-2)(x^2+x-a)$

$(x(x+2)-1(x+2))$

$(x+2)(x-1)$

$(x^2+x-a) = (x+2)(x+3)$

$= x^2+5+6$

$a = 6$

$(x^2+x-b)(x^2+5x+a)$

$(x^2+5x+6) = (x+2)(x+3)$

$= (x^2+2)(x-1)$

$= (x^2+x-2)$

$b = 2$

32. x^{23}

$x^2 - 3x + 2$

when $p(x)$ divided by $q(x)$ is result and $ax + b$ remainder

$x^2 - 3x + 2 = (x-1)(x-2)$

Now, we know,

$x^{23} = q(x) = (x-1)(x-2) + ax + b$

For $x = 1$

$1 = q(1) = (1-1)(1-2) + a + b = 1$

$a + b = 1$

For $x = 2$

$2^{23} = q(2) = (2-1)(2-2) + 2a + b = 2$

$2a + b = 2^{23}$

Finding remainder

$a + b = 1$

$2a + b = 2^{23}$

(–) (–) (–)

$-a = 1 - 2^{23}$

$a = (2^{23} - 1)$

$a = (2^{23} - 1)$

then $b = 1 - (2^{23} - 1)$

$b = 2 - 2^{23}$

Hence, remainder = $(2^{23} - 1)\,x + (2 - 2^{23})$

33. We know that, $ax^2 + bx + c$, if $b^2 = 4ac$

$m^2n^2 = 4lmln$

$m^2n^2 = 4l^2mn$

$(mn) = 4l^2$

34. $(a+b+c)^2 = a^2+b^2+c^2+2ab+\cancel{2bc}+\cancel{2ca}$

$(a+b-c)^2 = a^2+b^2+c^2+2ab-\cancel{2bc}-\cancel{2ca}$

$(c^2-a^2-b^2-2ab) = c^2-(a+b)^2$

$= (c-(a+b))(c+(a+b))$

$= \sqrt{\begin{array}{c}a^2+b^2+c^2+2ab+a^2+b^2+c^2+2ab\\ +2(c^2-a^2-b^2-2ab)\end{array}}$

$= \sqrt{\cancel{2a^2}+\cancel{2b^2}+2c^2+\cancel{4ab}+2c^2-\cancel{2a^2}-\cancel{2b^2}-\cancel{4ab}}$

$= \sqrt{4c^2} = \mathbf{2c}$

35. $$\frac{x^2}{abc} = \frac{\left(\sqrt{\dfrac{125a^6b^4c^2}{5a^4b^2}}\right)^2}{abc}$$

$$= \frac{125a^5b^3c}{5a^4b^2} = 25\ abc$$

36. $(x^2 + 6x + 8)\,(x^2 + 5x + 6)\,(x^2 + 7x + 12)$

$(x^2 + 4x + 2x + 8)\,(x^2 + 2x + 3x + 6)\,(x^2 + 4x + 3x + 10)$

$(x(x+4) + 2(x+4))\,(x(x+2) + 3(x+2))\,(x(x+4) + 3(x+4))$

$(x+2)(x+4)(x+3)(x+2)(x+3)(x+4)$

Root = $(x+2)(x+3)(x+4)$

Essay Type Questions

37. $x^4 + 6x^2 + 4x + 9 + \frac{12}{x} + \frac{4}{x^2}$

$$= (x^2)^2 + \left(\frac{2}{x}\right)^2 + (3)^2 + 2(x^2)\left(\frac{2}{x}\right) + 2\left(\frac{2}{x}\right)(3) + 2(x^2)(3)$$

$$= \left(x^2 + \frac{2}{x} + 3\right)^2$$

$$\therefore \sqrt{x^4 + 6x^2 + 4x + 9 + \frac{12}{x} + \frac{4}{x^2}}$$

$$= x^2 + \frac{2}{x} + 3.$$

38. $P(x) = x^4 - 2x^3 + 3x^2 - mx + n$

Since P(x) is divided by $(x-1)$, it leave the remainder 5.

$\therefore$ P(1) = 5

$1^4 - 2(1)^3 + 3(1)^2 - m(1) + n = 5$

$1 - 2 + 3 - m + n = 5$

$-m + n = 3$ ____________(1)

Since P(x) is divided by (x + 1), it leave the remainder 19.

$\therefore P(-1) = 19$

$(-1)^4 - 2(-1)^3 + 3(-1)^2 - m(-1) + n = 19$

$1 + 2 + 3 + m + n = 19$

$m + n = 13$ __________(2)

Solving (1) and (2)

$2n = 16$

$n = 8$

Substitute $n = 8$ in equation (1),

$-m + 8 = 3$

$-m = -5$

$m = 5$

$\therefore P(x) = x^4 - 2x^3 + 3x^2 - 5x + 8$

The remainder when P(x) is divided by $x - 2$ is P(2).

$\therefore P(2) = 2^4 - 2(2)^3 + 3(2)^2 - 5(2) + 8$

$= 16 - 16 + 12 - 10 + 8 = 10$

39.

	$4x^3 - 3x^2 + 2x - 1)$
$4x^3$	$16x^6 - 24x^5 + 25x^4 - 20x^3 + 10x^2 - 4x + 1)$
	$16x^6$
$8x^3 - 3x^2$	0
	$-24x^5 + 25x^4$
	$-24x^5 + 9x^4$
$8x^3 - 6x^2 - 2x$	$0 + 16x^4 - 20x^3 + 10x^2$
	$16x^4 - 12x^3 + 4x^2$
$8x^3 - 6x^2 + 4x - 1$	$-8x^3 + 6x^2 - 4x - 1$
	$-8x^3 + 6x^2 - 4x - 1$
	0

So $(4x^3 - 3x^2 + 2x - 1)^2 = 16x^6 + 25x^4 - 24x^5 - 20x^3 + 10x^2 - 4x + 1$

$= 4x^3 - 3x^2 + 2x - 1$

40. Let the polynomial be:

$Ax^2 + Bx + C = 0$

When divided by x, the remainder is 1, therefore, as per remainder theorem

when $x = 0$

$Ax^2 + Bx + C = 1$ (1)

similarly, when $x = 1$

$Ax^2 + Bx + C = 2$ (2)

and when $x = 2$

$Ax^2 + Bx + C = 9$ (3)

Substituting the values of x in equation (1), (2), and (3), we get 3 equations.

$A(0)^2 + B(0) + C = 1$

$\Rightarrow C = 1$

$A + B + 1 = 2$

$\Rightarrow A + B = 1$ (4)

$A(2)^2 + B(2) + C = 9$

$\Rightarrow 4A + 2B = 8$ (5)

On solving equation (4) and (5), simultaneously we get:

$A = 3$ and $B = -2$

therefore polynomial is

$3x^2 - 2x + 1 = 0$

41. We have,

$a^2(b + c) + b^2(c + a) + c^2(a + b) - 2b^2c$

$= a^2b + a^2c + b^2c + b^2a + c^2a + c^2b - 2b^2c$

$= a^2b + a^2c + b^2a + c^2a + c^2b - b^2c$

$= ab(a + b) + ac(a + c) + bc(c - b)$

Competition Wing

Level 1: Apply Your Concepts

1. $11x^2 - 88x^3 + 14x^4$ is called a biquadratic polynomial. It is a polynomial of the fourth degree.
2. $7x^3 y^{10} z^2 \Rightarrow 3 + 10 + 2 = 15$
3. $(a + b + c)^3 = a^3 + b^3 + c^3 (a + b) (b + c) (a + c)$

   $(a + b + c)^3 = a^3 + b^3 + c^3 + 3a^2 (b + c) + 3b^2 (a + c) + 3c^2 (a + b) + 6abc$ [Adding $3abc$ on both sides]

   $(a + b + c)^3 + 3abc = a^3 + b^3 + c^3 + 3a^2 (b + c) + 3b^2 (a + c) + 3c^2 (a + b) + 9abc$

   $(a + b + c)^3 - [3a^2 (b + c) + 3b^2 (a + c) + 3c^2 (a + b) + 9abc] = a^3 + b^3 + c^3 - 3abc$

   $(a + b + c)^3 - [3ab (a + b + c) + 3bc (a + b + c) + 3ac (a + b + c)] = a^3 + b^3 + c^3 - 3abc$

   $a^3 + b^3 + c^3 - 3abc = (a + b + c) [(a + b + c)^2 - 3ab - 3bc - 3ac]$

   $a^3 + b^3 + c^3 - 3abc = (a + b + c) [(a^2 + b^2 + c^2 - ab - bc - ac]$

   $a + b + c = 0,\ a^3 + b^3 + c^3 = 3abc$
4. Factors of $x^6 - y^6$ are

   $(x^2)^3 - (y^2)^3$ <$a^2 - b^2 = (a + b) (a - b)$>

   <$a^3 - b^3 = (a - b) (a^2 + ab + b^2)$>

   $(x^2 - y^2) (x^4 + x^2y^2 + y^4)$

   $(x + y) (x - y) (x^2 - xy + y^2) (x^2 + xy + y^2)$
5. The required sequential order of steps is BDAC.
6. $f(x, y) = 5x^5 - 3y^5 + 2x^3y^a - 7x^by$ is a homogenous expression of degree 5.

   $\therefore 3 + a = 5$ and $b + 1 = 5$

   $\Rightarrow a = 2$ and $b = 4$

   $\Rightarrow a - b = 2 - 4 = -2$.
7. Given,

   The HCF of $x^b y^c z^5$ and $x^a y^b z^4$ is $x^2 y^2 z^c$

   $\Rightarrow c = 4,\ b = 2,\ a \geq 2$

   The minimum value of $a + b + c$

   $= 2 + 2 + 4 = 8$
8. Degree of every term should be same.
9. Use factorization concept.
10. Use remainder theorem.
11. Find the common factors with the least exponents.
12. Let $f(x) = x^2 + 8x + a$ and a factor is $(x + 1)$

    $\Rightarrow f(-1) = 0$

    $\Rightarrow (-1)^2 + 8(-1) + a = 0$

    $\Rightarrow 1 - 8 + a = 0$

    $\Rightarrow a = 7$.
13. Given polynomials:

    $(x + 2)^2 (x + 3)^{2018}$ and

    $(x + 3)^{2017} (x - 3)^b$

    LCM $= (x - 3)^{2020} (x + 3)^a (x + 2)^2$

    $\therefore a = 2018$ and $b = 2020$

    $\therefore$ The HCF of 2018 and 2020 is 2.
14. An expression is symmetric if all the coefficients are equal.
15. Use $a^2 + b^2 + 2ab = (a + b)^2$ identity.
16. Use the concept of multiplication of polynomials.
17. Factorize the given polynomials.
18. Use the addition and subtraction concept of polynomials.
19. The degree of the homogeneous expression is 3.
20. (i) Factorize the given polynomials.

    (ii) Factorize the middle term such that product obtained is 22 and sum obtained is $-12\sqrt{2}$.
21. (i) Use factor theorem.

    (ii) Put $x = -1$.

    (iii) Check for what values of n, $(-1)^n + 1$ is divisible by $x + 1$.
22. Use division method to find p and q.
23. Apply the division method to find the square root.
24. Recall the concept of finding the square root of monomial.
25. Use algebraic identities.
26. Use the formula (LCM) (HCF) $= f(x) \cdot g(x)$
27. Use factor theorem.
28. Use factor theorem.
29. Find the square root.
30. (i) $x^n + y^n$ is always disable by $x + y$ if n is odd.

    (ii) $x^n - y^n$ is divisible by $x - y$, if n is odd number.
31. (i) The product of four consecutive numbers added to 1 is a perfect square.

    (ii) The continued product of 4 consecutive integers added by 1 is always a perfect square.

Level 2: Review Your Concepts

32. The required sequential order is CDBA.

33. $x^2 + \frac{7}{6}y^2 - 9$ is a polynomial.

34. Let $P(x) = x^n - y^n$

The remainder when $P(x)$ is divided by $(x - y)$ is $P(y)$.

$\therefore P(y) = y^n - y^n = 0$, for any natural number n.

35. We know that $(a + b)^2 + (a - b)^2 = 2a^2 + 2b^2$

$\therefore (2x + 3y)^2 + (2x - 3y)^2$

$= 2(2x)^2 + 2(3y)^2$

$= 8x^2 + 18y^2$.

36. (i) Use division algorithm.

(ii) $f(x) = g(x)Q(x) + [ax + b]$ where $Q(x)$ is quotient and $(ax + b)$ is the remainder.

(iii) Put $x = 1$ and $x = -1$, then find the values of a and b.

37. Given $f(x + 3) = x^2 - 2x + 8$----------------(1)

The remainder, when $f(x)$ is divided by $(x - 2)$ is $f(2)$

Put $x = -1$ in equation (1)

$f(-1 + 3) = (-1)^2 - 2(-1) + 8$

$\Rightarrow f(2) = 1 + 2 + 8 = 11$.

38. (i) LCM is the product of the all the factors with highest powers.

(ii) Use the LCM concept and find the values of a and b.

(iii) $a + b + c$ is least when $c = 0$.

39. (i) Find the common and uncommon factors with highest powers.

(ii) Find LCM of 195 and 221.

(iii) Find the LCM of the expressions given.

40. (i) Use factor theorem.

(ii) If $x - a$ is HCF of $f(x)$, then $f(a) = 0$.

(iii) Substitute $x = 2$ in $f(x)$ or $g(x)$ and obtained the value of k.

41. (i) HCF is the product of all common factors with least exponents.

(ii) Use the HCF concept and find the values of a, b and c.

42. (i) Use remainder theorem.

(ii) Put $x = 0$, $x = -1$, and $x = -2$ in the given expression, and obtain the corresponding reminders.

43. (i) Find the LCM of denominations and add the polynomials.

(ii) Take LCM.

(iii) Find the factors and simplify.

44. (i) Use algebraic identities to factorize the given polynomial.

(ii) Multiply the first three terms with xyz.

(iii) Now express the expression in $(a + b + c)^2$ form.

45. (i) Use algebraic identities to factorize the given polynomial.

(ii) Add and subtract 4 to the expression.

(iii) Express the expression of the form $a^2 - b^2$.

46. BCAD is the required sequential order of steps in solving the given problem.

47. CBDAE is the required sequential order.

48. Let $f(x) = 5x^5 - 3x^3 + 2x^2 - k$

$f(-1) = 1$ (given)

$\Rightarrow 5(-1)^5 - 3(-1)^3 + 2(-1)^2 - k = 1$

$-5 + 3 + 2 - k = 1$

$\therefore k = -1$.

49. Given, $x + \frac{1}{x} = 3$,

Let $\sqrt{x} + \frac{1}{\sqrt{x}} = k$

(Squaring on both sides)

$$\left(\sqrt{x}\right)^2 + \left(\sqrt{\frac{1}{x}}\right)^2 + 2\sqrt{x}.\sqrt{\frac{1}{x}} = K^2$$

$3 + 2 = K^2$

$K^2 = 5$

$K = \pm\sqrt{5}$

50. Degree of $f = 3$

Degree of $g = 4$

$\Rightarrow$ Degree of $(f - g) = 4$, since the term of degree 4 cannot be vanished.

51. $\dfrac{x^2}{9}+\dfrac{9}{4x^2}-\dfrac{x}{3}+\dfrac{3}{2x}-\dfrac{5}{4}$

$\dfrac{x}{3}$	$\dfrac{x^2}{9}+\dfrac{9}{4x^2}-\dfrac{x}{3}-\dfrac{3}{2x}+\dfrac{5}{4}$
$\dfrac{2x}{3}-\dfrac{1}{2}$	$\dfrac{9}{4x^2}-\dfrac{x}{3}-\dfrac{3}{2x}+\dfrac{5}{4}$
$\dfrac{2x}{3}-1+\dfrac{3}{2x}$	$\dfrac{9}{4x^2}-\dfrac{3}{2x}+1$ $\dfrac{9}{4x^2}-\dfrac{3}{2x}+1$
	0

$$\therefore\ \sqrt{\frac{x^2}{9}+\frac{9}{4x^2}-\frac{x}{3}-\frac{3}{2x}+\frac{5}{4}}=\frac{x}{3}-\frac{1}{2}+\frac{3}{2x}.$$

52. $(xy+xz-yz)^2-4xyz(x-y)$

$=(xy+z(x-y))^2-4(xy)\ [z(x-y)]$

$=[xy-z(x-y)]^2$

$[\because (a+b)^2-4ab=(a-b)^2]$

$=(xy-zx+yz)^2$

$=(xy+yz-zx)^2$

$\therefore$ The square root of the given expression is $(xy+yz-zx)$.

Level 3: Assess Your Concepts

53. (i) Find the square root and equate it to ax^2+bx+c.

(ii) Square on both sides and obtain the values of a, b, and c.

(iii) Verify the relation between a, b and c.

54. (i) Find average of the given polynomials and then apply the division method.

(ii) Average of a, b, and c is $\dfrac{a+b+c}{3}$.

(iii) Express the numerator in the form of $(a+b+c)^2$.

57.

$\dfrac{a}{2}$	$\dfrac{a^2}{4}+\dfrac{1}{a^2}-\dfrac{1}{a}+\dfrac{a}{2}-\dfrac{3}{4}-\dfrac{a^2}{4}$
$\dfrac{2a}{2}+\dfrac{1}{2}$	$\dfrac{a^2}{4}+\dfrac{1}{a^2}-\dfrac{1}{a}+\dfrac{a}{2}-\dfrac{3}{4}-\dfrac{a^2}{4}$
$a+1-\dfrac{1}{a}$	$\dfrac{1}{a^2}-\dfrac{1}{a}-1$ $\dfrac{1}{a^2}-\dfrac{1}{a}-1$
	0

$\therefore$ The square root of the given expression is $\dfrac{a}{2}-\dfrac{1}{a}+\dfrac{1}{2}$.

58. $\dfrac{(x+y)^3+(x-y)^3}{2}-(y^3+3x^2y)$

$=\dfrac{x^3+y^3+3x^2y+3xy^2+x^3-y^3-3x^2y+3xy^2}{2}$

$-y^3-3x^2y$

$=\dfrac{2x^3+6xy^2}{2}-y^3-3x^2y$

$=x^3-3x^2y+3xy^2-y^3$

$=(x-y)^3.$

59. $(4a+5b+5c)^2-(5a+4b+4c)^2+9a^2$

$=(4a+5b+5c+5a+4b+4c)\ (4a+5b+5c-5a-4b-4c)+9a^2$

$=(9a+9b+9c)(-a+b+c)+9a^2$

$=9(a+b+c)(-a+b+c)+9a^2$

$=9(b+c)^2-9a^2+9a^2$

$=9(b+c)^2.$

$\therefore$ The square root of the given expression is $\sqrt{9(b+c)^2}=3(b+c)$.

60. $\dfrac{(a-b)^3-(a+b)^3}{2}+a(a^2+3b^2)$

$=\dfrac{a^3-3a^2b+3ab^2-b^3-a^3-3a^2b-3ab^2-b^3}{2}$

$+a^3+3ab^2$

$=\dfrac{-6a^2b-2b^3}{2}+a^3+3ab^2$

$=a^3-3a^2b+3ab^2-b^3$

$=(a-b)^3.$

61. $(3a+2b+3c)^2-(2a+3b+2c)^2+5b^2$

$=(3a+2b+3c+2a+3b+2c)\ (3a+2b+3c-2a-3b-2c)+5b^2$

$=(5a+5b+5c)(a-b+c)+5b^2$

$=5(a+c+b)(a+c-b)+5b^2$

$=5[(a+c)^2-b^2]+5b^2$

$=5(a+c)^2$

$\therefore$ Square root of the given expression is $\sqrt{5(a+c)^2}=\sqrt{5}(a+c)$.

JEE Special Wing

Multiple-Answer Type Questions

1. Given that A and B are two polynomials of degree 10 each.

 (i) If $A = x^{10} + x^9$ and $B = -x^{10} + 2x^9$, then $A - B = x^{10} - x^9$.

 In this case, the degree of $A - B$ is 10.

 (ii) If $A = x^{10} + x^9$ and $B = x^{10} + 2x^9$, then $A - B = -x^9$.

 In this case, the degree of $A - B$ is 9.

 (iii) If $A = x^{10} + x^9 - x^8$ and $B = x^{10} + x^9 + 2x^8 + x^7$, then $A - B = -x^8 - x^7$.

 In this case, the degree of $A - B$ is 8.

 So, the degree of polynomial $A - B$ can be 10, 9, 8, 7, …

 Hence, choice (a, b, c, d) are correct.

2. Going by options:

 (a) $(3x^2 - 5yz^2)(3x^2 - 5yz^2) = (3x^2 - 5yz^2)^2$

 $= 9x^4 - 30x^2yz^2 + 25y^2z^4$, which is a trinomial.

 (b) $(3x^2 + 5yz^2)(3x^2 - 5yz^2) = (3x^2)^2 - (5yz^2)^2$

 $= 9x^4 - 25y^2z^4$, which is a binomial.

 (c) $(3x^2 + 5yz^2)(3x^2 + 5yz^2) = (3x^2 + 5yz^2)^2$

 $= 9x^4 + 30x^2yz^2 + 25y^2z^4$, which is a trinomial.

 (d) $(3x^2 + 5yz^2)(3x^2 - 5yz^2)(9x^4 + 25y^2z^4)$

 $= \left[(3x^2)^2 - (5yz^2)^2\right](9x^4 + 25y^2z^4)$

 $= (9x^4 - 25y^2z^4)(9x^4 + 25y^2z^4)$

 $= (9x^4)^2 - (25y^2z^4)^2$

 $= 81x^8 - 625y^4z^8$, which is a binomial.

 Hence, choice (a and c) are correct.

3. Given that the degree of polynomial $\frac{A}{B}$ is 4, which is the degree of A – degree of B.

 Going by options:

 (a) $12 - 3 = 9$, which is not the degree of $\frac{A}{B}$.

 (b) $8 - 2 = 6$, which is not the degree of $\frac{A}{B}$.

 (c) $6 - 2 = 4$, which is the degree of $\frac{A}{B}$.

 (d) $4 - 0 = 4$, which is the degree of $\frac{A}{B}$.

 Hence, choice (c and d) are correct.

4. Given that the LCM of $(3x + 2y^4)^n$ and $(3x + 2y^4)^{10}$ is $(3x + 2y^4)^n$.

 So, n can be 10, 11, 12, 13, …

 Hence, choice (b, c, d) are correct.

5. Given that the HCF of $(x + 3y)^2(2x - y)^n$ and $(x + 3y)^m(2x - y)^3$ is $(x + 3y)^m(2x - y)^n$.

 So, m can be 0, 1, or 2 and n can be 0, 1, 2, or 3.

 Now $m + n$ can be 0, 1, 2, 3, 4, or 5.

 Hence, choice (a, b, c, d) are correct.

6. Going by options:

 (a) $(y^2 - y + 1)^2 = (y^2)^2 + (-y)^2 + (1)^2 + 2(y^2)(-y) + 2(-y)(1) + 2(y^2)(1)$

 $= y^4 + y^2 + 1 - 2y^3 - 2y + 2y^2$

 $= y^4 - 2y^3 + 3y^2 - 2y + 1$

 Similarly, (d) $(-y^2 + y - 1)^2 = (y^2 - y + 1)^2$

 $= y^4 - 2y^3 + 3y^2 - 2y + 1$

 Hence, choice (a and d) are correct.

7. Given that $f(y) = y^4 + 2y^3 + y^2 + y + 1$

 $= y^4 + y^3 + y^3 + y^2 + y + 1$

 $= y^3(y + 1) + y^2(y + 1) + 1(y + 1)$

 $= (y + 1)(y^3 + y^2 + 1)$

 The factors of $f(y)$ are 1, $(y + 1)$, $(y^3 + y^2 + 1)$ and $y^4 + 2y^3 + y^2 + y + 1$.

 So, the degrees of factors of $f(y)$ are 0, 1, 3 and 4.

 Hence, choice (a, b, d) are correct.

8. $x^6 - y^6 = (x^3)^2 - (y^3)^2$

 $= (x^3 - y^3)(x^3 + y^3)$

 $= \left[(x - y)(x^2 + xy + y^2)\right]\left[(x + y)(x^2 - xy + y^2)\right]$

 Let us consider (i) $(x^2 + xy + y^2)(x^2 - xy + y^2)$

 $= (x^2 + y^2)^2 - (xy)^2$

 $= x^4 + 2x^2y^2 + y^4 - x^2y^2 = x^4 + x^2y^2 + y^4$

 Also, (ii) $(x - y)(x^2 - xy + y^2)$

 $= x^3 - x^2y + xy^2 - x^2y + xy^2 - y^3$

 $= x^3 - 2x^2y + 2xy^2 - y^3$

 Also, (iii) $(x + y)(x^2 + xy + y^2)$

 $= x^3 + x^2y + xy^2 + x^2y + xy^2 + y^3$

 $= x^3 + 2x^2y + 2xy^2 + y^3$

 Hence, choice (a, b, d) are correct.

9. $x^4 - 17x^2 + 16 = x^4 - 16x^2 - x^2 + 16$

$= x^2(x^2 - 16) - 1(x^2 - 16)$

$= (x^2 - 16)(x^2 - 1)$

$= (x^2 - 4^2)(x^2 - 1^2)$

$= (x+4)(x-4)(x+1)(x-1)$

Hence, choice (a, c, d)are correct.

Match The Column

Common Solutions for questions 10 to 15:

10. $x^3 + x^2 - 17x + 15 = x^3 - x^2 + 2x^2 - 2x - 15x + 15$

$= x^2(x-1) + 2x(x-1) - 15(x-1)$

$= (x-1)(x^2 + 2x - 15) = (x-1)(x-3)(x+5)$

Hence, choice (a, e, g)are correct.

11. $x^3 + 3x^2 - 22x - 24 = x^3 + x^2 + 2x^2 + 2x - 24x - 24$

$= x^2(x+1) + 2x(x+1) - 24(x+1)$

$= (x+1)(x^2 + 2x - 24) = (x+1)(x-4)(x+6)$

Hence, choice (d and h) are correct.

12. Let $f(x) = x^3 + 3x^2 - 28x - 60$

Clearly, $(x+1)$ and $(x-1)$ are not factors of $f(x)$.

Now $f(2) = 2^3 + 3(2)^2 - 28(2) - 60 \neq 0$

Now $f(-2) = (-2)^3 + 3(-2)^2 - 28(-2) - 60$

$= -8 + 12 + 56 - 60 = 0.$

So, $(x+2)$ is a factor of $f(x)$.

$x^3 + 3x^2 - 28x - 60 = x^3 + 2x^2 + x^2 + 2x - 30x - 60$

$= x^2(x+2) + x(x+2) - 30(x+2)$

$= (x+2)(x^2 + x - 30) = (x+2)(x-5)(x+6)$

Hence, choice (c and i) are correct.

13. Let $f(x) = x^3 - 15x^2 + 66x - 80$

Clearly, $(x+1)$ and $(x-1)$ are not factors of $f(x)$.

Now $f(2) = 2^3 - 15(2)^2 + 66(2) - 80$

$= 8 - 60 + 132 - 80 = 0.$

So, $(x-2)$ is a factor of $f(x)$.

$x^3 - 15x^2 + 66x - 80 = x^3 - 2x^2 - 13x^2 + 26x + 40x - 80$

$= x^2(x-2) - 13x(x-2) + 40(x-2)$

$= (x-2)(x^2 - 13x + 40) = (x-2)(x-5)(x-8)$

Hence, **choice (f) and choice (i)** are correct.

14. Let $f(x) = x^3 + 4x^2 - 17x - 60$

Clearly, $(x+1)$ and $(x-1)$ are not factors of $f(x)$.

Now $f(2) = 2^3 + 4(2)^2 - 17(2) - 60 \neq 0$

Now $f(-2) = (-2)^3 + 4(-2)^2 - 17(-2) - 60$

$= -8 + 16 + 34 - 60 \neq 0.$

Now $f(-3) = (-3)^3 + 4(-3)^2 - 17(-3) - 60$

$= -27 + 36 + 51 - 60 = 0.$

So, $(x+3)$ is a factor of $f(x)$.

$x^3 + 4x^2 - 17x - 60 = x^3 + 3x^2 + x^2 + 3x - 20x - 60$

$= x^2(x+3) + x(x+3) - 20(x+3)$

$= (x+3)(x^2 + x - 20) = (x+3)(x+5)(x-4)$

Hence, choice (b and h) are correct.

15. $x^4 - 5x^3 + 5x^2 + 5x - 6 = x^4 + 5x^2 - 5x^3 + 5x - 6$

$= x^4 - x^2 + 6x^2 - 5x^3 + 5x - 6$

$= x^4 - x^2 - 5x^3 + 5x + 6x^2 - 6$

$= x^2(x^2 - 1) - 5x(x^2 - 1) + 6(x^2 - 1)$

$= (x^2 - 1)(x^2 - 5x + 6) = (x+1)(x-1)(x-2)(x-3)$

Hence, choice (d, e, f, g) are correct.

Comprehension-Based Questions

Common Solutions for questions 16 to 20:

Give that $f(x-3) = x^3 - 6x^2 + 14x - 8$.

16. The remainder when $f(x)$ is divided by $(x-3)$ is $f(3)$.

Let us substitute $x = 6$ in $f(x-3)$ to get $f(3)$.

$f(x-3) = x^3 - 6x^2 + 14x - 8$

$f(6-3) = 6^3 - 6(6)^2 + 14(6) - 8$

$= 216 - 216 + 84 - 8 = 76.$

Hence, the correct option is (b).

17. The remainder when $f(x)$ is divided by $(x+2)$ is $f(-2)$.

Let us substitute $x = 1$ in $f(x-3)$ to get $f(-2)$.

$f(x-3) = x^3 - 6x^2 + 14x - 8$

$f(1-3) = 1^3 - 6(1)^2 + 14(1) - 8$

$f(-2) = 1 - 6 + 14 - 8 = 1.$

Hence, the correct option is (a).

18. Let us substitute $x = x - 1$ in $f(x-3)$ to get $f(x-4)$.

$f(x-3) = x^3 - 6x^2 + 14x - 8$

$f(x-1-3) = (x-1)^3 - 6(x-1)^2 + 14(x-1) - 8$

$f(x-4) = (x-1)^3 - 6(x-1)^2 + 14(x-1) - 8$

The divisor is $(x-1)$.

But $(x-1)^3 - 6(x-1)^2 + 14(x-1)$ is divisible by $(x-1)$.

The remainder = –8|

Hence, the correct option is (c).

19. Let us substitute $x = x+1$ in $f(x-3)$ to get $f(x-2)$.

$f(x-3) = x^3 - 6x^2 + 14x - 8$

$f(x+1-3) = (x+1)^3 - 6(x+1)^2 + 14(x+1) - 8$

$f(x-2) = (x+1)^3 - 6(x+1)^2 + 14(x+1) - 8.$

The divisor is $(x-2)$.

The remainder $= (2+1)^3 - 6(2+1)^2 + 14(2+1) - 8$

$= 27 - 54 + 42 - 8 = 7.$

Hence, the correct option is (c).

20. Let us substitute $x = x+2$ in $f(x-3)$ to get $f(x-1)$.

$f(x-3) = x^3 - 6x^2 + 14x - 8$

$f(x+2-3) = (x+2)^3 - 6(x+2)^2 + 14(x+2) - 8$

$f(x-1) = x^3 + 6x^2 + 12x + 8 - 6(x^2 + 4x + 4)$

$+14x + 28 - 8$

$= x^3 + 6x^2 + 12x + 8 - 6x^2 - 24x - 24 + 14x + 20$.

$= x^3 + 2x + 4.$

Hence, the correct option is (d).

Assertion and Reason Type Questions

Common Solutions for questions 21 to 25:

21. Assertion: Given that

$f(x) = 5x^7 + 6x^6 - 7x^5 + 8x^4.$

$f(1) = 5 + 6 - 7 + 8 - 5 - 6 + 7 - 8 = 0.$

So, $x-1$ is a factor of $f(x)$.

So, Assertion is true.

Reason: If the sum of the numerical coefficients of a polynomial is zero, then $x-1$ is a factor of the polynomial.

Reason is true and is the correct explanation to Assertion.

Hence, the correct option is (a).

22. Assertion: Given that

$f(x) = 5x^7 - 6x^6 - 7x^5 - 8x^4 - 5x^3 + 6x^2 + 7x + 18.$

$f(-1) = -5 - 6 + 7 - 8 + 5 + 6 - 7 + 18 = 10.$

So, $x+1$ is not a factor of $f(x)$.

So, Assertion is false.

Reason: If the sum of the numerical coefficients of even powers of variables is equal to the sum of the numerical coefficients of odd powers of variables of a polynomial, then $x+1$ is a factor of the polynomial.

Reason is true.

Hence, the correct option is (d).

23. Assertion: $x^2 - 7x + 10 = x^2 - 5x - 2x + 10$

$= x(x-5) - 2(x-5) = (x-5)(x-2).$

So, Assertion is true.

Reason: The maximum possible number of factors of a quadratic polynomial is two.

Reason is true, but not the correct explanation to Assertion.

Hence, the correct option is (b).

24. Assertion: Given that the LCM of two linear polynomials is $x^2 - 1$.

But $x^2 - 1 = (x+1)(x-1)$.

The two linear polynomials are $(x+1)$ and $(x-1)$.

The HCF of $(x+1)$ and $(x-1)$ is 1.

So, Assertion is true.

Reason: The HCF of $(x^2 - y^2)$ and $(x+y)$ is $(x+y)$.

So, Reason is false.

Hence, the correct option is (c).

25. Assertion: If the n is a positive even number, then the square root of $(4x^2 + 17x - 12)^n$ is $(4x^2 + 17x - 12)^{\frac{n}{2}}$.

Assertion is true.

Reason: The square of $x^2 + y^2$ is $(x^2 + y^2)^2$

$= x^4 + 2x^2y^2 + y^4.$

Reason is true, but not the correct explanation to Assertion.

Hence, the correct option is (b).

CHAPTER

6

Linear Equations in Two Variables

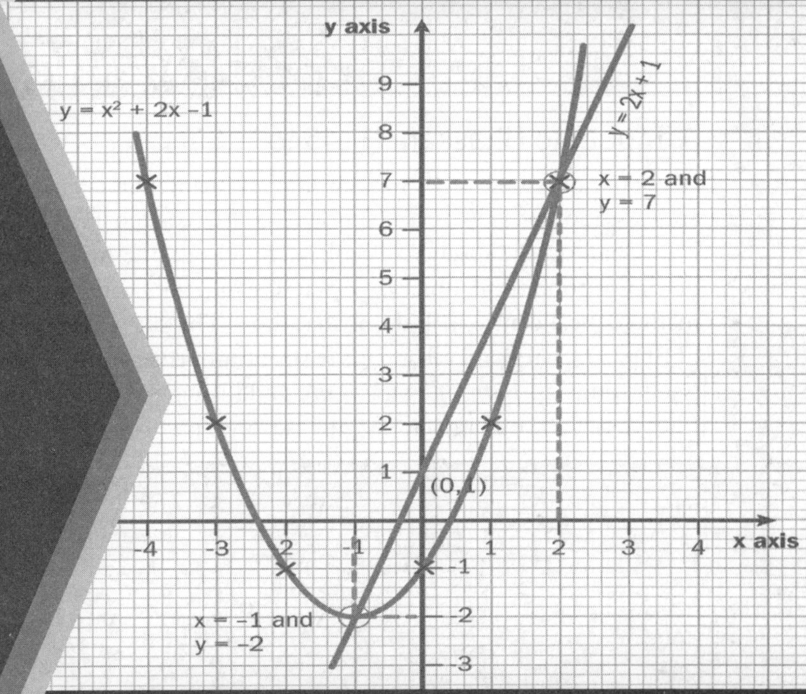

Remember

Before beginning this chapter, you should be able to:

- Understand basic terms such as linear equations and inequations in mathematics
- Solve word problems and applications of simple algebraic equations

Key Ideas

After completing this chapter, you should be able to:

- Solve two simultaneous linear equations
- Learn the graphical representation of linear equations and inequations
- Understand the application of simultaneous linear equations
- Solve word problems on linear equations and inequations
- Obtain the absolute value

Scientific Crypt

A Tribute to Bhaskara (1145 to 1185)

Bhaskara or Bhaskar II was an Indian mathematician and astronomer. He is also known as Bhaskaracharya, i.e., 'Bhaskara the teacher'. Bhaskaracharya became head of the astronomical observatory at Ujjain, the leading mathematical centre in India at that time. The six works of Bhaskaracharya are Lilavati (The Beautiful), Bijaganitha (seed counting or root extraction), Siddhanta Siromani (the first part on astronomy, the second part on the sphere), Vasanabhyasa of Mitaksara, the Karana Kutuhala (calculation of Astronomical wonders) and the Vivarana. Some of the contributions of Bhaskara to mathematics are a proof of the Pythagorean theorem, integer solutions of linear and quadratic indeterminate equations, etc. He was the first to give a general solution for 'Pell's equation' ($x^2 - ny^2 = 1$).

FUN TIME

CROSSWORD

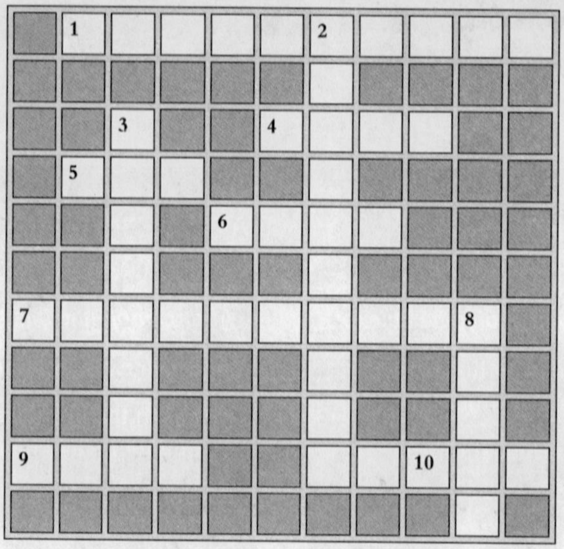

Across

1. $x > y$, $y > z$ and $x > z$, The name of this property.
4. The number of solutions of the inequation $x > 10$ and $x < 10$.
5. The number of solutions of the equation $x + 5 = 10$.
6. The number of pairs of integers whose product is 4.
7. A system of equations which has a solution, is said to be
9. Sentence which cannot be determined either true or false.
10. Two-fifth of a number is 16. Then one-fourth of the number.

Down

2. An open sentence which consists of an inequality symbol.
3. The number of solutions of the equation $x - 8 = 12 + y$.
8. The number of disjoint sets formed by a line in a plane.

INTRODUCTION

In this chapter, we learn how to frame and solve equations. Framing an equation is more difficult than solving it. Now, let us review the basic concepts related with equations and inequations.

Algebraic Expressions

Expressions of the form $2x$, $3x + 5$, $4x - 2y$, $2x^2 + 3\sqrt{y}$, $\frac{3x^3}{2\sqrt{y}}$ are algebraic expressions. $3x$ and 5 are the terms of $3x + 5$, and $4x$ and $2y$, are the terms of $4x - 2y$. Algebraic expressions are made up of numbers, symbols, and the basic arithmetical operations.

Open Sentences

Sentences which are true for some values of the variable and false for the other values of the variable are called **open sentences**. When a certain value is substituted for the variable, the sentence becomes a statement, either true or false.

Example: $x + 1 = 4$. This is an open sentence. When we substitute 3 for x, we get a true statement. When we substitute any other value, we get a false statement.

Example: $x + 1 < 3$. This is another open sentence. If we substitute any value less than 2 for x we get a true statement. If we substitute 2 or any number greater than 2, we get a false statement.

Equation

An open sentence containing the equality sign is an equation. In other words, an equation is a sentence in which there is an equality sign between two algebraic expressions.

Example: $2x + 5 = x + 3$, $3y - 4 = 20$, $5x + 6 = x + 1$ are equations.

Linear Equation

An equation, in which the highest index of the unknowns present is one, is a **linear equation**.

Example: $2(x + 5) = 18$, $3x - 2 = 5$, $x + y = 20$ and $3x - 2y = 5$ are some linear equations.

Simple Equation

A linear equation which has only one unknown is a **simple equation**.

$3x + 4 = 16$ and $2x - 5 = x + 3$ are examples of simple equations. The part of an equation which is to the left side of the equality sign is known as the left hand side, abbreviated as LHS. The part of an equation which is to the right side of the equality sign is known as the right-hand side, abbreviated as RHS. The process of finding the value of an unknown in an equation is called solving the equation. The value (values) of the unknown found after solving an equation is (are) called the solution(s) or the root(s) of the equation.

Before we learn how to solve an equation, let us review the basic properties of equality.

Solving an Equation in One Variable

The following steps are involved in solving an equation:

Step 1: Always ensure that the unknown quantities are on the LHS and the known quantities or constants on the RHS.

Step 2: Add all the terms containing the unknown quantities on the LHS and all the known quantities on the RHS so that each side of the equation contains only one term.

Step 3: Divide both sides of the equation by the coefficient of the unknown.

EXAMPLE 6.1 If $2x + 10 = 40$, find the value of x.

SOLUTION

Step 1: Group the known quantities as the RHS of the equation, i.e., $2x = 40 - 10$

Step 2: Simplify the numbers on the RHS $\Rightarrow 2x = 30$.

Step 3: Since 2 is the coefficient of x, divide both sides of the equation by 2.

$$\frac{2x}{2} = \frac{30}{2} \Rightarrow x = 15.$$

EXAMPLE 6.2 Solve for x: $5x - 8 = 3x + 22$.

SOLUTION

Step 1: $5x - 3x = 22 + 8$

Step 2: $2x = 30$

Step 3: $\frac{2x}{2} = \frac{30}{2} \Rightarrow x = 15.$

EXAMPLE 6.3 A teacher has 45 chocolates. After giving two chocolates to each student, she is left with 7 chocolates. How many students are there in the class?

SOLUTION

Let the number of students in the class be x.

Total number of chocolates distributed = $2x$

Total number of chocolates left with the teacher = 7

$2x + 7 = 45$

$\Rightarrow 2x = 45 - 7$

$\Rightarrow 2x = 38 \Rightarrow x = 19.$

There are 19 students in the class.

Simultaneous Linear Equations

We have learnt how to solve an equation with one unknown quantity. Very often we come across equations involving more than one unknown quantity. In such cases we require more than one condition or equation. Generally, when there are two unknowns, we require two equations to solve the problem. When there are three unknowns, we require three equations and so on.

We need to find the values of the unknowns that satisfy all the given equations. Since the values satisfy all the given equations we call them simultaneous equations. In this chapter, we deal with simultaneous (linear) equations with two unknowns.

Let us consider the equation, $3x + 4y = 15$, which contains two unknown quantities x and y.

Here, $4y = 15 - 3x$

$$\Rightarrow y = \frac{15 - 3x}{4} \quad (1)$$

In the above equation for every value of x, there exists a corresponding value for y.

When $x = 1$, $y = 3$.

When $x = 2$, $y = \frac{9}{4}$ and so on.

If there is another equation, of the same kind, say $5x - y = 2$, from this we get,

$$y = 5x - 2 \tag{2}$$

If we need the values of x and y such that both the equations are satisfied, then,

$$\frac{15 - 3x}{4} = 5x - 2 \Rightarrow 15 - 3x = 20x - 8$$

$$\Rightarrow 23x = 23 \Rightarrow x = 1.$$

On substituting the value of $x = 1$ in the first equation, we get,

$$y = \frac{15 - 3(1)}{4} \Rightarrow y = 3.$$

If both the equations are to be satisfied by the same values of x and y, there is only one solution.

Thus, we can say that when two or more equations are satisfied by the same values of unknown quantities then those equations are called simultaneous equations.

Solving Two Simultaneous Equations

When two equations, each in two variables are given, they can be solved in four ways.

1. Elimination by cancellation.
2. Elimination by substitution.
3. Adding the two equations and subtracting one equation from the other.
4. Graphical method.

Elimination by Cancellation

EXAMPLE 6.4 If $4x + 3y = 25$ and $5x + 2y = 26$, then find the values of x and y.

SOLUTION

$4x + 3y = 25$ (1)

$5x + 2y = 26$ (2)

Using this method, the two equations are reduced to a single variable equation by eliminating one of the variables.

Step 1: Here, let us eliminate the y term, and in order to eliminate the y term, equate the coefficient of y in both the equations.

$(4x + 3y = 25)2 \Rightarrow 8x + 6y = 50$ (3)

$(5x + 2y = 26)3 \Rightarrow 15x + 6y = 78$ (4)

Step 2: Subtract equation (3) from (4),

$(15x + 6y) - (8x + 6y) = 78 - 50 \Rightarrow 7x = 28$

$\Rightarrow x = 4.$

Step 3: Substitute the value of x in Eq. (1) or Eq. (2) to find the value of y. Substituting the value of x in the first equation, we have,

$4(4) + 3y = 25$

$\Rightarrow 3y = 25 - 16$

$\Rightarrow 3y = 9 \Rightarrow y = 3.$

$\therefore$ The solution of the given pair of equations is (x, y), i.e., $(4, 3)$.

Elimination by Substitution

EXAMPLE 6.5 If $3x - 2y = 12$ and $6x + y = 9$, then find the values of x and y.

SOLUTION

$3x - 2y = 12$ (1)

$6x + y = 9$ (2)

Using this method, the two equations are reduced to a single variable equation by substituting the value of one variable, obtained from one equation, in the other equation.

Step 1: Using the first equation, find x in terms of y, i.e., $3x - 2y = 12 \Rightarrow 3x = 12 + 2y$

$$\Rightarrow x = \frac{12+2y}{3} \quad (3)$$

Step 2: Substitute the value of x in the second equation to find the value of y, i.e., $6x + y = 9$

$$\Rightarrow 6\left(\frac{12+2y}{3}\right) + y = 9$$

Step 3: Simplify the equation in terms of y and find the value of y.

$2(12 + 2y) + y = 9$

$\Rightarrow 24 + 4y + y = 9$

$\Rightarrow 5y = 9 - 24 \Rightarrow y = -3.$

Step 4: Substituting the value of y in Eq. (3) we get $x = 2$.

$\therefore$ The solution for the given pair of equations is (x, y), i.e., $(2, -3)$.

Adding Two Equations and Subtracting One Equation from the Other

We use this method, in case of solving the system of linear equations of the form $ax + by = p$ and $bx + ay = q$.

EXAMPLE 6.6 Solve $4x + 5y = 37$ and $5x + 4y = 35$.

SOLUTION

Given, $4x + 5y = 37$ (1)

and $5x + 4y = 35$ (2)

Step 1: Adding both equations, we get

$9x + 9y = 72$

$\Rightarrow 9(x + y) = 9 \times 8$

$\Rightarrow x + y = 8$ (3)

Step 2: Subtracting Eq. (2) from the Eq. (1),

$(4x + 5y) - (5x + 4y) = 37 - 35$

$\Rightarrow -x + y = 2$ (4)

Step 3: Adding the Eqs. (3) and (4),

$(x + y) + (-x + y) = 8 + 2$

$\Rightarrow 2y = 10 \Rightarrow y = 5.$

Substituting $y = 5$ in any of the Eqs. (1), (2), (3) or (4), we get $x = 3$.

$\therefore$ The solution of the pair of equations is (x, y), i.e., $(3, 5)$.

Graphical Method: Plotting the Points

If we consider any point in a plane, then we can determine the location of the given point, i.e., we can determine the distance of the given point from X-axis and Y-axis. Therefore, each point in the plane represents the distance from both the axes. So, each point is represented by an ordered pair and it consists of x-coordinate and y-coordinate. The first element of an ordered pair is called x-coordinate and the second element of an ordered pair is called y-coordinate. In the first quadrant Q_1, both the x-coordinate and y-coordinate are positive real numbers. In the second quadrant Q_2, x-coordinates are negative real numbers and y-coordinates are positive real numbers. In the third quadrant Q_3 both the x-coordinate and y-coordinate are negative real numbers. In the fourth quadrant Q_4, x-coordinates are positive real numbers and y-coordinates are negative real numbers. And the origin is represented by (0, 0).

Konnect

Choosing a particular method to solve a pair of equations makes the simplification easier. One can learn which method is easiest to solve a pair of equations by becoming familiar with the different methods of solving the equation.

Consider the point (2, 3). Here, 2 is the x-coordinate and 3 is the y-coordinate. The point (2, 3) belongs to the first quadrant. The point (2, 3) is 2 units away from the Y-axis and 3 units away from the X-axis. If we consider the point (–3, –5), –3 is x-coordinate and –5 is y-coordinate. The point (–3, –5) belongs to Q_3 and is 3 units away from the Y-axis and 5 units away from the X-axis. The method of plotting a point in a co-ordinate plane was explained by a **René Descartes, a French mathematician.**

To plot a point say $P(-3, 4)$, we start from the origin and proceed 3 units towards the left-hand side along the X-axis (i.e., negative direction as x-coordinate is negative), and from there we move 4 units upwards along the Y-axis (i.e., positive direction as y-coordinate is positive).

EXAMPLE 6.7 Plot the following points on the coordinate plane:
$A(3, 5)$, $B(2, -4)$, $C(-2, 7)$, $D(-3, -4)$, $E(0, -5)$ and $F(5, 0)$

SOLUTION

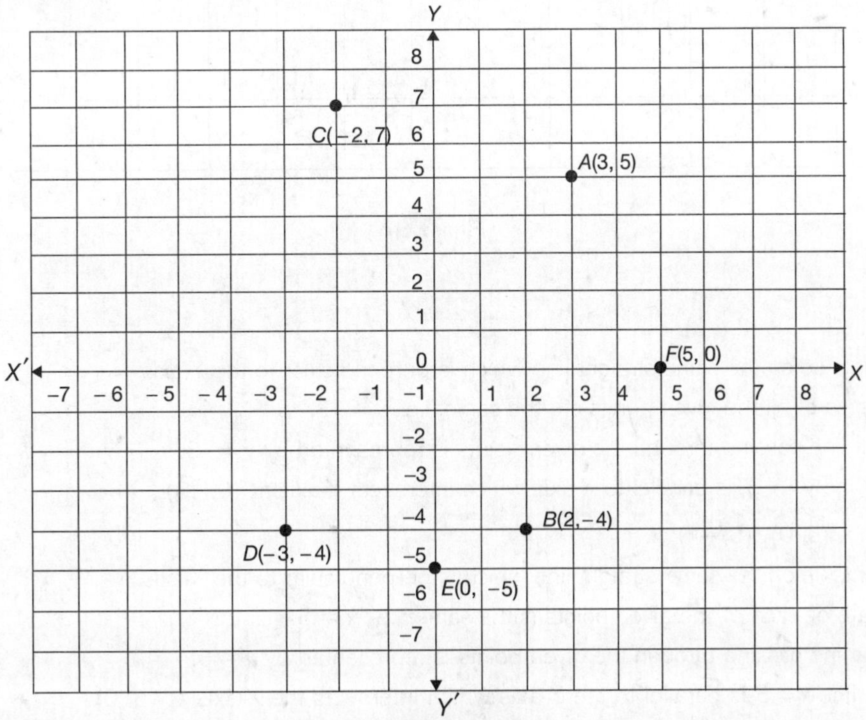

Figure 6.1

EXAMPLE 6.8 Plot the following points on the coordinate plane. What do you observe?

(a) (–2, –3), (–1, –3), (0, –3), (2, –3)
(b) (5, 3), (5, 2), (5, 1), (5, 0), (5, –1).

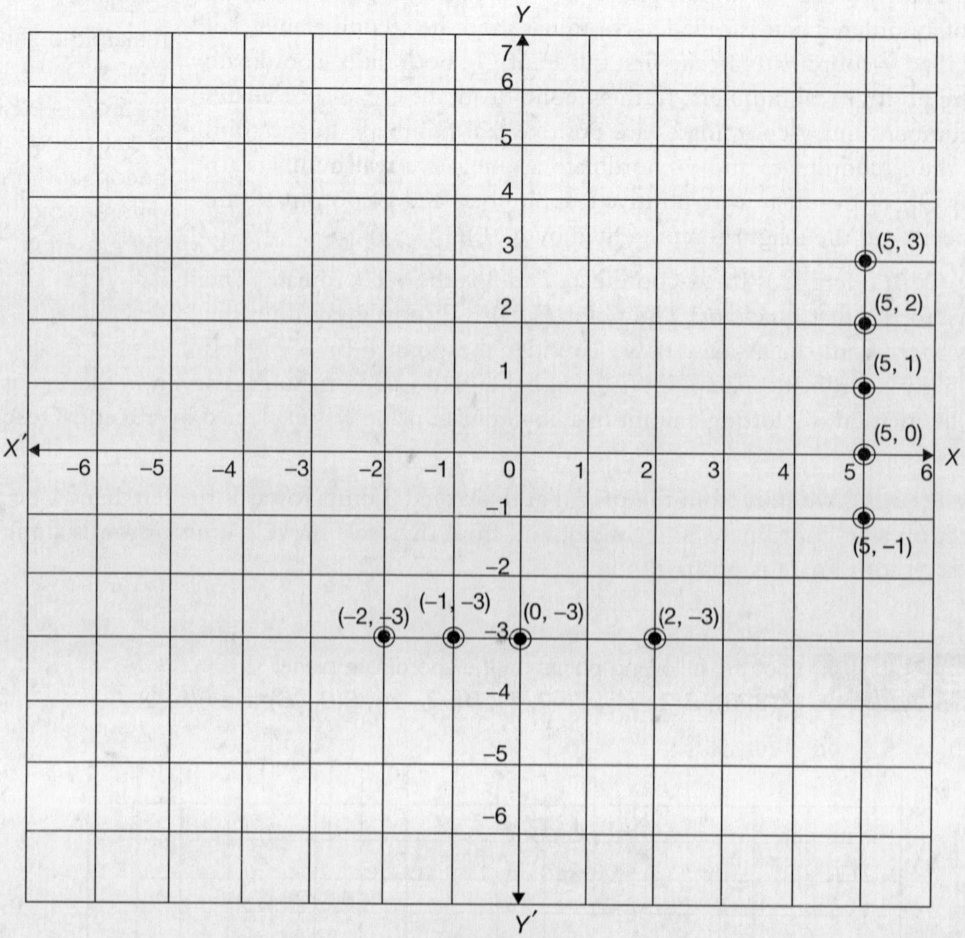

Figure 6.2

SOLUTION

(a) (–2, –3), (–1, –3), (0, –3), (2, –3)

(i) The above points lie on the same straight line which is perpendicular to the *Y*-axis.
(ii) The *y*-coordinates of all the given points are the same, i.e., $y = -3$.
(iii) So, the straight line passing through the given points is represented by $y = -3$.
(iv) Therefore, the line $y = -3$, is parallel to *X*-axis which intersects *Y*-axis at (0, –3).

(b) (5, 3), (5, 2), (5, 1), (5, 0), (5, –1)

(i) The above points lie on the same straight line which is perpendicular to the *X*-axis.
(ii) The *x*-coordinate of each of the given points is the same, i.e., $x = 5$.
(iii) So, the straight line passing through the given points is represented by $x = 5$.
(iv) Therefore, the line $x = 5$ is parallel to the *Y*-axis which intersects the *X*-axis at (5, 0).

Konnect

1. The y-coordinate of every point on the X-axis is zero, i.e., $y = 0$. Therefore, the X-axis is denoted by $y = 0$.
2. The x-coordinate of every point on the Y-axis is zero, i.e., $x = 0$. Therefore, the Y-axis is denoted by $x = 0$.

Example: The line $x = 4$ is parallel to Y-axis which intersects X-axis at (4, 0).

Example: The line $y = 5$ is parallel to X-axis which intersects Y-axis at (0, 5).

EXAMPLE 6.9

Plot the following points on the coordinate plane and what do you observe?
(–3, 3), (–2, 2), (–1, 1), (0, 0), (1, –1), (2, –2), (3, –3)

SOLUTION

(a) All the given points lie on the same straight line.
(b) Every point on the straight line represents $y = -x$.
(c) The above line with the given ordered pairs is represented by the equation $y = -x$.

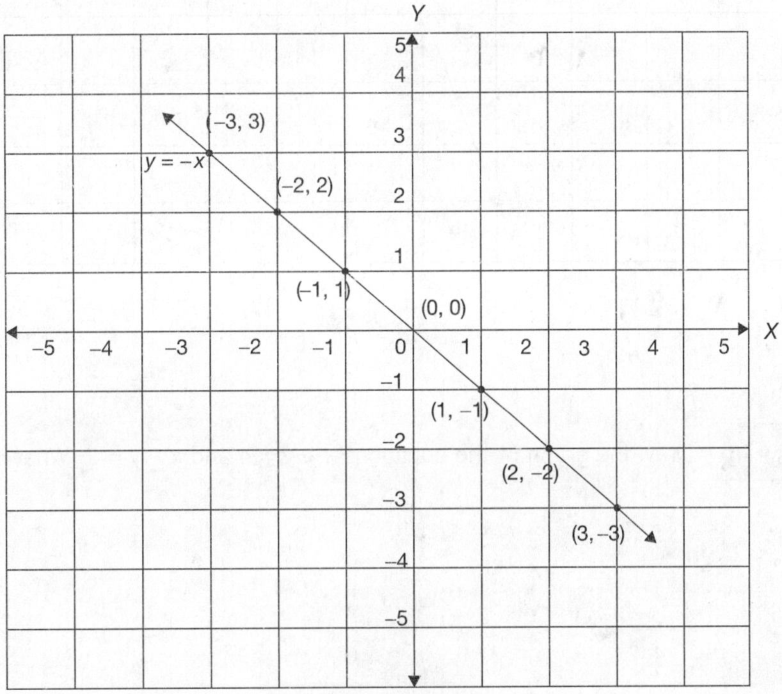

Figure 6.4

EXAMPLE 6.10

Draw the graph of the equation $y = 3x$ where R is the replacement set for both x and y.

SOLUTION

x	–2	–1	0	1	2
$y = 3x$	–6	–3	0	3	6

Some of the ordered pairs which satisfy the equation $y = 3x$ are (–2, –6), (–1, –3), (0, 0), (1, 3), (2, 6). By plotting the above points on the graph sheet, we get the following:

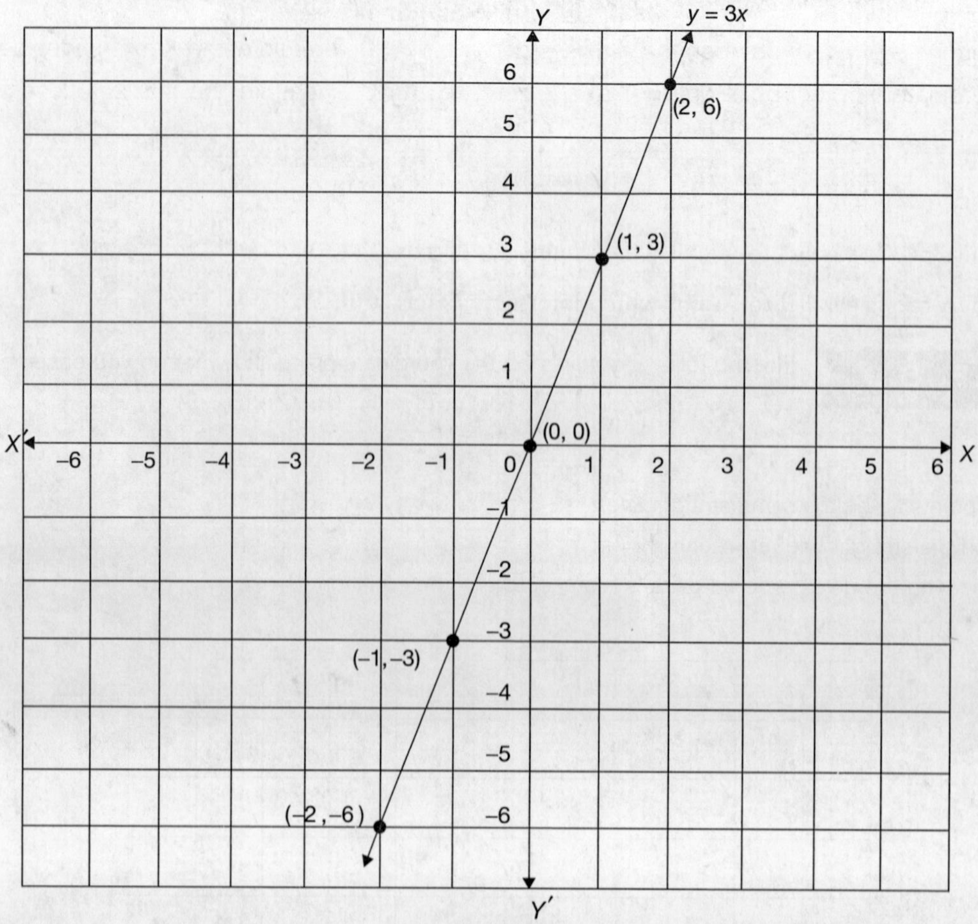

Figure 6.4

EXAMPLE 6.11 Draw the graph of the equations $x + y = 4$ and $x - y = 2$. What do you notice?

SOLUTION

(a) $x + y = 4$

x	–2	–1	0	1	2	3	4
$y = 4 - x$	6	5	4	3	2	1	0

Some of the ordered pairs which satisfy the equation $x + y = 4$ are (–2, 6), (–1, 5), (0, 4), (1, 3), (2, 2), (3, 1), (4, 0).

(b) $x - y = 2$

x	–2	–1	0	1	2	3	4	5
$y = x - 2$	–4	–3	–2	–1	0	1	2	3

∴ Some of the ordered pairs which satisfy the equation $x - y = 2$ are (–2, –4), (–1, –3), (0, –2), (1, –1), (2, 0), (3, 1), (4, 2), (5, 3).

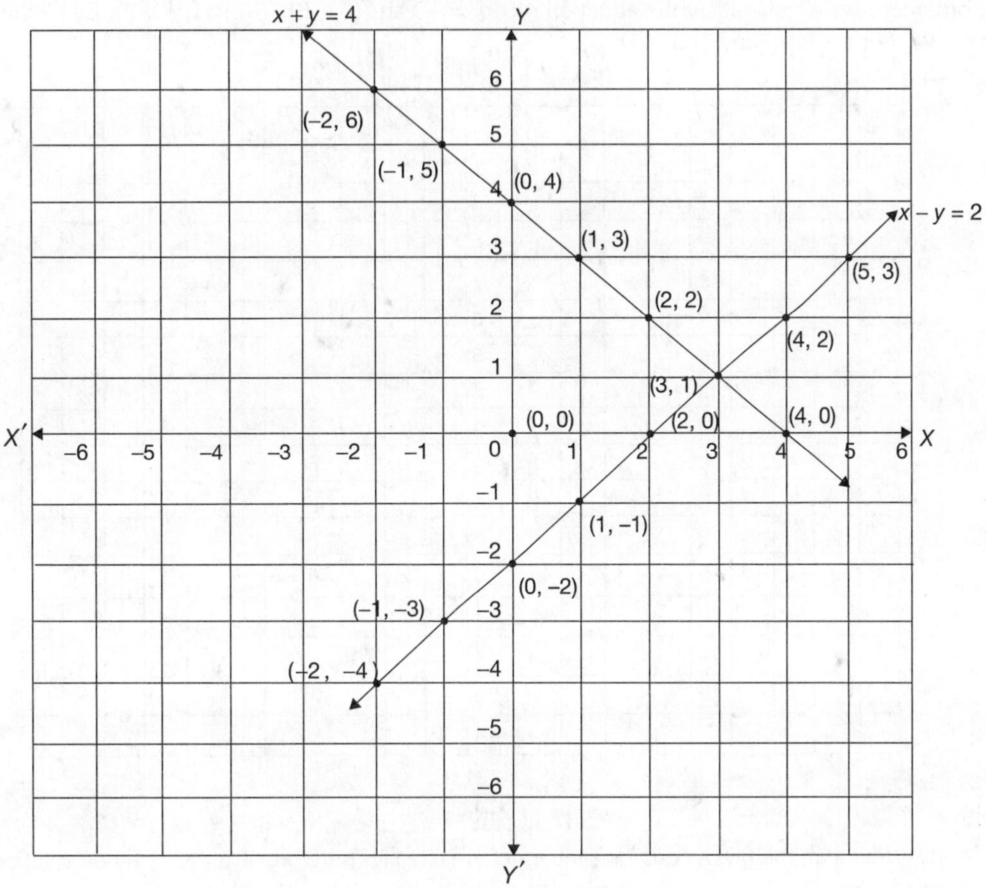

Figure 6.5

From the above graph, we notice that the two given equations intersect at the point (3, 1).

That is, $x + y = 4$ and $x - y = 2$ have a common point, (3, 1).Therefore, (3, 1) is the solution of the equations $x + y = 4$ and $x - y = 2$.

Verification:

$x + y = 4$ (1)

$x - y = 2$ (2)

Solving Eqs. (1) and (2), we get, $x = 3$ and $y = 1$.

$\therefore$ (3, 1) is the solution of $x + y = 4$ and $x - y = 2$.

EXAMPLE 6.12

Solve the following equations $x + 4y = 2$ and $4x - y = -9$ by the graphical method and check the result.

SOLUTION

(a) $x + 4y = 2$

x	2	6	−2	−6
$y = \frac{2-x}{4}$	0	−1	1	2

Some of the ordered pairs which satisfy the equation $x + 4y = 2$ are (2, 0), (6, −1), (−2, 1), (−6, 2).

(b) $4x - y = -9$

x	−1	−2	0
$y = 4x + 9$	5	1	9

Konnect

From the above example, we notice that we can find the solution for simultaneous equations by representing them in a graph, i.e., by using the graphical method.

Some of the ordered pairs which satisfy the equation $4x - y = -9$ are (–1, 5), (–2, 1), (0, 9). By plotting the above points on graph sheet, we get the following graph:

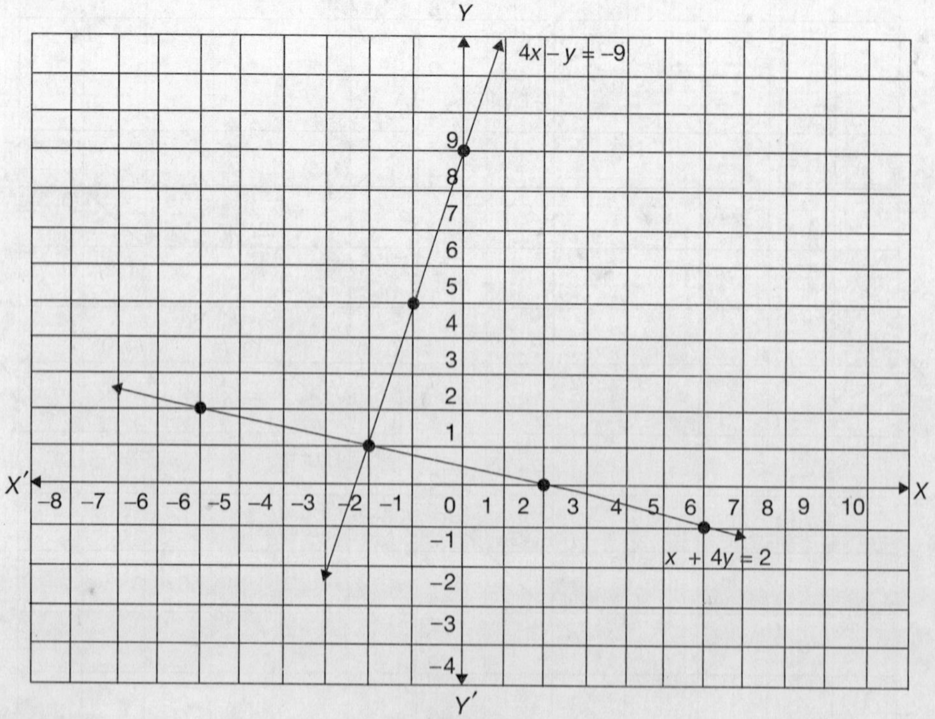

Figure 6.6

From the graph, it is clear that, the given equations intersect at (–2, 1). Therefore, it is the common solution for the equations $x + 4y = 2$ and $4x - y = -9$.

Verification:

$x + 4y = 2$ (1)

$4x - y = -9$ (2)

By solving Eqs. (1) and (2), we get $x = -2$ and $y = 1$.

∴ The solution is (–2, 1)

Nature of Solutions

When we try to solve a pair of equations, we could arrive at three possible results. They are having:

1. A unique solution.
2. An infinite number of solutions.
3. No solution.

Let the pair of equations be $a_1x + b_1y + c_1 = 0$ and $a_2x + b_2y + c_2 = 0$, where a_1, b_1, a_2, and b_2 are the coefficients of x and y terms, while c_1 and c_2 are the known constant quantities.

A Pair of Equations Having a Unique Solution

If, $\frac{a_1}{a_2} \neq \frac{b_1}{b_2}$, then there will be a unique solution.

We have solved such equations in the previous examples of this chapter.

A Pair of Equations Having Infinite Solutions

If $\frac{a_1}{a_2} = \frac{b_1}{b_2} = \frac{c_1}{c_2}$, then the pair of equations $a_1x + b_1y + c_1 = 0$ and $a_2x + b_2y + c_2 = 0$ will have an infinite number of solutions.

EXAMPLE 6.13 Find out the number of solutions for the following equations:

$3x + 4y = 8$

$9x + 12y = 24$

SOLUTION

For these two equations $a_1 = 3, a_2 = 9, b_1 = 4, b_2 = 12, c_1 = -8, c_2 = -24$.

$\therefore \frac{a_1}{a_2} = \frac{b_1}{b_2} = \frac{c_1}{c_2}$

Since, $\frac{3}{4} = \frac{4}{12} = \frac{-8}{-24}$

$\therefore$ The above pair of equations will have infinite solutions.

Konnect

In fact this means that there are no two equations as such and one of the two equations is simply obtained by multiplying the other with a constant. These equations are known as **dependent equations**.

A Pair of Equations Having no Solution

If $\frac{a_1}{a_2} = \frac{b_1}{b_2} \neq \frac{c_1}{c_2}$, then the pair of equations $a_1x + b_1y + c_1 = 0$ and $a_2x + b_2y + c_2 = 0$, will have no solution. Such lines are called parallel lines.

EXAMPLE 6.14 If $7x + ky = 9$ and $14x - 22y = 19$ have no common solutions, then the value of k is _____.

(a) 22 (b) −22 (c) 11 (d) −11

SOLUTION

Since $7x + ky = 9$ and $14x - 22y = 19$ have no common solution,

$\frac{a_1}{a_2} = \frac{b_1}{b_2} \neq \frac{c_1}{c_2}$

$\frac{7}{14} = \frac{k}{22}$

$k = -11$.

Konnect

1. In other words, the two equations will contradict each other or be inconsistent with each other.
2. A pair of equations are said to be consistent if they have a solution (finite or infinite).

Word Problems and Application of Simultaneous Equations

In this chapter, we have discussed earlier that it is essential to have as many equations as there are unknown quantities to be determined. In word problems also, it is required that there are as many independent conditions as there are unknown quantities to be determined.

Let us understand with the help of the following examples as to how word problems can be solved using simultaneous equations.

EXAMPLE 6.15 The sum of two numbers is 30 and the larger number exceeds the smaller by 6. Find the numbers.

SOLUTION

Let the numbers be a and b.

Given that $a + b = 30$ and $a - b = 6$.

By adding both the equations,

$2a = 36 \Rightarrow a = 18$

Substituting $a = 18$ in the first equation, $18 + b = 30$

$\Rightarrow b = 12$

$\therefore$ The two numbers are 18 and 12.

EXAMPLE 6.16 In a fraction, if unity is added to the numerator and subtracted from the denominator, it becomes $\frac{2}{3}$. Instead, if unity is subtracted from the numerator and added to the denominator, it becomes $\frac{1}{2}$. Find the fraction.

SOLUTION

Let the fraction be $\frac{x}{y}$, applying the first condition, we get,

$\frac{x+1}{y-1} = \frac{2}{3}$

$\Rightarrow 3x+3 = 2y-2$

$\Rightarrow 3x-2y = -5$ (1)

Applying the second condition, we get,

$\frac{x-1}{y+1} = \frac{1}{2}$

$\Rightarrow 2x-3 = 2y+1$

$\Rightarrow 2x-y = 3$ (2)

By solving the Eqs. (1) and (2) using any of the methods discussed earlier, we get $x = 11$ and $y = 19$.

$\therefore$ The fraction is $\frac{11}{19}$.

EXAMPLE 6.17 The sum of the digits of a two digit number is 8. If 18 is added to the number, then the resultant number is equal to the number obtained by reversing the digits of the original number. Find the original number.

SOLUTION

Let the number be in the form of $10x + y$, where x and y are the tens digit and the units digit, respectively. Applying the first condition, we get

$x + y = 8$ (1)

Applying the second condition, given in the problem,

$10x + y + 18 = 10y + x$

$\Rightarrow 9x - 9y = -18$

$\Rightarrow x - y = -2$ (2)

By solving Eqs. (1) and (2), we get,

$x = 3$ and $y = 5$ and the number is 35.

EXAMPLE 6.18 Five years ago, the age of a person was three years more than four times the age of his son. Three years hence, the age of the person will be six years less than thrice the age of his son. After how many years will their combined age be 80 years?

SOLUTION

Let the present ages of the person and his son be x and y years respectively.

Five years ago,

the age of person = $x - 5$

the age of son = $y - 5$

$x - 5 = 3 + 4(y - 5)$

$x - 4y = -12$ ------------- (1)

Three years hence,

the age of person = $x + 3$

the age of son = $y + 3$

$x + 3 = 3(y + 3) - 6$

$x - 3y = 0$ ------------- (2)

Solving (1) and (2),

we get $x = 36$, $y = 12$.

The sum of their present ages = 48 years.

$\therefore$ After 16 years, their combined age will be 80 years.

EXAMPLE 6.19 If $2x + 3y = 7$ and $4x + ky = 14$ are consistent equations, then the value of k is ____.

SOLUTION

Since $2x + 3y = 7$ and $4x + ky = 14$ are consistent equations,

$$\frac{a_1}{b_1} = \frac{b_1}{b_2} = \frac{c_1}{c_2} \text{ or } \frac{a_1}{a_2} \neq \frac{b_1}{b_2}$$

$$\frac{2}{4} = \frac{3}{k} = \frac{7}{14} \text{ or } \frac{2}{4} \neq \frac{3}{k}$$

$k = 6$ or $k \neq 6$

$\therefore$ For any real value of 'k', the given pair of equations are consistent.

POINTS TO REMEMBER

- ✔ Sentences which are true for some values of the variable and false for the other values of the variable are called open sentences.
- ✔ An equation is a sentence in which there is an equality sign between two algebraic expressions.
- ✔ An equation, in which the highest index of the unknowns present is one, is a linear equation.
- ✔ A linear equation which has only one unknown is a simple equation.
- ✔ The first element of an ordered pair is called x-coordinate and the second element of an ordered pair is called y-coordinate
- ✔ The method of plotting a point in a co-ordinate plane was explained by a René Descartes, a French mathematician

PRACTICE QUESTIONS CLASSROOM WING

Very Short Answer Type Questions

Directions of questions from 1 to 7:
Fill in the blanks.

1. The equations $\frac{x}{a}+\frac{y}{b}=1$ and $\frac{x}{b}+\frac{y}{a}=1$ are inconsistent if ______.

2. If sum of two numbers is 10 whereas their difference is 4, then the greater number is ______.

3. The number of solutions for $|x|+2=0$, where x is a real number is ________.

4. If a, b, c, d and e are positive real numbers such that $abcde = 32$, then the minimum value of $(1 + a)(1 + b)(1 + c)(1 + d)(1 + e)$ is ______.

5. What is the minimum value of $6 + |4 - 7x|$?

6. The maximum value of $30 - |x - 10|$ is ______.

7. The maximum value of $24 + |x - 18|$ is ______.

Directions of questions from 8 to 11:
State whether the following statements are true or false

8. If the system of linear equations is inconsistent, then the solution set is infinite. (True/False)

9. Every system of dependent equations is consistent. The converse is always true? (True/False)

10. Any line in a plane divides the plane into three disjoint parts. (True/False)

11. If the cost of 2 chocolates and 3 biscuits is ₹55 and that of 4 chocolates and 6 biscuits is ₹110, then the costs of one chocolate and one biscuit are necessarily ₹20 and ₹5, respectively. (True/False).

Short Answer Type Questions

12. The solution of the inequality $|2x + 1| < 0$ is ______.

13. If $2a + 3b + 5c = 9$ and $2a + b - c = 7$, then $a + b + c$ = ______

14. If $px + qy + r = 0$ and $qx + py + r = 0$ $(x \neq y)$, then show that the value of $x + y$ is $\frac{-r}{p}$ or $\frac{-r}{q}$.

15. Find the value of x, if $2x + 3y + k = 12$ and $x + 6y + 2k = 18$.

16. If $7x + 8y = 15$ and $14x + py = 30$ has infinite solutions, then find the value of p.

17. Father's age is 3 years more than thrice the son's age. After 5 years, father's age will be 12 years more than twice the son's age. Find the father's present age.

18. Sum of successors of two numbers is 40, whereas their difference is 6. Find the two numbers.

19. If the cost of 2 pencils and 3 erasers is ₹14. Whereas the cost of 3 pencils and 5 erasers is ₹22, then find the cost of one pencil and one eraser.

20. The sum of the digits of a two digit number is 7. If 9 is added to the number, the digits interchange their places. Find the number.

21. Harry has ₹2 and ₹5 coins with him. If he has a total of 33 coins worth ₹120 with him, how many ₹5 coins does he have?

Essay Type Questions

22. There are some chocolates with Tom and Jerry. If Tom gives certain number of chocolates to Jerry, then the number of chocolates with them will be interchanged. Instead, if Jerry gives same number of chocolates to Tom, then the number of chocolates with jerry will be one-fourth of the number of chocolates that Tom has. If the total number of chocolates with them is 100, then find the number of chocolates with Tom.

23. If $\frac{1}{x}+\frac{1}{y}=\frac{4}{3}$ and $\frac{1}{x}-\frac{1}{y}=\frac{1}{3}$, then $x =$ ________.

Direction for question 24 and 27:
Solve the questions graphically.

24. Find the two natural numbers so that their sum cannot exceed 6 and the difference between first and second number is positive and does not exceed 2 and also the resultant sum is maximum.

25. Find the pair of whole numbers so that their sum cannot exceed 10 and difference of twice the first number and thrice the second number cannot exceed 12.

26. A test has 150 questions. A candidate gets 2 marks for each correct answer and loses 1 mark for each wrong answer and loses $\frac{1}{2}$ mark for leaving the question unattempted. A student score 165 marks. If the student left 18 questions unattempted, find the number of questions he marked wrong.

27. In a school, the principal enquired and found that the number of students who use the "FaceBook" and "Twitter" were in the ratio 12 : 7. After the lecture on "Better use of Time" by the principal, 150 students stopped FaceBook and 100 students stopped using Twitter, the ratio became 7 : 4. Find the number of students who were using FaceBook at the beginning. (Assume that none of the students use both).

PRACTICE QUESTIONS COMPETITION WING

Level 1: Apply Your Concepts

Directions of questions from 1 to 4:
Fill in the blanks

1. The system of equations $a + b = 3$ and $3a + 3b = 9$ is ______.

2. The equations $px + qy + r = 0$ and $kpx + kqy + kr = 0$ are ______.

3. If the equations $4x + py = 12$ and $qx + 3y = 6$ are dependent, then the values of p and q are ______, and ______ respectively.

4. If $2x - 3y = 0$, then the value of $2x + 3y$ in terms of y is ______.

Directions of questions from 5 to 44:
Select the correct alternative from the given choices.

5. The number of solutions for $|x| - 4 = 0$ where x is a real number is ________.
   (a) 0 (b) 1
   (c) 2 (d) 3

6. Solve for x: $2x + 3 \geq 3x - 7$
   (a) $x \leq 10$ (b) $x \geq 10$
   (c) $-x \leq 10$ (d) $-x \geq 10$

7. If a, b are two natural numbers and $a + b = 5$, then which of the following can be the value of ab?
   (a) 2 (b) 6
   (c) 8 (d) 5

8. The maximum value of $23 - |2x + 3|$ is
   (a) 20 (b) 26
   (c) 17 (d) 23

9. The product of a number and 72 exceeds the product of the number and 27 by 360. Find the number.
   (a) 12 (b) 7
   (c) 8 (d) 11

10. The total cost of 10 erasers and 5 sharpeners is at least ₹65. The cost of each eraser cannot exceed ₹4. Find the minimum possible cost of each sharpener.
    (a) ₹6 (b) ₹5.50
    (c) ₹5 (d) ₹6.50

11. Find the solution of $|x + 1| < 5$.
    (a) $x < 6$ (b) $x > -5$
    (c) $-5 \leq x \leq 6$ (d) $-6 < x < 4$

12. The number of non-negative integer values of x that satisfy the inequation $x - 4 < 0$ is ________.
    (a) 1 (b) 2
    (c) 3 (d) 4

13. There is a group of cows and hens. The total number of legs is 14 more than twice the number of heads. Find the number of cows.
    (a) 14 (b) 10
    (c) 7 (d) 6

14. The age of a woman is thrice that of her daughter. When the woman was 29 years old, her only son, who is three years younger to her only daughter, was born. What is the present age of her son?
    (a) 8 years (b) 9 years
    (c) 10 years (d) 11 years

15. Solve the equations: $4(2^{x-1}) + 9(3^{y-1}) = 17$ and $3(2^x) - 2(3^y) = 6$.
    (a) $(x, y) = (2, 1)$ (b) $(x, y) = (-2, -1)$
    (c) $(x, y) = (1, 2)$ (d) $(x, y) = (2, -1)$

16. The solution set of $\frac{2}{x}+\frac{3}{y} = 2$ and $\frac{3}{x}+\frac{4}{y} = 20$ is:
    (a) $(4, -2)$ (b) $\left(-\frac{1}{2}, \frac{1}{4}\right)$
    (c) $(2, -4)$ (d) $\left(\frac{1}{4}, \frac{-1}{2}\right)$

17. Cost of 5 pens and 7 note books is ₹82 and cost of 4 pens and 4 note books is ₹52. Find the cost of 2 note books and 3 pens.
    (a) ₹34.50 (b) ₹30.50
    (c) ₹32.50 (d) ₹36.50

18. If $(a + b, a - b)$ is the solution of the equations $3x + 2y = 20$ and $4x - 5y = 42$, then find the value of b.
    (a) 8 (b) −2
    (c) −4 (d) 5

19. In a fraction, if numerator is increased by 2 and denominator is increased by 3, it becomes $\frac{3}{4}$ and if numerator is decreased by 3 and denominator is decreased by 6, it becomes $\frac{4}{3}$. Find the sum of the numerator and denominator.

(a) 16 (b) 18
(c) 20 (d) 14

20. If 100 cm is divided into two parts such that the sum of 2 times the smaller part and $\frac{1}{3}$ of the larger part, is less than 100 cm, then which of the following is correct?
(a) Larger portion is always less than 60.
(b) Smaller portion is always less than 60 and more than 40.
(c) Larger portion is always greater than 60.
(d) Smaller portion is always greater than 40.

21. If $\frac{3}{2}x + 2y = \frac{x}{4} - \frac{y}{2} = 1$, then $x - y =$

(a) 1 (b) 3
(c) 2 (d) 0

22. If we add 1 to the numerator and subtract 1 from the denominator a fraction becomes 1. It also becomes $\frac{1}{2}$ if we add 1 to the denominator. Then the sum of the numerator and denominator of the fraction is:

(a) 7 (b) 8
(c) 2 (d) 11

23. If $4x - 3y = 7xy$ and $3x + 2y = 18xy$, then $(x, y) =$

(a) $\left(\frac{1}{2}, \frac{1}{3}\right)$ (b) (3, 4)
(c) (4, 3) (d) $\left(\frac{1}{3}, \frac{1}{4}\right)$

Level 2: Review Your Concepts

24. If (1, 4) is the point of intersection of the lines whose equations are $2x + 3y = 14$ and $3y = 8 - ax$, then $a =$ ______.

(a) –4 (b) 2
(c) –2 (d) 4

25. If $73x + 69y = 256$ and $69x + 73y = 312$, then $y - x$ is ______.

(a) 10 (b) 14
(c) 16 (d) 18

26. Find the values of x and y, which satisfy the simultaneous equations $1010x + 1011y = 4040$ and $1011x + 1010y = 4044$.

(a) $x = 2, y = -4$ (b) $x = 0, y = 4$
(c) $x = 4, y = 4$ (d) $x = 4, y = 0$

27. If $3a + 5b + 6c = 33$ and $a + 3b + 4c = 19$, then $a + b + c =$ ______.

(a) 7 (b) 14
(c) 21 (d) 13

28. Shiva's age is three times that of Ram. After 10 years Shiva's age becomes less than twice the age of Ram. What can be the maximum present age (in complete years) of Shiva?

(a) 30 (b) 10
(c) 9 (d) 29

29. If a line $8x - 3y = 6$ passes through a point $(k - 1, k + 2)$, then $k =$ ______

(a) 3 (b) 4
(c) 2 (d) 5

30. If $2x + 3y = 6$ and $kx + 6y = 15$ has a unique solution, then find the set of values of k.

(a) N (b) N – {4}
(c) R (d) R – {4}

31. The following are two steps involved in finding the values of p and q from $3^p + 5^q = 52$ and $3^{p-1} + 5^{q-1} = 14$. Arrange them in sequential order.
(A) Let $x = 3^p$ and $y = 5^q$
(B) Solve for x and y
(C) Find p and q
(D) Rewrite the given equations in terms of x and y

(a) ABCD (b) ADCB
(c) ACBD (d) ADBC

32. If a, b, c, d are positive real numbers, the minimum value of the product $(a + b + c + d)\left(\frac{1}{a} + \frac{1}{b} + \frac{1}{c} + \frac{1}{d}\right)$ is ______.

(a) 16 (b) 32
(c) 24 (d) 36

33. X is a three-digit number. The number formed by reversing the digits of X is 891 less than X. Find its units digit.

(a) 0 (b) 1
(c) 2 (d) Cannot be determined

Level 3: Assess Your Concepts

34. An examination consists of 160 questions. One mark is given for every correct option. If one-fourth mark is deducted for every wrong option and half mark is deducted for every question left, then one person scores 79. And if half mark is deducted for every wrong option and one-fourth mark is deducted for every left question, the person scores 76, then find the number of questions he attempted correctly.
(a) 80 (b) 100
(c) 120 (d) 140

35. Runs scored by Sachin in a charity match is 10 more than the balls faced by Lara. The number of balls faced by Sachin is 5 less than the runs scored by Lara. Together they have scored 105 runs and Sachin faced 10 balls less than the balls faced by Lara. How many runs were scored by Sachin?
(a) 45 (b) 60
(c) 50 (d) 55

36. In an examination consisting of 100 questions, one mark is given for every correct answer and one-fourth mark is deducted for every wrong answer. A candidate attempts all the 100 questions and scores a total of 70 marks. Find the number of questions he marked correctly.
(a) 66 (b) 76
(c) 86 (d) 82

37. The number of possible pairs of successive prime numbers, such that each of them is greater than 40 and their sum is utmost 100, is
(a) 3 (b) 2
(c) 4 (d) 1

38. In an election the supporters of two candidates A and B were taken to polling booth in two different vehicles, capable of carrying 10 and 15 voters, respectively. If at least 90 vehicles were required to carry a total of 1200 voters, then find the maximum number of votes by which the elections could be won by the Candidate B.
(a) 900 (b) 600
(c) 300 (d) 500

39. A test has 60 questions. For each correct answer 2 marks are awarded and each wrong answer 1 mark is deducted. A candidate attempted all the questions in the test and scored 90 marks. Find the number of questions he attempted correctly.
(a) 54 (b) 48
(c) 49 (d) 50

40. Krishna and Sudheer have some marbles with them. If Sudheer gives 10 marbles to Krishna, Krishna will have 40 more marbles than Sudheer. If Sudheer gives 40 marbles to Krishna, Krishna will have 5 times as many marbles as Sudheer. Find the number of marbles with Sudheer.
(a) 65 (b) 55
(c) 70 (d) 50

41. If x, y are two natural numbers and $x + y = 7$, then which of the following cannot be the value of yx?
(a) 25 (b) 36
(c) 64 (d) 81

42. In a bag, the ratio of the number of coins of the denominations 25 paise, 10 paise and 5 paise is 1 : 2 : 3. The total amount in the bag is ₹30. The number of 5 paise coins in the bag is ______.
(a) 15 (b) 90
(c) 20 (d) 150

43. The sum of the ages of two married couples is 5 years more than three times the sum of the ages of their children. Five years ago sum of the ages of two couples and their children were in the ratio 9 : 2. Five years from now, if the ratio becomes 5 : 2, then find the total number of children.
(a) 4 (b) 5
(c) 6 (d) 7

44. Mr. P and Mr. Q are using the same mobile network on the same tariff plan. On 31st May, Mr. P had ₹72 and Mr. Q had ₹84 as balance respectively. Mr. P made calls of 80 minutes for the same network and 30 minutes for other networks and was left with a balance of ₹12. Mr. Q made calls of 90 minutes for the same network and 45 minutes for the other networks and was left with a balance ₹3. Find the details about the call rates of the tariff plan used by Mr. P and Mr. Q for the same and other network respectively.
(a) 30 paise/min, 120 paise/min
(b) 120 paise/min, 30 paise/min
(c) 20 paise/min, 100 paise/min
(d) 20 paise/ min, 120 paise/min

AT

PRACTICE QUESTIONS JEE SPECIAL WING

Multiple-Answer Type Questions

Directions for questions 1 to 10:
Each question has FOUR options (a), (b), (c), and (d). ONE OR MORE THAN ONE of these four option(s) is/are the correct answer(s).

1. If x and y are two positive integers such that $8x - 3y = 48$. Which of the following can be the sum of x and y?
   (a) 28 (b) 50
   (c) 83 (d) 105

2. Which of the following is (are) a solution (solutions) of $7x + 11y \leq -48$?
   (a) (2, –6) (b) (–3, –3)
   (c) (–9, 2) (d) (24, –25)

3. Which of the following is (are) a solution (solutions) of $|3 - x| + |x + 3| \geq 2030$?
   (a) 1020 (b) 1018
   (c) 1015 (d) 1013

4. If $26x - 52y + 91z = 936$ and $51x + 153y - 34z = 1326$, then which of the following is/are true?
   (a) $x + y + z = 30$ (b) $x + 13y - 9z = 6$
   (c) $x - 5y + 6z = 42$ (d) $x + 7y - 4z = 18$

5. Mr Manogna purchased x bananas at ₹4 each and y guavas at ₹9 each. Which of the following can be true about the given information, if he spent a total of ₹720 to purchase the bananas and guavas?
   (a) Manogna could purchase a minimum of four guavas.
   (b) Manogna could purchase a minimum of 85 fruits.
   (c) Manogna could purchase a maximum of 162 bananas.
   (d) Manogna could purchase a maximum of 170 fruits.

6. Madhu was born in the year 1978. The sum of 15 times her month of birth and 12 times her date of birth is 360. Which of the following can be true about month/date of her birth?
   (a) Madhu's month of birth is April.
   (b) Madhu's date of birth is 15.
   (c) Madhu was born on 20th August.
   (d) Madhu was born on 30th January.

7. The perimeter of a scalene triangle is 15 cm. Which of the following can be the difference between the longest and the shortest sides of the triangle?
   (a) 2 cm (b) 3 cm
   (c) 4 cm (d) 5 cm

8. If $x^2 - y^2 = 1001$, where x and y are two positive integers. Which of the following can be true about the given information?
   (a) The numbers are consecutive integers.
   (b) The difference between the numbers is always a prime number.
   (c) The smallest possible number is 32.
   (d) The greatest possible number is 501.

9. If x and y are two positive integers such that $\frac{1}{x} + \frac{1}{y} = \frac{1}{6}$, then which of the following can be true about the given information?
   (a) There exists five pairs of numbers.
   (b) The smallest possible number is 7.
   (c) The sum of the numbers is 27.
   (d) The difference of the numbers is 35.

10. Abhinav takes up an activity, on a given day, if he reaches the target, he will get ₹2500 otherwise he needs to payback ₹500. He works for thirty days. He does not reach the target on at least one day. Which of the following statements is/are true?
    (a) He has to reach the target for at least 5 days to avoid a negative payment.
    (b) The maximum possible amount that he could get is ₹72,000.
    (c) The minimum possible positive amount that he could get is ₹2500.
    (d) The ratio of the amounts that he could get when he reaches the target for 15 days and 25 days is 1 : 2.

Match The Column

Directions for questions 11 to 15:

Read the paragraph given below and answer the questions.

Liam and Olivia are twins, and they are good at Mathematics. One day, their teacher asked them to give a pair of natural numbers such that the sum of their reciprocals is $\frac{1}{20}$. They were able to give eight pairs of numbers in two minutes.

Match the values in Column A with those in Column B.

Column A (HCF of x and y)	Column B (LCM of x and y)
11. 9	(a) 40
12. 21	(b) 60
13. 24	(c) 210
14. 30	(d) 120
15. 40	(e) 180
	(f) 360
	(g) 420
	(h) 630

Comprehension-Based Questions

Directions for questions 16 to 20:

Read the paragraph given below and answer the questions.

Apoorva runs a book stall. She goes to a wholesale bookstore to purchase scales, marker pens and geometry boxes. The cost of each scale is ₹10, each marker pen is ₹40, and each geometry box is ₹50. She has to purchase 100 items by spending a total of ₹2800.

16. In how many ways can she purchase the items?

(a) 10 (b) 12
(c) 14 (d) 16

17. What is the maximum possible number of geometry boxes that can be purchased?

(a) 33 (b) 30
(c) 45 (d) 42

18. What is the minimum possible number of scales that can be purchased?

(a) 21 (b) 31
(c) 41 (d) 51

19. How many scales she should purchase if she purchases 27 geometry boxes?

(a) 49 (b) 37
(c) 25 (d) 13

20. How many marker pens she should purchase if she purchases 50 scales?

(a) 10 (b) 20
(c) 30 (d) 40

Assertion and Reason Type Questions

Directions for questions 21 to 25:

Read the options given below and answer the questions.

(a) Both assertion (A) and reason (R) are true, and the reason (R) is the correct explanation of the assertion (A).
(b) Both assertion (A) and reason (R) are true, and the reason (R) is not the correct explanation of the assertion (A).
(c) Assertion (A) is true, but reason (R) is false.
(d) Assertion (A) is false, and reason (R) is true.

21. Assertion: The number of common solutions of $6x - 4y = 33$ and $3x + 2y = -17$ is 1.

Reason: For a pair of linear equations $a_1x + b_1y = c_1$ and $a_2x + b_2y = c_2$ if $\frac{a_1}{a_2} \neq \frac{b_1}{b_2}$, then the pair of equations has unique solution.

22. Assertion: The pair of equations $6x - 4y = 32$ and $9x - 6y = 48$ has no solution.

Reason: For a pair of linear equations $a_1x + b_1y = c_1$ and $a_2x + b_2y = c_2$ if $\frac{a_1}{a_2} = \frac{b_1}{b_2} \neq \frac{c_1}{C_2}$, then the pair of equations has no solution.

23. Assertion: The pair of equations $21x + 14y = -210$ and $24x + 16y = -240$ has infinitely many solutions.

Reason: For a pair of linear equations $a_1x + b_1y = c_1$ and $a_2x + b_2y = c_2$ if $\frac{a_1}{a_2} = \frac{b_1}{b_2} \neq \frac{c_1}{c_2}$, then the pair of equations has infinitely many solutions.

24. **Assertion:** The pair of equations $x + y = 2030$ and $x - y = 2032$ is consistent.

Reason: For a pair of linear equations $a_1x + b_1y = c_1$ and $a_2x + b_2y = c_2$ if $\frac{a_1}{a_2} = \frac{b_1}{b_2} \neq \frac{c_1}{c_2}$, then given pair of equations is said be inconsistent

25. **Assertion:** If the pair of equations $5x + 10y = -a$ and $ax + 30y = -45$ is consistent, then a is any real number.

Reason: If the pair of linear equations $a_1x + b_1y = c_1$ and $a_2x + b_2y = c_2$ is consistent, then $\frac{a_1}{a_2} = \frac{b_1}{b_2} = \frac{c_1}{c_2}$ or $\frac{a_1}{a_2} \neq \frac{b_1}{b_2}$.

ANSWER KEYS

Crossword

Across

1. Transitive	4. Zero	5. One	6. Four	7. Consistent
9. Open	10. Ten			

Down

2. Inequation	3. Infinite	8. Three

Classroom Wing

Very Short Answer Type Questions

1. $a+b=0$	2. 7	3. x has no real value	4. 243	5. 6
6. 30	7. 24	8. False	9. False	10. True
11. False				

Short Answer Type Questions

12. The solution set is an empty set	13. $a+b+c=4$	15. 2	16. 16
17. 45 years	18. 22, 16	19. ₹6	20. 34
21. 18			

Essay Type Questions

22. 60	23. $\frac{6}{5}$	24. (4, 2)	26. 30	27. 1200

Competition Wing

Level 1: Apply Your Concepts

1. consistent	2. dependent	3. 6, 2	4. $6y$	5. (c)
6. (a)	7. (c)	8. (d)	9. (c)	10. (c)
11. (d)	12. (d)	13. (c)	14. (c)	15. (a)
16. (d)	17. (b)	18. (d)	19. (a)	20. (c)
21. (b)	22. (b)	23. (d)		

Level 2: Review Your Concepts

24. (a)	25. (b)	26. (d)	27. (a)	28. (d)
29. (b)	30. (d)	31. (d)	32. (a)	33. (a)

Level 3: Assess Your Concepts

34. (b)	35. (b)	36. (b)	37. (a)	38. (b)
39. (d)	40. (a)	41. (b)	42. (d)	43. (a)
44. (a)				

JEE Special Wing

Multiple-Answer Type Questions

1. (a, b, c, d) 2. (a, b, d) 3. (a, b, c) 4. (a, b, c, d) 5. (a, b)
6. (a, b, c) 7. (a, c, d) 8. (a, c, d) 9. (a, b, c, d) 10. (a, b, d)

Match The Column

11. (e) 12. (g) 13. (d) 14. (b) 15. (a)

Comprehension-Based Questions

16. (c) 17. (d) 18. (c) 19. (a) 20. (b)

Assertion and Reason Type Questions

21. (a) 22. (d) 23. (c) 24. (b) 25. (a)

Hints and Explanations

Classroom Wing

Very Short Answer Type Questions

1. $\frac{x}{a}+\frac{y}{b}=1, \frac{x}{b}+\frac{y}{a}=1$

$$\frac{xb+ya}{ab}=1, \frac{xa+yb}{ab}=1$$

$$bx+ay=ab, \ ax+by=ab$$

$$-ax+bx+ay-by=0$$

$$(b-a)(x-y)=0$$

So, $b-a=0$, if its consistent

but if $a+b=0$, then it will be inconsistent.

2. $x+y=10$

$$x-y=4$$

$$2x=14$$

$$x=7$$

$$y=10-7$$

$$y=3$$

So, here greater is 7

3. $|x|+2=0 \ |x|=-2$

$\therefore$ x has no real value.

4. For the minimum value of $(1+a)(1+b)(1+c)(1+d)(1+e)$, each of a, b, c, d and e is minimum.

Given, $abcde = 32 \Rightarrow$ The minimum value of each of a, b, c, d and e is 2, since $abcde = (2)^5$.

$\therefore$ $(1+a)(1+b)(1+c)(1+d)(1+e) = (2)^5 = 243.$

5. $6+|4-7x|$ will have the minimum value when $|4-7x|$ has the minimum value which is 0. Hence the minimum value of $6+|4-7x|$ is 6.

6. Since $|x-10|$ is always non-negative $30 - \ \leq 30$ for all real values of x.

$\therefore$ The maximum value is 30.

7. Given $f(x) = 24 + |x+8|$

Since $|x-8|$ is always non-negative, $|x-8| \geq 0$

$\therefore$ $24+|x-8| \geq 24$

The minimum value is 24.

8. Disagree, inconsistent has no solution.

There are some points which are not true for equation / inequality.

9. No, system of dependent equation is not always consistent.

10. True, any line in a plane directs the plane into 3 disjoint parts.

11. $2x+3y=55$

$4x+6y=110$

These 2 equations definite have many solutions so False.

Short Answer Type Questions

12. We know that $|x|$ is ≥ 0 for all $x \in$ R.

$\therefore$ No real value of x satisfies $|2x+1| < 0$

$\therefore$ The solution set is an empty set.

13. Given, $2a+3b+5c=9$ -------- (1)

$2a+b-c=7$ ----------- (2)

$(1)+(2) \Rightarrow 2a+3b+5c=9$

$\underline{2a+\ b-\ c=\ 7}$

$\underline{4a+4b+4c=16}$

$a+b+c=4.$

14. $px+qy+r=0$ and $qx+py+r=0$

$$px+qx+py+qy+2r=0$$

$$x(p+q)+y(p+q)=-2r$$

$$(p+q)(x+y)=-2r$$

$$x+y=\frac{-2r}{p+q} \qquad (1)$$

$$px-qx+qy-py=0$$

$$x(p-q)-y(p-q)=0$$

$$(x-y)(p-q)=0$$

we know that $x \neq y$

so, $p-q=0$

$$p=q \qquad (2)$$

Putting in the value of equation 2 in equation 1

$$x+y=\frac{-2r}{2p}=\frac{-r}{p}$$

Hence proved.

15. $-2(2x+3y+k=12)$

$x+6y+2k=18$

$-4x-6y-2k=-24$

$x+6y+2k=18$

$-3x=-6$

$x=2$

16. Given, $7x + 8y = 15$

$14x + py = 30$

The system has infinite solutions.

$\frac{7}{14}=\frac{8}{p}=\frac{15}{30}$

$\frac{8}{p}=\frac{1}{2}$

$p=16.$

17. Son current age is 'x' and Father's age is 'y'

equation 1 $\Rightarrow$ $y = 3x + 3$

equation 2 $\Rightarrow$ $(y + 5) = 2(x + 5) +12$

$y-3x=3$

$-y+2x=-17$

$-x=-14$

$x = 14$

$y-3\times 14=3$

$y-42=3$

$y = 45$ years

18. $x+1+y+1=40$

$x+y=38$

$x-y=6$

$2x=44$

$x = 22$

$y = 38 - 22 = 16$

$x = 22,\ y = 16$

19. $-3 \times (2x + 3y = 14)$

$2 \times (3x +5y = 22)$

$-6x-9y=-42$

$6x+10y=44$

$y=2$

$2x + 6 = 14$

$x=\frac{14-6}{2}$

$x = 4$

Pencil costs ₹4, Eraser costs ₹2 } Total = ₹6

20. Let the digits be x and y

$x + y = 7$

The number will be $(x + 10y)$

$x + 10y + 9 = 10x + y$

$9(x + y = 7)$

$9x - 9y = 9$

$9x+9y=63$

$9x-9y=9$

$18x=72$

$x=\frac{72}{18}=4$

$x = 4$

$y = 3$

Number $= 4 + 10 \times 3$

$= 34$

21. Let the number of ₹2 and ₹5 coins be x and y

$-2(x + y = 33)$

$2x+5y=120$

$-2x-2y=-66$

$3y=54$

$y = 18$

number of ₹5 coins are 18.

Essay Type Questions

22. Tom (x) Jerry (y)

$x-c=y \quad y+c=x$

$y-c=\frac{x+c}{4}$

$x+y=100$

$2y=\frac{5x+c}{4}$

$2y=\frac{5x+(x-y)}{4}$

$8y=6x-y$

$9y-6x=0$

$x+y=100$

$9y-6x=0$

$-9y-9x=-900$

$-15x=-900$

$$x = \frac{900}{15} = 60$$
$$x = 60$$
$$y = 40$$

23. Given, $\frac{1}{x} + \frac{1}{y} = \frac{4}{3}$ ______(1)

and $\frac{1}{x} - \frac{1}{y} = \frac{1}{3}$ ______(2)

$$(1)+(2) \Rightarrow \frac{1}{x} + \frac{1}{y} = \frac{4}{3}$$
$$\frac{1}{x} - \frac{1}{y} = \frac{1}{3}$$
$$\frac{2}{x} = \frac{5}{3}$$

$$\therefore \frac{1}{x} = \frac{5}{6} \Rightarrow x = \frac{6}{5}.$$

24.

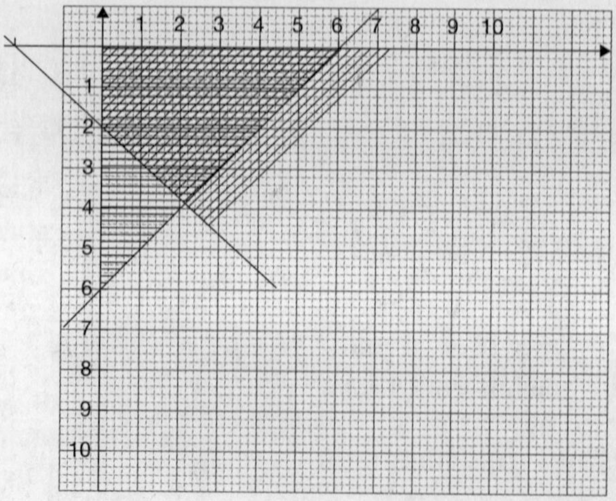

Let the numbers be x and y

$$x + y \le 6$$
$$x - y < 2$$

$x = 4, y = 2$

25.

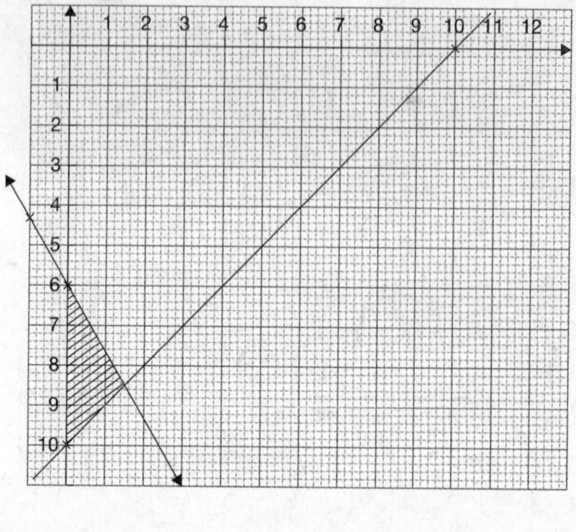

$$x + y > 10$$
$$2x - 3y > 12$$

7 and 2

$7 + 2 = 9$

$\therefore 9 < 10$

and

$7 - 2 = 5$

$5 < 12$

26 $x + y + z = 150$

$$2x - y - \frac{z}{2} = 165$$
$$x + y + 18 = 150$$
$$2x - y - 9 = 165$$
$$3x = 315 -$$
$$x = \frac{315-9}{3} = \frac{306}{3} = 102$$
$$102 + y + 18 = 150$$
$$y = 30$$

$\therefore$ He attempted 30 wrongly.

27. Let the number of students who use facebook be F and that of twitter be T.

$$\frac{F}{T} = \frac{12}{7} \text{ and } \frac{F-150}{T-100} = \frac{7}{4}$$

$\Rightarrow 7F = 12T$ and $4F - 600 = 7T - 700$

$\Rightarrow 7F = 12T$ and $4F - 7T = -100$

$$F = \frac{12}{7}T \Rightarrow 4\left(\frac{12}{7}\right)T - 7T = -100$$

$48T - 49T = -700 \Rightarrow T = 700$

$$\therefore F = \frac{12}{7} \times 700$$

$F = 1200$

$\therefore$ The number of students who were using facebook at the beginning = 1200.

Competition Wing

Level 1: Apply Your Concepts

1. The system of equations $a + b = 3$ and $3a + 3b = 9$ is consistent.

2. The equations $px + qy + r = 0$ and $Kpx + Kqy + Kr = 0$ are dependent.

3. $4x - py = 12$, $9x + 3y = 6$
as they are dependent
$$\frac{4}{q} = \frac{p}{3} = \frac{12}{6}$$
$$\frac{4}{q} = 2\ ,\ q = 2$$
$$p = 2 \times 3 = 6$$
$$p = 6$$

4. $2x - 3y = 0,\ x = \frac{3y}{2},\ y = \frac{2x}{3}$
$$2x + 3y = 2\left(\frac{3y}{2}\right) + 3y$$
$$= 3y + 3y$$
$$= 6y$$

5. $|x| - 4 = 0 \Rightarrow |x| = 4$
$\Rightarrow x = \pm 4$
$\therefore$ The given equations has two solutions.

6. $2x + 3 \geq 3x - 7$
$2x - 3x \geq -7 - 3$
$-x \geq -10$
$x \leq 10.$

7. Given, $a + b = 5$
Possibilities of $(a, b) = \{(1, 4), (2, 3), (3, 2), (4, 1)\}$
Possibilities of ab are 1, 8, 9, 4.
Choice (c) follows.

8. Since $|x|$ is always positive.
$\therefore a + |x| \leq a.$

9. Assume the number to be x and frame the equation.

10. Frame the inequations and proceed.

11. $|x + 1| < 5$
$\Rightarrow -5 < x + 1 < 5$
$\Rightarrow -6 < x < 4.$

12. Given, $x - 4 < 0$
$x < 4$ and $x \in$ W
$x \in \{0, 1, 2, 3\}.$

13. Let the number of cows and hens be x and y respectively.
$4x + 2y = 14 + 2(x + y)$
$4x + 2y = 14 + 2x + 2y$
$2x = 14$
$x = 7.$

14. Let the present ages of woman and daughter be x and y respectively
$x = 3y$ ---------- (1)
$x - y = 26$ ------------- (2)
From (1) and (2)
$3y - y = 26$
$2y = 26$
$y = 13$
Present age of son = (13 – 3) years.
= 10 years.

15. Assume $2^x = a$ and $3^y = b$ then solve.

16. Put $\frac{1}{x} = a, \frac{1}{y} = b$ and proceed.

17. Make algebraic equations and proceed.

18. $x = a + b$ and $y = a - b$.

19. (i) Frame equations according to the data.
(ii) Assume the numerator and denominator as x and y, respectively.
(iii) Frame the equations in terms of x and y and solve them.

20. Let the two parts be x and $(100 - x)$ and proceed.

21. Solve the equations for x and y.

22. Assume the fraction as $\frac{x}{y}$. Form equations in terms of x and y according to the given data and find the values of x and y.

23. Divide the two equations by xy. Assume $\frac{a}{x} = a;$ $\frac{1}{y} = b$ then solve for a and b.

Level 2: Review Your Concepts

24. Given (1, 4) is the point of intersection of $2x + 3y = 14$ and $3y = 8 - ax$.
$\therefore 3(4) = 8 - a$
$a = -4.$

25. Given, $73x + 69y = 256$ ------------ (1)

$69x + 73y = 312$ ------------ (2)

Eq (2) – eq (1), gives $4y - 4x = 56$

$\Rightarrow y - x = 14$

26. (i) First of all add given equations and then subtract from one another.

(ii) Subtract and add the given equations and then solve them for x and y.

27. Given, $3a + 5b + 6c = 33$ ------- (1)

$a + 3b + 4c = 19$ ----------- (2)

$$\begin{aligned}(1) - (2) \Rightarrow\ & 3a + 5b + 6c = 33 \\ & a + 3b + 4c = 19 \\ & - \quad - \quad - \quad - \\ \hline & 2a + 2b + 2c = 14 \\ & a + b + c = 7.\end{aligned}$$

28. (i) Frame inequation according to the data.

(ii) Assume the ages of Shiva and Ram as x and y years, respectively.

(iii) Frame the equation and inequation according to the data.

29. Given $8x - 3y = 6$ ----------- (1)

$(k - 1, k - 2)$ passes through the equation (1).

$8(k - 1) - 3(k + 2) = 6$

$8k - 8 - 3k - 6 = 6$

$5k = 20$

$k = 4.$

30. Given, $2x + 3y = 6$

$kx + 6y = 15$

The system has a unique solution

i.e. $\frac{2}{k} \neq \frac{3}{6} \Rightarrow k \neq 4$

∴ The value of k is any real number except 4.

31. It can be easily seen that the correct order is ADBC.

32. $(a+b+c+d)\left(\frac{1}{a}+\frac{1}{b}+\frac{1}{c}+\frac{1}{d}\right) = [1+1+1+1+$

$\left(\frac{a}{b}+\frac{b}{a}\right)+\left(\frac{a}{c}+\frac{c}{a}\right)+\left(\frac{a}{d}+\frac{d}{a}\right)+\left(\frac{b}{c}+\frac{c}{d}\right)$

$+\left(\frac{b}{d}+\frac{d}{b}\right)+\left(\frac{c}{d}+\frac{d}{c}\right) \geq [4+6(2)]\left(\because x+\frac{1}{x}\geq 2\right)$

$= 16$

∴ The minimum value is 16.

33. Let x be abc.

The number formed by reversing the digits = cba

$cba = abc - 891$, i.e., $891 = abc - cba$

$891 = 100a + 10b + c - (100c + 10b + a)$

$= 99(a - c)$

$9 = a - c$

i.e., $a = c + 9$

$c \geq 0$

∴ $a \geq 9$.

But $a \leq 9$.

∴ $a = 9$.

∴ $c = 0$.

Level 3: Assess Your Concepts

34. (i) Frame equations according to the data.

(ii) Frame the equations according to the data and then solve.

35. (i) Frame equations according to the data.

(ii) Assume runs scored by Sachin as x and balls faced by Sachin as y.

(iii) Frame the equation in terms of x and y according to the data and solve the equation.

36 Let 'c' be the number of questions marked correctly.

∴ The number of questions marked wrongly = $100 - c$

∴ $1c - \frac{1}{4}(100 - c) = 70$

$c - 25 + \frac{c}{4} = 70$

$\frac{5c}{4} = 95$

$c = 76$

∴ The number of questions marked correctly = 76.

37. (i) Write primes as per the given conditions.

(ii) Assume the prime numbers as x, y.

(iii) Find the possible values of x and y such that $x + y < 100$, where $x > y > 40$.

38. Find the values of x and y such that $x + y > 90$ and $10x + 15y = 1200$.

39. Let the number of questions attempted correctly by the candidate = C.

He attempted all the questions.

$\therefore$ Number of questions attempted wrongly by him = $60 - C$

$2C - 1(60 - C) = 90$

$2C - 60 + C = 90$

$C = 50.$

40. Let the number of marbles with Krishna and Sudheer be M and S, respectively.

$M + 10 = S - 10 + 40 \Rightarrow M = S + 20.$

$M + 40 = 5(S - 40) \Rightarrow S + 20 + 40 = 5(S - 40)$

$260 = 4S$, i.e., $S = 65.$

41. Given, $x + y = 7$

Possibilities of (x, y) are (1, 6), (2, 5), (3, 4), (4, 3), (5, 2), (6, 1)

Possibilities of y^x are 6, 25, 64, 81, 32 and 1.

Choice (2) follows.

42. Let the number of 25 paise 10 paise and 5 paise coins be x, $2x$ and $3x$ respectively.

$25x + 20x + 15x = 30 \times 100$

$60x = 3000$

$x = 50$

$\therefore$ The number of 5 paise coins = 3(50) = 150.

43. Let the sum of the ages of two married couples be 'x' years and the sum of the ages of their children be 'y' years.

$x = 3y + 5$

Let there be 'n' number of children in all together.

Five years ago; $\dfrac{x - 4(5)}{y - n(5)} = \dfrac{9}{2}$

$\Rightarrow 2x - 40 = 9y - 45n$

$2(3y + 5) - 40 = 9y - 45n$

$45n - 3y = 30$ (1)

Five years hence,

$\dfrac{x + 4(5)}{y + 5n} = \dfrac{5}{2}.$

$2x + 40 = 5y + 25n$

$2(3y + 5) + 40 = 5y + 25n$

$y - 25n = -50$

$y = 25n - 50$ (2)

On solving (1) and (2), we get

$n = 4$ and $y = 50 \Rightarrow x = 155$

$\therefore$ There are four children in total.

44. Let cost for a minute to the same network be ₹x and that for the other networks be ₹y.

Mr. P

$80x + 30y = 72 - 12$

$80x + 30y = 60$

$8x + 3y = 6 \rightarrow (1)$

Mr. Q

$90x + 45y = 84 - 3$

$90x + 45y = 81$

$10x + 5y = 9 \rightarrow (2)$

Equation (1) × 5 – equation (2) × 3

$\Rightarrow 40x + 15y = 30$

$30x + 15y = 27$

$10x = 3$

$x = ₹\dfrac{3}{10}$

$x = \dfrac{300}{10}$ paise

$x = 30$ paise per minute.

From (1), $8\left(\dfrac{3}{10}\right) + 3y = 6$

$3y = 6 - \dfrac{12}{5}$

$3y = \dfrac{18}{5}$

$y = \dfrac{6}{5}$ $y = ₹1.20$

$y = 120$ paise per minute.

$\therefore$ The tariff plan is 30 paise per 1 minute for the same network and 120 paise per 1 minute for the other networks.

JEE Special Wing

Multiple-Answer Type Questions

1. Given that x and y are two positive integers such that $8x - 3y = 48$.

$\Rightarrow x = \dfrac{48 + 3y}{8}$

$\Rightarrow x = 6 + \dfrac{3y}{8}$

y	8	16	24	32	40	48	56	64	72	...
x	9	12	15	18	21	24	27	30	33	...
$x+y$	17	28	39	50	61	72	83	94	105	...

Hence, choice (a, b, c, d) are correct.

2. Given that $7x + 11y \le -48$.

Going by options:

(a) (2, –6):

$7(2) + 11(-6) = 14 - 66 = -52 < -48.$

(b) (–3, –3):

$7(-3) + 11(-3) = -21 - 33 = -54 < -48.$

(c) (–9, 2):

$7(-9) + 11(2) = -63 + 22 = -41 > -48.$

(d) (24, –25):

$7(24) + 11(-25) = 168 - 275 = -107 < -48.$

Hence, **choice (a, b, d)** are correct.

3. Given that of $|3 - x| + |x + 3| \ge 2029.$

Going by options:

(a) $x = 1020$

$|3 - x| + |x + 3| = |3 - 1020| + |1020 + 3|$

$= |-1017| + |1023| = 1017 + 1023 = 2040 \ge 2030.$

(b) $x = 1018$

$|3 - x| + |x + 3| = |3 - 1018| + |1018 + 3|$

$= |-1015| + |1021| = 1015 + 1021 = 2036 \ge 2030.$

(c) $x = 1015$

$|3 - x| + |x + 3| = |3 - 1015| + |1015 + 3|$

$= |-1012| + |1018| = 1012 + 1018 = 2030 \ge 2030.$

(d) $x = 1013$

$|3 - x| + |x + 3| = |3 - 1013| + |1013 + 3|$

$= |-1010| + |1016| = 1010 + 1016 = 2026 < 2030.$

Hence, choice (a, b, c) are correct.

4. Given that:

$26x - 52y + 91z = 936 \Rightarrow 2x - 4y + 7z = 72$ (1)

$51x + 153y - 34z = 1326 \Rightarrow 3x + 9y - 2z = 78$ (2)

(a) Adding both the equations we get $5x + 5y + 5z = 150$.

$\Rightarrow x + y + z = 30.$

(b) Eqn (2) – Eqn (1): $x + 13y - 9z = 6$

(c) $4 \times$ Eqn (1) – Eqn (2):

$4 \times (2x - 4y + 7z = 72) - (3x + 9y - 2z = 78)$

$\Rightarrow 8x - 16y + 28z - (3x + 9y - 2z) = 288 - 78$

$\Rightarrow 5x - 25y + 30z = 210$

$\Rightarrow x - 5y + 6z = 42.$

(d) $3 \times$ Eqn (2) – $2 \times$ Eqn (1):

$3 \times (3x + 9y - 2z = 78) - 2 \times (2x - 4y + 7z = 72)$

$\Rightarrow 9x + 27y - 6z - 4x + 8y - 14z = 234 - 144$

$\Rightarrow 5x + 35y - 20z = 90$

$\Rightarrow x + 7y - 4z = 18.$

Hence, choice (a, b, c, d) are correct.

5. Given that Mr Manogna purchased x bananas at ₹4 and y guavas at ₹9. Also, he spent a total of ₹ 720.

$\Rightarrow 4x + 9y = 720$

$\Rightarrow y = 80 - \dfrac{4x}{9}$ where x and y are positive integers.

Also, x is also divisible by 9.

x	9	18	27	36	45	54	...	162	171
y	76	72	68	64	60	56	...	8	4
$x+y$	85	90	95	100	105	110	...	170	175

(a) Manogna could purchase a minimum of four guavas which is a true statement.

(b) Manogna could purchase a minimum of 85 fruits which is a true statement.

(c) Manogna could purchase a maximum of 162 bananas which is a false Reason because she could purchase a maximum of 171 bananas.

(d) Manogna could purchase a maximum of 170 fruits which is a false Reason because she could purchase a maximum of 175 fruits.

Hence, choice (a and b) are correct.

6. Given that Madhu was born in the year 1978. The sum of 15 times her month of birth and 12 times her date of birth is 360.

Let the month of birth be m and the date of birth be b, where $1 \le m \le 12$ and $1 \le d \le 31$.

As per the given data, $15m + 12d = 360$.

$\Rightarrow 5m + 4d = 120.$

$\Rightarrow d = 30 - \frac{5m}{4}$ where m and d are positive integers.

Also, m is also divisible by 4.

m	4	8	12
d	25	20	15

Madhu may be born on 25th April or 20th August or 15th December.

Hence, choice (a, b, c) are correct.

7. Given that the perimeter of a scalene triangle is 15 cm. Let the sides of the triangle be a, b and c.

$\Rightarrow a + b + c = 15$

$\Rightarrow (a, b, c) = (7, 2, 6); (7, 3, 5); (6, 4, 5)$

(Since the sum of any two sides is greater than the third side and the difference of any two sides is less than the third side)

The difference between the longest and the shortest sides of the triangle:

$7 - 2 = 5; 7 - 3 = 4; 6 - 4 = 2$

Hence, choice (a, c, d) are correct.

8. Given that x and y are two positive integers such that $x^2 - y^2 = 1001$.

$\Rightarrow (x + y)(x - y) = 7 \times 11 \times 13.$

Case (i): $x + y = 77$ and $x - y = 13$

$\Rightarrow x = 45$ and $y = 32$.

Case (ii): $x + y = 91$ and $x - y = 11$

$\Rightarrow x = 51$ and $y = 40$.

Case (iii): $x + y = 143$ and $x - y = 7$

$\Rightarrow x = 75$ and $y = 68$.

Case (iv): $x + y = 1001$ and $x - y = 1$

$\Rightarrow x = 501$ and $y = 500$.

Now going by options:

(a) The numbers are consecutive integers which is a true statement when $x = 501$ and $y = 500$.

(b) The difference between the numbers is always a prime number which is a false statement when 501 and $y = 500$.

(c) The smallest possible number is 32 which is a true statement.

(d) The greatest possible number is 501 which is a true statement.

Hence, choice (a, c, d) are correct.

9. Given that x and y are two positive integers such that $\frac{1}{x} + \frac{1}{y} = \frac{1}{6}$.

$\Rightarrow \frac{1}{y} = \frac{1}{6} - \frac{1}{x}$

$\Rightarrow \frac{1}{y} = \frac{x - 6}{6x}$

$\Rightarrow y = \frac{6x}{x - 6}$

x	7	8	9	10	12
y	42	24	18	15	12
$x + y$	49	32	27	25	24
$x - y$	35	16	9	5	0

So, all the given statements are true.

Hence, choice (a, b, c, d) are correct.

10. The amount that Abhinav receives on reaching the target = ₹2500.

The amount that Abhinav payback for not reaching the target = ₹500.

Let the number of days that he reaches the target be n.

The total amount that Abhinav receive

$= (₹2500 \times n) - (30 - n) \times ₹500$

$= ₹3000 \times n - ₹15000$

$= ₹3000 \times (n - 5).$

(a) He has to reach the target for at least 5 days to avoid a negative payment, which is a true statement.

(b) As he does not reach the target on at least one day he works, he has to reach the target in 29 days to get the maximum possible amount.

The maximum possible amount that he could get is $₹3000 \times (n - 5)$

$= ₹3000 \times (29 - 5)$

$= ₹3000 \times 24 = ₹72,000.$

So, statement (b) is true.

(c) To get the minimum possible positive amount, he has to reach the target for six days.

The minimum possible positive amount that he could get is get is $₹3000 \times (n - 5)$

$= ₹3000 \times (6 - 5)$

$= ₹3000 \times 1 = ₹3000.$

So, statement (c) is wrong.

(d) The required ratio

$= [₹3000 \times (15-5)] : [₹3000 \times (25-5)]$

$= 10 : 20 = 1 : 2$. So, statement (d) is true.

Hence, choice (a, b, d) are correct.

Match The Column

Solutions for questions 11 to 15:

Given that x and y are two natural such that $\frac{1}{x}+\frac{1}{y}=\frac{1}{20}$.

$\Rightarrow \frac{1}{y}=\frac{1}{20}-\frac{1}{x}$

$\Rightarrow \frac{1}{y}=\frac{x-20}{20x}$

$\Rightarrow y=\frac{20x}{x-20}$

x	21	22	24	25	28	30	36	40
y	420	220	120	100	70	60	45	40
HCF (x, y)	21	22	24	25	14	30	9	40
LCM (x, y)	420	220	120	100	140	60	180	40

11. When HCF (x, y) is 9, LCM (x, y) is 180.
Hence, the correct option is (e).

12. When HCF (x, y) is 21, LCM (x, y) is 420.
Hence, the correct option is (g).

13. When HCF (x, y) is 24, LCM (x, y) is 120.
Hence, the correct option is (d).

14. When HCF (x, y) is 30, LCM (x, y) is 60.
Hence, the correct option is (b).

15. When HCF (x, y) is 40, LCM (x, y) is 40.
Hence, the correct option is (a).

Comprehension-Based Questions

Solutions for questions 16 to 20:

Let the number of scales, marker pens and geometry boxes to be purchased x, y and z respectively.

Given that $x+y+z=100$ … (1)

Also $10x+40y+50z=2800$

$\Rightarrow x+4y+5z=280$ … (2)

Eqn (2) – Eqn (1): $3y+4z=180$

$\Rightarrow z=45-\frac{3y}{4}$ where z and y are positive integers. Also, y is also divisible by 4.

y	4	8	12	16	20	24	28	…	56
z	42	39	36	33	30	27	24	…	3
x	54	53	52	51	50	49	48	…	41

16. She can purchase the items in fourteen ways.
Hence, the correct option is (c).

17. The maximum number of geometry boxes that Apoorva can purchase is 42.
Hence, the correct option is (d).

18. The minimum number of scales that Apoorva can purchase is 41.
Hence, the correct option is (c).

19. If $z=27$, then $x=49$ and $y=24$.
She should purchase 49 scales.
Hence, the correct option is (a).

20. If $x=50$, then $y=20$ and $z=30$.
She should purchase 20 marker pens.
Hence, the correct option is (b).

Assertion and Reason Type Questions

Solutions for questions 21 to 25:

21. **Assertion:** Given that $6x-4y=33$ and $3x+2y=-17$.

$\Rightarrow \frac{a_1}{a_2}=\frac{6}{3}=2$ and $\frac{b_1}{b_2}=\frac{-4}{2}=-2$

As $\frac{a_1}{a_2}\neq\frac{b_1}{b_2}$, the pair of equations has unique solution.

So, Assertion is true.

Reason: For a pair of linear equations $a_1x+b_1y=c_1$ and $a_2x+b_2y=c_2$ if $\frac{a_1}{a_2}\neq\frac{b_1}{b_2}$, then the pair of equations has unique solution.

So, Reason is true and is the correct explanation of the Assertion.

Hence, the correct option is (a).

22. **Assertion:** Given that $6x-4y=32$ and $9x-6y=48$.

$\Rightarrow \frac{a_1}{a_2}=\frac{6}{9}=\frac{2}{3}, \frac{b_1}{b_2}=\frac{-4}{-6}=\frac{2}{3}$ and $\frac{c_1}{c_2}=\frac{32}{48}=\frac{2}{3}$

As $\frac{a_1}{a_2}=\frac{b_1}{b_2}=\frac{c_1}{c_2}$, the pair of equations has infinitely many solutions.

So, Assertion is false.

Reason: For a pair of linear equations $a_1x + b_1y = c_1$ and $a_2x + b_2y = c_2$ if $\frac{a_1}{a_2} = \frac{b_1}{b_2} \neq \frac{c_1}{c_2}$, then the pair of equations has no solution.

So, Reason is true.

Hence, the correct option is (d).

23. **Assertion:** Given that $21x + 14y = -210$ and $24x + 16y = -240$.

$\Rightarrow \frac{a_1}{a_2} = \frac{21}{24} = \frac{7}{8}, \frac{b_1}{b_2} = \frac{14}{16} = \frac{7}{8}$ and $\frac{c_1}{c_2} = \frac{-210}{-240} = \frac{7}{8}$.

As $\frac{a_1}{a_2} = \frac{b_1}{b_2} = \frac{c_1}{c_2}$, the pair of equations has infinitely many solutions.

So, Assertion is true.

Reason: For a pair of linear equations $a_1x + b_1y = c_1$ and $a_2x + b_2y = c_2$ if $\frac{a_1}{a_2} = \frac{b_1}{b_2} \neq \frac{c_1}{c_2}$, then the pair of equations has no solution.

So, Reason is false.

Hence, the correct option is (c).

24. **Assertion:** Given that $x + y = 2030$ and $x - y = 2032$.

$\Rightarrow \frac{a_1}{a_2} = 1$ and $\frac{b_1}{b_2} = -1$

As $\frac{a_1}{a_2} \neq \frac{b_1}{b_2}$, the pair of equations has unique solution.

The pair of equations is said to be consistent.

So, Assertion is true.

Reason: For a pair of linear equations $a_1x + b_1y = c_1$ and $a_2x + b_2y = c_2$ if $\frac{a_1}{a_2} = \frac{b_1}{b_2} \neq \frac{c_1}{c_2}$, then given pair of equations is said be inconsistent

So, Reason is true but not the correct explanation of the Assertion.

Hence, the correct option is (b).

25. **Assertion:** Given that the pair of equations $5x + 10y = -a$ and $ax + 30y = -45$ is consistent.

$\Rightarrow \frac{a_1}{a_2} = \frac{b_1}{b_2} = \frac{c_1}{c_2}$ or $\frac{a_1}{a_2} \neq \frac{b_1}{b_2}$.

$\Rightarrow \frac{5}{a} = \frac{10}{30} = \frac{-a}{-45}$ or $\frac{5}{a} \neq \frac{10}{30}$

$\Rightarrow \frac{5}{a} = \frac{1}{3} = \frac{-a}{-45}$ or $\frac{5}{a} \neq \frac{1}{3}$

$\Rightarrow a = 15$ or $a \neq 15$.

When $a = 15$, the pair of equations has infinitely many solutions.

When $a \neq 15$, the pair of equations has unique solution.

As the given pair of equations is consistent, Assertion is true.

Reason: If the pair of linear equations $a_1x + b_1y = c_1$ and $a_2x + b_2y = c_2$ is consistent, then $\frac{a_1}{a_2} = \frac{b_1}{b_2} = \frac{c_1}{c_2}$ or $\frac{a_1}{a_2} \neq \frac{b_1}{b_2}$.

So, Reason is true and is the correct explanation of the Assertion.

Hence, the correct option is (a).

CHAPTER

7

Sets and Relations

Remember

Before beginning this chapter, you should be able to:

- Understand the concepts of percentage.
- Understand the basic definitions of sets.
- Apply basic operations on sets.

Key Ideas

After completing this chapter, you should be able to:

- Calculate percentage of absolute values given.
- Learn about sets, representation of sets, and some definitions related to sets.
- Apply operations on sets.
- Understand the Venn diagrams.
- Obtain cartesian products of sets.
- Know about relation of sets, its representation, types, properties, and to find its domain and range.
- Understand the functions of sets.

Scientific Crypt

A Tribute to Georg Cantor (1845-1918)

Georg Ferdinand Ludwig Philipp Cantor, a renowned mathematician, is celebrated for his pioneering work in set theory and the concept of infinity. He stands as a visionary mathematician whose brilliance transcended conventional boundaries and forever reshaped our understanding of infinity.

Born on March 3, 1845, in Saint Petersburg, Russia, Georg Cantor displayed an early aptitude for mathematics and enrolled at the Imperial University of Saint Petersburg. While initially studying physics, his interests soon gravitated towards mathematics. He pursued a doctorate from the University of Berlin and crafted a thesis on number theory, guided by the esteemed mathematician Eduard Heine.

FUN TIME

CROSSWORD

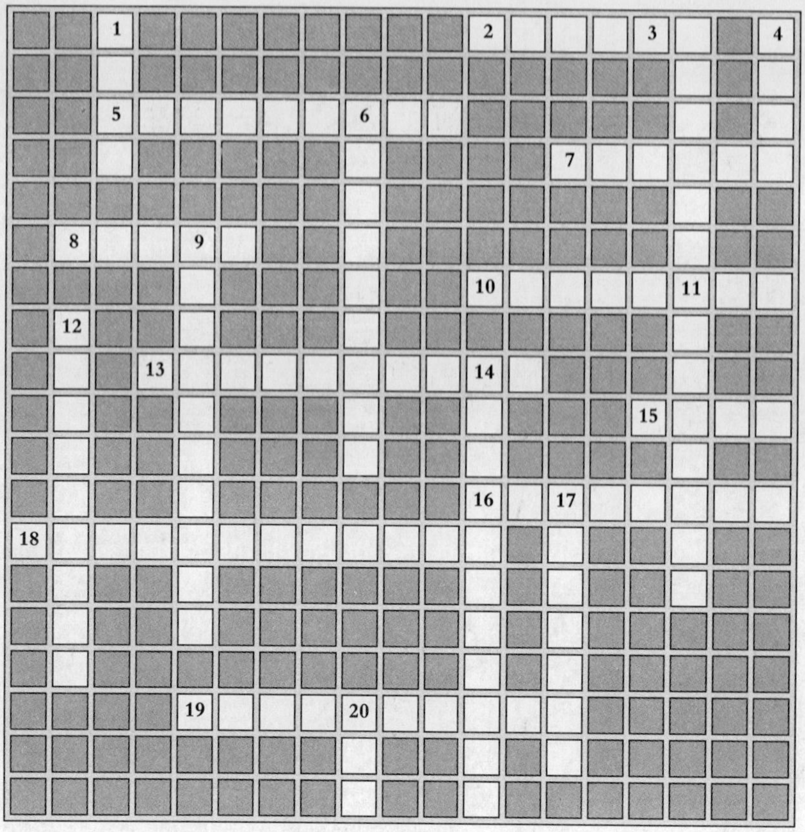

Across

2. In this method, a set is described by listing out all the elements in the set.
5. The complement of the null set is ___ set.
7. The set of the first coordinates of all ordered pairs of a relation.
8. Set A has all the subsets of B only. A is ___ set of B.
10. It is a subset of the cartesian product of two sets.
13. A, B, and C are three no-empty sets. If C has only the elements of A, but not the elements of B. C is ____ of A and B.
15. The set of the second coordinates of all ordered pairs of a relation.
16. These sets have no common elements.
18. For every $x \in$ A, $(x, x) \in$ R.
19. For every $(x, y) \in$ R and $(y, z) \in$ R, if there exists $(x, z) \in$ R, then R is a ___ relation.

Down

1. The cardinal number of $\{1, \{2, 3\}, 4, 5\}$.
3. Another name for an object of a set.
4. He introduced the pictorial representation of sets.
6. The inverse of a relation is equal to itself.
9. $\{1, 2, 3\}$ and $\{a, b, c\}$ are ____ sets.
11. R = $\{(a, a), (b, b), (b, b)\}$ is the ____ relation on $\{a, b, c\}$.
12. The set of natural numbers neither prime nor composite is a ____ set.
14. The number of elements in a set.
17. The number of subsets of $\{a, \{a, c\}, b, c\}$.
20. A well-defined collection of objects.

INTRODUCTION

In everyday life, we come across different collections of objects. For example, a herd of sheep, a cluster of stars, a posse of policemen, etc. In mathematics, we call such collections as sets. The objects are referred to as the elements of the sets.

Set

A set is a well-defined collection of objects. Let us understand what we mean by a well-defined collection of objects.

We say that a collection of objects is well-defined if there is some reason or rule by which we can say whether a given object of the universe belongs to or does not belong to the collection.

Elements of a Set

The objects in a set are called elements or members of the set. We usually denote the sets by capital letters A, B, C or X, Y, Z, etc.

If a is an element of a set A, then we say that a belongs to A and we write, $a \in A$.

If a is not an element of A, then we say that a does not belong to A and we write, $a \notin A$.

To understand the concept of a set, let us look at some examples.

Examples:

1. Let us consider the collection of odd natural numbers less than or equal to 15.
   In this example, we can definitely say what the collection is. The collection comprises the numbers 1, 3, 5, 7, 9, 11, 13, and 15.
2. Let us consider the collection of students in a class who are good at painting. In this example, we cannot say precisely which students of the class belong to our collection. So, this collection is not well-defined.

Hence, the first collection is a set where as the second collection is not a set. In the first example given, the set of odd natural numbers less than or equal to 15 can be represented as set $A = \{1, 3, 5, 7, 9, 11, 13, 15\}$.

Some Sets of Numbers and Their Notations

N = Set of all natural numbers = $\{1, 2, 3, 4, 5, \ldots\}$.

W = Set of all whole numbers = $\{0, 1, 2, 3, 4, 5, \ldots\}$.

Z or I = Set of all integers = $\{0, \pm1, \pm2, \pm3, \ldots\}$.

Q = Set of all rational numbers = $\left\{\frac{p}{q} \text{ where } p, q \in Z \text{ and } q \neq 0\right\}$.

Cardinal Number of a Set

The number of elements in a set A is called its cardinal number. It is denoted by $n(A)$. A set which has finite number of elements is a finite set and a set which has infinite number of elements is an infinite set.

Examples:

1. Set of English alphabets is a finite set.
2. Set of number of days in a month is a finite set.
3. The set of all even natural numbers is an infinite set.
4. Set of all the lines passing through a point is an infinite set.
5. The cardinal number of the set $X = \{a, c, c, a, b, a\}$ is $n(X) = 3$ as in sets only distinct elements are counted.

Representation of Sets

We represent sets by the following methods:

Roster or List Method

In this method, a set is described by listing out all the elements in the set.

Examples:

1. Let W be the set of all letters in the word JANUARY. Then we represent W as, $W = \{A, J, N, R, U, Y\}$.
2. Let M be the set of all multiples of 3 less than 20. Then we represent the set M as, $M = \{3, 6, 9, 12, 15, 18\}$.

Set Builder Method

In this method, a set is described by using a representative and stating the property or properties which the elements of the set satisfy, through the representative.

Examples:

1. Let D be the set of all days in a week. Then we represent D as,
   $D = \{x: x \text{ is a day in a week}\}$.
2. Let N be the set of all natural numbers between 10 and 20, then we represent the set N as, $N = \{x: 10 < x < 20$ and $x \in N\}$.

Some Simple Definitions of Sets

Empty Set or Null Set or Void Set

A set with no elements in it is called an **empty set (or) void set (or) null set**. It is denoted by { } or ϕ. (read as 'phi')

Examples:

1. Set of all positive integers less than 1 is an empty set.
2. Set of all mango trees with apples is an empty set.

Singleton Set

A set consisting of only one element is called a **singleton set**.

Examples:

1. The set of all vowels in the word MARCH is a singleton, as A is the only vowel in the word.
2. The set of whole numbers which are not natural numbers is a singleton, as 0 is the only whole number which is not a natural number.

Equivalent Sets

Two sets A and B are said to be equivalent if their cardinal numbers are equal. We write this symbolically as $A \sim B$ or $A \leftrightarrow B$.

Examples:

1. Sets, $X = \{2, 4, 6, 8\}$ and
   $Y = \{a, b, c, d\}$ are equivalent as $n(X) = n(Y) = 4$.
2. Sets, $X = \{\text{Dog, Cat, Rat}\}$ and
   $Y = \{\triangle, \bigcirc, \square\}$ are equivalent.
3. Sets, $X = \{-1, -7, -5\}$ and
   $Y = \{\text{Delhi, Hyderabad}\}$ are not equivalent as $n(X) \neq n(Y)$.

Konnect

If the sets A and B are equivalent, we can establish a one-to-one correspondence between the two sets. That is, we can pair up elements in A and B such that every element of set A is paired with a distinct element of set B and every element of B is paired with a distinct element of A.

Equal Sets

Two sets A and B are said to be equal if they have the same elements.

Examples:

1. Set, $A = \{a, e, i, o, u\}$ and $B = \{x: x \text{ is a vowel in the English alphabet}\}$ are equal sets.
2. Set, $A = \{1, 2, 3\}$ and $B = \{x, y, z\}$ are not equal sets.
3. Set, $A = \{1, 2, 3, 4, \ldots\}$ and $B = \{x: x \text{ is a natural number}\}$ are equal sets.

Info Bytes!

If A and B are equal sets, then they are equivalent but the converse need not be true.

Disjoint Sets

Two sets A and B are said to be disjoint, if they have no elements in common.

Examples:

1. Sets $X = \{3, 6, 9, 12\}$ and $Y = \{5, 10, 15, 20\}$ are disjoint as they have no elements in common.
2. Sets $A = \{a, e, i, o, u\}$ and $B = \{e, i, j\}$ are not disjoint as they have elements e and i in common.

Subset

Let A and B be two sets. If every elements of set A is also an element of set B, then A is said to be a subset of B or B is said to be a superset of A. If A is a subset of B, then we write $A \subseteq B$ or $B \supseteq A$.

Examples:

1. Set $A = \{2, 4, 6, 8\}$ is a subset of set $B = \{1, 2, 3, 4, 5, 6, 7, 8\}$.
2. Set of all primes except 2 is a subset of the set of all odd natural numbers.
3. Set $A = \{1, 2, 3, 4, 5, 6, 7, 8\}$ is a superset of set $B = \{1, 3, 5, 7\}$.

Proper Subset and Superset

If $A \subseteq B$ and $A \neq B$, then A is called a **proper subset of *B*** and is denoted by $A \subset B$. If $A \subset B$, then B is called a superset of A and is denoted as $B \supset A$.

Konnect

1. Empty set is a subset of every set.
2. Every set is a subset of itself.
3. If a set A has n elements, then the number of subsets of A is 2^n.
4. If a set A has n elements, then the number of non-empty subsets of A is (2^{n-1}).

Power Set

The set of all subsets of a set A is called **power set of *A***. It is of A denoted by $P(A)$.

Example: Let $A = \{x, y, z\}$. Then the subsets of A are ϕ, $\{x\}$, $\{y\}$, $\{z\}$, $\{x, y\}$, $\{x, z\}$, $\{y, z\}$, $\{x, y, z\}$.

So, $P(A) = \{\phi, \{x\}, \{y\}, \{z\}, \{x, y\}, \{x, z\}, \{y, z\}, \{x, y, z\}\}$.

We observe that the cardinality of $P(A)$ is $8 = 2^3$.

Konnect

1. If a set A has n elements, then the number of subsets of A is 2^n, i.e., the cardinality of the power set is 2^n.
2. If a set A has n elements, then the number of proper subsets of A is $2^n - 1$.
3. If a set A has n elements, then the number of non-empty proper subsets is $2^n - 2$.

Universal Set

A set which consists of all the sets under consideration or discussion is called the **universal set**. It is usually denoted by U or μ.

Example:

Let $A = \{a, b, c\}$, $B = \{c, d, e\}$ and $C = \{a, e, f, g, h\}$. Then, the set {a, b, c, d, e, f, g, h} can be taken as the universal set here.

$\therefore \quad \mu = \{a, b, c, d, e, f, g, h\}$.

Complement of a Set

Let μ be the universal set and $A \subseteq \mu$. Then, the set of all those elements of μ which are not in set A is called the complement of the set A. It is denoted by A' or A^c.

$$A' = \{x : x \in \mu \text{ and } x \notin A\}.$$

Examples:

1. Let $\mu = \{3, 6, 9, 12, 15, 18, 21, 24\}$ and $A = \{6, 12, 18, 24\}$. Then, $A' = \{3, 9, 15, 21\}$.
2. Let $\mu = \{x$: x is a student and $x \in$ class X}.
   And $B = \{x$: x is a boy and $x \in$ class X}.
   Then, $B' = \{x$: x is a girl and $x \in$ class X}.

Info Bytes!

1. A and A' are disjoint sets.
2. $\mu' = \phi$ and $\phi' = \mu$.

Operations on Sets

Union of Sets

Let A and B be two sets. Then, the union of A and B, denoted by $A \cup B$, is the set of all those elements which are either in A or in B or in both A and B.

That is, $A \cup B = \{x: x \in A \text{ or } x \in B\}$.

Examples:

1. Let $A = \{-1, -3, -5, 0\}$ and $B = \{-1, 0, 3, 5\}$ then, $A \cup B = \{-5, -3, -1, 0, 3, 5\}$.
2. Let $A = \{x: 5 \leq 5x < 25 \text{ and } x \in N\}$ and $B = \{x: 5 \leq (10x) \leq 20 \text{ and } x \in N\}$, then, $A \cup B = \{x: 5 \leq 5x \leq 20 \text{ and } x \in N\}$.

Intersection of Sets

Let A and B be two sets. Then the intersection of A and B, denoted by $A \cap B$, is the set of all those elements which are common to both A and B.

That is, $A \cap B = \{x: x \in A \text{ and } x \in B\}$.

Konnect

1. If $A \subseteq B$, then $A \cup B = B$.
2. $A \cup \mu = \mu$ and $A \cup \phi = A$.
3. $A \cup A' = \mu$.

Examples:

1. Let $A = \{1, 2, 3, 5, 6, 7, 8\}$ and $B = \{1, 3, 5, 7\}$. $A \cap B = \{1, 3, 5, 7\}$.
2. Let A be the set of all English alphabet and B be the set of all consonants. $A \cap B$ is the set of all consonants in the English alphabet.
3. Let E be the set of all even natural numbers and O be the set of all odd natural numbers. $E \cap O = \{\ \}$ or ϕ.

Konnect

1. If A and B are disjoint sets, then $A \cap B = \phi$ and $n(A \cap B) = 0$.
2. If $A \subseteq B$, then $A \cap B = A$.
3. $A \cap \mu = A$ and $A \cap \phi = \phi$.
4. $A \cap A' = \phi$

Difference of Sets

Let A and B be two sets. Then the difference $A - B$ is the set of all those elements which are in A but not in B. That is, $A - B = \{x: x \in A \text{ and } x \notin B\}$.

Example: Let $A = \{3, 6, 9, 12, 15, 18\}$ and $B = \{2, 6, 8, 10, 14, 18\}$.

$A - B = \{3, 9, 12, 15\}$ and $B - A = \{2, 8, 10, 14\}$.

> **Info Bytes!**
>
> 1. $A - B \neq B - A$ unless $A = B$.
> 2. For any set A, $A' = \mu - A$.

Symmetric Difference of Sets

Let A and B be two sets. Then the symmetric difference of A and B, denoted by $A \Delta B$, is the set of all those elements which are either in A or in B but not in both, i.e., $A \Delta B = \{x: x \in A \text{ and } x \notin B \text{ or } x \in B \text{ and } x \notin A\}$.

Example: Let $A = \{1, 2, 4, 6, 8, 10, 12\}$ and $B = \{3, 6, 12\}$. $A \Delta B = (A - B) \cup (B - A) = \{1, 2, 4, 8, 10\} \cup \{3\} = \{1, 2, 3, 4, 8, 10\}$.

> **Konnect**
>
> $A \Delta B = (A - B) \cup (B - A)$ (or) $A \Delta B = (A \cup B) - (A \cap B)$.

EXAMPLE 7.1

If $A = \{3, 5, 7, 8\}$ and $B = \{7, 8, 9, 10\}$, then find the value of $(A \cup B) - (A \cap B)$. The following are the steps involved in solving the above problem. Arrange them in sequential order.

(A) $A \cup B = \{3, 5, 7, 8, 9, 10\}$ and $A \cap B = \{7, 8\}$.

(B) Given $A = \{3, 5, 7, 8\}$ and $B = \{7, 8, 9, 10\}$.

(C) $(A \cup B) - (A \cap B) = \{3, 5, 9, 10\}$.

(D) $(A \cup B) - (A \cap B) = \{3, 5, 7, 8, 9, 10\} - \{7, 8\}$.

SOLUTION

The sequential order is BADC.

Some Results

For any three sets A, B, and C, we have the following results:

1. **Commutative law:**
   (i) $A \cup B = B \cup A$
   (ii) $A \cap B = B \cap A$
   (iii) $A \Delta B = B \Delta A$
2. **Associative law:**
   (i) $(A \cup B) \cup C = A \cup (B \cup C)$
   (ii) $(A \cap B) \cap C = A \cap (B \cap C)$
   (iii) $(A \Delta B) \Delta C = A \Delta (B \Delta C)$
3. **Distributive law:**
   (i) $A \cup (B \cap C) = (A \cup B) \cap (A \cup C)$
   (ii) $A \cap (B \cup C) = (A \cap B) \cup (A \cap C)$
4. **De-Morgan's law:**
   (i) $(A \cup B)' = A' \cap B'$
   (ii) $(A \cap B)' = A' \cup B'$
   (iii) $A - (B \cup C) = (A - B) \cap (A - C)$
   (iv) $A - (B \cap C) = (A - B) \cup (A - C)$
5. **Identity law:**
   (i) $A \cup \phi = \phi \cup A = A$
   (ii) $A \cap \mu = \mu \cap A = A$
6. **Idempotent law:**
   (i) $A \cup A = A$
   (ii) $A \cap A = A$
7. **Complement law:**
   (i) $(A')' = A$
   (ii) $A \cup A' = \mu$
   (iii) $A \cap A' = \phi$

Dual of an Identity

An identity obtained by interchanging ∪ and ∩, and ϕ and μ in the given identity is called **the dual of that identity**.

Examples:

1. Consider the identity, $A \cup B = B \cup A$. Dual of the identity is $A \cap B = B \cap A$.
2. Consider the identity, $A \cup \mu = \mu$. Dual of the identity is $A \cap \phi = \phi$.

Venn Diagrams

We also represent sets pictorially by means of diagrams called **Venn diagrams.** In Venn diagrams, the universal set is usually represented by a rectangular region and its subsets by closed regions inside the rectangular region. The elements of the set are written in the closed regions and the elements which belong to the universal set are written in the rectangular region.

Example: Let $\mu = \{1, 2, 3, 4, 5, 6, 7, 8, 9, 10\}$, $A = \{1, 2, 4, 6, 7, 8\}$ and $B = \{2, 3, 4, 5, 9\}$. We represent these sets in the form of Venn diagram as in Fig. 7.1.

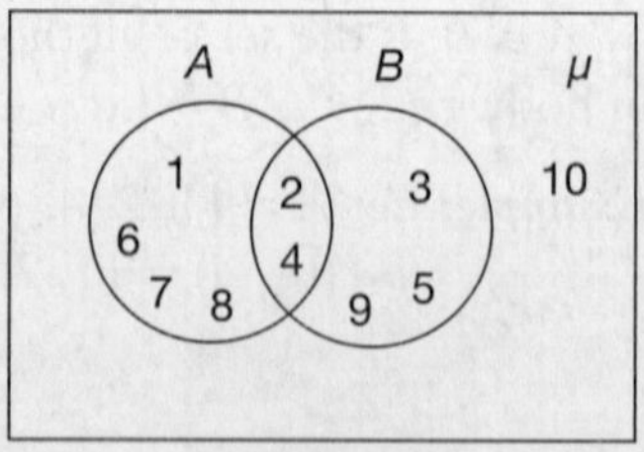

Figure 7.1

We can also represent the sets in Venn diagrams by shaded regions.

Examples:

1. Venn diagram of $A \cup B$, where A and B are two overlapping sets and it is shown in Fig. 7.2:

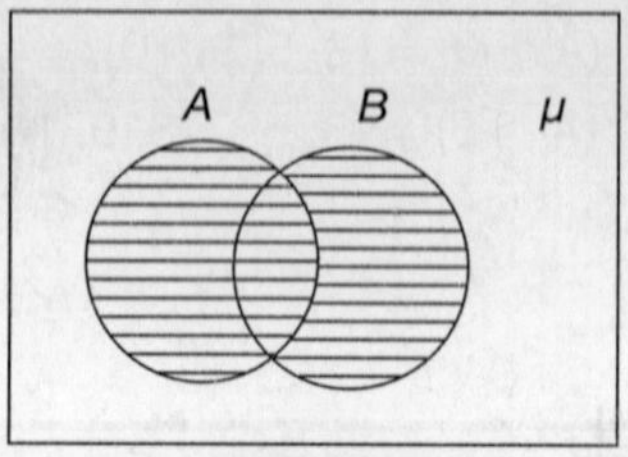

Figure 7.2

2. Let A and B be two overlapping sets. Then, the Venn diagram of $A \cap B$ is as shown in Fig. 7.3:

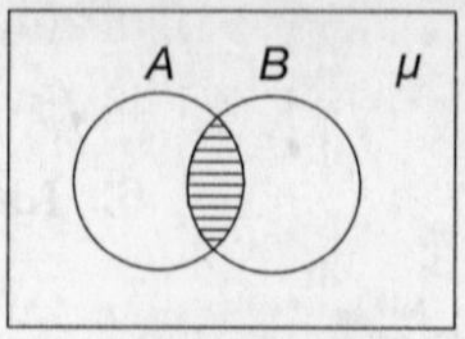

Figure 7.3

3. For a non-empty set A, Venn diagram of A' is as shown in Fig. 7.4:

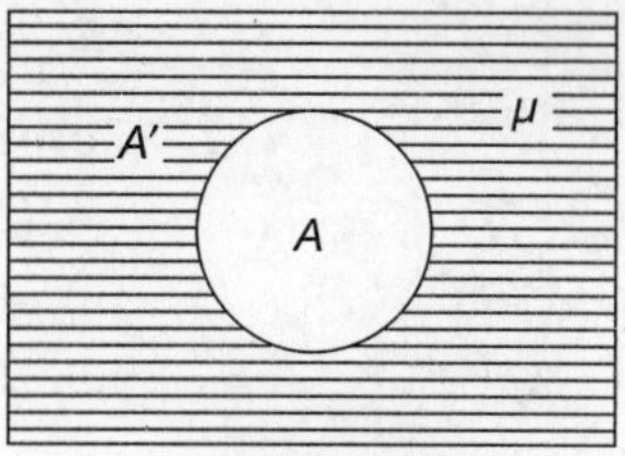

Figure 7.4

4. Let A and B be two overlapping sets. Then, the Venn diagram of $A - B$ is as shown in Fig. 7.5:

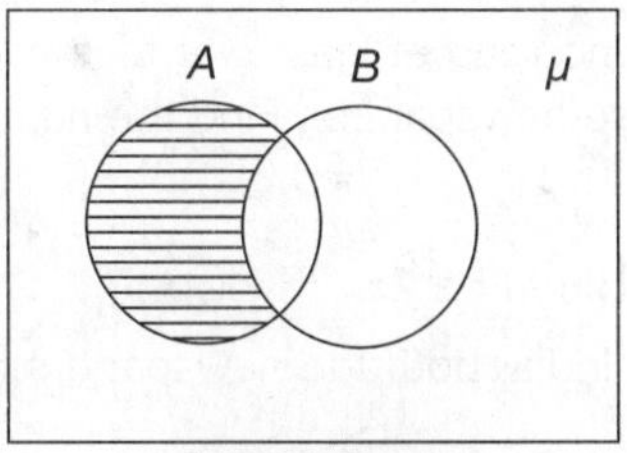

Figure 7.5

5. Let A and B be two sets such $A \subseteq B$. We can represent this relation using Venn diagram as shown in Fig. 7.6:

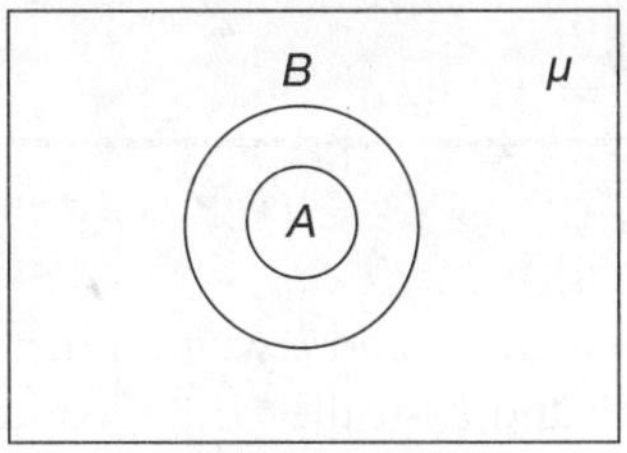

Figure 7.6

Some Formulae on the Cardinality of Sets

Let $A = \{1, 2, 3, 5, 6, 7\}$ and $B = \{3, 4, 5, 8, 10, 11\}$. Then, $A \cup B = \{1, 2, 3, 4, 5, 6, 7, 8, 10, 11\}$ and $A \cap B = \{3, 5\}$.

In terms of the cardinal numbers, $n(A) = 6$, $n(B) = 6$, $n(A \cap B) = 2$ and $n(A \cup B) = 10$.

So, $n(A) + n(B) - n(A \cap B) = 6 + 6 - 2 = 10 = n(A \cup B)$.

We have the following formulae:

For any three sets A, B and C.

1. $n(A \cup B) = n(A) + n(B) - n(A \cap B)$.

2. $n(A \cup B \cup C) = n(A) + n(B) + n(C) - n(A \cap B) - n(B \cap C) - n(C \cap A) + n(A \cap B \cap C)$.

EXAMPLE 7.2 If A, B and C are any three non–empty sets, then $(A \cup B')' \cap (B \cup C)$ is

SOLUTION

$(A \cup B')' \cap (B \cup C)$

$= (A' \cap B) \cap (B \cup C)$

$= (A' \cap B \cap B) \cup (A' \cap B \cap C)$

$= (A' \cap B) \cup (A' \cap B \cap C)$

$= A' \cap B$

EXAMPLE 7.3 If $n(A) = 8$ and $n(B) = 6$, and the sets A and B are disjoint, then find $n(A \cup B)$.

SOLUTION

Given, $n(A) = 8$ and $n(B) = 6$. A and B are disjoint.

$\Rightarrow A \cap B = \phi \Rightarrow n(A \cap B) = 0$.

$\therefore n(A \cup B) = n(A) + n(B) - n(A \cap B) = 8 + 6 - 0 = 14$.

Konnect

If A and B are two disjoint sets, then $n(A \cup B) = n(A) + n(B)$.

EXAMPLE 7.4 In a locality, the number of residents who read only The Hindu, only The Times of India, both the newspapers, and neither of the newspapers are in the ratio 2 : 3 : 4 : 1. The number of residents who read at least one of these newspapers is 160 more than those who read neither of these newspapers. Find the number of residents in the locality.

SOLUTION

Let the number of residents who read only The Hindu be $2x$.

$\therefore$ Number of residents who read The Times of India, both the newspapers and neither of the newspapers are $3x$, $4x$, and x, respectively.

$2x + 3x + 4x = x + 160$

$8x = 160 \Rightarrow x = 20$

Number of residents in the locality

$= 2x + 3x + 4x + x = 10x = 200.$

Ordered Pair

Let A be a non-empty set and $a, b \in A$. The elements a and b written in the form (a, b) is called an **ordered pair**. In the ordered pair (a, b), a is called the first coordinate and b is called the second coordinate.

Konnect

Two ordered pairs are said to be equal only when their first as well as the second coordinates are equal, i.e., $(a, b) = (c, d) \Leftrightarrow a = c$ and $b = d$.

So, $(1, 2) \neq (2, 1)$ and if $(a, 5) = (3, b) \Rightarrow a = 3$ and $b = 5$.

Cartesian Product of Sets

Let A and B be two non-empty sets. The Cartesian product of A and B, denoted by $A \times B$, is the set of all ordered pairs (a, b), such that $a \in A$ and $b \in B$.

That is, $A \times B = \{(a, b): a \in A, b \in B\}$.

Example: Let $A = \{1, 2, 3\}$ and $B = \{2, 4\}$. $A \times B = \{(1, 2), (1, 4), (2, 2), (2, 4), (3, 2), (3, 4)\}$ and $B \times A = \{(2, 1), (2, 2), (2, 3), (4, 1), (4, 2), (4, 3)\}$.

We observe that, $A \times B \neq B \times A$ and $n(A \times B) = 6 = n(B \times A)$.

Info Bytes!

1. $A \times B \neq B \times A$, unless $A = B$.
2. For any two sets A and B, $n(A \times B) = n(B \times A)$.
3. If $n(A) = p$ and $n(B) = q$, then $n(A \times B) = pq$.

Some Results on Cartesian Product

1. $A \times (B \cup C) = (A \times B) \cup (A \times C)$ (or) $(A \cup B) \times (A \cup C)$.
2. $A \times (B \cap C) = (A \times B) \cap (A \times C)$ (or) $(A \cap B) \times (A \cap C)$.
3. If $A \times B = \phi$, then either,
   (i) $A = \phi$
   (ii) $B = \phi$
   (iii) both $A = \phi$ and $B = \phi$.

Cartesian product of sets can be represented in following ways:

1. Arrow diagram
2. Tree diagram
3. Graphical representation

Representation of $A \times B$ Using Arrow Diagram

EXAMPLE 7.5 If $A = \{a, b, c\}$ and $B = \{1, 2, 3\}$, then find $A \times B$.

SOLUTION

In order to find $A \times B$, represent the elements of A and B as shown in the diagram; 7.7.
Now draw the arrows from each element of A to each element of B.
Now, represent all the elements related by arrows in ordered pairs in a set, which is the required $A \times B$.
That is, $A \times B = \{(a, 1), (a, 2), (a, 3), (b, 1), (b, 2), (b, 3), (c, 1), (c, 2), (c, 3)\}$.

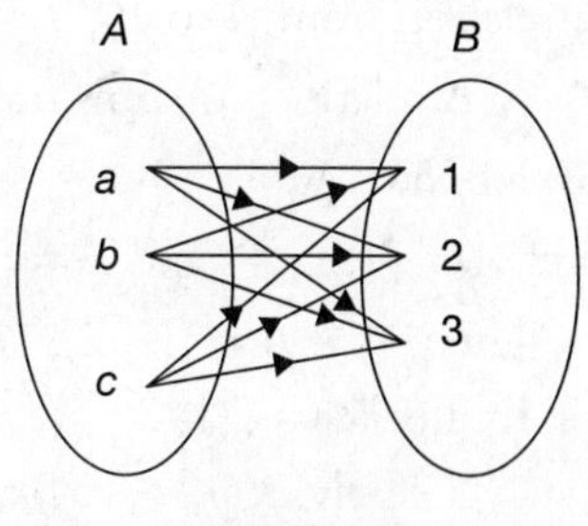

Figure 7.7

Representation of $A \times B$ Using a Tree Diagram

EXAMPLE 7.6 If $A = \{a, b, c\}$ and $B = \{1, 2, 3\}$, then find $A \times B$.

SOLUTION

To represent $A \times B$ using tree diagram, write all the elements of A vertically and then for each element of A, write all the elements of B and draw arrows as shown in the diagram,
$\therefore A \times B = \{(a, 1), (a, 2), (a, 3), (b, 1), (b, 2), (b, 3), (c\ 1), (c, 2), (c, 3)\}$.

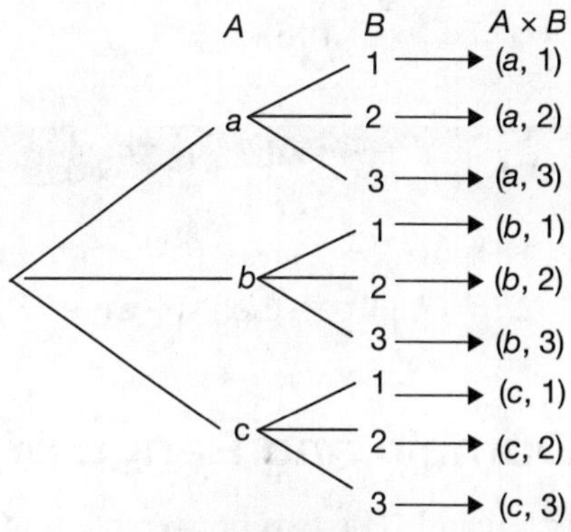

Figure 7.8

Graphical Representation of $A \times B$

EXAMPLE 7.7 If $A = \{1, 2, 3\}$ and $B = \{3, 4, 5\}$, then find $A \times B$.

SOLUTION

Consider the elements of A on the X-axis and the elements of B on the Y-axis and mark the points (see Fig. 7.9).
$\therefore A \times B = \{(1, 3), (1, 4), (1, 5), (2, 3), (2, 4), (2, 5), (3, 3), (3, 4), (3, 5)\}$.

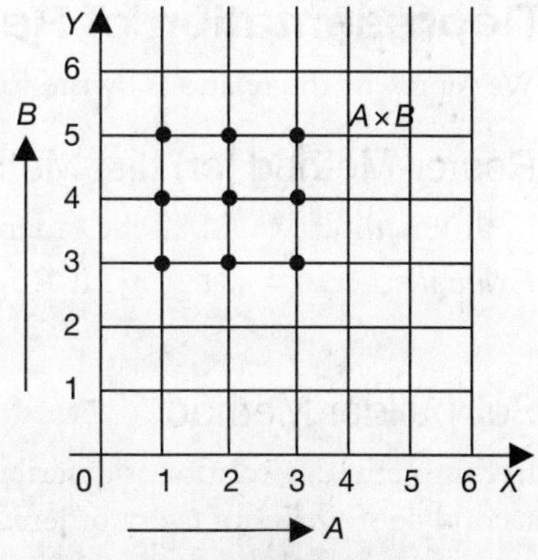

Figure 7.9

Relation

We come across certain relations in real life and also in basic geometry, like *is father of, is a student of, is parallel to, is similar to*, etc.

Definition

Let A and B be two non-empty sets and $R \subseteq A \times B$. R is called a relation from the set A to B (any subset of $A \times B$ is called a relation from A to B).

$\therefore$ A relation contains ordered pairs as elements. Hence, 'A relation is a set of ordered pairs'.

Examples:

Let $A = \{1, 2, 4\}$ and $B = \{2, 3\}$.

Then, $A \times B = \{(1, 2), (1, 3), (2, 2), (2, 3), (4, 2), (4, 3)\}$.

1. Let $R_1 = \{(1, 2), (1, 3), (2, 3)\}$

Clearly, $R_1 \subseteq A \times B$ and we also notice that, for every ordered pair $(a, b) \in R_1$, $a < b$.

So, R_1 is the relation *is less than* from A to B.

2. Let $R_2 = \{(4, 2), (4, 3)\}$.

Clearly, $R_2 \subseteq A \times B$ and we also notice that, for every ordered pair $(a, b) \in R_2$, $a > b$.

So, R_2 is the relation *is greater than* from A to B.

Konnect

1. If $n(A) = p$ and $n(B) = q$, then the number of relations possible from A to B is $2pq$.
2. If $(x, y) \in R$, then we write xRy and read as x is related to y.

Domain and Range of a Relation

Let A and B be two non-empty sets and R be a relation from A to B, we note the following:

1. The set of first coordinates of all ordered pairs in R is called **the domain of R**.
2. The set of second coordinates of all ordered pairs in R is called **the range of R**.

Example: Let $A = \{1, 2, 4\}$, $B = \{1, 2, 3\}$ and $R = \{(1, 1), (1, 2), (2, 1), (2, 3), (4, 3)\}$ be a relation from A *to* B. Then, domain of $R = \{1, 2, 4\}$ and range of $R = \{1, 2, 3\}$.

Representation of Relations

We represent the relations by the following methods:

Roster-Method (or) List Method

In this method, we list all the ordered pairs that satisfy the rule or property given in the relation.

Example: Let $A = \{1, 2, 3\}$. If R is a relation on the set A having the property *is less than*, then the roster form of R is, $R = \{(1, 2), (1, 3), (2, 3)\}$.

Set-builder Method

In this method, a relation is described by using a representative and stating the property or properties, which the first and second coordinates of every ordered pair of the relation satisfy, through the representative.

Example: Let $A = \{1, 2, 3\}$. If R is a relation on the set A having the property *is greater than or equal to*, then the set builder form of R is, $R = \{(x, y) \mid x, y \in A \text{ and } x \geq y\}$.

Arrow Diagram

In this method, a relation is described by drawing arrows between the elements which satisfy the property or properties given in the relation.

Example: Let $A = \{1, 2, 4\}$ and $B = \{2, 3\}$. Let R be a relation from A to B with the property *is less than*. Then, the arrow diagram of R is as shown in Fig. 7.10.

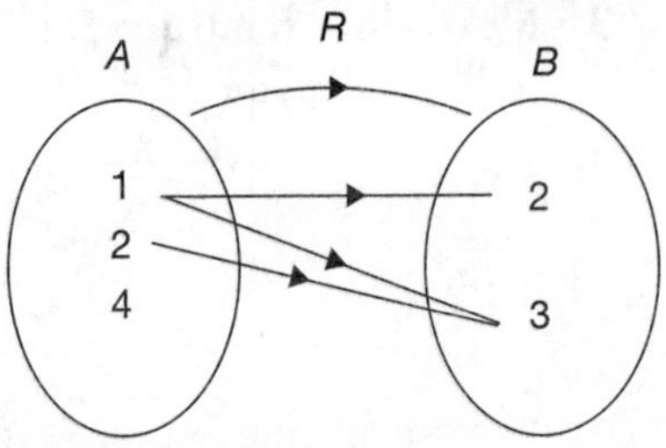

Figure 7.10

Inverse of a Relation

Let R be a relation from A to B. The inverse relation of R, denoted by R^{-1}, is defined as, $R^{-1} = \{(y, x)/(x, y) \in R\}$.

Example: Let $R = \{(1, 1), (1, 2), (2, 1), (2, 3), (4, 3)\}$ be a relation from A to B, where $A = \{1, 2, 4\}$ and $B = \{1, 2, 3\}$. Then, $R^{-1} = \{(1, 1), (1, 2), (2, 1), (3, 2), (3, 4)\}$.

Konnect

1. Domain of R^{-1} = Range of R.
2. Range of R^{-1} = Domain of R.
3. If R is a relation from A to B, then R^{-1} is a relation from B to A.
4. If $R \subseteq A \times A$, then R is called a binary relation or simply a relation on the set A.
5. For any relation R, $(R^{-1})^{-1} = R$.

Types of Relations

1. **One-one relation:** A relation $R: A \rightarrow B$ is said to be one-one relation if different elements of A are paired with different elements of B, i.e., $x \neq y$ in $A \Rightarrow f(x) \neq f(y)$ in B.

   Example:

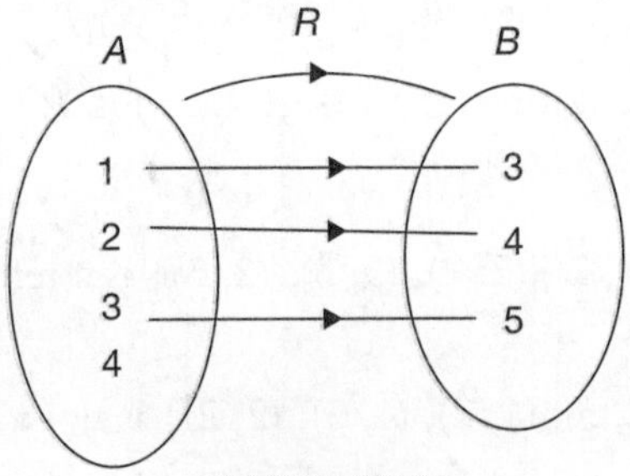

Figure 7.11

   Here, the relation $R = \{(1, 3), (2, 4), (3, 5)\}$.

2. **One-many relation:** A relation $R: A \rightarrow B$ is said to be one-many relation if at least one element of A is paired with two or more elements of B.

   Example:

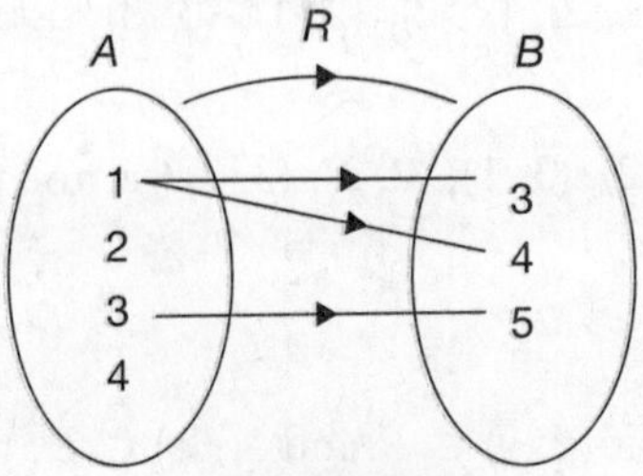

Figure 7.12

   Here, the relation $R = \{(1, 3), (1, 4), (3, 5)\}$.

3. **Many-one relation:** A relation $R: A \rightarrow B$ is said to be many-one relation if two or more elements of A are paired with an element of B.

Example:

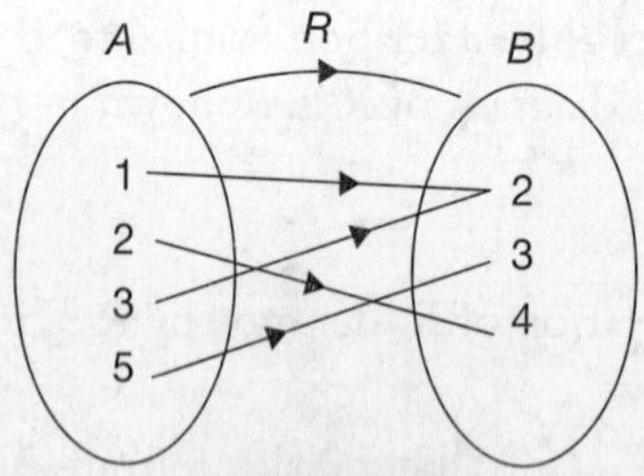

Figure 7.13

Here, the relation $R = \{(1, 2), (2, 4), (3, 2), (5, 3)\}$.

4. **Many-many relation:** A relation $R: A \rightarrow B$ is said to be many-many relation if two or more elements of A are paired with two or more elements of B.

Example:

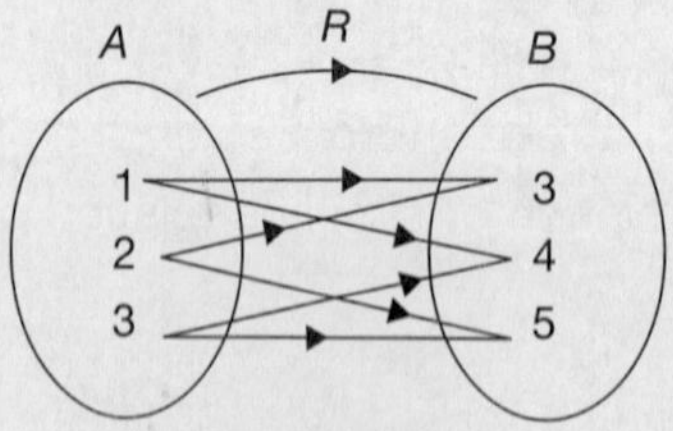

Figure 7.14

Here, the relation $R = \{(1, 3), (1, 4), (2, 3), (2, 5), (3, 4), (3, 5)\}$.

Properties of Relations

Reflexive Relation

A relation R on a set A is said to be reflexive if for every $x \in A$, $(x, x) \in R$.

Examples:

1. Let $A = \{1, 2, 3\}$ then, $R = \{(1, 1), (1, 2), (2, 2), (3, 3), (2, 3)\}$ is a reflexive on A.
2. Let $A = \{1, 2, 3\}$ then, $R = \{(1, 1), (2, 3), (1, 2), (1, 3), (2, 2)\}$ is not a reflexive relation as $3 \in A$ but $(3, 3) \notin R$.

Konnect

Number of reflexive relations defined on a set having n elements is 2^{n^2-n}.

Symmetric Relation

A relation R on a set A is said to be symmetric, if for every $(x, y) \in R$, $(y, x) \in R$.

Examples:

1. Let $A = \{1, 2, 3\}$. Then, $R = \{(1, 1), (1, 2), (2, 2), (2, 1), (3, 3)\}$ is a symmetric relation on A.
2. Let $A = \{1, 2, 3\}$. Then, $R = \{(1, 1), (1, 2), (3, 1), (2, 2), (3, 3)\}$ is not a symmetric relation as, $(1, 2) \in R$ but $(2, 1) \notin R$.

Info Bytes!

A relation R on a set A is symmetric if $R = R^{-1}$, i.e., R is symmetric if $R = R^{-1}$.

Transitive Relation

A relation R on a set A is said to be transitive if $(x, y) \in R$ and $(y, z) \in R$, then $(x, z) \in R$.

That is, R is said to be transitive, whenever $(x, y) \in R$ and $(y, z) \in R \Rightarrow (x, z) \in R$.

Examples:

1. If $A = \{1, 2, 3\}$, then, $R = \{(1, 1), (1, 2), (1, 3), (2, 1), (3, 1), (2, 2), (3, 3)\}$ is a transitive relation.
2. Let $A = \{1, 2, 3\}$. Then, $R = \{(1, 2), (2, 2), (2, 1), (3, 3), (1, 3)\}$ is not a transitive relation as $(1, 2) \in R$ and $(2, 1) \in R$ but $(1, 1) \notin R$.

Anti-symmetric Relation

A relation R on a set A is said to be anti-symmetric if $(x, y) \in R$ and $(y, x) \in R$, then $x = y$., i.e., R is said to be anti-symmetric if for $x \neq y$, $(x, y) \in R \Rightarrow (y, x) \notin R$.

Examples:

1. Let $A = \{1, 2, 3\}$. Then, $R = \{(1, 1), (1, 2), (3, 3)\}$ is an anti-symmetric relation.
2. Let $A = \{1, 2, 3\}$. Then, $R = \{(1, 1), (1, 2), (1, 3), (2, 1), (3, 3)\}$ is not an anti-symmetric relation as $(1, 2) \in R$ and $(2, 1) \in R$ but $1 \neq 2$.

Equivalence Relation

A relation R on a set A is said to be an equivalence relation if it is,

1. Reflexive
2. Symmetric
3. Transitive

Konnect

For any set A, $A \times A$ is an equivalence relation. In fact it is the largest equivalence relation.

Identity Relation

A relation R on a set A defined as, $R = \{(x, x) \mid x \in A\}$ is called an **identity relation on A**. It is denoted by I_A.

Example: *Let* $A = \{1, 2, 3\}$. Then, $R = \{(1, 1), (2, 2), (3, 3)\}$ is the identity relation on A.

Info Bytes!

Identity relation is the smallest equivalence relation on a set A.

POINTS TO REMEMBER

- ✔ A set consisting of only one element is called a singleton set.
- ✔ A set with no elements in it is called an empty set (or) void set (or) null set.
- ✔ Two sets A and B are said to be equivalent if their cardinal numbers are equal.
- ✔ Two sets A and B are said to be equal if they have the same elements.
- ✔ Two sets A and B are said to be disjoint, if they have no elements in common.
- ✔ The set of all subsets of a set A is called power set of A. It is of A denoted by P(A).
- ✔ If every elements of set A is also an element of set B, then A is said to be a subset of B or B is said to be a superset of A.
- ✔ A set which consists of all the sets under consideration or discussion is called the universal set.
- ✔ An identity obtained by interchanging $\cup$ and $\cap$, and ϕ and μ in the given identity is called the dual of that identity.
- ✔ If A and B are two disjoint sets, then $n(A \cup B) = n(A) + n(B)$.
- ✔ The set of first coordinates of all ordered pairs in R is called the domain of R.
- ✔ The set of second coordinates of all ordered pairs in R is called the range of R.
- ✔ Number of reflexive relations defined on a set having n elements is 2^{n^2-n}
- ✔ A relation R on a set A is said to be transitive if $(x, y) \in R$ and $(y, z) \in R$, then $(x, z) \in R$.
- ✔ A relation R on a set A defined as, $R = \{(x, x) \mid x \in A\}$ is called an identity relation on A.

DW

PRACTICE QUESTIONS CLASSROOM WING

Very Short Answer Type Questions

Directions of questions from 1 to 5:
Fill in the blanks.

1. If $n(A \cup B) = 16$ and $n(A \cap B) = 4$, then the number of elements in the symmetric difference of A and B is ________.
2. If A is universal set, then $((A')')'$ is ________.
3. If $n(P) = 2$ and $n(Q) = 5000$, then $n(P \times Q) =$ ________.
4. If $n(P) = 2439$ and $Q = \phi$ then $n(P \times Q) =$ ________.
5. If $(x, 2p + q) = (y, p + 2q)$ then $p - q =$ ________.

Directions of questions from 6 and 7:
State whether the following statements are true or false

6. The symmetric difference of A and B is commutative. (True/False)
7. The order in which the elements are placed plays an important role in sets. (True/False)

Directions of questions from 8 to 21:
Answer the following questions.

8. If $P = \{1, 2, 3, 4, 5, 6, 7\}$ and $Q = \{2, 5, 8, 9\}$, then find $P \cup Q$.
9. If $P = \{1, 2, 3, 4, 5, 6, 7\}$ and $Q = \{2, 5, 8, 9\}$, then find $P - Q$.
10. If $P = \{1, 2, 3, 4, 5, 6, 7\}$ and $Q = \{2, 5, 8, 9\}$, then find $P \cap Q$.
11. The cardinal number of a set is 5. Find the cardinal number of the power set.
12. If $V = \{a, e, i, o, u\}$, then find the number of non-empty proper subsets of V.
13. If a set has 510 non-empty proper subsets, then find the cardinal number of the set.
14. Let $A = \{a, b, c\}$ and $B = \{p, q\}$. Draw the arrow diagram of $A \times B$.
15. If $n(A) = 6$ and $n(B) = 3$, then find the number of subsets of $A \times B$.
16. If $n(A) = 40$ and $n(B) = 23$, then find $n(A - B)$ and $n(B - A)$ when $B \subset A$.
17. Find $n(P \times Q)$, if $n(Q - P) = 10$ and $n(P - Q) = 13$ and $n(P \cap Q) = 8$.
18. Find the number of relations from A to A, where $A = \{1, 2, 3, 4\}$.
19. A relation $R = \{(a, b), (a, a), (a, c), (x, x), (x, y), (y, y), (d, d), (d, c)\}$.Write a relation $E \subset R$ such that x is equal to y.
20. $A = \{1, 2, 3, 4\}$, $B = \{3, 4\}$ and $R = \{(3, 1), (3, 2), (4, 1), (4, 2), (4, 3)\}$ is a relation from B into A. Write R in set-builder form.
21. $P = \{3, 5, 6, 8, 9\}$, $Q = \{6, 10, 12, 16, 17\}$ and $R = \{(x, y)/(x, y) \in P \times Q, 2x = y\}$ is a relation from P into Q, write R in list form.

Short Answer Type Questions

22. If $A = \{2, 3, 4, 6, 7, 9, 10, 12\}$, $B = \{1, 3, 5, 8, 9, 10, 11, 15\}$, $C = \{3, 4, 7, 10, 11, 13, 15\}$ and $\mu = \{1, 2, 3, \ldots, 15\}$. Then, find $(A \cup B)'$.
23. If $n(X - Y) = 30 + a$, $n(Y - X) = 20 + 2a$, $n(X \cup Y) = 100$ and $n(X \cap Y) = 15 + 2a$, then find a.
24. If $n(P \Delta Q) = n(P \cup Q)$, then find the values of P and Q.
25. If $n(A - B) = 25$, $n(B - A) = 15$ and $n(A \cup B) = 60$, then find $n(A \cap B)$.
26. If $n(P \cap Q) = 12$ and $n(Q) = 37$, then find the value of $n(P' \cap Q)$
27. In a colony of 170 members, 70 subscribe Deccan Chronicle and 120 subscribe Times of India. How many subscribe only Deccan Chronicle? (Each subscribes at least one.)
28. $A = \{1, 2, 3, 4\}$ and $f(x) = 2x^2$, $x \in A$. If $f(x) = 18$, then find x.
29. A, B and C are three different sets and $A \times (B \cap C) = (A \times B) \cap (A \times C)$. Judge the given statements by

taking any three non-empty sets A, B and C. State whether it is true and false.

30. Given that $R = \{(1, 1), (3, 3), (2, 3), (3, 2), (2, 2)\}$ on the set $A = \{1, 2, 3\}$. Which property is not satisfied by R on A?

31. (A) What type of relation does R define on the set of integers, if $x + y = 8$?

(B) What type of relation does R define on the set of integers, if $x + y = 2021$?

32. In a class of 50 students 20 take Sanskrit but not Hindi and 37 take Sanskrit. How many students take Hindi but not Sanskrit? (Each student takes either Sanskrit or Hindi.)

33. In a class of 60 students, 25 speak Hindi, 45 speak English. How many of them speak both English and Hindi, if each student speaks either English or Hindi?

34. In term examination, 40% students failed in English, 32% failed in Physical Science. What is the pass percentage, if 10% failed in both?

Essay Type Questions

35. The following figure depicts the number of families subscribed for three different newspapers, i.e., Eenadu (E), Hindu (H) and Vaartha (V).

Find the number of people who read:

(i) atleast two papers
(ii) atmost two papers
(iii) atleast three papers
(iv) atmost three papers
(v) atleast one paper.
(vi) atmost one paper.

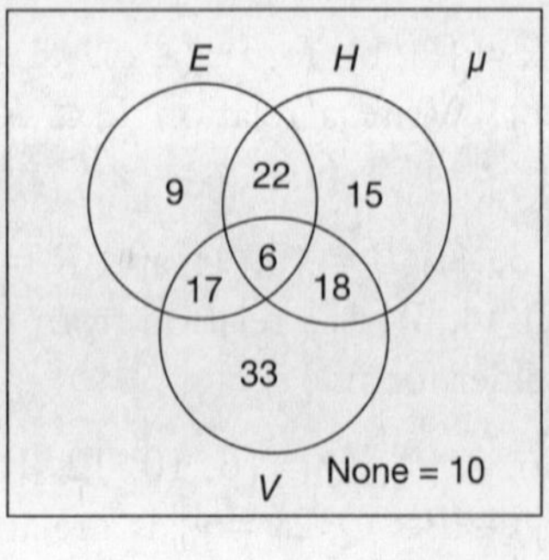

36. On the set of all colleges in a state, a relation R is defined such that 'two colleges are related if they belong to the same district'. Find the properties satisfied by R.

37. In a set of students studying in the same class, two students are related 'if their weights are not equal'. Find the properties satisfied by it.

38. If a set A has 4 elements and a reflexive relation R defined in set A has x elements, then what is the range of x?

39. In a club 45% plays cricket, 20% plays only football. Find the percentage of members who plays only cricket if 10% play both (each plays at least one.)

PRACTICE QUESTIONS COMPETITION WING

Level 1: Apply Your Concepts

Directions of questions from 1 to 5:
Fill in the blanks.

1. If $X \subset Y$ and $Y \subset X$, then ________.
2. The complement of ϕ' is ________.
3. $A \cap A' =$ ________.
4. If P and Q are disjoint, then $(P \cap Q)'$ is ________.
5. If P and Q are disjoint, then $P - Q =$ ________ and $Q - P =$ ________.

Directions of questions from 6 to 59:
Select the correct alternative from the given choices.

6. If A_n is the set of all factors of n and P is the set of prime numbers less than 50, then $n\left(\bigcup_{n\in P} A_n\right) =$
(a) 14 (b) 15
(c) 16 (d) 20

7. If A and B are two sets such that $n(A) = 5$ and $n(B) = 7$, then the minimum number of elements in $(A - B) \cup (B - A)$ is
(a) 12 (b) 4
(c) 6 (d) 2

8. If $A = \{1, 2, 3, 4\}$ and R is a transitive relation defined on A, then the maximum number of elements in R is
(a) 16 (b) 15
(c) 14 (d) 13

9. Relations $R = \{(2, 4), (4, 6)\}$ and S are defined on the set $A = \{2, 4, 6\}$. Find the minimum number of elements in S, such that $R \cup S$ is a reflexive and symmetric relation.
(a) 4 (b) 5
(c) 6 (d) 7

10. If $X = \{x: x^2 - 12x + 20 = 0\}$ and $Y = \{x: x^2 + 5x - 14 = 0\}$, then $X - Y =$
(a) $\{2\}$ (b) $\{10\}$
(c) $\{-7\}$ (d) $\{\ \}$

11. The number of subsets of $A \times B$ if $n(A) = 3$ and $n(B) = 3$ is:
(a) 512 (b) 256
(c) 511 (d) 255

12. If $A = \{1, 2, 3, 4\}$, then how many subsets of A contain the element 3?
(a) 24 (b) 28
(c) 8 (d) 16

13. In 'aRb' if 'a and b have the same teacher', then R is ________.
(a) Reflexive (b) Symmetric
(c) Transitive (d) Equivalence

14. A relation $R: Z \rightarrow Z$ is such that $R = \{(x, y) \mid y = 2x + 1\}$ is a
(a) One to one relation. (b) Many to one relation.
(c) One to many relation. (d) Many to many relation.

15. If P_n is the set of first n prime numbers, then $\bigcup_{n=2}^{10} P_n =$
(a) $\{2, 3, 5, 7, 11, 13, 17, 19\}$
(b) $\{3, 5\}$
(c) $\{2, 3, 5, 7, 11, 13, 17, 19, 23, 29\}$
(d) $\{2, 3\}$

16. If P_n is the set of first n prime numbers, then $\bigcap_{n=3}^{10} P_n$ is:
(a) $\{3, 5, 7, 11, 13, 17, 19\}$
(b) $\{2, 3, 5\}$
(c) $\{2, 3, 5, 7, 11, 13, 17\}$
(d) $\{3, 5, 7\}$

17. If $n(\mu) = 100$, $n(A) = 50$, $n(B) = 20$ and $n(A \cap B) = 10$, then $n[(A \cup B)^c] =$
(a) 60 (b) 30
(c) 40 (d) 20

18. Let Z denote the set of integers, then $\{x \in Z: |x - 3| < 4 \cap \{x \in Z: |x - 4| < 5\} =$
(a) $\{-1, 0, 1, 2, 3, 4\}$
(b) $\{-1, 0, 1, 2, 3, 4, 5\}$
(c) $\{0, 1, 2, 3, 4, 5, 6\}$
(d) $\{-1, 0, 1, 2, 3, 5, 6, 7, 8, 9\}$

19. If $A = \left\{n : \dfrac{n^3 + 5n^2 + 2}{n}\right.$ is an integer and n itself is an is an integer$\left.\right\}$, then the number of elements in the set A is:

(a) 1 (b) 2
(c) 3 (d) 4

20. Relations $R = \{(1, 3), (3, 5)\}$ and S are defined on the set $A = \{1, 3,5\}$. Find the minimum number of elements in S, such that $R \cup S$ is an equivalence relation.
(a) 5 (b) 6
(c) 7 (d) 8

21. $A = \{a, b, c\}$ and R is a symmetric relation defined on A, then the minimum number of elements in R is
(a) 0 (b) 3
(c) 5 (d) 9

22. If A and B are two sets such that $n(A) = 10$ and $n(B) = 8$, then the maximum number of elements in $(A - B) \cup (B - A)$ is
(a) 16 (b) 10
(c) 2 (d) 18

23. If X, Y and Z are any three non–empty sets, then $(X \cap Y^c)^c \cup (Y \cap Z)$ is
(a) $X \cap Y^c$ (b) $X^c \cup Y$
(c) $X \cap Y$ (d) $X^c \cup Y^c$

24. The relation 'is not equal to' is defined on the set of real numbers is satisfies which of the following?
(a) Reflexive only (b) Symmetric only
(c) Transitive only (d) Equivalence

25. If $R = \{(a, b)/ |a + b| = |a| + |b|\}$ is a relation on a set $\{-1, 0, 1\}$ then R is ______.
(a) Reflexive (b) Symmetric
(c) Anti symmetric (d) Equivalence

26. For all p, such that $1 \le p \le 100$, if $n(A_p) = p + 2$ and $A_1 \subset A_2 \subset A_3 \subset \cdots \subset A_{100}$ and $\bigcap_{p=3}^{100} A_p = A$, then $n(A) =$
(a) 3 (b) 4
(c) 5 (d) 6

27. If $R = \{(a, b)/a + b = 4\}$ is a relation on N, then R is ______.
(a) Reflexive (b) Symmetric
(c) Anti-symmetric (d) Transitive

28. Let R be a relation defined on S, the set of squares on a chess board, such that xRy, for $x, y \in S$, if x and y share a common side. Then, which of the following is false for R?
(a) Reflexive (b) Symmetric
(c) Transitive (d) All the above

29. $A = \{$ONGC, BHEL, SAIL, GAIL, IOCL$\}$ and R is a relation defined as 'two elements of A are related if they share exactly one common letter'. For instance, BHEL and SAIL are related as they have a common letter L. The relation R is ______.
(a) Anti-symmetric (b) Only transitive
(c) Only symmetric (d) Equivalence

30. X is the set of all engineering colleges in the state of A.P and R is a relation on X defined as two colleges are related iff they are affiliated to the same university then R is
(a) Only reflexive. (b) Only symmetric.
(c) Only transitive. (d) Equivalence.

31. In a class, each student likes either cricket or football, 40% of the students like football, 80% of the students like cricket. The number of students who like only cricket is 40 more than the number of students who like only football. What is the strength of the class?
(a) 80 (b) 100
(c) 120 (d) 150

32. For all p, such that $1 \le p \le 100$, $n(A_p) = p + 1$ and $A_1 \subset A_2 \subset \ldots \subset A_{100}$. Then $\bigcup_{p=1}^{100} A_p$ contains ______ elements.
(a) 99 (b) 100
(c) 101 (d) 102

Level 2: Review Your Concepts

33. In a class, 70 students wrote two tests, *viz.*, Test-I and Test-II. 50% of the students failed in Test-I and 40% of the students failed in Test-II. How many students passed in both the tests?
(a) 21 (b) 7
(c) 28 (d) 14

34. Every man in a group of 20 men likes either mangoes or an apple. Every man who likes apples also likes mangoes. 9 men like mangoes but not apples. How many like mangoes and apples?
(a) 9 (b) 11
(c) 10 (d) 12

35. If $A = \{1, 2, 3, 4\}$, then how many subsets of A contain the element 1, but not 4?

(a) 16 (b) 4
(c) 8 (d) 24

36. A relation $R: Z \to Z$ defined by $R = \{(x, y)/y = x^2 - 1\}$ is

(a) One to one relation.
(b) Many to one relation.
(c) One to many relation.
(d) Many to many relation.

37. If a set A has 13 elements and R is a reflexive relation on A with n elements, $n \in Z^+$, then:

(a) $13 \le n \le 26$ (b) $0 \le n \le 26$
(c) $13 \le n \le 169$ (d) $0 \le n \le 169$

38. Example of an equivalence relation among the following is:

(a) Is a father of (b) Is less than
(c) Is congruent to (d) Is an uncle of

39. If $A = \{p \in N; p$ is a prime and $p = \dfrac{7n^2 + 3n + 3}{n}$ for some $n \in N\}$, then the number of elements in the set A is

(a) 1 (b) 2
(c) 3 (d) 4

40. 'aRb' if 'a is the father of b'. Then R is ________.

(a) Reflexive (b) Symmetric
(c) Transitive (d) None of these

41. Let A be a set of compartments of a train. Then the relation R is defined on A as 'aRb if and only if a and b have the link between them'. Then which of the following is true for R?

(a) Reflexive (b) Symmetric
(c) Transitive (d) All of these

42. A relation $R: N \to N$ defined by $R = \{(x, y)/y = x^2 + 1\}$ is

(a) One to one. (b) One to many.
(c) Many to one. (d) Many to many.

43. Set-builder form of the relation $R = \{(-2, -7), (-1, -4), (0, -1), (1, 2), (2, 5)\}$ is:

(a) $R = \{(x, y)/y = 2x - 3; x, y \in Z\}$
(b) $R = \{(x, y)/y = 3x - 1; x, y \in Z\}$
(c) $R = \{(x, y)/y = 3x - 1; x, y \in N\}$
(d) $R = \{(x, y)/y = 3x - 1; -2 \le x < 3 \text{ and } x \in Z\}$

44. A group of 30 men participate in a survey on language skills. The number of men who know both English and Hindi was equal to the number of men who know neither of these languages. The number of men who know English is 4 more than those who know Hindi. How many know Hindi?

(a) 11 (b) 12
(c) 13 (d) 14

45. In a locality, the number of people buying only The Times of India is 80% of the number of people buying both The Times of India and The Hindu. The number of people buying only The Hindu is 60% less than the number who buy both. The number of people buying neither of these is 22,000 less than the number of people in the locality. How many people buy both newspapers?

(a) 10,000 (b) 20,000
(c) 25,000 (d) 30,000

46. Find the number of subsets of $A \times B$, if $n(A) = 2$ and $n(B) = 4$.

The following are the steps involved in solving the above problem. Arrange them in sequential order.

(A) The number of elements in $A \times B$ is $4 \times 2 = 8$.
(B) The number of subsets of a set with n elements $= 2^n$.
(C) Given $n(A) = 2$ and $n(B) = 4$.
(D) Required number of subsets is $2^8 = 256$.

(a) CBAD (b) CABD
(c) CDAB (d) CBDA

47. If $\mu = \{1, 2, 3, 4, 5, 6\}$ and $A = \{1, 2, 3, 4\}$ and $B = \{3, 4, 5, 6\}$, then find $A^c \cap B^c$. The following are the steps involved in solving the above problem. Arrange them in sequential order.

(A) $A^c = \{5, 6\}$ and $B^c = \{1, 2\}$
(B) $A^c \cap B^c = \{5, 6\} \cap \{1, 2\}$
(C) We know that $A^c = \mu - A$ and $B^c = \mu - B$.
(D) $A^c \cap B^c = \phi$

(a) CBAD (b) CDBA
(c) CABD (d) CADB

48. The number of subsets of $\{\{a\}, \{b, c\}, d, e\}$ is ________.

(a) 32 (b) 16
(c) 8 (d) 20

49. If $R = \{(a, a), (a, c), (b, c), (b, b), (c, c), (a, b)\}$ on the set $X = \{a, b, c\}$, then how many subsets of R are reflexive relations?

(a) 15 (b) 16
(c) 8 (d) 9

50. The relation $R = \{(2, 2), (1, 1), (1, 3), (3, 1)\}$ on the set $A = \{1, 2, 3\}$ is ______.

(a) Reflexive (b) Symmetric
(c) Transitive (d) Both (b) and (c)
(a) A and B (b) A, B, and C
(c) B, C, and D (d) D

51. If A and B are two non-empty sets and $n(A \times B) = 36$, then which of the following cannot be equal to $n(B)$?

(a) 9 (b) 6
(c) 8 (d) 12

52. If the number of reflexive relations defined on a set A is 64, then the number of elements in A is ______.

(a) 3 (b) 2
(c) 6 (d) 5

Level 3: Assess Your Concepts

53. In a rehabilitation programme, a group of 50 families were assured new houses and compensation by the government. Number of families who got both is equal to the number of families who got neither of the two. The number of families who got new houses is 6 greater than the number of families who got compensation. How many families got houses?

(a) 22 (b) 28
(c) 23 (d) 25

54. In an office, every employee likes at least one of tea, coffee, and milk. The number of employees who like only tea, only coffee, only milk and all the three are all equal. The number of employees who like only tea and coffee, only coffee and milk, and only tea and milk are equal and each is equal to half the number of employees who like all the three. Then a possible value of the number of employees in the office is ______.

(a) 65 (b) 90
(c) 77 (d) 84

55. In a school, on the Republic day, three dramas A, B, and C are performed on the dais. In a group of people, who attended the function and who like at least one of the three dramas, 16 people like A, 20 people like B, 15 people like C, 4 people like both A and B, 3 people like both A and C, 3 people like both B and C and 2 people like all the three. Then how many people like at most two?

(a) 59 (b) 41
(c) 4 (d) 6

56. The students of a class like at least one of the games out of Chess, Caroms, and Judo. The number of students who like only Chess and Caroms, only Caroms and Judo, only Chess and Judo and the number of those who like all the three are equal. The number of students who like only Chess, only Caroms, only Judo and the number of those who like all the three are equal. A possible value of the number of students in the class is:

(a) 30 (b) 40
(c) 50 (d) 70

57. There are a total of 70 ladies who watch at least one of the channels, i.e., Zee TV, Sony TV and Star Plus. The total number of ladies who watch Zee or Sony but not Star plus, the number of ladies who watch Sony or Star Plus but not Zee and the number of ladies who watch Star Plus or Zee but not Sony is 90. How many ladies watch at least two of these channels if 10 ladies watch all the three channels?

(a) 25 (b) 30
(c) 40 (d) 35

58. Which of the following cannot be the number of reflexive relations defined on a set A?

(a) 1 (b) 4
(c) 4096 (d) 512

59. In a class, the number of students who like only Chess, only Caroms, both the games and neither of the games are in the ratio 2 : 4 : 1 : 3. The number of students who like at least one of these games is 120 more than those who like neither of the games. Find the number of students in the class.

(a) 300 (b) 240
(c) 270 (d) 360

AT

PRACTICE QUESTIONS JEE SPECIAL WING

Multiple-Answer Type Questions

Directions for questions 1 to 10:
Each question has FOUR options (a), (b), (c), and (d). ONE OR MORE THAN ONE of these four option(s) is/are the correct answer(s).

1. Which of the following collections is/are sets?
   (a) Ten good books in the Library of Alexandria.
   (b) Seven most talented persons in the world.
   (c) Six distinct digits in the decimal expansion of $\frac{1}{7}$.
   (d) Five vowels in the letters of English alphabet.

2. Which of the following is/are void sets?
   (a) The set of names in the months of the calendar whose spelling doesn't include any vowel.
   (b) The set of natural numbers between any two positive consecutive integers.
   (c) The set of single digit natural numbers which have exactly five factors.
   (d) The set of months of the year 2176 which have exactly 29 days.

3. Which of the following sets have 32 subsets?
   (a) $A=\{a, c, h, r, m\}$
   (b) $B=\{a, u, \{g, u\}, s, t\}$
   (c) $C=\{s, e, p, \{t, e, m\}, \{b, e, r\}\}$
   (d) $D=\{o, c, t, \{o\}, \{b, e, r\}\}$

4. If A and B are two non-empty sets, then which of the following is/are true?
   (a) $(A \cap B) \subseteq A$ (b) $(B - A) \subseteq B$
   (c) $(A \Delta B) \subseteq (A \cup B)$ (d) $(A \cup B) \subseteq (A \Delta B)$

5. If A and B are two non-empty sets, then which of the following is/are true?
   (a) If $n(A \cup B) = n(A) + n(B)$, then A and B are disjoint sets.
   (b) If $n(A \cup B) = n(A) + n(B)$, then A and B are equal sets.
   (c) If $n(A \cup B) = n(A \cap B)$, then A and B are disjoint sets.
   (d) If $n(A \cup B) = n(A \cap B)$, then A and B are equal sets.

6. If R_1, R_2, R_3 and R_4 are defined on $S=\{a,i,m\}$, then which of the following is/are reflexive relations?
   (a) $R_1 = \{(a,a),(i,i),(m,m)\}$
   (b) $R_2 = \{(a,a),(i,i),(m,m),(a,i),(i,m)\}$
   (c) $R_3 = \{(a,a),(i,i),(m,m),(a,i),(i,m),(a,m)\}$
   (d) $R_4 = \{(a,a),(i,i),(m,m),(a,i),(i,m),(a,m),(i,a),(m,i),(m,a)\}$

7. If R_{11}, R_{22}, R_{33} and R_{44} are defined on $U=\{t,i,m,e\}$, then which of the following is/are symmetric relations?
   (a) $R_{11} = \{(t,t),(i,i),(m,m),(e,e)\}$
   (b) $R_{22} = \{(t,t),(i,i),(m,e),(e,m)\}$
   (c) $R_{33} = \{(t,t),(i,m),(m,e),(e,m)\}$
   (d) $R_{44} = \{(t,m),(m,e),(m,t),(e,m)\}$

8. If R_{111}, R_{222}, R_{333} and R_{444} are defined on $P=\{a,e,p,l\}$, then which of the following is/are transitive relations?
   (a) $R_{111} = \{(a,a),(e,e),(p,p),(l,l)\}$
   (b) $R_{222} = \{(e,a),(e,e),(e,p),(a,l)\}$
   (c) $R_{333} = \{(a,e),(e,p),(p,l),(a,p),(e,l)\}$
   (d) $R_{444} = \{(a,e),(e,p),(p,l),(a,p),(e,l),(a,l)\}$

9. If R_a, R_b, R_c and R_d are defined on $E=\{t,o,p\}$, then which of the following is/are anti-symmetric relations?
   (a) $R_a = \{(t,o),(o,p)\}$
   (b) $R_b = \{(t,p),(o,t),(p,o)\}$
   (c) $R_c = \{(p,o),(t,p),(o,p)\}$
   (d) $R_d = \{(t,p),(p,o),(p,t),(o,p)\}$

10. If R_p, R_q, R_r and R_s are defined on $R=\{r,a,n,k\}$, then which of the following is/are equivalence relations?
   (a) $R_p = \{(r,r),(a,a),(n,n),(k,k)\}$
   (b) $R_q = \{(r,r),(a,a),(n,n),(k,k),(n,k),(k,n)\}$
   (c) $R_r = \{(r,r),(a,a),(n,n),(k,k),(n,k),(k,n),(r,n),(n,r),(r,k),(k,r)\}$
   (d) $R_s = R \times R$

Match The Column

Directions for questions 11 to 15:

Read the paragraph given below and answer the questions.

In a school, there are five sections in class IX and each section has 50 students. Of these 150 students play kabaddi, 100 students play football, and 125 students play tennis. Also, 60 students play both kabaddi and football, 50 students play both football and tennis, 40 students play both tennis and kabaddi. Please note that ten students do not play any game.

Column A	Column B
11. Number of students who play all the three games	(a) 5
12. Number of students who play only football	(b) 10
13. Number of students who play exactly two games	(c) 15
14. Number of students who play at most one game	(d) 90
15. Number of students who play football or tennis but not kabaddi	(e) 100
	(f) 105
	(g) 115
	(h) 130
	(i) 140

Comprehension-Based Questions

Directions for questions 16 to 20:

Read the paragraph given below and answer the questions.

Given that P is a set of prime numbers less than 50, Q is the set of composite numbers less than 30 and R is the set of composite numbers more than 30 and less than 50.

16. How many subsets of P consists of all the prime numbers lesser than 10?

(a) 2^{15} (b) 2^{11}
(c) 2^8 (d) 2^4

17. How many subsets of Q doesn't contain any of the composite numbers less than 20?

(a) 2^{15} (b) 2^{11}
(c) 2^8 (d) 2^4

18. How many subsets of R doesn't contain any of the composite numbers less than 40 and consist of the composite numbers more than 40?

(a) 2^{15} (b) 2^{11}
(c) 2 (d) 1

19. How many subsets of $(P \cup Q)$ consist of all the numbers more than 10 and less than 20?

(a) 2^{24} (b) 2^{33}
(c) 2^9 (d) 2^{10}

20. How many subsets of $(P \cup Q \cup R)$ consist of all the prime numbers but not any of the composite numbers?

(a) 2^{32} (b) 2^{15}
(c) 2 (d) 1

Directions for questions 21 to 25:

Read the paragraph given below and answer the questions.

In a school, there are 350 students in class IX (all the sections together). Each student scored grade A in at least one of the subjects Mathematics and Sciences.

Further information is as follows:

(i)

	The number of students who secured grade A in			
	Maths	Sciences	Both	Total
Boys	80			
Girls				
Total			50	350

(ii) The number of girls is 50 more than that of the boys.

(iii) The number of boys who secured A grade in science is $25\frac{5}{7}\%$ of the total students.

(iv) The ratio of the total number of students who secured grade A in mathematics and that in sciences is 3 : 5.

21. How many boys secured grade A in both the subjects?

(a) 10 (b) 15
(c) 20 (d) 25

22. How many girls secured grade A in sciences?
(a) 120 (b) 130
(c) 150 (d) 160

23. How many boys secured grade A only in one of the subjects?
(a) 120 (b) 130
(c) 150 (d) 170

24. How many students secured grade A in maths?
(a) 140 (b) 150
(c) 180 (d) 200

25. How many girls secured grade A only in maths?
(a) 40 (b) 45
(c) 70 (d) 75

Assertion and Reason Type Questions

Directions for questions 26 to 30:
Read the options given below and answer the questions.

(a) Both assertion (A) and reason (R) are true, and the reason (R) is the correct explanation of the assertion (A).
(b) Both assertion (A) and reason (R) are true, and the reason (R) is not the correct explanation of the assertion (A).
(c) Assertion (A) is true, but reason (R) is false.
(d) Assertion (A) is false, and reason (R) is true.

26. **Assertion:** Given that $M = \{j, u, n, e\}$. The relation $\{(j, j), (u, u), (n, n), (e, e)\}$ is an identity relation defined on M.
Reason: If A is a non-empty set and $n(A) = x$, then the number of possible identity relations defined on A is 1.

27. **Assertion:** Given that R is a reflexive relation defined on $N = \{m, a, y\}$, then the number of possible reflexive relations is 256.
Reason: If A is a non-empty set and $n(A) = x$, then the number of possible reflexive relations defined on A is $2^{x^2 - x}$.

28. **Assertion:** The number of relations defined from $P = \{m, a, r, c, h\}$ to $Q = \{j, u, l, y\}$ is 2^{20}.
Reason: A and B are two non-empty sets. If and $n(A) = x$ and $n(B) = y$, then the number of possible relations defined from A to B, is $2^{x \times y} - x \times y$.

29. **Assertion:** $\left(\left((P')'\right)'\right)' \cap \left((P')'\right)' = \varnothing$
Reason: $\left(\left((P')'\right)'\right)'^{\ldots n \text{ times}}$ is equal to P when n is even and P' when n is odd. If A and B are disjoint sets, then $(A \cap B) = \varnothing$.

30. **Assertion:** Given that $A = \{a, b, c\}$ and $B = \{p, q\}$. If R is relation defined from A to B where $R = A \times B$, then $R^{-1} = \{(p, a), (q, a), (p, b), (q, b), (p, c), (q, c)\}$.
Reason: R is a relation from A to B. The inverse relation of R, denoted by R^{-1}, is defined as, $R^{-1} = \{(y, x) /$ for every $(x, y) \in R\}$.

ANSWER KEYS

Crossword

Across

2. Roster 5. Universal 7. Domain 8. Power 10. Relation
13. Difference 15. Range 16. Disjoint 18. Reflexive 19. Transitive

Down

1. Four 3. Element 4. Venn 6. Symmetric 9. Equivalent
11. Identity 12. Singleton 14. Cardinality 17. Sixteen 20. Set

Classroom Wing

Very Short Answer Type Questions

1. 12 2. ϕ 3. 10000 4. 0 5. 0
6. True 7. False 8. {1, 2, 3, 4, 5, 6, 7, 8, 9} 9. {1, 3, 4, 6, 7}
10. {2, 5} 11. 32 12. 30 13. 9 15. 2^{18}
16. 17, 0 17. 378 18. 2^{16} 19. $E = \{(a, a), (x, x), (y, y), (d, d)\}$
20. $R = \{(x, y)/(x, y) \in B \times A, x > y\}$ 21. $R = \{(3, 6), (5, 10), (6, 12), (8, 16)\}$

Short Answer Type Questions

22. {13, 14} 23. $a = 7$ 24. disjoint 25. 20 26. 25
27. 50 28. $x = 3$ 29. True 30. anti-symmetric property
31. (A) one to one type of relations (B) One to one relation 32. 13 33. 10
34. 38%

Essay Type Questions

35. (i) 63 (ii) 124 (iii) 6 (iv) 130 (v) 120 (vi) 67 36. reflexive, symmetric, transitive
37. only symmetric property 38. $4 \le x \le 2^{12}$ 39. 35%

Competition Wing

Level 1: Apply Your Concepts

1. $X = Y$ 2. ϕ 3. ϕ 4. μ 5. P, Q
6. (c) 7. (d) 8. (a) 9. (b) 10. (b)
11. (a) 12. (c) 13. (d) 14. (a) 15. (c)
16. (b) 17. (c) 18. (c) 19. (d) 20. (c)
21. (a) 22. (d) 23. (b) 24. (b) 25. (d)
26. (c) 27. (b) 28. (c) 29. (c) 30. (d)
31. (b) 32. (c)

Level 2: Review Your Concepts

33. (b) 34. (b) 35. (b) 36. (b) 37. (c)
38. (c) 39. (a) 40. (d) 41. (b) 42. (a)
43. (d) 44. (c) 45. (a) 46. (b) 47. (c)
48. (b) 49. (c) 50. (b) 51. (c) 52. (a)

Level 3: Assess Your Concepts

53. (b) 54. (c) 55. (b) 56. (d) 57. (c)
58. (d) 59. (a)

JEE Special Wing

Multiple-Answer Type Questions

1. (c, d) 2. (a, b, c) 3. (a, b, c, d) 4. (a, b, c) 5. (a, d)
6. (a, b, c, d) 7. (a, b, d) 8. (a, d) 9. (a, b) 10. (a, b, c, d)

Match The Column

11. (c) 12. (a) 13. (f) 14. (h) 15. (d)

Comprehension-Based Questions

16. (b) 17. (c) 18. (c) 19. (a) 20. (d)
21. (c) 22. (d) 23. (b) 24. (b) 25. (a)

Assertion and Reason Type Questions

26. (b) 27. (d) 28. (c) 29. (a) 30. (a)

Hints and Explanations

Classroom Wing

Very Short Answer Type Questions

1. $n(A \Delta B) = n(A \cup B) - n(A \cap B)$
$= 16 - 4 = 12$

2. If A is universal set, then $((A')')'$ is:
ϕ, A' is null set
$(A')'$ is universal set
$((A')')'$ is null set

3. If $n(P) = 2$ and $n(Q) = 5000$, $n(P \times Q) = 10000$

4. As one set is empty, nothing can be mapped into it.

5. $x = y$
$2p + q = p + 2q$
$2p - p = 2q - q$
$p - q = 0$

6. The symmetric difference of A and B is commutative.

7. The order in which the elements are placed does not play an important role in set.

8. $P \cup Q = \{1, 2, 3, 4, 5, 6, 7\} \cup \{2, 5, 8, 9\}$
$= \{1, 2, 3, 4, 5, 6, 7, 8, 9\}$

9. $P - Q = \{1, 3, 4, 6, 7\}$

10. $P \cap Q = \{2, 5\}$

11. $2^5 = 32$

12. $2^n - 2$
$2^5 - 2$
$32 - 2 = 30$

13. $2^n - 2 = 510$
$2^n = 512$
$\therefore n = 9$

14.

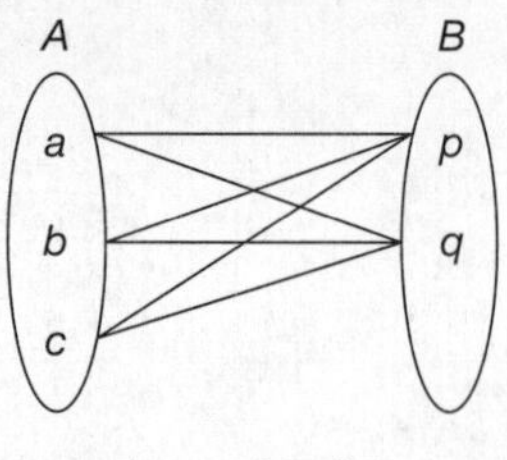

15. Number of Subsets $= 2^{pq}$
$= 2^{6\times3}$
$= 2^{18}$

16. $n(A - B) = 17$
$(40 - 23)$
As $B \subset A$, $A - B$ contains all elements of A other than B.
$n(B - A) = 0$
As $B \subset A$, $B - A$ contains Nothing

17.

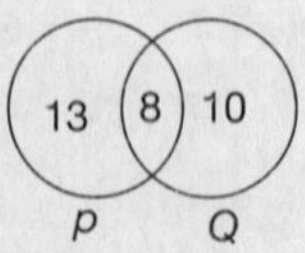

Elements in $P = 13 + 8 = 21$
$n(Q) = 10 + 8$
$= 18$
$n(P \times Q) = 21 \times 18$
$= 378$

18. 2^{pq} As the relation is form A to A'
$P = Q = 4$
$2^{4\times4} = 2^{16}$

19. Rel^n E must have the same letters
$\therefore E = \{(a, a)\ (x, x)\ (y, y)\ (d, d)\}$

20. $R = \{(x, y) \,/\, (x, y) \in B \times A, x > y\}$
Number in set B is referred as x and Number in set A is referred as y.

21. $R = \{(3, 6)\ (5, 10)\ (6, 12)\ (8, 16)\}$

Short Answer Type Question

22. $A \cup B = \{1, 2, 3, 4, 5, 6, 7, 8, 9, 10, 11, 12, 15\}$
$(A \cup B)' = \{13, 14\}$

23. $n(X \cup Y) = n(X) + n(Y) - n(X \cap Y)$
$n(X) = n(X - Y) + n(X \cap Y)$
$\therefore 100 = (30 + a + 15 + 2a) + (20 + 2a + 15 + 2a) - (15 + 2a)$
$100 - 65 = 5a$
$a = 7$

24. We know, $n(P \Delta Q) = n(P \cup Q) - n(P \cap Q)$
$n(P \cap Q)$ must be 0 if $n(P \Delta Q) = n(P \cup Q)$
$\therefore$ P and Q are disjoint.

25. We know,
$n(A \cup B) = n(A) + n(B) - n(A \cap B)$

$n(A) = n(A - B) + n(A \cap B)$

$n(A \cap B) = n(A) + n(A \cap B) + n(B - A) + n(A \cap B) - n(A \cup B)$

$n(A \cap B) = 25 + n(A \cap B) + 15 + n(A \cap B) - 60$

$n(A \cap B) = -20 + 2\,n(A \cap B)$

$n(A \cap B) = 20$

26.

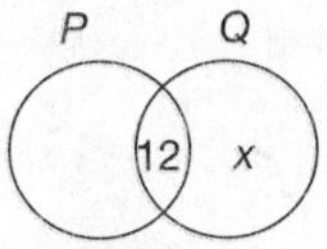

$12 + x = 37$

$x = 37 - 12$

$x = 25$

27. $n(\cup) = n(\text{OUT}) = 170$

Deccan chronicle $\Rightarrow n(D) = 70$

Times of India $\Rightarrow n(T) = 120$

Only Deccan chronicle $= n(D) - n(T)$

$= 120 - 70$

$= 50$

28. We know $f(x) = 2x^2 = 18$

$\therefore x^2 = \dfrac{18}{2}$

$x^2 = 9$

$x = 3$

29. Because putting in the value 0 in place of all the number will give $0 = 0$ so valid statement.

30. Anti-symmetric property

31. (A) One-to-one relationship

As it is a straight line x will have 1 value of y, so one to one rel^{n}

(B) $y = 2021 - x$

Let $x_1, x_2, \in$ domain, $f(x_1) = f(x_2)$.

$\Rightarrow 2021 - x_1 = 2021 - x_2$

$\Rightarrow x_1 = x_2$

$\therefore x + y = 2021$ is one to one relation.

32.

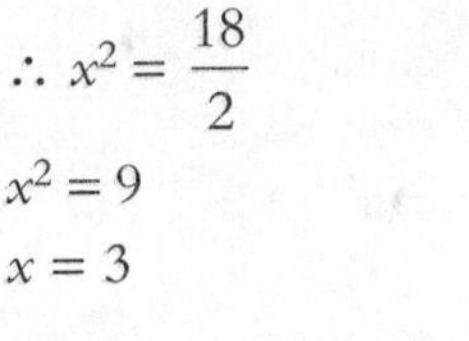

$x + 20 = 37$

$x = 17$

$y + x + 20 = 50$

$y = 30 - 17$

$y = 13$

Hindi = 13

33. $n(\cup) = n(\text{HUE}) = 60$

Hindi $n(H) = 25$

English $n(E) = 45$

$n(H \cap E) = n(H) + n(E) - n(H \cup E)$

$= 25 + 45 - 60$

$= 10$

34. English $n(E) = 40\%$

Physical Science $n(S) = 32\%$

$n(E \cap S) = 10\%$

People failed $n(E \cap S) = n(E) + n(S) - n(E \cap S)$

$= 40\% + 32\% - 10\%$

$= 62\%$

$\therefore$ Pass percentage

$\Rightarrow n(E \cup S)' = 100\% - n(E \cup S)$

$= 100\% - 62\%$

$n(E \cup S)' = 38\%$

Essay Type Questions

35.

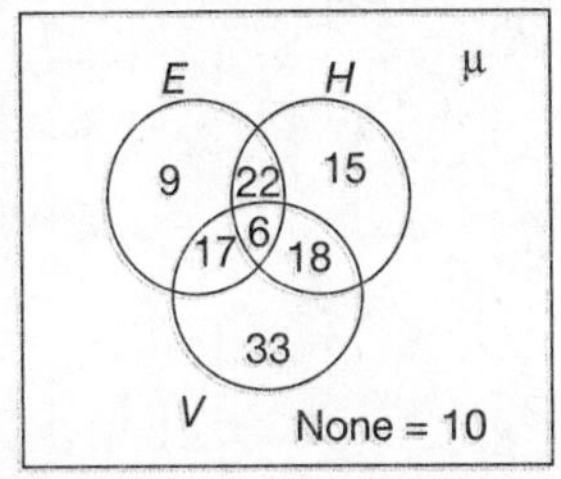

(i) At least two papers.

This means either 2 or 3 paper subscription.

$n(E \cap H) + n(H \cap V) + n(E \cap V) + n(E \cap H \cap V)$

$22 + 18 + 17 + 6 = 63$

(ii) At most two papers.

This means 0, 1 or 2 subscription of paper

$\therefore n(\mu') + n(E) + n(E \cap H) + n(H) + n(H \cap V) + n(V) + n(E \cap V)$

$10 + 9 + 22 + 15 + 18 + 33 + 17 = 124$

(iii) At least 3 papers

This means minimum 3 paper subscription.

i.e., $n(E \cap H \cap V) = 6$

(iv) At most 3 papers

This means 0, 1, 2, 3 paper subscription.

i.e $n(\mu') + n(E) + n(H) + n(V) + n(E \cap H) + n(E \cap V) + n(H \cap V) + n(E \cap H \cap V)$

$10 + 9 + 15 + 33 + 22 + 18 + 17 + 6 = 130$

(v) At least one paper

Minimum 1 and maximum 3 subscription of paper

$n(E) + n(H) + n(V) + n(E \cap H) + n(E \cap V) + n(H \cap V) + n(E \cap H \cap V)$

$9 + 15 + 33 + 22 + 18 + 17 + 6 = 120$

(vi) At most one paper

None or one paper subscription

$n(\mu') + n(E) + n(H) + n(V)$

$10 + 9 + 15 + 33 = 67$

36. $S = \{S_1, S_2, S_3, \ldots\ldots\}$

Here $S_1 = S_1$

So, Reflexive property

Here $S_1 = S_2$ $\quad S_2 = S_1$

So, Symmetric property and also

$S_1 = S_2$ $\quad S_2 = S_3$

So, $S_1 = S_3$

Hence Transitive also

So, Reflexive, Symmetric and Transitive

37. Only symmetric as student A = student B means student B = student A.

38. In a set of 4 Minimum Reflexive can be '4'

Max value is 2^{n^2-n}

2^{4^2-4}

$2^{16-4} = 2^{12}$

$4 \leq x \leq 2^{12}$

39. 45% - Cricket

20% - Football

10% - Both

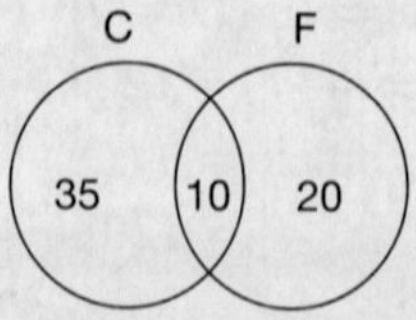

$45 - 10$

Cricket = 35%

Competition Wing

Level 1: Apply Your Concepts

1. $X = Y$

2. ϕ, Null set contains nothing and complement of it is also null.

3. ϕ, A' contains all the elements that is not in set A Intersection of it will be a null set.

4. If P and Q are disjoint, then $(P \cap Q)'$ is μ.

5. $P - Q = P$
If P and Q are disjoint, $P - Q$ contains only elements of P
$Q - P = Q$
If P and Q are disjoint, $Q - P$ contains only elements of Q.

6. Given P = {2, 3, 5, 7, 11, 13, 17, 19, 23, 29, 31, 37, 41, 43, 47}
$n(P) = 15$
$\therefore A_2 = \{1, 2\}; A_3 = \{1, 3\}; A_5 = \{1, 3\}; \ldots\ldots A_{47} = \{1, 47\}$
$\therefore A_2 \cup A_3 \cup \ldots \cup A_{47} = \{1, 2, 3, 5 \ldots . 47\}$
$\therefore n\left(\bigcup_{n \in P} A_n\right) = 16$

7. Since $n(A) < n(B)$ If $A \subseteq B$, then $(A - B) \cup (B - A)$ has least number of elements.
$\therefore n(A \Delta B) = n(A \cup B) - n(A \cap B)$
$= n(B) - n(A)$ ($\because A \subseteq B$)
$= 7 - 5 = 2$

8. We know that $A \times A$ is largest equivalence relation.
$\therefore A \times A$ is also transitive.
$\therefore$ The number of elements in R is 16.

9. Given $R = \{(2, 4), (4, 6)\}$ and A = {2, 4, 6}
For $R \cup S$ to be reflexive, S must contain the ordered pairs (2,2), (4, 4) and (6, 6).
For $R \cup S$ to be symmetric, S must contain the ordered pairs (4,2) and (6, 4)
$\therefore$ Minimum number of ordered pairs in S is 5.

10. Solve the two equations for x then write X and Y. Now find $X - Y$.

11. Number of subsets = $2^{n(A \times B)}$.

12. The number of subsets of A containing one particular element is 2^{n-1}.

13. Use the definition of reflexive, symmetric, and transitive.

14. Recall one-one relation.

15. (i) Recall the definition of union of sets and subsets.
(ii) If $A \subset B$, then $A \cup B = B$.
(iii) $\bigcup_{n=2}^{10} P_n = P_2 \cup P_3 \cup \ldots \cup P_{10} = P_{10}$.

16. (i) Recall the definition of intersection of sets and subsets.
(ii) If $A \subset B$, then $A \cap B = A$.
(iii) $\bigcap_{n=3}^{10} P_n = P_3 \cap P_4 \cap \ldots \cap P_{10} = P_3$.

17. (i) $n(A \cup B)' = n(\mu) - n(A \cup B)$.
(ii) $n(A \cup B) = n(A) + n(B) - n(A \cap B)$.
(iii) $n[(A \cup B)^C] = n(\mu) - n(A \cup B)$.

18. $|x| < a \Rightarrow -a < x < a$.

19. List out value of n, such that $2/n$ is an integer.

20. Given, $R = \{(1, 3), (3, 5)\}$ and $A = \{1, 3, 5\}$
For $R \cup S$ to be reflexive, S must contain the ordered pairs (1, 1), (3, 3), (5, 5).
For $R \cup S$ to be symmetric, S must contain the ordered pairs (3, 1) and (5, 3).
For $R \cup S$ to be transitive, S must contain the ordered pairs (1, 5) and (5, 1).
$\therefore$ Required minimum number of ordered pairs in S is 7.

21. $A = \{a, b, c\}$ Null relation is a symmetric relation.
$\therefore$ The minimum number of elements in R is 0.

22. If A and B are disjoints sets, then $(A - B) \cup (B - A)$ contain the maximum number of elements.
When $A \cap B = \emptyset$, $A - B = A$ and $B - A = B$
$\therefore$ The number of elements in
$(A - B) \cup (B - A) = n(A - B) + n(B - A) = n(A) + n(B) = 10 + 8 = 18$

23. Given,
$(X \cap Y^c)^c \cup (Y \cap Z)$
$= (X^c \cup Y) \cup (Y \cup Z)$
$= [(X^c \cup Y) \cup Y] \cap [(X^c \cup Y) \cup Z]$ (distributive law)
$= (X^c \cup Y) \cap [(X^c \cup Y) \cup Z]$
$= X^c \cup Y$ ($\therefore X^c \cup Y \subset (X^c \cup Y) \cup Z$)

24. Recall the definitions of reflexive, symmetric, and transitive relations.

25. (i) Write all the elements of R.
(ii) $R = \{(0, 0), (1, 1), (-1, -1), (0, -1), (-1, 0), (1, 0), (0, 1)\}$.
(iii) Check the properties, which R satisfy.

26. (i) When $A_1 \subset A_2 \subset \ldots \subset A_n$ then $\bigcap_{i=1}^{n} A_i = A_1$

(ii) If $A \subset B$, then $A \cap B = A$.

(iii) $\bigcap_{p=3}^{100} A_p = A_3$.

(iv) Find $n(A_3)$ by using $n(A_p) = p + 2$.

27. (i) Write all possibilities for (a, b).

(ii) $R = \{(1, 3), (2, 2), (3, 1)\}$.

(iii) Check the properties, which R satisfy.

28. (i) Check by taking examples.

(ii) Consider the three squares of the board as follows.

1	2	3

Squares 1 and 2 share a common side and squares 2 and 3 share a common side, but squares 1 and 3 does not share a common side.

29. (i) Write the elements of R.

(ii) Write all the elements of R and verify.

30. (i) Verify the reflexive, symmetric and transitive properties of relations.

(ii) Take an example and proceed.

31. (i) $n(F \cup C) = n(F) + n(C) - n(F \cap C)$.

(ii) Let the total number of students be x.

(iii) 80% of x – 40% of x = 40. Find x.

32. (i) Recall the definition of union of sets and subsets.

(ii) If $A \subset B$, then $A \cup B = B$.

(iii) $\bigcup_{n=1}^{100} A_n = A_{100}$.

(iv) Now evaluate $n(A_{100})$ by using the given condition.

Level 2: Review Your Concepts

33. $n(A \cup B) = n(A) + n(B) - n(A \cap B)$.

34. Apply concept of subsets.

35. The number of subsets of A that contain a particular element and does not contain another particular element is 2^{n-2}.

36. (i) Write some possibilities of (x, y).

(ii) (2, 3) and (–2, 3) are the two elements of R.

(iii) Now check which type of relation is R.

37. (i) Recall the properties of identity relation.

(ii) If $n(A) = p$ and R is reflexive defined on A, then $p \le n(R) \le p^2$.

38. Use the definition of reflexive, symmetric and transitive.

39. Substitute $n = 1$ and $n = 3$.

40. Use the definition of reflexive, symmetric, and transitive.

41. (i) Verify the reflexive, symmetric and transitive properties of relations.

(ii)

1	2	3

Compartments 1 and 2 are linked and compartments 2 and 3 are linked but compartments 1 and 3 are not linked.

42. (i) Write some elements of R and then check.

(ii) (2, 3) and (–2, 3) are the two elements of R.

(iii) Now check which type of relation is R.

43. Select from options.

44. (i) $n(E \cup H) = n(E) + n(H) - n(E \cap H)$

(ii)

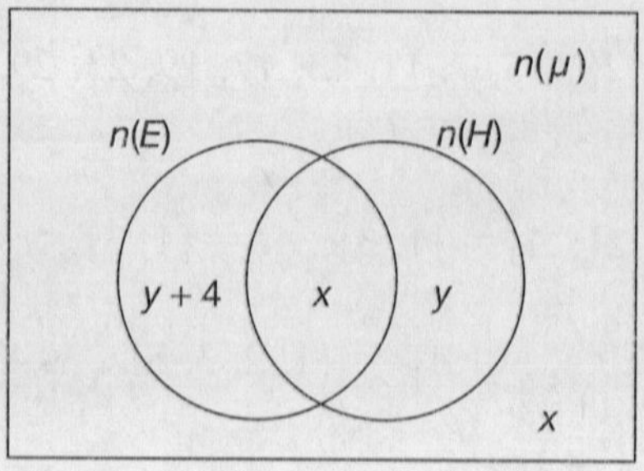

(iii) $(4 + y) + (x) + (y) + x = 30$.

(iv) The number of men who knows Hindi is $x + y$.

45. (i) Use Venn diagrams.

(ii) Take the number of families who buy both the news papers, The Times of India, and The Hindu as x.

(iii) $n(A \cup B) = 0.8x + x + 0.4x$.

(iv) Use $2.2x = 22000$, then find x.

46. The sequential order is CABD.

47. The sequential order is CABD.

48. Let $A = \{\{a\}, \{b, c\}, d, e\} \Rightarrow n(A) = 4$

$\therefore$ The number of subsets of $A = 2^4 = 16$.

49. Given $R = \{(a, a), (a, c), (b, c), (b, b), (c, c), (a, b)\}$

$\therefore$ The number of reflexive relations = The number of subsets formed by the elements(a, c), (b, c), and (a, b) = $2^3 = 8$.

50. Given, $A = \{1, 2, 3\}$ and $R = \{(2, 2), (1, 1), (1, 3), (3, 1)\}$

Here, $3 \in A$ but $(3, 3) \notin R$. Hence, R is not reflexive.

Also, $(3, 1) \in R$, and $(1, 3) \in R$ but $(3, 3) \notin R$. R is not transitive. But $\forall (x, y) \in R$, there exist $(y, x) \in R$.

Hence R is symmetric. (3, 1), (1, 3), $\in R$ but (3, 3) $\notin R$. Hence, R is not transitive.

51. $n(A \times B) = n(A) \times n(B) \Rightarrow n(A)$ and $n(B)$ should be the factors of $n(A \times B)$.
$\therefore n(B)$ cannot be 8.

52. We have number of reflexive relations defined on A is 2^{n^2-n}, where n is the cardinal number of A.

Given, $2^{n^2-n} = 64 \Rightarrow 2^{n^2-n} = 2^6$
$\Rightarrow n^2 - n = 6 \Rightarrow n(n-1) = 3 \times 2$
$\therefore n = 3.$

Level 3: Assess Your Concepts

53. (i) Use Venn diagram.

(ii) Given data can be expressed as follows:

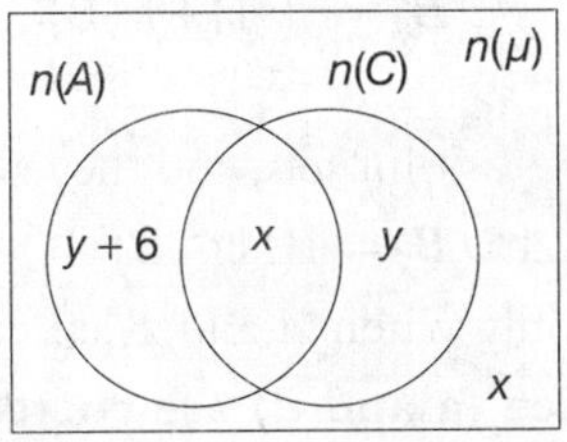

(iii) $(y + 6) + (x) + (y) + (x) = 50.$

(iv) Number of families who got houses $= x + y + 6$.

54. (i) Use Venn diagrams.

(ii) The given information can be expressed as:

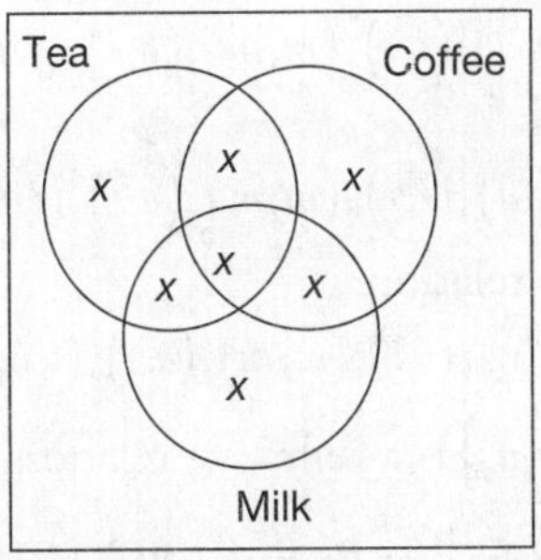

(iii) Total number of employees is $7x$, i.e., a multiple of 7.

55. (i) Use Venn diagrams.

(ii) Given data can be expressed as follows:

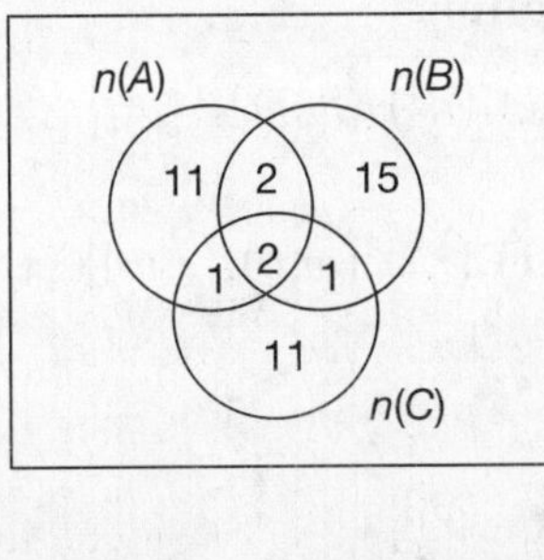

(iii) Number of people who like at most two dramas = Number of people who like only one drama + Number of people who like only two of the dramas.

56. (i) Use Venn diagram.

(ii) Given data can be expressed as:

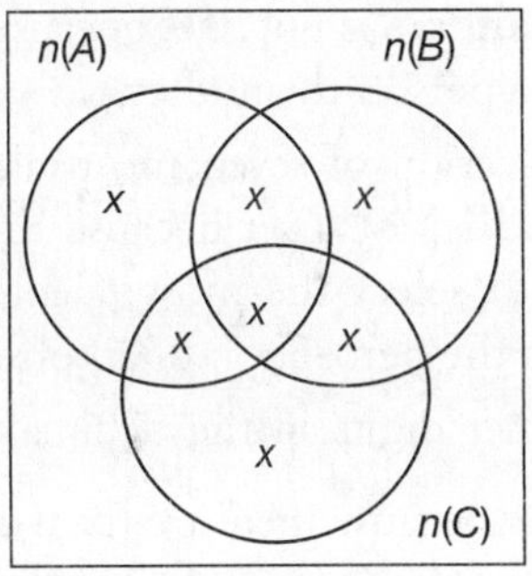

(iii) Total number of students is $7x$.

57. (i) Use Venn diagram.

(ii)

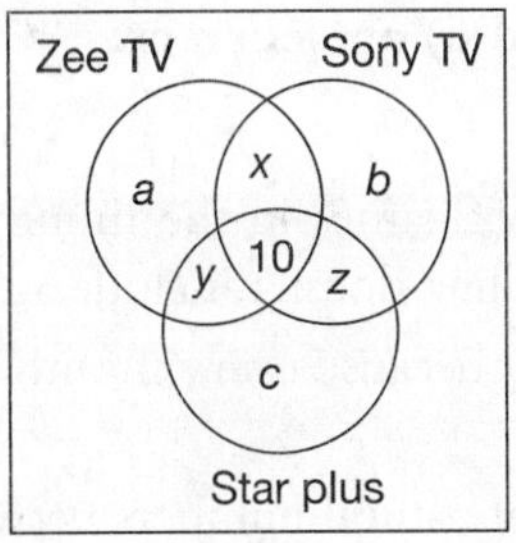

(iii) $(a + b + c) + (x + y + z) + 10 = 70.$

(iv) $(a + x + b) + (b + z + c) + (a + y + c) = 90.$

(v) Using the above information find $(x + y + z + 10)$.

58. We have the number of reflexive relations defined on A is 2^{n^2-n}.

Option (a) $\Rightarrow 2^{n^2-n} = 2^0$
$\Rightarrow n(n-1) = 1 \times 0 \Rightarrow n = 1.$
Option (b) $\Rightarrow 2^{n^2-n} = 2^2$
$\Rightarrow n(n-1) = 2 \times 1 \Rightarrow n = 2.$
Option (c) $\Rightarrow 2^{n^2-n} = 2^{12}$
$\Rightarrow n(n-1) = 4 \times 3 \Rightarrow n = 4.$
Option (d) $\Rightarrow 2^{n^2-n} = 2^9 \Rightarrow n(n-1) = 9.$
No integer value of n satisfies the above condition.
$\therefore$ 512 cannot be the number of reflexive relations defined on a set A.

59. Let the number of students who like only Chess be $2x$. The number of students who like only Carroms, both the games and neither of the games are $4x$, x, and $3x$, respectively.
Given, $2x + 4x + x = 3x + 120$
$\Rightarrow 4x = 120 \Rightarrow x = 30$
$\therefore$ The total number of students $= 2x + 4x + x + 3x = 10x = 300.$

JEE Special Wing

Multiple-Answer Type Questions

1. A well-defined collection of objects is a set.
   (a) The collection of ten good books in the **Library of Alexandria** is not a set because goodness varies from one person to another.
   (b) The collection of seven most talented persons in the world is not a set because there is no proper criteria to select the most talented persons. It is based on the perception of an observer.
   (c) Six distinct digits in the decimal expansion of $\frac{1}{7}$ form a set because there are fixed digits in the decimal expansion, they are 1, 2, 4, 5, 7, 8.
   (d) Five vowels in the English alphabet: $\{a, e, i, o, u\}$ is a set.

   Hence, choice (c and d) are correct.

2. **Going by options:**
   (a) Given that the set of names in the months of the calendar whose spelling doesn't include any vowel. It is a void (null) set because every month includes at least one vowel.
   (b) Given that the set of natural numbers between any two positive consecutive integers.
   As there are no natural numbers between any two positive consecutive integers, it is a void set.
   (c) Given that the set of single digit natural numbers which have exactly five factors.
   As there are no such single digit numbers, it is a void set.
   (d) The set of months of the year 2176 which have exactly 29 days = {February} which is a singleton set.

   Hence, choice (a, b, c) are correct.

3. **Going by options:**
   (a) $A=\{a, c, h, r, m\}$
   $\Rightarrow n(A)=5$
   The number of subsets of A is 2^5 i.e., 32.
   (b) $B=\{a, u, \{g, u\}, s, t\}$
   $\Rightarrow n(B)=5$
   The number of subsets of B is 2^5 i.e., 32.
   (c) $C=\{s, e, p, \{t, e, m\}, \{b, e, r\}\}$
   $\Rightarrow n(C)=5$
   The number of subsets of C is 2^5 i.e., 32.
   (d) $D=\{o, c, t, \{o\}, \{b, e, r\}\}$
   $\Rightarrow n(D)=5$
   The number of subsets of D is 2^5 i.e., 32.

   Hence, choice (a, b, c, d) are correct.

4. **Going by options:**
   (a) $(A\cap B)\subseteq A$ is true, since $A\cap B$ is common to both A and B.
   (b) $(B-A)\subseteq B$ is true, since $(B-A)$ is a part of A.
   (c) $(A\Delta B)\subseteq(A\cup B)$ is true, since $A\Delta B=(A\cup B)-(A\cap B)$ i.e., $(A\Delta B)$ is a part of $(A\cup B)$.
   (d) $(A\cup B)\subseteq(A\Delta B)$ which is false.

   Hence, choice (a, b, c) are correct.

5. **Going by options:**
   Given that $n(A\cup B)=n(A)+n(B)$.
   $\Rightarrow n(A\cap B)=0$.
   $\Rightarrow$ A and B are disjoint sets, and they are not equal sets.
   Given that $n(A\cup B)=n(A\cap B)$.
   It is possible only when A and B are equal sets.

   Hence, choice (a and d) are correct.

6. A relation R on a set A is said to be reflexive if for every $x\in A$, $(x, x)\in R$.
   Given that $S=\{a, i, m\}$.
   Going by options:
   (a) $R_1=\{(a,a),(i,i),(m,m)\}$ is a reflexive relation.
   (b) $R_2=\{(a,a),(i,i),(m,m),(a,i),(i,m)\}$ is a reflexive relation.
   (c) $R_3=\{(a,a),(i,i),(m,m),(a,i),(i,m),(a,m)\}$ is a reflexive relation.
   (d) $R_4=\{(a,a),(i,i),(m,m),(a,i),(i,m),(a,m),(i,a),(m,i),(m,a)\}$ is a reflexive relation.

   Hence, choice (a, b, c, d) are correct.

7. A relation R on a set A is said to be symmetric, if for every $(x, y)\in R$, $(y, x)\in$ R.
   Given that $U=\{t, i, m, e\}$.
   Going by options:
   (a) $R_{11}=\{(t,t),(i,i),(m,m),(e,e)\}$ is a symmetric relation.
   (b) $R_{22}=\{(t,t),(i,i),(m,e),(e,m)\}$ is a symmetric relation.

(c) $R_{33} = \{(t,t),(i,m),(m,e),(e,m)\}$ is not a symmetric relation, since $(i,m) \in R_{33}$ but $(m,i) \notin R_{33}$.

(d) $R_{44} = \{(t,m),(m,e),(m,t),(e,m)\}$ is a symmetric relation.

Hence, choice (a, b, d) are correct.

8. A relation R on a set A is said to be transitive if $(x, y) \in R$ and $(y, z) \in R$, then $(x, z) \in R$.

Given that $P = \{a, e, p, l\}$.

Going by options:

(a) $R_{111} = \{(a,a),(e,e),(p,p),(l,l)\}$ is a transitive relation.

(b) $R_{222} = \{(e,a),(e,e),(e,p),(a,l)\}$ is not a transitive relation, since $(e,a) \in R_{222}$ and $(a,l) \in R_{222}$ but $(e,l) \notin R_{222}$.

(c) $R_{333} = \{(a,e),(e,p),(p,l),(a,p),(e,l)\}$ is not a transitive relation, since $(a,p) \in R_{333}$ and $(p,l) \in R_{333}$ but $(a,l) \notin R_{333}$.

(d) $R_{444} = \{(a,e),(e,p),(p,l),(a,p),(e,l),(a,l)\}$ is a transitive relation.

Hence, choice (a and d) are correct.

9. A relation R on a set A is said to be anti-symmetric if $(x, y) \in R$ and $(y, x) \in R$, then $x = y$, i.e., R is said to be anti-symmetric if for $x \neq y$, $(x, y) \in R \Rightarrow (y, x) \notin R$.

Given that $E = \{t, o, p\}$.

Going by options:

(a) $R_a = \{(t,o),(o,p)\}$ is an anti-symmetric relation.

(b) $R_b = \{(t,p),(o,t),(p,o)\}$ is an anti-symmetric relation.

(c) $R_c = \{(p,o),(t,p),(o,p)\}$ is not an anti-symmetric relation, since $(p,o) \in R_c$ and $(o,p) \in R_c$.

(d) $R_d = \{(t,p),(t,o),(p,t),(o,t)\}$ is not an anti-symmetric relation, since $(t,o) \in R_d$ and $(o,t) \in R_d$.

Hence, choice (a and b) are correct.

10. A relation R on a set A is said to be an equivalence relation if it is reflexive, symmetric, and transitive.

Given that $R = \{r, a, n, k\}$.

Going by options:

(a) $R_p = \{(r,r),(a,a),(n,n),(k,k)\}$ is an equivalence relation.

(b) $R_q = \{(r,r),(a,a),(n,n),(k,k),(n,k),(k,n)\}$ is an equivalence relation.

(c) $R_r = \{(r,r),(a,a),(n,n),(k,k),(n,k),(k,n),(r,n),(n,r),(r,k),(k,r)\}$ is an equivalence relation.

(d) $R_s = R \times R$ is an equivalence relation.

Hence, choice (a, b, c, d) are correct.

Match The Column

Common Solutions for questions 11 to 15:

The total number of students = 50 × 5 = 250.

The number of students who play kabaddi = 150

The number of students who play football = 100.

The number of students who play tennis = 125.

The number of students who play kabaddi and football = 60.

The number of students who play tennis and football = 50.

The number of students who play kabaddi and tennis = 40.

The number of students who play none of the games = 10.

Let the number of the students who play all the games be x.

The number of students who play only kabaddi
$= 150 - (60 - x) - (40 - x) - x = 50 + x$.

The number of students who play only football
$= 100 - (60 - x) - (50 - x) - x = x - 10$.

The number of students who play only tennis
$= 125 - (40 - x) - (50 - x) - x = 35 + x$.

The above data can be depicted as follows:

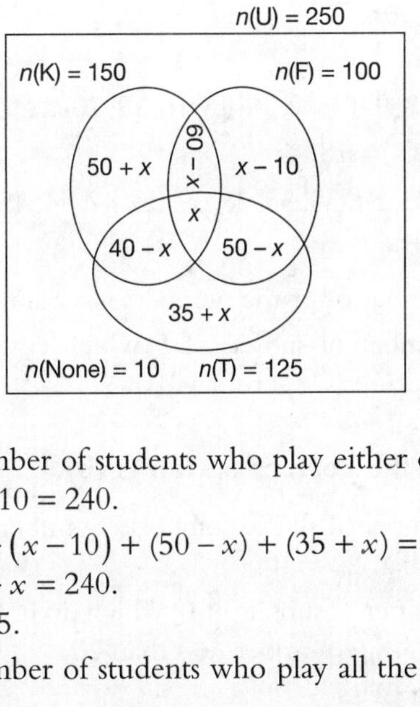

11. The number of students who play either of the games = 250 – 10 = 240.

$\Rightarrow 150 + (x - 10) + (50 - x) + (35 + x) = 240.$

$\Rightarrow 225 + x = 240.$

$\Rightarrow x = 15.$

The number of students who play all the three games = 15.

Hence, the correct option is (c).

12. The number of students who play only football $= x - 10$ $= 15 - 10 = 5$.

Hence, the correct option is (a).

13. The number of students who play exactly two games $= (60 - x) + (50 - x) + (40 - x)$

$= 150 - 3x = 150 - 45 = 105$.

Hence, the correct option is (f).

14. The number of students who play at most one game = The number of students who play only one game + The number of students who play none of the games

$= (50 + x + x - 10 + 35 + x) + 10$

$= 85 + 3x = 85 + 45 = 130$.

Hence, the correct option is (h).

15. The number of students who play football or tennis but not kabaddi

$= (x - 10) + (50 - x) + (35 + x)$

$= 75 + x$

$= 75 + 10 = 90$.

Hence, the correct option is (d).

Comprehension-Based Questions

Directions for questions 16 to 20:

These questions are based on the following information.

Given that P is a set of prime numbers less than 50, Q is the set of composite numbers less than 30 and R is the set of composite numbers more than 30 and less than 50.

$\Rightarrow P = \{2, 3, 5, 7, 11, 13, 17, 19, 23, 29, 31, 37, 41, 43, 47\}$

$\Rightarrow n(P) = 15$.

$Q = \{4, 6, 8, 9, 10, 12, 14, 15, 16, 18, 20, 21, 22, 24, 25, 26, 27, 28\} \Rightarrow n(Q) = 18$.

$R = \{32, 33, 34, 35, 36, 38, 39, 40, 42, 44, 45, 46, 48, 49\}$

$\Rightarrow n(R) = 14$.

16. The number of prime numbers less than 10 is 4.

The number of subsets of P which consist of all the prime numbers lesser than $10 = 2^{15-4}$

$= 2^{11}$.

Hence, the correct option is (b).

17. The number of all the composite numbers of Q which are less than 20 = 10.

The number of subsets of Q which do not consist of all the composite numbers less than 20

$= 2^{18-10} = 2^8$.

Hence, the correct option is (c).

18. The number of all the composite numbers of R which are less than 40 and more than 40 = 13.

The number of subsets of R which do not consist of all the composite numbers less than 40 and consists of the composite numbers more than 40 $= 2^{14-13} = 2^1 = 2$.

Hence, the correct option is (c).

19. As P and Q are disjoint sets, $n(P \cup Q) = N(P) + n(Q)$.

Now, $n(P \cup Q) = 15 + 18 = 33$.

The number of numbers of $P \cup Q$ which are more than 10 and less than 20 = 9.

The number of subsets of $P \cup Q$ which consists of all the numbers more than 10 and less than 20 $= 2^{33-9} = 2^{24}$.

Hence, the correct option is (a).

20. As P, Q and R are mutually disjoint sets, $n(P \cup Q \cup R) = N(P) + n(Q) + n(R)$.

Now, $n(P \cup Q \cup R) = 15 + 18 + 14 = 47$.

Please note that $(P \cup Q \cup R)$ does not have any numbers other than prime and composite numbers.

The number of subsets of $(P \cup Q \cup R)$ which consist of all the prime numbers but not the composite numbers $= 2^{47-47} = 2^0 = 1$.

Hence, the correct option is (d).

Common Solutions for questions 21 to 25:

Given that:

(i)

The number of students who secured grade A in				
	Maths	Sciences	Both	Total
Boys	80			
Girls				
Total			50	350

(ii) The number of girls is 50 more than that of the boys.

(iii) The number of boys who secured A grade in science is $25\frac{5}{7}\%$ of the total students.

(iv) The ratio of the total number of students who secured grade A in mathematics and that in sciences is 3 : 5.

Let the number of boys be b and the number of girls be g.

From (i) and (ii), $g + b = 350$ and $g - b = 50$.

$\Rightarrow g = 200$ and $b = 150$.

From (iii), the number of boys who secured A grade in science is $25\frac{5}{7}\% \times 350$

$= \frac{180}{7 \times 100} \times 350 = 90$.

We know that the number boys who secured grade A in maths + the number of boys who secured grade A in sciences – the number of boys who secured grade A in both the subjects = The total number of boys.

80 + 90 – the number of boys who secured grade A in both the subjects = 150.

The number of boys who secured grade A in both the subjects = 170 – 150 = 20.

Now, the number of girls who secured grade A in both the subjects = 50 – the number of boys who secured grade A in both the subjects = 50 – 20 = 30.

From (iv), $3x + 5x - 50 = 350$.

$\Rightarrow 8x = 400 \Rightarrow x = 50$.

The total number of students who secured grade A in mathematics = $3x$ = 150.

The total number of students who secured grade A in sciences = $5x$ = 250.

$\Rightarrow$ The number of girls who secured grade A in mathematics = 150 – 80 = 70.

The number of girls who secured grade A in sciences = 250 – 90 = 160.

Now, the final data can be tabulated as follows:

	The number of students who secured grade A in			
	Maths	Sciences	Both	Total
Boys	80	90	20	150
Girls	70	160	30	200
Total	150	250	50	350

21. The number of boys secured grade A in both the subjects = 20.

Hence, the correct option is (c).

22. The number of girls secured grade A in sciences = 160.

Hence, the correct option is (d).

23. The number of boys secured grade A only in one of the subjects = (80 – 20) + (90 – 20) = 130.

Hence, the correct option is (b).

24. The number of students who secured grade A in maths = 150.

Hence, the correct option is (b).

25. The number girls who secured grade A only in maths = 70 – 30 = 40.

Hence, the correct option is (a).

Assertion and Reason Type Questions

26. Assertion: Given that R is an identity relation defined on $M = \{j, u, n, e\}$.

A relation R on a set A defined as $R = \{(x, x) \mid \text{for every } x \in A\}$, is called an identity relation on A.

The identity relation is $\{(j, j), (u, u), (n, n), (e, e)\}$.

So, Assertion is true.

Reason: If A is a non-empty set and $n(A) = x$, then the number of possible identity relations defined on A is 1.

Reason is true, but not the correct explanation for Assertion.

Hence, the correct option is (b).

27. Assertion: If R is a reflexive relation defined on $N = \{m, a, y\}$.

$\Rightarrow n(N) = 3$.

$\Rightarrow n(N \times N) = 3 \times 3 = 9$.

A relation R on a set A is said to be reflexive if for every $x \in A$, $(x, x) \in R$.

So, the required relation should consist of $(m, m), (a, a), (y, y)$.

Therefore, the number possible reflexive relations is $= 2^{9-3} = 2^6 = 64$.

So, Assertion is false as it is given as 256.

Reason: If A is a non-empty set and $n(A) = x$, then the number of possible reflexive relations defined on A is $2^{x^2 - x}$.

Reason is true.

Hence, the correct option is (d).

28. Assertion: A relation is defined from $P = \{m, a, r, c, h\}$ to $Q = \{j, u, l, y\}$.

$\Rightarrow n(P) = 5$ and $n(Q) = 4$.

$\Rightarrow n(P \times Q) = 5 \times 4 = 20$.

The number of relations defined from P to $Q = 2^{20}$.

Reason: A and B are two non-empty sets. If and $n(A) = x$ and $n(B) = y$, then the number of possible relations defined from A to B, is $2^{x \times y}$.

So, Reason is false.

Hence, the correct option is (c).

29. Assertion: $\left(\left((P')'\right)'\right)' \cap \left((P')'\right)' = P \cap P'$

$= \varnothing$ since P and P' are disjoint sets.

So, Assertion is true.

Reason: $\left(\left((P')'\right)'\right)^{\prime\ldots n\text{ times}}$ is equal to P when n is even or P' when n is odd. If A and B are disjoint sets, then $(A \cap B) = \varnothing$.

Reason is true and is the correct explanation for Assertion.

Hence, the correct option is (a).

30. **Assertion:** Given that $A = \{a, b, c\}$, $B = \{p, q\}$ and $R = A \times B$.

$\Rightarrow R = \{(a, p), (a, q), (b, p), (b, q), (c, p), (c, q)\}$.

$R^{-1} = \{(p, a), (q, a), (p, b), (q, b), (p, c), (q, c)\}$.

Assertion is true.

Reason: R is a relation from A to B. The inverse relation of R, denoted by R^{-1}, is defined as, $R^{-1} = \{(y, x)/$ for every $(x, y) \in R\}$.

Reason is true and is the correct explanation for Assertion.

Hence, the correct option is (a).

CHAPTER

8

Logarithms

Remember

Before beginning this chapter, you should be able to:

- Explain laws of indices
- Solve exponential equations

Key Ideas

After completing this chapter, you should be able to:

- Understand the system of logarithms
- Learn properties and laws of logarithms
- Understand variation of logax with x and learn the signs of logax for different values of x and a
- Find the log of a number using log tables obtain the antilog from a given problem

Scientific Crypt

A Tribute to John Napier (1550-1617)

Napier (1550 – 1617) was a mathematician, physicist, astronomer and astrologer who lived in Merchiston, Edinburgh. He is well known for his contribution to the study of logarithms. Though Michel Stifel was the founder of an early form of logarithms, Napier is remembered as the inventor of logarithms and Napier bones, a multiplication tool meant for mechanically multiplying, dividing and taking square roots and cube roots using a set of numbered rods. He developed a mnemonic for formulae, that are used in solving spherical triangles and two formulae known as Napier's analogies. His other contributions include exponential expressions for trigonometric functions. He introduced the decimal notation for fractions.

Among his works 'Mirifici Logarithmorum canons descripto' is the most famous. It is written on natural logarithms and theorems in spherical trigonometry. This book contains tables of numbers related to natural logarithms.

As a mark of respect for his knowledge in astronomy, a crater on the moon was named after him, which is now called Neper.

FUN TIME

CROSSWORD

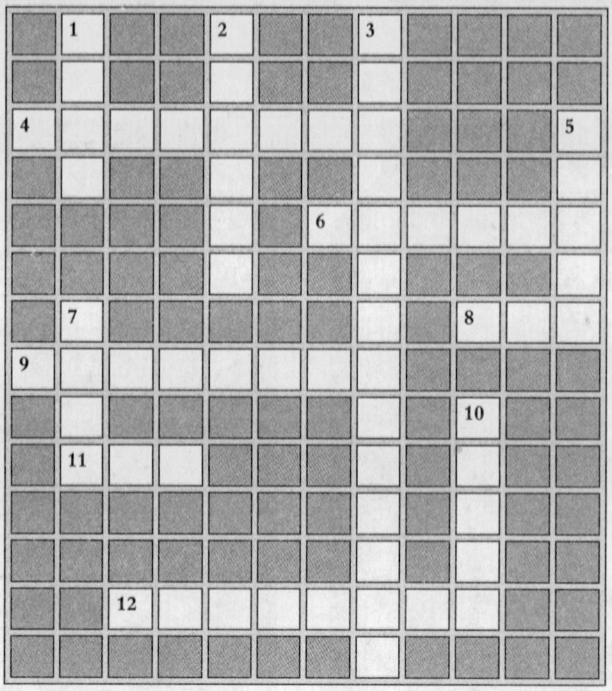

Across

4. The decimal part of the log of a number is said to be
6. The mathematician who discovered natural logarithms
8. The base of common logarithms
9. The log of a number which is greater than 1 with a weak base
11. Log of a number to the same base
12. The logs are defined for ______ real numbers

Down

1. In logarithms, the bases which are lesser than 1 are said to be
2. The mathematician who discovered common logarithms
3. The integral part of the log of a number said to be
5. In logarithms the bases which are greater than 1 are said to be
7. Log of 1 to any base
10. If $\log x = 2.3426$, then the number of digits in x

INTRODUCTION

One of the results in the previous classes, we learnt is that if $2^x = 2^3$, $x = 3$ and if $4^x = 4^y$, then $x = y$, i.e., if two powers of the same base are equal and the base is not equal to −1, 0 or 1, then the indices are equal.

But when $3^x = 5^2$, just by using the knowledge of indices, we cannot find the numerical value of x. The necessity of the concept of logarithms arises here. Logarithms are useful in long calculations involving multiplication and division.

Definition

The logarithm of any positive number to a given base (a positive number not equal to 1) is the index of the power of the base which is equal to that number. If N and a ($\neq 1$) are any two positive real numbers and x is some real number, then $a^x = N$. Where x is said to be logarithm of N to the base a. i.e., if $a^x = N$, then $x = \log_a N$.
From the definition of logs, we get the following results:

When $a > 0$, $b > 0$ and $b \neq 1$,

1. $\log_a a^n = n$, e.g., $\log_4 4^3 = 3$
2. $a^{\log_a b} = b$, e.g., $2^{\log_2 16} = 16$.

If in a particular relation, all the log expressions are to the same base, we normally do not specify the base.

Examples:

1. $2^3 = 8 \Rightarrow \log_2 8 = 3$
2. $5^4 = 625 \Rightarrow \log_5 625 = 4$

Systems of Logarithms

There are two systems of logarithms, which are used most often.

1. **Natural logarithms** were discovered by Napier. They are calculated to the base e which is approximately equal to 2.71. These are used in higher mathematics.
2. Logarithms to the base 10 are known as **common logarithms**. This system was introduced by Briggs, a contemporary of Napier.

For the rest of this chapter, we shall use the short-form log rather than logarithm.

Properties

1. Logarithms are defined only for positive real numbers.
2. Logarithms are defined only for positive bases different from 1.
3. In $\log_b a$, neither a nor b is negative but the value of $\log_b a$ can be negative.
   Example: As $10^{-2} = 0.01$, $\log_{10} 0.01 = -2$
4. Logs of different numbers to the same base are different, i.e., if $a \neq b$, then $\log_m a \neq \log_m b$. In other words, if $\log_m a = \log_m b$, then $a = b$.
   Example: $\log_{10} 2 \neq \log_{10} 3$
   $\log_{10} 2 = \log_{10} y \Rightarrow y = 2$

5. Logs of the same number to different bases have different values, i.e., if $m \neq n$, then $\log_m a \neq \log_n a$. In other words, if $\log_m a = \log_n a$, then $m = n$.

   Example: $\log_2 16 \neq \log_4 16$

   $\log_2 16 = \log_n 16 \Rightarrow n = 2$

6. Log of 1 to any base is 0.

   Example: $\log_2 1 = 0$ ($\because 2^0 = 1$)

7. Log of a number to the same base is 1

   Example: $\log_4 4 = 1$.

8. Log of 0 is not defined.

Laws

1. $\log_m(ab) = \log_m a + \log_m b$

   Example: $\log 15 = \log(5 \times 3) = \log 5 + \log 3$

2. $\log_m\left(\frac{a}{b}\right) = \log_m a - \log_m b$

   Example: $\log\left(\frac{15}{20}\right) = \log 15 - \log 20$

3. $\log a^m = m\log a$

   Example: $\log 36 = \log 6^2 = 2\log 6$

4. $\log_b a \log_c b = \log_c a$ (chain rule)

   Example: $\log_2 4 \log_4 16 = \log_2 16$

5. $\log_b a = \dfrac{\log_c a}{\log_c b}$

   Example: $\log_4 16 = \dfrac{\log_2 16}{\log_2 4}$ (change of base rule)

   In this relation, if we take $a = c$, we get the following result:

   $$\log_b a = \frac{1}{\log_a b}.$$

Variation of $\log_a x$ with x

For $1 < a$ and $0 < p < q$, $\log_a p < \log_a q$

For $0 < a < 1$ and $0 < p < q$, $\log_a p > \log_a q$

Example: $\log_{10} 2 < \log_{10} 3$ and $\log_{0.1} 2 > \log_{0.1} 3$

Bases which are greater than 1 are called strong bases and bases which are less than 1 are called weak bases. Therefore, for strong bases log increases with number and for weak bases log decreases with number.

Sign of $\log_a x$ for Different Values of x and a

Strong bases ($a > 1$)

1. If $x > 1$, $\log_a x$ is positive.

   Example: $\log_2 10$, $\log_5 25$ are positive.

2. If $0 < x < 1$, then $\log_a x$ is negative.

   Example: $\log_3 0.2$, $\log_{10} 0.25$ are negative.

   Consider $\log_3 0.2 = \dfrac{\log 0.2}{\log 3} = \dfrac{\log 2 - \log 10}{\log 3}$

   $\log 2 < \log 10$ and $0 < \log 3$ for strong bases.

   As $\dfrac{\log 2 - \log 10}{\log 3} < 0$, $\log_3 0.2 < 0$

Weak bases ($0 < a < 1$)

3. If $x > 1$, then $\log_a x$ is negative.

   Example: Consider $\log_{0.4} 2 = \dfrac{\log 2}{\log 0.4} = \dfrac{\log 2}{\log 4 - \log 10}$

   $\log 4 < \log 10$ (for any base)

   $\log 4 - \log 10 < 0$

   $\dfrac{\log 2}{\log 4 - \log 10} < 0$. (for strong bases)

4. If $0 < x < 1$, then $\log_a x$ is positive. For example, $\log_{0.1} 0.2$, $\log_{0.4} 0.3$ are positive. To summarize, log of big numbers (>1) to strong bases and small numbers (<1) to weak bases are positive.

EXAMPLE 8.1 If $a^x = b^y = c^z$ and $y^2 = xz$, what is the value of $\frac{(\log_b a)}{(\log_c b)}$?

SOLUTION

$x \log a = y \log b = z \log c = k$

$\frac{\log_b a}{\log_c b} = \frac{(\log a)(\log c)}{(\log b)(\log b)}$ $[(\because \log_n{}^m = (\log m)/(\log n)]$

$\left(\frac{y}{x}\right)\left(\frac{y}{z}\right) = y^2/xz = 1$

EXAMPLE 8.2 $\frac{1}{\log_2 \log_2 \log_3 81} =$

SOLUTION

$\frac{1}{\log_2 \log_2 \log_3 81} = \frac{1}{\log_2 \log_2 4\log_3 3}$

$= \frac{1}{\log_2 \log_2 2^2} = \frac{1}{\log_2 2} = \frac{1}{1} = 1$

EXAMPLE 8.3 If $\log 2 = 0.3010$, then the number of digits in 2^{1000} is ______.

SOLUTION

$\log (2)^{1000} = 1000 (\log 2)$

$= 1000 \times (0.3010)$ (given)

$= 301.0$

Number of digits = 301 + 1 = 302.

To Find the log of a Number to Base 10

Consider the following numbers:

2, 20, 200, 0.2, and 0.02.

We see that $20 = 10(2)$ and $200 = 100(2)$

$\therefore \log 20 = 1 + \log 2$ and $\log 200 = 2 + \log 2$

Similarly, $\log 0.2 = -1 + \log 2$ and $\log 0.02 = -2 + \log 2$

From the tables, we see that $\log 2 = 0.3010$. (Using the tables, this is explained in more detail in later examples.)

$\therefore \log 20 = 1.3010$, $\log 200 = 2.3010$, $\log 0.2 = -1 + 0.3010$ and $\log 0.02 = -2 + 0.3010$.

We note two points:

1. Multiplying or dividing by a power of 10 changes only the integral part of the log, not the fractional part.
2. For numbers less than 1, (for example 0.2) it is more convenient to leave the log value as $-1 + 0.3010$ instead of changing it to -0.6090. We refer to the first form (in which the fraction is positive) as the standard form and the second form as the normal form. Both the forms represent the same number.

   For numbers less than 1, it is more convenient to express the log in the standard form. As the negative sign refers only to the integral part, it is written above the integral part, rather than in front, i.e., $\log 0.2 = \bar{1}.3010$ and not -1.3010.

   The convenience of the standard form will be clear when we learn how to take the antilog, which is explained in more detail later.

   antilog (-0.6090) = antilog $(-1 + 0.3010)$ = antilog $\bar{1}.3010 = 0.2$.

   When the logs of numbers are expressed in the standard form, (for numbers greater than 1, the standard form of the log is the same as the normal form), the integral part is called the characteristic and the fractional part (which is always positive) is called the *mantissa.*

EXAMPLE 8.4 Express -0.5229 in the standard form and locate it on the number line.

SOLUTION

$-0.5229 = -1 + 1 - 0.5229 = \bar{1}.4771$

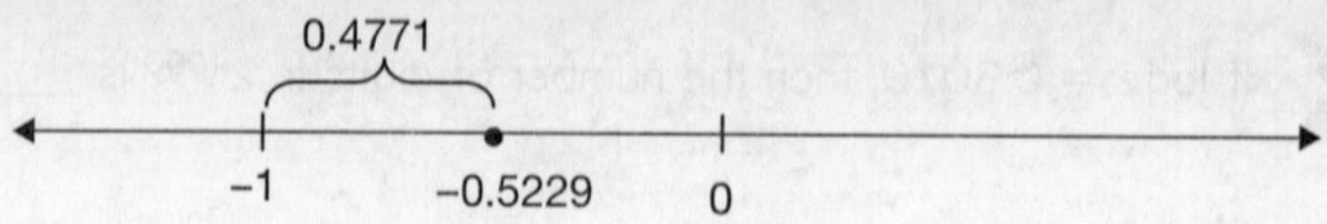

The Rule to Obtain the Characteristic of log *x*

1. If $x > 1$ and there are n digits in x, the characteristic is $n - 1$.
2. If $x < 1$ and there are m zeroes between the decimal point and the first non-zero digit of x, the characteristic is $-m$, more commonly written as $\bar{m}$.

Info Bytes!

$-4 = \bar{4}$ but $-4.01 \neq \bar{4}.01$

To Find the log of a Number from the log Tables

EXAMPLE 8.5 Find the value of $\log 25$, $\log 250$, and $\log 0.025$.

SOLUTION

In the log table, we find the number 25 in the left-hand column. In this row, in the next column (under 0), we find 0.3979 (the decimal point is dropped in other columns).

For the log of all numbers whose significant digits are 25 and this number 0.3979, is the *mantissa*. Prefixing the characteristics we have,

$\log 25 = 1.3979$

$\log 250 = 2.3979$

$\log 0.025 = \bar{2}.3979.$

EXAMPLE 8.6 Find the value of log 2.54, log 0.254, and log 25400.

SOLUTION

In the log table, we locate 25 in the first column. In this row, in the column under 4, we find 0.4048. As done in the earlier example, the same line as before gives the *mantissa* of logarithms of all numbers which begin with 25. From this line we pick out the *mantissa* which is located in the column numbered 4. This gives 4048 as the *mantissa* for all numbers whose significant digits are 254.

$\log 2.54 = 0.4048$

$\log 0.254 = \bar{1}.4048$

$\log 25400 = 4.4048.$

EXAMPLE 8.7 Find the value of log 2.546 and log 25460.

SOLUTION

As found in the above example, we can find the mantissa for the sequence of digits 4048.

Since there are four significant digits in 2546, in the same row where we have found 4048, under column 6 in the mean difference column, we find the number 10, the mantissa of the logarithm of 2546 will be 4048 + 10 = 4058.

Thus, $\log 2.546 = 0.4058$

$\log 0.2546 = \bar{1}.4058$

$\log 25460 = 4.4058.$

Antilog

As $\log_2 8 = 3$, 8 is the antilogarithm of 3 to the base 2. Antilog b to base m is m^b.

In example 2.7 above, we saw that, $\log 2.546 = 0.4058$. Therefore,
Antilog $0.4058 = 2.546$

> **Info Bytes!**
> An antilogarithm is the reverse operation of a logarithm. Given a logarithm, the antilog gives you back the number. It's like the process of "undoing" the logarithm

EXAMPLE 8.8 Find the antilog of 1.301.

SOLUTION

Step 1: In the antilog table, we find the number 30 in the left-hand column. In that row in the column under 1, we find 2000.

Step 2: As the characteristic is 1, we place the decimal after two digits from the left. That is, antilog 1.301 = 20.00.

If the characteristic was 2, we would place the decimal after three digits from the left. That is, antilog 2.301 = 200.0.

If the characteristic was 3, we would place the decimal after four digits from the left. That is, antilog 3.301 = 2000.

EXAMPLE 8.9 Find the antilog of 2.3246.

SOLUTION

We have to locate 0.32 in the left- hand column and slide along the horizontal line and pick out the number in the vertical column headed by 4. We see that the number is 2109. The mean difference for 6 in the same line is 3.

The significant digits in the required number are = 2109 + 3 = 2112. As the characteristic is 2, the required antilog is 211.2.

EXAMPLE 8.10 Find the value of $\frac{5.431\times0.061}{12.38\times0.041}$ to four significant digits.

SOLUTION

log of a fraction = (log of numerator) – (log of denominator)

log of numerator = $\log 5.431 + \log 0.061 = 0.7349 + \bar{2}.7853 = \bar{1}.5202$

log of denominator = $\log 12.38 + \log 0.041 = 1.0927 + \bar{2}.6128 = \bar{1}.7055$

log of given expression = $\bar{1}.5202 - \bar{1}.7055 = \bar{1}.8147$

antilog of 8147 is 6516 + 11 = 6527

Since the characteristic is $\bar{1}$, the decimal should be kept before the four digits.

∴ The answer is 0.6527.

EXAMPLE 8.11 If $\log_{10} 2 = 0.3010$ then $\log_{10} 50$ ______.

SOLUTION

Given, $\log_{10} 2 = 0.3010$

$\log_{10} 50 = \log_{10} 10\times5 = \log_{10} 10 + \log_{10} 5$

$= 1 + \log_{10}\frac{10}{2} = 1 + \log_{10} 10 - \log_{10} 2$

= 1 + 1 – 0.3010

= 1.6990

POINTS TO REMEMBER

- ✔ Natural logarithms were discovered by Napier. They are calculated to the base e which is approximately equal to 2.71. These are used in higher mathematics.
- ✔ Logarithms to the base 10 are known as common logarithms. This system was introduced by Briggs, a contemporary of Napier.
- ✔ Logarithms are defined only for positive real numbers.
- ✔ For $1 < a$ and $0 < p < q$, $\log_a p < \log_a q$
- ✔ For $0 < a < 1$ and $0 < p < q$, $\log_a p < \log_a q$
- ✔ Multiplying or dividing by a power of 10 changes only the integral part of the log, not the fractional part.
- ✔ When the logs of numbers are expressed in the standard form, (for numbers greater than 1, the standard form of the log is the same as the normal form), the integral part is called the characteristic and the fractional part (which is always positive) is called the *mantissa*.
- ✔ As $\log_2 8 = 3$, 8 is the antilogarithm of 3 to the base 2. Antilog b to base *m* is m^b.

PRACTICE QUESTIONS CLASSROOM WING

Very Short Answer Type Questions

Directions of questions from 1 to 11:
Fill in the blanks.

1. $3^{\log_3 7} + 5^{\log_5 6} =$ ______.
2. $\log_{2\sqrt{2}} \sqrt{32} =$ ________.
3. $\log_{\sqrt{k}} \sqrt{k\sqrt{k\sqrt{k\sqrt{k}}}} =$ ________.
4. If $x = \log_5 3$ and $y = \log_5 8$, then $\log_5 24$ in terms of x, y is equal to ________.
5. If $3^x = 2^y = 6$, then $\dfrac{x+y}{xy} =$ ________.
6. $\log_2 7 \log_3 5 \log_7 2 \log_5 3 =$ ________.
7. $10^{\log_{10} 3} + 6^{\log_6 5} =$ ________.
8. If $\log_{10} 25 = 1.3979$, then $\log_{10} 5 =$ ________.
9. If $\log_{10} 3 = 0.4771$, then $\log_{10} 300 =$ ________.
10. $\log_y x \times \log_z y \times \log_x z =$ ______.
11. Given, antilog(2.375) = x. Characteristic of $\log x$ is ______.

Directions of questions from 12 to 22:
Answer the following questions.

12. Expand $\log_3\left(\dfrac{xy^2}{z^3}\right)$.
13. Can we write $\log_x \dfrac{a}{b}$ as $\dfrac{\log_x a}{\log_x b}$?
14. Express $0.001 = (0.1)^3$ in the logarithmic form.
15. Evaluate $3 - \log_{10}100$.
16. When $0 < a < 1$ and $m < n$, then which is greater, $\log_a m$ (or) $\log_a n$?
17. Find the value of $\log_{\sqrt{8}}16$.
18. If $\log 2 = 0.3010$, $\log 3 = 0.4771$ and $\log 7 = 0.8451$, then find the values of $\log 210$.
19. If $\log(21.73) = 1.3371$, then find the values of $\log(2.173)$.
20. If antilog (0.2156) = 1.643, then find the values of antilog (1.2156).
21. Without using the logarithm tables find the value of $3\log_3 27$.
22. Find the value of $\log_{0.6}\left(\dfrac{9}{25}\right)$.

Short Answer Type Questions

23. Prove that $\log 5040 = 4\log 2 + 2\log 3 + \log 5 + \log 7$.
24. Find the value of $\log_{2^{-1}}(0.0625)$.
25. Express the following as a single logarithm. $\dfrac{1}{3}\log x - \dfrac{8}{5}\log y + \dfrac{7}{2}\log z$.
26. If $x^2 + y^2 = 25xy$, then prove that $2\log(x + y) = 3\log 3 + \log x + \log y$.
27. If $x^2 + y^2 = z^2$, then prove that $\log_y(z + x) + \log_y(z - x) = 2$.
28. If $7^x = 8^y = 3136$, then $\dfrac{1}{x} + \dfrac{1}{y} =$ ________.
29. $\log_3 10 \ \log_2 25 \ \log_{10} 3 \ \log_5 2,=$ ________.
30. If $\log 2 = 0.3010$, $\log 3 = 0.4771$ and $\log 7 = 0.8451$, then find the value of $\log 75$.
31. If $x = \log_3 2$, then $\dfrac{1}{x+1} + 1 =$ ______
32. Prove that
$$2\log\frac{35}{192} + 2\log\frac{114}{91} + \log 48 + 2\log\left(\frac{13}{19}\right) = \log\left(\frac{75}{64}\right).$$
33. Solve for x:
$\log x + \log 5 = 2 + \log 64$
34. If $x^6 - y^6 = z^6$, then prove that $\log_z(x^2 - y^2) + \log_z(x^2 + y^2 - xy) + \log_z(x^2 + y^2 + xy) = 6$.

35. Using the tables find the value of $\sqrt[4]{(32)^3}$.

36. Using the tables find the value of $\sqrt{(0.12)^3}$.

37. Given $\log 3 = 0.4771$, then the number of digits in 3^{1000} is ______.

Essay Type Questions

38. If If $x = \log_5 10$, then $x + \frac{1}{x} + 2 =$ ______.

39. If $a = b^{1/3} = c^{1/5} = d^{1/7} = e^{1/9}$, find $\log_a abcde$.

40. Arrange the following in ascending order.

$A = \log_9 6561$ $\quad B = \log_{\sqrt{5}} 625$

$C = \log_{\sqrt{3}} 243$ $\quad D = \log_{\sqrt{2}} 256$

41. If $\log_y x - \log_{y^3} x^2 = 9(\log_{xy} y)^2$ and $x = 9y$, find y.

42. $\log\left(\frac{a^2}{b}\right) + \log\left(\frac{a^4}{b^3}\right) + \log\left(\frac{a^6}{b^3}\right) + \cdots + \log\left(\frac{a^{2n}}{b^n}\right) = ?$

43. If $\frac{\log x}{y - z} = \frac{\log y}{z - x} = \frac{\log z}{x - y}$, then find the value of $x^x \times y^y \times z^z$.

PRACTICE QUESTIONS COMPETITION WING

Level 1: Apply Your Concepts

Directions of questions from 1 to 5:
Fill in the blanks

1. $(5)^{2\log_5 2} =$ _______.

2. $\log_5 2 + \log_5 20 - \log_5 8 =$ _______.

3. The value of $\dfrac{3+\log_{10}(10)^2}{\log_5 5}$ is _______.

4. Given $3 = \log_2 x + 4\log_2 8$. Then the value of $x =$ _______.

5. If $\log_{10} 2 = 0.3010$, then $\log_{10} 5 =$ _______.

Directions of questions from 6 to 69:
Select the correct alternative from the given choices.

6. For which of the following numbers, logarithm is not defined?
(a) 0 (b) 1
(c) $\sqrt{2}$ (d) 0.1

7. $\dfrac{1}{\log_a abc} + \dfrac{1}{\log_b abc} + \dfrac{1}{\log_c abc} =$ _______.
(a) 0 (b) 1
(c) 2 (d) $\dfrac{1}{2}$

8. $\log_3 2.\log_4 3.\log_5 4 \ldots\ldots\ldots \log_{2048} 2047 =$ _______.
(a) 0 (b) 1
(c) 11 (d) $\dfrac{1}{11}$

9. Which of the following cannot be the base of a logarithm of a number?
(a) $\dfrac{1}{2}$ (b) 1
(c) $\sqrt{2}$ (d) 0.1

10. If a, b are the lengths of the sides and c is the length of the hypotenuse of a right-angled triangle, where $c - b \neq 1$ and $c + b \neq 1$,
then $\dfrac{1}{\log_{(c+b)} a} + \dfrac{1}{\log_{(c-b)} a} =$ _______.
(a) 1 (b) 0
(c) 2 (d) $\dfrac{1}{2}$

11. $\log(a^3 + b^3) - \log(a + b) - \log(a^2 - ab + b^2) =$ _______.
(a) $a^3 - b^3$ (b) 0
(c) $\log 1$ (d) Both (b) and (c)

12. Which is greatest among the following:
(a) $\log_2 20$ (b) $\log_7 35$
(c) $\log_5 70$ (d) $\log_3 68$

13. $\log(a + b) + \log(a - b) - \log(a^2 - b^2) =$ _______.
(a) 0 (b) 1
(c) $(a^2 - b^2)$ (d) $a^2 + b^2$

14. If $\dfrac{\log x}{\log y} = \dfrac{\log 49}{\log 7}$, then the relation between x and y.
(a) $x = \sqrt{y}$ (b) $x = y^3$
(c) $y = x^2$ (d) $x = y^2$

15. $\log(x) - \log(2x - 3) = 1$, then $x =$?
(a) $\dfrac{30}{19}$ (b) $\dfrac{20}{19}$
(c) $\dfrac{19}{30}$ (d) $\dfrac{19}{20}$

16. If $2\log(x + 4) = \log 16$, then $x =$?
(a) 0, –8 (b) –8
(c) –2 (d) 0

17. The value of x when $\log_x 343 = 3$, is:
(a) 7 (b) 8
(c) 3 (d) 27

18. $\log_{16} 3 \cdot \log_{17} 4 \cdot \log_9 17 =$ _______.
(a) $\dfrac{1}{2}$ (b) $\dfrac{1}{4}$
(c) $\dfrac{1}{8}$ (d) $\dfrac{2}{3}$

19. $\log_2 [\log_2 \{\log_2 (\log_3 81)\}] =$
(a) 1 (b) 0
(c) $\log 3$ (d) Undefined

20. $\log_{121}\left(\dfrac{\sqrt{14641}}{121}\right) =$ _______.
(a) 11 (b) 121
(c) 0 (d) 1

21. $\frac{\log_3 729+\log_6 216}{4+\log_2 16-2\log_4 64}$ = ______.

(a) 9 (b) 4

(c) $\frac{9}{2}$ (d) $\frac{1}{2}$

22. If $\log_{x^n} y^m = k\log_x y$, then the value of k is

(a) $\frac{m}{n}$ (b) mn

(c) m^n (d) n^m

23. If $\log_y x = 2$, then $_a\log_a{}^{(\log_x y)}$ = ______.

(a) −2 (b) 4

(c) $\frac{1}{2}$ (d) $\frac{-1}{4}$

24. If $p = \log_6 216$ and $q = \log_3 25$ then p^q = ______.

(a) 3 (b) 25

(c) 15 (d) Cannot be determined

25. $2^{(16-\log_2 1024)}$ = ______.

(a) 16 (b) 32

(d) 64 (d) 8

26. $2^{3\log_2 2} + 3^{2\log_3 2}$ = ______.

(a) 8 (b) 4

(c) 9 (d) 2

27. $\log_{a+b}(a^3+b^3) - \log_{a+b}(a^2 - ab + b^2)$ = ______.

(a) $\log_{a+b}(a-b)$ (b) 2

(c) $a+b$ (d) 1

28. $4^{\log_{16} 25}$ = ______.

(a) 25 (b) 5

(c) 16 (d) 4

29. $\frac{1}{\log_{xy} x} + \frac{1}{\log_{xy} y}$ = ______?

(a) 1 (b) 2

(c) 0 (d) $\frac{1}{\log_{xy} x \times \log_{xy} y}$

30. If $y = \log_{x-3}(x^2 - 6x + 9)$, then find y.

(a) 4 (b) 8

(c) 2 (d) 32

Level 2: Review Your Concepts

31. If $\log_{10} 2 = 0.3010$, then the number of digits in 16^{12} is:

(a) 14 (b) 15

(c) 13 (d) 16

32. If $\log_{64} p^2 = 1\frac{2}{3}$, then $\log_2 \frac{p}{16}$ = ______.

(a) 16 (b) 2

(c) 32 (d) 1

33. $\log_2 \log_2 \log_5 125$ = ______.

(a) 4 (b) 8

(c) −1 (d) 1

34. If $\log_x y = \frac{\log_a y}{p}$, then the value of p is

(a) $\log_y x$ (b) $\log_x a$

(c) $\log_a x$ (d) $\log_a y$

35. $\log\left[\frac{\sqrt[3]{x^2} \times y}{\sqrt[5]{z^2}}\right]$ = ______

(a) $\log x^{2/3} - \log z^{2/5} + \log y$

(b) $\log x^{3/2} + \log y - \log z^{5/2}$

(c) $\log x^{2/3} - \log y + \log z^{2/5}$

(d) None of these

36. If $\log[4 - 5\log_{32}(x + 3)] = 0$, find x.

(a) 32 (b) 8

(c) 3 (d) 5

37. If $x = \log_3 \log_2 \log_2 256$, then $2^{\log_4 2^{2^x}}$ = ______.

(a) 4 (b) 8

(c) 2 (d) 1

38. If $\log_a\left(\frac{13^2}{\sqrt{2^3} \times 5}\right) = 2\log_a 13 - \log_a 5 - x$ then

(a) $a^x = 2^{3/2}$ (b) $x^a = 2^{3/2}$

(c) $a^x = 2^{2/3}$ (d) $x^a = 2^{2/3}$

39. If $\log 81 - \log 3 = \log a$, then $4_9^{\log a}$ = ______.

(a) 4 (b) 16

(c) 2 (d) 8

40. If $a^{\log_a n} = 3$ then $a^{2\log b} - b^{\log a}$ = ______.

(a) 6 (b) 9

(c) 3 (d) Cannot be determined

41. If $\log_3(x-5)+\log_3(x+2)=\log_3 8$, then $x=$ ________.

(a) -3 (b) 6
(c) $6, -3$ (d) $3, -6$

42. If $\log(x+y)=\log x+\log y$, then $x=$ ________.

(a) $\frac{-y}{1+y}$ (b) $\frac{-y}{1-y}$
(c) 1 (d) $\frac{y}{1+y}$

43. If $2^{\log 5}\cdot 5^{\log 2}=2^{\log x}$, then $\log_5 \sqrt[3]{x^2}=$ ________.

(a) $\frac{4}{3}$ (b) $\frac{3}{4}$
(c) $\frac{1}{3}$ (d) 3

44. If $3^{\log x}+x^{\log 3}=54$, find $\log x$.

(a) 3 (b) 2
(c) 4 (d) Cannot be determined

45. If $\log_{10}x-\log_{10}y=1$ and $x+y=11$, then $x=$ ________.

(a) 10 (b) 1
(c) 11 (d) 2

46. If $\log_{49}3\times\log_9 7\times\log_2 8=x$, then find the value of $\frac{4x}{3}$.

(a) 3 (b) 7
(c) 8 (d) 1

47. The value of $\log_{a-b}(a^3-b^3)-\log_{a-b}(a^2+ab+b^2)$ is ______. $(a>b)$

(a) 0 (b) 1
(c) 3 (d) Undefined

48. If $\log_3 2=x$, then the value of $\frac{\log_{10}72}{\log_{10}24}$ is:

(a) $\frac{1+x}{1-x}$ (b) $\frac{2+3x}{1+3x}$
(c) $\frac{2-3x}{2+3x}$ (d) $\frac{3x+1}{3x+2}$

49. $\log\left(\frac{1}{2}\right)+\log\left(\frac{2}{3}\right)+\log\left(\frac{3}{4}\right)+\cdots+\log\left(\frac{99}{100}\right)=$ ______.

(a) -2 (b) -1
(c) 0 (d) 2

50. If $x^2-y^2=1$, $(x>y)$, then find the value of $\log_{(x-y)}(x+y)$.

(a) -2 (b) 2
(c) -1 (d) 1

51. If $3^{\log_3 5}+5^{\log_x 3}=8$, then find the value of x.

(a) 3 (b) 5
(c) 4 (d) 8

52. $\log_2 1\cdot\log_3 2\cdot\log_4 3\cdot\log_5 4\cdot\log_6 5\ \ldots\ \log_{200}199$ = ________.

(a) ∞ (b) 0
(c) 1 (d) Cannot be determined

53. If $x^2+y^2-3xy=0$ and $x>y$, then find the value of $\log_{xy}(x-y)$.

(a) $\frac{1}{4}$ (b) 4
(c) $\frac{1}{2}$ (d) 2

54. If $\log 3=0.4771$, then find the number of digits in 3^{100}.

(a) 47 (b) 48
(c) 49 (d) 50

Level 3: Assess Your Concepts

55. If $\log_5 x-\log_5 y=\log_5 4+\log_5 2$ and $x-y=7$, then $x=$ ______.

(a) 1 (b) 8
(c) 7 (d) 6

56. If $\log_2\left[-1+\sqrt{x^2-14x+49}\right]=4$, then $x=$ ______.

(a) 24 (b) -10
(c) $24, -10$ (d) 10

57. If $\frac{\log p}{2}=\frac{\log q}{4}=\frac{\log r}{8}=k$ and $pqr=100$, then k = ______.

(a) 14 (b) $\frac{1}{6}$
(c) $\frac{1}{7}$ (d) 2

58. If $\log_{10}2 = 0.3010$ and $\log_{10}3 = 0.4771$, then the value of $\log_{10}\left(\dfrac{2^3 \times 3^2}{5^2}\right)$ is :

(a) 0.4592. (b) 0.5492.
(c) 0.4529. (d) 0.5429.

59. The value of $\dfrac{1}{1+\log_{ab} c}+\dfrac{1}{1+\log_{ac} b}+\dfrac{1}{1+\log_{bc} a}$ equals:

(a) 2 (b) 0
(c) 1 (d) $\log abc$

60. If $x^2 + y^2 = z^2$, then $\dfrac{1}{\log_{(z+x)}y}+\dfrac{1}{\log_{(z-x)}y}=$ ______.

(a) 4 (b) 3
(c) 2 (d) 1

61. If $\log 2 = 0.301$, then find the number of digits in 2^{1024}.

(a) 307 (b) 308
(c) 309 (d) 310

62. If $x^2 - y^2 = 1$, $(x > y)$, then find the value of $\log_{(x-y)}(x + y)$.

(a) −2 (b) 2
(c) −1 (d) 1

63. If $2^{\log_3 9} + 25^{\log_9 3} = 8^{\log_x 9}$, then $x =$ ______.

(a) 9 (b) 8
(c) 3 (d) 2

64. If $\log_a x = m$ and $\log_b x = n$, then $\log_{\left(\frac{a}{b}\right)} x =$ ______.

(a) $\dfrac{m}{m-n}$ (b) $\dfrac{mn}{m-n}$
(c) $\dfrac{n}{m-n}$ (d) $\dfrac{mn}{n-m}$

65. $\dfrac{\log_5 6}{\log_5 2+1}=$

(a) $\log_2 6$ (b) $\log_2 5$
(c) $\log_{10} 6$ (d) $\log_{10} 30$

66. If $x = \log_3 27$ and $y = \log_9 27$, then $\dfrac{1}{x}+\dfrac{1}{y}=$ ______.

(a) $\dfrac{1}{3}$ (b) $\dfrac{1}{9}$
(c) 3 (d) 1

67. If $\log_6 x + 2\log_{36} x + 3\log_{216} x = 9$, then $x =$ ______.

(a) 6 (b) 36
(c) 216 (d) None of these

68. If $\log_4 \log_3 |x| < 1$, then the region in which 'x' lies is

(a) $|x| > 9$ (b) $|x| > 81$
(c) $|x| < 81$ (d) $|x| < 9$

69. If $n = 1 \times 2 \times 3 \times \ldots.. 2019$, then find the value of $\dfrac{1}{\log_{2^{2019}} n}+\dfrac{1}{\log_{3^{2019}} n}+\ldots+\dfrac{1}{\log_{2019^{2019}} n}$.

(a) 2018 (b) 2019
(c) 2017 (d) None

AT

PRACTICE QUESTIONS JEE SPECIAL WING

Multiple-Answer Type Questions

Directions for questions 1 to 10:
Each question has FOUR options (a), (b), (c), and (d). ONE OR MORE THAN ONE of these four option(s) is/are the correct answer(s).

1. Which of the following logarithms is/are defined?
   (a) $\log_4 5$ (b) $\log_3 4$
   (c) $\log_2 3$ (d) $\log_1 2$

2. If the value of $\log_x 5$ is a negative real number, the value of x can be ________.
   (a) 0.2 (b) 0.3
   (c) 0.5 (d) 0.7

3. Which of the following is/are equivalent to $\log_{28} 784$?
   (a) $\log_4 5 \times \log_5 6 \times \log_6 7 \times \log_7 8 \times \ldots \times \log_{15} 16$
   (b) $2028^{\log_{2028} 2}$
   (c) $\log_{216} 36 + \log_{343} 49 + \log_{512} 64$
   (d) $\dfrac{1}{\log 10 - \log_{1296} 36}$

4. If x and y are two positive integers such that $\log_2\left(x^2 - y^2\right) = 5$, then which of the following can be the values of $x + y$?
   (a) 32 (b) 16
   (c) 8 (d) 4

5. If $\log_p 3 \times \log_{\frac{p}{3}} 3 = \log_{\left(\frac{p}{9}\right)^6} 3$, then which of the following is/are the values of p?
   (a) 3 (b) 9
   (c) 27 (d) 81

6. Which of the following is/are equal to $\dfrac{1}{\log_p pqr} + \dfrac{1}{\log_q pqr} + \dfrac{1}{\log_r pqr}$
   (a) $\log_{14} 15 \times \log_{15} 16 \times \log_{16} 14$
   (b) $11^{\log_{11} 1}$
   (c) $\log_{(24\times25)} 15 + \log_{(20\times30)} 40$
   (d) $\log_{(x-y)}\left(x^3 - y^3\right) - \log_{(x-y)}\left(x^2 + y^2 + xy\right)$

7. If $\log_2 \log_3 \log_6\left(x^2 - 9\right) = \log_3 \log_3 \log_3 27$, then which of the following is/are the value(s) of x?
   (a) −15 (b) −5
   (c) 5 (d) 15

8. Which of the following statements is/are true?
   (a) $\dfrac{1}{7} < \log_{100} 2 < \dfrac{1}{6}$ (b) $\dfrac{1}{5} < \log_{100} 3 < \dfrac{1}{4}$
   (c) $\dfrac{1}{4} < \log_{100} 5 < \dfrac{1}{3}$ (d) $\dfrac{1}{2} < \log_{100} 11 < 1$

9. If $\dfrac{1}{\log x} = \dfrac{2}{\log y} = \dfrac{3}{\log z}$, then which of the following statements is/are true?
   (a) $xy = z$ (b) $xz = y^2$
   (c) $yz = x^5$ (d) $xyz = 6$

10. If $\log 3 = 0.4771$, then which of the following statements are true?
    (a) An integral part of $\log 300$ is 2.
    (b) The decimal part of $\log 300$ is 4771.
    (c) $\log 0.003 = \bar{3}.4771$.
    (d) $\log\left(3 \times 10^{10}\right) = 10.4771$.

Match The Column

Directions for questions 11 to 15:
Read the paragraph given below and answer the questions.

$\log 2 = 0.3010$
$\log 3 = 0.4771$
$\log 5 = 0.6990$
$\log 7 = 0.8451$
$\log 11 = 1.0414$

Match the values in Column A with those in Column B.

Column A	Column B (Number of Digits in the Expansion)
11. 2^{250}	(a) 70
12. 3^{150}	(b) 71
13. 5^{105}	(c) 72
14. 7^{90}	(d) 73
15. 11^{70}	(e) 74
	(f) 75
	(g) 76
	(h) 77

Comprehension-Based Questions

Directions for questions 16 to 20:
Read the paragraph given below and answer the questions.

Given that :

$p = \log_2 199$
$q = \log_3 599$
$r = \log_{11} 999$
$s = \log_7 1999$
$t = \log_5 19999$

16. Which of the following is a negative number?
    (a) $p - r - s$ (b) $q + r - t$
    (c) $p + r - q - t$ (d) $p + q - s - t$

17. Which of the following is a positive number?
    (a) $t - p$ (b) $r - s$
    (c) $s - t$ (d) $q - r$

18. Which of the following is closer to 6?
    (a) p (b) q
    (c) r (d) s

19. Which of the following lies between 11 and 13?
    (a) $q + t$ (b) $r + s$
    (c) $s + t$ (d) $p + r$

20. Which of the following statements is true?
    (a) $p > q > t$ (b) $r > s > p$
    (c) $q > r > s$ (d) $p > t > r$

Assertion and Reason Type Questions

Directions for questions 21 to 25:
Read the options given below and answer the questions.

(a) Both assertion (A) and reason (R) are true, and the reason (R) is the correct explanation of the assertion (A).
(b) Both assertion (A) and reason (R) are true, and the reason (R) is not the correct explanation of the assertion (A).
(c) Assertion (A) is true, but reason (R) is false.
(d) Assertion (A) is false, and reason (R) is true.

21. **Assertion:** $\log_5 5 = \log_4 4 = \log_3 3 = \log_2 2 = \log_1 1$.
    Reason: $\log_a a$ where a is any positive real number other than 1.

22. **Assertion:** If $x^{\log_7 5} + 5^{\log_7 x} = 10$, then the number of possible values for x is only one.
    Reason: $a^{\log_b c} = c^{\log_b a}$.

23. **Assertion:** $\dfrac{\log_5 4}{\log_5 2} = 2$.
    Reason: $\dfrac{\log_b x}{\log_b y} = \dfrac{x}{y}$.

24. **Assertion:** $\log_5 3x > \log_5 (x+6)$ is true for all the real values of x more than 3.
    Reason: If $\log_c a > \log_c b$ and $c > 1$, then $a > b$.

25. **Assertion:** If $\log 2 = 0.3010$, then $\log 5 = 0.699$.
    Reason: $\log\left(\dfrac{a}{b}\right) = \log a - \log b$.

ANSWER KEYS

Crossword

Across

4. Mantissa 6. Napier 8. Ten 9. Negative 11. One 12. Positive

Down

1. Weak 6. Briggs 8. Characteristic 9. Strong 10. Three 11. Zero

Classroom Wing

Very Short Answer Type Questions

1. 13 2. $\frac{5}{3}$ 3. $\frac{15}{8}$ 4. $x + y$ 5. 1
6. $\log_2 2$ 7. 8 8. 0.6989 9. 2.4771 10. 1
11. 2 12. $\log_3 x + 2\log_3 y - 3\log_3 z$ 13. No
14. $\log_{0.1}(0.001) = 3$ 15. 1 16. $\log_a m$ 17. $\frac{8}{3}$ 18. 2.3222
19. 0.3370 20. 16.43 21. 9 22. 2

Short Answer Type Questions

24. 4 25. $\log\left(\frac{x^{1/3}z^{7/2}}{y^{8/5}}\right)$ 28. $\frac{1}{2}$ 29. $\log_5 25$ 30. 1.8751
31. $\log_6 18$ 33. $x = 1280$ 35. 13.45 36. 0.04158 37. 478

Essay Type Questions

38. $\frac{(\log_{50})^2}{\log_5 . \log_{10}}$ 39. 25 40. ABCD 41. 3 42. $\log \frac{a^{n(n+1)}}{b^{\frac{n(n+1)}{2}}}$
43. 1

Competition Wing

Level 1: Apply Your Concepts

1. 4 2. 1 3. 5 4. $\frac{1}{512}$ 5. 0.6990
6. (a) 7. (b) 8. (d) 9. (b) 10. (c)
11. (d) 12. (a) 13. (a) 14. (d) 15. (a)
16. (d) 17. (a) 18. (b) 19. (b) 20. (c)
21. (c) 22. (a) 23. (c) 24. (b) 25. (c)
26. (b) 27. (d) 28. (b) 29. (d) 30. (c)

Level 2: Review Your Concepts

31. (b)	32. (d)	33. (c)	34. (c)	35. (a)
36. (d)	37. (c)	38. (a)	39. (d)	40. (a)
41. (b)	42. (b)	43. (a)	44. (a)	45. (a)
46. (d)	47. (b)	48. (b)	49. (a)	50. (c)
51. (b)	52. (b)	53. (c)	54. (b)	

Level 3: Assess Your Concepts

55. (b)	56. (c)	57. (c)	58. (a)	59. (a)
60. (c)	61. (c)	62. (c)	63. (b)	64. (d)
65. (c)	66. (d)	67. (c)	68. (c)	69. (b)

JEE Special Wing

Multiple-Answer Type Questions

1. (a, b, c)	2. (a, b, c, d)	3. (a, b, c, d)	4. (a, b, c)	5. (c, d)
6. (a, b, c, d)	7. (a, d)	8. (a, b, d)	9. (a, b, c)	10. (a, b, c, d)

Match The Column

11. (g)	12. (c)	13. (e)	14. (h)	15. (d)

Comprehension-Based Questions

16. (c)	17. (d)	18. (b)	19. (a)	20. (d)

Assertion and Reason Type Questions

21. (d)	22. (a)	23. (c)	24. (a)	25. (a)

Hints and Explanations

Classroom Wing

Very Short Answer Type Questions

1. $3^{\log_3 7} + 5^{\log_5 6}$ $\left(\because a^{\log_a k} = k\right)$

$= 7 + 6 = 13$

2. $\log_{2\sqrt{2}} \sqrt{32} \;\; \log_{\sqrt{8}} \sqrt{32}$

$= \log_{8} 32$

$= \dfrac{5}{3} \log_2 2$

$= \dfrac{5}{3}$

3. Given, $\log_{\sqrt{k}} \sqrt{k\sqrt{k\sqrt{k\sqrt{k}}}} = \log_{k^{1/2}} k^{\frac{1}{2}+\frac{1}{4}+\frac{1}{8}+\frac{1}{16}}$

$= \log_{k^{1/2}} k^{15/16}$

$= \dfrac{\left(\dfrac{15}{16}\right)}{\left(\dfrac{1}{2}\right)} \log_k k$

$= \dfrac{15}{8}.$

4. $x = \log_5 3 \quad y = \log_5 8$

$\log_5 24 = \log_5 (3 \times 8)$

$= \log_5 3 + \log_5 8$

$= x + y$

5. $3^x = 2^y = 6$

$3^x = 6$	$2^y = 6$
$x = \log_3 6$	$y = \log_2 6$
$\dfrac{1}{x} = \log_6 3$	$\dfrac{1}{y} = \log_6 2$

$\dfrac{1}{x} + \dfrac{1}{y} = \log_6 3 + \log_6 2$

$\dfrac{x+y}{xy} = \log_6 6 = 1$

6. $\log_2 7 \log_3 5 \log_7 2 \log_5 3$

$= \dfrac{\log 7}{\log 2} \dfrac{\log 5}{\log 3} \dfrac{\log 2}{\log 7} \dfrac{\log 3}{\log 5}$

$= 1 = \log_2 2.$

7. $10^{\log_{10} 3} + 6^{\log_6 5} = 3 + 5 = 8.$

8. $\log_{10} 25 = 1.3979$

$\log_{10} 5^2 = 1.3979$

$2\log_{10} 5 = 1.3979$

$\log_{10} 5 = \dfrac{1.3979}{2} = 0.6989$

9. Given, $\log_{10} 3 = 0.4771$

$\log_{10} 300 = \log_{10} 3 + 2\log_{10} 10$

$= 0.4771 + 2$

$= 2.4771.$

10. $\log_y x \times \log_z y \times \log_x z$

$= \log_z x \times \log_x z = 1$

11. Antilog $(2.375) = x$

$\log x = 2.375$

So, characteristic is 2

12. $\log_3 \left[\dfrac{xy^2}{z^3}\right] = \log_3 x + \log_3 y^2 - \log_3 z^3$

$= \log_3 x + 2\log_3 y - 3\log_3 z$

13. No, because according to the identity

$\log \dfrac{A}{B} = \log A - \log B$

So, $\log_x \dfrac{a}{b} = \dfrac{\log_x a}{\log_x b}$

14. $(0.1)^3 = 0.001$

$(0.1) = \sqrt[3]{0.001}$

$\log_3 (0.001) = (0.1)$

15. $3 - \log_{10} 100$

$= 3 - \log_{10} 10^2$

$= 3 - 2\log_{10} 10$

$= 1$

16. $0 < a < 1$ and $m < n$

So $\log_a m$ is greater than $\log_a n$

17. $\log_{\sqrt{8}} 16$

$\log_{\sqrt{8}} 16 = x$

$16 = \left(\sqrt{8}\right)^x$

$2^4 = \left(2^3\right)^{\frac{x}{2}}$

$2^4 = 2^{\frac{3x}{2}}$

When bases are same powers are equal.

$4 = \frac{3x}{2}$

$x = \frac{8}{3}$

18. $\log 2 = 0.3010$, $\log 3 = 0.4771$ and $\log 7 = 0.8451$

$\log 210 = \log (7 \times 3 \times 10)$

$= \log 7 + \log 3 + \log 10$

$= 0.4771 + 0.8451 + 1$

$= 2.3222$

19. $\log_{10} (21.73) = 1.3371$

$21.73 = 10^{1.3370}$

Dividing both sides by 10:

$2.173 = 10^{1.3370 - 1}$

$\log (2.173) = 0.3370$

20. antilog $(0.2156) = 1.643$

$\log(1.643) = 0.2156$

$10 \times 1.643 = 10^{0.2156} \times 10$

$16.43 = 10^{1.2156}$

$\log_{10} (16.43) = 1.2156$

antilog $(1.2156) = 16.43$

21. $3 \log_3 27$

$3 \log_3 3^3$

$3 \times 3 \times \log_3 (3) = 9$

22. $\log_{0.6} \left(\frac{3^2}{5^2}\right) = x$

$2 \left(\frac{3}{5}\right)^2 = 0.6^x$

$(0.6)^2 = (0.6)^x$

$x = 2$

Short Answer Type Questions

23. $4 \log 2 + 2 \log 3 + \log 5 + \log 7$

$= \log 2^4 + \log 3^2 + \log 5 + \log 7$

$= \log (2^4 \times 3^2 \times 5 \times 7)$

$= \log (16 \times 9 \times 5 \times 7)$

$= \log (5040)$

Hence proved.

24. Let $\log_{2^{-1}} (0.0625) = x$

$\frac{0.0625}{10000} = 2^{-x}$

$\frac{625}{10000} = 2^{-x}$

$\frac{25}{400} = 2^{-x}$

$\frac{1}{16} = \frac{1}{2^x}$

$\Rightarrow \quad 2^x = 16$

$2^x = 2^4$

$x = 4$

25. $\frac{1}{3}\log x - \frac{8}{5}\log y + \frac{7}{2}\log z$

$= \log x^{\frac{1}{3}} - \log y^{\frac{8}{5}} + \log z^{\frac{7}{2}}$

$= \log \frac{x^{\frac{1}{3}} z^{\frac{7}{2}}}{y^{\frac{8}{5}}}$

26. $x^2 + y^2 = 25\, xy$

$2 \log(x + y) = 3 \log 3 + \log x + \log y$

$= \log (3^3 \times x \times y)$

$\log (x + y)^2 = \log 27\, xy \quad (1)$

$(x + y)^2 = x^2 + y^2 + 2xy$

$(x + y)^2 = 25\, xy + 2\, xy$

$= 27\, xy$

$\log (x + y)^2 = \log 27\, xy \quad (2)$

(1) and (2) $\Rightarrow$ Hence proved.

27. $x^2 + y^2 = z^2$

$\log_y (z + x) + \log_y (z - x) = 2$

$= \log_y ((z + x)(z - x))$

$= \log_y (z^2 - x^2)$

$= \log_y (y)^2$

$= 2 \log_y y$

$= 2$

Hence proved.

28. Given, $7^x = 8^y = 3136$

$7^x = 3136$	$8^y = 3136$
$x = \log_7 3136$	$y = \log_8 3136$

$$\frac{1}{x} + \frac{1}{y} = \log_{3136} 7 + \log_{3136} 8$$

$$= \log_{(56)^2} 56 = \frac{1}{2} = \log_{(56)} 56 = \frac{1}{2}$$

29. $\log_3 10 \log_2 25 \log_{10} 3 \log_5 2$

$$\frac{\log 10}{\log 3} \times \frac{2\log 5}{\log 2} \times \frac{\log 3}{\log 10} \times \frac{\log 2}{\log 5}$$

$= 2$

$= \log_5 25.$

30. $\log 2 = 0.3010$, $\log 3 = 0.4771$, $\log 7 = 0.8451$

$\log 10 = 1$

first here to find $\log (2 \times 5) = 1$

$\log 2 + \log 5 = 1$

$\log 5 = 1 - 0.3010$

$= 0.699$

$\log 75 = \log (5 \times 5 \times 3)$

$= 2 \log 5 + \log 3$

$= 2 (0.699) + .4771$

$= 1.8751$

31. $X = \log_3 2$

$$\frac{1}{x+1} = \frac{1}{\log_3 2 + 1} = \frac{1}{\log_3 2 + \log_3 3}$$

$$\frac{1}{\log_3 6} = \log_6 3$$

$$\frac{1}{x+1} + 1 = \log_6 3 + \log_6 6 = \log_6 18.$$

32. $2\left[\log \frac{35}{192} + \log \frac{114}{91} + \log \frac{13}{19}\right] + \log 48$

$$2\left[\log \frac{\cancel{35}^{\,5}}{\cancel{192}_{\,\cancel{96}\,32}} \times \frac{\cancel{114}^{\,\cancel{57}\,\cancel{3}}}{\cancel{91}_{\,\cancel{7}}} \times \frac{\cancel{13}}{\cancel{19}}\right] + \log 48$$

$$2 \log\left(\frac{5}{32}\right) + \log 48$$

$$\log\left[\frac{25 \times 48}{32 \times 32}\right] = \log\left[\frac{25 \times 24}{16 \times 32}\right]$$

$$= \log\left(\frac{25 \times 3}{4 \times 16}\right)$$

$$= \log\left(\frac{75}{64}\right)$$

Hence proved.

33. $\log x + \log 5 = 2 + \log 64$

$\log (5x) = \log (100 \times 64)$

$5x = 100 \times 64$

$x = 20 \times 64$

$x = 1280$

34. We know $x^6 - y^6 = z^6$

$\log_z [(x^2 - y^2)(x^2 + y^2 - xy)(x^2 + y^2 + xy)] = 6$

$(x^2 - y^2)(x^2 + y^2)^2 - x^2y^2 = z^6$

$(x^2 - y^2)(x^4 + y^4 + 2x^2y^2 - x^2y^2) = z^6$

$(x^2 - y^2)(x^4 + y^4 + x^2y^2) = z^6$

$x^6 + \cancel{x^2y^4} + \cancel{x^4y^2} - \cancel{x^4y^2} - y^6 - \cancel{x^2y^4} = z^6$

$\Rightarrow x^6 - y^6 = z^6$

Hence proved.

35. $\log \sqrt[4]{(32)^3} = \log x$

$$\log (32)^{\frac{3}{4}} = \log x$$

$$\log 2^{\frac{15}{4}} = \log x$$

$$x = 2^{\frac{15}{4}}$$

$x = 13.45$

36. $\sqrt{(0.12)^3} = x$

$\frac{3}{2}\log(0.12) = \log x$

antilog (–1.3812) = x =0.04158

37. log 3 = 0.4771

Digits in 3^{1000} = 477.1

Hence 477 + 1 digits.

So, 478 digits

Essay Type Questions

38. Given, $x = \log_5^{10}$

$\Rightarrow \frac{1}{x} = \log_{10}^{5}$

$x + \frac{1}{x} + 2 = (x+1) + \left(\frac{1}{x} + 1\right)$

$= \left(\log_5^{10} + \log_5^{5}\right) + \left(\log_{10}^{5} + \log_{10}^{10}\right)$

$= \log_5^{50} + \log_{10}^{50}$

$= \frac{\log_{50}}{\log_5} + \frac{\log_{50}}{\log_{10}}$

$= \log_{50}\left[\frac{1}{\log_5} + \frac{1}{\log_{10}}\right]$

$= \log_{50}\left[\frac{\log_5 + \log_{10}}{\log_5 \log_{10}}\right]$

$= \log_{50}\frac{\log_{50}}{\log_5 . \log_{10}} = \frac{(\log_{50})^2}{\log_5 . \log_{10}}$.

39. $a = b^{\frac{1}{3}} = c^{\frac{1}{5}} = d^{\frac{1}{7}} = e^{\frac{1}{9}}$

$\log_a a = \frac{1}{3}\log_a b = \frac{1}{5}\log_a c = \frac{1}{7}\log_a d = \frac{1}{9}\log_a e$

$\Rightarrow \log_a a + \log_a b + \log_a c + \log_a d + \log_a e$

$= 1 + 3 + 5 + 7 + 9$

$= 25$

40. $A = \log_9 6561 = \log_9 9^4 = 4$

$B = \log_{\sqrt{5}} 625 = \log_{\sqrt{5}}(\sqrt{5})^8 = 8$

$C = \log_{\sqrt{3}} 243 = \log_{\sqrt{3}}(\sqrt{3})^{10} = 10$

$D = \log_{\sqrt{2}} 256 = \log_{\sqrt{2}}(\sqrt{2})^{16} = 16$

So, $A < B < C < D$

41. $\log_y x - \log_y x^2 = 9(\log_x y)^2$

$\log_y x - \frac{2\log_y x}{3} = \frac{9}{(\log_y x)^2}$

Let $\log_y x$ = 'A'

$A - \frac{2A}{3} = \frac{9}{A^2}$

$\frac{A}{3} = \frac{9}{A^2}$

$A^3 = 27$

$A = 3$

$\Rightarrow \quad \log_y x = 3$

$x = y^3$

$9y = y^3$

$y^2 = 9$

$\Rightarrow \quad y = 3$

42. $\log\left[\frac{a^2}{b^1}\cdot\frac{a^4}{b^2}\cdot\frac{a^6}{b^3}\cdots\cdots\frac{a^{2n}}{b^n}\right]$

We know that

$a^2 \cdot a^4 \cdot a^6 \cdots\cdots a^{2n}$

$= a^{2+4+6\cdots\cdots 2n}$

$= \frac{a^{2[1+2+3\cdots n]}}{b^{[1+2+3+4\cdots n]}}$

Sum of $(1 + 2 \cdots n)$

$= n\frac{(n+1)}{2}$

$= \frac{a^{2\left(\frac{n(n+1)}{2}\right)}}{b^{\frac{n(n+1)}{2}}}$

43. Let $\frac{\log x}{y - z} = \frac{\log y}{z - x} = \frac{\log z}{x - y} = c$ (say)

$\Rightarrow \log x = c(y - z) \Rightarrow x \log x = cx(y - z)$

Similarly $\log y = c(z - x) \Rightarrow y \log y = cy(z - x)$

$\log z = c(x - y) \Rightarrow z \log z = cz(x - y)$

$\therefore x \log x + y \log y + z \log z = c\,(xy - zx + yz - xy + zx - yz) = 0$

$\Rightarrow \log(x^x \times y^y \times z^z) = 0$

$\therefore x^x \times y^y \times z^z = 1$

Competition Wing

Level 1: Apply Your Concepts

1. $5^{2\log_5 2} = 5^{\log_5 4}$

$x^{\log_a b} = b^{\log_a x}$

$= 4^{\log_5 5}$

$= (4)^1 = 4$

2. $\log_5 2 + \log_5 20 - \log_5 8$

$= \log_5 \left(\frac{2\times 20}{8}\right)$

$= \log_5 (5)$

$= 1$

3. $\frac{3+\log_{10}(10)^2}{\log_5 5} = \frac{3+2\log_{10} 10}{\log_5 5} = 3+2 = 5$

4. $3 = \log_2 x + 4\log_2 8$

$3 = \log_2 x + 4\log_2 2^3$

$3 = \log_2 x + \log_2 2^{12}$

$3 = \log_2 ((x)\cdot(2^{12}))$

$\Rightarrow 8 = 2^{12}x$

$x = \frac{2^3}{2^{12}} = 2^{-9} = \frac{1}{2^9} = \frac{1}{512}$

5. $\log_{10} 2 = 0.3010$

$\log_{10} 2 = \log_{10} (10)^{0.3010}$

$\log_{10} 2 = \log_{10} (2)^{0.3010} + \log_{10} (5)^{0.3010}$

$\log_{10} 2 = (0.3101)(\log_{10} 2) + (0.3010)(\log_{10} 5)$

$0.3101 = (0.3101)^2 + (0.3101)(\log_{10} 5)$

$1 = 0.3101 + \log_{10} 5$

$\log_{10} 5 = 1 - 0.3101$

$= 0.6990$

6. Logarithm is defined for only positive real numbers.

7. $\frac{1}{\log_a abc} + \frac{1}{\log_b abc} + \frac{1}{\log_c abc}$

$\log_{abc} a + \log_{abc} b + \log_{abc} c$

$\log_{abc} abc = 1$

8. $= \log_3 2.\log_4 3.\log_5 4.........\log_{2048} 2047$

$= \log_{2048} 2$

$= \log_{2^{11}} 2 = \frac{1}{11}\log_2 2 = \frac{1}{11}$

9. Base of a logarithm is a positive real number which is not equal to 1.

10. $c^2 - a^2 + b^2$

$\Rightarrow c^2 - b^2 = a^2$

$\frac{1}{\log_{c+b} a} + \frac{1}{\log_{c-b} a} = \log_a c+b+\log_a c-b$

$\log_a (c+b)(c-b) = \log_a c^2 - b^2$

$= \log_a a^2 = 2\log_a a = 2$

11. (i) $\log x - \log y - \log z = \log\left(\frac{x}{yx}\right)$

(ii) $\log M - \log N = \log\left(\frac{M}{N}\right)$ and $\log M + \log N = \log MN$.

12. (i) $\log_2 16 < \log_2 20 < \log_2 32$

(ii) Given four options are to be compared.

(iii) For example, $\log_2 16 < \log_2 20 < \log_2 32$
$\Rightarrow 4 < \log_2 20 < 5$.

(iv) $7 < 35 < 7^2$; $5^2 < 70 < 5^3$; $3^3 < 68 < 3^4$ Apply logarithms to suitable bases and evaluate $\log_7 15$, $\log_5 70$ and $\log_3 68$.

13. (i) Use the identity $\log m + \log n - \log p = \log mn/p$

(ii) Use $\log x + \log y = \log xy$ and $\log p - \log q = \log(p/q)$.

14. (i) Use the identity $\frac{\log a}{\log b} = \log_b a$

(ii) $\frac{\log x}{\log y} = 2 \Rightarrow \log_y x = 2$

(iii) $\log_b a = n \Rightarrow a = b^n$.

15. (i) Use $\log m - \log n = \log\frac{m}{n}$

(ii) Use $\log m - \log n = \log\frac{m}{n}$ and simplify LHS.

(iii) Write 1 as $\log_{10} 10$ and proceed.

16. (i) Use $\log m = \log n \Rightarrow m = n$.

(ii) Remove logarithms to set $(x + 4)^2 = 16$, then find x.

17. (i) Use $\log m = \log n \Rightarrow m = n$.

(ii) Use, $\log_b a = N \Rightarrow a = b^N$.

18. Apply laws of logarithms.

19. (i) $\log_b a^m = m\log_b a$ and $\log_a a = 1$

(ii) Express 81 as 3^4 and then use $\log a^m = m \log a$ and proceed until all the brackets are removed.

20. Find $\sqrt{14641}$.

21. Simplify the expression by applying laws of logarithms.

22. Apply laws of logarithm.

23. Apply laws of logarithm.

24. Find p and q.

25. Write 1024 as a power of 2.

26. Apply laws of logarithm.

27. Apply laws of logarithm.

28. (i) Recall the laws of logarithm.
(ii) Use $a\log_a N = N$ after simplifying the given term.

29. (i) Simplify and then use laws of logarithm.
(ii) Take LCM and simplify.
(iii) Use $\log_a x + \log_a y = \log_a xy$.

30. (i) Use $\log_a a = 1$ to find y and then substitute y value.
(ii) Write $x^2 - 6x + 9$ as $(x-3)^2$ and use $\log_a a = 1$.

Level 2: Review Your Concepts

31. Find the value of 16^{12} by applying logarithm.

32. $(64)^{\frac{5}{3}} = p^2$, give p = 32.

33. Apply laws of logarithm.

34. (i) Recall the laws of logarithm.
(ii) $p = \dfrac{\log a^y}{\log x^y}$. Use $\log p^q = q\log p$.

35. (i) Use the identities $\log mn = \log m + \log n$, $\log\dfrac{m}{n} = \log m - \log n$ and $\log x^n = n\log x$
(ii) $\log\left(\dfrac{\sqrt[3]{x^2}\cdot y}{\sqrt[5]{z^2}}\right) \log\left(\left(\dfrac{x^{2/3}\cdot y}{z^{2/5}}\right)\right)$
(iii) Use $\log\left(\dfrac{a}{b}\right) = \log a - \log b$ and $\log ab = \log a + \log b$ simplify.

36. (i) $\log x = 0 \Rightarrow x = 1$
(ii) $\log x = 0 \Rightarrow x = 1$
(iii) Use $\log_b a = \dfrac{1}{n}\log_b a$
(iv) $x = a\log n \Rightarrow a^x = n$.

37. Find x.

38. Apply laws of logarithm.

39. Find a.

40. Substitute the value of $a^{\log b}$.

41. Apply laws of logarithm.

42. (i) $\log(a) = \log(b) \Rightarrow a = b$
(ii) $\log(x+y) = \log xy$
(iii) $\Rightarrow x + y = xy$.

43. (i) $a^{\log b} = b^{\log a}$
(ii) $5^{\log 2} = 2^{\log 5}$
(iii) $a^m = a^n \Rightarrow m = n$.

44. (i) $a^{\log b} = b^{\log a}$
(ii) $x^m = x^n \Rightarrow m = n$.

45. Apply laws of logarithm and solve for x.

46. $\log_{49}3 \times \log_9 7 \times \log_2 8 = x$

$$\frac{\log 3}{2\log 7} \times \frac{\log 7}{2\log 3} \times \frac{3\log 2}{\log 2} = x$$

$$\frac{3}{4} = x \Rightarrow \frac{4x}{3} = \frac{4}{3} \times \frac{3}{4} = 1.$$

47. $\log_{a-b}(a^3 - b^3) - \log_{a-b} a^2 + ab + b^2$

$$= \log_{a-b}\left(\frac{a^3 - b^3}{a^2 + ab + b^2}\right)$$

$$= \log_{a-b}\frac{(a-b)(a^2+ab+b^2)}{(a^2+ab+b^2)}$$

$$= \log_{a-b}(a-b) = 1.$$

48. Given, $\log_3 2 = x$

$$\frac{\log_{10} 72}{\log_{10} 24} = \log_{24} 72 = \log_{24}(24 \times 3)$$

$$= \log_{24} 24 + \log_{24} 3 = 1 + \frac{\log 3}{\log 24}$$

$$= 1 + \frac{\log_3 3}{\log_3 24}$$

$$= 1 + \frac{1}{\log_3(3 \times 8)}$$

$$= 1 + \frac{1}{\log_3 3 + \log_3 8}$$

$$= 1 + \frac{1}{1 + \log_3 2^3}$$

$$= 1 + \frac{1}{1 + 3\log_3 2}$$

$$= \frac{1 + 3\log_3 2 + 1}{1 + 3\log_3 2} = \frac{2 + 3x}{1 + 3x}.$$

49. $\log\left(\frac{1}{2}\right)+\log\left(\frac{2}{3}\right)+\cdots+\log\left(\frac{99}{100}\right)$

$= \log 1-\log 2+\log 2-\log 3+\cdots + \log 99-\log 100$

$= \log 1-\log 100 = 0-\log 10^2$

$= -2\log 10 = -2.$

50. Given $x^2 - y^2 = 1$

Applying log on both the sides, we get,

$(x^2 - y^2) = \log 1$

$\Rightarrow \log[(x + y)(x - y)] = 0$

$\Rightarrow \log(x + y) + \log(x - y) = 0$

$\Rightarrow \log(x + y) = -\log(x - y)$

$\frac{\log(x+y)}{\log(x-y)} = -1$

$\Rightarrow \log_{(x-y)}(x + y) = -1.$

51. $3^{\log_3 5} + 5^{\log_x 3} = 8$

$\Rightarrow 5+5^{\log_x 3} = 8$

$\Rightarrow 5^{\log_x 3} = 3$

$3^{\log_x 5} = 3$

$\Rightarrow \log_x 5 = 1$

$\Rightarrow x = 5.$

52. As $\log_2 1 = 0$, $\log_2 1 \cdot \log_3 2 \cdot \log_4 3 \ldots \log_{199} 200 = 0$

53. Given $x^2 + y^2 - 3xy = 0$

$x^2 + y^2 - 2xy = xy$

Applying log on both sides,

$\log(x - y)^2 = \log xy$

$2\log(x - y) = \log xy$

$\Rightarrow \frac{\log(x-y)}{\log xy} = \frac{1}{2}$

$\Rightarrow \log_{xy}(x - y) = \frac{1}{2}.$

54. Let $x = 3^{100}$

$\Rightarrow \log x = \log 3^{100}$

$\Rightarrow \log x = 100 \log 3$

$\Rightarrow \log x = 100\ (0.4771)$

$\Rightarrow \log x = 47.71$

The characteristic is 47

The number of digits in 3^{100} is 48.

Level 3: Assess Your Concepts

55. Apply laws of logarithm.

56. (i) $\log_a x = b \Rightarrow a^b = x.$

(ii) Write $\sqrt{x^2-14x+49} = 16+1 = 17$ and solve for x.

(iii) Then verify for what values of x, $\log f(x)$ is defined.

57. (i) Find the value of p, q, r then find pqr.

(ii) Express p, q, and r in terms of k.

(iii) Substitute the above values in $pqr = 100$ and find k.

58. (i) Apply laws of logarithm.

(ii) Use $\log\left(\frac{a}{b}\right) = \log a - \log b$ and $\log a^m = m\log a$.

59. $\frac{1}{1+\log_{ab} c} = \frac{1}{\log_{ab} ab+\log_{ab} c} = \frac{1}{\log_{ab} abc}$

$= \log_{abc} ab \quad \frac{1}{1+\log_{ac} b} = \frac{1}{\log_{ac} ac+\log_{ac} b}$

$= \frac{1}{\log_{ac} abc} = \log_{abc} ac \quad \frac{1}{1+\log_{bc} a} +$

$\frac{1}{\log_{bc} bc+\log_{bc} a} = \frac{1}{\log_{bc} abc} \log_{abc} bc$

Hence, the value of the required expression.

$= \log_{abc} ab + \log_{abc} ac + \log_{abc} bc$

$= \log_{abc}[(ab)(ac)(bc)] = \log_{abc}(abc)^2 = 2.$

60. Given that, $x^2 + y^2 = z^2$

$\Rightarrow z^2 - x^2 = y^2 \qquad (1)$

$\therefore \frac{1}{\log_{z+x} y} + \frac{1}{\log_{(z-x)} y}$

$= \log_y(z + x) + \log_y(z - x)$

$= \log_y(z^2 - x^2) = \log_y y^2$ {from (1)}

$= 2.$

61. Let $x = 2^{1024}$

$\Rightarrow \log x = \log 2^{1024}$

$= 1024 \log 2 = 1024(0.301)$

$\Rightarrow \log x = 308.22$

$\Rightarrow$ The characteristic is 308

$\therefore$ The number of digits in 2^{1024} is 309.

62. Given $x^2 - y^2 = 1$

Applying log on both the sides, we get $\log(x^2 - y^2) = \log 1$

$\Rightarrow \log[(x+y)(x-y)] = 0$

$\Rightarrow \log(x+y) + \log(x-y) = 0$

$\Rightarrow \log(x+y) = -\log(x-y)$

$$\frac{\log(x+y)}{\log(x-y)} = -1$$

$\Rightarrow \log_{(x-y)}(x+y) = -1.$

63. $2^{\log_3 9} + 25^{\log_9 3} = 8^{\log_x 9}$

$\Rightarrow 2^{\log_3 3^2} + 25^{\log_{3^2} 3} = 8^{\log_x 9}$

$\Rightarrow 2^2 + 25^{1/2} = 8^{\log_x 9}$

$\Rightarrow 9 = 8^{\log_x 9}$

$\Rightarrow \log_x 9 = \log_8 9$

$\Rightarrow x = 8.$

64. $\log_a x = m$, $\log_b x = n$

$$\log_{\left(\frac{a}{b}\right)} x = \frac{\log x}{\log\left(\frac{a}{b}\right)} = \frac{\log_x x}{\log_x\left(\frac{a}{b}\right)}$$

$$= \frac{1}{\log_x a - \log_x b}$$

$$= \frac{1}{\frac{1}{\log_x a} - \frac{1}{\log_b x}}$$

$$= \frac{1}{\frac{1}{m} - \frac{1}{n}} = \frac{1}{\left(\frac{n-m}{mn}\right)} = \frac{mn}{n-m}.$$

65. $$\frac{\log_5 6}{\log_5 2 + 1} = \frac{\log_5 6}{\log_5 2 + \log_5 5} = \frac{\log_5 6}{\log_5(2\times 5)}$$

$$= \frac{\log_5 6}{\log_5 10} \log_{10} 6.$$

66. $x = \log_3 27$ | $y = \log_9 27$

$\Rightarrow x = \log_3 3^3$ | $y = \log_{3^2} 3^3$

$\Rightarrow x = 3$ | $y = \frac{3}{2}$

$$\therefore \frac{1}{x} + \frac{1}{y} = \frac{1}{3} + \frac{1}{\left(\frac{3}{2}\right)} = \frac{1}{3} + \frac{2}{3} + \frac{3}{3} = 1.$$

67. $\log_6 x + 2\log_{36} x + 3\log_{216} x = 9$

$\Rightarrow \log_6 x + \log_6 x + \log_6 x = 9$

$\Rightarrow 3\log_6 x = 9 \Rightarrow \log_6 x = 3$

$\Rightarrow x = 6^3$

$\therefore x = 216.$

68. $\log_4 (\log_3 |x|) < 1$

$\Rightarrow \log_4 (\log_3 |x|) < \log_4 4$

$\Rightarrow \log_3 |x| < 4$

$\Rightarrow \log_3 |x| < \log_3 3^4$

$\Rightarrow |x| < 3^4 \Rightarrow |x| < 81.$

69. $$\frac{1}{\log_{2^{2019}} n} + \frac{1}{\log_{3^{2019}} n} + \ldots + \frac{1}{\log_{2019^{2019}} n}.$$

$= \log_n 2^{2019} + \log_n 3^{2019} + \log_n 4^{2019} + \ldots \log_n 2019^{2019}$

$= \log_n(2 \times 3 \times 4 \times 5 \ldots\ldots\ldots\ldots \times 2019)^{2019}$

$= \log_n n^{2019} = 2019.$

JEE Special Wing

Multiple-Answer Type Questions

1. Logarithms are defined only for positive real numbers and positive bases different from 1.

Hence, $\log_4 5$, $\log_3 4$ and $\log_2 3$ are defined.

Also, $\log_1 2$ is not defined as the base is 1.

Hence, choice (a, b, c) follow.

2. Let $\log_x 5 = a$, where a is a negative number.

Also let $-a = b$.

$\Rightarrow x^a = 5$

$\Rightarrow \frac{1}{x^b} = 5$, where b is a positive number.

So, $0 < x < 1$.

Hence, choice (a, b, c, d) follow.

3. $\log_{28} 784 = \log_{28} (28)^2 = 2$.

Going by options:

(a) $\log_4 5 \times \log_5 6 \times \log_6 7 \times \log_7 8 \times \ldots \times \log_{15} 16$

$= \frac{\log 5 \times \log 6 \times \log 7 \times \log 8 \times \ldots \times \log 16}{\log 4 \times \log 5 \times \log 6 \times \log 7 \times \ldots \times \log 15}$

$= \frac{\log 16}{\log 4}$

$= \log_4 16$

$= \log_4 4^2$

$= 2 \times \log_4 4 = 2$.

(b) $2028^{\log_{2028} 2} = 2$. $\left(\text{Since } a^{\log_a N} = N\right)$

(c) $\log_{216} 36 + \log_{343} 49 + \log_{512} 64$

$= \log_{6^3} 6^2 + \log_{7^3} 7^2 + \log_{8^3} 8^2$

$= \frac{2}{3} \times \log_6 6 \times \frac{2}{3} \times \log_7 7 \times \frac{2}{3} \times \log_8 8$

$= \frac{2}{3} + \frac{2}{3} + \frac{2}{3} = \frac{6}{3} = 2$.

(d) $\frac{1}{\log 10 - \log_{1296} 36} = \frac{1}{1 - \log_{36^2} 36^1}$

$= \frac{1}{1 - \frac{1}{2}}$

$= \frac{1}{\frac{1}{2}} = 2$.

Hence, choice (a, b, c, d) follow.

4. Given that x and y are two positive integers such that $\log_2 \left(x^2 - y^2\right) = 5$.

$\Rightarrow x^2 - y^2 = 2^5$

$\Rightarrow (x + y)(x - y) = 32$, where x and y are positive integers.

Also, $x > y$.

So, $x + y$ must be more than $x - y$.

Hence, $x + y$ can be 32, 16, 8.

Hence, choice (a, b, c) follow.

5. Given that $\log_p 3 \times \log_{\frac{p}{3}} 3 = \log_{\left(\frac{p}{9}\right)^6} 3$

$\Rightarrow \frac{1}{\log_3 p \times \log_3 \frac{p}{3}} = \frac{1}{\log_3 \left(\frac{p}{9}\right)^6}$

$\Rightarrow \frac{1}{\log_3 p \times (\log_3 p - \log_3 3)} = \frac{1}{6 \times (\log_3 p - \log_3 9)}$

$\Rightarrow \frac{1}{\log_3 p \times (\log_3 p - 1)} = \frac{1}{6 \times \left(\log_3 p - \log_3 3^2\right)}$

$\Rightarrow \frac{1}{\log_3 p \times (\log_3 p - 1)} = \frac{1}{6 \times (\log_3 p - 2)}$

Let $\log_3 p$ be x.

The above equation becomes $\frac{1}{x \times (x - 1)} = \frac{1}{6 \times (x - 2)}$

$\Rightarrow x \times (x - 1) = 6 \times (x - 2)$

$\Rightarrow x^2 - x = 6x - 12$

$\Rightarrow x^2 - 7x + 12 = 0$

$\Rightarrow x^2 - 3x - 4x + 12 = 0$

$\Rightarrow x(x - 3) - 4(x - 3) = 0$

$\Rightarrow (x - 3)(x - 4) = 0$.

$\Rightarrow x = 3$ (or) $x = 4$.

$\Rightarrow \log_3 p = 3$ (or) $\log_3 p = 4$.

$\Rightarrow p = 3^3 = 27$ (or) $p = 3^4 = 81$

Hence, choice (c and d) follow.

6. $\frac{1}{\log_p pqr} + \frac{1}{\log_q pqr} + \frac{1}{\log_r pqr}$

$= \log_{pqr} p + \log_{pqr} q + \log_{pqr} r$

$= \log_{pqr} pqr = 1$.

Going by options:

(a) $\log_{14} 15 \times \log_{15} 16 \times \log_{16} 14$.

$= \frac{\log 15 \times \log 16 \times \log 14}{\log 14 \times \log 15 \times \log 16} = 1$

(b) $11^{\log_{11} 1} = 11^0 = 1.$

(c) $\log_{(24\times25)} 15 + \log_{(20\times30)} 40$

$= \log_{(600)} 15 + \log_{(600)} 40$

$= \log_{(600)} (15\times 40) = \log_{(600)} (600) = 1.$

(d) $\log_{(x-y)} (x^3 - y^3) - \log_{(x-y)} (x^2 + y^2 + xy)$

$= \log_{(x-y)} \dfrac{(x^3 - y^3)}{(x^2 + y^2 + xy)}$

$= \log_{(x-y)} \dfrac{(x^2 + y^2 + xy)(x - y)}{(x^2 + y^2 + xy)}$

$= \log_{(x-y)} (x - y) = 1.$

Hence, choice (a, b, c, d) follow.

7. Given that $\log_2 \log_3 \log_6 (x^2 - 9) = \log_3 \log_3 \log_3 27.$

$\Rightarrow \log_2 \log_3 \log_6 (x^2 - 9) = \log_3 \log_3 \log_3 3^3$

$\Rightarrow \log_2 \log_3 \log_6 (x^2 - 9) = \log_3 \log_3 3$

$\Rightarrow \log_2 \log_3 \log_6 (x^2 - 9) = \log_3 1$

$\Rightarrow \log_2 \log_3 \log_6 (x^2 - 9) = 0$

$\Rightarrow \log_3 \log_6 (x^2 - 9) = 2^0$

$\Rightarrow \log_3 \log_6 (x^2 - 9) = 1$

$\Rightarrow \log_6 (x^2 - 9) = 3^1$

$\Rightarrow \log_6 (x^2 - 9) = 3$

$\Rightarrow x^2 - 9 = 6^3$

$\Rightarrow x^2 = 225$

$\Rightarrow x = \pm 15$

Hence, choice (a and d) follow.

8. Going by options:

(a) We know that $128 > 100 > 64$

$\Rightarrow 2^6 > 100 > 2^7$

$\Rightarrow \log_2 2^7 > \log_2 100 > \log_2 2^6$

$\Rightarrow 7 > \log_2 100 > 6$

$\Rightarrow \dfrac{1}{7} < \log_{100} 2 < \dfrac{1}{6}.$

(b) We know that $243 > 100 > 81$

$\Rightarrow 3^5 > 100 > 3^4$

$\Rightarrow \log_3 3^5 > \log_3 100 > \log_3 3^4$

$\Rightarrow 5 > \log_3 100 > 4$

$\Rightarrow \dfrac{1}{5} < \log_{100} 3 < \dfrac{1}{4}.$

(c) We know that $125 > 100 > 25$

$\Rightarrow 5^3 > 100 > 5^2$

$\Rightarrow \log_5 5^3 > \log_5 100 > \log_5 5^2$

$\Rightarrow 3 > \log_5 100 > 2$

$\Rightarrow \dfrac{1}{3} < \log_{100} 5 < \dfrac{1}{2}.$

(d) We know that $121 > 100 > 11$

$\Rightarrow 11^6 > 100 > 11^7$

$\Rightarrow \log_{11} 11^7 > \log_{11} 100 > \log_{11} 11^6$

$\Rightarrow 2 > \log_2 100 > 1$

$\Rightarrow \dfrac{1}{2} < \log_{100} 2 < 1.$

Hence, choice (a, b, d) follow.

9. Let $\dfrac{1}{\log x} = \dfrac{2}{\log y} = \dfrac{3}{\log z} = k.$

$\Rightarrow \log x = \dfrac{1}{k}$, $\log y = \dfrac{2}{k}$ and $\log z = \dfrac{3}{k}$

(a) $\log x + \log y = \dfrac{1}{k} + \dfrac{2}{k}$

$\Rightarrow \log xy = \dfrac{3}{k}$

$\Rightarrow \log xy = \log z \Rightarrow xy = z.$

(b) $\log x + \log z = \dfrac{1}{k} + \dfrac{3}{k}$

$\Rightarrow \log xz = \dfrac{4}{k}$

$\Rightarrow \log xz = 2 \times \dfrac{2}{k}$

$\Rightarrow \log xz = 2 \times \log y \Rightarrow xz = y^2.$

(c) $\log y + \log z = \dfrac{2}{k} + \dfrac{3}{k}$

$\Rightarrow \log yz = \dfrac{5}{k}$

$\Rightarrow \log yz = 5 \times \dfrac{1}{k}$

$\Rightarrow \log yz = 5 \times \log x \Rightarrow yz = x^5.$

(d) $\log x + \log y + \log z = \dfrac{1}{k} + \dfrac{2}{k} + \dfrac{3}{k}$

$\Rightarrow \log xyz = \dfrac{6}{k}$

$\Rightarrow xyz = (10)^{\frac{6}{k}} \neq 1.$

Hence, choice (a, b, c) follow.

10. Given that $\log 3 = 0.4771.$

As 300 has three digits, $\log 300 = 2.4771.$

An integral part of $\log 300$ is 2.

The decimal part of $\log 300$ is 4771.

As 0.003 has two zeroes between the decimal point and non-zero number,
$\log 0.003 = \bar{3}.4771$.
As 3×10^{10} has eleven digits, $\log\left(3\times10^{10}\right) = 10.4771$.
Hence, choice (a, b, c, d) follow.

Match The Column

Common Solutions for questions 11 to 15:

Given that:
$\log 2 = 0.301$
$\log 3 = 0.4771$
$\log 5 = 0.699$
$\log 7 = 0.8451$
$\log 11 = 1.0414$

11. $\log 2^{250} = 250\times\log 2$
$= 250\times0.301 = 75.25$
$\therefore$ The number of digits in the expansion of 2^{250} is $75 + 1 = 76$.
Hence, the correct option is (g).

12. $\log 3^{150} = 150\times\log 3$
$= 150\times0.4771 = 71.565$
$\therefore$ The number of digits in the expansion of 2^{250} is $71 + 1 = 72$.
Hence, the correct option is (c).

13. $\log 5^{105} = 105\times\log 5$
$= 105\times0.699 = 73.395$
$\therefore$ The number of digits in the expansion of 5^{105} is $73 + 1 = 74$.
Hence, the correct option is (e).

14. $\log 7^{90} = 90\times\log 7$
$= 90\times0.8451 = 76.059$
$\therefore$ The number of digits in the expansion of 7^{90} is $76 + 1 = 77$.
Hence, the correct option is (h).

15. $\log 11^{70} = 70\times\log 11$
$= 70\times1.0414 = 72.898$
$\therefore$ The number of digits in the expansion of 11^{70} is $72 + 1 = 73$.
Hence, the correct option is (d).

Comprehension-Based Questions

Common Solutions for questions 16 to 20:

Given that:
$p = \log_2 199$
$q = \log_3 599$
$r = \log_{11} 999$
$s = \log_7 1999$
$t = \log_5 19999$

(i) We know that $128 < 199 < 256 \Rightarrow 2^7 < 199 < 2^8$
$\Rightarrow \log_2 2^7 < \log_2 199 < \log_2 2^8$
$\Rightarrow 7 < \log_2 199 < 8 \Rightarrow 7 < p < 8$.

(ii) We know that $243 < 599 < 729 \Rightarrow 3^5 < 599 < 3^6$
$\Rightarrow \log_3 3^5 < \log_3 599 < \log_3 3^6$
$\Rightarrow 5 < \log_3 599 < 6 \Rightarrow 5 < q < 6$.

(iii) We know that $121 < 999 < 1131 \Rightarrow 11^2 < 999 < 11^3$
$\Rightarrow \log_{11} 11^2 < \log_{11} 999 < \log_{11} 11^3$
$\Rightarrow 2 < \log_{11} 999 < 3 \Rightarrow 2 < r < 3$.

(iv) We know that $343 < 1999 < 2401 \Rightarrow 7^3 < 1999 < 7^4$
$\Rightarrow \log_7 7^3 < \log_7 1999 < \log_7 7^4$
$\Rightarrow 3 < \log_7 1999 < 4 \Rightarrow 3 < s < 4$.

(v) We know that $15625<19999<78125 \Rightarrow 5^6 < 19999 < 5^7$
$\Rightarrow \log_5 5^6 < \log_5 19999 < \log_5 5^7$
$\Rightarrow 6 < \log_5 19999 < 7 \Rightarrow 6 < t < 7$.
So, $p > t > q > s > r$.

16. Going by options:
(a) $p - r - s = p - (r + s) > 0$
(Since $7 < p < 8$ and $5 < (r + s) < 7$)
(b) $q + r - t > 0$ (Since $7 < q + r < 9$ and $6 < t < 7$)
(c) $p + r - q - t = p + r - (q + t) < 0$
(Since $9 < p + r < 11$ and $11 < (q + t) < 13$)
(d) $p + b - s - t = p + q - (s + t) > 0$
(Since $12 < (p + q) < 11$ and $9 < s + t < 11$)
Hence, the correct option is (c).

17. Going by options:
(a) $t - p < 0$ (Since $6 < t < 7$ and $7 < p < 8$)
(b) $r - s < 0$ (Since $2 < r < 3$ and $3 < s < 4$)
(c) $s - t < 0$ (Since $3 < s < 4$ and $6 < t < 7$)
(d) $q - r > 0$ (Since $5 < q < 6$ and $2 < r < 3$)
Hence, the correct option is (D).

18. We have:
$7 < p < 8$
$5 < q < 6$
$2 < r < 3$
$3 < s < 4$
Among p, q, r and s, q is closer to 6.
Hence, the correct option is (b).

19. We have:
$7 < p < 8$
$5 < q < 6$

$2 < r < 3$
$3 < s < 4$
$6 < t < 7$
Going by options: $11 < q + t < 13$
$5 < r + s < 7$
$9 < s + t < 11$
$9 < p + r < 11$
Hence, $q + t$ lies between 11 and 13.
Hence, the correct option is (a).

20. We have So, $p > t > q > s > r$.
So, $p > t > r$ is a true statement.
Hence, the correct option is (d).

Assertion and Reason Type Questions

Solutions for questions 21 to 25:

21. Assertion: $\log_5 5 = \log_4 4 = \log_3 3 = \log_2 2 = 1$.
And $\log_1 1$ is not defined.
So, Assertion is false.
Reason: $\log_a a$ where a is any positive real number other than 1.
Reason is true.
Hence, the correct option is (d).

22. Assertion: Given that $x^{\log_7 5} + 5^{\log_7 x} = 10$.
$5^{\log_7 x} + 5^{\log_7 x} = 10$ (Since $a^{\log_b c} = c^{\log_b a}$)
$2 \times 5^{\log_7 x} = 10$
$5^{\log_7 x} = 5$
$\log_7 x = 1$
$x = 7$.
So, Assertion is true.
Reason: $a^{\log_b c} = c^{\log_b a}$
Reason is true, and is the correct explanation to Assertion.
Hence, the correct option is (a).

23. Assertion: $\dfrac{\log_5 4}{\log_5 2} = \dfrac{\frac{\log 4}{\log 5}}{\frac{\log 2}{\log 5}}$
$= \dfrac{\log 4}{\log 2}$
$= \log_2 4$
$= \log_2 2^2 = 2.$
So, Assertion is true.
Reason: $\dfrac{\log_b x}{\log_b y} = \dfrac{\log x}{\log y}$.
So, Reason is false.
Hence, the correct option is (c).

24. Assertion: Given that $\log_5 3x > \log_5 (x+6)$.
$3x > x + 6$
$2x > 6$
$x > 3$.
So, Assertion is true.
Reason: If $\log_c a > \log_c b$ and $c > 1$, then $a > b$.
Reason is true, and is the correct explanation to Reason.
Hence, the correct option is (a).

25. Assertion: $\log 5 = \log\left(\dfrac{10}{2}\right)$
$= \log 10 - \log 2 \quad \because \left(\log\left(\dfrac{a}{b}\right) = \log a - \log b\right)$
$= 1 - 0.3010 = 0.699.$
So, Assertion is true.
Reason: $\log\left(\dfrac{a}{b}\right) = \log a - \log b$.
Reason is true, and is the correct explanation to Assertion.
Hence, the correct option is (a).

CHAPTER 9

Geometry

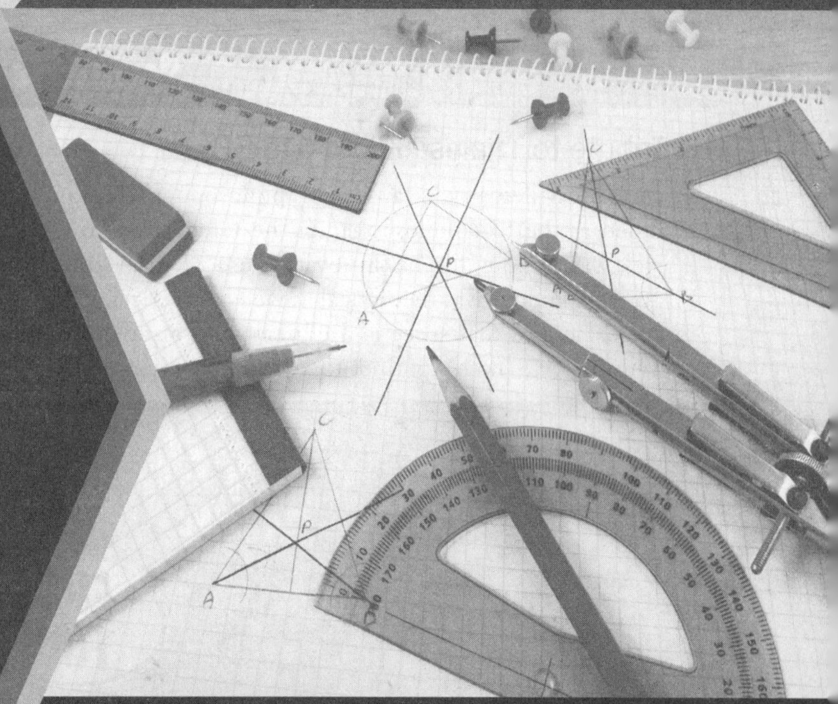

Remember

Before beginning this chapter, you should be able to:

- State the simple definitions on plane, lines, angles, etc.
- Use the constructions of plane figures

Key Ideas

After completing this chapter, you should be able to:

- State the axioms and postulates
- Know different types of angles, like adjacent, linear pair, vertically opposite, complementary, and supplementary angles
- Review triangles, their types, properties, and congruency
- Know types, properties of quadrilaterals
- Know some theorems on triangles, like mid-point theorem, basic proportionality theorem
- Understand Pythagoras's theorem and its converse
- Construct polygons, triangles, quadrilaterals, and circles

Scientific Crypt

A Tribute to Thales (625 to 546 BC)

Thales of Miletus was a Greek philosopher. He is regarded as the first philosopher in the Greek tradition. Thales was famous for his innovative use of geometry. His understanding was theoretical as well as practical. For instance, he said that space is the greatest, as it contains everything. He used to find the heights of pyramids by using the knowledge of similar triangles and right triangles. He concluded that at that time of the day when his own shadow was equal to his height, the length of the shadow of a pyramid was also equal to the height of the pyramid.

FUN TIME

CROSSWORD

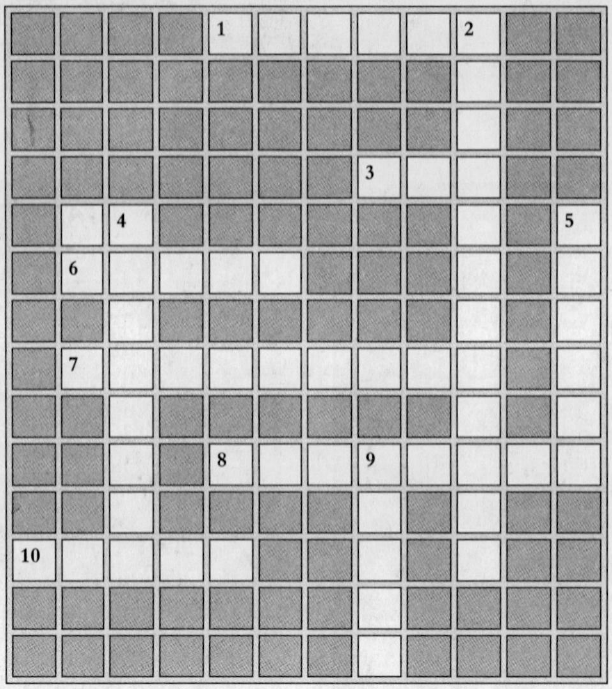

Across

1. A quadrilateral in which the opposite angles are supplementary.
3. The part of a circle.
6 The largest angle subtended by a chord of a circle on the circumference of the circle.
7. It is a cyclic parallelogram.
8. The locus of a point which is equidistant from the sides of a triangle.
10. The number of points required to construct a unique circle.

Down

2. The point of concurrence of the perpendicular bisectors of sides of a triangle.
4. The locus of a point in a plane which equidistant from the arms of an angle is ___ of the angle.
5. For all triangles, the incentre lies in its
9. Angles in the same segment.

INTRODUCTION

We will learn the definitions of a point, line, collinear points, and angles. We will also learn the properties of parallel lines and construction related to lines and angles. Further, we will discuss the types of triangles, concurrent lines, properties of triangles, similarity and congruence of triangles. In addition to the constructions of triangles, we will also focus on various types of quadrilaterals as well as other polygons. Finally, we will revise the definition of a circle and study the theorems based on chords and angles. We will conclude with the constructions of circles. Let us begin with some basic concepts.

Line

A line is a set of infinite points. It has no end points. It is infinite in length. Figure 9.1 shows line l that extends to infinity on either side. If A and B are any two points on l, we denote line l as $\overleftrightarrow{AB}$, read as line AB.

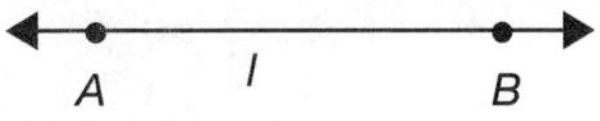

Figure 9.1

Info Bytes!

A line has infinite length.

Line Segment

A line segment is a part of a line. The line segment has two end points and it has a finite length.

In Fig. 9.2, AB is a line segment. It is a part of line l, consisting of the points A, B and all points between A and B. Line segment AB is denoted as $\overline{AB}$. A and B are the end points of AB.

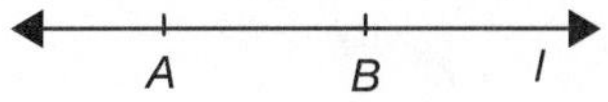

Figure 9.2

Ray

A ray has one end point and it extends infinitely on the other side.

In Fig. 9.3, AP is a ray which has only one end point A. A ray with end point A is denoted as $\overrightarrow{AP}$ which is different from $\overrightarrow{AP}$ (but $\overline{AP}$ is similar to $\overline{QA}$). If A lies between P and Q, $\overrightarrow{AP}$ and $\overrightarrow{AQ}$ are said to be opposite rays.

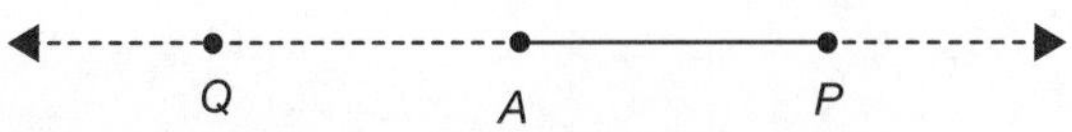

Figure 9.3

Collinear Points

Three or more points lying on the same line are collinear points.

Coplanar Lines

Two or more lines lying in a plane are coplanar lines.

Intersecting Lines

Two lines which have a common point are known as intersecting lines. In Fig. 9.4, l_1 and l_2 are intersecting lines.

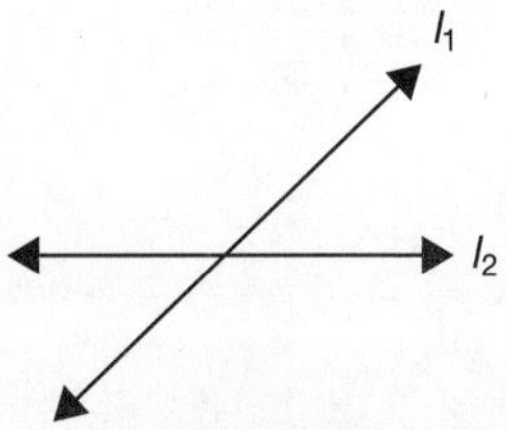

Figure 9.4

Concurrent Lines

Three or more lines passing through a common point are known as concurrent lines.

Angle

Two rays which have a common end point form an angle.

In Fig.9.5, $\overrightarrow{OQ}$ and $\overrightarrow{OP}$ are two rays which have O as the common end point and an angle with a certain measure is formed. The point O is called the vertex of the angle and $\overrightarrow{OQ}$ and $\overrightarrow{OP}$ are called the sides or arms of the angle. We denote this angle as $\angle QOP$ or $\angle POQ$ (or sometimes as $\angle O$). We observe that $\angle QOP = \angle POQ$ (These are two ways of representing the same angle). Angles are measured in a unit called degrees. This unit is denoted by a small circle placed above and to the right of the number. Thus $x°$ is read as x degrees.

The angle formed by two opposite rays is called a straight angle. We define the unit of degree such that the measure of a straight angle is 180°.

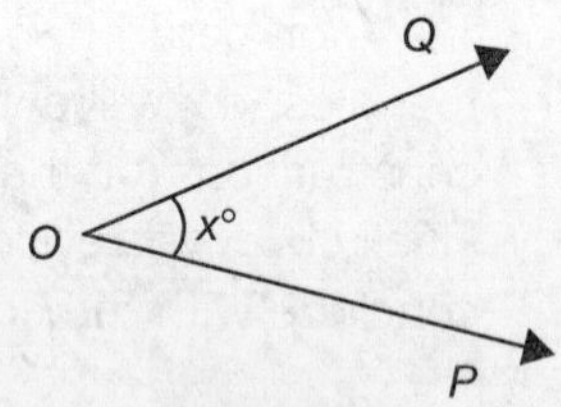

Figure 9.5

Types of Angles

Let the measure of an angle be x.

1. If $0° < x < 90°$, then x is called an **acute angle**.

Example:

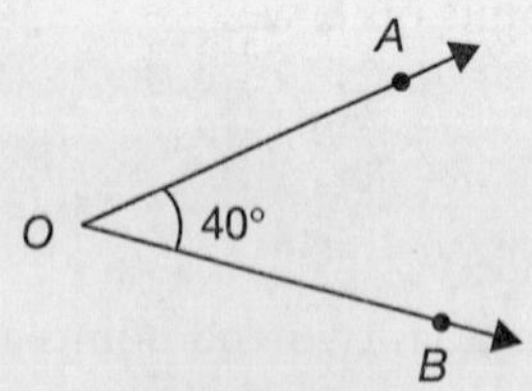

Figure 9.6

In the figure given above (Fig.9.6), $\angle AOB$ is an acute angle.

2. If $x = 90°$, then x is called a **right angle**.

Example:

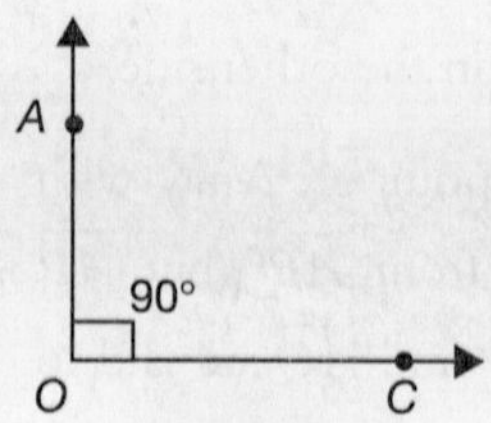

Figure 9.7

In the figure given above (Fig.9.7), $\angle AOC$ is a right angle.

3. If $90° < x < 180°$, then x is called an **obtuse angle**.

Example:

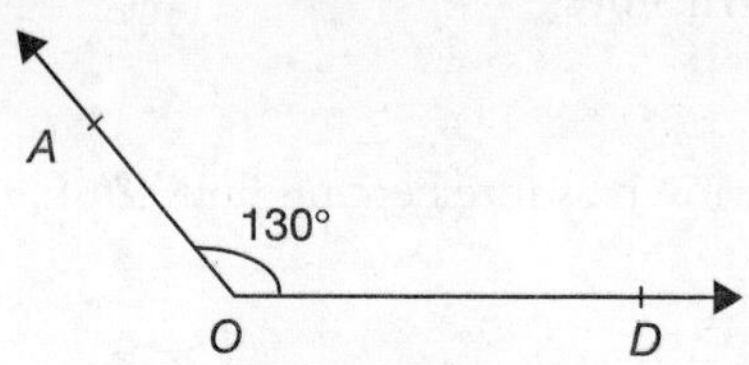

Figure 9.8

In the figure given above (Fig.9.8), $\angle AOD$ is an obtuse angle.

Info Bytes!

- The word "angle" comes from the Latin word "angulus", which means "a corner".
- The largest angle ever measured in a scientific experiment is that of the curvature of spacetime around a black hole, which can approach 180° but never quite reaches it.

4. If $x = 180°$, then it is the **angle of a straight line**.

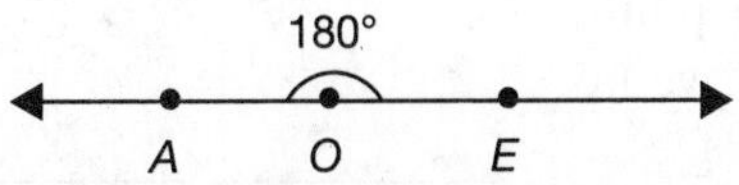

Figure 9.9

In the Fig.9.9, $\angle AOE = 180°$, $\overline{AE}$ is a straight line and O is a point on the line AE.

5. If both the rays coincide, then the angle formed is a **zero angle**.

Perpendicular Lines

Two intersecting lines making an angle of 90° are called perpendicular lines.

In Fig. 9.10, l_1 and l_2 are perpendicular lines. We write $l_1 \perp l_2$ and read it as l_1 is perpendicular to l_2.

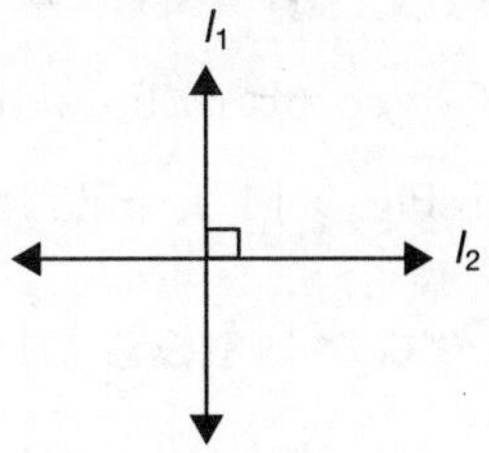

Figure 9.10

Perpendicular Bisector

If a line divides a line segment into two equal parts and is also perpendicular, then it is a perpendicular bisector.

Complementary Angles

When the sum of two angles is 90°, then the two angles are said to be complementary angles.

Example: If $x + y = 90°$, x and y are the complementary angles.

Supplementary Angles

When the sum of two angles is 180°, then the two angles are called supplementary angles.

Example: If $a + b = 180°$, then a and b are called supplementary angles.

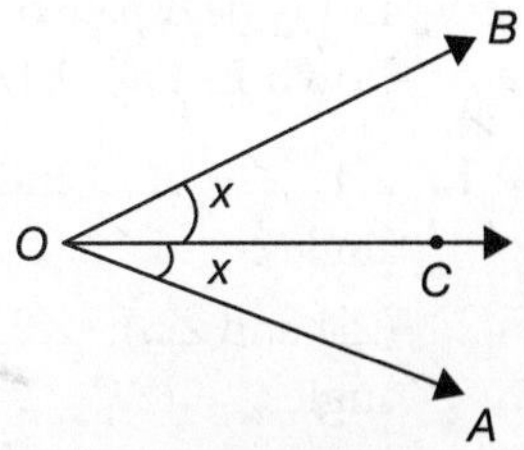

Figure 9.11

Bisector of an Angle

If a line divides an angle into two angles of equal magnitudes, then it is the bisector of that angle.

In Fig. 9.11, $\overrightarrow{OC}$ is the bisector of $\angle AOB$.

Adjacent Angles

If two angles have a common end point and a common side and the other two sides lie on either side of the common side, they are said to be adjacent angles.

In Fig. 9.12, $\angle AOD$ and $\angle DOC$ are adjacent angles. $\angle DOC$ and $\angle COB$ are also adjacent angles.

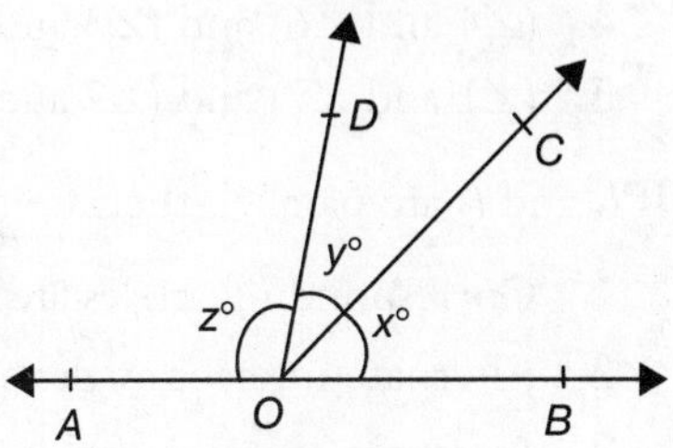

Figure 9.12

Linear Pair

In a pair of adjacent angles, if the non-common sides are opposite rays, then the angles are said to form a linear pair. Alternately, if O is a point between A and B, P is a point not on $\overleftrightarrow{AB}$, then $\angle AOP$ and $\angle POB$ forms a linear pair. The angles of a linear pair are supplementary.

Vertically Opposite Angles

When two lines intersect each other at a point, four angles are formed. Two angles which have no common arm are called vertically opposite angles.

In Fig. 9.13, $\overleftrightarrow{AB}$ and $\overleftrightarrow{PQ}$ intersects at O. $\angle AOP$ and $\angle BOQ$ are vertically opposite angles. $\angle POB$ and $\angle QOA$ are also vertically opposite angles.

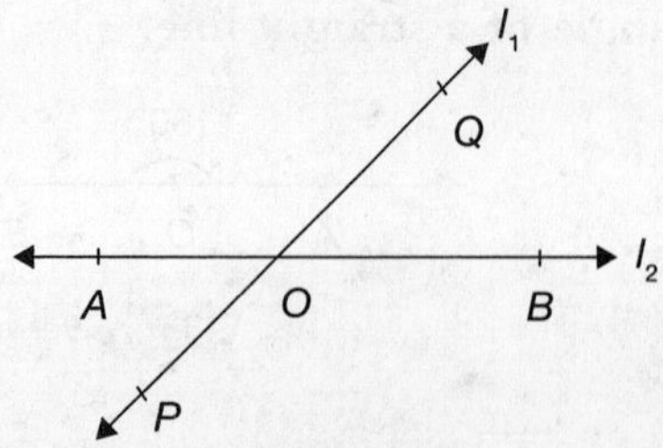

Figure 9.13

Konnect

Vertically opposite angles are equal.

Parallel Lines

Two co-planar lines that do not have a common point are called parallel lines.

In Fig. 9.14, l_1 and l_2 are parallel lines. We write $l_1 \parallel l_2$ and read as l_1 is parallel to l_2.

Figure 9.14

Properties of Parallel Lines

1. The perpendicular distance between two parallel lines is equal everywhere.
2. Two lines lying in the same plane and perpendicular to the same line are parallel to each other.
3. If two lines are parallel to the same line, then they are parallel to each other.
4. One and only one parallel line can be drawn to a given line through a given point which is not on the given line.

Transversal

A straight line intersecting a pair of straight lines in two distinct points is a transversal for the two given lines.

Let l_1 and l_2 be a pair of lines and t be a transversal.

As shown in Fig. 9.15, a total of eight angles are formed.

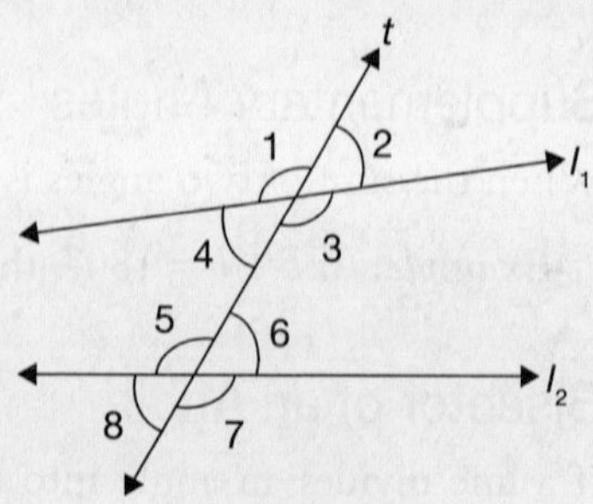

Figure 9.15

1. $\angle 1$, $\angle 2$, $\angle 7$, and $\angle 8$ are exterior angles and $\angle 3$, $\angle 4$, $\angle 5$, and $\angle 6$ are interior angles.
2. ($\angle 1$ and $\angle 5$), ($\angle 2$ and $\angle 6$), ($\angle 3$ and $\angle 7$) and ($\angle 4$ and $\angle 8$) are pairs of corresponding angles.
3. ($\angle 1$ and $\angle 3$), ($\angle 2$ and $\angle 4$), ($\angle 5$ and $\angle 7$), and ($\angle 6$ and $\angle 8$) are pairs of vertically opposite angles.
4. ($\angle 4$ and $\angle 6$) and ($\angle 3$ and $\angle 5$) are pairs of alternate interior angles.
5. ($\angle 1$ and $\angle 7$) and ($\angle 2$ and $\angle 8$) are pairs of alternate exterior angles.

If l_1 and l_2 are parallel, then we can draw the following conclusions:

1. Corresponding angles are equal, i.e., $\angle 1 = \angle 5$, $\angle 2 = \angle 6$, $\angle 3 = \angle 7$ and $\angle 4 = \angle 8$.
2. Alternate interior angles are equal, i.e., $\angle 4 = \angle 6$ and $\angle 3 = \angle 5$.
3. Alternate exterior angles are equal, i.e., $\angle 1 = \angle 7$ and $\angle 2 = \angle 8$.
4. Exterior angles on the same side of the transversal are supplementary, i.e., $\angle 1 + \angle 8 = 180°$ and $\angle 2 + \angle 7 = 180°$.
5. Interior angles on the same side of the transversal are supplementary, i.e., $\angle 4 + \angle 5 = 180°$ and $\angle 3 + \angle 6 = 180°$.

Intercepts

If a transversal t intersects two lines l_1 and l_2 in two distinct points P and Q, respectively, then the lines l_1 and l_2 are said to make an intercept PQ on t.

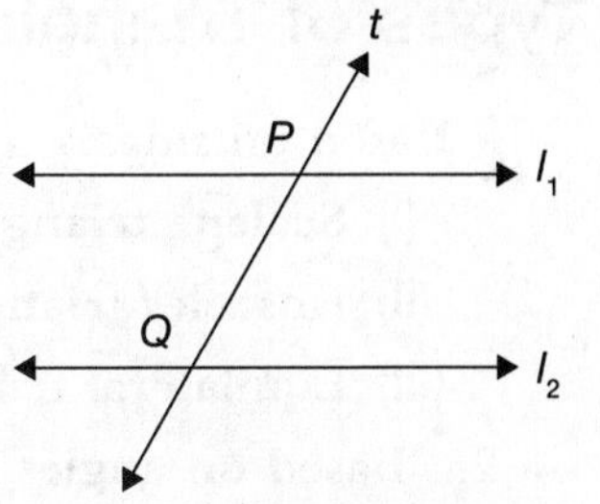

Figure 9.16

In Fig. 9.16, $\overline{PQ}$ is an intercept on t.

A pair of parallel lines make equal intercepts on all transversals which are perpendicular to them.

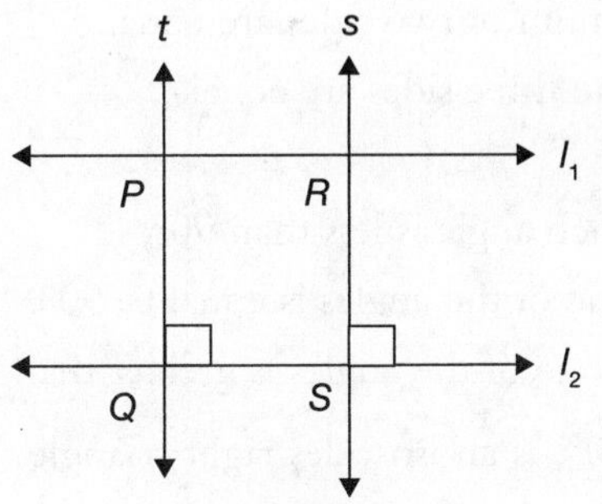

Figure 9.17

In the above figure, l_1 and l_2 are parallel lines. Transversals t and s are perpendicular to them. The intercepts PQ and RS are equal.

Equal Intercepts

If three parallel lines make equal intercepts on one transversal, then they will make equal intercepts on any other transversal as well.

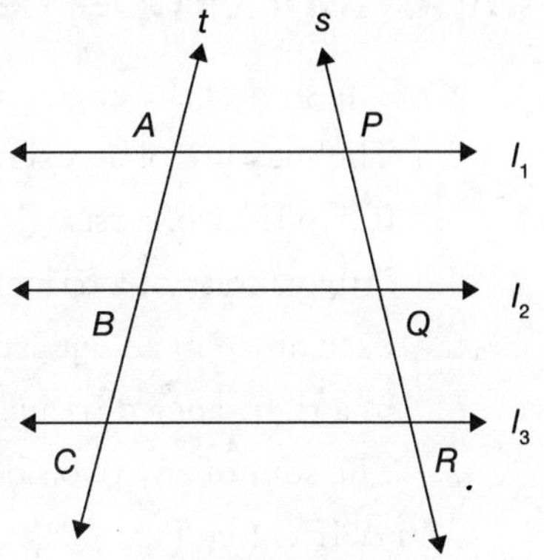

Figure 9.18

In Fig. 9.18, l_1, l_2 and l_3 are parallel lines. They make intercepts AB and BC on transversal t and intercepts PQ and QR on transversal s.

If $AB = BC$, then $PQ = QR$.

Now, let us consider four parallel lines l_1, l_2, l_3, and l_4.

In Fig. 9.19, l_1, l_2, l_3, and l_4 are four parallel lines making intercepts on the transversals t and s.

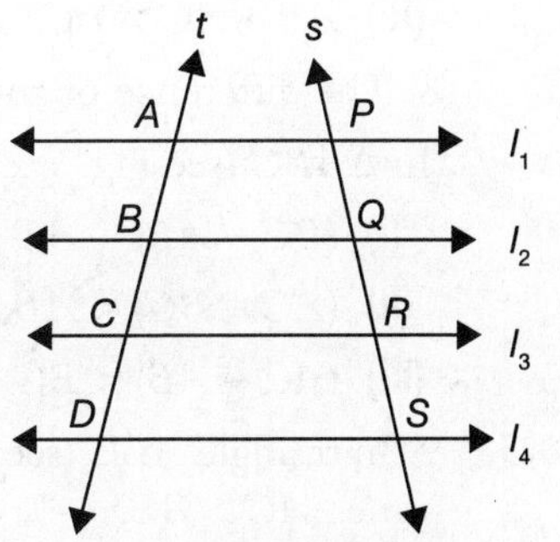

Figure 9.19

The lines, l_1, l_2, l_3, and l_4, make intercepts AB, BC, and CD on transversal t and intercepts PQ, QR, and RS on transversal s. If $AB = BC = CD$, then $PQ = QR = RS$. Hence, we can say that if three or more parallel lines make equal intercepts on a transversal, they will also make equal intercepts on any other transversal. This is known as **equal intercepts property**.

Triangles

A triangle is a simple three-sided closed plane figure. The point of intersection of any two sides of a triangle is called a vertex. Hence, there are three vertices in a triangle. For example, in ΔABC, the vertices are A, B, and C.

When one of the sides is produced (as shown in the Fig. 9.20), the angle ($\angle ABD$) thus formed is called the exterior angle and the angles $\angle BAC$ and $\angle ACB$ are called its interior opposite angles.

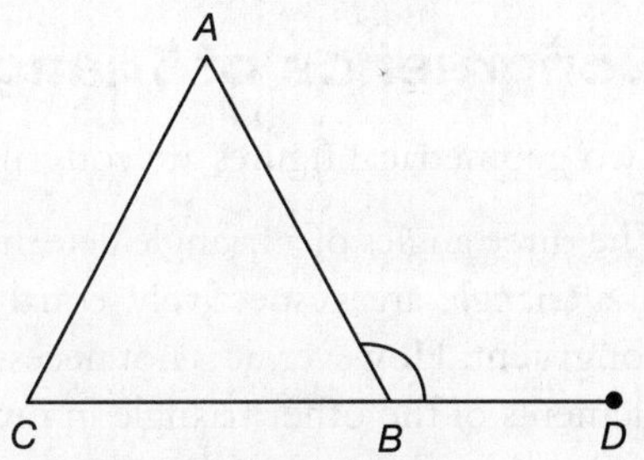

Figure 9.20

Types of Triangles

1. **Based on sides:**
   - (i) **Scalene triangle:** A triangle in which no two sides are equal.
   - (ii) **Isosceles triangle:** A triangle in which a minimum of two sides are equal.
   - (iii) **Equilateral triangle:** A triangle in which all the three sides are equal.
2. **Based on angles:**
   - (i) **Acute-angled triangle:** A triangle in which each angle is less than 90°.
   - (ii) **Right-angled triangle:** A triangle in which one of the angles is equal to 90°.
   - (iii) **Obtuse-angled triangle:** A triangle in which one of the angles is greater than 90°.

A triangle in which two sides are equal and one angle is 90°, is an isosceles right triangle. The hypotenuse is $\sqrt{2}$ times of each equal side.

Important Properties of Triangles

1. The sum of the angles of a triangle is 180°.
2. The measure of an exterior angle is equal to the sum of the measures of its interior opposite angles.
3. If two sides of a triangle are equal, then the angles opposite to them are also equal.
4. If two angles of a triangle are equal, then the sides opposite to them are also equal.
5. Each angle in an equilateral triangle is equal to 60°.
6. In a right-angled triangle the square of the hypotenuse is equal to the sum of the squares of the other two sides.
7. The sum of any two sides of a triangle is always greater than the third side.
   In ΔABC (see Fig. 9.21):
   - (i) $AB + BC > AC$
   - (ii) $BC + AC > AB$
   - (iii) $AB + AC > BC$

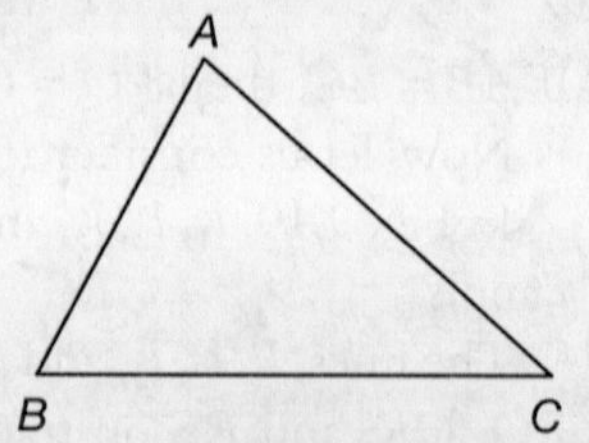

Figure 9.21

8. The difference of any two sides of a triangle is less than the third side.
   In ΔABC (see Fig. 9.21):
   - (i) $(BC - AB) < AC$
   - (ii) $(AC - BC) < AB$
   - (iii) $(AC - AB) < BC$
9. In triangle ABC (see Fig. 9.21), if $\angle B > \angle C$, then the side opposite to $\angle B$ is longer than the side opposite to $\angle C$, i.e., $AC > AB$.
10. In triangle ABC (see Fig. 9.21), if $AC > BC$, then the angle opposite to side AC is greater than the angle opposite to side BC, i.e., $\angle B > \angle A$.

Congruence of Triangles

Two geometrical figures are congruent if they have the same shape and the same size.

The three angles of a triangle determine its shape and its three sides determine its size. If the three angles and the three sides of a triangle are, respectively, equal to the corresponding angles and sides of another triangle, then the two triangles are congruent. However, it is not necessary that each of the six elements of one triangle have to be equal to the corresponding elements of the other triangle in order to conclude that the two triangles are congruent.

Based on the study and experiments, the following results can be applied to establish the congruence of two triangles.

Side-Side-Side (SSS) Congruence Property

By the SSS congruence property, two triangles are congruent if the three sides of one triangle are, respectively, equal to the corresponding three sides of the other triangle.

ABC and *PQR* are two triangles (see Fig. 9.22) such that $AB = PQ$, $BC = QR$ and $CA = RP$, then ΔABC is congruent to ΔPQR.

We write this as $\Delta ABC \cong \Delta PQR$.

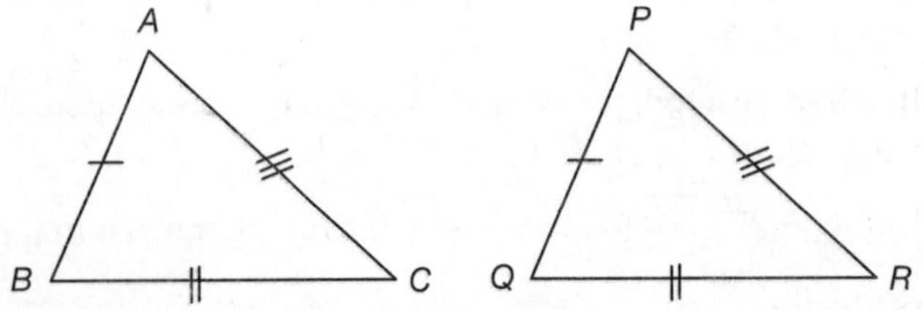

Figure 9.22

Side-Angle-Side (SAS) Congruence Property

By the SAS congruence property, two triangles are congruent if the two sides and the included angle of one triangle are, respectively, equal to the corresponding two sides and the included angle of the other triangle.

If *ABC* and *PQR* are two triangles (see Fig. 9.23) such that $AB = PQ$, $BC = QR$ and $\angle ABC = \angle PQR$, then $\Delta ABC \cong \Delta PQR$.

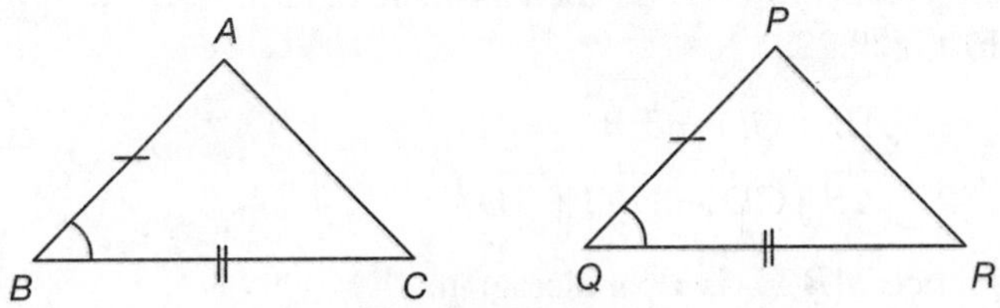

Figure 9.23

Angle-Side-Angle (ASA) Congruence Property

By the ASA congruence property, two triangles are congruent if any two angles and a side of one triangle are, respectively, equal to the corresponding parts of the other triangle.

In Fig. 9.24, $\angle BAC = \angle QPR$ and $\angle ABC = \angle PQR$ and $AB = PQ$. It follows that $\Delta ABC \cong \Delta PQR$.

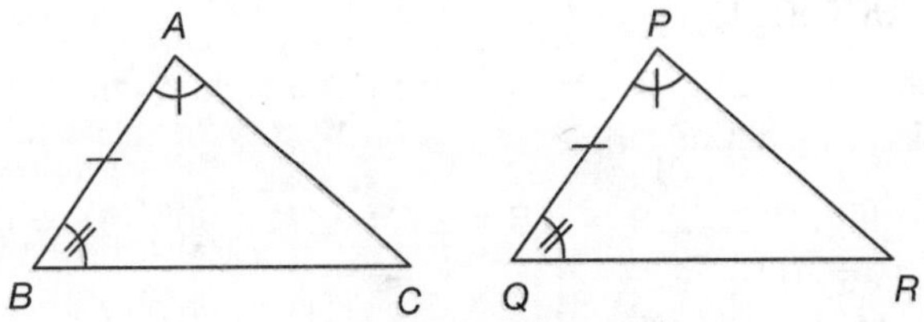

Figure 9.24

Right Angle-Hypotenuse-Side Congruency Property

The RHS congruence property states that two right triangles are congruent, if the hypotenuse and one side of a triangle are respectively equal to the hypotenuse and the corresponding side of the other right triangle.

In ΔABC and ΔPQR (see Fig. 9.25), $AB = PQ$, $AC = PR$ and $\angle ABC = \angle PQR = (90°)$, then $\Delta ABC \cong \Delta PQR$.

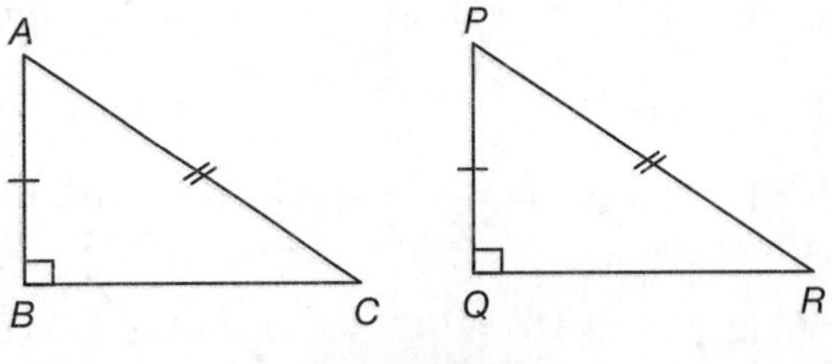

Figure 9.25

Quadrilaterals

A closed figure bounded by four line segments is called a quadrilateral. A quadrilateral *PQRS* has the following elements (see Fig. 9.26):

1. Four vertices *P*, *Q*, *R* and *S*.
2. Four sides $\overline{PQ}$, $\overline{QR}$, $\overline{RS}$ and $\overline{SP}$.
3. Four angles $\angle P$, $\angle Q$, $\angle R$ and $\angle S$.
4. Two diagonals $\overline{PR}$ and $\overline{QS}$.
5. Four pairs of adjacent sides $(\overline{PQ}, \overline{QR})$, $(\overline{QR}, \overline{RS})$, $(\overline{RS}, \overline{SP})$ and $(\overline{SP}, \overline{PQ})$.
6. Two pairs of opposite sides $(\overline{PQ}, \overline{RS})$ and $(\overline{QR}, \overline{PS})$.
7. Four pairs of adjacent angles $(\angle P, \angle Q)$ $(\angle Q, \angle R)$, $(\angle R, \angle S)$ and $(\angle S, \angle P)$.
8. Two pairs of opposite angles $(\angle P, \angle R)$ and $(\angle Q, \angle S)$.
9. The sum of the four angles of a quadrilateral is 360°.

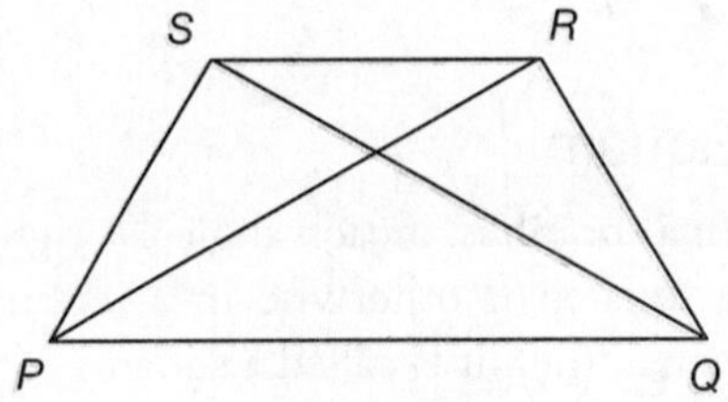

Figure 9.26

Different Types of Quadrilaterals

Trapezium

In a quadrilateral, if one pair of opposite sides are parallel to each other, then it is called a trapezium.

In Fig. 9.27, $\overline{AB} \parallel \overline{CD}$, hence $ABCD$ is a trapezium.

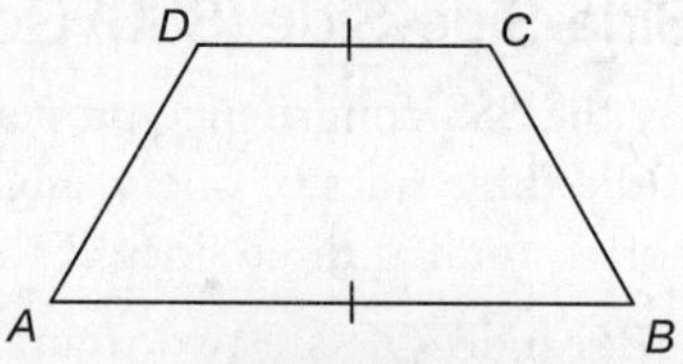

Figure 9.27

Parallelogram

In a quadrilateral if both the pairs of opposite sides are parallel, then it is called a parallelogram.
In Fig. 9.28:

1. $AB = CD$ and $BC = AD$.
2. $\overline{AB} \parallel \overline{CD}$ and $\overline{BC} \parallel \overline{AD}$.

Hence, $ABCD$ is a parallelogram.

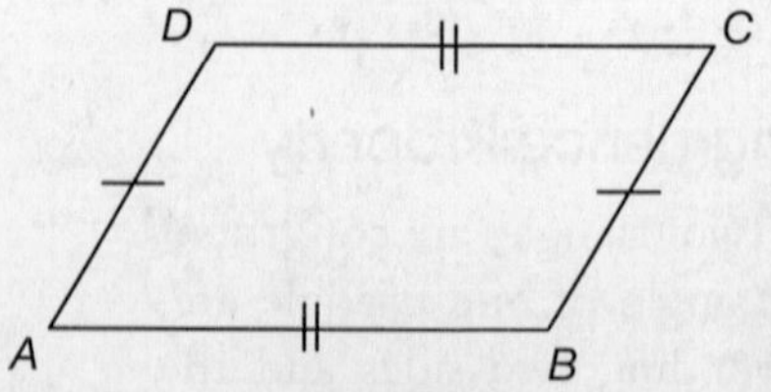

Figure 9.28

Konnect

In a parallelogram, diagonals need not be equal, but they bisect each other.

Rectangle

In a parallelogram, if each angle is a right angle (90°), then it is called a rectangle.

In Fig. 9.29, $\angle A = \angle B = \angle C = \angle D = 90°$, $AB = CD$ and $BC = AD$.

Hence, $ABCD$ is a rectangle.

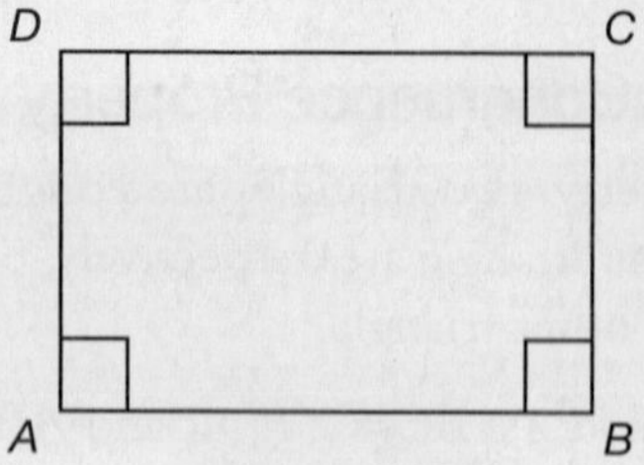

Figure 9.29

Info Bytes!

In a rectangle, the diagonals are equal, i.e., $AC = BD$.

Rhombus

In a parallelogram, if all the sides are equal, then it is called a rhombus.

In Fig. 9.30, $AB = BC = CD = AD$, hence $ABCD$ is a rhombus.

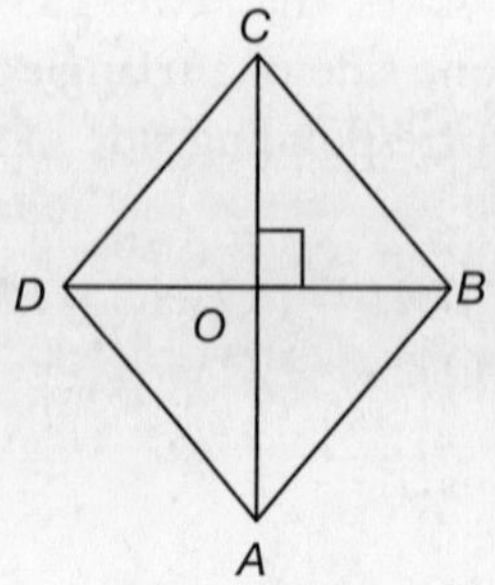

Figure 9.30

Konnect

1. In a rhombus, the diagonals need not be equal.
2. In a rhombus, the diagonals bisect each other at right angles, i.e., $AO = OC$, $BO = OD$ and $\overline{AC} \perp \overline{DB}$.

Square

In a rhombus, if each angle is a right angle, then it is called a square, or otherwise in a rectangle, if all the sides are equal, then it is called a square.

In Fig. 9.31, $AB = BC = CD = DA$ and $\angle A = \angle B = \angle C = \angle D = 90°$.

Hence, $ABCD$ is a square.

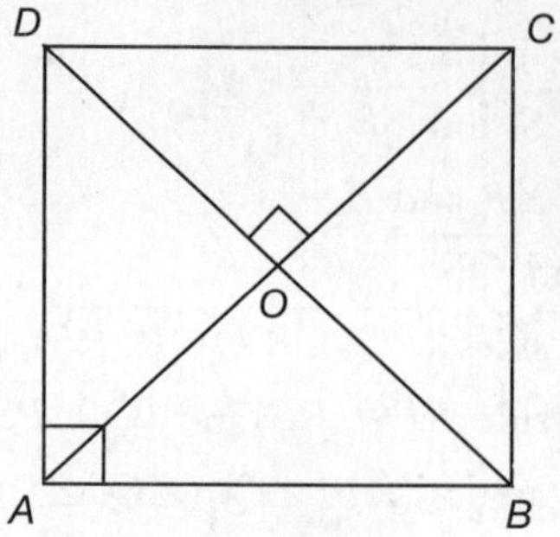

Figure 9.31

Info Bytes!

1. In a square, the diagonals bisect each other at right angles.
2. In a square, the diagonals are equal.

Isosceles Trapezium

In a trapezium, if the non-parallel opposite sides are equal, then it is called an isosceles trapezium.

In Fig. 9.32, $\overline{AB} \parallel \overline{CD}$ and $BC = AD$.
Hence, $ABCD$ is an isosceles trapezium.
$\Rightarrow \angle A = \angle B$ and $\angle C = \angle D$.

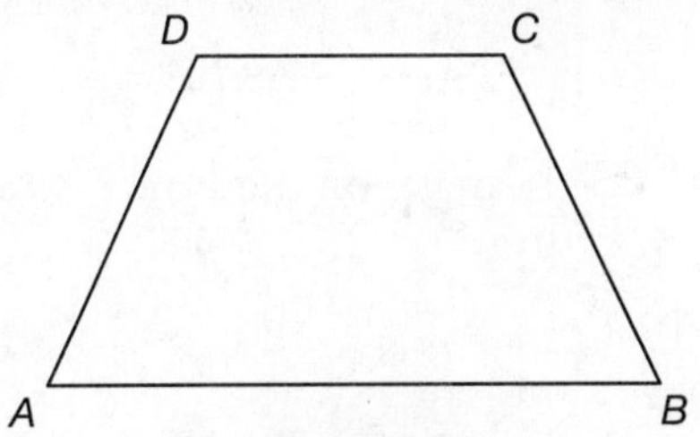

Figure 9.32

Kite

In a quadrilateral, if two pairs of adjacent sides are equal and other two sides of adjacent sides are not equal, then it is called a kite.

In Fig. 9.33, $AB = AD$ and $BC = CD$.
Hence, $ABCD$ is a kite.

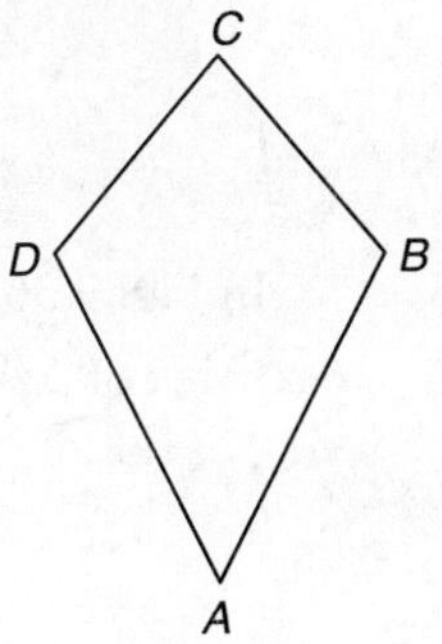

Figure 9.33

Geometrical Results on Areas

1. Parallelograms on the same base and between the same parallels are equal in area.

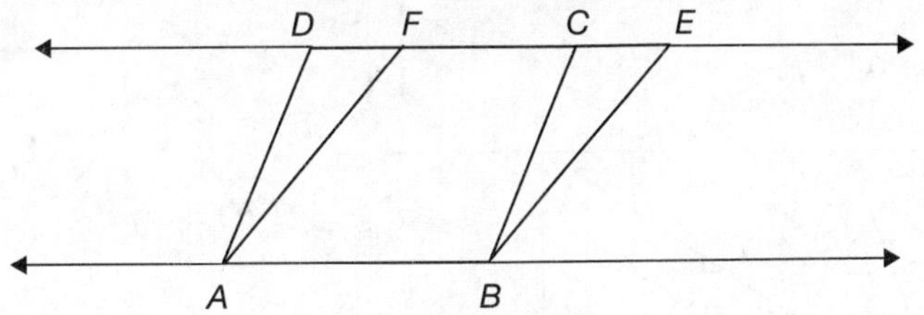

Figure 9.34

In Fig. 9.34, parallelogram $ABCD$ and parallelogram $ABEF$ are on the same base $\overline{AB}$ and between the same parallels $\overleftrightarrow{AB}$ and $\overleftrightarrow{CD}$.
∴ Area of parallelogram $ABCD$ = Area of parallelogram $ABEF$.

> **Konnect**
> A parallelogram and a rectangle on the same base and between the same parallels are equal in area.

2. The area of a triangle is half the area of the parallelogram, if they lie on the same base and between the same parallels.

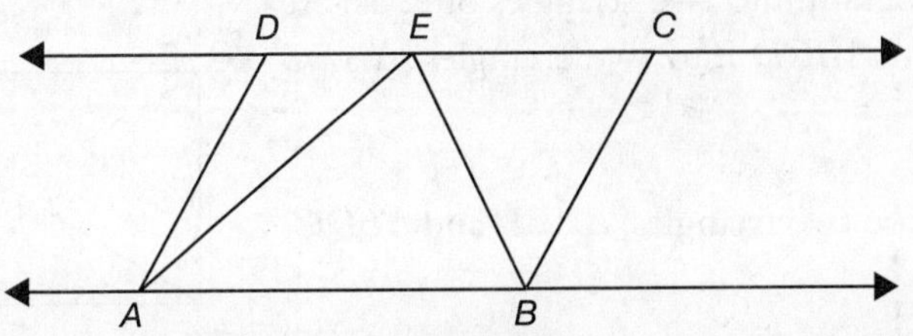

Figure 9.35

In Fig. 9.35, parallelogram $ABCD$ and ΔABE are on the same base $\overline{AB}$ and between the same parallels $\overline{AB}$ and $\overline{CD}$.

$\therefore$ Area of $\Delta ABE = \frac{1}{2}$ Area of parallelogram $ABCD$.

3. Triangles on the same base and between the same parallels are equal in area.

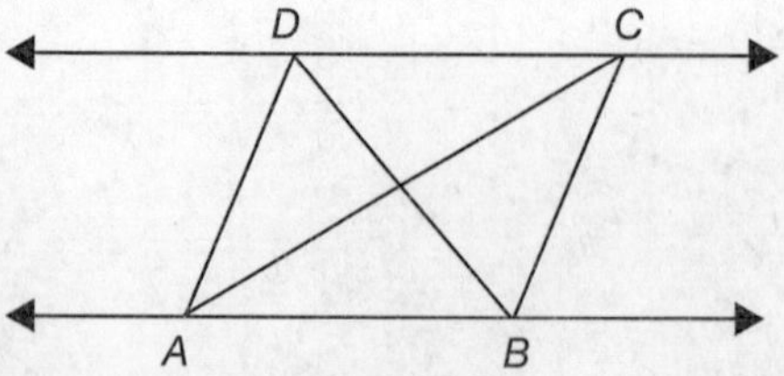

Figure 9.36

In Fig. 9.36, ΔABC and ΔABD are on the same base $\overline{AB}$ and between the same parallels $\overline{AB}$ and $\overline{CD}$.

$\therefore$ Area of ΔABC = Area of ΔABD.

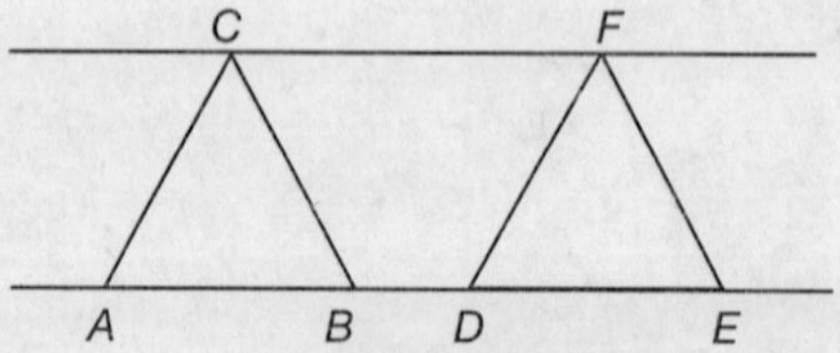

Figure 9.37

Info Bytes!

Triangles with equal bases and between the same parallels are equal in area.

In Fig. 9.37, in ΔABC and ΔDEF,

$AB = DE$ and $\overline{AE} \parallel \overline{CF}$.

$\therefore$ Area of ΔABC = Area of ΔDEF.

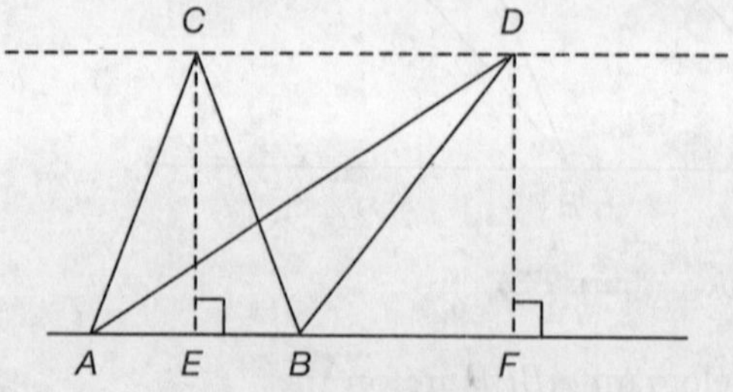

Figure 9.38

Konnect

In this case (Fig. 9.38), altitudes CE and DF are equal.

4. Triangles with equal bases and with equal areas lie between the same parallels.

In Fig. 9.38, if Area of ΔABC = Area of ΔABD, then $\overline{AB} \parallel \overline{CD}$.

5. A diagonal of a parallelogram divides the parallelogram into two triangles of equal area.

In Fig. 9.39, diagonal $\overline{AC}$ divides parallelogram $ABCD$ into two triangles, ΔABC and ΔACD.

Here, area of ΔABC = area of ΔACD.

Similarly, diagonal BD divides the parallelogram into two triangles, ΔABD and ΔBDC.

Hence, the area of ΔABD = area of ΔBCD.

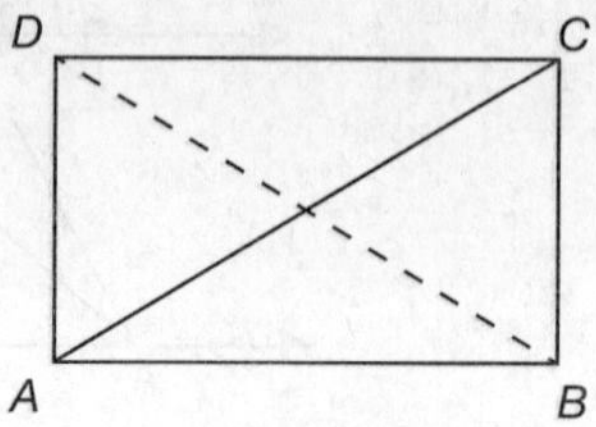

Figure 9.39

Some Theorems on Triangles

Mid-point Theorem

In a triangle, the line segment joining the mid-points of any two sides is parallel to the third side and also half of it.

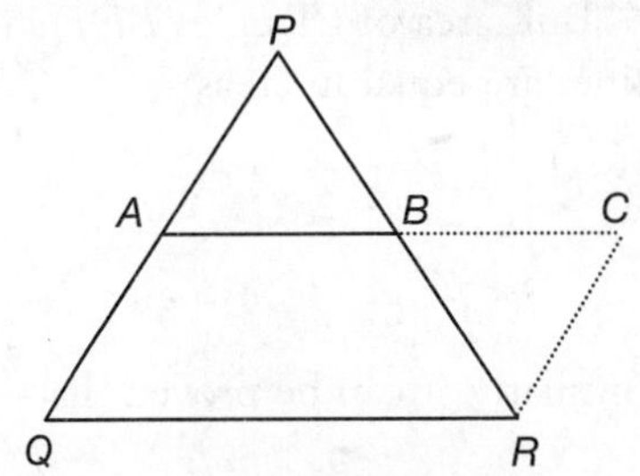

Figure 9.40

Given: In ΔPQR, A and B are the mid-points of $\overline{PQ}$ and $\overline{PR}$. respectively.

RTP: $\overline{AB} \parallel \overline{QR}$ and $AB = \frac{1}{2} QR$

Construction: Draw $\overline{RC}$ parallel to $\overline{QA}$ to meet produced $\overline{AB}$ at C (see Fig. 9.40).

Proof:

1. In ΔABP and ΔCBR,

   $\angle PBA = \angle RBC$ (vertically opposite angles)

   $\angle PAB = \angle RCB$ (alternate angles and $\overline{CR} \parallel \overline{PQ}$)

   $PB = BR$ (B is mid-point of PR).

   By AAS congruence property,

   $\Delta ABP \cong \Delta CBR$

   $\therefore PA = CR$ and $AB = BC$ (corresponding parts of congruent triangles)

   $$\Rightarrow AQ = CR. \qquad (\because PA = AQ)$$

   In quadrilateral $ACRQ$, $AQ = CR$ and $\overline{AQ} \parallel \overline{CR}$.

   $\therefore ACRQ$ is a parallelogram.

   $$\therefore \overline{AC} \parallel \overline{QR} \Rightarrow \overline{AB} \parallel \overline{QR}$$

2. $AC = QR$ (opposite sides of parallelogram)

   $$\Rightarrow QR = AB + BC$$
   $$\Rightarrow QR = 2AB \; (\because AB = BC)$$
   $$\Rightarrow AB = \frac{1}{2} QR.$$

Basic Proportionality Theorem

In a triangle, if a line is drawn parallel to one side of the triangle, then it divides the other two sides in the same ratio.

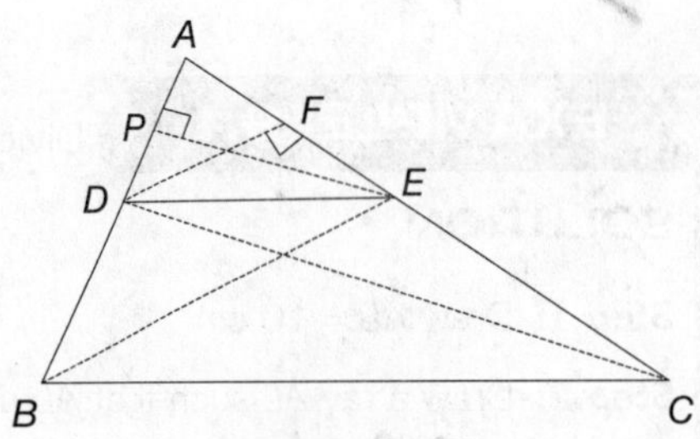

Figure 9.41

Given: In ΔABC, $\overline{DE}$ is drawn parallel to $\overline{BC}$.

RTP: $\dfrac{AD}{DB} = \dfrac{AE}{EC}$

Construction: Draw $\overline{EP} \perp \overline{AB}$ and $\overline{DF} \perp \overline{AC}$. Join DC and BE (see Fig. 9.41).

Proof:

$$\frac{\text{Area of triangle } ADE}{\text{Area of triangle } BDE} = \frac{\frac{1}{2} \times AD \times PE}{\frac{1}{2} \times BD \times PE} = \frac{AD}{BD}$$

$$\text{and } \frac{\text{Area of triangle } ADE}{\text{Area of triangle } CDE} = \frac{\frac{1}{2} \times AE \times DF}{\frac{1}{2} \times EC \times DF} = \frac{AE}{EC}.$$

But, area of triangles *BDE* and *CDE* are equal. ($\because$ Two triangles lying on the same base and between the same parallel lines are equal in areas).

$$\therefore \frac{AD}{DB} = \frac{AE}{EC}.$$

Similarly, it can be proved that $\frac{AB}{AD} = \frac{AC}{AE}$ and $\frac{AB}{BD} = \frac{AC}{CE}$.

Converse of Basic Proportionality Theorem

If a line divides two sides of a triangle in the same ratio, then that line is parallel to the third side.

In Fig. 9.42, $\frac{AD}{DB} = \frac{AE}{EC} \Rightarrow \overline{DE} \parallel \overline{BC}$.

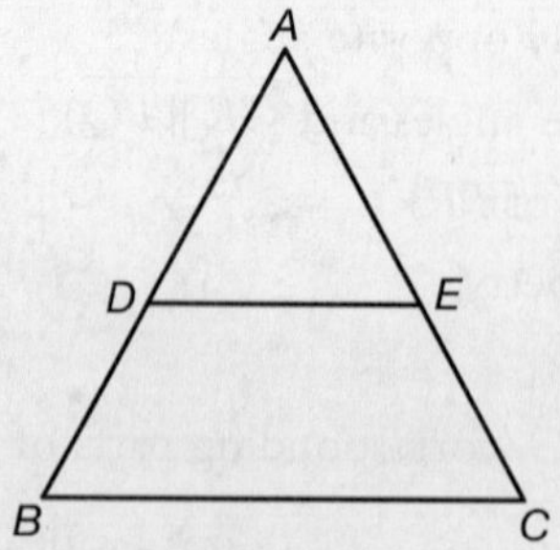

Figure 9.42

Konnect

The intercepts made by three or more parallel lines on any two transversals are proportional.

In Fig. 9.43, the parallel lines l_1, l_2, and l_3 make intercepts *AB* and *BC* on transversal *t* and intercepts *PQ* and *QR* on transversal *s*.

Then, $\frac{AB}{BC} = \frac{PQ}{QR}$.

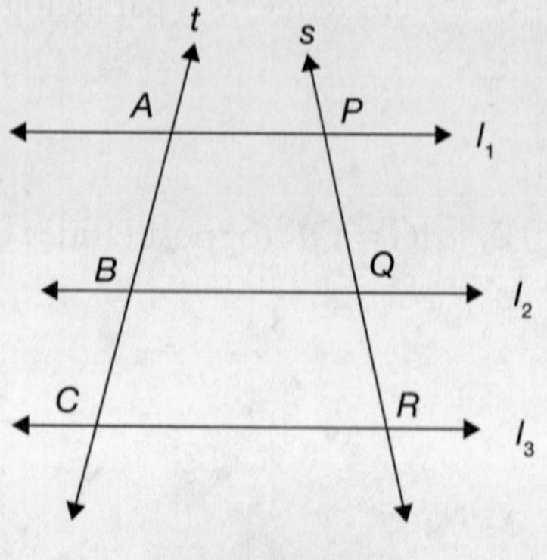

Figure 9.43

EXAMPLE 9.1 Divide line segment *AB* = 10 cm into six equal parts.

SOLUTION

Step 1: Draw *AB* = 10 cm.

Step 2: Draw a ray *AL* such that *AL* does not coincide with *AB*.

Step 3: Mark six equal line segments *AC*, *CD*, *DE*, *EF*, *FG*, and *GH* on ray *AL* with convenient length, using a compass.

Step 4: Join *HB*.

Step 5: Draw lines parallel to *HB* through the points *C*, *D*, *E*, *F*, and *G* intersecting the line segment *AB* at *P*, *Q*, *R*, *S*, and *T*. respectively. The line segments *AP*, *PQ*, *QR*, *RS*, *ST*, and *TB* are the required six equal parts of the line segment *AB* (see Fig. 9.44).

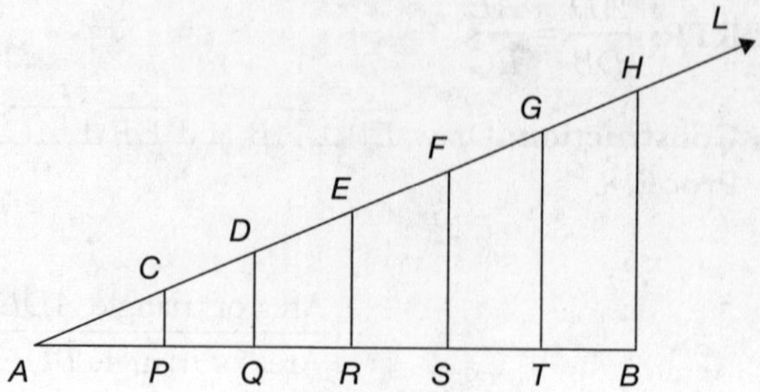

Figure 9.44

Pythagorean Theorem

In a right triangle, the square of the hypotenuse is equal to the sum of the squares of the other two sides.

Given: In ΔABC, $\angle B = 90°$.

To prove: $AC^2 = AB^2 + BC^2$

Construction: Draw $\overline{BP}$ perpendicular to $\overline{AC}$ (see Fig. 9.54).

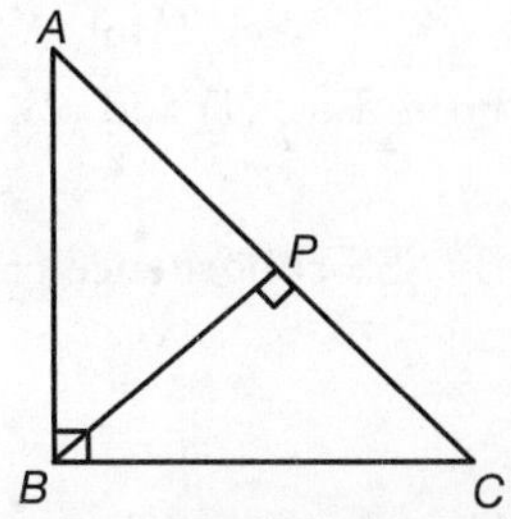

Figure 9.54

Proof: In ΔAPB and ΔABC,

$\angle APB = \angle ABC$ (right angles)

$\angle A = \angle A$ (common)

$\therefore$ Triangle APB is similar to triangle ABC.

$$\Rightarrow \frac{AP}{AB} = \frac{AB}{AC}$$

$\Rightarrow AB^2 = (AP)(AC)$.

Similarly, $BC^2 = (PC)(AC)$

$\therefore AB^2 + BC^2 = (AP)(AC) + (PC)(AC)$

$AB^2 + BC^2 = (AC)(AP + PC)$

$AB^2 + BC^2 = (AC)(AC)$

$\Rightarrow AC^2 = AB^2 + BC^2$.

Hence proved.

Converse of Pythagorean Theorem

In a triangle, if the square of one side is equal to the sum of the squares of the other two sides, then the angle opposite to the first side is a right angle.

Given: In ΔXYZ, $XZ^2 = XY^2 + YZ^2$ (see Fig. 9.55).

To prove: $\angle Y = 90°$

Construction: Construct ΔMNO, such that $XY = MN$, $YZ = NO$ and $\angle N = 90°$ (see Fig. 9.56).

Proof: In ΔMNO, $\angle N = 90°$.

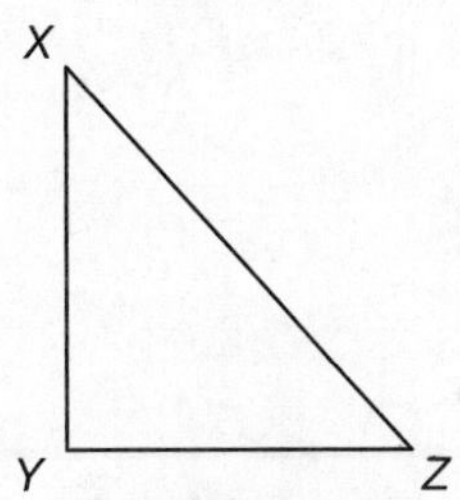

Figure 9.55

$$\therefore OM^2 = MN^2 + NO^2 \text{ (Pythagorean theorem)}$$

$$\Rightarrow OM^2 = XY^2 + YZ^2 \text{ (construction)} \quad (1)$$

$$\text{But, } XZ^2 = XY^2 + YZ^2 \text{ (Given)} \quad (2)$$

From Eqs. (1) and (2), we get:

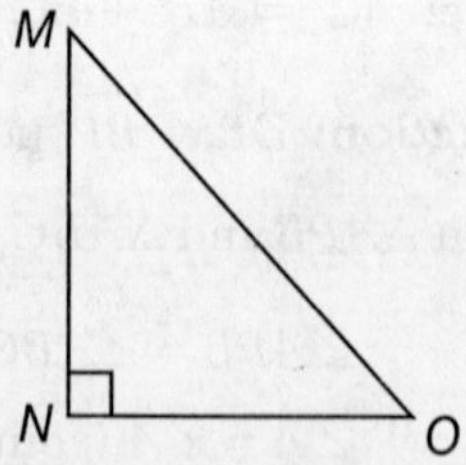

$$OM^2 = XZ^2 \Rightarrow OM = XZ$$

By SSS congruence criterion, we get:

$$\Delta XYZ \cong \Delta MNO$$

$$\therefore \angle Y = \angle N = 90°.$$

Hence, $\angle Y = 90°$.

EXAMPLE 9.2 In the given figure (not to scale), ABC is an isosceles triangle in which $AB = AC$. $AEDC$ is a parallelogram. If $\angle CDF = 70°$ and $\angle BFE = 100°$, then find $\angle FBA$.

(a) 30° **(b)** 40° **(c)** 50° **(d)** 80°

SOLUTION

(i) In a parallelogram, any pair of adjacent angles are supplementary.

(ii) $\angle EFG = \angle FGC = \angle AGB$ and $\angle ACB$

$= \angle ABC = \angle CDE.$ $\left(\because \overline{AC} \parallel \overline{DE}\right)$

(iii) Use the above data and find $\angle BAC$, and then $\angle ABG$.

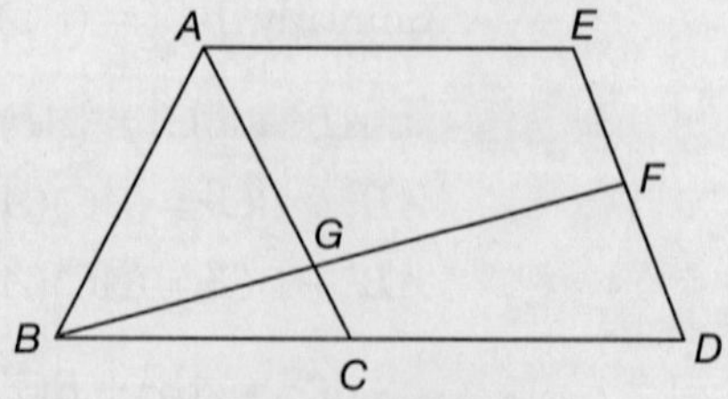

Figure 9.56

EXAMPLE 9.3 In the given figure, $\angle PQR = \angle QSR$. If $PS = 1$ cm and $SR = 4$ cm, then $QR =$ ______ cm.

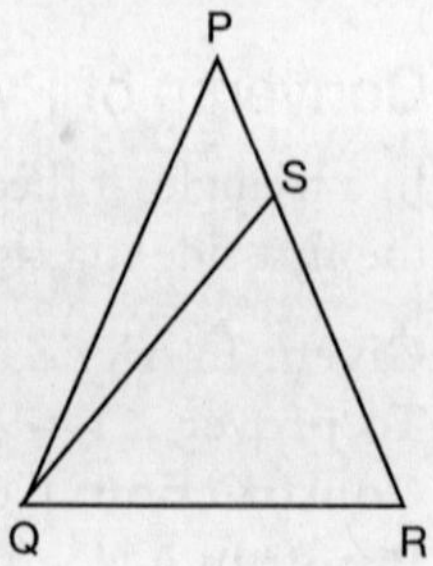

SOLUTION

$\angle PQR = \angle QSR$ (given)

$\angle R = \angle R$ (common)

$\Delta PQR \sim \Delta QSR$ ($\because$ AA similarity)

$$\Rightarrow \frac{PR}{QR} = \frac{QR}{SR}$$

$$\Rightarrow \frac{5}{QR} = \frac{QR}{4}$$

$$\Rightarrow QR^2 = 20 \Rightarrow QR = 2\sqrt{5} \text{ cm}$$

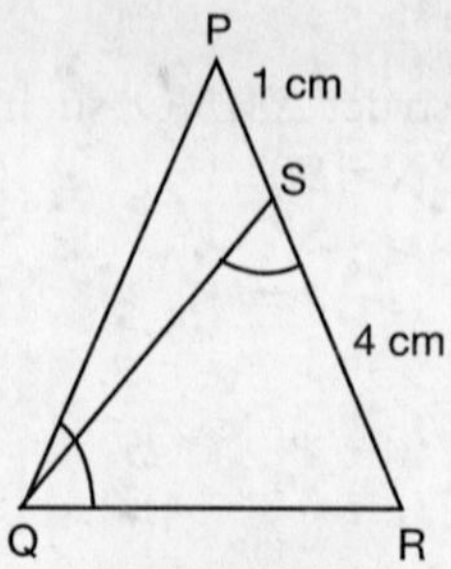

Figure 9.57

Polygons

A closed plane figure bounded by three or more line segments is called a polygon.

1. Each line segment is called a side of the polygon.
2. The point at which any two adjacent sides intersect is called a vertex of the polygon.

Different polygons, the number of their sides and their names are given in the following table.

Number of Sides	3	4	5	6	7	8	9	10
Name of the polygon	Triangle	Quadrilateral	Pentagon	Hexagon	Septagon	Octagon	Nonagon	Decagon
Corresponding figure		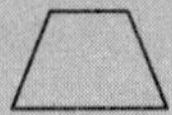	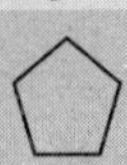	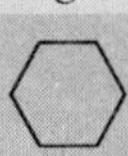	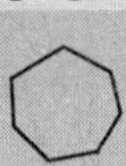	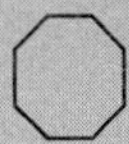	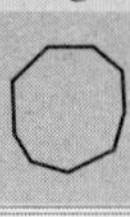	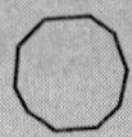

Polygons can also be classified as-

1. Convex polygons
2. Concave polygons.

Convex Polygon and Concave Polygon

A polygon in which each interior angle is less than 180° is called a convex polygon (Fig. 9.58). Otherwise it is called concave polygon (Fig. 9.59).

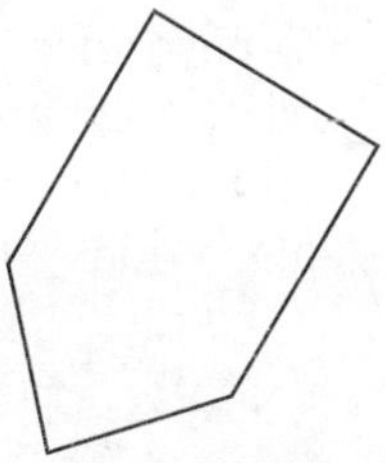

Figure 9.58

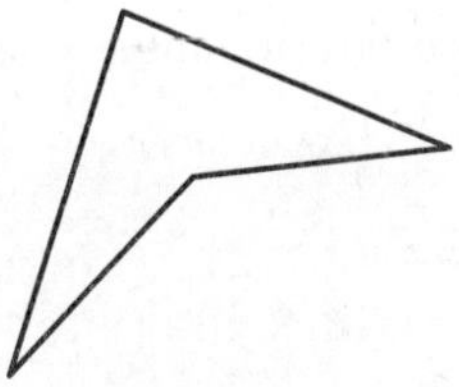

Figure 9.59

Konnect

Unless otherwise mentioned, we refer to convex polygons simply as polygons.

Some Important Results on Polygons

1. **Diagonals of a polygon:** A line segment joining any two non-consecutive vertices of a polygon is called its diagonal.

Info Bytes!

The number of diagonals of a polygon with n sides is given by $\frac{n(n-3)}{2}$.

EXAMPLE 9.4 Find the number of diagonals of a 10-sided polygon.

SOLUTION

Here, $n = 10$

$\therefore$ Number of diagonals $= \frac{10(10-3)}{2} = 35.$

2. The sum of the interior angles of an n-sided polygon is $(2n - 4)\ 90°$ or $(n - 2) \times 180°$.

EXAMPLE 9.5 Which of the following is the sum of the interior angles of a polygon?

SOLUTION

The sum of the interior angles of a polygon = $(2n - 4) \times 90° = (n - 2) \times 180°$

From the given options, only 1980° is the multiple of 180°.

3. The sum of all the exterior angles of a polygon is 360°.

4. In a polygon, if all the sides are equal and all the angles are equal, then it is called a regular polygon.

In case, all the sides are not equal, then the polygon is called an irregular polygon.

5. Each interior angle of regular polygon of n sides is $\left(\frac{(2n-4)90}{n}\right)^{\circ}$.

6. Each exterior angle of a regular polygon of n sides is $\left(\frac{360}{n}\right)^{\circ}$.

7. The number of sides n of a regular polygon whose exterior angle $x°$ is $= \left(\frac{360}{x}\right)^{\circ}$.

Konnect

In case of a regular polygon, all the interior angles are equal and all the exterior angles are also equal.

Construction of Triangles

In the earlier classes, we have learnt construction of triangles, when

1. all the three sides are given.
2. two sides and an angle are given.
3. two angles and an included side are given.
4. a side and the hypotenuse of a right triangle are given.

In the present section, we will discuss construction of triangles in some more cases.

1. To construct a triangle when the base and the sum of the other two sides and one base angle are given.

EXAMPLE 9.6 Construct a triangle ABC, in which base $BC = 6$ cm, $AB + AC = 9$ cm, and $\angle ABC = 45°$.

SOLUTION

Step 1: Draw $BC = 6$ cm.

Step 2: Draw $\overrightarrow{BX}$, such that $\angle CBX = 45°$.

Step 3: With B as the centre and the radius as $AB + AC = 9$ cm, draw an arc to meet $\overrightarrow{BX}$ at D. Join CD.

Step 4: Draw the perpendicular bisector of $\overline{CD}$ to intersect $\overline{BD}$ at A. Join CA. ΔABC is the required triangle.

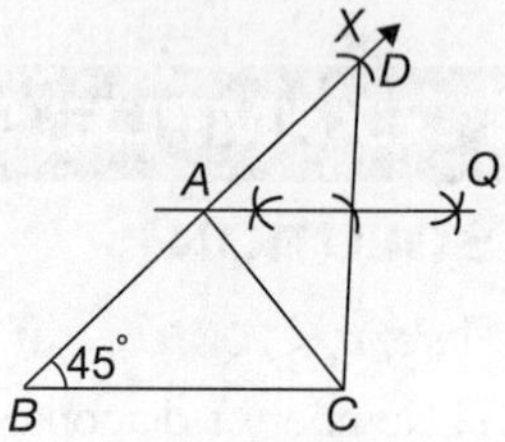

Figure 9.60

Proof: As AQ is the perpendicular bisector of CD, ACD is an isosceles triangle, hence $AD = AC$ and $AB + AC = AB + AD = BD = 9$ cm.

2. Construction of a triangle when its perimeter and the base angles are given.9.7

EXAMPLE 9.7 Construct ΔABC, whose perimeter is 10 cm and base angles are 60° and 44°.

SOLUTION

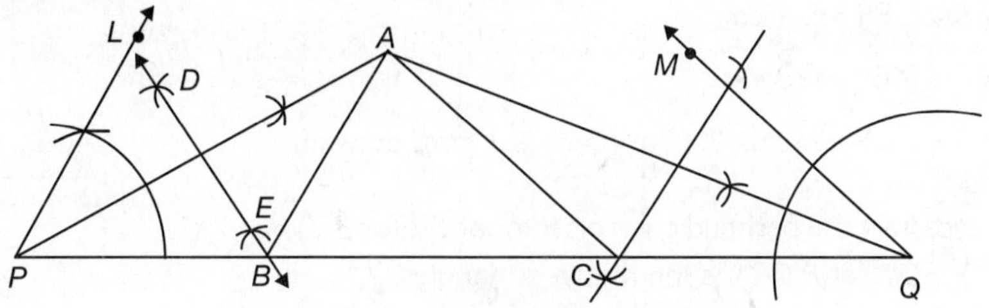

Figure 9.61

Step 1: Draw $PQ = AB + BC + CA = 10$ cm.

Step 2: Draw $\angle LPQ$ equal to $\angle B$ and $\angle MQP$ equal to $\angle C$.

Step 3: Draw the angle bisectors of $\angle LPQ$ and $\angle MQP$. Let these bisectors meet at A.

Step 4: Draw the perpendicular bisectors of $\overline{AP}$ and $\overline{AQ}$ to meet PQ at B and C, respectively.

Step 5: Join AB and AC to form the required ΔABC.

3. To construct a triangle when its base, one base angle and the difference of the remaining sides are given.

EXAMPLE 9.8 Construct a triangle PQR, in which $QR = 4.5$ cm, $\angle Q = 44°$ and $PQ - PR = 2$ cm.

SOLUTION

Step 1: Draw a line segment $QR = 4.5$ cm.

Step 2: Draw $\overrightarrow{QX}$, such that $\angle RQX = 44°$.

Step 3: With Q as the centre and radius = 2 cm, draw an arc to intersect $\overrightarrow{QX}$ at S.

Step 4: Join SR and draw the perpendicular bisector of SR to intersect $\overrightarrow{QX}$ at P.

Step 5: Join P and R. PQR is the required triangle.

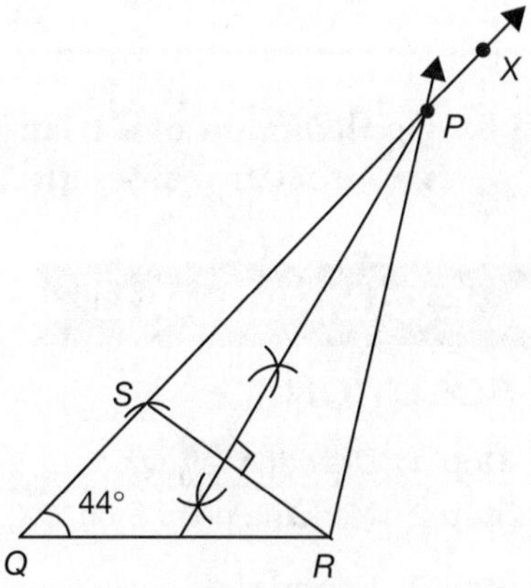

Figure 9.62

4. Construction of a triangle, when the base, the angle at the vertex and the sum of the other two sides are given.

EXAMPLE 9.9 Construct ΔPQR in which $QR = 2.1$ cm, $\angle P = 46°$ and $PQ + PR = 5.1$ cm.

SOLUTION

Step 1: Construct $\angle QS = PQ + PR = 5.1$ cm.

Step 2: Construct $\angle QSR = \frac{1}{2}(46°) = 23°$.

Step 3: With Q as the centre and the radius 2.1 cm ($QR = 2.1$ cm), draw an arc to intersect SX at R and R'.

Step 4: Join QR (or QR') and draw the perpendicular bisector of SR (or SR') to intersect $\overline{QS}$ at P (or P'). PQR (or $P'QR'$) is the required triangle.

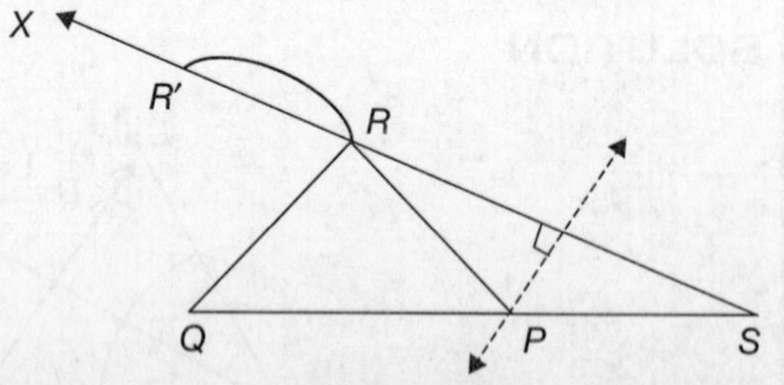

Figure 9.63

5. To construct a triangle when two sides and the median drawn on the third side are given.

EXAMPLE 9.10 Construct a triangle PQR, such that $PQ = 3.8$ cm, $QR = 4.3$ cm and the median from Q to PR is 3.5 cm.

SOLUTION

Step 1: Draw a line segment QR of length 4.3 cm.

Step 2: Draw the perpendicular bisector of $\overleftrightarrow{QR}$ and mark the mid-point of QR as S.

Step 3: Taking Q as the centre and radius equal to 3.5 cm, draw an arc.

Step 4: Taking S as the centre and radius = 1.9 cm $\left(\frac{1}{2}PQ\right)$, draw another arc intersecting the already drawn arc (in Step 3) at T.

Step 5: Join R and T and produce RT to X.

Step 6: With Q as the centre and radius = 3.8 cm, draw an arc to intersect $\overrightarrow{RX}$ at P. Join PQ. ΔPQR is the required triangle.

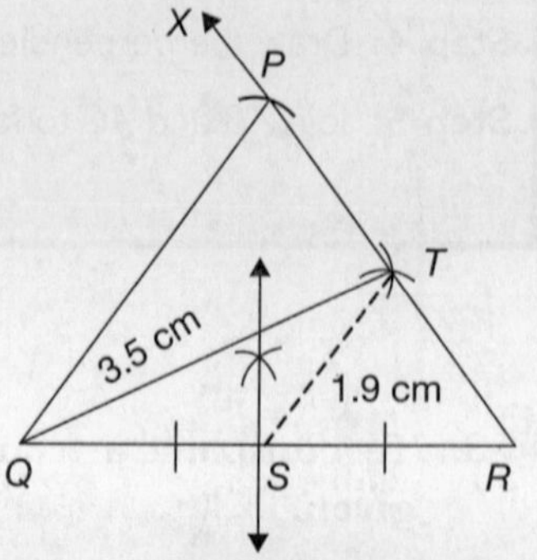

Figure 9.64

6. Construction of a triangle when the base, the angle between the other two sides and the difference of the other two sides are given.

EXAMPLE 9.11 Construct ΔPQR in which $QR = 3.4$ cm, $\angle P = 50°$ and $PQ - PR = 1.2$ cm.

SOLUTION

Step 1: Draw the ray, QX.

Step 2: Mark the point S on $\overrightarrow{QX}$, such that $QS = 1.2$ cm.

Step 3: Construct an angle equal to $180 - \frac{1}{2}(180 - 50) = 115°$ at S, such that $\angle QSY = 115°$.

Step 4: With Q as the centre and radius = 3.4 cm, draw an arc to meet SY at R.

Step 5: Join Q and R.

Step 6: Draw the perpendicular bisector of SR intersecting QX at P.

Step 7: Join PR. PQR is the required triangle.

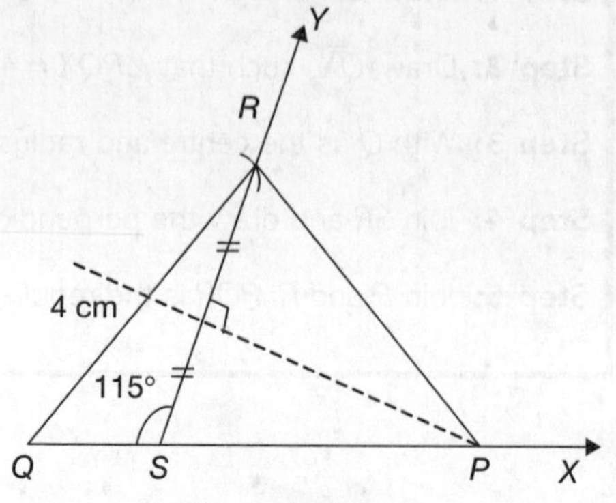

Figure 9.65

7. Construction of a triangle when the base, sum of the remaining sides and the difference of the base angles are given.

EXAMPLE 9.12 Construct ΔPQR in which $QR = 3.2$ cm, $PQ + PR = 5.9$ cm and $\angle R - \angle Q = 60°$.

SOLUTION

Step 1: Draw line segment $QR = 3.2$ cm.

Step 2: Draw $\overrightarrow{RX}$, such that $\angle QRX = \left(90° + \frac{\angle R - \angle Q}{2}\right) = 90° + 30° = 120°$.

Step 3: Taking Q as the centre and a radius equal to 5.9 cm ($PQ + PR$), draw an arc intersecting $\overrightarrow{RX}$ at S.

Step 4: Join Q and S.

Step 5: Draw RY, such that $\angle QRY = \left(\frac{\angle R - \angle Q}{2}\right) = 30°$, intersecting QS at T.

Step 6: Draw the perpendicular bisector of $\overline{RT}$ intersecting $\overline{QS}$ at P.

Step 7: Join P and R. PQR is the required triangle.

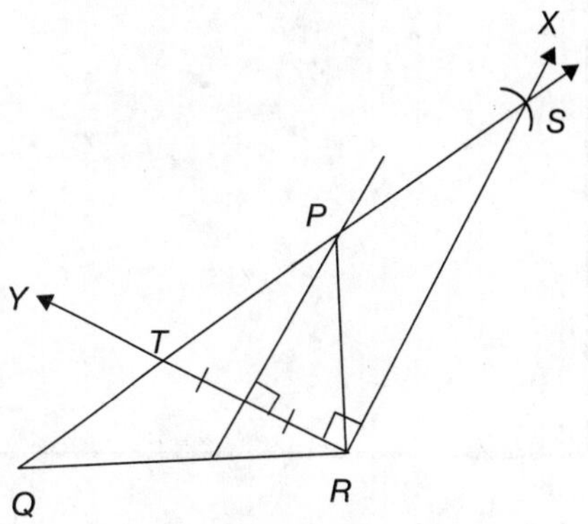

Figure 9.66

8. Construction of a triangle when the base, difference of the remaining two sides and the difference of the base angles are given.

EXAMPLE 9.13 Construct a triangle PQR in which $QR = 4.7$ cm, $PR - PQ = 2.3$ cm and $\angle Q - \angle R = 50°$.

SOLUTION

Step 1: Draw line segment $QR = 4.7$ cm.

Step 2: Draw $\overrightarrow{QX}$, such that $\angle RQX = \frac{1}{2}(\angle Q - \angle R) = 25°$.

Step 3: With R as the centre and the radius = 2.3 cm, draw an arc intersecting $\overrightarrow{QX}$ at A.

Step 4: Join RA and produce $\overline{RA}$.

Step 5: Draw the perpendicular bisector of QA to intersect RA produced at P.

Step 6: Join PQ. PQR is the required triangle.

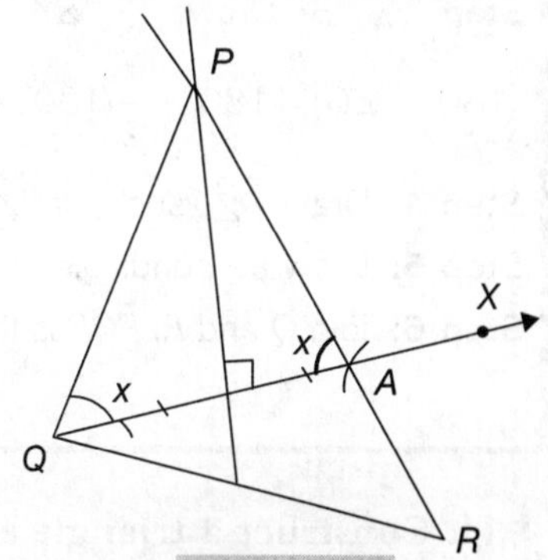

Figure 9.67

9. Construction of a triangle when two angles and the sum of the sides are given.

EXAMPLE 9.14 Construct ΔPQR in which $\angle P = 96°$, $\angle Q = 40°$, and $PQ + PR = 6$ cm.

SOLUTION

Step 1: Draw a line segment $\overline{RS} = 6$ cm.

Step 2: Draw $\overrightarrow{RX}$, such that $\angle SRX = 44°$.

Step 3: Draw $\overline{SY}$, such that $\angle RSY = \frac{1}{2}\angle P = 48°$, intersecting $\overrightarrow{RX}$ at Q.

Step 4: Draw the perpendicular bisector of QS to intersect RS at P.

Step 5: Join P and Q. PQR is the required triangle.

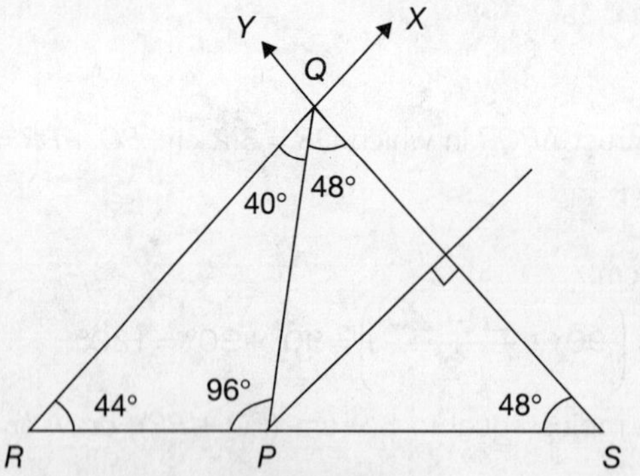

Figure 9.68

10. Construction of a triangle with two angles and the difference between two sides are given.

EXAMPLE 9.15 Construct a triangle PQR, such that $\angle P = 50°$, $\angle Q = 30°$, and $PQ - QR = 1.4$ cm.

SOLUTION

Step 1: Draw $\overrightarrow{PX}$.

Step 2: Locate the point S on $\overrightarrow{PX}$, such that $PS = 1.4$ cm.

Step 3: Draw $\overline{SY}$, such that $\angle PSY = 180° - \frac{1}{2}(180° - \angle Q) = 180° - \frac{1}{2}(180° - 30°) = 105°$.

Step 4: Draw $\overrightarrow{PZ}$, such that $\angle SPZ = 50°$, intersecting $\overrightarrow{SY}$ at R.

Step 5: Draw perpendicular bisector of $\overline{RS}$ intersecting $\overrightarrow{PX}$ at Q.

Step 6: Join Q and R. PQR is the required triangle.

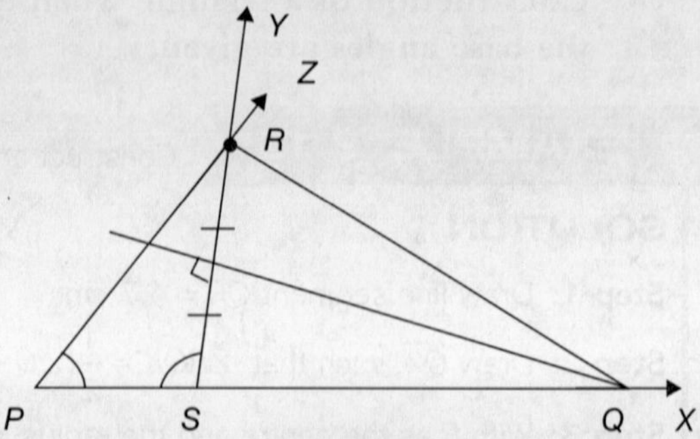

Figure 9.69

11. Construct a triangle equal to the area of a given convex quadrilateral.

Let $PQRS$ be the given quadrilateral.

Step 1: Join QS.

Step 2: Through R, draw a line parallel to $\overline{QS}$.

Step 3: Produce PQ to meet the parallel line drawn through R at T.

Step 4: Join ST. PST is the required triangle.

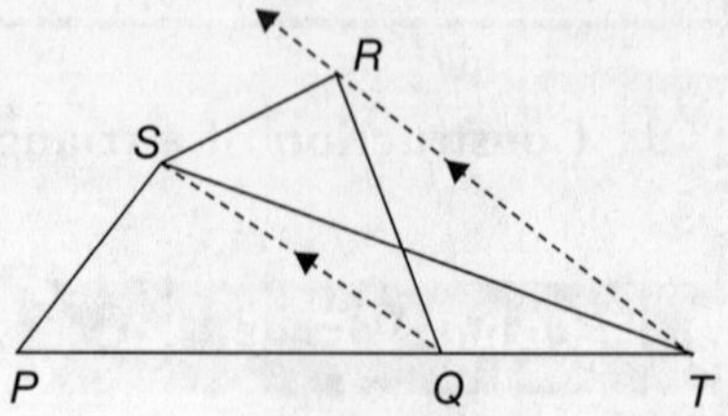

Figure 9.70

Justification

$Ar(\Delta QSR) = Ar(\Delta QST) \rightarrow$ Eq. 1. ($\because$ They lie on the same base $\overline{SQ}$, and lie between the same parallels).

Area of quadrilateral $PQRS = Ar(\Delta PQS) + Ar(\Delta QSR)$.

$= Ar(\Delta PQS) + Ar(\Delta QST)$ (From Eq. 1)

$\therefore$ Area of quadrilateral $PQRS$ = Area of ΔPST.

12. Construct a triangle equal to the area of a given pentagon.

Step 1: Construct a pentagon *ABCDE*.
Step 2: Join *BD* and *AD*.
Step 3: Draw lines parallel to $\overline{BD}$ and $\overline{AD}$ through *C* and *E*, respectively, to meet *AB* produced and *BA* produced at *F* and *G*. respectively.
Step 4: Join *DF* and *DG* to form ΔDGF which is equal to the area of the pentagon *ABCDE*.

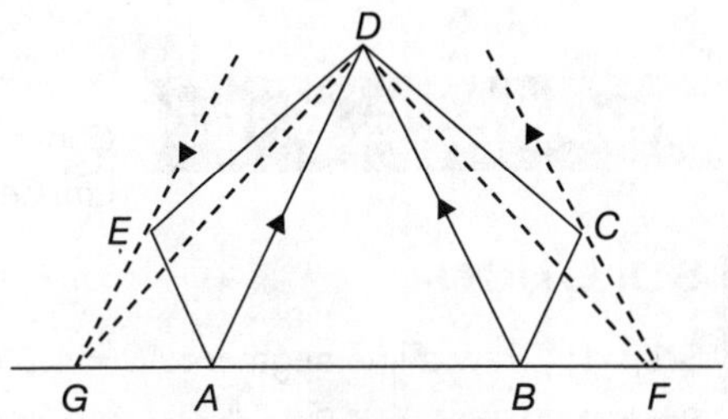

Figure 9.71

Justification

Area of ΔBDC = Area of ΔBDF

Area of ΔADE = Area of ΔADG ($\because$ They lie on the same bases, $\overline{BD}$ and $\overline{AD}$, and between the same parallels.)

Area of pentagon *ABCDE* = Sum of the areas of ΔAED, ΔABD, ΔDBC
= Sum of the areas of ΔADG, ΔABD and ΔBDF
= Area of ΔGDF

$\therefore$ The area of the pentagon *ABCDE* is equal to the area of ΔGDF.

Construction of Quadrilaterals

1. When four sides and one angle are given.

EXAMPLE 9.16 Construct a quadrilateral *ABCD* in which $AB = 4.2$ cm, $\angle A = 80°$, $BC = 2.4$ cm, $CD = 3.3$ cm, and $AD = 2.4$ cm.

SOLUTION

Step 1: Draw a line segment $AB = 4.2$ cm.
Step 2: Draw $\angle BAX = 80°$.
Step 3: Mark *D* on $\overrightarrow{AX}$, such that $AD = 2.4$ cm.
Step 4: Taking *D* as the centre and 3.3 cm as the radius, draw an arc, and taking *B* as the centre and 2.4 cm as radius, draw another arc to intersect the previous arc at *C*.
Step 5: Join *CD* and *BC*. *ABCD* is the required quadrilateral.

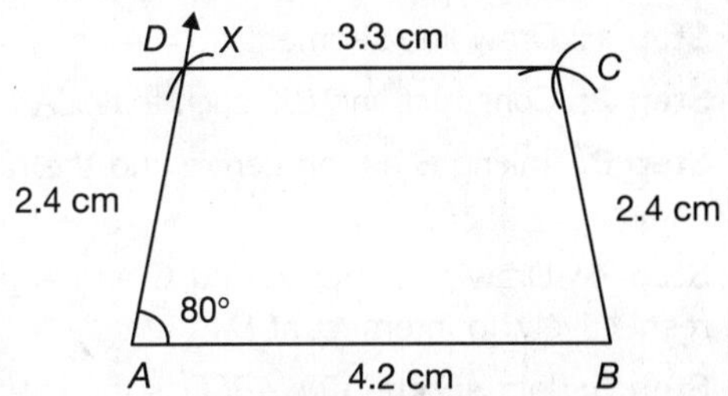

Figure 9.72

2. When three consecutive sides and two included angles are given.

EXAMPLE 9.17 Construct a quadrilateral *ABCD* with $AB = 4$ cm, $BC = 2.8$ cm, $CD = 4$ cm, $\angle B = 75°$, and $\angle C = 105°$.

SOLUTION

Step 1: Draw a line segment $AB = 4$ cm.
Step 2: Draw $\overrightarrow{BX}$, such that $\angle ABX = 75°$.
Step 3: With *B* as the centre and a radius of 2.8 cm, draw an arc to cut $\overrightarrow{BX}$ at *C*.
Step 4: Draw $\overrightarrow{CY}$ which makes an angle 105° with $\overline{BC}$.
Step 5: Mark *D* on $\overrightarrow{CY}$, such that $CD = 4$ cm.
Step 6: Join *AD*. *ABCD* is the required quadrilateral.

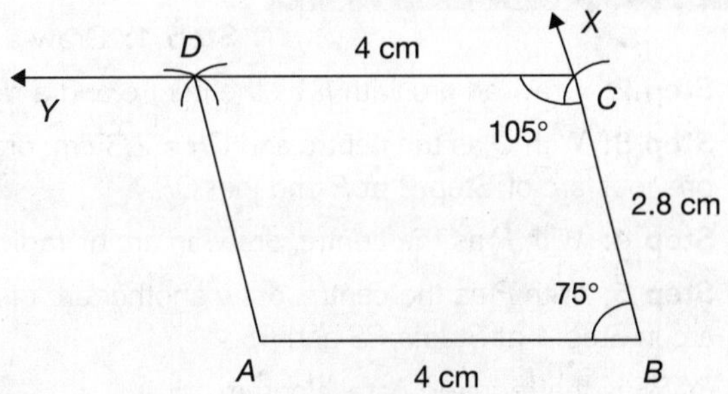

Figure 9.73

3. When four sides and one diagonal are given.

EXAMPLE 9.18 Construct a quadrilateral *ABCD* in which *AB* = 4.6 cm, *BC* = 2.6 cm, *CD* = 3.5 cm, *AD* = 2.6 cm, and the diagonal *AC* = 4.9 cm.

SOLUTION

Step 1: Draw a line segment *AB* = 4.6 cm.

Step 2: With *A* and *B* as the centres, draw two arcs of radii 4.9 cm and 2.6 cm respectively to intersect each other at *C*.

Step 3: With *C* and *A* as the centres, draw two arcs of radii 3.5 cm and 2.6 cm, respectively, to intersect at *D*.

Step 4: Join *BC*, *CD* and *AD* to form quadrilateral *ABCD*.

ABCD is the required quadrilateral.

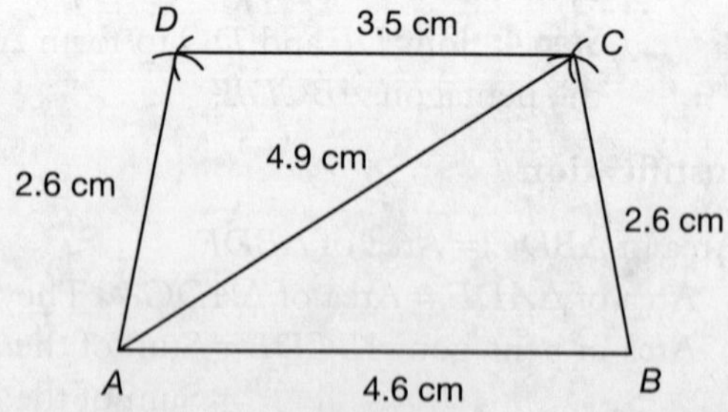

Figure 9.74

4. To construct a parallelogram, when two consecutive sides and the included angle are given.

EXAMPLE 9.19 Construct a parallelogram *ABCD*, when *AB* = 4 cm, *BC* = 2.5 cm and ∠*B* = 100°.

SOLUTION

Step 1: Draw line segment *AB* = 4 cm.

Step 2: Construct line *BX*, such that ∠*ABX* = 100°.

Step 3: Taking *B* as the centre and the radius = 2.5 cm, cut $\overline{BX}$ at the point *C* with an arc.

Step 4: Draw two arcs taking *C* and *A* as centres and 4 cm and 2.5 cm as radii, respectively, to intersect at *D*.

Step 5: Join *AD* and *CD*. *ABCD* is the required parallelogram.

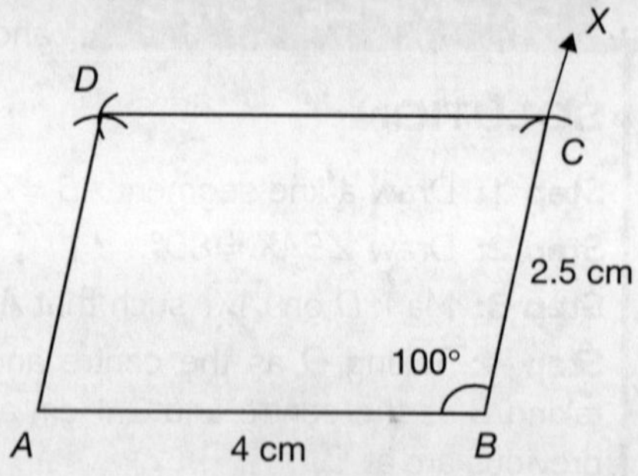

Figure 9.75

5. Construction of a parallelogram when two adjacent sides and one diagonal are given.

EXAMPLE 9.20 Construct a parallelogram *PQRS*, when *PQ* = 3.7 cm, *QR* = 2.3 cm and *PR* = 4.8 cm.

Step 1: Draw a line segment *PQ* = 3.7 cm.

Step 2: Draw an arc with *P* as the centre and a radius of 4.8 cm.

Step 3: With *Q* as the centre and *QR* = 2.3 cm, draw another arc to intersect the previous arc of Step 2 at *R* and join *QR*.

Step 4: With *R* as the centre, draw an arc of radius 3.7 cm.

Step 5: With *P* as the centre, draw another arc of radius 2.3 cm to intersect the arc in Step 4 at *S*. Join *RS* and *PS*.

PQRS is the required parallelogram.

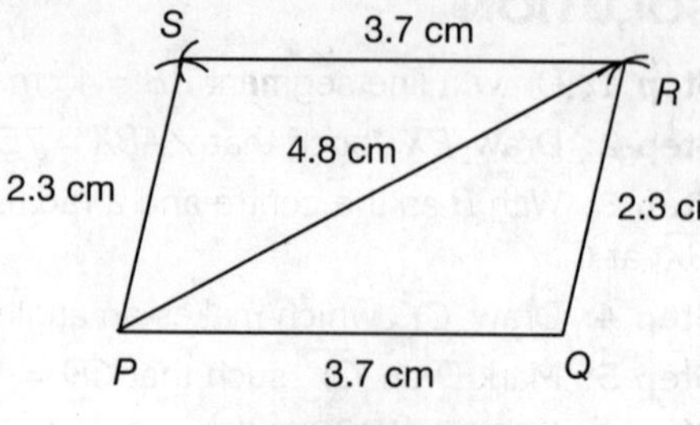

Figure 9.76

6. Construction of a parallelogram when both the diagonals and the angle between them are given.

EXAMPLE 9.21 Construct a parallelogram $PQRS$ with $PR = 3$ cm, $QS = 4.2$ cm and the angle between the diagonals equal to 75°.

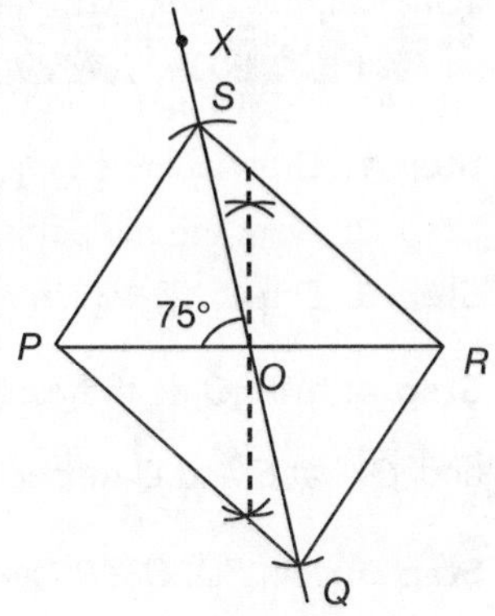

Figure 9.77

SOLUTION

Step 1: Draw the diagonal $PR = 3$ cm.

Step 2: Bisect PR to mark the mid-point of PR as O.

Step 3: Construct an angle of 75°at O, such that $\angle POX = 75°$.

Step 4: Taking O as the centre and radius $= \frac{1}{2}(QS) = \frac{1}{2} \times 4.2 = 2.1$ cm, draw arcs on the angular line constructed in Step 3 to cut at Q and S.

Step 5: Join PQ, QR, RS, and SP to obtain the required parallelogram $PQRS$.

7. Construction of a rectangle when two adjacent sides are given.

EXAMPLE 9.22 Construct a rectangle $PQRS$ with $PQ = 5.2$ cm and $QR = 2.6$ cm.

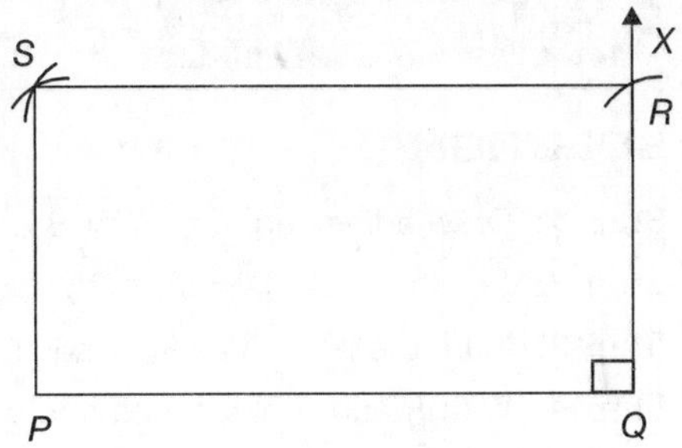

Figure 9.78

Step 1: Draw $PQ = 5.2$ cm.

Step 2: At Q, construct a right angle, such that $\angle PQX = 90°$.

Step 3: Taking Q as the centre and 2.6 cm as radius, draw an arc to cut $\overrightarrow{QX}$ at R.

Step 4: With R and P as centres, draw two arcs with radii 5.2 cm and 2.6 cm, respectively, to cut each other at S. Join PS and RS. $PQRS$ is the required rectangle.

8. Construction of a rectangle when a side and a diagonal are given.

EXAMPLE 9.23 Construct a rectangle $PQRS$ with $PQ = 5.3$ cm and diagonal $PR = 5.8$ cm.

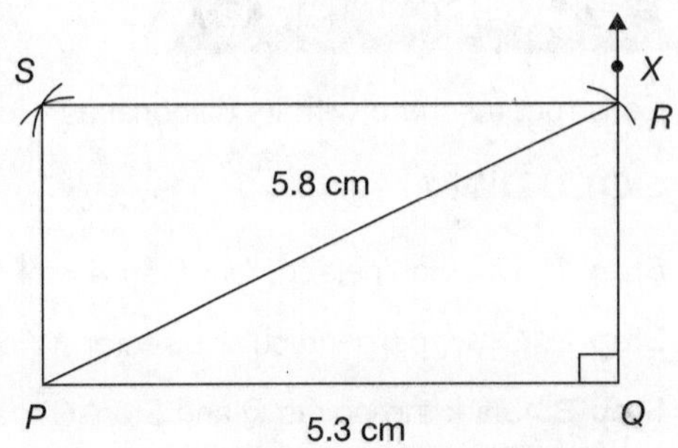

Figure 9.79

SOLUTION

Step 1: Draw a line segment $PQ = 5.3$ cm.

Step 2: At Q, construct $\angle PQX = 90°$.

Step 3: Taking P as the centre and 5.8 cm as radius, draw an arc to cut $\overrightarrow{QX}$ at R.

Step 4: With R and Q as centres, 5.3 cm and 5.8 cm respectively as radii, draw two arcs to intersect each other at S.

Step 5: Join RS and PS to form the required rectangle $PQRS$.

9. Construction of a rectangle when one diagonal and the angle between two diagonals are given.

EXAMPLE 9.24

Construct a rectangle *PQRS*, such that *PR* = 5.2 cm and the angle between the diagonals is 50°.

Step 1: Draw a line segment *PR* = 5.2 cm.

Step 2: Mark the midpoint of *PR* as *O*.

Step 3: Draw $\overleftrightarrow{XY}$ which makes an angle of 50° with $\overline{PR}$ at the point *O*.

Step 4: With *O* as the centre and with radius equal to $\frac{1}{2}(PR) = 2.6$ cm, cut $\overrightarrow{OX}$ and $\overrightarrow{OY}$ at *S* and *Q* respectively.

Step 5: Join *PQ*, *QR*, *RS* and *PS* to form the required rectangle *PQRS*.

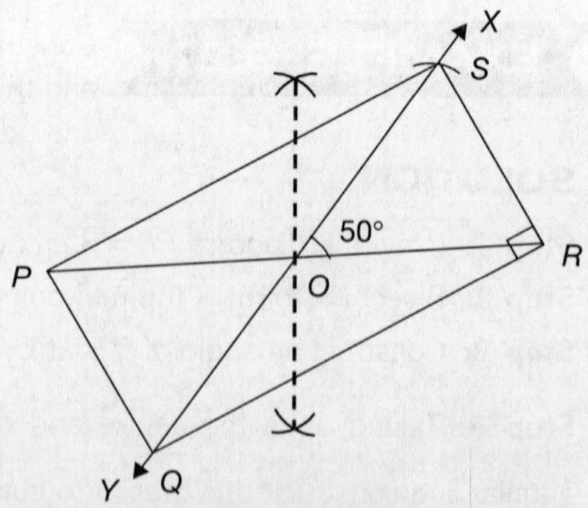

Figure 9.80

10. Construction of a square when one side is given.

EXAMPLE 9.25

Construct a square of side 3 cm.

SOLUTION

Step 1: Draw a line segment *PQ* = 3 cm.

Step 2: Construct ∠*PQX* = 90°.

Step 3: Mark the point *R* on $\overrightarrow{QX}$, such that *QR* = 3 cm.

Step 4: With *R* and *P* as centres and with radii of 3 cm each draw two arcs to intersect each other at *S*.

Step 5: Join *PS* and *RS* to form the required square *PQRS*.

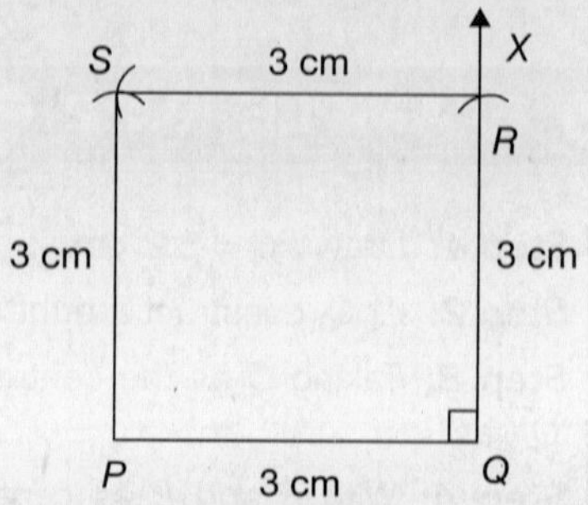

Figure 9.81

11. Construction of a square when a diagonal is given.

EXAMPLE 9.26

Construct a square with its diagonal as 4 cm.

SOLUTION

Step 1: Draw a line segment *PR* = 4 cm.

Step 2: Draw perpendicular bisector *XY* of $\overline{PR}$ to bisect $\overline{PR}$ at *O*.

Step 3: Mark the points *Q* and *S* on $\overrightarrow{OY}$ and $\overrightarrow{OX}$, respectively, such that *OQ* = *OS* = 2 cm.

Step 4: Join *PS*, *RS*, *PQ*, and *QR* to form the required square *PQRS*.

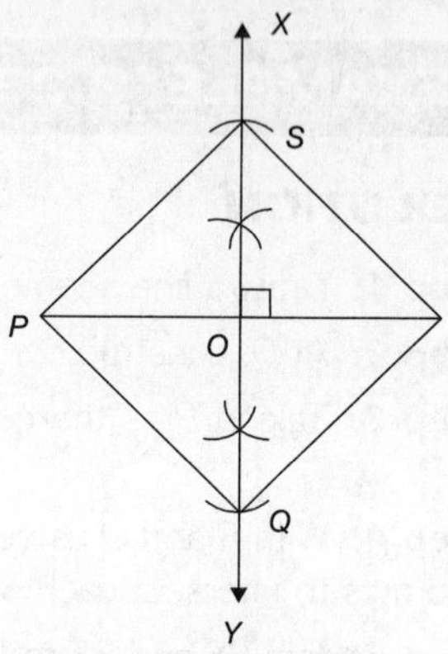

Figure 9.82

12. Construction of a rhombus when one side and one angle are given.

EXAMPLE 9.27 Construct a rhombus $PQRS$ with $PQ = 3.6$ cm and $\angle P = 50°$.

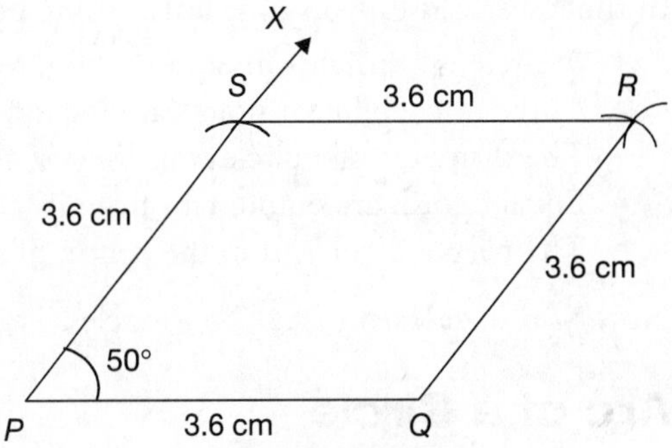

Figure 9.83

SOLUTION

Step 1: Draw a line segment $PQ = 3.6$ cm.

Step 2: Construct $\angle QPX = 50°$.

Step 3: Taking P as the centre and a radius equal to 3.6 cm, draw an arc to cut $\overline{PX}$ at S, such that $PS = 3.6$ cm.

Step 4: From Q and S, draw two arcs with radii 3.6 cm each to meet each other at R.

Step 5: Join QR and SR to form the required rhombus $PQRS$.

13. Construction of rhombus when one side and one diagonal are given.

EXAMPLE 9.28 Construct a rhombus $PQRS$, such that $PQ = 3.2$ cm and $PR = 4.2$ cm.

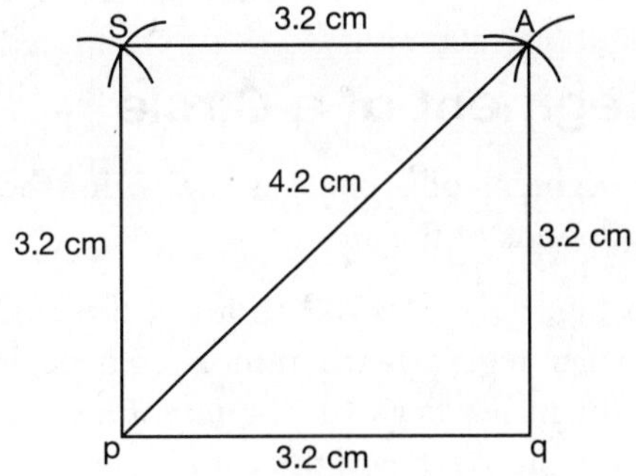

Figure 9.84

SOLUTION

Step 1: Draw a line segment $PQ = 3.2$ cm.

Step 2: Taking P as the centre and radius equal to 4.2 cm, draw an arc and taking Q as centre, radius as 3.2 cm draw another arc to cut the previous arc at R.

Step 3: With R and P as centres and the radii equal to 3.2 cm each, draw two arcs to meet at S.

Step 4: Join PS, RS, and QR to form rhombus $PQRS$.

14. Construction of a rhombus when both the diagonals are given.

EXAMPLE 9.29 Construct a rhombus $PQRS$ with diagonal $PR = 3.4$ cm and $QS = 3.6$ cm.

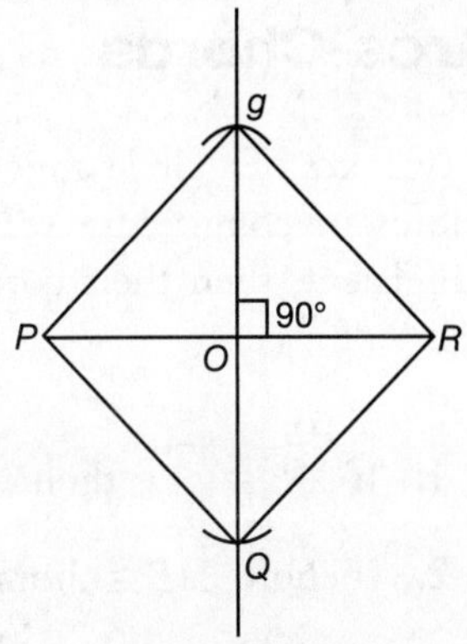

Figure 9.85

SOLUTION

Step 1: Draw a line segment $PR = 3.4$ cm.

Step 2: Bisect PR and mark its mid-point as O.

Step 3: With O as the centre and radii 1.8 cm each, draw arcs on either sides of PR to cut perpendicular bisector of PR at Q and S.

Step 4: Join PS, PQ, QR, and RS to form the required rhombus $PQRS$.

Circles

In the lower classes, you have learnt some properties of a circle, like:

- A circle is a simple closed round figure.
- Three non-collinear points are required to construct a unique circle.
- The diameter of a circle is its longest chord.
- Equal chords are equidistant from its centre.
- The perpendicular from the centre of a circle to a chord in the circle bisects it.

Now, you shall learn more about circles.

Arc of a Circle

An arc is a part of a circle. In Fig. 9.86, the two parts of the circle between A and B are arcs. When the two arcs are unequal, the shorter one is called the minor arc and the longer one is called the major arc.

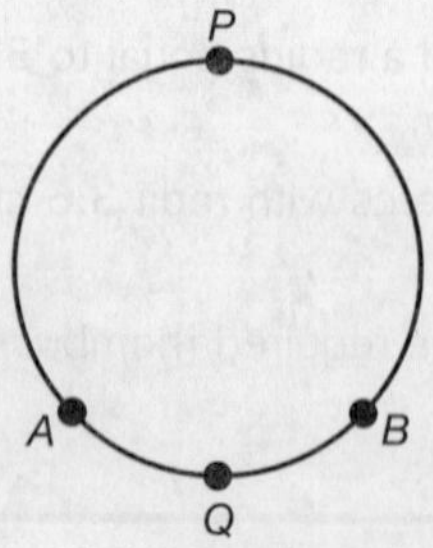

Figure 9.86

Konnect

In Fig. 9.86, *AQB* is the minor arc and *APB* is the major arc.

Semi-circle

The diameter of a circle divides it into two equal arcs. Each arc is called a semi-circle.

Segment of a Circle

A segment of a circle is the region between the arc of the circle and the chord joining the endpoints of the arc.

In Fig. 9.87, AB is a chord of the circle. Chord AB divides the circle into two regions. The smaller region is the minor segment and the larger region is the major segment. The minor segment lies between the minor arc ACB and chord AB. The major segment lies between the major arc ADB and the chord AB.

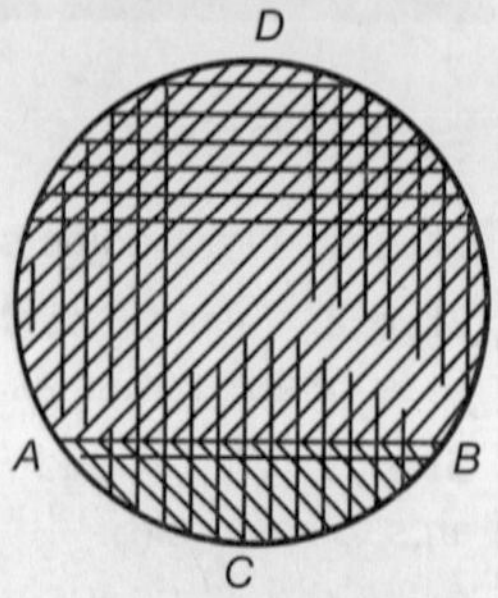

Figure 9.87

Congruence of Circles

Circles having equal radii are congruent. Two arcs of a circle (or of congruent circles), which subtend equal angles at the centre (or at the corresponding centres) are equal in length. Two chords of the same or different circles are said to be congruent, if they have the same length.

Arcs-Chords

If two arcs of a circle are congruent, then their corresponding chords are congruent. Conversely, if two chords of a circle are congruent, then their corresponding arcs are congruent (see Fig. 9.88).

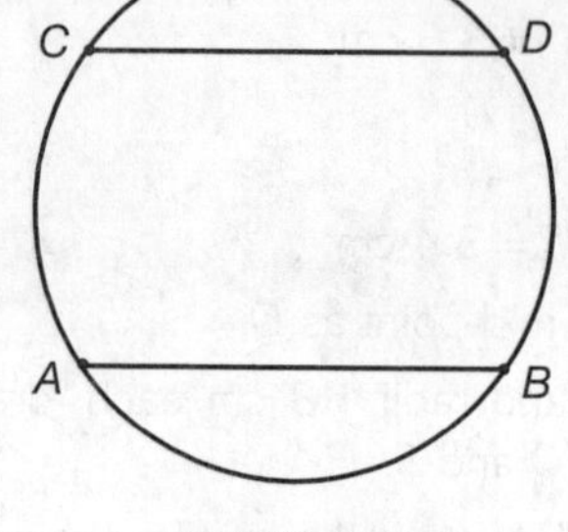

Figure 9.88

Info Bytes!

The theorem of arcs-chords holds good for two congruent circles also.

1. If $\overset{\frown}{AB} \cong \overset{\frown}{CD}$, then chord $AB \cong$ chord CD.
2. If chord $AB \cong$ chord CD, then $\overset{\frown}{AB} \cong \overset{\frown}{CD}$.

If two circles C_1 and C_2 are congruent, and PQ is a chord in C_1 and RS is a chord in C_2, such that $\overline{PQ} \cong \overline{RS}$, then $\widehat{PQ} \cong \widehat{RS}$.

Theorem 1

The angle subtended by an arc at the centre of a circle is double the angle subtended by the same arc at any point on the remaining part of the circle.

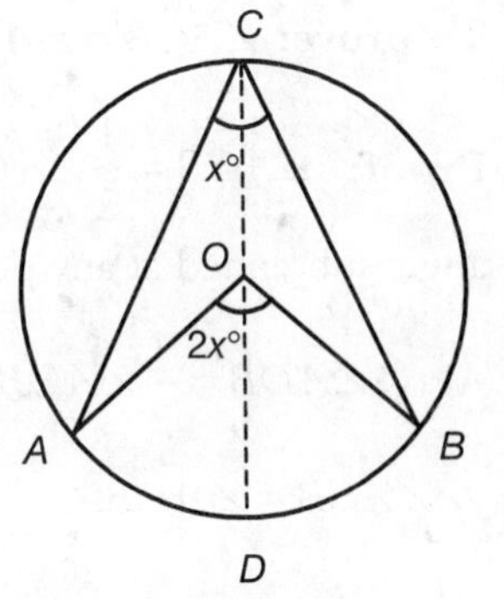

Figure 9.89

Given: In Fig. 9.89, $\angle AOB$ is subtended by the $\widehat{AB}$ at the centre O and $\angle ACB$ is subtended by the same arc AB at a point C on the remaining part of the circle.

The centre of the circle O may lie in the interior, the exterior or on $\angle ACB$.

Case 1: Centre O lies in the interior of $\angle ACB$.

Case 2: Centre O lies on $\angle ACB$.

Case 3: Centre O lies in the exterior of $\angle ACB$.

Construction: Join C and O and produce CO to D.

Proof

Case 1: Centre O lies in the interior of $\angle ACB$.

In triangle OCA,

$\angle OCA = \angle OAC$ (Angles opposite to equal sides OC, OA, the radii of the circle.)

$\angle AOD = \angle OCA + \angle OAC$ (Exterior angle is equal to the sum of the interior opposite angles)

$= 2\angle OCA.$

Similarly, $\angle DOB = 2\angle OCB$

$\therefore \angle AOB = 2\angle OCA + 2\angle OCB$

$\Rightarrow \angle AOB = 2\angle ACB.$

Hence, proved.

Similarly, it can be proved in the other two cases mentioned above.

EXAMPLE 9.30 In the figure, 'O' is the centre of the circle. ΔABC is inscribed in the circle. $\angle ACD$ is the exterior angle of ΔABC. If $\angle AOB = \angle ACD$, then find the value of $\angle ACB$.

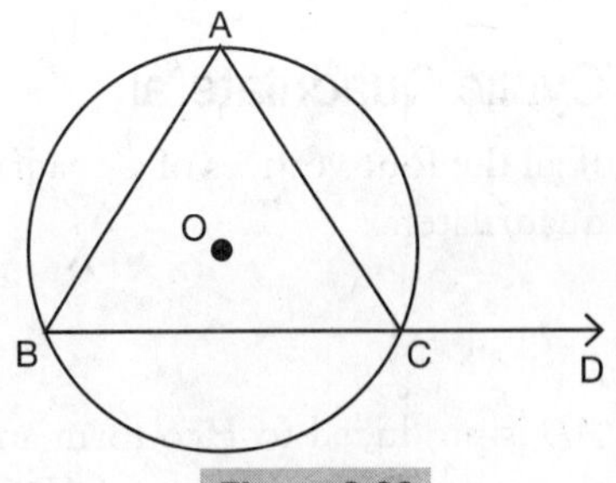

Figure 9.90

SOLUTION

Given $\angle AEB = 36°$ and arc AB = arc BC

$\Rightarrow \angle AEB = \angle BDC = 36°$

$\angle AOC = \angle AOB + \angle BOC$

$= 2(\angle AEB + \angle BDC) = 2(2 \times 36°) = 144°$

$\therefore$ Reflex $\angle AOC = 360° - 144° = 216°$.

EXAMPLE 9.31 In the figure, O is the centre of the circle. If $\angle POR = 120°$ and $\angle ORQ = 70°$, then $\angle OPQ$ measures ______.

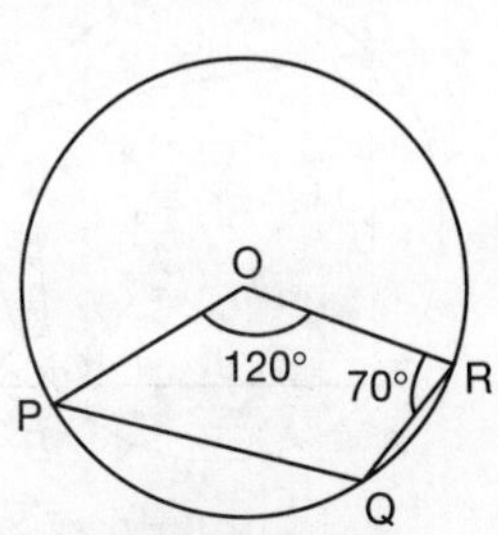

Figure 9.91

SOLUTION

$\angle PQR = 180° - \dfrac{120°}{2}$

$= 180° - 60° = 120°.$

$\therefore \angle OPQ = 360° - (120° + 120° + 70°) = 360° - 310° = 50°$

Theorem 2

Angles in the same segment of a circle are equal.

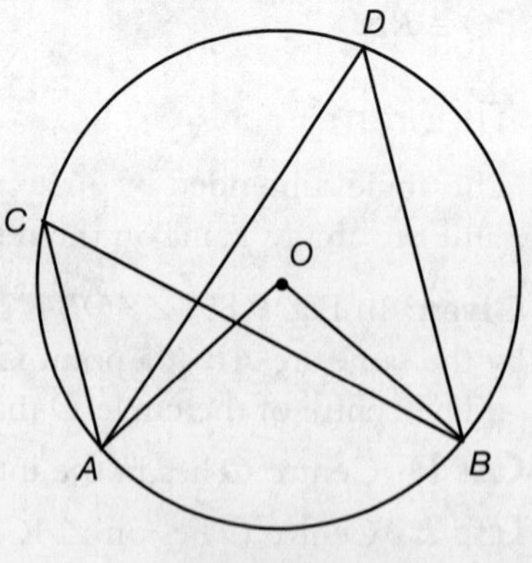

Figure 9.92

Given: O is the centre of the circle. A, B, C and D are the points on the circle as shown in Fig. 9.92.
To prove: $\angle ACB = \angle ADB$.

Proof: $\angle ACB = \frac{1}{2}\angle AOB$ (Angle subtended by an arc at the centre is double the angle subtended at any point on the remaining part of the circle.)

Also, $\angle ADB = \frac{1}{2}\angle AOB$ (Using the above rule).

$\therefore \angle ACB = \angle ADB$.

Theorem 3

An angle in a semi-circle is a right angle.

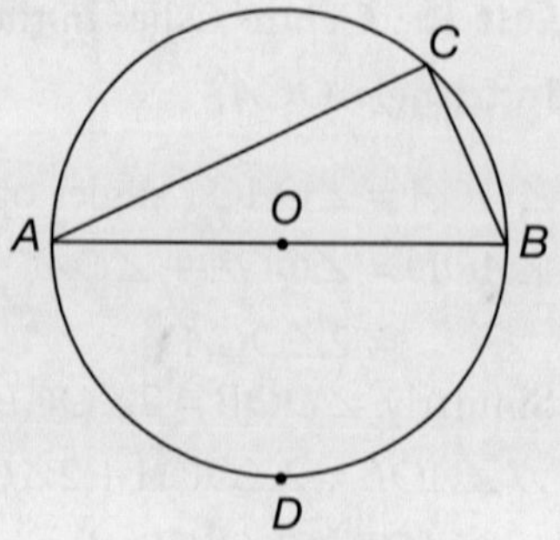

Figure 9.93

Given: AB is the diameter of the circle (see Fig. 9.93).
To prove: $\angle ACB = 90°$

Proof: $\overset{\frown}{ADB}$ is an arc, making an angle 180° at the centre O. (AOB is a straight line).

$$\therefore \angle ACB = \frac{1}{2}\angle AOB = \frac{1}{2}(180°).$$

$\therefore \angle ACB = 90°$.

Corollary If an arc of a circle subtends a right angle at any point on the remaining part of the circle, it is a semi-circle.

Cyclic Quadrilateral

If all the four vertices of a quadrilateral lie on one circle, then the quadrilateral is called a cyclic quadrilateral.

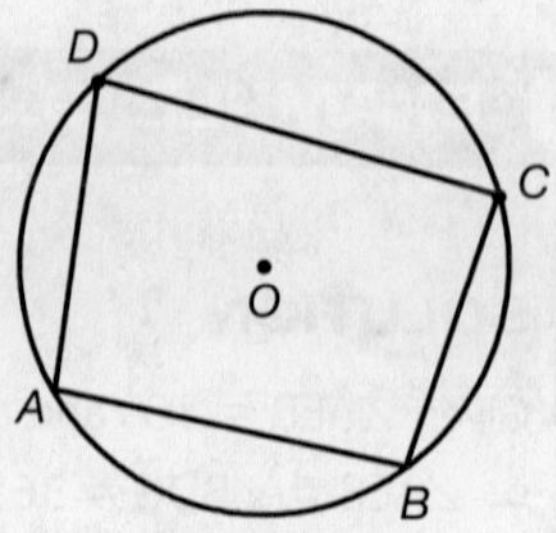

Figure 9.94

In Fig. 9.95, $ABCD$ is a cyclic quadrilateral.

AB is produced to E to form an exterior angle, $\angle CBE$ and it is equal to the interior angle at the opposite vertex, i.e., $\angle ADC$.

$\therefore \angle CBE = \angle ADC$

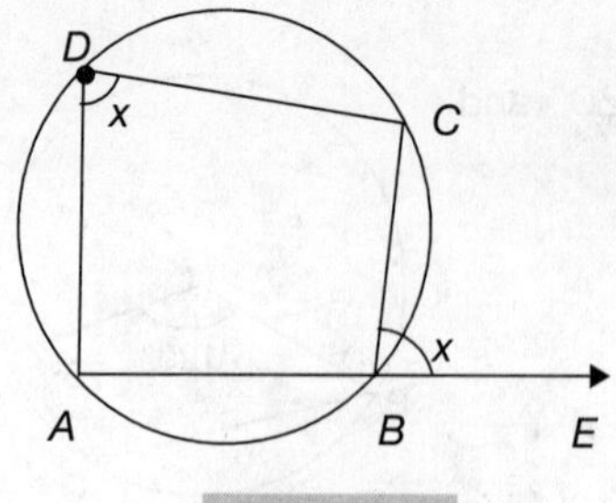

Figure 9.95

Konnect

1. Opposite angles in a cyclic quadrilateral are **supplementary**.
2. In a quadrilateral, if the opposite angles are supplementary, then the quadrilateral is a cyclic quadrilateral.
   In Fig. 9.93, $ABCD$ is a cyclic quadrilateral.
   $$\angle A + \angle C = 180° \text{ and } \angle B + \angle D = 180°$$
3. Exterior angle of a cyclic quadrilateral is equal to the interior opposite angle.

EXAMPLE 9.32

In the given figure, 'O' is the centre of the circle and A, E and C are collinear. If AB = BC If ∠ADE = 45° then ∠ACB = ______.

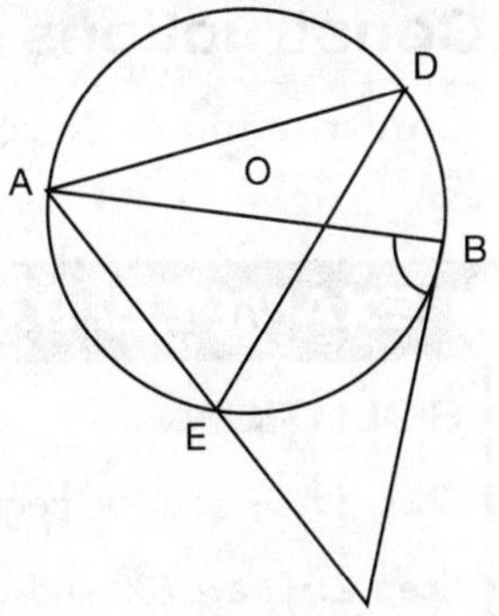

SOLUTION

Given, ∠ADE = 45°

Join BE

∠ABE = ∠ADE = 45°

(∵ Angles in the same segment of a circle are equal)

∠AEB = 90° (∵ An angle in a semicircle is a right angle)

In ΔABE,

∠ABE + ∠BEA + ∠EAB = 180°

45° + 90° + ∠EAB = 180°

∠EAB = 45°

⇒ ∠CAB = 45°

∴ (A = BC) ∠ACB = ∠CAB = 45°

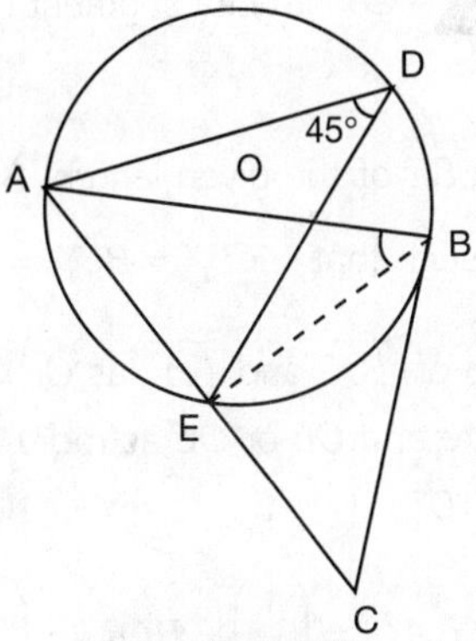

Figure 9.96

EXAMPLE 9.33

A and *B* are the centres of the circles as shown in the given figure. The circles intersect at *C* and *D*. Find ∠*CED* + ∠*CFD*.

(a) 90° **(b)** 135° **(c)** 120° **(d)** 150°

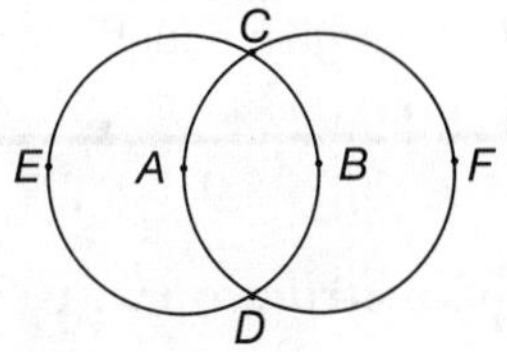

SOLUTION

(i) Join *AB*, which is the radius of both the circles.

(ii) *AC* = *AD* = *BC* = *BD* = radius.

(iii) Δ*ABC* and Δ*ABD* are equilateral triangles. ∠*CAD* = ∠*BAD* = 120°.

(iv) $\angle CED = \angle CFD = \frac{1}{2}\angle CAD = \frac{1}{2}\angle CBD.$

(Angle at the centre is equal to half the angle at the circumference).

EXAMPLE 9.34

In the figure, two congruent circles intersect each other at P and Q, each circle is passing through the centre of the other circle.

If AQB is a straight line and PA = PB, then find the value of ∠PDQ.

(a) 60° **(b)** 30° **(c)** 90° **(d)** 45°

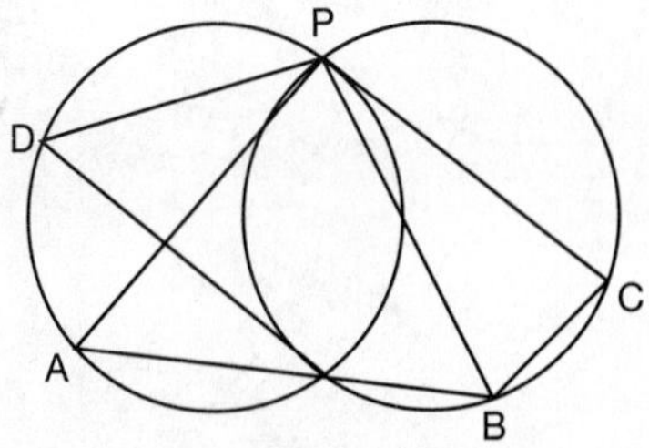

SOLUTION

Let C_1, C_2 are the centers of the circle.

Join PQ.

Since PA = PB, PQ ⊥ AB

Since $PC_1 = PC_2 = C_1C_2$ (radii)

$\angle C_1PC_2 = 60°$ ⇒ ∠APQ = 30° and ∠AQP = 90°

⇒ ∠PAQ = 60°

⇒ ∠PDQ = 60° (Angles in the same segment)

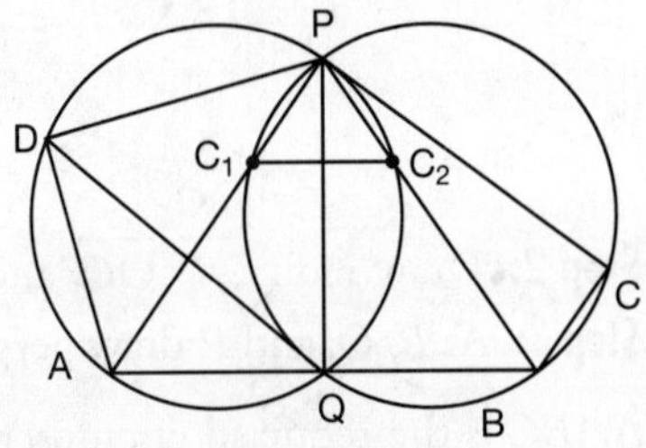

Constructions Related to Circles

Construction 1: To construct a segment of a circle, on a given chord and containing a given angle.

EXAMPLE 9.35 Construct a segment of a circle with a chord of length 8.5 cm and containing an angle of 55°.

SOLUTION

Step 1: Draw a line segment BC of the given length, 8.5 cm.

Step 2: Draw $\overline{BX}$ and $\overline{CY}$, such that $\angle CBX = BCY = \dfrac{180-2\theta}{2} = 35°$.

Step 3: Mark the intersection of $\overrightarrow{BX}$ and $\overrightarrow{CY}$ as O.

Step 4: Taking O as the centre and OB or OC as radius, draw $\widehat{BAC}$.

Step 5: In ΔBOC, $\angle BOC = 110°$

$$\Rightarrow \angle BAC = \left(\frac{1}{2}\right)\angle BOC = \left(\frac{1}{2}\right)(110°) = 55°.$$

$\therefore \angle BAC = 55°$.

The region bounded by $\widehat{BAC}$ and $\overline{BC}$ is the required segment.

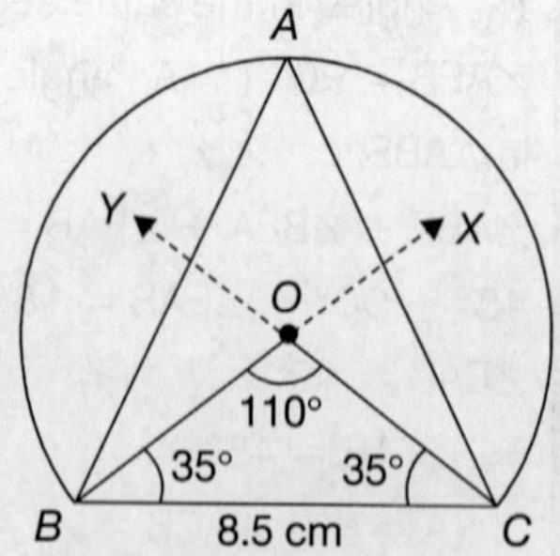

Figure 9.97

Construction 2: Construct an equilateral triangle inscribed in a circle of radius 3.5 cm.

Step 1: Draw a csircle of radius 3.5 cm and mark its centre as O.
Step 2: Draw radii $\overline{OA}$, $\overline{OB}$ and $\overline{OC}$, such that $\angle AOB = \angle BOC = 120°$.
Step 3: Join AB, BC and CA, which is the required equilateral ΔABC in the given circle.

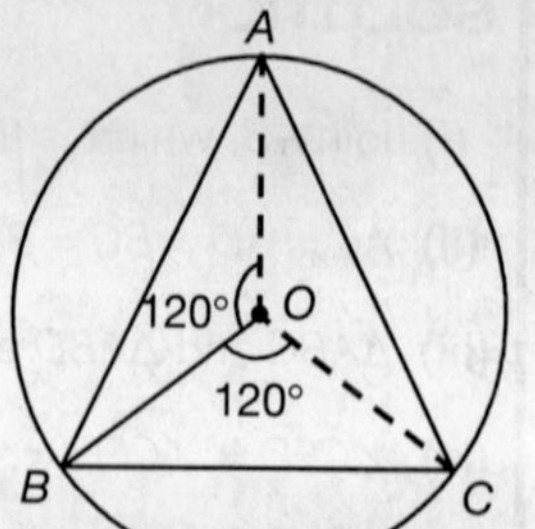

Figure 9.98

Construction 3: Construct an equilateral triangle circumscribing a circle of radius 3 cm.

Step 1: Draw a circle of radius 3 cm with centre O.

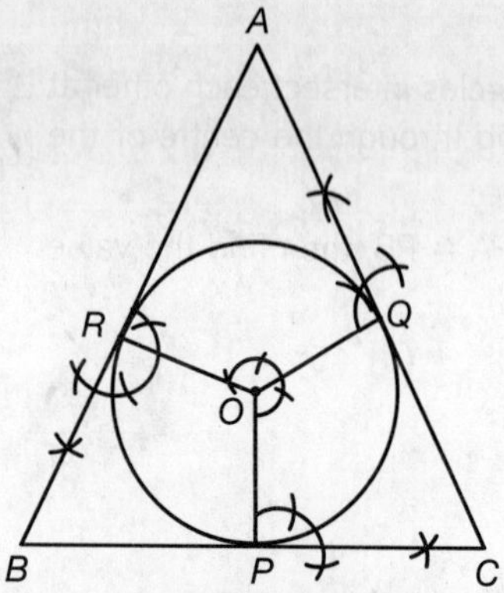

Figure 9.99

Step 2: Draw radii $\overline{OP}$, $\overline{OQ}$ and $\overline{OR}$, such that $\angle POR = \angle ROQ = 120°$.
Step 3: At P, Q, and R draw perpendiculars to $\overline{OP}$, $\overline{OQ}$, and $\overline{OR}$, respectively, to form ΔABC.

ΔABC is the required circumscribing equilateral triangle.

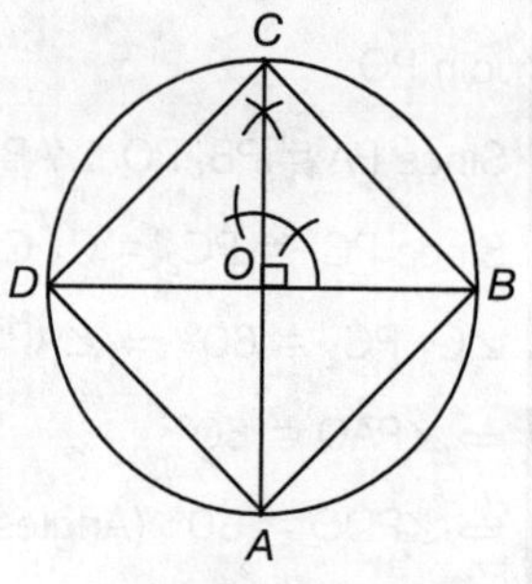

Figure 9.100

Construction 4: Construct a square inscribed in a circle of radius 3 cm.

Step 1: Draw a circle of radius 3 cm and mark the centre as O.

Step 2: Draw diameters $\overline{AC}$ and $\overline{BD}$, such that $\overline{AC} \perp \overline{BD}$.

Step 3: Join AB, BC, CD and DA. Quadrilateral $ABCD$ is the required square inscribed in the given circle.

Construction 5: Construct a square circumscribing a circle of radius 2.5 cm.

Step 1: Draw a circle of radius 2.5 cm.

Step 2: Draw two mutually perpendicular diameters $\overline{PR}$ and $\overline{SQ}$.

Step 3: At P, Q, R, and S, draw lines perpendicular to OP, OQ, OR, and OS to form square $ABCD$ as shown in Fig. 9.101.

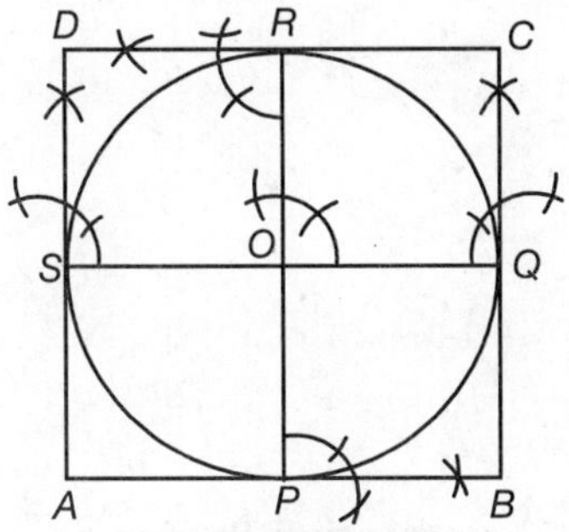

Figure 9.101

Construction 6: Inscribe a regular hexagon in a circle of radius 3 cm.

Step 1: Draw a circle of radius 3 cm taking the centre as O.

Step 2: Draw radius $\overline{OA}$. With radius equal to OA and starting with A as the centre, mark points B, C, D, E, and F one after the other.

Step 3: Join A, B, C, D, E, and F. Polygon $ABCDEF$ is the required hexagon.

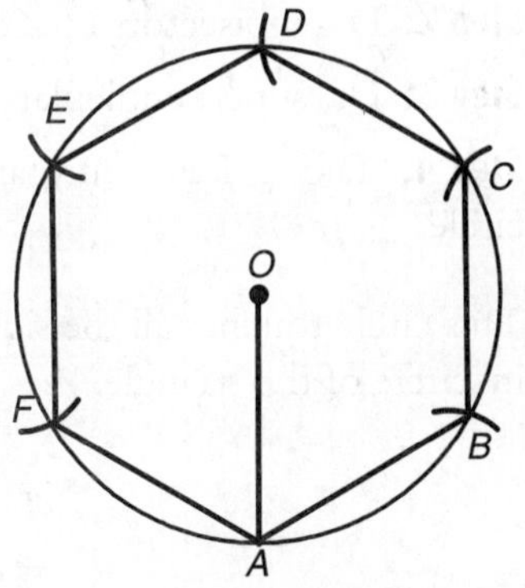

Figure 9.102

Construction 7: Construct a regular hexagon circumscribing a circle of radius 3.5 cm.

Step 1: Draw a circle of radius 3.5 cm and mark its centre as O.

Step 2: Draw radii $\overline{OP}, \overline{OQ}, \overline{OR}, \overline{OS}, \overline{OT}$ and $\overline{OU}$, such that the angle between any two adjacent radii is 60°.

Step 3: Draw lines at P, Q, R, S, T, and U perpendicular to $\overline{OP}, \overline{OQ}, \overline{OR}, \overline{OS}, \overline{OT}$, and $\overline{OU}$, respectively, to form the required hexagon $ABCDEF$.

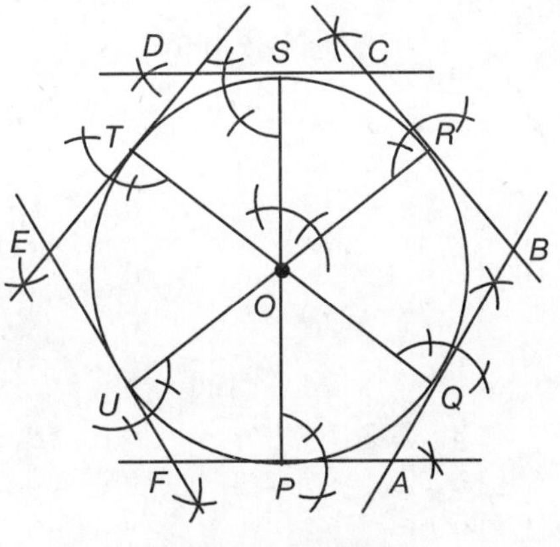

Figure 9.103

Construction 8: Draw the circum-circle of a given triangle.

Step 1: Draw ΔABC with the given measurements.

Step 2: Draw perpendicular bisectors of $\overline{AB}$ and $\overline{AC}$ to intersect each other at S.

Step 3: Taking S as the centre and radius equal to AS or BS or CS, draw a circle. The circle passes through all the vertices A, B, and C of the triangle.

∴ The circle drawn is the required circum-circle.

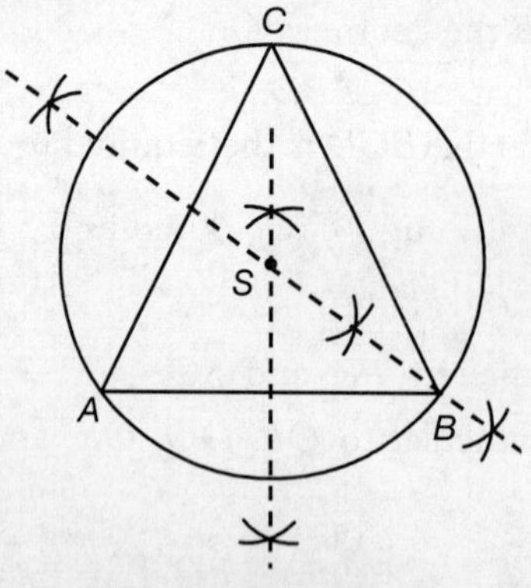

Figure 9.104

Konnect

The circum-centre is equidistant from the vertices of the triangle.

Construction 9: Construct the in-circle of a given triangle ABC.

Step 1: Draw a ΔABC with the given measurements.

Step 2: Draw bisectors of $\angle B$ and $\angle C$ to intersect at I.

Step 3: Draw perpendicular $\overline{IM}$ from I onto $\overline{BC}$.

Step 4: Taking I as centre and IM as the radius, draw a circle.

This circle touches all the sides of the triangle. This is the in-circle of the triangle.

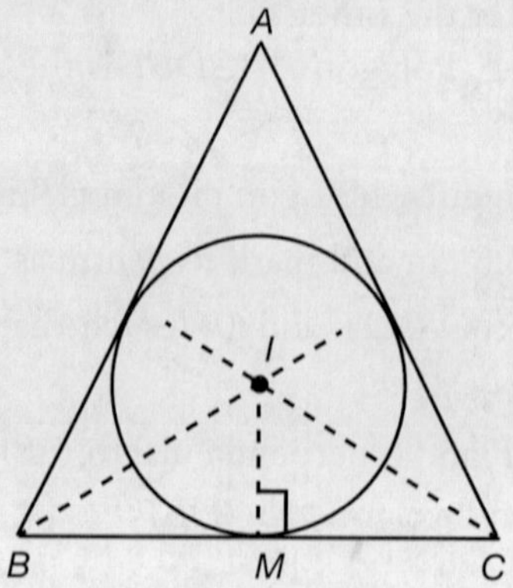

Figure 9.105

Info Bytes!

The in-centre is equidistant from all the sides of the triangle.

POINTS TO REMEMBER

- ✔ A line is a set of infinite points. It has no end points. It is infinite in length.
- ✔ A line segment is a part of a line. The line segment has two end points and it has a finite length.
- ✔ A ray has one end point and it extends infinitely on the other side.
- ✔ Two rays which have a common end point form an angle.
- ✔ Two intersecting lines making an angle of 90° are called perpendicular lines.
- ✔ If a line divides a line segment into two equal parts and is also perpendicular, then it is a perpendicular bisector.
- ✔ When the sum of two angles is 90°, then the two angles are said to be complementary angles.
- ✔ When the sum of two angles is 180°, then the two angles are called supplementary angles.
- ✔ If a line divides an angle into two angles of equal magnitudes, then it is the bisector of that angle.
- ✔ If two angles have a common end point and a common side and the other two sides lie on either side of the common side, they are said to be adjacent angles.
- ✔ Two co-planar lines that do not have a common point are called parallel lines.
- ✔ A straight line intersecting a pair of straight lines in two distinct points is a transversal for the two given lines.
- ✔ A closed figure bounded by four line segments is called a quadrilateral.
- ✔ In a parallelogram, if all the sides are equal, then it is called a rhombus.
- ✔ In a quadrilateral, if two pairs of adjacent sides are equal, then it is called a kite.
- ✔ In a triangle, the line segment joining the mid-points of any two sides is parallel to the third side and also half of it.
- ✔ In a triangle, if a line is drawn parallel to one side of the triangle, then it divides the other two sides in the same ratio.
- ✔ Two figures are said to be congruent, if they have the same shape and same size. But the figures of the same shape need not have the same size.
- ✔ A closed plane figure bounded by three or more line segments is called a polygon.
- ✔ A polygon in which each interior angle is less than 180° is called a convex polygon otherwise it is called concave polygon.
- ✔ The diameter of a circle divides it into two equal arcs. Each arc is called a semi-circle.

DW

PRACTICE QUESTIONS CLASSROOM WING

Very Short Answer Type Questions

Directions of questions from 1 to 7:
Fill in the blanks.

1. Two circles cannot intersect in more than _____ points.

2. In a quadrilateral, $ABCD$, $\angle DAB + \angle BCD = 180°$, then the quadrilateral $ABCD$ is ________.

3. In the figure, O is the centre of the circle. If $\angle AOC = x°$, then $\angle ABC$ is _______.

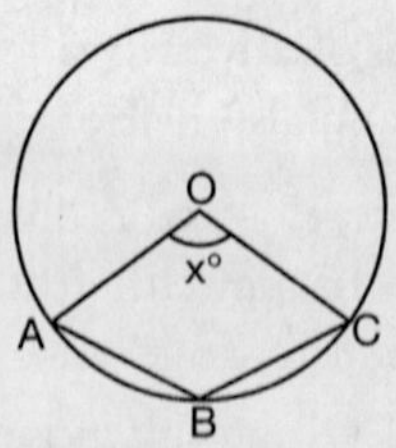

4. The sum of all the altitudes in a triangle is _______ the sum of all the sides. (equal to/less than/greater than)

5. Two lines AB and CD intersect at point O. $\angle AOD : \angle BOD = 3 : 1$, then $\angle AOD =$ ___________.

6. If the longest chord of a circle is of length 14 cm, then the circumference of the circle is ________ cm.

7. If AB and CD are two chords of a circle and $AB > CD$, then the chord which is nearer to the centre is ________.

Directions of questions from 8 to 19:
Answer the following questions.

8. In the given figure, O is centre of the circle and ABC is a straight line. BD = CD. If $\angle ABD = 140°$, then $\angle BCO =$ _____.

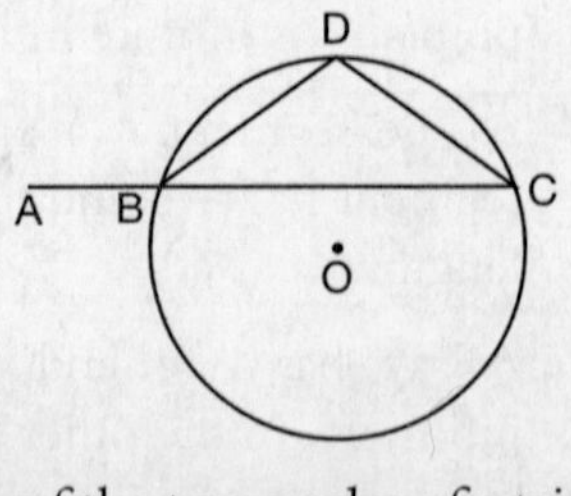

9. Can the sum of the two angles of a triangle be less than the third angle?
10. If all the sides of a polygon are equal, then all its interior angles must be equal. Is the given statement true?
11. Two quadrilaterals of equal perimeters occupy equal areas. Is this statement always true?
12. Can a polygon have the sum of all its interior angles equal to 810°?
13. If four lines intersect in a plane, at the maximum how many triangles are formed?
14. If all the angles of a quadrilateral are equal, then all its sides must be equal. Is the above statement true?
15. An angle is $\frac{2}{3}$ times its supplementary angle. What is the angle?
16. Are all the diagonals of a regular polygon always concurrent?
17. Are the diagonals of a regular polygon equal in length?
18. Can the length of the median in a triangle to a side be less than the corresponding altitude?
19. In a triangle ABC, D is a point on BC, such that AD is the shortest distance from A to BC and $\angle ADC = 70°$. Is it possible?

Short Answer Type Questions

20. In the following figure, $PQ \parallel RS$. If $\angle TRS = 105°$, $\angle PTR = 35°$, $\angle QPT = a°$, find the value of a.

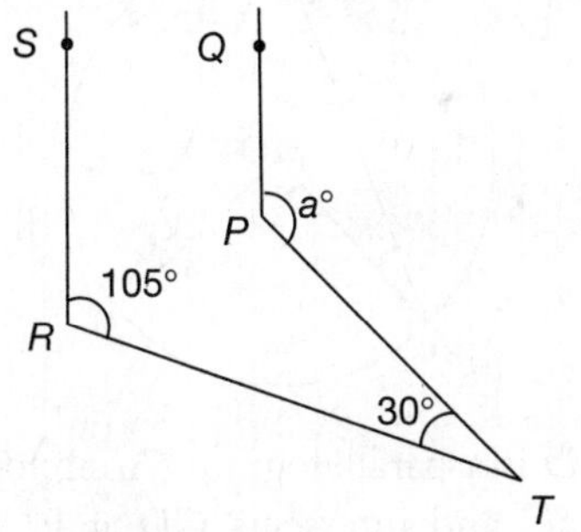

21. In the given figure, KLMN is a rhombus. P and Q are the mid-points of ML and MN respectively. If the area (KPMQ) = 24 cm^2, then find the area of the rhombus. (in cm^2)

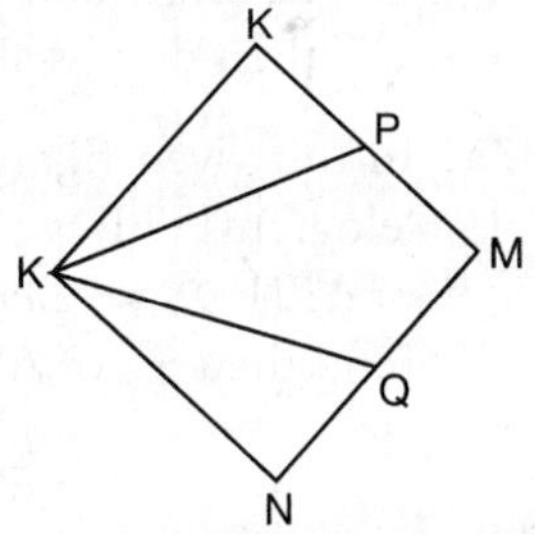

22. In the given figure, 'O' is the centre of a circle. AB and CD are two equal and parallel chords of the circle. If the distance between them is 14 cm and AB = 48 cm, then the radius of the circle is _______.

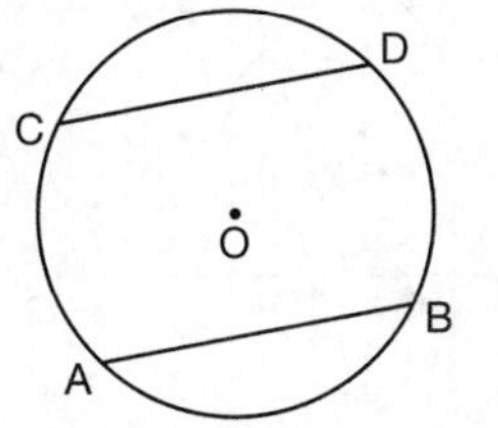

23. In the figure, O is the centre of the circle, ABC is a triangle inscribed in the circle. If ∠AOB = 100°, then find the value of the exterior angle ACD of the triangle ABC.

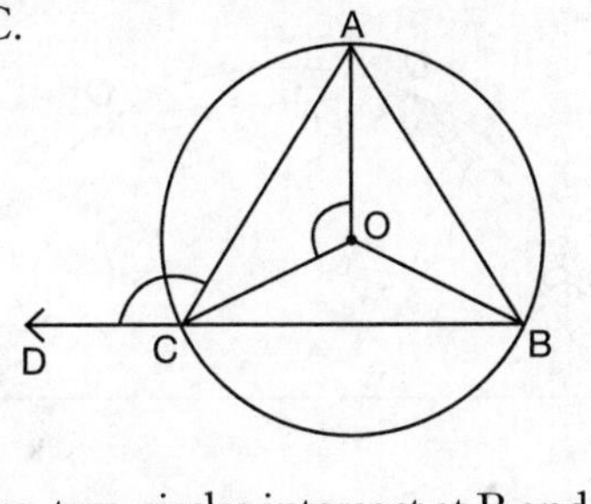

24. In the figure, two circles intersect at B and E. ABC, DEF are straight lines. If ∠CDF = 78°, then find ∠AFD.

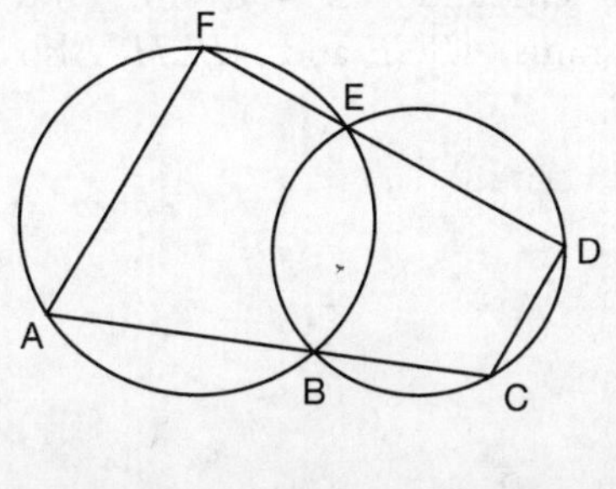

25. In the following figure, $\overline{CB}$ is produced to the point A. Find $\angle BDC$.

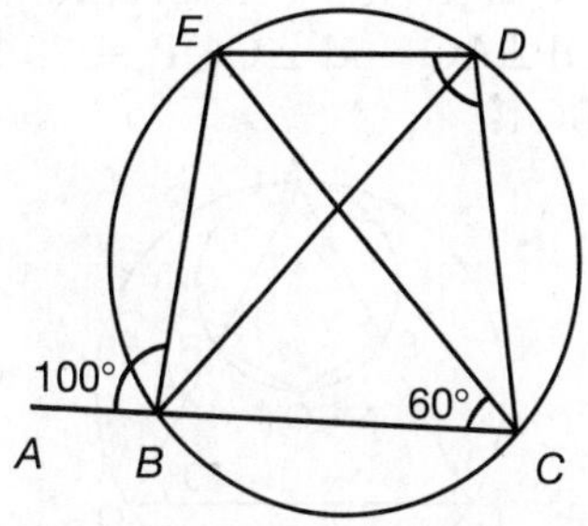

26. If the sum of the interior angles of a polygon is 2340°, then find the number of sides of the polygon.

27. In the following figure, if O is the centre of the circle and $\overline{AB}$ is the diameter, then find $\angle ACB$.

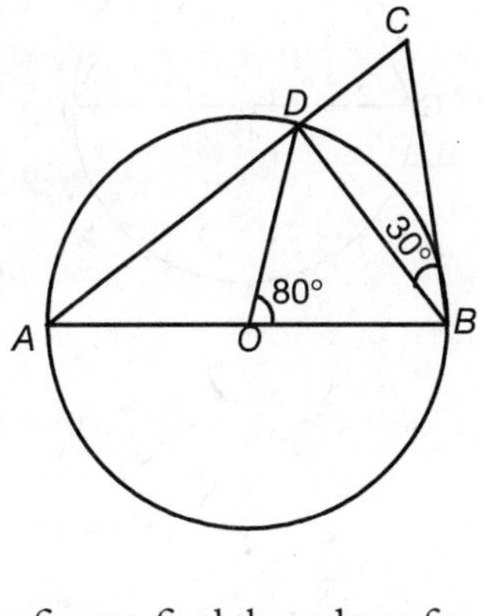

28. In the above figure, find the value of z, if x is two-third of y which is a complement of 45°.

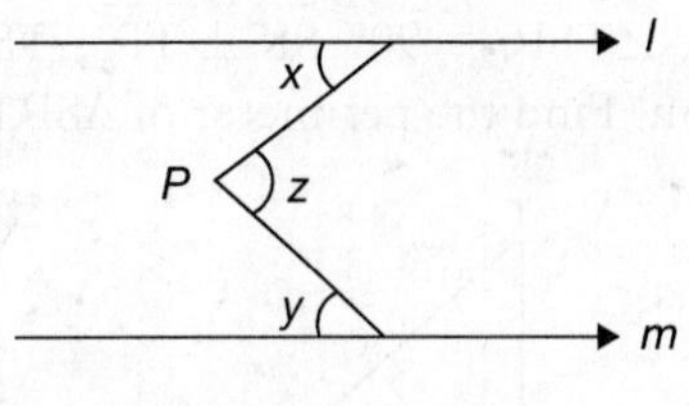

29. In the figure, A, B, C D and E are the points on the circle. If ∠DFB = 90°, AF = FB and ∠EAF = 24°, then find the value of ∠BCD.

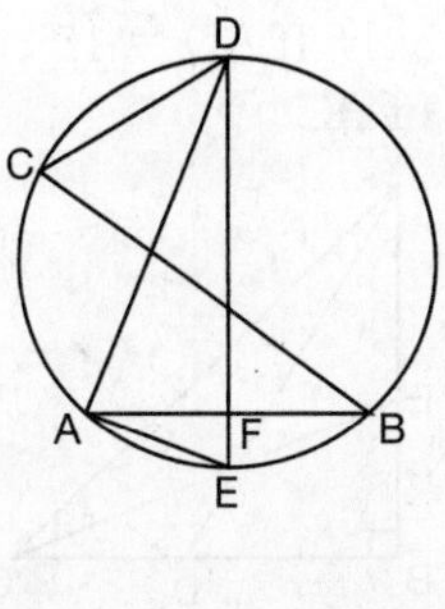

30. In the figure, O is the centre of the bigger circle. The smaller circle is touching the bigger circle internally at A and passing through the centre of the bigger circle. The straight lines ABC and APQ are intersecting the smaller circle at B and P respectively. If OB = OP, OB⊥AC, OP⊥AQ and ∠CQP = 79°, then find the value of ∠BOP.

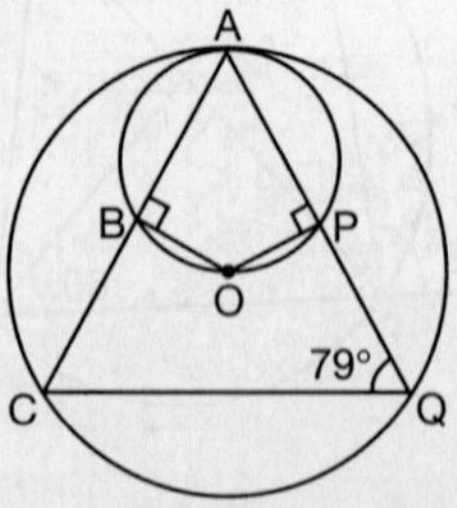

31. In the given figure, O is the centre of the circle. GJ, JI and IH are chords of the circle. GH is a diameter of the circle and GJ = OH = HI. ∠HIJ = ______.

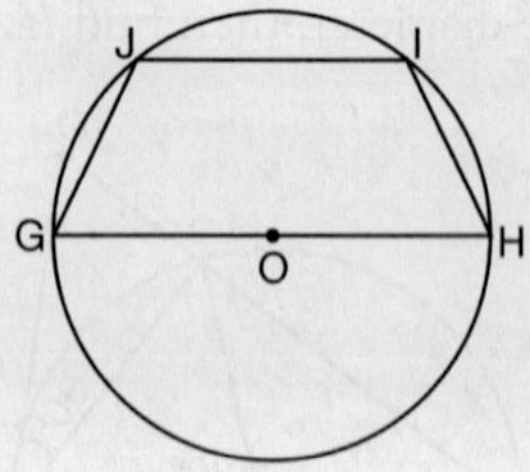

32. (A) In the following figure, O is the centre of the circle. If $x = 40°$ and $x : y = 4 : 3$, find the value of z.

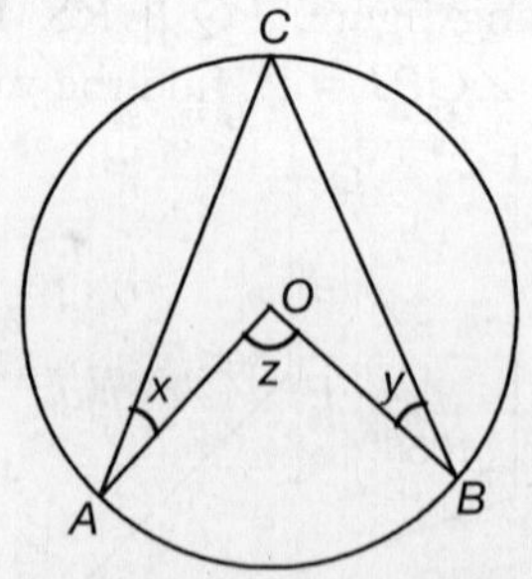

(B) *ABCD* is a parallelogram. A circle passes through A, B, C and intersects *CD* at E. If *BC* = 8 cm, then discuss about the measure of *AE*.

33. In the given figure, *PQRS* and *QRTV* are two parallelograms, *TV* is produced to meet *PQ* at *W*. The area of Δ*PWUS* = 72 cm² and the area of Δ*VWQ* = 24 cm². Find the area of Δ*TUR*.

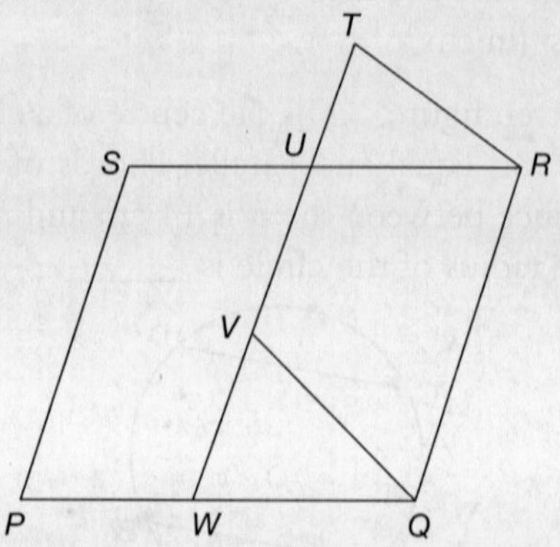

Essay Type Questions

34. In ΔTSR, ∠TSR = 90° $\overline{SK} \perp \overline{TR}$, TS = 5 cm and TK = 3 cm. Find the perimeter of ΔSRK (in cm).

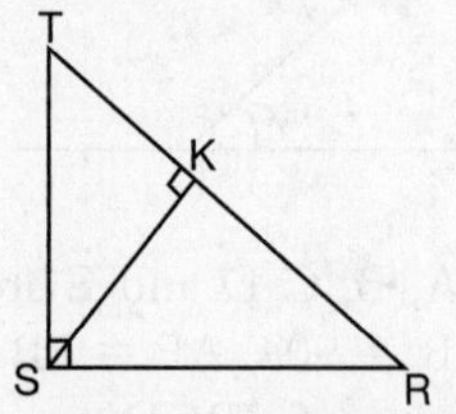

35. In ΔABC, ∠B = 90°, D and E are the midpoints of BC and AB respectively. If AD = 15 cm, CE = $\sqrt{360}$ cm, find the length of AC.

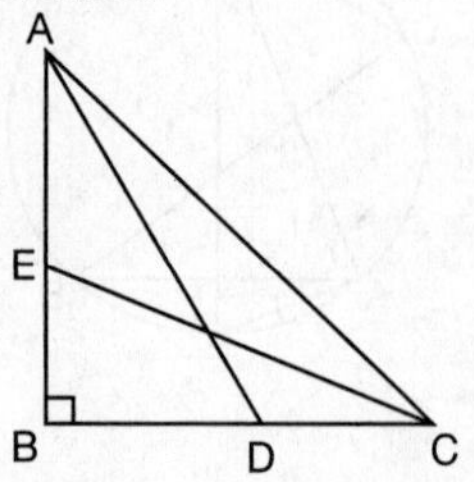

36. Find ∠*DBA*, ∠*DAB*, and ∠*AED* in the following figure, where *ABCDE* is a semi-circle.

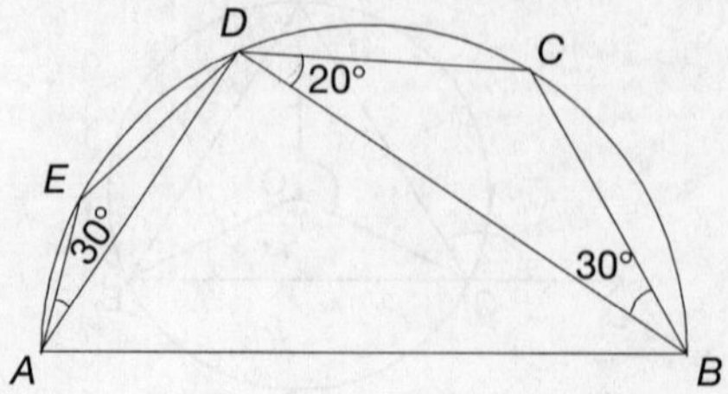

37. In the following figure, *ABDG* is a rectangle with *AB* = 10 cm and *AG* = 6 cm. Find the areas of parallelograms *ABCF* and *ABEH*. Also find the area of Δ*AEB*.

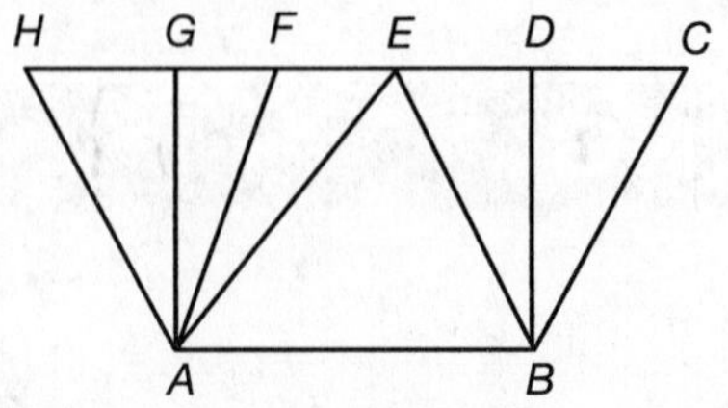

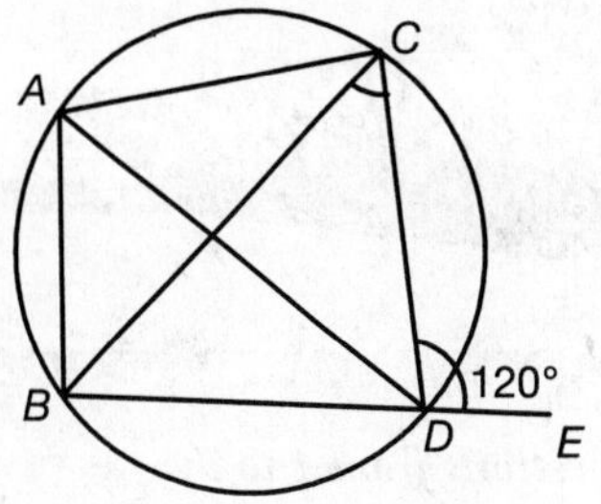

38. In the following figure, $\overline{BD}$ is produced to E. If $\overline{AD}$ is the angle bisector of $\angle A$, then find $\angle BCD$.

PRACTICE QUESTIONS COMPETITION WING

Level 1: Apply Your Concepts

Directions of questions from 1 to 5:
Fill in the blanks

1. The areas of parallelograms on the same base and between the same parallel lines are ________.
2. If a circle passes through four points, then the four points are said to be __________.
3. The exterior angle of a regular polygon is 60°. The number of sides of the polygon is _______.
4. A line l intersects a pair of parallel lines. The exterior angles on the same side of line l are in the ratio 5 : 4. The measure of the bigger angle of the two is __________.
5. When all the sides of a quadrilateral are equal, then it is either a _________ or a ________.

Directions of questions from 6 to 60:
Select the correct alternative from the given choices.

6. The number of diagonals of a 21–sided polygon is _______.
(a) 189 (b) 170
(c) 231 (d) 190
7. A cyclic polygon has n sides such that each of its interior angle measures 144°. What is the measure of the angle subtended by each of its side at the geometrical centre of the polygon?
(a) 144° (b) 30°
(c) 36° (d) 54°
8. Which of the following is the locus of a point equidistant from all the sides of the triangles?
(a) Incenter (b) Circumcenter
(c) Orthocenter (d) Centroid
9. Which of the following is the locus of a point equidistant from the arms of the angle 60°?
(a) circle
(b) the bisector of the angle
(c) two parallel lines
(d) None of these
10. The difference between the number of sides of two regular polygons is 2 and the difference between the number of diagonals of those polygons is 15. Find the number of diagonals of the polygon which has the least number of sides.
(a) 20 (b) 27
(c) 35 (d) 14
11. In ΔPQR, M and N are points on PQ and PR, respectively, such that $\overline{MN} \parallel \overline{QR}$. If $PM = x$, $PR = x + 9$, $PQ = x + 13$ and $PN = x - 2$, then find x.
(a) 10 (b) 11
(c) 13 (d) 15
12. In the following figure (not to scale), the chords AC and BD intersect at E and $\angle BAE = \angle ECD + 20°$. If $\angle CDE = 60°$, find $\angle ABE$.

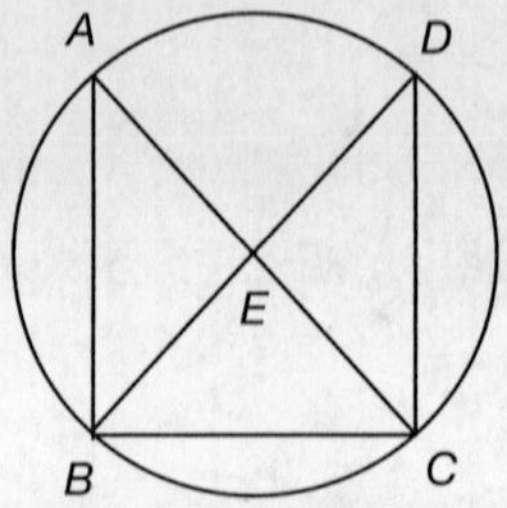

(a) 40° (b) 60°
(c) 80° (d) None of these
13. ABCD is a cyclic quadrilateral in which the opposite angles are equal. Which of the following is necessarily be true about ABCD?
(a) Isosceles trapezium
(b) Square
(c) Kite
(d) Rectangle
14. Which of the following is not the sum of the interior angles of a polygon?
(a) 1080° (b) 1260°
(c) 1640° (d) 1800°
15. In the following figure, O is the centre of the circle. If $\angle MPN = 55°$, then find the value of $\angle MON + \angle OMN + \frac{1}{2}\angle MNO$.

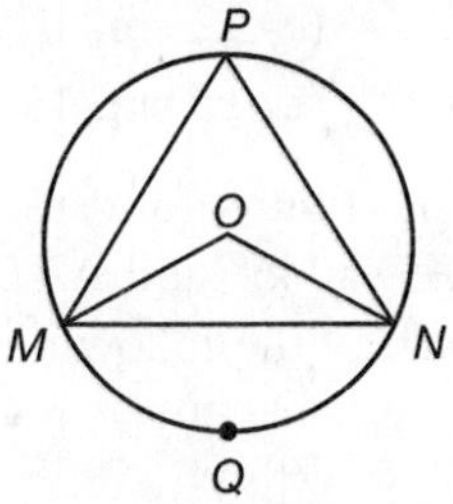

(a) 145° (b) $162\frac{1}{2}^\circ$

(c) $158\frac{1}{2}^\circ$ (d) 180°

16. In the following figure, ΔPQR is right-angled at R and S is the mid-point of hypotenuse PQ. If $RS = 25$ cm and $PR = 48$ cm, then find QR.

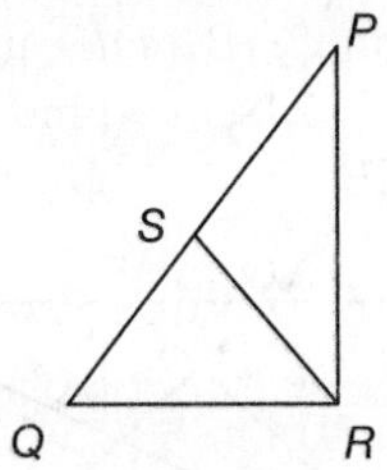

(a) 7 cm (b) 25 cm
(c) 14 cm (d) Cannot be determined

17. The number of diagonals of a polygon is six times the number of sides of the polygon. Find the number of diagonals of the polygon.
(a) 15 (b) 90
(c) 120 (d) 150

18. In the given figure, ABCD is a parallelogram. ABED is a cyclic quadrilateral. If ∠BAD = 70°, then find the value of ∠EDC.

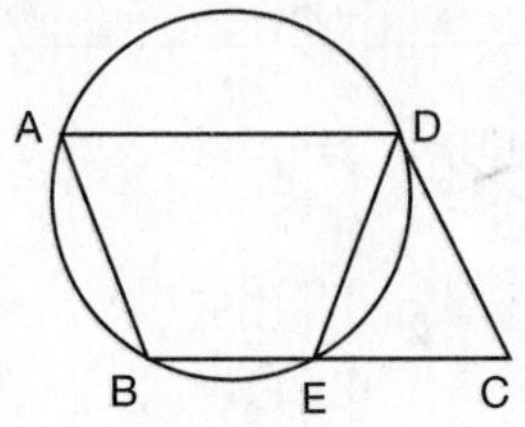

(a) 40° (b) 50°
(c) 70° (d) Cannot be determined

19. The angle subtended by a minor arc in its alternate segment is ________.
(a) Acute (b) Obtuse
(c) 90° (d) Reflex angle

20. The number of diagonals of a regular polygon is 27. Then, each of the interior angles of the polygon is ________.

(a) $\left(\frac{500}{3}\right)^\circ$ (b) 140°

(c) 128° (d) 154°

21. ABC is a triangle inscribed in a circle, AC being the diameter of the circle. The length of AC is as much more than the length of BC as the length of BC is more than the length of AB. Find $AC : AB$.
(a) 5 : 3 (b) 5 : 4
(c) 6 : 5 (d) 3 : 2

22. $\overset{\frown}{MN}$ is the arc of the circle with centre O. If $\angle MOR = 100^\circ$ and $\angle NOR = 135^\circ$, then $\frac{1}{2}\angle ORN + \frac{1}{4}\angle ORM$ is ________.

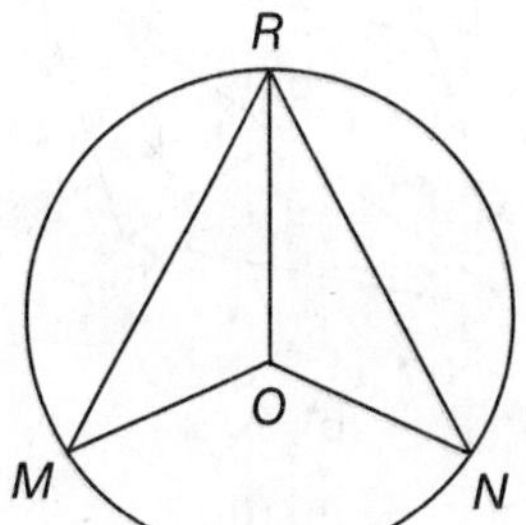

(a) $22\frac{1}{2}^\circ$ (b) 40°

(c) 125° (d) $21\frac{1}{4}^\circ$

23. In the following figure (not to scale), $\angle BCD = 40^\circ$, $\angle EDC = 35^\circ$, $\angle CBF = 30^\circ$ and $\angle DEG = 40^\circ$. Find $\angle BAE$.

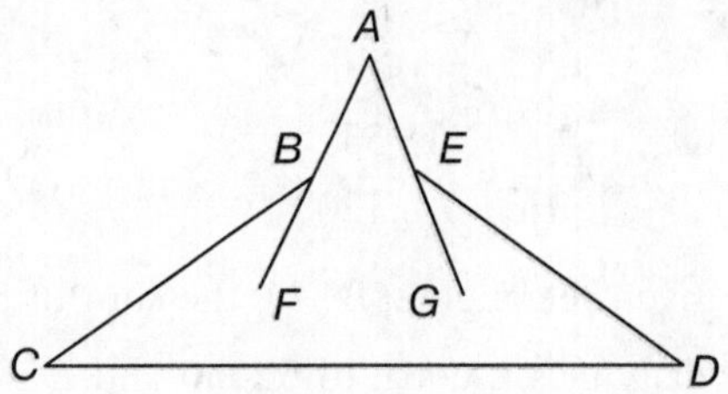

(a) 70° (b) 50°
(c) 110° (d) 35°

24. In the following figure (not to scale), $\overline{AB} \parallel \overline{CD}$. If $\angle BAE = 25^\circ$ and $\angle DCE = 30^\circ$, then find $\angle AEC$.

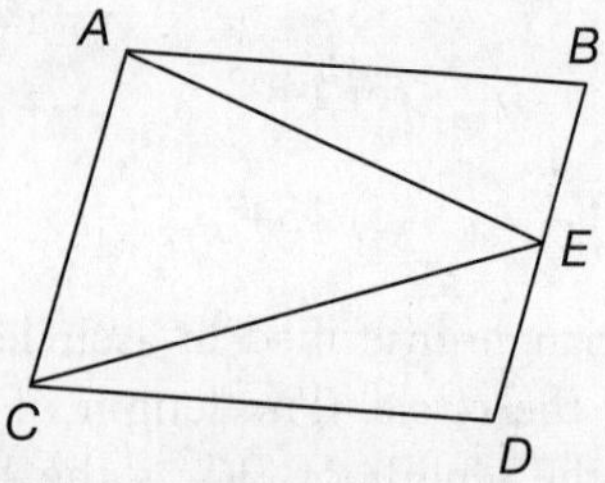

(a) 30° (b) 45°
(c) 50° (d) 55°

25. In the given figure, ABCD is a parallelogram and BDEC is a square. BD < AC. If the length of the shorter diagonal of the parallelogram is 5 cm, then the length of the longer diagonal of the parallelogram is ____ cm.

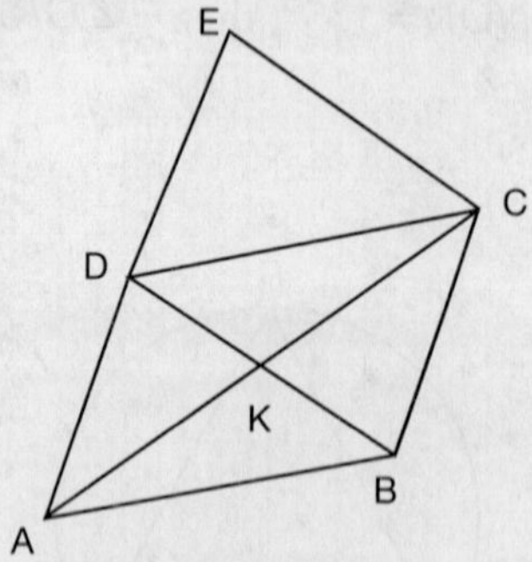

(a) $5\sqrt{2}$ (b) $5\sqrt{3}$
(c) $5\sqrt{5}$ (d) $10\sqrt{2}$

26. In the given figure, AC is the diameter. AB and AD are equal chords. If $\angle AED = 110°$, then find $\angle BAD$.

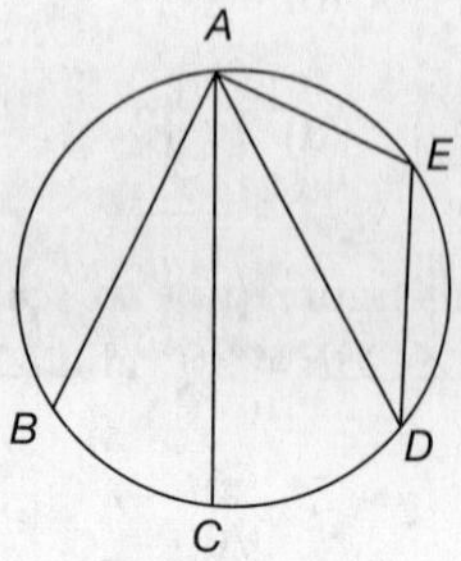

(a) 40° (b) 55°
(c) 110° (d) 120°

27. In the given rectangle $ABCD$, the sum of the lengths of two diagonals is equal to 52 cm and E is a point in AB, such that $\overline{OE}$ is perpendicular to $\overline{AB}$. Find the lengths of the sides of the rectangle, if $OE = 5$ cm.

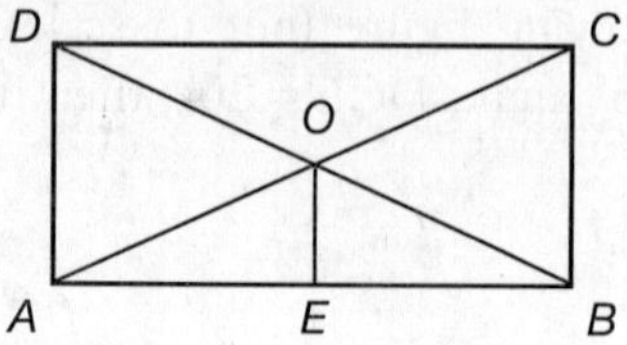

(a) 24 cm, 10 cm (b) 12 cm, 10 cm
(c) 24 cm, 5 cm (d) 12 cm, 15 cm

28. In the following figure (not to scale), AD bisects $\angle BAC$. If $\angle BAD = 45°$ and ΔABC is inscribed in a circle, then which of the following is the longest?

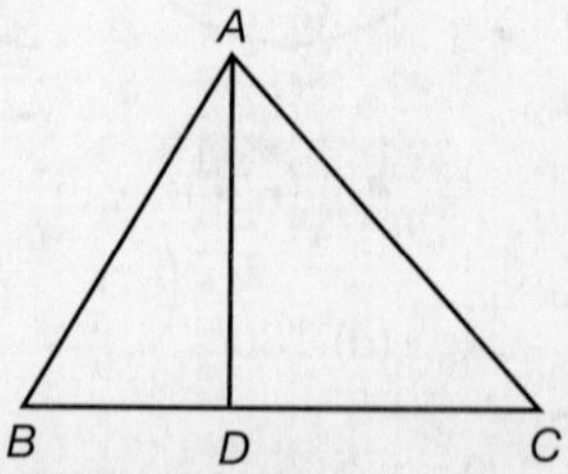

(a) AB (b) AD
(c) AC (d) BC

29. In the given figure, $\overline{AB} \parallel \overline{DE}$ and area of the parallelogram $ABFD$ is 24 cm². Find the areas of ΔAFB, ΔAGB, and ΔAEB.

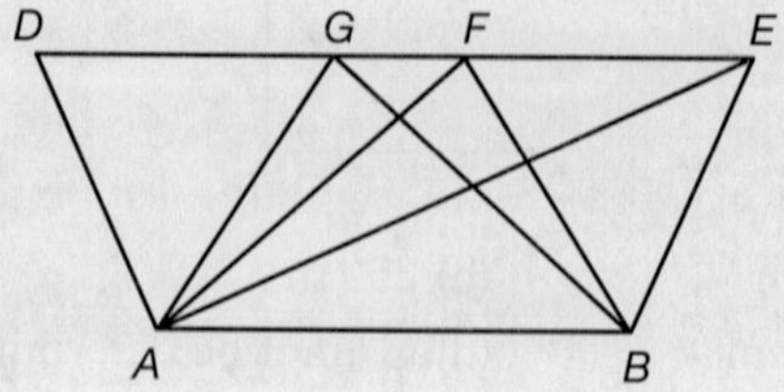

(a) 8 cm² (b) 12 cm²
(c) 10 cm² (d) 14 cm²

30. In the given figure, $\overline{AD}$ and $\overline{BE}$ intersect at C, such that $BC = CE$, $\angle ABC = 40°$ and $\angle DEC = 85°$. Find $\angle BAC - \angle CDE$.

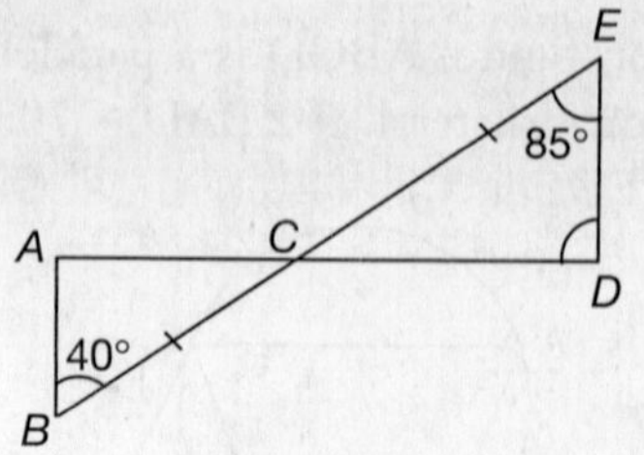

(a) 45° (b) 125°
(c) 55° (d) 110°

31. In the given figure, DEF is a triangle. If DF is the longest side and EF is the shortest side, then which of the following is true?

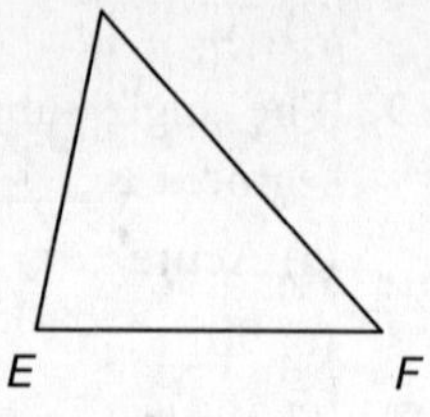

(a) $\angle E > \angle D > \angle F$
(b) $\angle D < \angle F < \angle E$
(c) $\angle D < \angle E < \angle F$
(d) None of these

32. The ratio between the exterior angle and the interior angle of a regular polygon is 1 : 3. Find the number of the sides of the polygon.
(a) 12 (b) 6
(c) 8 (d) 10

33. Find each interior and exterior angle of a regular polygon having 30 sides.
(a) 144°, 36° (b) 156°, 24°
(c) 164°, 16° (d) 168°, 12°

Level 2: Review Your Concepts

34. If $BC : CD = 2 : 3$, $AE : EC = 3 : 4$ and $BC : AE = 2 : 3$, then find the ratio of the area of ΔECD to the area of ΔAEB.
(a) 2 : 1 (b) 2 : 3
(c) 3 : 5 (d) 4 : 3

35. In the given figure (not to scale), O is the centre of the circle. If $PB = PC$, $\angle PBO = 25°$ and $\angle BOC = 130°$, then find $\angle ABP + \angle DCP$.

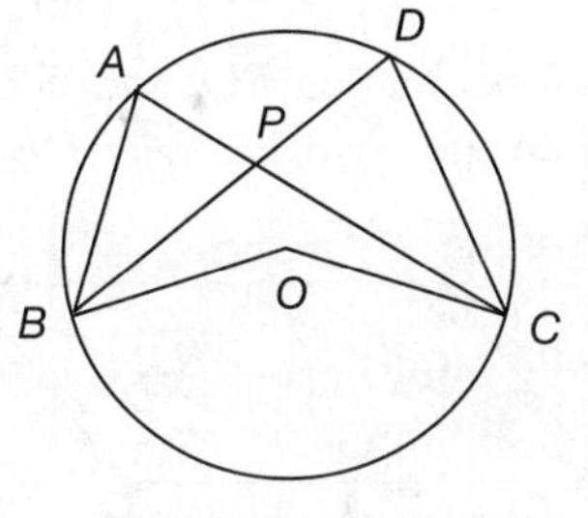

(a) 10° (b) 30°
(c) 40° (d) 50°

36. In a polygon, the greatest angle is 110° and all the angles are distinct in integral measures (in degrees) Find the maximum number of sides it can have.
(a) 4 (b) 5
(c) 6 (d) 7

37. In the given figure, $ABCD$ is a rectangle inscribed in a semi-circle. If the length and the breadth of the rectangle are in the ratio 2 : 1. What is the ratio of the perimeter of the rectangle to the diameter of the semicircle?

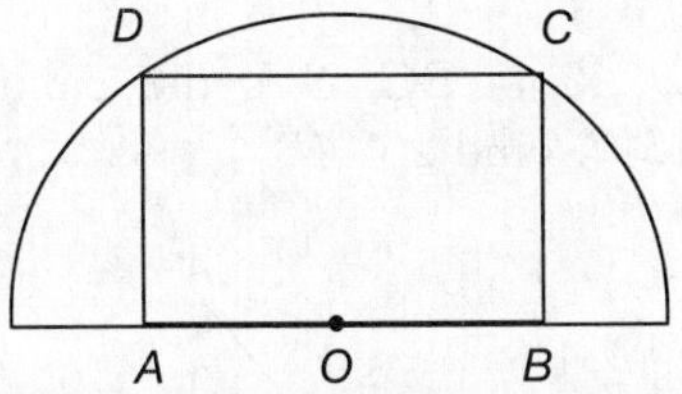

(a) $3 : \sqrt{2}$ (b) $2 : \sqrt{3}$
(c) $2 : \sqrt{5}$ (d) $3 : \sqrt{5}$

38. In the given figure (not to scale), the points M, R, N, S, and Q are concyclic. Find $\angle PQR + \angle OPR + \angle NMS + \angle OSN$, if O is the centre of the circle.

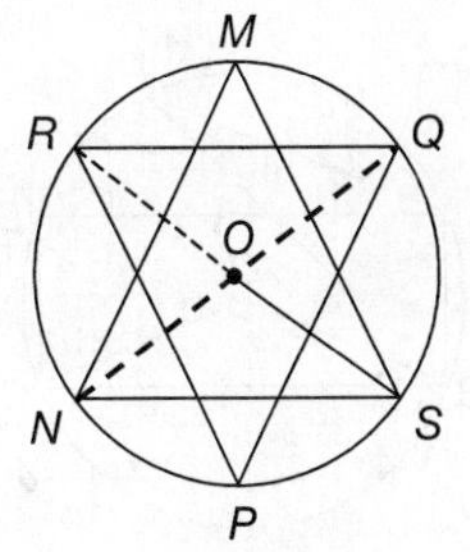

(a) 90° (b) 180°
(c) 270° (d) Data inadequate

39. In the given figure (not to scale), AC is the diameter of the circle and $\angle ADB = 20°$, then find $\angle BPC$.

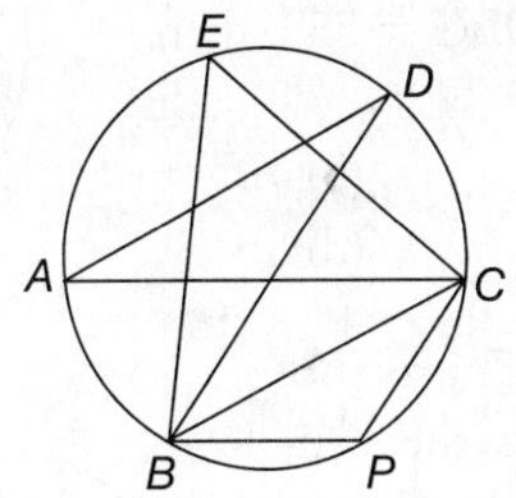

(a) 50° (b) 70°
(c) 90° (d) 110°

40. In the following figure, O is the centre of the circle and $CD = DE = EF = GF$. If $\angle COD = 40°$, then find reflex $\angle COG$.

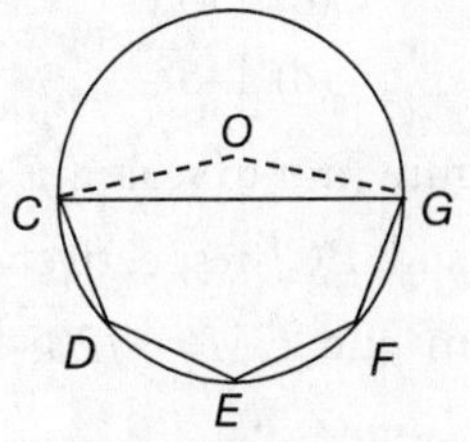

(a) 200° (b) 90°
(c) 80° (d) 160°

41. In the given figure (not to scale), AC is the median as well as altitude to BD. In ΔACE, AD is the median to CE. Which of the following is true?

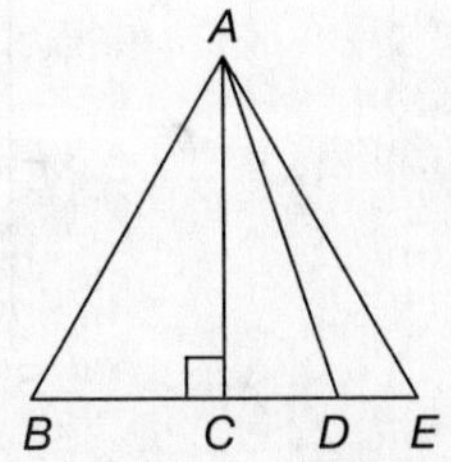

(a) $AB + CD > AE$
(b) $AB + BC = AE$
(c) $AB + DE < AE$
(d) None of the above

42. In the given figure, (not to scale), rectangle $ABCD$ and triangle ABE are inscribed in the circle with centre O. If $\angle AEB = 40°$, then find $\angle BOC$.

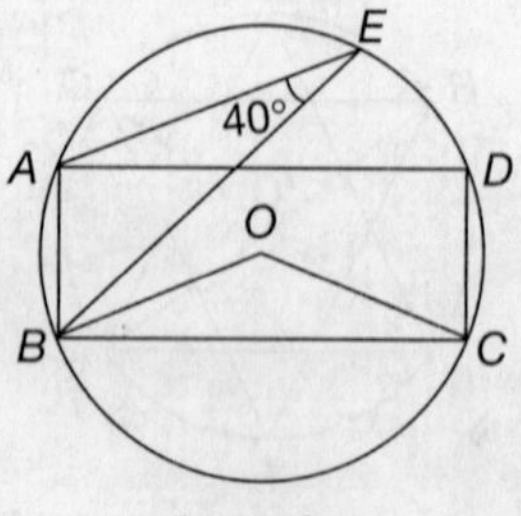

(a) 60° (b) 80°
(c) 100° (d) 120°

43. In the given figure (not to scale), O is the centre of the circle. BC and CD are equal chords. If $\angle OBC = 55°$, then find $\angle BAC$.

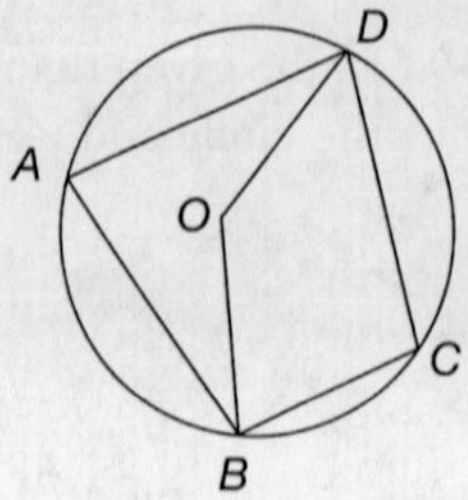

(a) 60° (b) 70°
(c) 80° (d) 90°

44. In the given figure (not to scale), O is the centre of the circle C_1 and AB is the diameter of the circle C_2. Quadrilateral $PQRS$ is inscribed in the circle with centre O. Find $\angle QRS$.

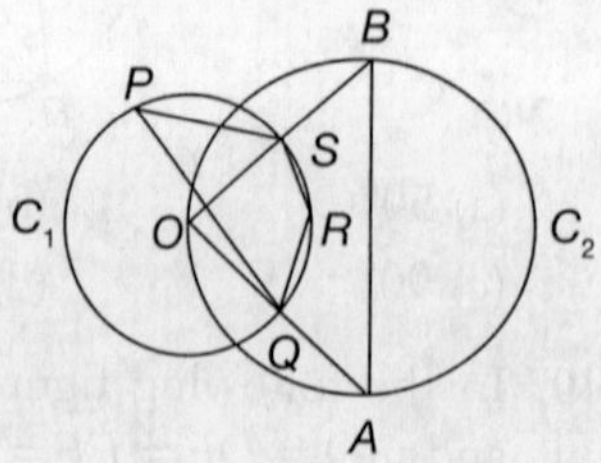

(a) 105° (b) 115°
(c) 135° (d) 145°

45. In the given figure (not to scale), E and D are the mid-points of AB and BC, respectively. Also, $\angle B = 90°$, $AD = \sqrt{292}$ cm and $CM = \sqrt{208}$ cm. Find AC.

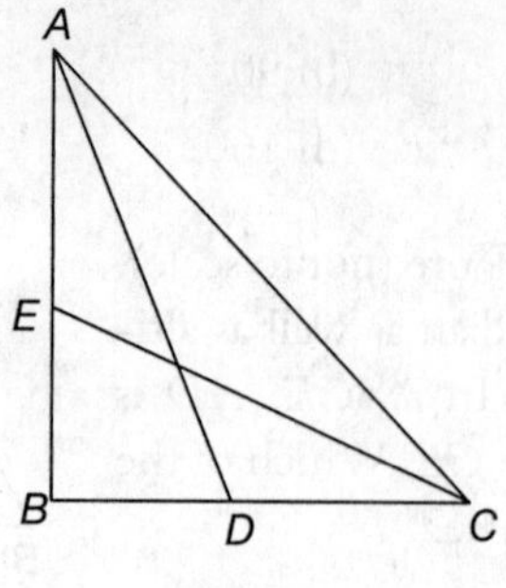

(a) 15 (b) 18
(c) 20 (d) 24

46. Show that each diagonal of a parallelogram divide it into two congruent triangles.
The following are the steps involved in showing the above result. Arrange them in sequential order.
(A) In ΔABC and ΔCDA, $AB = DC$ and $BC = AD$ ($\because$ opposite angles of parallelogram) $AC = AC$ (common side).
(B) Let $ABCD$ be a parallelogram. Join AC.
(C) By SSS congruence property, $\Delta ABC \cong \Delta CDA$.
(D) Similarly, BD divides the triangle into two congruent triangles.

(a) BACD (b) BDAC
(c) BADC (d) BDCA

47. In the given figure, $PQRS$ is a parallelogram. A and B are the mid-points of $\overline{PQ}$ and $\overline{SR}$, respectively. If $PS = BR$, then the quadrilateral $ADBC$ is a ______.

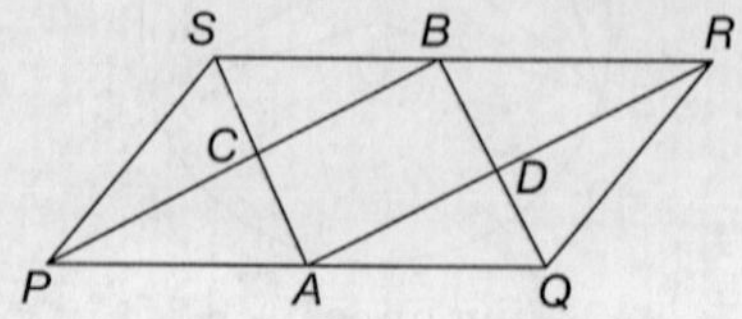

(a) Rhombus (b) Trapezium
(c) Square (d) Rectangle

48. The sides of a triangle are 2006 cm, 6002 cm and m cm, where m is a positive integer. Find the number of such possible triangles.
(a) 1 (b) 2006
(c) 3996 (d) 4011

49. If a, b and c are the lengths of the sides of a right triangle ABC with $c = 2a$ and $b^2 - 3a^2 = 0$, then $\angle ABC =$ ______.
(a) 60° (b) 30°
(c) 45° (d) 90°

50. In ΔABC, $AC = BC$, S is the circum-centre and $\angle ASB = 150°$. Find $\angle CAB$.

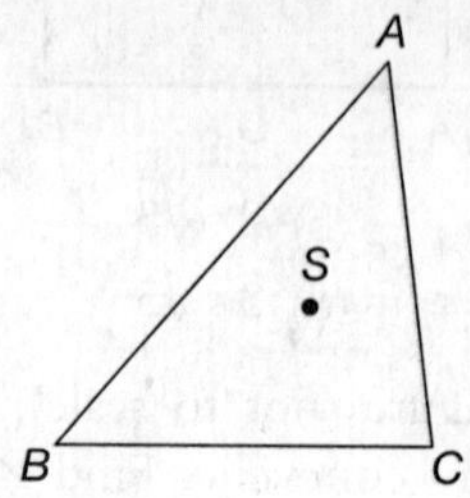

(a) $55\frac{1}{2}^{\circ}$ (b) $52\frac{1}{2}^{\circ}$

(c) $62\frac{1}{2}^{\circ}$ (d) $35\frac{1}{2}^{\circ}$

51. In the given figure, P, Q, R, and S are concyclic points, and O is the mid-point of the diameter QS.

If $\angle QPR = 25^{\circ}$, then find $\angle SOR$.

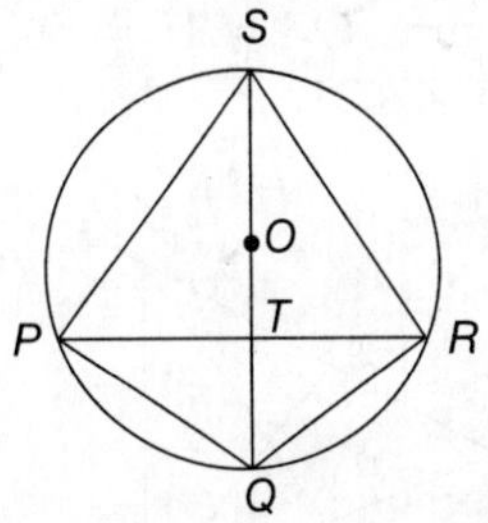

(a) 130° (b) 120°

(c) 75° (d) 100°

Level 3: Assess Your Concepts

52. In ΔABC, $\angle B = 90^{\circ}$. P, Q and R are the mid-points of $\overline{AB}$, $\overline{BC}$, and $\overline{AC}$, respectively. Then which of the following is true?

(a) A, P, Q and R are concyclic points

(b) B, P, R and Q are concyclic points

(c) C, Q, P and R are concyclic points

(d) All of these

53. If p, q, and r are the lengths of the sides of a right triangle, PQR, and the hypotenuse $r = \sqrt{2pq}$, then $\angle QPR =$ ________.

(a) 50° (b) 45°

(c) 60° (d) 30°

54. In a triangle PQR, $PQ = QR$. A and B are the mid-points of $\overline{QR}$ and $\overline{PR}$, respectively. A circle passes through P, Q, A, and B. Then which of the following is necessarily true?

(a) ΔPQR is equilateral

(b) ΔPQR is right isosceles

(c) PQ is a diameter

(d) Both (a) and (c)

55. In the figure given below (not to scale), D is a point on the circle with centre A and C is a point on the circle with centre B. $\overline{AD} \perp \overline{BD}$ and $\overline{BC} \perp \overline{CA}$. Then which of the following is true?

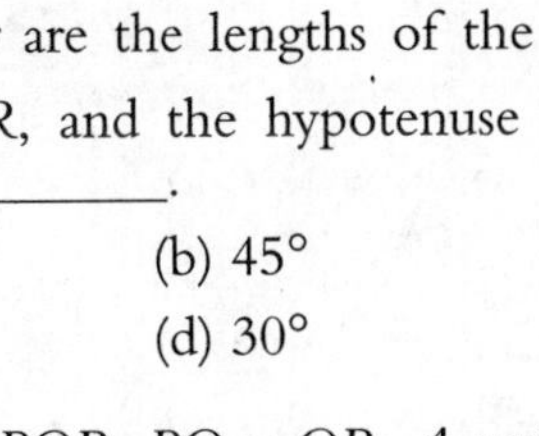

(a) $BD = AC$, when $\overline{AD} = \overline{BC}$

(b) $BD = AC$, when $\overline{AD} \parallel \overline{BC}$

(c) Both (a) and (b)

(d) $BD = AC$ is always true

56. In the given figure, the angles $\angle ADE$ and $\angle ABC$ differ by 15°. Find $\angle CAE$.

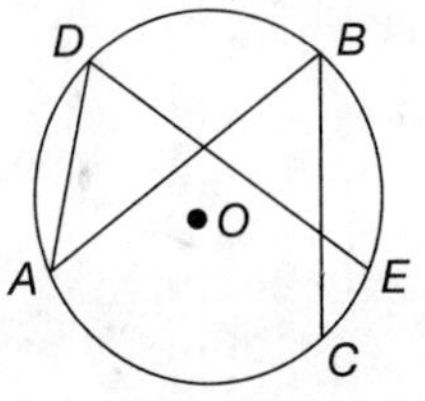

(a) 10°

(b) $7\frac{1}{2}^{\circ}$

(c) 15°

(d) 30°

57. In the given figure, $ABCD$ is a cyclic quadrilateral, $\angle ABC = 70^{\circ}$, $\overrightarrow{FG}$ bisects $\angle CFA$, $\overrightarrow{EG}$ bisects $\angle DEB$, $\angle DCE = 60^{\circ}$ and $\angle EGF = 90^{\circ}$. Find $\angle HEC$.

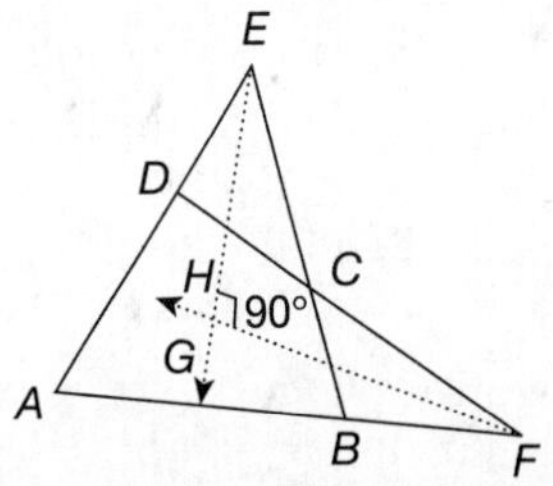

(a) 20° (b) 40°

(c) 25° (d) 45°

58. In the given figure, A, D, B, E, and C are concyclic. If $\angle ACB = 60^{\circ}$ and $\angle AED = 50^{\circ}$, then find $\angle DEB$.

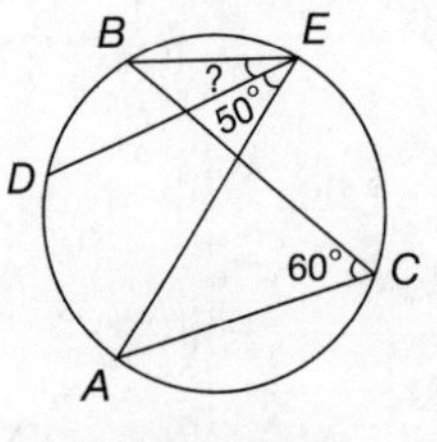

(a) 15° (b) 10°

(c) 20° (d) 5°

59. In the given figure, $OA = AB = BC = CD = OD$. Find the measure of $\angle AOD$.

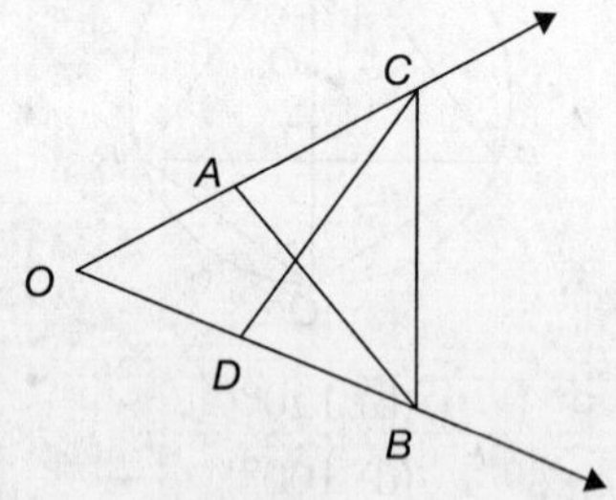

(a) 46^0 (b) 36^0
(c) 63^0 (d) 49^0

60. In a ΔABC, D is a point on AC such that $AD = 2$ cm, $DC = 6$ cm and $\angle ADB = \angle ABC$. Which of the following cannot be the measure of BC?

(a) 9 cm (b) 10 cm
(c) 11 cm (d) 12 cm

AT

PRACTICE QUESTIONS JEE SPECIAL WING

Multiple-Answer Type Questions

Directions for questions 1 to 10:
Each question has FOUR options (a), (b), (c), and (d). ONE OR MORE THAN ONE of these four option(s) is/are the correct answer(s).

1. Which of the following is/are the number of diagonals of a polygon?
(a) 4850 (b) 2015
(c) 860 (d) 350

2. Which of the following angles represents an exterior angle of a regular polygon?
(a) 15° (b) 20°
(c) 25° (d) 30°

3. *ABCD* is a quadrilateral. Which of the following statements should be necessarily true for *ABCD* to be a rhombus?
(a) $\angle A = 60°$, $\angle B = 120°$, $\angle C = 60°$, and $\angle D = 120°$.
(b) $AC \perp BD$.
(c) $AC = BD$.
(d) *AC* and *BD* bisect to each other.

4. STAR is a quadrilateral. A circle passes through the four vertices of the quadrilateral. Which of the following can be true about the quadrilateral?
(a) Trapezium (b) Isosceles Trapezium
(c) Kite (d) Rectangle

5. The area of ΔRTM is 144 sq cm. If *S* and *P* are the midpoints *TR* and *MR*, then which of the following statements is/are true?
(a) The area of ΔRSP is 36 sq cm.
(b) The area of $\square MPST$ is 108 sq cm.
(c) The area of ΔSPT is 36 sq cm.
(d) The area of ΔPTM is 72 sq cm.

6. In the given figure, ΔSKY and ΔERT are two triangles in which *A* is the midpoint of both *SY* and *ET*. *B* is the midpoint of both *KY* and *ER*. Which of the following statements is/are true?

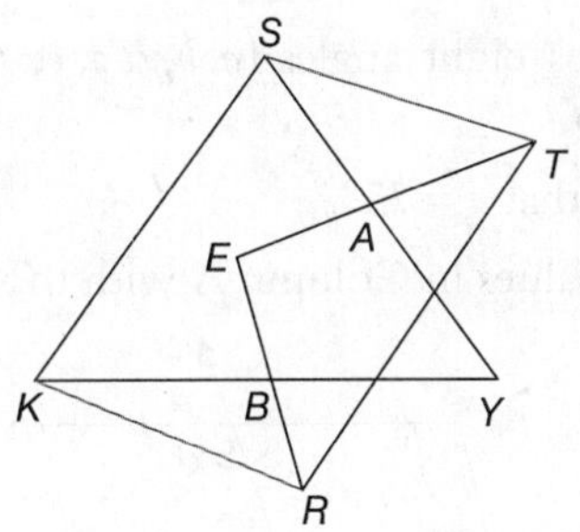

(a) $\overline{SK} \parallel \overline{TR}$ (b) $SK = TR$
(c) $\overline{ST} \parallel \overline{KR}$ (d) $ST = KR$

7. *PQRS* is a parallelogram. *A*, *B*, *C*, and *D* are points on *PS*, *SR*, *QR*, and *PQ* respectively such that $AS : AP = BS : BR = CQ : CR = DQ : DP = 1 : 2$. Which of the following statements are true?
(a) $AC = BD$.
(b) $AC \perp BD$.
(c) *AC* and *BD* bisect each other.
(d) *ABCD* is a parallelogram.

8. *P* and *Q* are two regular polygons. The number of sides of *P* and *Q* are in the ratio is 1 : 3. The ratio of the interior angles of *P* and *Q* is 6 : 7. Which of the following statements is/are true?
(a) The difference of the number of sides of the polygons is 18.
(b) The sum of an exterior angle of *P* and an exterior angle of *Q* is 48°.
(c) The sum of the number of diagonals of *P* and *Q* is 440.
(d) The difference of an interior angle of *P* and an interior angle of *Q* is 24°.

9. *PQRS* is a cyclic quadrilateral. *PQ* is extended to *T* and *RS* is extended to *U*. Which of the following is/are necessarily be true?
(a) $\overline{PQ} \parallel \overline{SR}$ (b) $\angle P + \angle R = 180°$
(c) $SR = QR$ (d) $\angle PSU = \angle PQR$

10. *P*, *R*, and *Q* are the three points on a circle with centre *O*. $\angle POR = 120°$. Which of the following statements can be true?
(a) $\angle PQR = 30°$ (b) $\angle PQR = 60°$
(c) $\angle PQR = 120°$ (d) $\angle PQR = 150°$

Match The Column

Directions for questions 11 to 15:
Read the paragraph given below and answer the questions.
In the given figure, *PQRS* is a parallelogram.

Line l is a transversal of *PQ* and *SR* of the parallelogram.

Line l makes eight angles (a, b, c, d, e, f, g, h) with *PQ* and *SR*.

Also, given that $a = 75°$.

Match the values in Column A with those in Column B.

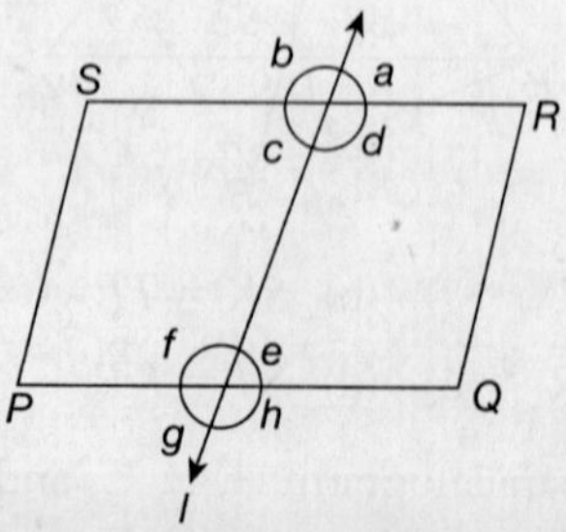

Column A	Column B
11. $\frac{g}{3}$	(a) 12°
12. $\frac{b}{3}$	(b) 15°
13. $\frac{b+e}{15}$	(c) 18°
14. $h - c$	(d) 20°
15. $\frac{h}{5}$	(e) 21°
	(f) 25°
	(g) 30°
	(h) 35°

Directions for questions 16 to 20:
Read the paragraph given below and answer the questions.
ABCD is a quadrilateral.

A quadrilateral in which a pair of opposite sides are parallel is a trapezium.

A trapezium in which non-parallel sides are equal is an isosceles trapezium.

A quadrilateral in which both the pairs of opposite sides are parallel is a parallelogram.

A parallelogram in which an angle is a right angle is a rectangle.

A quadrilateral in which two pairs of adjacent sides are equal is a kite.

Match the values in Column A with those in Column B.

Column A (Type of Quadrilateral)	Column B (Angles of Quadrilateral in Order)
16. Trapezium with no two sides equal	(a) 90°, 90°, 90°, 90°
17. Isosceles trapezium but not a rectangle	(b) 70°, 90°, 110°, 90°
18. Rectangle	(c) 111°, 69°, 69°, 111°
19. Parallelogram but not a rectangle	(d) 90°, 80°, 80°, 110°
20. Cyclic kite but not a square	(e) 101°, 89°, 71°, 99°
	(f) 121°, 59°, 63°, 117°
	(g) 121°, 89°, 71°, 99°
	(h) 131°, 49°, 131°, 49°

Comprehension-Based Questions

Directions for questions 21 to 25:
Read the paragraph given below and answer the questions.
Spandana is a collaborative and engaging math teacher from a school called Spoorthy Excellence of Education. She prefers to teach mathematics by a method of learning by doing. One day she taught types of triangles and also properties of triangles. She divided the class 9 students into nine groups and gave an activity to test their knowledge and understanding of the concepts pertaining to properties of triangles. The data of the task is as follows:

Three sides of a triangle are 265 cm, 565 cm and x cm, where x is an integer.

The tasks and four alternatives for each task are given below.

21. How many triangles exist in all?
(a) 309 (b) 419
(c) 529 (d) Infinite

22. How many triangles are isosceles?
(a) 0 (b) 1
(c) 2 (d) 3

23. Which of the following cannot be the sum of any two sides?

(a) 595 (b) 895

(c) 1095 (d) 1395

24. Which of the following cannot be the perimeter of one of the triangles?

(a) 1661 (b) 1551

(c) 1241 (d) 1131

25. Which of the following cannot be the difference of any two sides?

(a) 232 (b) 343

(c) 454 (d) 565

Assertion and Reason Type Questions

Directions for questions 26 to 30:

Read the options given below and answer the questions.

(a) Both assertion (A) and reason (R) are true, and the reason (R) is the correct explanation of the assertion (A).

(b) Both assertion (A) and reason (R) are true, and the reason (R) is not the correct explanation of the assertion (A).

(c) Assertion (A) is true, but reason (R) is false.

(d) Assertion (A) is false, and reason (R) is true.

26. **Assertion:** Rhombus $ABCD$ can be constructed when $AC = 8$ cm and $BD = 7$ cm.

Reason: We cannot construct a rhombus when two diagonals are given.

27. **Assertion:** In the given figure PQ is a common chord of two concentric circles with centre O. The chord intersects the smaller circle at A and B. If $OS \perp AB$, then $PA = QB$.

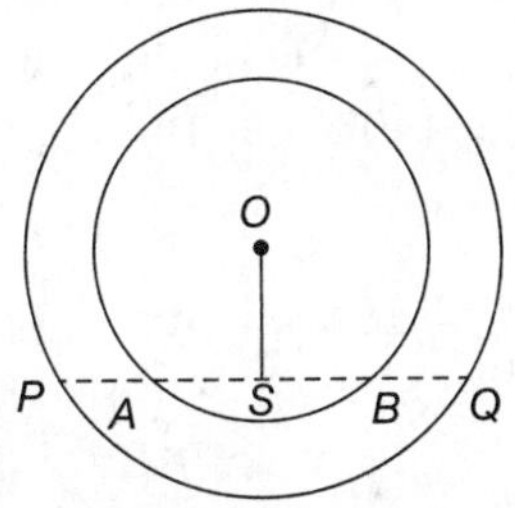

Reason: The perpendicular drawn from the centre of a circle bisects its chord.

28. **Assertion:** $ABCD$ is a rectangle in which AC and BD intersect at O. By SSS congruence property $\Delta OBA \cong \Delta OBC$.

Reason: SSS congruence property states that two triangles are said to be congruent if the three sides of a triangle are respectively equal to the corresponding three sides of another triangle.

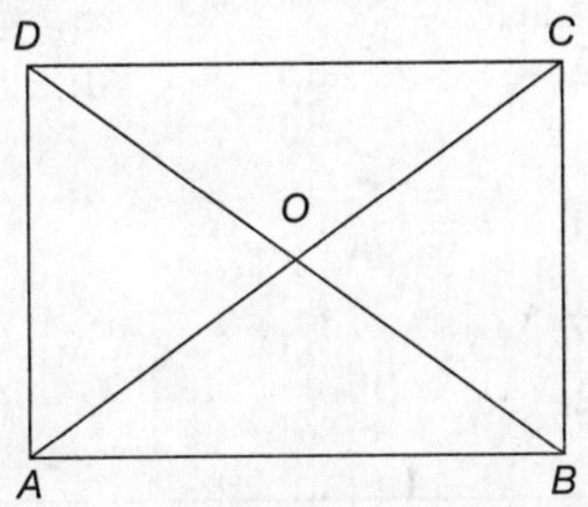

29. **Assertion:** $ABCD$ is a rhombus. P is a point CD such that $CP : DP = 1 : 2$. The area of ΔABP is equal to the area of ΔBCD.

Reason: If a triangle and a parallelogram lie on the same base and lie between the same parallels, then the area of the triangle is one-third of the area of the parallelogram.

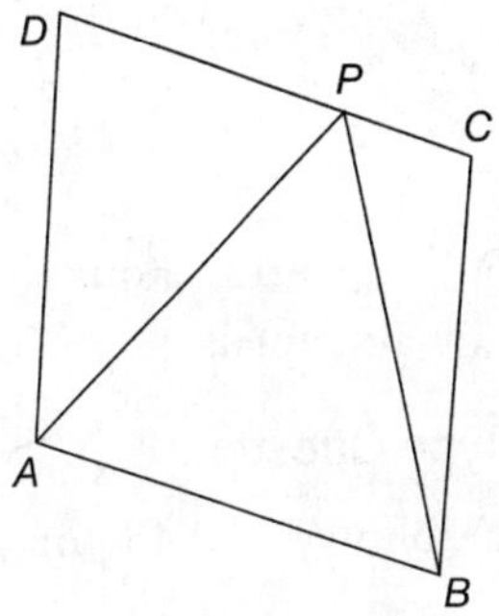

30. **Assertion:** As shown in the figure, A, B, C, and D are concyclic points. If $\angle ACB = 33°$, then $\angle ADB = 33°$.

Reason: The opposite angles of a cyclic quadrilateral are supplementary. Also, an exterior angle of a cyclic quadrilateral is equal to its interior opposite angle.

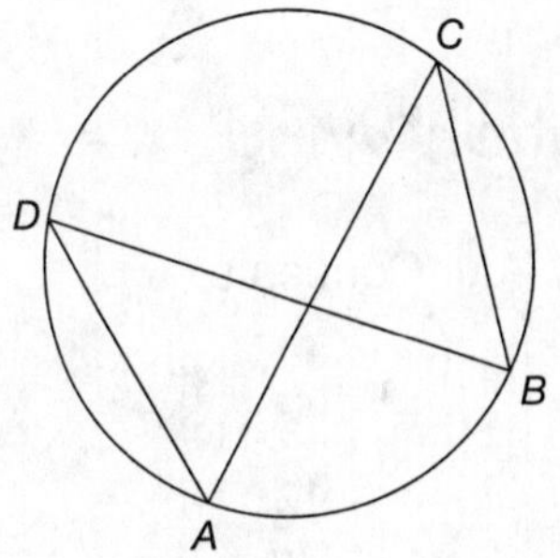

ANSWER KEYS

Crossword

Across

1. Cyclic
3. Arc
6. Right
7. Rectangle
8. Incentre
10. Three

Down

2. Circumcentre
4. Bisector
5. Inside
9. Equal

Classroom Wing

Very Short Answer Type Questions

1. True
2. cyclic
3. $180° - \frac{x°}{2}$
4. less than
5. 135°
6. 44
7. AB
8. 10°
9. Yes
10. True
11. No
12. No
13. Four
14. No
15. 72°
16. No
17. No, not always equal.
18. No
19. No

Short Answer Type Questions

20. (a) and (c) follows
21. 48 cm^2
22. 25 cm
23. 130°
24. 102°
25. 40°
26. 15
27. 60°
28. 75°
29. 66°
30. 158°
31. 120°
32. (A) $z = 140°$ (B) 8 cm
33. 24 cm^2

Essay Type Questions

34. 16 cm
35. $6\sqrt{13}$ cm
36. $\angle ABD = 40°$, $\angle DAB = 50°$, $\angle AED = 140°$
37. 60 cm^2, 30 cm^2
38. $\angle BCD = 60°$

Competition Wing

Level 1: Apply Your Concepts

1. equal
2. concyclic
3. 6
4. 100°
5. square, rhombus
6. (a)
7. (c)
8. (a)
9. (b)
10. (a)
11. (c)
12. (a)
13. (d)
14. (c)
15. (b)
16. (c)
17. (b)
18. (a)
19. (a)
20. (b)
21. (a)
22. (d)
23. (d)
24. (d)
25. (c)
26. (a)
27. (a)
28. (d)
29. (b)
30. (a)
31. (b)
32. (c)
33. (d)

Level 2: Review Your Concepts

34. (a)
35. (b)
36. (b)
37. (a)
38. (b)
39. (d)
40. (a)
41. (a)
42. (c)
43. (b)

44. (c)	45. (c)	46. (a)	47. (d)	48. (d)
49. (a)	50. (b)	51. (a)		

Level 3: Assess Your Concepts

52. (b)	53. (b)	54. (d)	55. (c)	56. (c)
57. (c)	58. (b)	59. (b)	60. (d)	

JEE Special Wing

Multiple-Answer Type Questions

1. (a, b, c, d)	2. (a, b, d)	3. (b, d)	4. (b, d)	5. (a, b, c, d)
6. (a, b, c, d)	7. (c, d)	8. (b, c, d)	9. (b, d)	10. (b, c)

Match The Column

11. (f)	12. (h)	13. (a)	14. (g)	15. (e)
16. (f)	17. (c)	18. (a)	19. (h)	20. (b)

Comprehension-Based Questions

21. (c)	22. (b)	23. (d)	24. (a)	25. (d)

Assertion and Reason Type Questions

26. (c)	27. (a)	28. (d)	29. (c)	30. (b)

Hints and Explanations

Classroom Wing

Very Short Answer Type Questions

1. True, 2 circles cannot intersect in more than 2 points.
2. If, sum of diagonally opposite angles = 180°, then quadrilateral is Cyclic quadrilateral.
3. $\angle ABC = \frac{1}{2}$ Reflex $\angle AOC$

$= \frac{1}{2}[360° - x°]$

$= 180° - \frac{x°}{2}$

4. Sum of all the altitudes in a triangle is always less than the sum of all sides.
5. 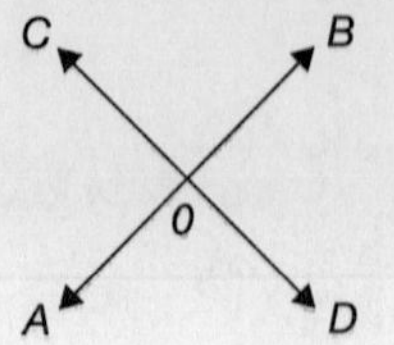

$\angle AOD : \angle BOD = 3 : 1$

Let the angles be $3x$, x

Since $\angle AOD$ and $\angle BOD$ form Linear pair.

$\therefore \quad 3x + x = 180°$

$4x = 180°$

$x = 45°$

Therefore, $\angle AOD = 3 \times 45° = 135°$

$\angle BOD = 45°$

6. Longest chord in a circle = diameter of the circle.

$\Rightarrow$ diameter = 14 = 2 × (radius)

Circumference = $2\pi r = 14 \times \frac{22}{7}$ cm = 44 cm

7. 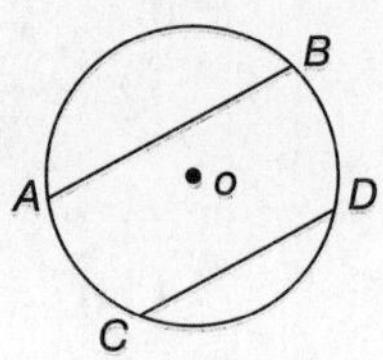

If $AB > CD$

$\Rightarrow AB$ is a closer to centre.

8. 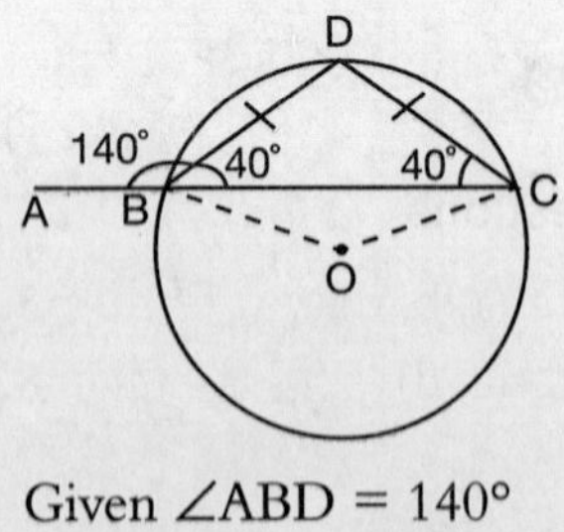

Given $\angle ABD = 140°$

$\Rightarrow \angle CBD = 180° - 140° = 40°$

As BD = CD, $\angle BCD = \angle CBD = 40°$

$\angle BOC = 2\angle BCD + 2\angle CBD = 2(40° + 40°) = 160°$

Now $\angle BCO = \angle CBO = \frac{180° - 160°}{2} = 10°$

9. Yes, the sum of 2 angles can be less than the 3rd angle in a triangle.
10. True, if all sides of a polygon are equal then all interior angles will also be equal.
11. No, the given statement is not always True.
12. Sum of all interior angles of a polygon of n sides is:

Sum = $(n - 2) \times 180°$

According to the question

$(n - 2) \times 180° = 810°$

$(n - 2) = \frac{810}{180} = \frac{9}{2} = 4.5$

$\Rightarrow n = 4.5 + 2 = 6.5$

Since, n should be an integer

Sum of all interior angles cannot be equal to 810°

13. If four lines intersect in a plane, then at maximum 4 triangles are formed.
14. No, the given statement is not always true.
15. Let the angle be x, then its supplementary will be $\frac{2}{3}x$

Now, $x + \frac{2}{3}x = 180°$

$5x = 180 \times 3$

$x = \frac{180 \times 3}{5} = 108°$

Other angle is $\frac{2}{3} \times 108° = 72°$

16. No, all the diagonals of a regular polygon are not always concurrent.

17. No, not always equal.

18. No, length of the median to a side cannot be less than the attitude.

19. No, not possible because shortest distance from a point to a line is altitude, which is always perpendicular. Hence, $\angle ADC = 90°$.

Short Answer Type Questions

20. 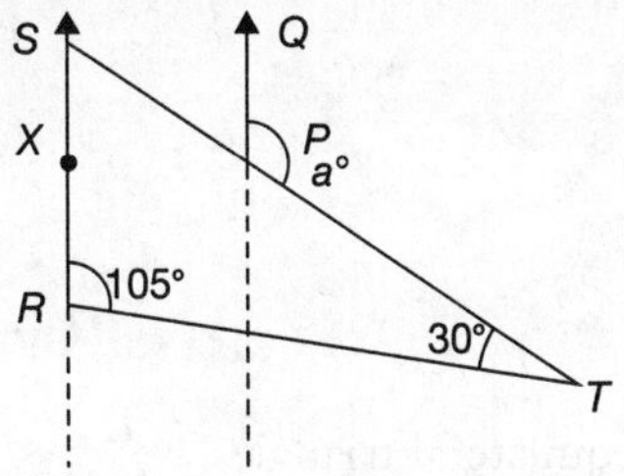

Since, $SR \parallel PQ$

$\Rightarrow \angle SXT = \angle QPT$ (corresponding angles)

$\Rightarrow \angle SXT = a°$

Now, $\angle RXT = 180° - a°$ (Linear Pair)

In ΔRXT

$\angle RXT + \angle T + \angle R = 180°$

$(180 - a) + 30° + 105° = 180°$

$\Rightarrow \quad a = 135°$

21. KLMN is a rhombus

P and Q are the midpoints of LM and NQ respectively.

Join K and M.

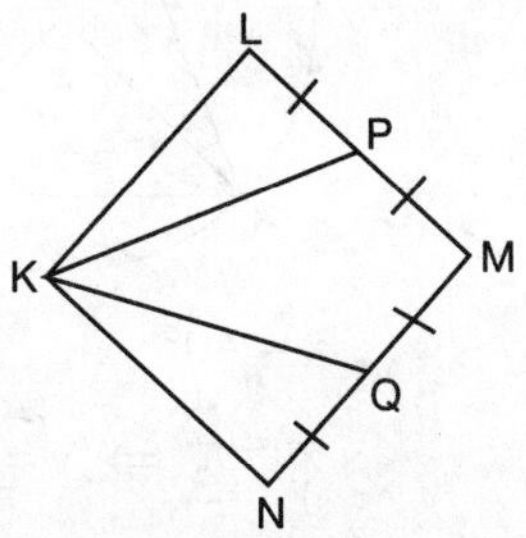

Ar(rhombus KLMN)

= Ar(ΔKLM) + Ar(ΔKNM)

= 2 Ar(ΔKPM) + 2 Ar(ΔKQM)

= 2 Ar(KPMQ)

= 2(24 cm^2)

= 48 cm^2

22. 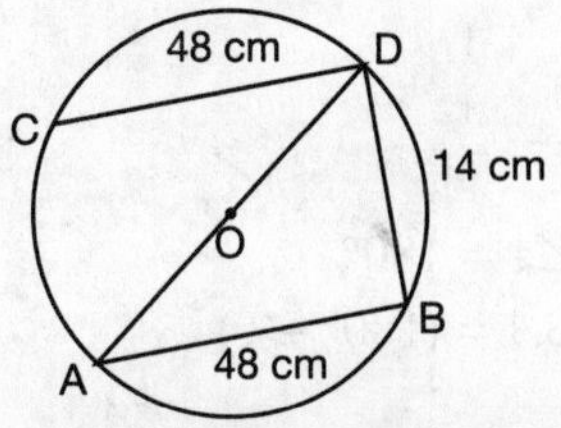

Given, AB = CD = 48 cm and AC = BD = 14 cm

ΔABD is a right angled triangle

$AD^2 = AB^2 + DB^2$

$AD^2 = 2304 + 196$

$AD^2 = 2500 \Rightarrow AD = 50$

$\therefore$ required radius $= \dfrac{AD}{2} = \dfrac{50}{2} = 25$ cm

23. From the figure,

$\angle AOB = 2\angle ACB$

$100° = 2\angle ACB$

$\Rightarrow \angle ACB = 50°$

$\therefore \angle ACD = 180° - \angle ACB$

$= 180° - 50°$

$= 130°$.

24. $\angle CDF = \angle EBA = 78°$

(Exterior angle of a cyclic quadrilateral)

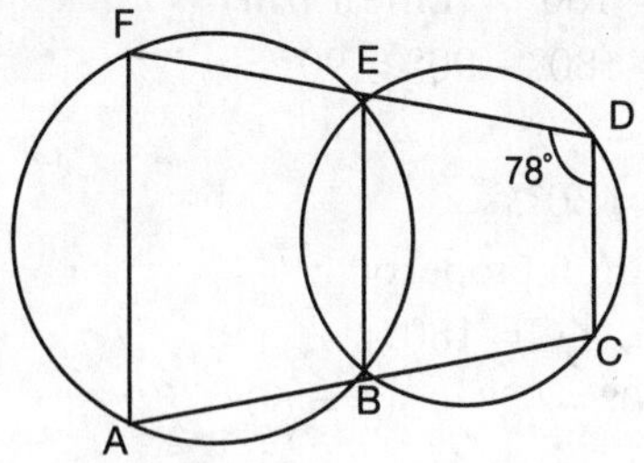

$\angle AFD + \angle ABE = 180°$

(opposite angles °f a cycle quadrilateral)

$\angle AFD + 78° = 180°$

$\angle AFD = 180° - 78° = 102°$.

25. 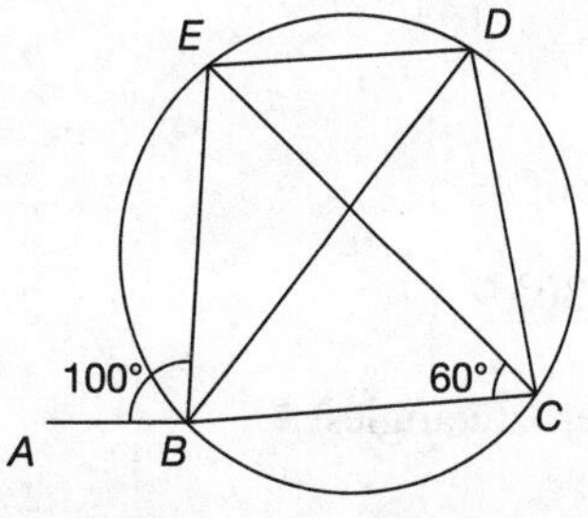

In ΔBEC

$\angle ABE = \angle BEC + \angle ECB$ (Exterior angle = sum of opposite interior angles)

$100° = 60° + \angle BEC$

$\angle BEC = 40°$

Now, $\angle BEC = \angle BDC$ (angle subtended by the same chord)

$\Rightarrow \quad \angle BDC = 40°$.

26. Sum of interior angles of an n-sided polygon is:

Sum = $(n - 2)\, 180°$

Now, according to question:

$(n - 2)\, 180° = 2340°$

$(n - 2) = \dfrac{2340}{180} = 13$

$n - 2 = 13$

$\Rightarrow \quad n = 15.$

27.

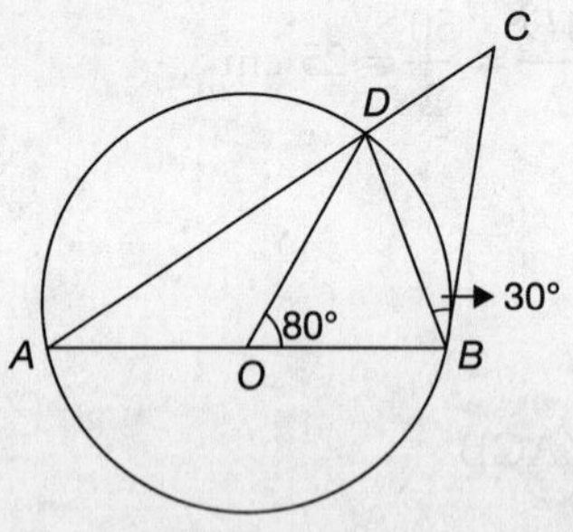

In ΔADB

$\angle ADB = 90°$ (angle subtended by diameter on circumference = 90°)

$\angle ADB + \angle BDC = 180°$ (Linear pair)

$\angle BDC = 180° - 90° = 90°$

In $\Delta\ BDC$, $\angle BDC = 90°$,

$\angle DBC = 30°$,

Therefore by angle sum property

$\angle BDC + \angle DBC + \angle C = 180°$

$\angle C = 180° - 90° - 30° = 60°$

$\angle ABC = 60°$.

28.

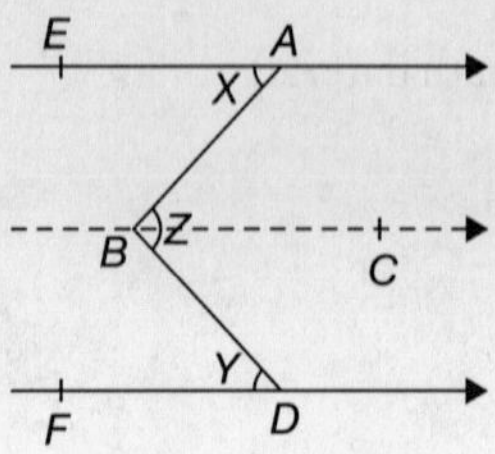

$y = 45°$ (compliment of 45°)

$x = \frac{2}{3} \times y = \frac{2}{3} \times 45° = 30°$

$x = \angle ABC$ (alternate angles)

$\angle ABC = 30°$

$y = \angle DBC$ (alternate angles)

$\Rightarrow \quad y = \angle DBC = 45°$

Now, $\angle ABC + \angle DBC = \angle ABD = Z$

$\Rightarrow \quad Z = 45° + 30° = 75°$

$Z = 75°$

29. Join EC.

DE is the perpendicular bisector of the chord AB.

∴ DE is the diameter of the circle.

$\Rightarrow \angle ECD = 90°$

$\angle ECB = \angle EAB = 24°$

(Angles in the same segment)

$\Rightarrow \angle BCD = \angle ECD - \angle ECB$

$= 90° - 24°$

$= 66°$.

30. Since AC = AQ

$\angle AQC = \angle ACQ = 79°$

$\Rightarrow \angle CAQ = 180° - 2 \times 79°$

$= 180° - 158°$

$= 22°$

$\therefore \angle BOP = 180° - 22°$

$= 158°$.

31.

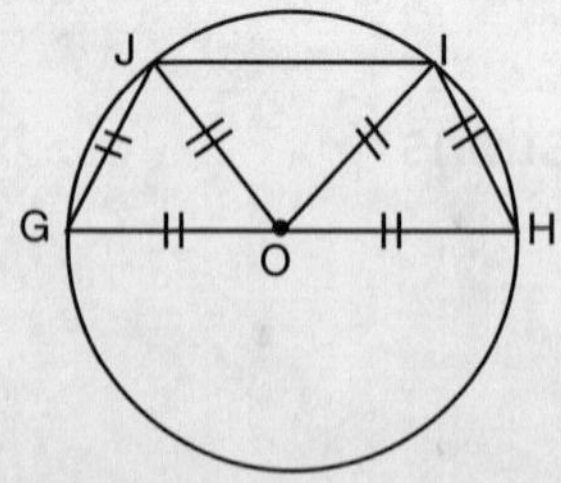

Join OJ, OI

HI = OG = OJ = GJ

ΔOHI and ΔOJG are equilateral triangles.

$\Rightarrow \angle H = 60$

But $\angle HIJ + \angle G = 180°$

$\Rightarrow \angle HIJ = 180° - 60° = 120°$

32. (A)

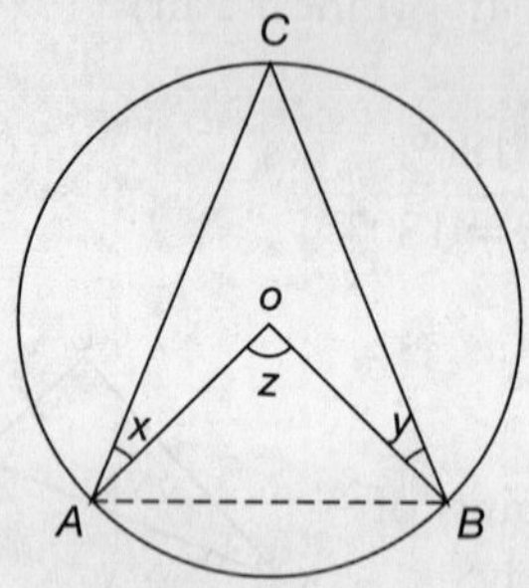

$x = 40°$

$\frac{x}{y} = \frac{4}{3} \Rightarrow y = \frac{3x}{4} = \frac{3 \times 40}{4}$

$\Rightarrow y = 30°$

now, $z = 2\angle C$ (angle subtended at centre is twice than the angle subtended y same chord on circumference)

$\Rightarrow \angle C = \frac{z}{2}$ (*)

In ΔAOB

$\angle OAB + \angle OBA + \angle z = 180°$

$\angle OAB + \angle OBA = (180° - z)$ (1)

In ABC,

$\angle C + \angle A + \angle B = 180°$

$\frac{z}{2} + x + \angle OAB + y + \angle OBA = 180°$

using equation (1) and value of x, y:

$$30 + 40 + \frac{z}{2} + 180 - z = 180°$$

$$70 - \frac{z}{2} = 0$$

$$z = 140°$$

(B) $BC = 8$ cm

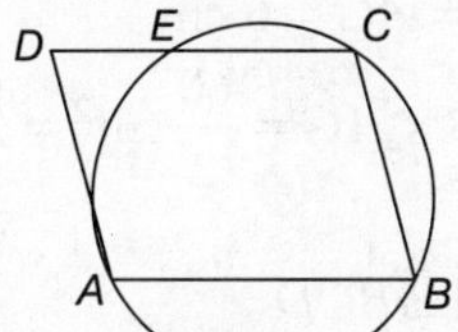

$ABCD$ is a parallelogram

$\Rightarrow \angle B = \angle D$ (1)

$ABCE$ is a cyclic quadrilateral

$\angle AED = \angle B$

($\therefore$ Exterior angle of a cyclic quadrilateral) (2)

From (1) and (2), $\angle D = \angle AED$

$\Rightarrow AE = AD$

$\Rightarrow AE = BC$ ($\therefore AD = BC$)

$\Rightarrow AE = 8$ cm

33. In ΔTUR and ΔVWQ

$\angle UTR = \angle WVQ \left(\overline{TR} \,||\, \overline{VQ}\right)$

$\angle TUR = \angle VWQ \left(\overline{UR} \,||\, \overline{WQ}\right)$

$TR = VQ$ (opposite sides of a parallelogram

$\therefore \Delta TUR \cong \Delta VWQ$

$\Rightarrow$ area (ΔTUR) = area (ΔVWQ) = 24 cm^2

Essay Type Questions

34.

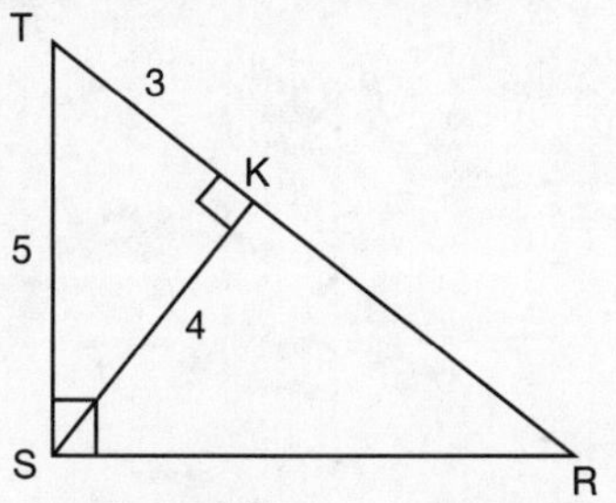

In ΔTSR, $\angle TSR = 90°$ and $\overline{SK} \perp \overline{TR}$

Given that TS = 5 cm and TK = 3 cm

$\Rightarrow SK = \sqrt{5^2 - 3^2} = 4$ cm

Now, $\angle T = \angle T$ (common)

$\Rightarrow \angle TKS = \angle TSR = 90°$

$\Rightarrow \Delta TKS \sim \Delta TSR$ ($\because$ AA similarity)

$$\Rightarrow \frac{TK}{TS} = \frac{KS}{SR} = \frac{TS}{TR}$$

$$\Rightarrow \frac{3}{5} = \frac{4}{SR} = \frac{5}{3 + KR}$$

$$\Rightarrow SR = \frac{20}{3}$$

and $3 + KR = \dfrac{25}{3}$

$$\Rightarrow KR = \frac{25}{3} - 3 = \frac{16}{3}$$

Perimeter ΔSRK = SK + KR + SR

$$= \left(4 + \frac{16}{3} + \frac{20}{3}\right) \text{ cm}$$

$$= \left(4 + \frac{36}{3}\right) = 16 \text{ cm}$$

35.

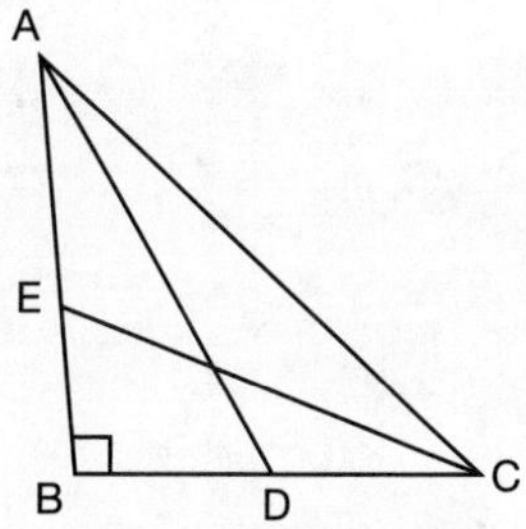

Given $\angle B = 90°$,

E and D are the mid points of AB and BC respectively.

We know that $4(AD^2 + CE^2)$

$= 5AC^2$

$$\therefore 4\left(15^2 + \left(\sqrt{360}\right)^2\right) = 5AC^2$$

$4(225 + 360) = 5AC^2$

$4 \times 585 = 5AC^2$

$\therefore AC^2 = 4 \times 117$

$AC^2 = 4 \times 9 \times 13$

$AC = 2 \times 3\sqrt{13}$

$AC = 6\sqrt{13}$ cm

36.

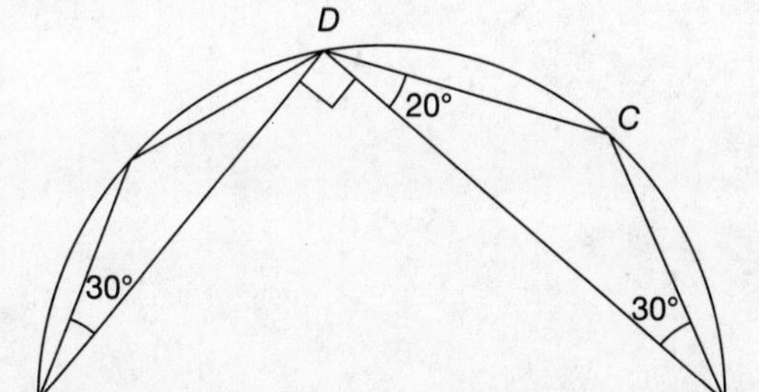

$\angle ADB = 90°$ (angle subtended by diameter on circumference)

$\angle C + 20° + 30° = 180°$

$\angle C = 130°$

In quadrilateral $ABCD$,

$\Rightarrow \angle C + \angle A = 180°$ (diagonally opposite angles in cyclic quadr.)

$\Rightarrow \angle A = 180 - \angle C$

$\Rightarrow \angle A = 180 - 130 = 50°$

$\Rightarrow \angle DAB = 50°$

In ΔADB

$\angle DAB + \angle ADB + \angle DBA = 180°$

$50° + 90° + \angle DBA = 180°$

$\angle DBA = 40°$

In quadrilateral $ABDE$

$\angle B + \angle E = 180°$ (diagonally opposite angles in cyclic quadr)

$\angle E = 180° - 40° = 140°$

$\angle AED = 140°$

37. 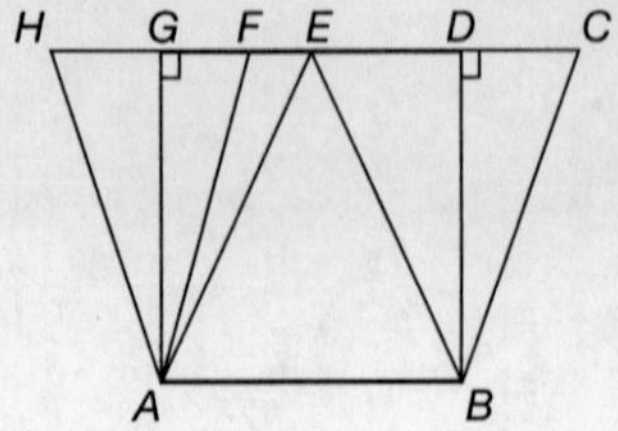

$AB = 10$ cm

$AG = 6$ cm

In ||gm $ABCF$,

base $= AB = 10$ cm

height $= BD = AG = 6$ cm (since $BD = AG$, sides of rectangle)

Area of $ABCF = b \times h$

$= 10 \times 6 = 60$ cm^2.

In ||gm $ABEH$,

base $= AB = 10$ cm

height $= AG = 6$ cm

Area $= AB \times AG = 60$ cm^2

In ΔAEB, base $= AB = 10$ cm

height $= AG = 6$ cm

Area $= \frac{1}{2} \times AB \times AG = \frac{60}{2}$ cm^2 $= 30$cm^2

38. In quadrilateral $ABCD$

$\angle A + \angle D = 180°$ (diagonally opposite angles) (1)

Also $\angle CDE + \angle CDB = 180°$ (Linear Pair)

$\Rightarrow \angle CDB = 180° - 120° = 60°$

Using this in equation (1),

$\angle A + 60° = 180°$

$\Rightarrow \angle A = 120°$

Since, AD is a bisector $\Rightarrow \angle BAD = 60°$

Also, $\angle BAD = \angle BCD = 60°$ (angle subtended by common chord subtend equal angles)

$\Rightarrow \angle BCD = 60°$

$x + y > 10$

$2x - 3y > 12$

7 and 2

$7 + 2 = 9$

$\therefore 9 < 10$

and

$7 - 2 = 5$

$5 < 12$

Competition Wing

Level 1: Apply Your Concepts

1. 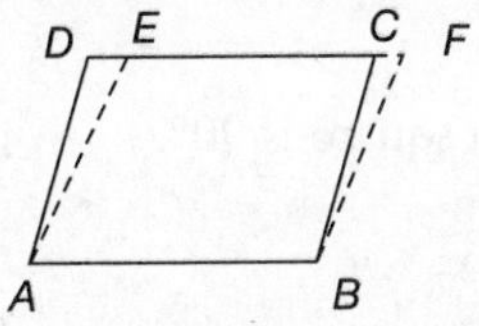

| |gm $ABCD$, $ABFE$ have same base AB and are between same | | line.

Area of | |gm = Base × (distance between | | lines)

$\Rightarrow$ area of | |gm $ABCD$ = area of | |gm $ABFE$

Equal.

2. Concyclic points.

3. Sum of all exterior angles = 360°

Let the polygon has 'n' sides

$\Rightarrow n \times$ (exterior angle) = 360°

$n \times 60° = 360°$

$n = \frac{360}{60} = 6$

Polygon has 6 sides.

4. 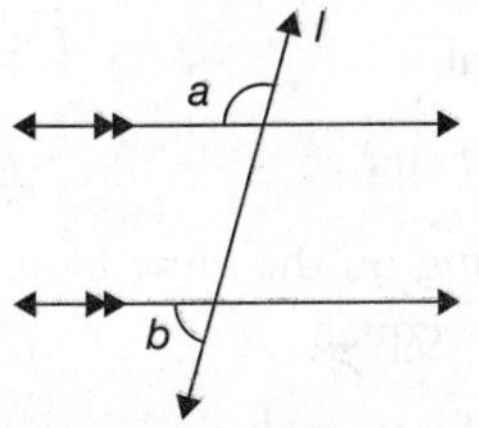

Let a and b be the 2 exterior angles on the same side of line.

$\frac{a}{b} = \frac{5}{4}$ (according to Questions).

Let a, b equal to $5x$ and $4x$.

Also, sum of exterior angle = 180°

$\Rightarrow \quad 5x + 4x = 180°$

$9x = 180°$

$x = 20°$

$\Rightarrow a = 5x = 100°$, $b = 4x = 80°$

5. When all sides of a quadrilateral are equal, then it is either a Square or Rhombus

6. Given, number of sides (n) = 21

Number of diagonals of an n – sided polygon

$= \frac{n(n-3)}{2}$, where $n = 21$.

$= \frac{21(21-3)}{2} = \frac{21(18)}{2} = 189.$

7. Find the number of sides of the polygon, angle subtended at the centre $= \frac{360°}{n}$.

8. Incenter is equidistant from all the sides of the triangle.

9. The bisector of the angle is the required locus.

10. Let m, n be the number of sides of the polygons, where $m < n$.

$\Rightarrow n - m = 2$

$\Rightarrow n = m + 2$

Also $\frac{n(n-3)}{2} - \frac{m(m-3)}{2} = 15$

$\frac{(m+2)(m+2-3)}{2} \frac{m(m-3)}{2} = 15$

$(m + 2)(m - 1) - m(m - 3) = 30$

$m^2 - m + 2m - 2 - m^2 + 3m = 30$

$4m = 32$

$m = 8$

$\therefore n = m + 2 = 8 + 2 = 10$

$\therefore$ The number of diagonals of the polygon having 8 sides

$= \frac{8(8-3)}{2}$

$= \frac{8 \times 5}{2} = 20$

11. (i) Use BPT.

(ii) By BPT, $\frac{PM}{PQ} = \frac{PN}{PR}$.

12. $\angle CDE = \angle BAE$ ($\because$ angles in the same segment).

13. ABCD is a cyclic, quadrilateral,

$\Rightarrow \angle A + \angle C = \angle B + \angle D = 180°$

Given that the opposite angles are equal.

$\Rightarrow \angle A = \angle C$ and $\angle B = \angle D$

$\Rightarrow \angle A = \angle C = \angle B = \angle D = 90$

Hence, ABCD is a rectangle.

14. The sum of the interior angles of a polygon is the even multiple of 90°. Here, in the given options, 1640° is not a multiple of 90°.

15. Angle subtended by an arc at the centre is double the angle subtended by it on the remaining part of the circle.

16. $RS = \frac{1}{2} PQ$.

17. Let n be the number of sides.

Given, $6n = \dfrac{n(n-3)}{2}$

$\Rightarrow 6 = \dfrac{n-3}{2}$

$\Rightarrow n = 12 + 3 = 15$

Number of diagonals

$= \dfrac{15(15-3)}{2}$

$= 90$

18. ABCD is a parallelogram. $\angle BAD = 70°$

$\angle C = \angle BAD = 70°$ ($\because$ Opposite angles of a parallelogram)

ABED is a cyclic quadrilateral.

$\Rightarrow \angle DEC = \angle BAD = 70°$

($\because$ exterior angle of a cyclic quadrilateral)

$\Rightarrow \angle EDC = 180° - \angle DEC - \angle C = 180° - 70° - 70°$

$= 40°$

19. Angle subtended by a minor arc is always less than 90°.

20. Number of diagonals of a polygon with n sides $= \dfrac{n(n-3)}{2}$

21. $AC^2 = AB^2 + BC^2$. Consider AB as x, BC as $x + k$ and AC as $x + 2k$.

22. ΔMOR and ΔNOR are isosceles triangles.

23. (i) Produce AF and AG to meet CD.

(ii) Exterior angle of a triangle is equal to the sum of its interior opposite angles.

(iii) Sum of the angles in a triangle is always 180°.

24. Draw a parallel line to AB through E.

25.

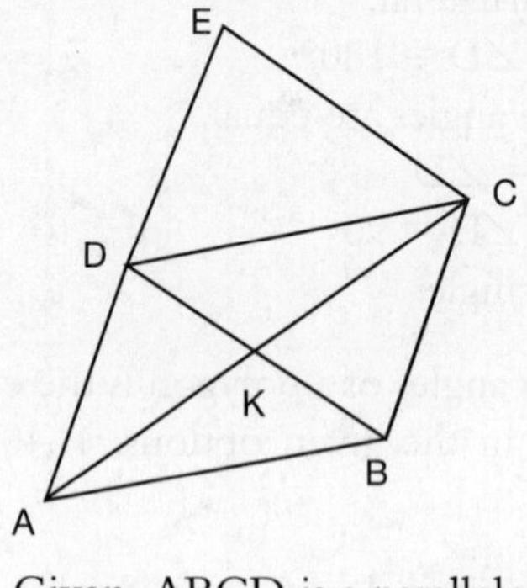

Given, ABCD is a parallelogram. BDEC is a square.

Given, BD = 5 cm. ($\because$ BD is the shorter diagonal of the parallelogram)

BC = CE = ED = DB = 5 cm

($\because$ BDEC is a square)

AC and BD bisect each other at K (say) ($\because$ ABCD is a parallelogram).

$\therefore$ BK $= \dfrac{5}{2}$ cm.

We know that each angle in a square is 90°.

$\therefore \angle CBD = 90°$

In ΔBKC, $CK^2 = BK^2 + BC^2$

$CK^2 = \left(\dfrac{5}{2}\right)^2 + (5)^2$

$CK^2 = \dfrac{25}{4} + 25$

$CK^2 = \dfrac{125}{4}$

$CK = \dfrac{5\sqrt{5}}{2}$

$\therefore$ required diagonal length = AC

= AK + CK = 2 CK ($\because$ AK = CK)

$= 2\left(\dfrac{5\sqrt{5}}{2}\right) = 5\sqrt{5}$ cm

26. Join BD, $ABDE$ is a cyclic quadrilateral.

27. Find the length of the diagonal.

28. $\angle BAC = 90°$ and BC is a diameter.

29. Areas of the parallelograms lying on the same base and between same parallel lines are equal.

30. Use the angle sum property of a triangle.

31. Apply the concept of inequality property of a triangle.

32. Sum of the exterior and interior angles of a polygon = 180°.

33. Find one exterior angle.

Level 2: Review Your Concepts

34. (i) As $BC : CD = 2 : 3$, Area (ΔABC) : Area(ΔACD) $= 2 : 3$.

Let area of $\Delta ABC = 2x$ and (ΔACD) $= 3x$.

(ii) As $AE : EC = 3 : 4$, Area (ΔAEB) $= \dfrac{3}{7}(2x)$ and

Area (ΔECD) $= \dfrac{4}{7}(3x)$.

35. (i) As $PB = PC$, $\angle PBO = \angle PCO$.

(ii) As $\angle BOC = 130°$, $\angle BAC = \angle BDC = 65°$.

36. (i) As the greatest interior angle is 110°, the least exterior angle is (180° – 110°).

(ii) Sum of all the exterior angles = 360°.

(iii) All exterior angles are distinct.

37. (i) Join OC and find the relation between OB and BC.

(ii) $OB = BC$ and $OC : OB = \sqrt{2} : 1$.

38. (i) $\angle PQR = \frac{1}{2}(\angle POR)$; $\angle NMS = \frac{1}{2}(\angle NOS)$.

(ii) If $\angle OPR = x$, then $\angle ROP = 180° - 2x$.

39. (i) Join DC and use properties of cyclic quadrilateral

(ii) Use $\angle ADC = 90°$ and find $\angle BDC$.

(iii) $BDCP$ is cyclic.

40. (i) Join OD, OE and OF.

(ii) Equal chords subtend equal angles at the centre.

41. (i) In a triangle median is same as altitude drawn on same side, then the remaining two sides are equal.

(ii) As AC is median as well as altitude to BD, $AB = AD$.

(iii) In ΔADE, $AD + DE > AE$.

(iv) As AD is median, $CD = DE$.

42. (i) Join OA and use properties of arcs.

(ii) $\angle AOB = 2\angle AEB$.

(iii) AOC is the diameter, i.e., $\angle AOB + \angle BOC = 180°$.

43. (i) Join OC, and apply the concept of equal chords.

(ii) $\angle OBC = \angle OCB$.

(iii) As $BC = CD$, $\angle BOC = \angle COD$.

(iv) $\angle BAC = \frac{1}{2}\angle BOC$.

44. (i) As AB is the diameter, $\angle AOB = 90°$.

(ii) $\angle QPS = \frac{1}{2}(\angle QOS)$.

(iii) $PQRS$ is a cyclic quadrilateral.

45. (i) Use Pythagoras's theorem.

(ii) Let $AE = BE = x$ and $BD = CD = y$.

(iii) Use Pythagoras's theorem in the right triangles ABD and BEC and obtain the equations in terms of x and y.

(iv) Add the above equations and obtain AC, i.e., $4x^2 + 4y^2$.

46. BACD is the required sequential order.

47. Since B is the mid-point of $\overline{SR}$ and $PS = BR$, $PS = BS = PA = AB$.

$\therefore$ $PABS$ is a rhombus, and similarly, $AQRB$ is a rhombus.

$\therefore \angle BCA = \angle ADB = 90°$.

As PB and QB are bisectors of $\angle P$ and $\angle Q$, $\angle PBQ = 90°$.

$\therefore CADB$ is a rectangle.

48. From the inequality of triangles, we have:

$6002 + 2006 > m$ and

$6002 - 2006 < m$

$\Rightarrow 3996 < m < 8008$

Since m is an integer, it can take (8008 – 3996 – 1) or 4011 values.

49.

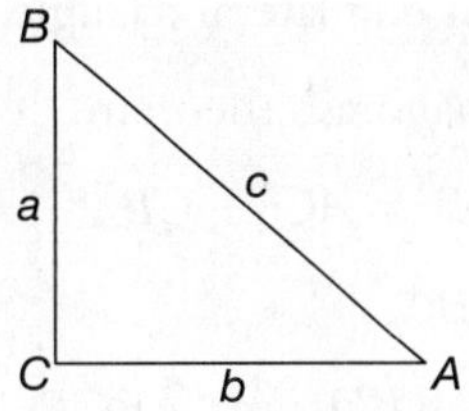

Given that, $c = 2a$ and $b^2 - 3a^2 = 0. \Rightarrow b = \sqrt{3}a$.

$a : b : c = a : \sqrt{3}a : 2a = 1 : \sqrt{3} : 2$.

$\therefore \angle A = 30°, \angle B = 60°$ and $\angle C = 90°$.

So, $\angle ABC = 60°$.

50. Since, $SA = SB = SC$, S is the circum-centre

$\angle ASB = 150°$ (given) $\Rightarrow \angle ACB = 75°$.

Since, $AC = BC$, $\angle CAB = \angle CBA = \left(\frac{180° - 75°}{2}\right)$

$= 52\frac{1}{2}°$.

51. Given, $\angle QPR = 25°$.

Since, QS is the diameter, $\angle QPS = 90°$.

$\Rightarrow \angle SPR = 90 - 25° = 65°$

$\therefore \angle SOR = 2 \times 65° = 130°$.

Level 3: Assess Your Concepts

52. (i) Draw the figure and mark the points P, Q and R on sides AB, BC, and AC, respectively.

(ii) Angle $B = 90°$ and $\angle PRQ$ is formed by lines PR and RQ, which are parallel to lines BC and AB (mid-point theorem).

(iii) Since BC and AB are perpendicular, PR and RQ are also perpendicular, i.e., $\angle PRQ = 90°$.

(iv) Quadrilateral joining $BPRQ$ is a cyclic quadrilateral.

53. (i) Draw the figure and mark the points on it.

(ii) Use Pythagoras's theorem.

(iii) We will get $p^2 + q^2 = 2pq$ which gives $p = q$.

54. (i) Draw the figure and mark the points on it.

(ii) Join BQ, now BQ is the median to PR. Since $PQ = QR$, BQ is also the altitude to PR.

(iii) PBQ is a right triangle, right angled at B. Thus, PQ is the diameter.

(iv) Joining PA, we get another right triangle PAQ which is right angled at A.

PBQ and PAQ are congruent angles.

(v) $PR = QR$, so ΔPQR is an equilateral triangle.

55. (i) Join AB. Now using Pythagoras's theorem,

$AB^2 = AD^2 + DB^2$ and $AB^2 = AC^2 + CB^2$.

(ii) If $BD = AC$, then $AD = BC$.

(iii) If $\overline{AD} \parallel \overline{BD}$, then $\overline{AC} \parallel BD$, so $ABCD$ is a rectangle.

56.

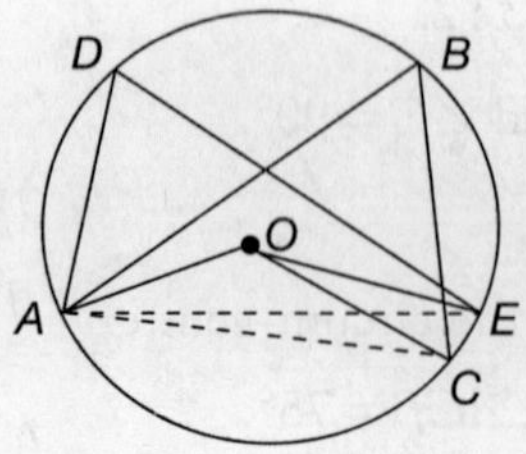

From the given figure,

$AE > AC$

$\Rightarrow \angle ADE > \angle ABC$

$\Rightarrow (\angle ADE - \angle ABC) = 15°$

$\Rightarrow \dfrac{\angle AOE}{2} - \dfrac{\angle AOC}{2} = 15°$

$\Rightarrow \angle AOE - \angle AOC = 30°$

$\Rightarrow \angle COE = 30°$.

$\therefore \angle COE = \dfrac{1}{2}\angle COE = 15°$.

57.

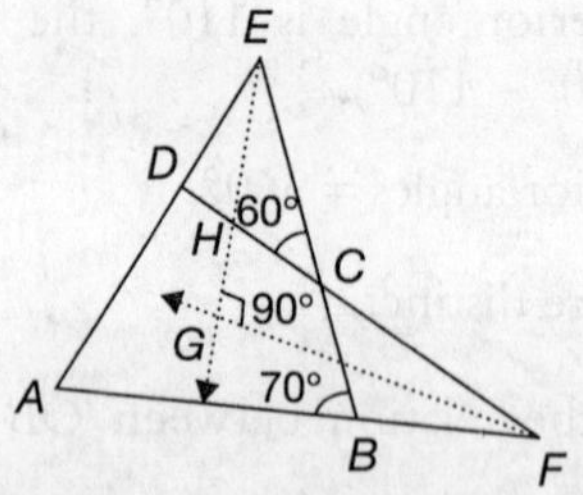

$\angle DAB = \angle DCE = 60°$ and $\angle EDC = \angle CBA = 70°$. (Exterior angle of a cyclic quadrilateral.)

In ΔABE, $\angle DEC = 180 - (60° + 70°) = 50°$.

Since, $\overline{FG}$ bisects $\angle F$

$\therefore \angle HEC = \dfrac{\angle DEC}{2} = \dfrac{50°}{2} = 25°$.

58.

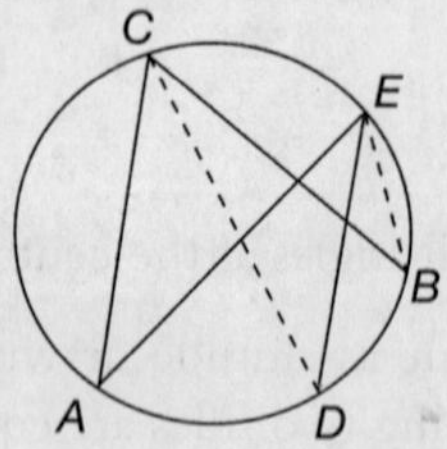

Join CD and EB

$\angle ACD = \angle AED = 50°$ (angles in the same segment and $\angle AED = 50°$)

$\angle ACB = 60°$ (given)

$\Rightarrow \angle DCB = \angle ACB - \angle ACD = 60° - 50° = 10°$.

$\angle DEB = \angle DCB = 10°$. (angles in the same segment)

59. $OA = AB = BC = CD = OD$

Let $\angle O = x$

As $AO = AB$, $\angle O = \angle ABO = x$

$\Rightarrow \angle CAB = \angle O + \angle ABO = 2x$

As $AB = BC$, $\angle CAB = \angle BCA = 2x$

As $OD = DC$, $\angle O = \angle OCD = x$

$\angle CDB = \angle O + \angle OCD = 2x$

As $CD = CB$, $\angle CDB = \angle CBO = 2x$

In $DOCB$, $\angle O + \angle BCO + \angle CBO = 180°$

$\Rightarrow x + 2x + 2x = 180°$

$\Rightarrow 5x = 180° \Rightarrow x = 36°$

60. In ΔABC and ΔADB

$\angle A = \angle A$ (common)

$\angle ABC = \angle ADB$ (given)

By AA similarity

$\Delta ABC \sim \Delta ADB$

$\Rightarrow \dfrac{AB}{AD} = \dfrac{AC}{AB}$

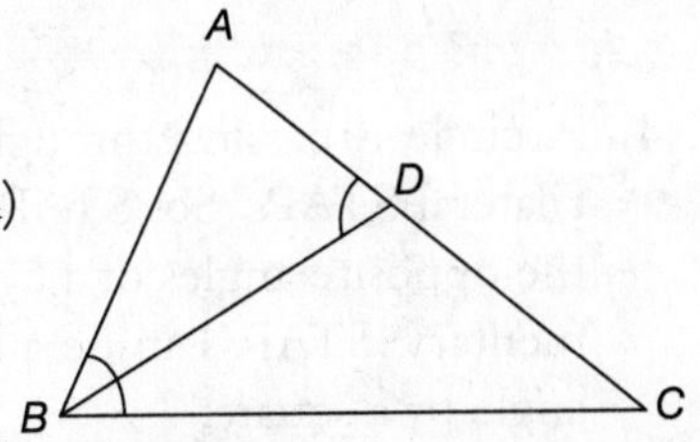

$AB^2 = AD \times AC$

$= 2(2 + 6) = 16$

$AB = 4$ cm

In ΔABC

$AC - AB < BC < AC + AB$

$8 - 4 < BC < 8 + 4$

$4 < BC < 12$

JEE Special Wing

Multiple-Answer Type Questions

1. The number of diagonals of a polygon of n sides $=\dfrac{n(n-3)}{2}$.

Going by options:

(a) $\dfrac{n(n-3)}{2}=4850$

$n(n-3)=9700$

$n(n-3)=100\times 97=100(100-3)$

$\Rightarrow n=100$

(b) $\dfrac{n(n-3)}{2}=2015$

$n(n-3)=4030$

$n(n-3)=65\times 62=65(65-3)$

$\Rightarrow n=65$

(c) $\dfrac{n(n-3)}{2}=860$

$n(n-3)=1720$

$n(n-3)=43\times 40=43(43-3)$

$\Rightarrow n=43$

(d) $\dfrac{n(n-3)}{2}=350$

$n(n-3)=700$

$n(n-3)=28\times 25=28(28-3)$

$\Rightarrow n=28$

Hence, choice (a), choice (b), choice (c), and choice (d) are follows.

2. An exterior angle of a regular polygon of n sides is given by $\dfrac{360°}{n}$.

So, exterior angle of a regular polygon is a factor of 360 in degree.

Therefore, the angles given in all the options are factors of 360.

Hence, choice (a), choice (b), and choice (d) are follows.

3. Given that $ABCD$ is a quadrilateral.

If $ABCD$ is a rhombus, then the diagonals bisect to each other at right angles.

Hence, choice (b) and choice (d) are follows.

4. A circle is passing through the four vertices of quadrilateral STAR. So, STAR is a cyclic quadrilateral. As the opposite angles of a cyclic quadrilateral are supplementary, STAR can be an isosceles trapezium, a rectangle or a square.

Hence, choice (b) and choice (d) are follows.

5. Given that the area of ΔRTM is 144 sq cm.

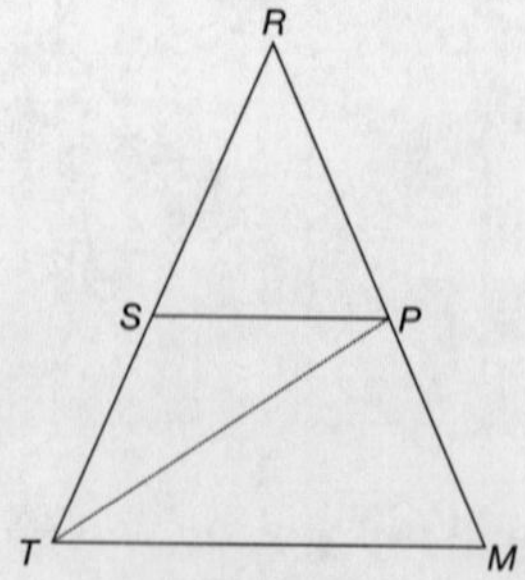

S and P are the midpoints TR and MR.

(a) The area of ΔRSP is one-fourth of the area of ΔRTM

$=\dfrac{1}{4}\times 144 = 36$ sq cm.

(b) The area of $\square MPST$ is 144 sq cm - 36 sq cm = 108 sq cm.

As S and P are the midpoints TR and MR, $TM = 2SP$.

And also, $\overline{TM} \parallel \overline{SP}$.

Let h be the distance between TM and SP.

We have the area of $\square MPST$ = 108 sq cm.

$\dfrac{h}{2}(SP+TM)=108$

$\dfrac{h}{2}(SP+2SP)=108$

$\dfrac{h}{2}(3SP)=108$

$h(SP)=72$

(c) The area of $\Delta SPT=\dfrac{h}{2}(SP)=\dfrac{72}{2}=36$ sq cm.

(d) The area of $\Delta PMT=\dfrac{h}{2}(TM)=\dfrac{h}{2}(2SP)=h(SP)$ = 72 sq cm.

Hence, choice (a, b, c, d) are follows.

6. Given that SKY and ERT are two triangles.

A is the midpoint of both SY and ET.

B is the midpoint of both KY and ER.

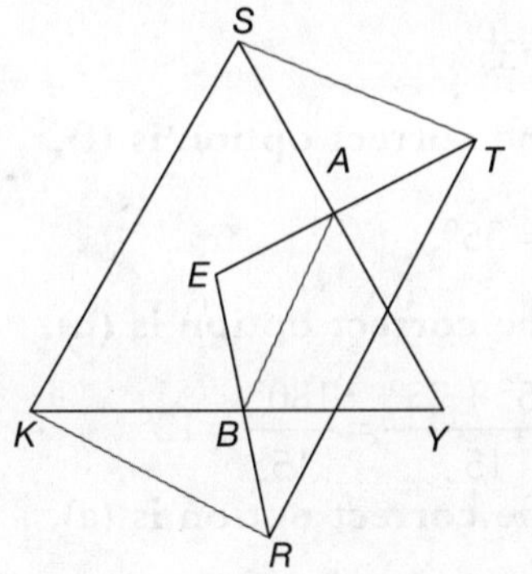

By midpoint theorem, $AB = \frac{SK}{2} = \frac{TR}{2} \Rightarrow SK = TR$.

Also, $\overline{SK} \parallel \overline{AB} \parallel \overline{TR}$.

So, *STRK* is a parallelogram.

Hence, choice (a), choice (b), choice (c) and choice (d) are follows.

7. Given that *PQRS* is a parallelogram.
A, *B*, *C*, and *D* are the points on *PS*, *SR*, *QR*, and *PQ* respectively such that $AS : AP = BS : BR = CQ : CR = DQ : DP = 1 : 2$.

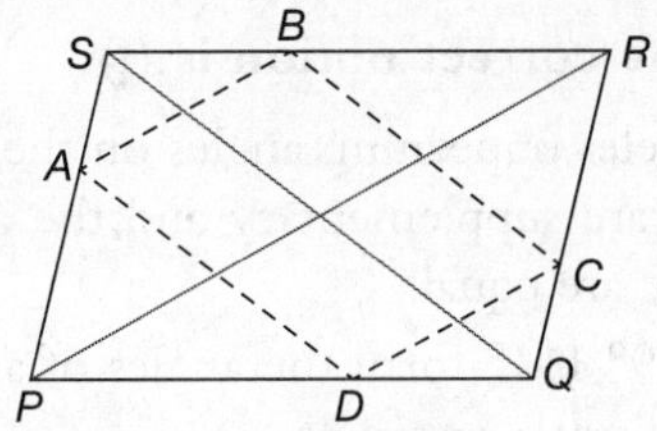

In ΔSPR, $AS : AP = BS : BR$.

$\overline{AB} \parallel \text{PR}$ (By Basic proportionality theorem)

In ΔQPR, $CQ: CR = DQ : DP$.

$\overline{CD} \parallel \text{PR}$ (By Basic proportionality theorem)

$\Delta \overline{AB} \parallel \overline{CD}$ (1)

In ΔRSQ, $BS : BR = CQ : CR$.

$\overline{BC} \parallel \overline{SQ}$ (By Basic proportionality theorem)

In ΔPSQ, $DQ : DP = AS : AP$.

$\overline{AD} \parallel \overline{SQ}$ (By Basic proportionality theorem)

$\Delta \overline{BC} \parallel \overline{AD}$ (2)

From (1) and (2), *ABCD* is a parallelogram.

So, *AC* and *BD* bisect to each other.

Hence, choice (c) and choice (d) are follows.

8. *P* and *Q* are two regular polygons.
The number of sides of *P* and *Q* are in the ratio is 1 : 3.
Let the number of sides be *n* and 3*n*.
Also, given that the ratio of the interior angles of *P* and *Q* is 6 : 7.

$$\frac{(n-2)180°}{n} : \frac{(3n-2)180°}{3n} = 6:7$$

$$(n-2) : \frac{(3n-2)}{3} = 6:7$$

$$\frac{3n-6}{3n-2} = \frac{6}{7}$$

$$\frac{n-2}{3n-2} = \frac{2}{7}$$

$$7n - 14 = 6n - 4$$

$$n = 10.$$

The number of sides of $P(n) = 10$

The number of sides of $Q(3n) = 30$.

(a) The difference of the number of the number of sides of the polygons = 30 – 10 = 20.

(b) The sum of an exterior angle of *P* and an exterior angle of $Q = \frac{360°}{10} + \frac{360°}{30}$
$= 36° + 12° = 48°$.

(c) The sum of the number of diagonals of *P* and *Q*
$= \frac{n(n-3)}{2} + \frac{3n(3n-3)}{2}$
$= \frac{10(10-3)}{2} + \frac{30(30-3)}{2}$
$= 35 + 405 = 440$.

(d) The difference of an interior angle of *P* and an interior angle of *Q*
$= \frac{(3n-2)180°}{3n} - \frac{(n-2)180°}{n}$
$= \frac{(30-2)180°}{30} - \frac{(10-2)180°}{10}$
$= 168° - 144° = 24°$.

Hence, choice (b), choice (c) and choice (d) are follows.

9. 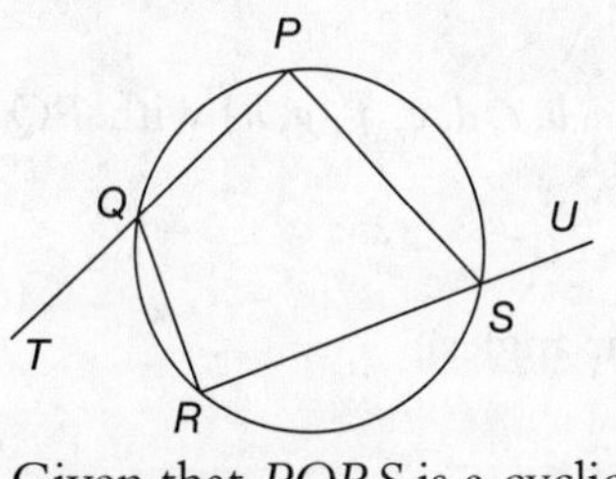

Given that *PQRS* is a cyclic quadrilateral.

PQ is extended to *T* and *RS* is extended to *U*.

In a cyclic quadrilateral, the opposite angles are supplementary, and an exterior angle is equal to its interior opposite angle.

So, $\angle P + \angle R = \angle Q + \angle S = 180°$.

$\angle PSU = \angle PQR$ and $\angle RQT = \angle PSR$

Hence, choice (b) and choice (d) are follows.

10. 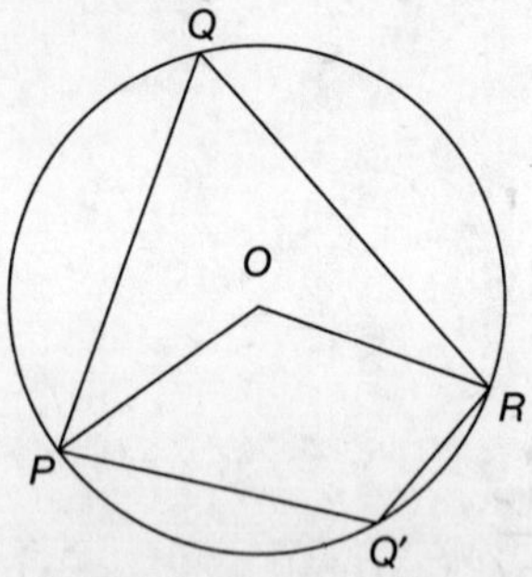

Given that P, R, and Q are the three points on a circle with centre O.

$\angle POR = 120°$.

The position of Q can be as follows.

Let it be Q or Q′.

$\angle PQR = \frac{\angle POR}{2} = \frac{120°}{2} = 60°.$

$\angle PQR + \angle PQ'R = 180°$

$60° + \angle PQ'R = 180°$

$\angle PQ'R = 120°$

Hence, choice (b) and choice (c) are follows.

Match The Column

Common Solutions for questions 11 to 15:

Given that $PQRS$ is a parallelogram.

Line l is a transversal of PQ and SR of the parallelogram.

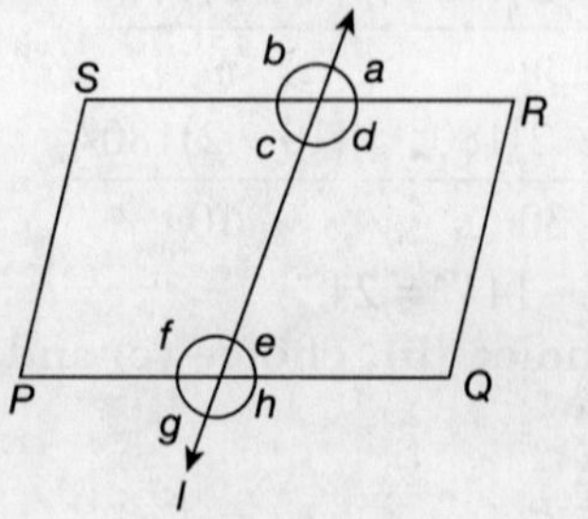

Line l makes eight angles (a, b, c, d, e, f, g, h) with PQ and SR.

Also, given that $a = 75°$.

$a + b = 180°$ (Linear pair angles)

$75° + b = 180°$

$b = 105°$

$c = a = 75°$ (Vertically opposite angles)

$d = b = 105°$ (Vertically opposite angles)

$e = a = 75°$ (Corresponding angles)

$f = b = 105°$ (Corresponding angles)

$g = c = 75°$ (Corresponding angles)

$h = d = 105°$ (Corresponding angles)

11. $\frac{g}{3} = \frac{75°}{3} = 25°.$

Hence, the correct option is (f).

12. $\frac{b}{3} = \frac{105°}{3} = 35°.$

Hence, the correct option is (h).

13. $\frac{b+e}{15} = \frac{105° + 75°}{15} = \frac{180°}{15} = 12°.$

Hence, the correct option is (a).

14. $h - c = 105° - 75° = 30°.$

Hence, the correct option is (g).

15. $\frac{h}{5} = \frac{105°}{5} = 21°.$

Hence, the correct option is (e).

Common Solutions for questions 16 to 20:

Given that $ABCD$ is a quadrilateral.

16. In a trapezium, angles on the same side of a transversal are supplementary.

$121°, 59°, 63°, 117°$ form the angles of a trapezium with no two sides are equal.

Hence, the correct option is (f).

17. In an isosceles trapezium, angles on the same side of a transversal are supplementary and the angles on each parallel side are equal.

$111°, 69°, 69°, 111°$ form the angles of an isosceles trapezium but not a rectangle.

Hence, the correct option is (c).

18. In a rectangle, each angle is a rectangle.

$90°, 90°, 90°, 90°$ are the angles of a rectangle.

Hence, the correct option is (a).

19. In a parallelogram, the adjacent angles are equal, and the opposite angles are equal.

$131°, 49°, 131°, 49°$ form the angles of a parallelogram but not a rectangle.

Hence, the correct option is (h).

20. In a cyclic kite, a pair of opposite angles are right angles.

$70°, 90°, 110°, 90°$ form the angles of a cyclic kite but not a square.

Hence, the correct option is (b).

Comprehension-Based Questions

Common Solutions for questions 21 to 25:

Given that:

Three sides of a triangle are 265 cm, 565 cm and x cm, where x is an integer.

We know that the sum of any two sides of a triangle is greater than the third side and the difference between any two sides is lesser than the third side.

So, $565 - 265 < x < 265 + 565$.

$300 < x < 830$, where x is an integer.

21. We have $300 < x < 830$, where x is an integer.
 So, x can be 301, 302, 303, ... 829.
 There exists, 529 (= 829 – 300) triangles.
 Hence, the correct option is (c).

22. Two sides of the triangle are 265 cm and 565 cm.
 Also, the triangles is isosceles.
 The third side is either 265 cm or 565 cm.
 But $300 < x < 830$.
 So, x must be 565 cm.
 There exists, only one isosceles triangle.
 Hence, the correct option is (b).

23. We have $300 < x < 830$, where x is an integer.
 If we consider one of the sides as 265 cm, then the sum of any two sides can be as follows:
 $300 + 265 < x + 265 < 830 + 265$
 $565 < x + 265 < 1095$ (1)
 If we consider one of the sides as 565 cm, then the sum of any two sides can be as follows:
 $300 + 565 < x + 565 < 830 + 565$
 $865 < x + 565 < 1395$ (2)
 From (1) and (2), $565 <$ sum of any two sides < 1395
 Hence, the sum of any two sides cannot be 1395 cm.
 Hence, the correct option is (d).

24. We have $300 < x < 830$, where x is an integer.
 $300 + 265 + 565 < x + 265 + 565 < 830 + 265 + 565$
 $1130 < x + 265 + 565 < 1660$
 Hence, the perimeter of the triangle cannot be 1661 cm.
 Hence, the correct option is (a).

25. We have $300 < x < 830$, where x is an integer.
 If we consider one of the sides as 265 cm, then the difference of any two sides can be as follows:
 $300 - 265 < x - 265 < 830 - 265$
 $35 < x - 265 < 565$ (1)
 If we consider one of the sides as 565 cm, then the sum of any two sides can be as follows:
 $|300 - 565| < |x - 565| < |830 - 565|$
 $|x - 565|$ can lie between 0 and 265, where 0 is included (2)
 From (1) and (2), $0 \leq$ difference of any two sides < 565.
 Hence, the difference of any two sides cannot be 565 cm.
 Hence, the correct option is (d).

Assertion and Reason Type Questions

26.

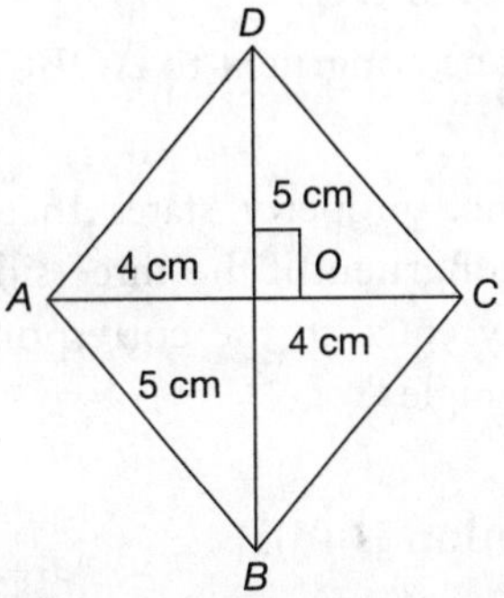

Assertion: Rhombus $ABCD$ can be constructed when $AC = 8$ cm and $BD = 7$ cm.

As shown in the figure, we can construct a rhombus with the given measurements. So, Assertion is true.

Reason: We can construct a rhombus when two diagonals are given. So, Reason is false.

Hence, the correct option is (c).

27. **Assertion:** In the given figure PQ is a common chord of two concentric circles with centre O.

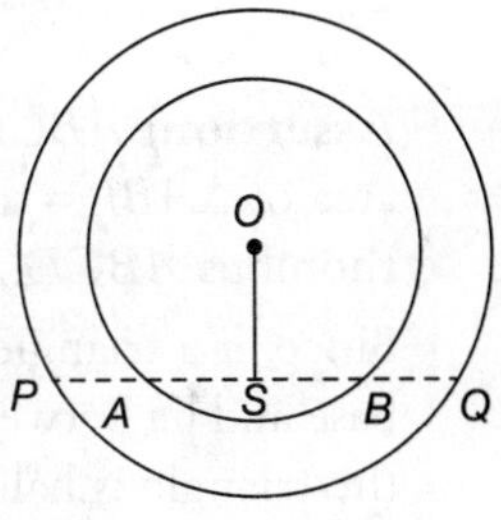

The chord intersects the smaller circle at A and B.

Also, $OS \perp AB$.

We know that the perpendicular drawn from the centre of a circle bisects its chord.

So, $PS = QS$ and $AS = BS$.

Now $PS - AS = QS - BS$.

$PA = QB$.

So, Assertion is true.

Reason: The perpendicular drawn from the centre of a circle bisects its chord.

Reason is true and is the correct explanation to Assertion.

Hence, the correct option is (a).

28.

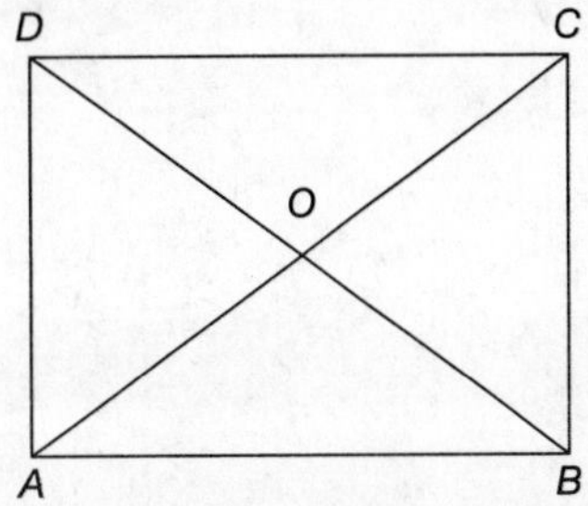

Assertion: $ABCD$ is a rectangle in which AC and BD intersect at O.

In ΔOBA and ΔOBC:

$OB = OD$ (Diagonals bisect to each other)

$OC = OC$ (Common side)

But BC need not be equal to DC.

Hence, ΔOBA need not be congruent to ΔOBC.

So, Assertion is false.

Reason: SSS congruence property states that two triangles are said to be congruent if the three sides of a triangle are respectively equal to the corresponding three sides of another triangle.

Reason is true.

Hence, the correct option is (d).

29. 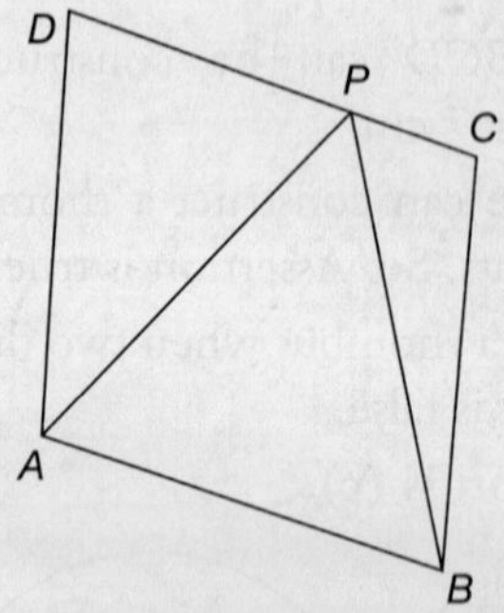

Assertion: $ABCD$ is a rhombus. P is a point CD. The area of ΔABP = the area of ΔBCD = half of the area of rhombus $ABCD$.

Since, if a triangle and a parallelogram lie on the same base and lie between the same parallels, then the area of the triangle is half the area of the parallelogram.

So, Assertion is true.

Reason: If a triangle and a parallelogram lie on the same base and lie between the same parallels, then the area of the triangle is half the area of the parallelogram.

So, Reason is false.

Hence, the correct option is (c).

30. 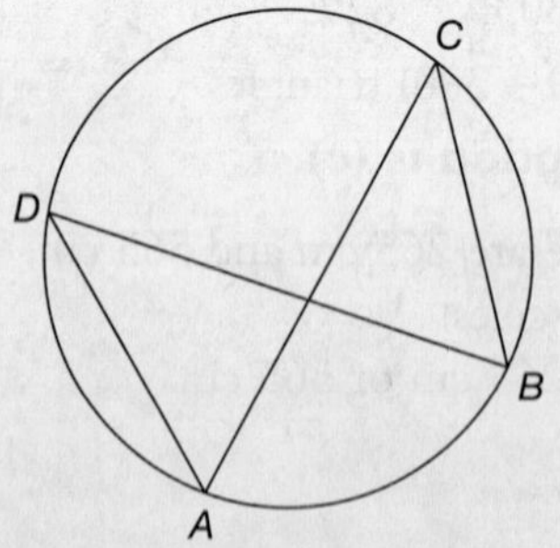

Assertion: Given that A, B, C, and D are concyclic points.

We know that the angles in a same segment are equal.

$\angle ADB = \angle ACB = 33°$.

So, Assertion is true.

Reason: The opposite angles of a cyclic quadrilateral are equal. Also, an exterior angle of a cyclic quadrilateral is equal to its interior opposite angle.

Reason is true but not the correct explanation to Assertion.

Hence, the correct option is (b).

CHAPTER 10

Mensuration

Remember

Before beginning this chapter, you should be able to:

- Understand the concepts of plane figures.
- Calculate the areas of plane figures.
- Obtain volume of simple solid figures.

Key Ideas

After completing this chapter, you should be able to:

- Know about polygons and calculate the area of different types of polygons.
- Learn about circles, circumference of a circle, sector of a circle, and area of a ring.
- Understand different solids and find their volumes.
- Find lateral surface areas, total surface areas and volumes of prism, cube, cuboid, cylinder, pyramid, cone, torus, sphere, and polyhedrons (tetrahedron and octahedron).

Scientific Crypt

A Tribute to Golenischev Mathematical Papyrus (1850 BC)

A papyrus (plural-papyri) is a manuscript written on paper-like sheets made from the stem of an aquatic plant. Papyrus – found mainly in North Africa. The oldest papyrus that has come down to us is the Golenischev Mathematical Papyrus (GMP), which dates to around 1850 BC. This has been named after the Russian Egyptologist, Vladimir Golenischev, who bought it around in 1892 (AD) in Thebes. At present, the GMP is in the Pushkin State Museum of Fine Arts in Moscow. One problem in the GMP shows that the ancient Egyptians knew the formula for the volume of a frustum of a pyramid. At present, we do not know how the ancient Egyptians arrived at this formula.

FUN TIME

CROSSWORD

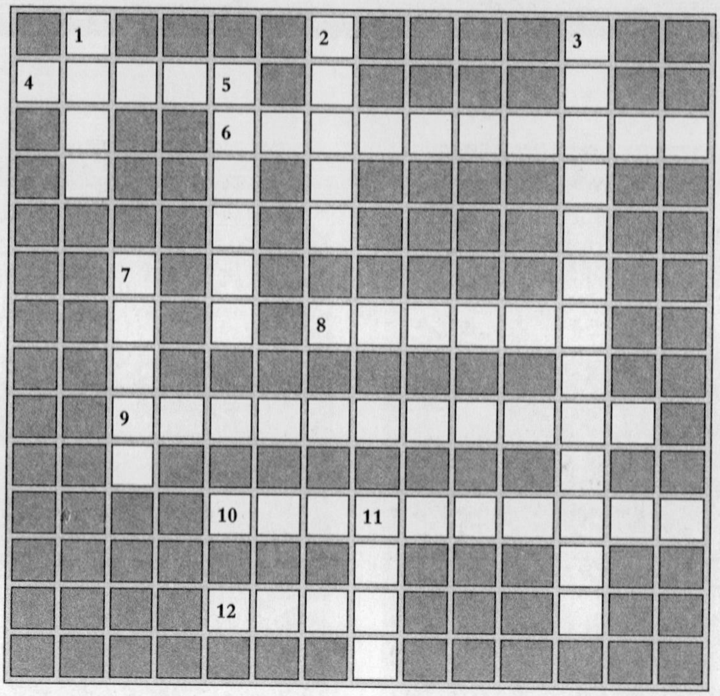

Across

4. A fully inflated tube
6. A solid bounded by plane figures
8. The amount of space enclosed by a solid
9. A polyhedron with four faces
10. A polyhedron with eight faces
12. A cuboid in which all the edges are equal

Down

1. A special type of pyramid
2. An object occupying space
3. Each lateral face of a right prism
5. A marble
7. Total length of the edges (in units) of a cube of edge 5 units
11. The magnitude of a plane region

INTRODUCTION

Mensuration is a branch of mathematics. It deals with computation of geometric magnitudes, such as the length of a line segment, area of a surface, and volume of a solid. In this chapter, we will deal with computation of areas and perimeters of plane figures and surface areas and volume of solid figures. To be precise, we will learn to find the perimeters and areas of plane figures including triangles, quadrilaterals, etc. Further, we will study prisms, cubes, cuboids, and cylinder. Then we will learn how to compute area and volume of pyramids, cones, cone frustums, tetrahedrons, and octahedrons. Finally, we will discuss spheres, hemispheres, hollow spheres, hollow hemispheres, and torus.

Plane Figure

A figure lying in a plane is called a **plane (or planar) figure**. Triangles, rectangles, circles are some examples of plane figures. A plane figure is a closed figure if it has no free end. It is called a simple closed figure if it does not cross itself.

A plane figure is made up of line segments or curves or both. A plane figure is called a **rectilinear figure**, if it is made up of only line segments. Triangles, squares, pentagons, etc., are some examples of rectilinear figures. A circle is not a rectilinear figure. The part of the plane which is enclosed by a simple closed figure is called a **plane region**. The magnitude of a plane region is called its **area**.

A line segment has one dimension, i.e., length. Hence, its size is measured in terms of its length.

A planar region has two dimensions, i.e., length and breadth. Hence, its size is measured in terms of its area.

The perimeter of a closed planar figure is the total length of the lines bounding the figure.

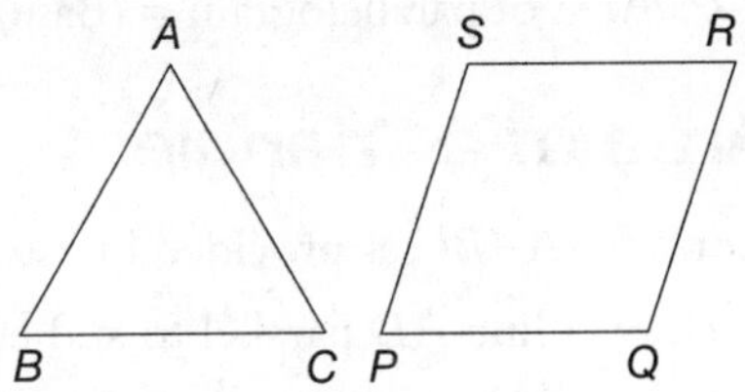

Figure 10.1

In Fig. 10.1, ABC is a triangle and $PQRS$ is a quadrilateral.

The perimeter of the ΔABC is $AB + BC + CA$.

The perimeter of the quadrilateral $PQRS$ is $PQ + QR + RS + SP$.

The perimeter of a rectangle of length l and breadth b is $2(l + b)$.

The perimeter of a square of side s is $4s$.

Units of Measurement

The length of a line is measured in units, such as centimetres, inches, metres, feet. Area is measured in sq units, such as square centimetres, square inches, square metres, square feet.

Estimating Areas

The area of a plane figure can be estimated by finding the number of unit squares that can fit into a whole figure.

Observe the square $ABCD$ (Fig. 10.2), in the square $ABCD$, there are 16 unit squares. Therefore, its area is 16 sq. units.

In Fig. 10.3, PQR is a right triangle. All the small units are not squares. Just as the length of a line need not be a whole number of units, the area of a plane figure also need not be a whole number of units.

In the figure, the triangle PQR does not cover 8 unit squares. But, its area is equal to that of 8 unit squares. This is because, the partial units, when added, are equal to 2 unit squares. Besides this, there are 6 unit squares. Hence, its area is equal to 8 unit squares.

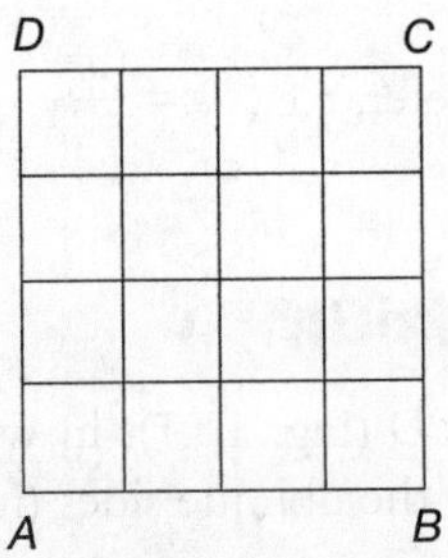

Figure 10.2

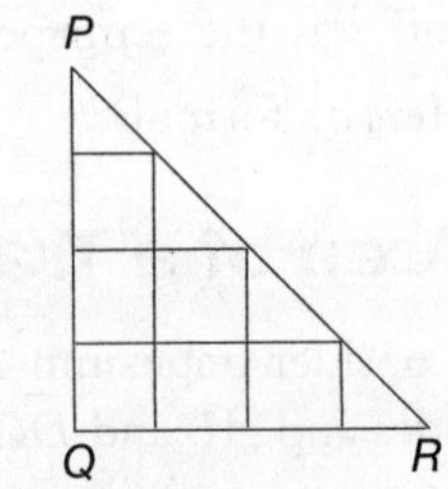

Figure 10.3

Area of a Rectangle

A rectangle is a four-sided closed figure in which both pairs of opposite sides are equal and each angle measures 90°. In Fig. 10.4, *ABCD* is a rectangle.

In rectangle *ABCD*, *AB* = 5 cm and *BC* = 4 cm. Each of the small squares measure 1 cm by 1 cm and the area occupied by each small square is 1 cm^2. There are 4 rows, and each row consists of 5 unit squares.

∴ The area occupied by the rectangle = (4)(5) = 20 cm^2.

The number of unit squares in the rectangle *ABCD* is equal to the product of the number of unit squares along the length and the number of unit squares along the breadth. Thus, we observe that the area of a rectangle = (length)(breadth).

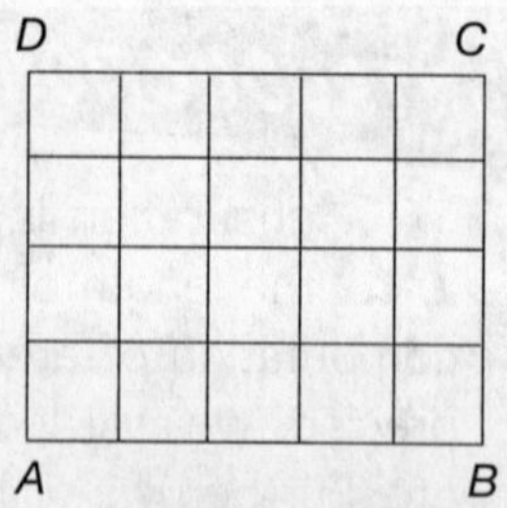

Figure 10.4

Area of a Parallelogram

Consider parallelogram *ABCD* as provided in Fig. 10.5:

Draw a perpendicular $\overline{DE}$ from *D* to $\overline{AB}$.

Draw a perpendicular $\overline{CF}$ from *C* to $\overline{AX}$ (*AB* extended).

By the ASA congruency property, the area of Δ*AED* is equal to the area of Δ*BFC*.

∴ The area of parallelogram *ABCD* = The area of rectangle *DEFC*.

⇒ (*EF*)(*FC*) = (*AB*)(*DE*)

∴ Area of parallelogram = (Base)(Corresponding height).

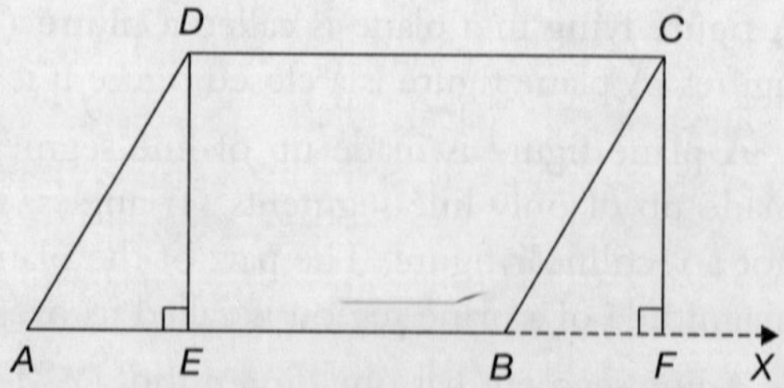

Figure 10.5

Area of a Triangle

Consider Δ*ABC* as provided in Fig. 10.6:

Draw a line *AD* parallel to and equal to *BC*.

Join *CD*.

ABCD is a parallelogram.

By ASA axiom, the area of triangle *ABC* is equal to the area of triangle *ADC*.

∴ The area of triangle *ABC* = $\left(\frac{1}{2}\right)$ (Area of a parallelogram)

(Where *AE* is the height of the triangle or parallelogram.)

∴ The area of a triangle = $\left(\frac{1}{2}\right)$ (Base)(Height)

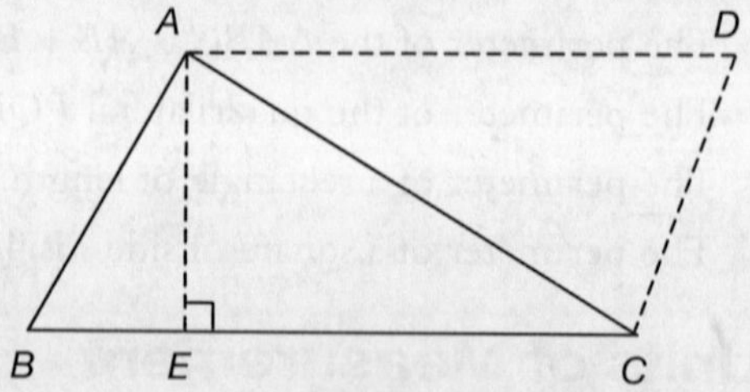

Figure 10.6

The area of a triangle is also given by $\sqrt{s(s-a)(s-b)(s-c)}$, where *a*, *b*, and *c* are the lengths of the sides of the triangle and *s* is the semi-perimeter, i.e., $s = \frac{(a+b+c)}{2}$. This relation is known as Heron's formula.

Area of a Trapezium

Consider trapezium *ABCD* (Fig. 10.7), in which *AD* and *BC* are the parallel sides and *AB* and *DC* are the oblique sides (not parallel).

Join *BD*.

DE is the perpendicular distance between *AD* and *BC*.

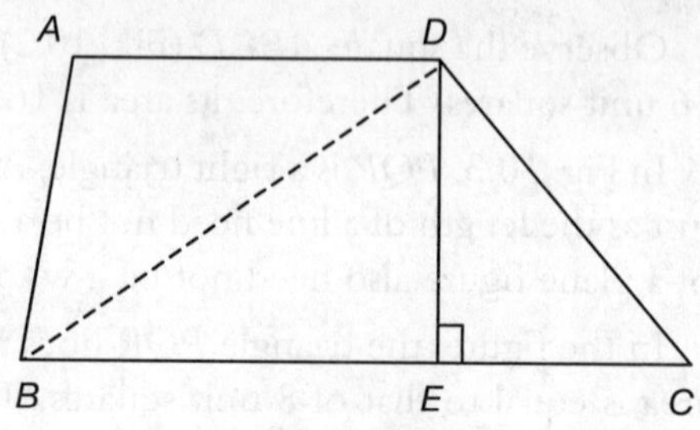

Figure 10.7

The area of the trapezium is equal to the sum of the areas of the ΔABD and ΔBCD.

$$= \left(\frac{1}{2}\right)(AD)(DE) + \left(\frac{1}{2}\right)(BC)(DE)$$

$$= \left(\frac{1}{2}\right)(AD + BC)(DE)$$

$\therefore$ Area of a trapezium $= \left(\frac{1}{2}\right)$(Sum of the parallel sides)(Distance between them).

Area of a Rhombus

A rhombus is a parallelogram in which all sides are equal. Consider rhombus $PQRS$ (Fig. 10.8), in which PR and SQ are the diagonals of the rhombus.

In a rhombus, the diagonals bisect each other at right angles at the point O.

$\therefore \angle POS = 90°$ and $\angle POQ = 90°$.

Area of the rhombus $PQRS$ = Area of ΔPRS + Area of ΔPQR

$$= \left(\frac{1}{2}\right)(PR)(OS) + \left(\frac{1}{2}\right)(PR)(OQ)$$

$$= \left(\frac{1}{2}\right)(PR)(OS + OQ) = \left(\frac{1}{2}\right)(PR)(SQ)$$

$\therefore$ Area of rhombus $= \left(\frac{1}{2}\right)$ (product of the diagonals).

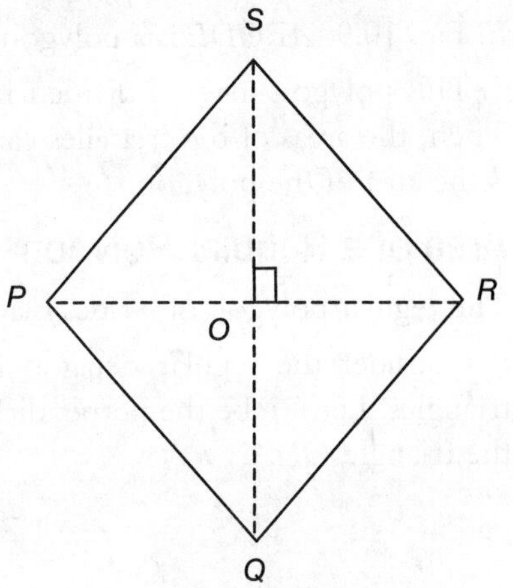

Figure 10.8

Area of a Square

A square is a rectangle in which all the sides are equal.

$$\text{Area of a rectangle} = (\text{Length})(\text{Breadth})$$

In a square, Length = Breadth

$$\therefore \quad \text{Area of a square} = (\text{Side})(\text{Side}) = (\text{Side})^2$$

Perimeter of a square = 4(Side)

Diagonal of a square $= \sqrt{2}$ (Side)

$$\therefore \quad \text{Area of a square} = \frac{(\text{Diagonal})^2}{2}.$$

Polygon

A polygon is a closed rectilinear figure that has three or more sides.

The following is a list of different types of polygons:

Name	Number of Sides
Triangle	3
Quadrilateral	4
Pentagon	5

(Continued)

Name	Number of Sides
Hexagon	6
Septagon	7
Octagon	8
Nonagon	9
Decagon	10

In a polygon, if all the sides are equal, and all the angles are equal, then it is a regular polygon.

Area of a Polygon

In Fig. 10.9, *ABCDE* is a polygon.

This polygon may be divided into triangles by joining points *B* and *E*, *E* and *C*. Then, the areas of the triangles can be found. The sum of the areas of these triangles is the area of the polygon.

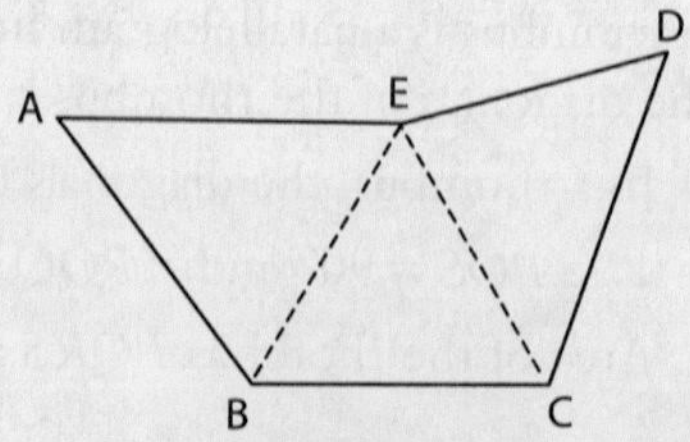

Figure 10.9

Area of a Regular Polygon

The regular polygon of *n* sides may be divided into *n* triangles of equal areas.

Consider the regular octagon in Fig. 10.10. The octagon can be divided into 8 equal triangles. Let *OP* be the perpendicular distance from centre *O* to side *AH*. *OP* is the height of the triangle *OHA*.

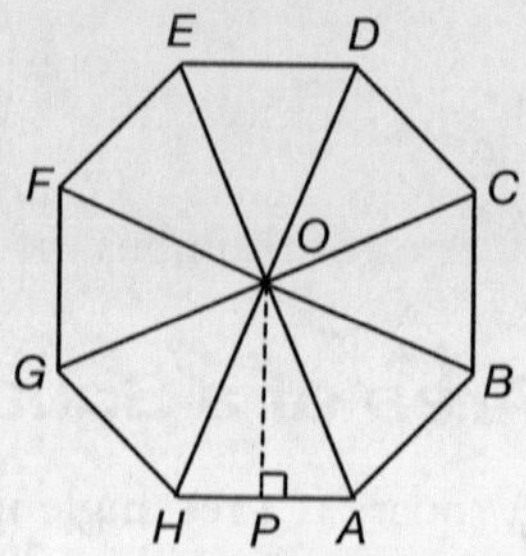

Figure 10.10

$$\text{Area of triangle } OHA = \left(\frac{1}{2}\right)(AH)(OP)$$

Since the octagon consists of 8 equal triangles, the area of the octagon $= (8)\left(\frac{1}{2}\right)(AH)(OP)$.

But, the perimeter of the octagon $= 8(AH)$.

$\therefore$ The area of a regular polygon $= \left(\frac{1}{2}\right)$(Perimeter of the polygon) (Perpendicular distance from the centre to any side).

Area of an Equilateral Triangle

In Fig. 10.11, *ABC* is an equilateral triangle.

Let $AB = BC = CA = a$

Draw perpendicular $\overline{AD}$ from *A* to $\overline{BC}$.

AD is the height of the triangle.

ADC is a right triangle, where $DC = \frac{a}{2}$ and $AC = a$.

$$AD = \sqrt{(a)^2 - \left(\frac{a}{2}\right)^2} = \frac{\sqrt{3}}{2}a.$$

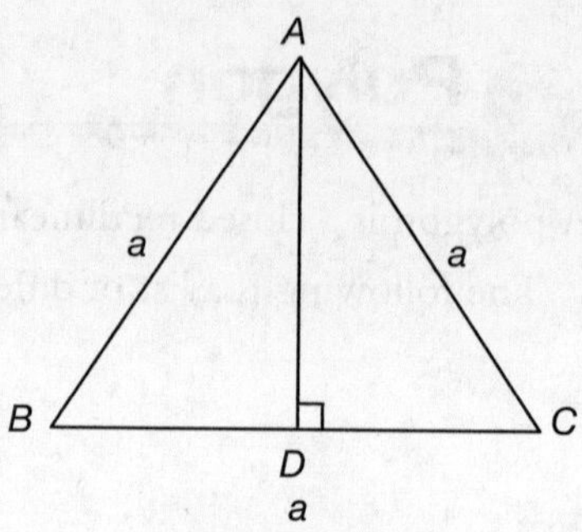

Figure 10.11

$\therefore$ The height of the triangle $\frac{\sqrt{3}}{2}a$.

$$\text{The area of the triangle } = \frac{1}{2}(a)\left(\frac{\sqrt{3}}{2}a\right) = \left(\frac{\sqrt{3}}{4}a^2\right).$$

$\therefore$ The area of an equilateral triangle $= \frac{\sqrt{3}}{4}(\text{side})^2$ sq. units.

Area of an Isosceles Triangle

An isosceles triangle has two equal sides. Generally, the base is considered to be the unequal side. Consider ΔABC (Fig. 10.12), in which $AB = AC$.

Let $AB = AC = a$ and $BC = b$.

Draw perpendicular AD from A to D on BC. In an isosceles triangle, AD is the altitude as well as the median.

As D is the mid-point of BC, $DC = \dfrac{b}{2}$.

ADC is a right triangle,

$$AD = \sqrt{a^2 - \left(\frac{b}{2}\right)^2} = \frac{\sqrt{4a^2 - b^2}}{2}.$$

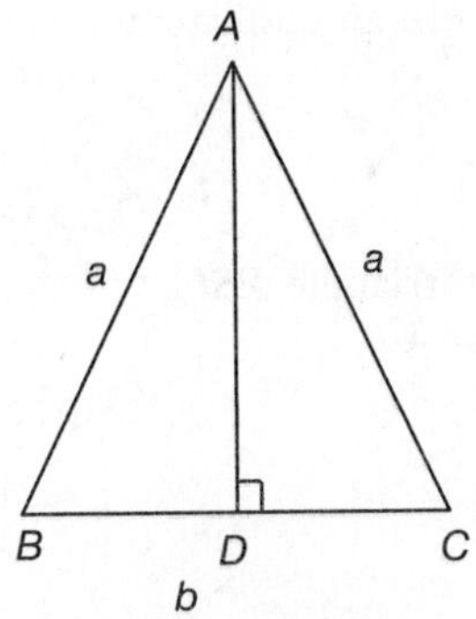

Figure 10.12

$$\text{The area of triangle } ABC = \left(\frac{1}{2}\right)(BC)(AD)$$

$$= \left(\frac{1}{2}\right)(b)\left(\frac{\sqrt{4a^2 - b^2}}{2}\right) = \frac{b}{4}\sqrt{4a^2 - b^2} \text{ sq. units.}$$

Area of Right Triangle

In Fig. 10.13, ABC is a right triangle and right angled at B.

Since AB is perpendicular to the base BC of the triangle, AB is the altitude of the triangle.

$$\therefore \text{ The area of right } \Delta ABC = \left(\frac{1}{2}\right)(b)(a) = \frac{ab}{2} \text{ sq. units.}$$

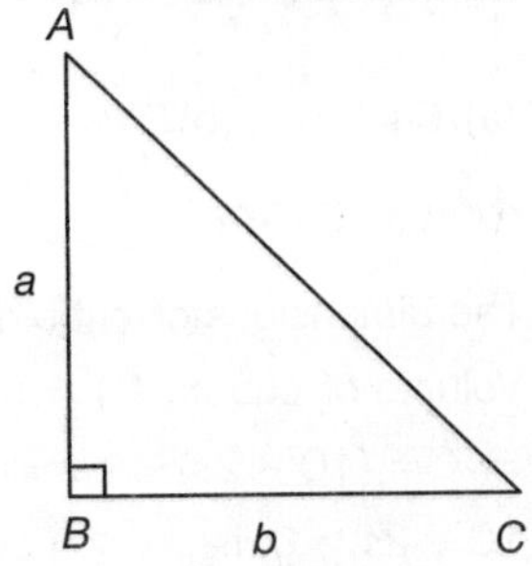

Figure 10.13

Isosceles Right Triangle

A right triangle in which the perpendicular sides are equal is an isosceles right triangle.

In Fig. 10.14, ABC is an isosceles right triangle, where $AB = BC = a$ units.

$$\text{The area of the triangle } ABC = \frac{1}{2}(a)(a) = \frac{a^2}{2} \text{ sq. units.}$$

From Pythagorean theorem, we have

$$AB^2 + BC^2 = AC^2$$

$$\Rightarrow \quad a^2 + a^2 = AC^2 \quad \Rightarrow \quad AC = \sqrt{2}a \text{ units.}$$

$$\therefore \quad AB : BC : CA = a : a : \sqrt{2}a = 1 : 1 : \sqrt{2}.$$

The hypotenuse is the longest side of a right triangle. The hypotenuse is $\sqrt{2}$ times of each of the equal sides.

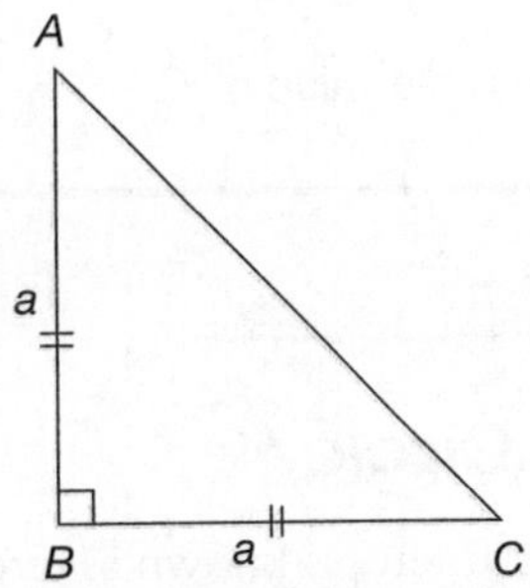

Figure 10.14

Info Bytes!

1. In-radius (r) of a triangle is given by the formula, $r = \dfrac{\Delta}{s}$.
2. Circum-radius (R) of a triangle is given by the formula, $R = \dfrac{abc}{4\Delta}$.

Where Δ is area of the triangle with sides a, b, and c, and s is the semi-perimeter.

Special Right Triangle with Angles 30°, 60° and 90°

In the right triangle (Fig. 10.15), $\angle PSQ = 90°$.

We have to determine the ratio of the sides PQ, QS, and PS.

Construction: Produce $\overline{QS}$ to the point R, such that $SR = SQ$ (see Fig. 10.16).

$\therefore \Delta PSQ \cong \Delta PSR$ (SAS Congruence property)

Let $PQ = QR = PR = a$. Since PS is also the median to QR, $QS = \frac{a}{2}$.

In an equilateral triangle, altitude is $\frac{\sqrt{3}}{2}$ times its side.

$$\therefore \qquad PS = \frac{\sqrt{3}}{2}a.$$

In triangle PSQ,

$$SQ : SP : PQ = \frac{a}{2} : \frac{\sqrt{3}}{2}a : a$$
$$= 1 : \sqrt{3} : 2.$$

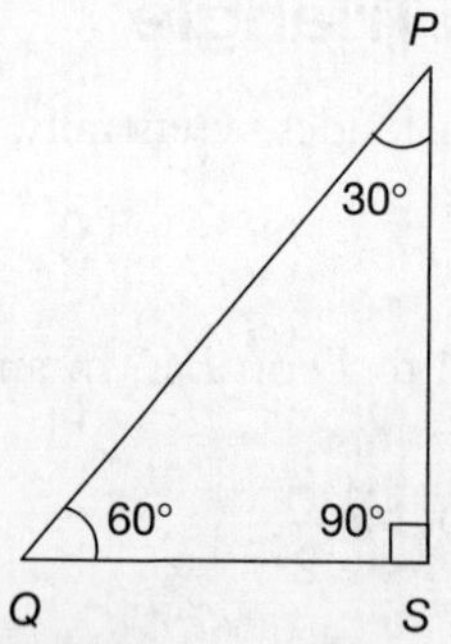

Figure 10.15

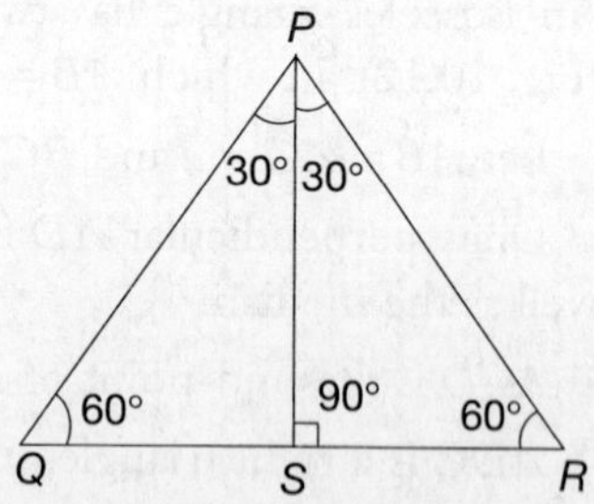

Figure 10.16

$\therefore$ In a right triangle with angles 30°, 60° and 90°, the ratio of the sides opposite to these angles is $1 : \sqrt{3} : 2$.

EXAMPLE 10.1 From each corner of a square sheet of side 10 cm, a square of side s cm is cut, where s is an integer. The remaining sheet is folded into a cuboid of volume C cubic cm. Which of the following cannot be a value of C?

(a) 64 (b) 72 (c) 48 (d) 30

SOLUTION

The dimensions of cuboid are $l = b = (10 - 2s)$ cm and $h = s$ cm.

Volume of cuboid $(c) = (10 - 2s)\ (10 - 2s)s$

$\Rightarrow C = (10 - 2s)^2 s$ cubic cm.

$10 - 2s > 0$, i.e., $s < 5$ and s is an integer.

$\therefore s = 1, 2, 3,$ or 4.

When $s = 1$, $C = 64$

When $s = 2$, $C = 72$

When $s = 3$, $C = 48$

When $s = 4$, $C = 16$

$\therefore$ Only option (d) cannot be a possible value of C.

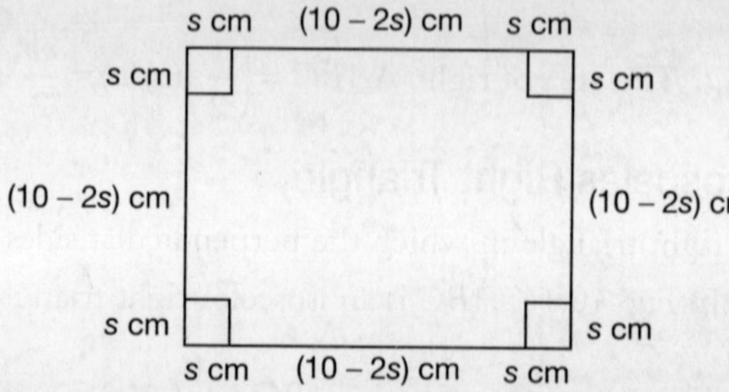

Circles

Circumference of a Circle

Since a circle is a closed arc, its perimeter is known as circumference. The circumference of a circle is π (read as pie) times its diameter. π is an irrational number. For numerical work, we use the approximate value of π as 3.14 or $\frac{22}{7}$.

The circumference of a circle $= \pi d = 2\pi r$.

The area of a circle $= \pi r^2$.

Area of a Ring

The region enclosed between two concentric circles is known as a ring.

In Fig. 10.17, the shaded region represents a ring. Let the radius of the smaller circle, OA, be r and the radius of the bigger circle, OB, be R.

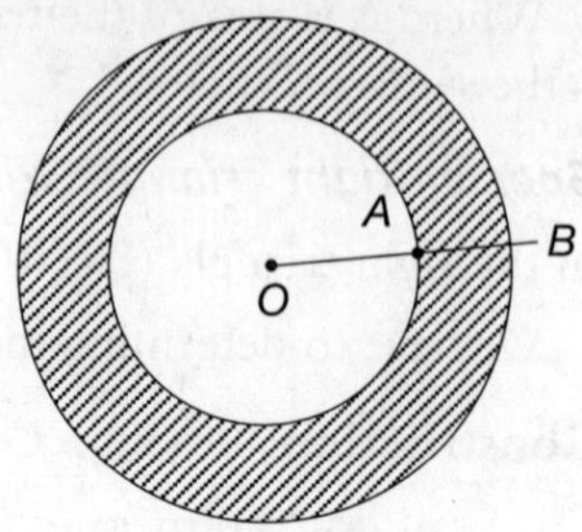

Figure 10.17

The area of the ring = (Area of the bigger circle) – (Area of the smaller circle)

$$= \pi R^2 - \pi r^2 = \pi\,(R^2 - r^2).$$

Sector of a Circle

A sector is formed when the endpoints of an arc of a circle are joined with two radii of the circle.

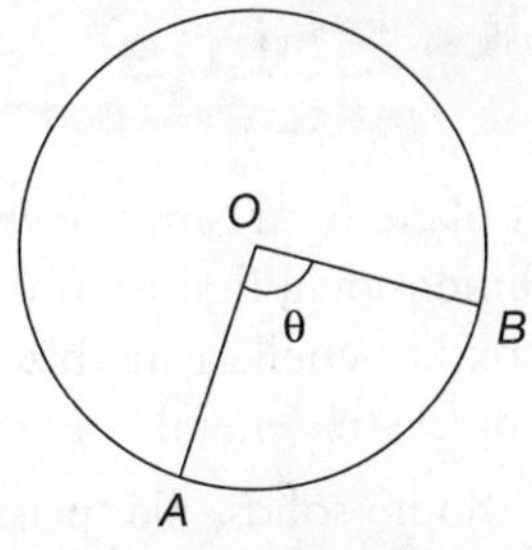

Figure 10.18

In the circle with centre O, AB is an arc of the circle (see Fig. 10.18). The endpoints of the arc A and B are joined with two radii OA and OB of the circle. AOB is a sector of the circle. The arc makes an angle θ at the centre of the circle. This is also known as central angle **or** sector angle.

The length of an arc of the sector of a circle is proportional to the central angle of the sector of the circle.

$\therefore$ The length of an arc of the sector of a circle $(l) = \frac{\theta}{360°} \times 2\pi r$, where r is the radius of the circle.

The perimeter of the sector of the circle $= l + 2r$.

The area of the sector of a circle is proportional to the central angle of the sector of the circle.

$\therefore$ The area of the sector of a circle $= \frac{\theta}{360°}(\pi r^2)$ or $\frac{lr}{2}$.

EXAMPLE 10.2 A circle of radius 6 cm is inscribed in an equilateral triangle. Find the area of the equilateral triangle (in sq cm).

SOLUTION

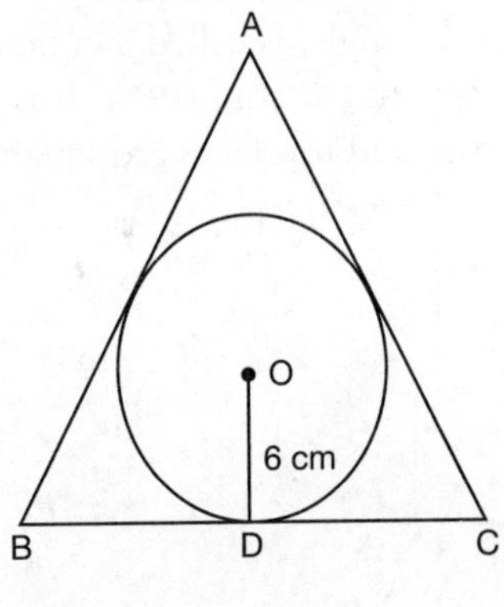

Let a be the length of the side of the equilateral triangle.

$\Rightarrow$ In radius, $\frac{1}{3}\left(\frac{\sqrt{3}a}{2}\right) = 6$

$\Rightarrow a = 12\sqrt{3}$ cm

Area of the equilateral triangle $= \frac{\sqrt{3}}{4}a^2$

$= \frac{\sqrt{3}}{4} \times \left(12\sqrt{3}\right)^2 = \frac{\sqrt{3}}{4} \times 144 \times 3 = 108\sqrt{3}\,\text{cm}^2$.

EXAMPLE 10.3 A right triangle is inscribed in a circle of radius 8 cm. One of the angles of the triangle is 30°, then find the area of the triangle (in sq cm).

SOLUTION

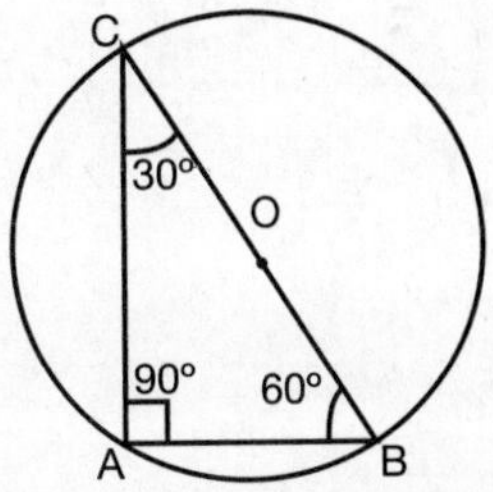

Since OB = 8 cm, BC = 16 cm

$\Rightarrow$ AB = 8 cm (opposite to 30°) and AC = $8\sqrt{3}$ cm (opposite to 60°)

Area of the triangle $= \frac{1}{2}$ AB × AC $= \frac{1}{2} \times 8 \times 8\sqrt{3} = 32\sqrt{3}$ sq cm.

Solids

A plane figure may have one dimension or two dimensions. Triangles and quadrilaterals have two dimensions. For two-dimensional figures, the dimensions are length and breadth or width or height. But many objects such as a brick, a match box, a pencil, a marble, a tank, an ice cream, and a cone have a third dimension. Thus, a solid is a three-dimensional object. In general, any object occupying space can be called a solid.

Some solids, like prisms, cubes, and cuboids have plane or flat surfaces, while some solids, like cone a cylinder have curved surfaces as well as flat surfaces. Spheres have only curved surfaces. Lateral surface area of a solid having a curved surface is referred to as curved surface area.

Volume of a Solid

The amount of space enclosed by the bounding surface or surfaces of a solid is called the volume of the solid. It is measured in cubic units.

Prisms

A prism is a solid in which two congruent and parallel polygons form the top and the bottom faces. The lateral faces are parallelograms.

The line joining the centres of the two parallel polygons is called the axis of the prism and the length of the axis is referred to as the height of the prism.

If two parallel and congruent polygons are regular and, if the axis is perpendicular to the base, then the prism is called a right prism. The lateral surfaces of a right prism are rectangles.

Consider two congruent and parallel triangular planes ABC and PQR. If we join the corresponding vertices of both the planes, i.e., A to P, B to Q and C to R, then the resultant solid formed is a triangular prism. A right prism, whose base is a rectangle, is called a cuboid and the one, the base of which is a pentagon, is called a pentagonal prism. If all the faces of a prism are congruent, it is a cube. In case of a cube or a cuboid, any face may be the base of the prism. A prism whose base and top faces are squares, but the lateral faces are rectangular is called a square prism (see Fig. 10.19).

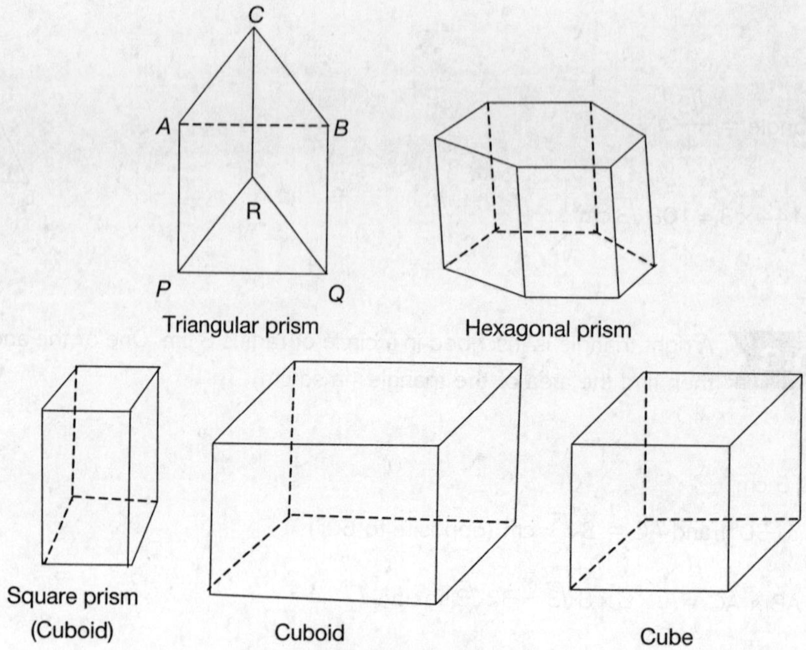

Figure 10.19

Konnect

The following points hold good for all prisms.

1. The number of lateral faces = The number of sides of the base.
2. The number of edges of a prism = The number of sides of the base × 3.
3. The sum of the lengths of the edges = 2(The perimeter of base) + The number of sides × Height.
4. For a prism, whose base is a polygon,
   Number of vertices + Number of faces = Number of edges + 2.
   This is known as Euler's formula, i.e., $V + F = E + 2$.

Lateral Surface Area (LSA) of a Prism

$$\text{LSA} = \text{Perimeter of base} \times \text{Height} = ph$$

Total Surface Area (TSA) of a Prism

$$\text{TSA} = \text{LSA} + 2(\text{Area of base})$$

Volume of a Prism

$$\text{Volume} = \text{Area of base} \times \text{Height} = Ah$$

Info Bytes!

The volume of water flowing in a canal in an hour = The cross-section of the canal × The speed of water in an hour.

EXAMPLE 10.4 The volume of a pentagonal prism is 1296 cu cm. The length of the edge joining the corresponding vertices of the pentagonal bases is 12 cm. Find the area of the base.

SOLUTION

Volume of the prism = Area of the base × height

⇒ 1296 = Area of the base × 12

Area of the base = 108 sq cm.

Cuboid and Cube

Cuboid

In a right prism, if the base is a rectangle, then it is called a cuboid (see Fig. 10.20). A match box, a brick, a room, etc., are in the shape of a cuboid.

The three dimensions of the cuboid, i.e., its length (l), breadth (b), and height (h) are, generally, denoted by $l \times b \times h$ and read as l by b by h.

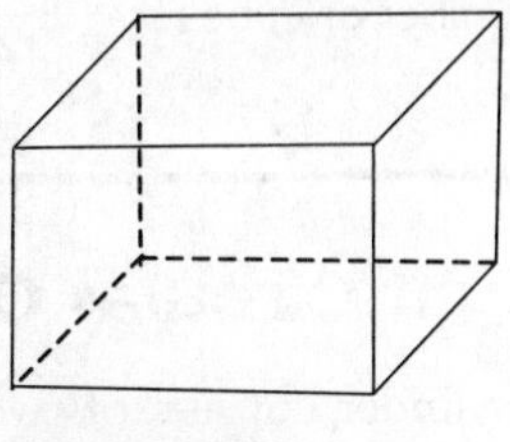

Figure 10.20 A Cuboid

1. The lateral surface area of a cuboid $= ph = 2(l + b)h$ sq. units, where p is the perimeter of the base.
2. The total surface area of a cuboid = LSA + 2(Base area) $= 2(l + b)h + 2lb = 2(lb + bh + lh)$ sq. units.
3. The volume of a cuboid $= Ah = (lb)h = lbh$ cubic units, where A is the area of the base.
4. Diagonal of a cuboid $= \sqrt{l^2 + b^2 + h^2}$ units.

Konnect

If a closed wooden box of thickness t has inner dimensions of l, b, and h, then the outer length $= l + 2t$, the outer breadth $= b + 2t$, and the outer height $= h + 2t$.

Cube

In a cuboid, if all the dimensions, i.e., its length, breadth, and height are equal, then it is called a cube. All the edges of a cube are equal in length (see Fig. 10.21). Thus, the size of a cube is completely determined by its edge.

If the edge of a cube is a units, then

1. The lateral surface area of the cube = $4a^2$.
2. The total surface area of the cube = LSA + 2(Area of base) = $4a^2 + 2a^2 = 6a^2$.
3. The volume of the cube = a^3.
4. The diagonal of the cube = $\sqrt{a^2 + a^2 + a^2} = \sqrt{3}\,a$.

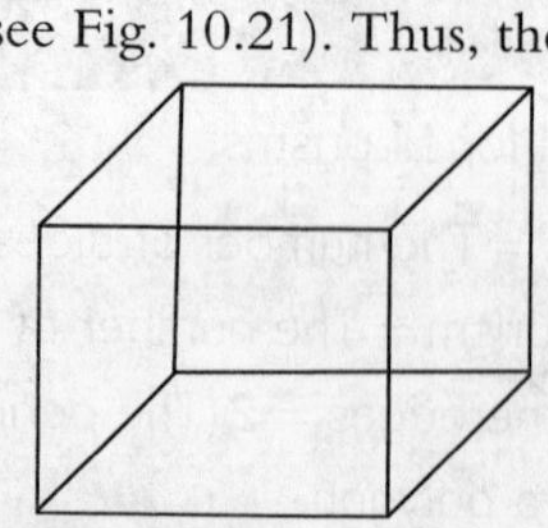

Figure 10.21 A Cube

Konnect

If the inner edge of a cubical wooden box of thickness t is a units, then the outer edge of the cube is given by $a + 2t$ units.

EXAMPLE 10.5 The dimensions $l \times b \times h$ of a room are 12 m × 7 m × 5 m. Find:

(a) The diagonal of the room.

(b) The cost of flooring at the rate of ₹2 per m².

(c) The cost of white-washing of the inside of the room excluding the floor at the rate of ₹3 per m².

SOLUTION

(a) The diagonal of the room $= \sqrt{l^2 + b^2 + h^2} = \sqrt{12^2 + 7^2 + 5^2} = \sqrt{144 + 49 + 25} = \sqrt{218}$ m.

(b) To find the cost of flooring, we should know the area of the base.

Base area = $lb = 12 \times 7 = 84$ m².

∴ Cost of flooring = 84 × 2 = ₹168.

(c) Total area to be white-washed

= LSA + area of roof = $2(l + b)h + lb$

= 2(12 + 7)5 + 12 × 7 = 2(19) (5) + 84 = 190 + 84 = 274 m².

∴ Cost of white-washing = 274 × 3 = ₹822.

EXAMPLE 10.6 How many identical cubes of an edge 14 cm can be placed in a cubical box of inner edge 420 cm with least empty space in the box?

SOLUTION

$$\text{Number of cubes} = \frac{420 \times 420 \times 420}{14 \times 14 \times 14} = 30 \times 30 \times 30 = 27000.$$

Right Circular Cylinder

A cylinder consists of two congruent and parallel circular regions which are connected by a curved surface. Each of the circular regions is called a base of the cylinder. A road roller, water pipe, power cables, round pillars are some of the cylinder-shaped objects.

In Fig. 10.22, a right circular cylinder is shown. Let A be the centre of the top face and A' be the centre of the base. The line joining the centres (i.e., AA') is called the axis of the cylinder. The length AA' is called the height of the cylinder. The radius r of the base of the cylinder and the height h completely describe the cylinder.

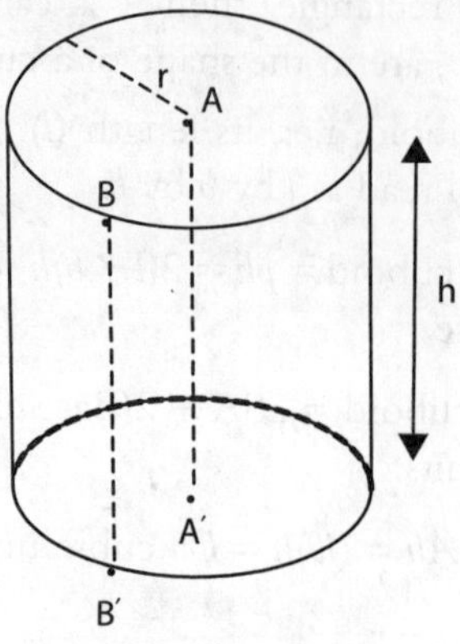

Figure 10.22

Info Bytes!

If a plastic pipe of length l is such that its outer radius is R and the inner radius is r, then the volume of the plastic content of the pipe is $l\pi(R^2 - r^2)$ cubic units.

Lateral (curved) surface area = Perimeter of base × Height = $2\pi rh$

The total surface area = LSA + 2(Base area)

$$= 2\pi rh + 2(\pi r^2) = 2\pi r(h + r)$$

Volume = Area of base × Height = $\pi r^2 h$.

EXAMPLE 10.7 The height of a solid cylinder exceeds its radius by 7 cm. If the lateral surface area of the solid is 616 cm^2, then find the volume of the solid (in cm^3).

SOLUTION

(Let 'h' and 'r' be the height and the radius of the cylinder respectively.

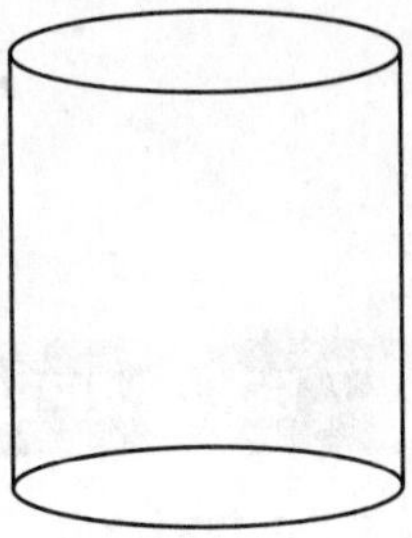

Given: $h - r = 7$ cm.

$\Rightarrow h = r + 7$

Given: lateral surface area = $2\pi rh = 616$ cm^2

$\Rightarrow 2 \times \frac{22}{7} \times r(r + 7) = 616$

$\Rightarrow r(r + 7) = 14 \times 7$

$\Rightarrow r = 7$ cm.

$h = 14$ cm

Volume of the cylinder = $\pi r^2 h = \frac{22}{7} 7^2 \times 14 = 2156$ cm^3

Pyramid

A pyramid is a solid obtained by joining the vertices of a polygon to a point in the space by straight lines. The polygon is the base of the pyramid. Triangles are formed with each side of the base and the point in the space. The fixed point in space where all the triangles (i.e., lateral faces) meet is called the vertex of the pyramid.

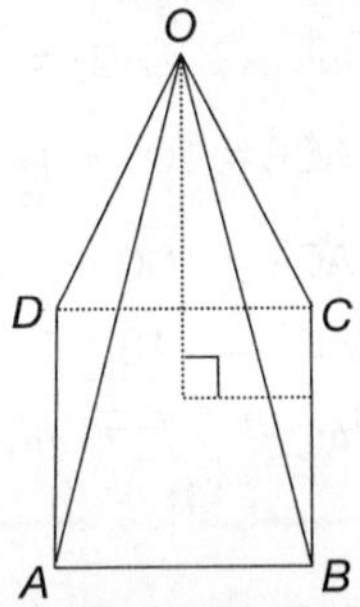

Figure 10.23

In Fig. 10.23, base $ABCD$ is a quadrilateral. All the vertices of the base are joined to a fixed point O in space by straight lines. The resultant solid obtained is a pyramid with a quadrilateral as the base. The straight line joining the vertex of the pyramid and the centre of the base is called the axis of the pyramid. If the axis is not perpendicular to the base, it is an **oblique pyramid**.

Right Pyramid

If the line joining the vertex of the pyramid and the centre of the base is perpendicular to the base, then the pyramid is called a right pyramid (see Fig. 10.24).

The length of the line segment joining the vertex of the pyramid and the centre of the base of a right pyramid is called the height of the pyramid. It is represented by h. The perpendicular distance between the vertex of the pyramid and the mid-point of any of the sides of the base (i.e., regular polygon) of a right pyramid is called its slant height. It is represented by l.

For a right pyramid with perimeter of base = p, height = h, and slant height = l:

1. Lateral surface area $= \frac{1}{2}$(perimeter of base) × (slant height) $= \frac{1}{2}pl$
2. Total surface area = lateral surface area + area of base.
3. Volume of pyramid $= \frac{1}{3}$ × area of base × height.

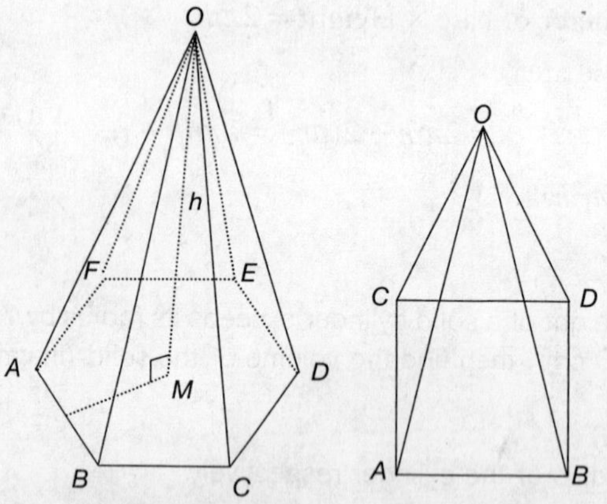

Hexagonal pyramid   Square pyramid

Figure 10.24

EXAMPLE 10.8 A regular hexagonal pyramid is 10 cm high and side of the base is 8 cm. Find the slant height of the pyramid (in cm).

SOLUTION

Given: height (h) = 10 cm.

Side of the base (a) = 8 cm.

Six equal equilateral triangles constitute the base of the regular hexagonal pyramid.

$\therefore BC = \frac{\sqrt{3}}{2} \times 8 = 4\ 4\sqrt{3}$ cm

In ΔABC, $AC^2 = AB^2 + BC^2$

$AC^2 = 10^2 + \left(4\sqrt{3}\right)^2$

$AC^2 = 100 + 48$

$AC^2 = 148$

$AC = 2\sqrt{37}$ cm

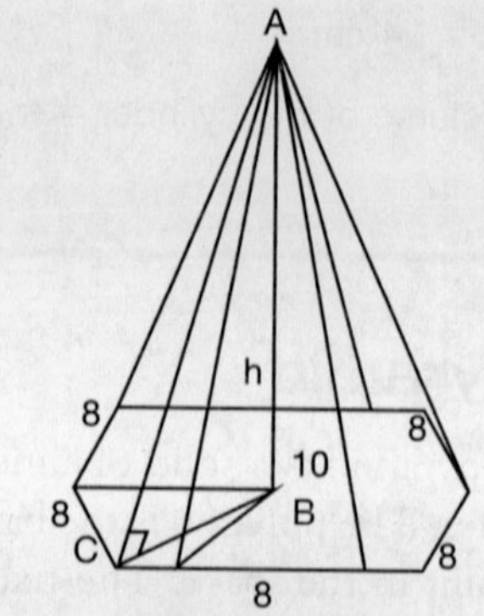

Figure 10.25

Circular Cone

A circular cone is a solid pointed figure with a circular base as shown in Fig. 10.26. A circular cone is a kind of pyramid whose base is a circle.

A cone has one vertex, one plane surface (i.e., the base) and a curved surface. The line joining the vertex to the centre of base (i.e., *AO*) is called the axis of the cone. If the axis is not perpendicular to the base of a cone, then it is an **oblique cone**. An ice cream cone and a conical tent are some of the examples of conical objects.

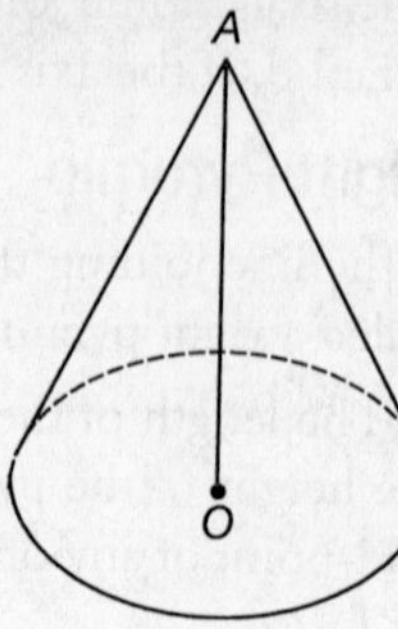

Figure 10.26

Right Circular Cone

In a circular cone, if the line joining the vertex and the centre of the base of the cone is perpendicular to the base, then it is a right circular cone. In other words, if the axis of the cone is perpendicular to the base of the cone, then it is a right circular cone. The length of the line segment *AO* is called the height of the cone. In this chapter, we deal with problems on right circular cones.

We can also define a right circular cone as a solid obtained by the revolution of a right-angled triangle about one of its two perpendicular sides.

If we consider any point B on the periphery of the base of the cone, then the line joining B and the vertex A is called the slant height of the cone and is denoted by l. Since AO is perpendicular to OB, ΔAOB is right-angled (see Fig. 10.27).

$$\therefore \quad l = \sqrt{r^2 + h^2}.$$

Earlier, we have studied about sector. We may recall that sector is a figure bounded by an arc of a circle with its two (see Fig. 10.28).

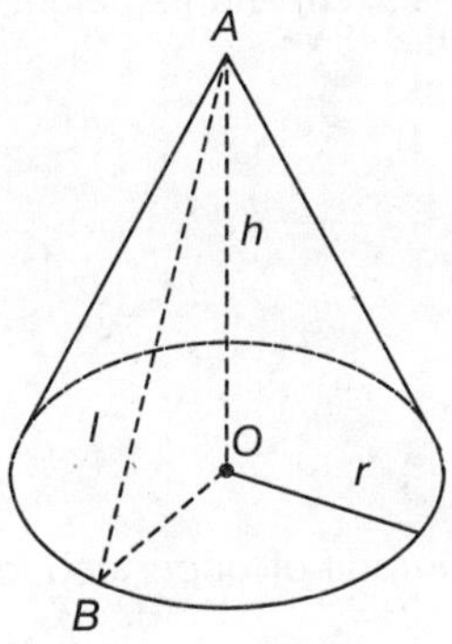

Figure 10.27

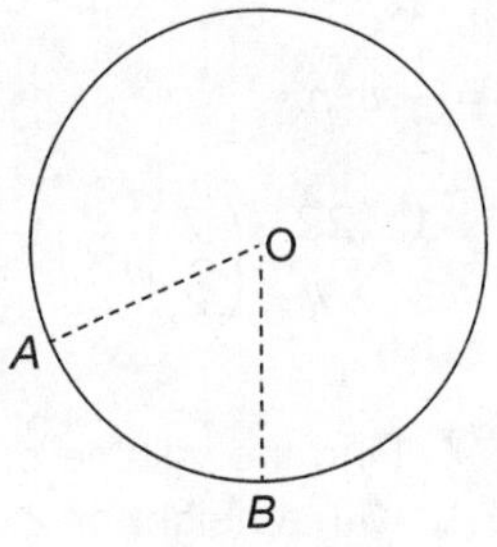

Figure 10.28

Now, consider the sector AOB. If we roll the sector up and bring (join) together the radii OA and OB such that they coincide, then the figure formed will be a cone. The radius of the circle becomes the slant height of the cone and the length of the arc of the sector becomes the perimeter of the base of the cone.

For a cone of radius r, height h, and slant height l:

1. Curved surface area of a cone = πrl sq. units.
2. Total surface area of a cone

   = Curved surface area + Area of base = $\pi rl + \pi r^2 = \pi r(r + l)$ sq. units.
3. Volume of a cone $= \frac{1}{3}\pi r^2 h$ cubic units.

Cone Frustum (or a Conical Bucket)

If a right circular cone is cut by a plane perpendicular to its axis (i.e., a plane parallel to the base), then the solid portion containing the base of the cone is called the **frustum** of the cone.

From Fig. 10.29, we observe that a frustum is in the shape of a bucket.

Let radius of the upper base be R, radius of the lower base be r, height of the frustum be h and slant height of the frustum be l.

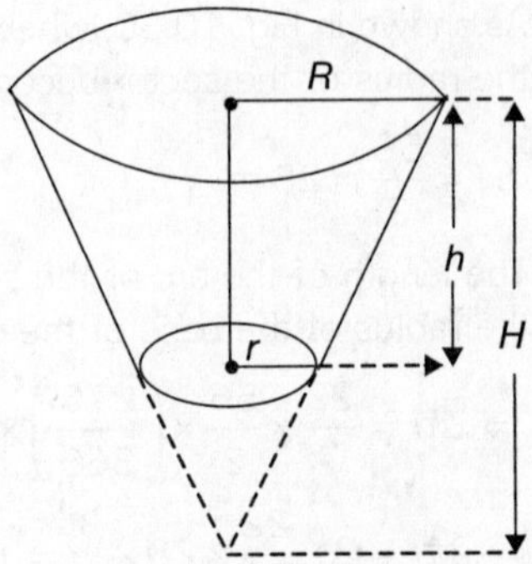

Figure 10.29

1. Curved surface area of a frustum = $\pi l(R + r)$ sq. units.
2. Total surface area of a frustum

   = Curved surface area + Area of lower base + Area of upper base = $\pi l(R + r) + \pi r^2 + \pi R^2$ sq. units.
3. Volume of a frustum $= \frac{1}{3}\pi h(R^2 + Rr + r^2)$ cubic units.
4. Slant height (l) of a frustum $= \sqrt{(R - r)^2 + h^2}$ units.

EXAMPLE 10.9 The height of a cone is 24 cm and the radius of the base is 7 cm. Find the curved surface area of the cone (in sq cm).

SOLUTION

CSA of the cone $= \pi rl = \pi r \times \sqrt{h^2 + r^2} = \frac{22}{7} \times 7 \times \sqrt{24^2 + 7^2} = \frac{22}{7} \times 7 \times 25 = 550$ sq cm.

EXAMPLE 10.10 The inner diameter of an ice cream cone is 7 cm and its height is 12 cm. Find the volume of ice cream that the cone can contain.

SOLUTION

Volume of ice cream (cone) $= \frac{1}{3}\pi r^2 h.$

$$= \frac{1}{3} \times \frac{22}{7} \times \left(\frac{7}{2}\right)^2 \times 12 = 22 \times 7 = 154 \text{ cm}^3.$$

EXAMPLE 10.11 Find the volume of a cone frustum whose radii of upper and lower ends are 14 cm, 10 cm with a height of 21 cm (in cu cm).

SOLUTION

R = 14 cm, r = 10 cm h = 21 cm

Volume of a cone frustum $= \frac{1}{3}\pi\left(R^2 + Rr + r^2\right)h$

$= \frac{1}{3} \times \frac{22}{7}$ $((14)^2 + (14)(10) + (10)^2) \times 21$

$= 22\ (196 + 140 + 100)$

$= 22 \times 436$

$= 9592$ cu cm.

EXAMPLE 10.12 From a circular canvas of diameter 56 m, a sector of 270° was cut out and a conical tent was formed by joining the straight ends of this piece. Find the radius and the height of the tent.

SOLUTION

As shown in Fig. 10.30, when the free ends of the canvas cut-out are joined to form a cone, the radius of the sector becomes the slant height (l) of the cone.

$\therefore l = \frac{56}{2} = 28$ m.

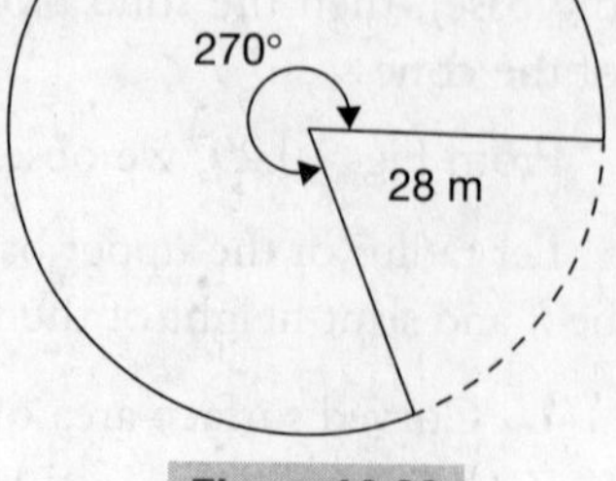

Figure 10.30

The length of the arc of the sector becomes the circumference of the base of the cone. Let the radius of the base of the cone = r.

$$\Rightarrow 2\pi r = \frac{22}{7} \times \frac{56}{2} \times \left(\frac{270}{360}\right) \times 2$$

$$\Rightarrow 2\pi r = 2 \times \frac{22}{7} \times 28 \times \frac{3}{4} \Rightarrow r = 21 \text{ m}.$$

$\therefore$ Height, $h = \sqrt{l^2 - r^2}$

$$= \sqrt{28^2 - 21^2} = \sqrt{7^2(4^2 - 3^2)}$$

$$= 7\sqrt{16 - 9} = 7\sqrt{7} \text{ m}$$

$\therefore h = 7\sqrt{7}$ m and $r = 21$ m.

Torus (Solid Ring)

A fully-inflated bicycle tube, tennikoit ring, and a life belt are some examples of a torus. A torus is a three-dimensional figure formed by the revolution of a circle about an axis lying in its plane, but not intersecting the circle.

If r is the radius of a circle that rotates and a is the distance of the centre of rotating circle from the axis (see Figs. 10.31 and 10.32), then:

Surface area of torus = $4\pi^2 ra$ sq. units and

Volume of torus = $2\pi^2 r^2 a$ cubic units.

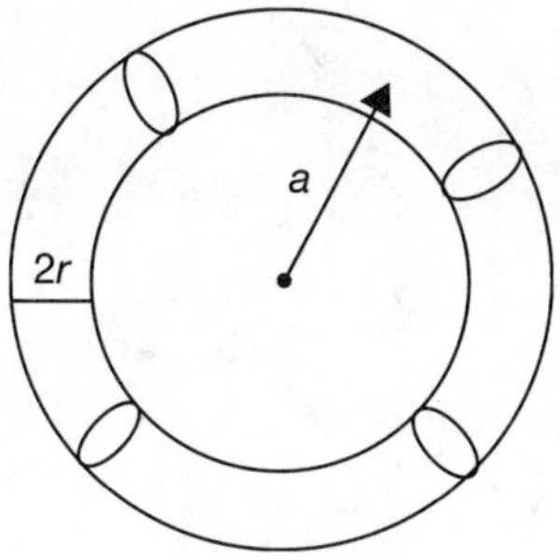

Figure 10.31

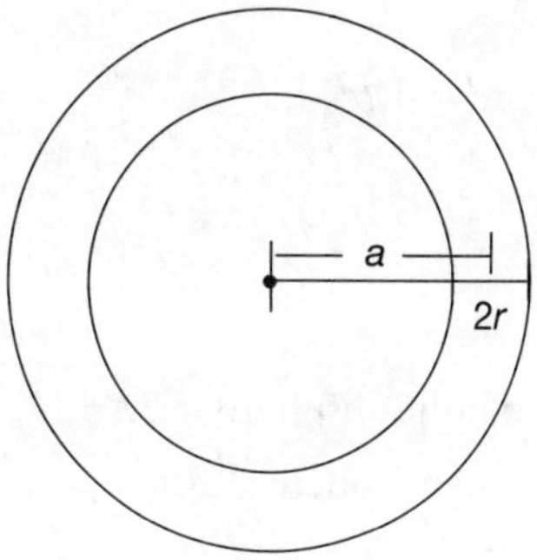

Figure 10.32

EXAMPLE 10.13 The radius of cross-section of a car tube is 7 cm. The outer radius of the tube is 16 cm. Find the surface area and the volume of the tube.

SOLUTION

Here, $r = 7$ cm, hence $a = 16 - r = 16 - 7 = 9$ cm.

$$\text{Surface area} = 4\pi^2 ra = 4 \times \frac{22}{7} \times \frac{22}{7} \times 7 \times 9 = \frac{17424}{7} \text{ cm}^2.$$

$$\text{Volume} = 2\pi^2 r^2 a$$

$$= 2 \times \frac{22}{7} \times \frac{22}{7} \times 7 \times 7 \times 9 = 8712 \text{ cm}^3.$$

Sphere

Sphere is a set of points in the space which are equidistant from a fixed point. The fixed point is called the centre of the sphere, and the distance is called the radius of the sphere. A lemon, a football, the moon, globe, small lead balls used in cycle bearings are some example of spherical-shaped objects.

A line joining any two points on the surface of sphere and passing through the centre of the sphere is called its diameter. The size of sphere can be completely determined by knowing its radius or diameter.

Solid Sphere

A solid sphere is the region in the space bounded by a sphere. The centre of a sphere is also a part of solid sphere, whereas the centre is not a part of hollow sphere. Marbles, lead shots, etc., are examples of solid spheres, while a tennis ball is a hollow sphere.

Hemisphere

If a sphere is cut into two halves by a plane passing through the centre of sphere, then each of the halves is called a **hemisphere** (see Fig, 10.33).

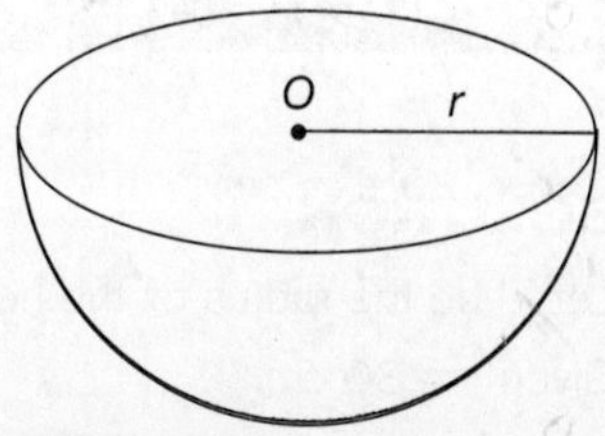

Figure 10.33 Hemisphere

Spherical Shell

The region bounded in the space between two concentric solid spheres is called a spherical shell. The thickness of the shell is given by the difference in radii of the two spheres.

Hemispherical Shell

A hemispherical shell is shown in Fig. 10.34.

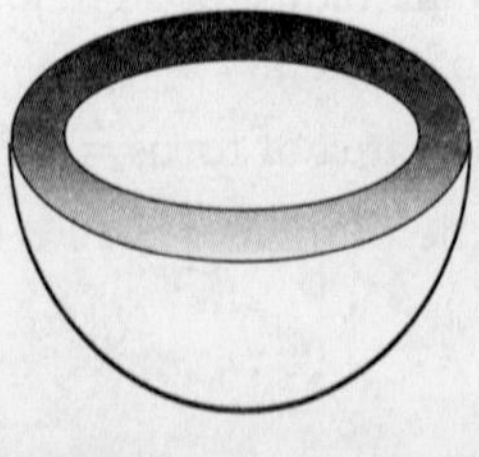

Figure 10.34 Hemispherical shell

Formulas to Memorize

Sphere

1. Surface area of a sphere = $4\pi r^2$
2. Volume of a sphere $= \frac{4}{3}\pi r^3$

Hemisphere

1. Curved surface area of a hemisphere = $2\pi r^2$
2. Total surface area of a hemisphere = $3\pi r^2$
3. Volume of a hemisphere $= \frac{2}{3}\pi r^3$

Spherical Shell

1. Thickness = $R - r$, where R = outer radius and r = inner radius.
2. Volume $= \frac{4}{3}\pi R^3 - \frac{4}{3}\pi r^3$
3. Total surface area of a hemispherical shell
   = (curved surface area of outer hemisphere + curved surface area of inner hemisphere + area of ring)
   $= 3\pi R^2 + \pi r^2$.

EXAMPLE 10.14 If the surface area of a sphere is 5024 cm^2, then find the radius of the sphere. (Take $\pi = 3.14$)

SOLUTION

Let 'r' be the radius of the sphere.

Surface area of the sphere = $4\pi r^2$

$4\pi r^2 = 5024$

$r^2 = \frac{5024}{4 \times 3.14}$

$r^2 = 400$

$r = 20$ cm.

EXAMPLE 10.15 If the radius of a hemisphere is 30 cm, then find the total surface area of the hemisphere (in sq cm).
(Take $\pi = 3.14$)

SOLUTION

Let 'r' be the radius of the hemisphere.

Given $r = 30$ cm.

Total surface area of the hemisphere = $3\pi r^2 = 3 \times (3.14) \times (30) \times 30 = 8478$ cm^2.

EXAMPLE 10.16 A thin hollow hemispherical sailing vessel is made of metal surmounted by a conical canvas tent. The radius of the hemisphere is 14 m and the total height of the vessel (including the height of tent) is 28 m. Find the area of the metal sheet and the canvas required.

SOLUTION

The vessel (with the conical tent) is shown in Fig. 10.36.

Total height, $H = 28$ m

Radius of hemisphere $= r = 14$ m.

$\therefore$ Height of conical tent $= h = H - r = 28 - 14$

$= 14$ m.

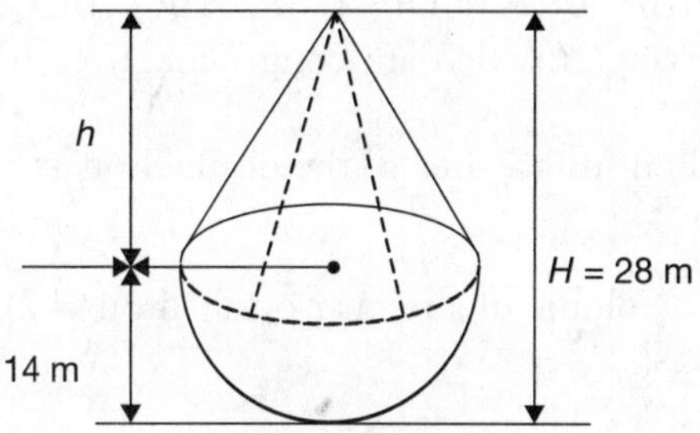

Figure 10.36

We can observe that radius of the base of the cone

= Radius of the hemisphere = 14 m.

$\therefore$ Area of canvas required $= \pi rl$.

$$= \frac{22}{7} \times 14 \times \sqrt{14^2 + 14^2} = 44 \times 14\sqrt{2} = 616\sqrt{2}\ \text{m}^2.$$

Area of metal sheet required = Surface area of hemisphere

$$= 2\pi r^2 = 2 \times \frac{22}{7} \times 14 \times 14 = 1232\ \text{m}^2.$$

Polyhedrons

A solid bounded by plane polygons is a polyhedron. The bounding polygons are known as the faces and the intersection of the faces are edges. The points where three or more edges intersect are called the vertices.

A polyhedron having four faces is a tetrahedron, one having six faces is a hexahedron and one having eight faces is an octahedron.

If all the faces of a polyhedron are regular polygons which are congruent, then it is a regular polyhedron. However, further discussion on regular polyhedrons can be made in higher classes.

Regular Tetrahedron

A regular tetrahedron is a tetrahedron having all of its faces as equilateral triangles (see Fig. 10.37). The line joining the vertex of the tetrahedron and the centre of the base is the vertical height of a regular tetrahedron. The line joining the mid-point of the side of the base and the vertex of a regular tetrahedron is its slant height.

The lateral surface area of a regular tetrahedron $= \frac{1}{2} \times$ Perimeter of base $\times$ Slant height

$$= \frac{1}{2} \times 3a \times \frac{\sqrt{3}}{2} a$$

$$= \frac{3\sqrt{3}}{4} a^2 \text{ (where } a \text{ is the edge).}$$

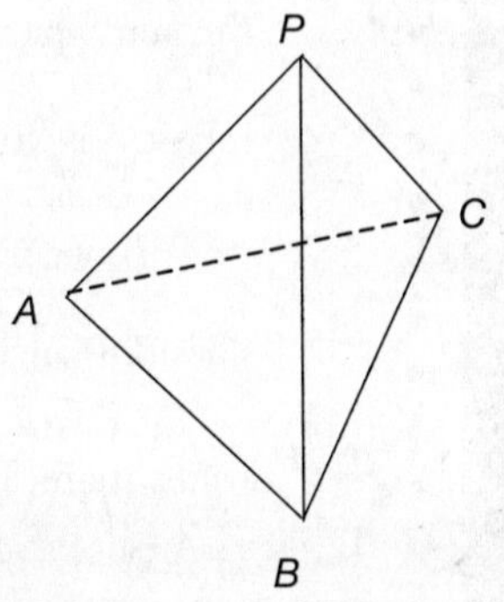

Figure 10.37 Regular Tetrahedron

The total surface area of a regular tetrahedron = LSA + Area of base

$$= \frac{3\sqrt{3}}{4} a^2 + \frac{\sqrt{3}}{4} a^2$$

$$= \sqrt{3}\, a^2.$$

Volume of a regular tetrahedron $= \frac{1}{3} \times$ Area of base $\times$ Vertical height

$$= \frac{1}{3} \times \frac{\sqrt{3}}{4} a^2 \times \frac{\sqrt{2}}{\sqrt{3}} a = \frac{a^3}{6\sqrt{2}}.$$

Regular Octahedron

A regular octahedron is an octahedron whose faces are all congruent equilateral triangles.

Figure 10.38 is an example of regular octahedron, where *ABCD* is a square; *ABP, BCP, CDP, DAP, ABQ, BCQ, CDQ,* and *DAQ* are eight equilateral triangles which are congruent. If each side of an equilateral triangle is *a* units,

then surface area of the octahedron $= 8\times\frac{\sqrt{3}}{4}a^2 = 2\sqrt{3}\,a^2$ sq. units.

Volume of a regular octahedron $= 2\left(\frac{1}{3}\times a^2\times\frac{a}{\sqrt{2}}\right) = \sqrt{\frac{2}{3}}a^3$ cu units.

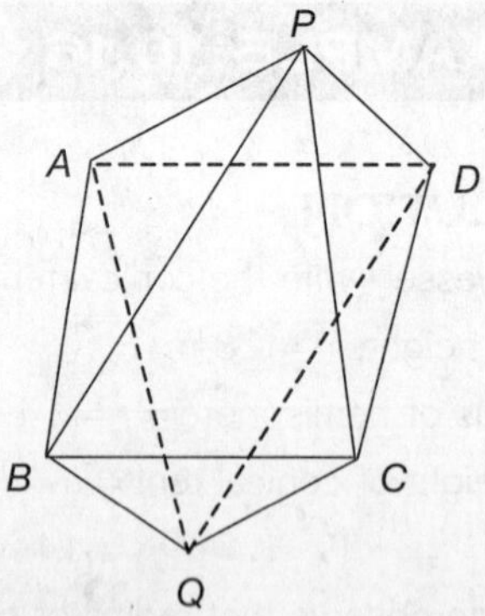

Figure 10.38 Regular Octahedron

POINTS TO REMEMBER

- ✔ A figure lying in a plane is called a plane (or planar) figure.
- ✔ A plane figure is made up of line segments or curves or both. A plane figure is called a rectilinear figure.
- ✔ The part of the plane which is enclosed by a simple closed figure is called a plane region. The magnitude of a plane region is called its area.
- ✔ The area of a triangle is also given by $\sqrt{s(s-a)(s-b)(s-c)}$, where *a, b,* and *c* are the lengths of the sides of the triangle and *s* is the semi-perimeter, i.e., $s = \frac{(a+b+c)}{2}$. This relation is known as Heron's formula.

  $\therefore$ Area of a trapezium $= \left(\frac{1}{2}\right)$(Sum of the parallel sides)(Distance between them).
- ✔ In a square, Length = Breadth

  $\therefore$ Area of a square = (Side)(Side) = $(\text{Side})^2$

  Perimeter of a square = 4(Side)

  Diagonal of a square $= \sqrt{2}$ (Side)

  $\therefore$ Area of a square $= \frac{(\text{Diagonal})^2}{2}$.

  $\therefore$ The area of a regular polygon $= \left(\frac{1}{2}\right)$(Perimeter of the polygon) (Perpendicular distance from the centre to any side).
- ✔ The area of an equilateral triangle $= \frac{\sqrt{3}}{4}(\text{side})^2$ sq. units.

  In-radius (*r*) of a triangle is given by the formula, $r = \frac{\Delta}{s}$.

  Circum-radius (*R*) of a triangle is given by the formula, $R = \frac{abc}{4\Delta}$.
- ✔ The area of the ring = (Area of the bigger circle) − (Area of the smaller circle) $= \pi R^2 - \pi r^2 = \pi(R^2 - r^2)$.

✔ The volume of a cuboid = $Ah = (lb)h = lbh$ cubic units, where A is the area of the base.

✔ Diagonal of a cuboid $= \sqrt{l^2 + b^2 + h^2}$ units.

✔ The lateral surface area of the cube = $4a^2$.

The total surface area of the cube = LSA + 2(Area of base) = $4a^2 + 2a^2 = 6a^2$.

The volume of the cube = a^3.

The diagonal of the cube $= \sqrt{a^2 + a^2 + a^2} = \sqrt{3}\,a$.

✔ For a right pyramid with perimeter of base = p, height = h, and slant height = l:

Lateral surface area $= \frac{1}{2}$(perimeter of base) × (slant height) $= \frac{1}{2}pl$

Total surface area = lateral surface area + area of base.

Volume of pyramid $= \frac{1}{3}$ × area of base × height.

✔ Let radius of the upper base be R, radius of the lower base be r, height of the frustum be h and slant height of the frustum be l.

Curved surface area of a frustum = $\pi l(R + r)$ sq. units.

Total surface area of a frustum

= Curved surface area + Area of lower base + Area of upper base = $\pi l(R + r) + \pi r^2 + \pi R^2$ sq. units.

Volume of a frustum $= \frac{1}{3}\pi rh(R^2 + Rr + r^2)$ cubic units.

Slant height (l) of a frustum

$= \sqrt{(R - r)^2 + h^2}$ units.

✔ Volume of a regular octahedron

$= 2\left(\frac{1}{3} \times a^2 \times \frac{a}{\sqrt{2}}\right) = \sqrt{\frac{2}{3}}a^3$ cu units.

✔ **Sphere**

- Surface area of a sphere = $4\pi r^2$
- Volume of a sphere $= \frac{4}{3}\pi r^3$

✔ **Hemisphere**

- Curved surface area of a hemisphere = $2\pi r^2$
- Total surface area of a hemisphere = $3\pi r^2$
- Volume of a hemisphere $= \frac{2}{3}\pi r^3$.

✔ **Spherical Shell**

- Thickness = $R - r$, where R = outer radius and r = inner radius.
- Volume $= \frac{4}{3}\pi R^3 - \frac{4}{3}\pi r^3$
- Total surface area of a hemispherical shell

  = (curved surface area of outer hemisphere + curved surface area of inner hemisphere + area of ring)

  = $3\pi R^2 + \pi r^2$.

Volume of a regular octahedron

$= 2\left(\frac{1}{3} \times a^2 \times \frac{a}{\sqrt{2}}\right) = \sqrt{\frac{2}{3}}a^3$ cu units.

PRACTICE QUESTIONS CLASSROOM WING

Very Short Answer Type Questions

Directions of questions from 1 to 10:
Fill in the blanks.

1. The area of a triangle whose sides are 17 cm, 8 cm and 15 cm, is ______.
2. The number of vertices of a pyramid whose base is a pentagon is ________.
3. The number of edges of a tetrahedron is ______.
4. A circle of radius 2 cm is inscribed in an equilateral triangle. The area of the circle circumscribing the triangle is _______.
5. By joining the mid-points of the adjacent sides of a quadrilateral of area 26 cm^2 a _____ is formed and its area, is _____.
6. The longest needle that can be placed in a cylinder of volume $\pi r^2 h$, is ______.
7. The base of a pyramid is an equilateral triangle with side a and the height of the pyramid is h. Then the volume of the pyramid is ______.
8. The heights of two cylinders are equal and their radii are in the ratio of 3 : 2. The ratio of their curved surface areas is ______.
9. The ratio of the radii of two cones having equal heights is 2:3 then ratio of their volumes is ________.
10. The radii of two spheres are 2 cm and 3 cm, respectively. The ratio of their surface areas is ________.

Directions of questions from 11 to 20:
Answer the following questions.

11. A triangle has a perimeter of 9 cm. How many combinations of its sides exist, if their lengths in cm are integers?
12. What is the volume of a pyramid whose base area is $(2+\sqrt{3})$ cm^2 and its height being $(2-\sqrt{3})$ cm?
13. If the edge of a cube increases by 20%, then find the percentage increase in its volume.
14. If a sphere, cone, cuboid, pyramid, and cube have the same surface area, then which of these solid figure have the maximum volume?
15. What is the volume of a hemispherical shell with outer radius of x units and thickness of y units?
16. If the volume of a solid hemisphere and its total surface area are numerically equal, then find its radius.
17. What is the volume of the prism whose base is a hexagon of side 6 cm and height $12\sqrt{3}$ cm?
18. If the dimensions of a cuboid are 5 cm × 4 cm × 3 cm, then find the maximum volume of the cube that can be carved out of it.
19. Find the lateral surface area and the length of the diagonal of a cube of side 8 cm.
20. Find the number of soaps of size 2 cm × 3 cm × 5 cm, that can be arranged in a cuboidal box of dimensions 6 cm × 3 cm × 15 cm.

Short Answer Type Questions

Directions of questions from 21 to 35:
Answer the following questions.

21. In the given figure, $AB = 6.4$ cm, $CF = 2.6$ cm, $AD = 3.2$ cm. Find the area of the triangle ABC and length of the side BC.

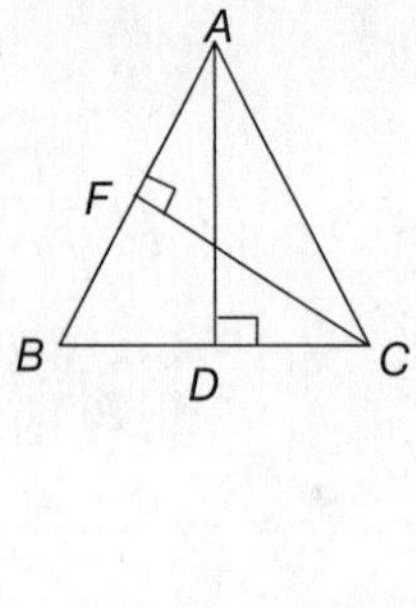

22. From the given figure, find the length of the major arc AB.

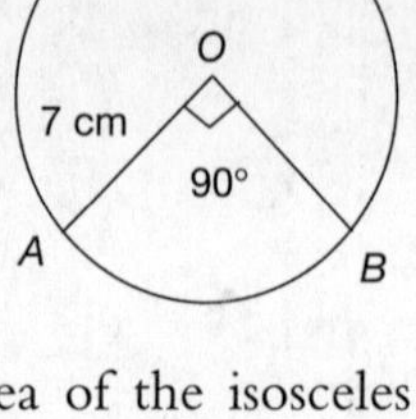

23. Find the area of a circle, if the area of the isosceles right-angle triangle inscribed in it is 18 sq. cm.

24. The perimeter of a rectangle is a two digits number whose units digit and tens digit represent the length and breadth of the rectangle, respectively. Find its area.

25. Three equilateral triangles are cut from an equilateral triangle of area 36 cm^2, such that a regular hexagon is left. Find the area of the hexagon.

26. If $a+b$, $a-b$, and $2\sqrt{ab}$ are the sides of a cuboid, then find the longest stick that can be placed in it.

27. A square plate of side 28 cm is made into a cylinder by joining two edges of it. Find the base area of the cylinder formed.

28. From a cylindrical wooden log of length 30 cm and base radius $7\sqrt{2}$ cm, maximum cuboid of square base is made. Find the volume of wood wasted.

29. In the given figure, AB = 15 cm, BC = 12 cm and CD = AF = 2 cm. Find the area of the polygon AFEDCA (in cm^2).

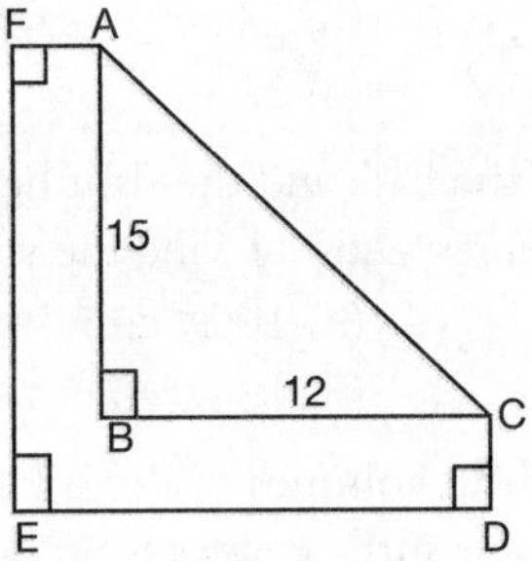

30. A sphere fits exactly in a hollow cube. Find the ratio of the volumes of the cube and the sphere.

31. The diameters of the circular ends of a bucket are 14 cm and 7 cm. If the height of the bucket is 12 cm, then find the total surface area of the bucket.

32. A cow is tied by a rope of length 14 m, to a pole at a corner of a grassy field of length 100 m and breadth 80 m. What is the area of the field it can graze?

33. The base of a right pyramid is a regular hexagon. The perimeter of the base is 36 cm. If the vertical height of the pyramid is 12 cm, then find the volume of the right pyramid.

34. The area of the base of a pyramid, which is an equilateral triangle, is $16\sqrt{3}$ cm^2, and its slant height is 3 cm. What is its lateral surface area?

35. The base radius of a conical tent is 120 cm and its slant height is 750 cm. Find the area of the canvas required to make 10 such tents (in m^2). (Take π = 3.14).

Essay Type Questions

Directions of questions from 36 to 42:
Answer the following questions.

36. An open metallic conical tank is 6 m deep and its circular top has a diameter of 16 m. Find the cost of tin plating in its inner surface at the rate of ₹0.8 per 100 cm^2. (Take $\pi = 3.14$).

37. A drum in the shape of a frustum of a cone with radii 20 ft and 14 ft and height 5 ft is full of water. The drum is emptied into a cuboidal tank of base 73 ft × 44 ft. Find the rise in the height of the water level in the tank.

38. The radius of a cross-section of a tube of a truck is 28 cm. The outer radius of the tube itself is 63 cm. What is the surface area of the tube?

39. If the thickness of a hemispherical bowl is 12 cm and its outer diameter is 10.24 m, find the inner surface area of the hemisphere. (Take $\pi = 3.14$)

40. The internal surface area of a hollow hemisphere is 77 cm^2 and its external surface area is 308 cm^2. What is the thickness of the hollow hemisphere?

41. In the given figure, *ABCD* is a parallelogram and *ADB* is an equilateral triangle. If the diagonal BD = 8 cm, then find the area of the parallelogram and find the length of the diagonal *AC*.

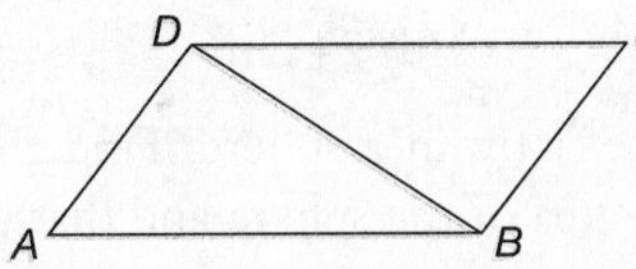

42. There is a rectangular shed of dimensions 8 m × 6 m inside a field. A cow is tied at one corner of this shed with a rope of 6 m long. What is the maximum area that the cow can graze in the field, outside of the shed?

PRACTICE QUESTIONS COMPETITION WING

Level 1: Apply Your Concepts

Directions of questions from 1 to 4:
Fill in the blanks.

1. The diagonal of a square is 10 cm. What is its area?
2. If the circumference of a circle is numerically equal to its area, then what is the radius of the circle?
3. A solid object has 8 vertices and 12 edges. It has ______ faces.
4. The number of vertices of a pyramid, whose base is a pentagon, is ______.

Directions of questions from 5 to 60:
Select the correct alternative from the given choices.

5. The perimeter of a right triangle is 72 cm and its area is 216 cm^2. Find the sum of the lengths of its perpendicular sides (in cm).
   (a) 36 (b) 32
   (c) 42 (d) 50

6. In the given figure, ABCD is a rectangle. DE = EC, CF = FB, EH = HC and CG = GF. If the area of ABCD is 96 cm^2, then find area of ΔHCG.

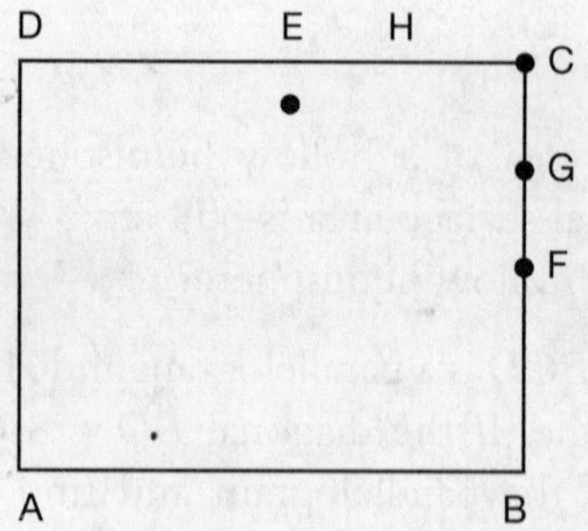

   (a) 3 cm^2 (b) 6 cm^2
   (c) 12 cm^2 (d) 24 cm^2

7. A cube fits exactly in a sphere. Find the ratio of the total surface area of the sphere and that of the cube.
   (a) $\pi : 2$ (b) $\pi : 3$
   (c) $\pi : 6$ (d) $\pi : 2$

8. A horse is tied by a rope of length 12 m to a pole at a corner of the square shaped grassy field of length 50 m. What is the area of the field it can graze?
   (a) 16 π m^2 (b) 25 π m^2
   (c) 36 π m^2 (d) 49 π m^2

9. An edge of a regular tetrahedron is $4\sqrt{3}$ cm. Find the slant height of the tetrahedron. (in cm).
   (a) $8\sqrt{3}$ (b) 6
   (c) 8 (d) $6\sqrt{3}$

10. The radius of the base of a cone is 7 cm and its slant height is 25 cm. The volume of the cone is ______.
   (a) 3696 cm^3 (b) 1232 cm^3
   (c) 2464 cm^3 (d) 1864 cm^3

11. The side of a square is equal to the diagonal of a cube. The square has an area of 1728 m^2. Calculate the side of the cube.
   (a) 12 m (b) 24 m
   (c) 27 m (d) 36 m

12. The radius of the base and the slant height of a cone is 5 cm and 13 cm, respectively. Find the volume of the cone.
   (a) 88π cm^3 (b) 100π cm^3
   (c) 92π cm^3 (d) 106π cm^3

13. If the ratio of the volumes of the spheres is 8 : 27, then the ratio of their surface areas is ______.
   (a) 4 : 9 (b) 9 : 4
   (c) 4 : 3 (d) 2 : 9

14. The volume of a hemisphere is 18π cm^3. What is the total surface area of the hemisphere?
   (a) 18π cm^2 (b) 27π cm^2
   (c) 21π cm^2 (d) 24π cm^2

15. In a polyhedron, if the number of faces is 4 and the number of edges is 6, then the number of vertices of that polyhedron is ______.
   (a) 1 (b) 2
   (c) 3 (d) 4

16. Fifteen identical spheres are made by melting a solid cylinder of 10 cm radius and 5.4 cm height. Find the diameter of each sphere.
   (a) 6 cm (b) 3 cm
   (c) 2 cm (d) 4 cm

17. If the radius of a sphere is increased by 25%, then the percentage increase in its volume is ______. (approximately)
   (a) 90% (b) 95%
   (c) 83% (d) 78%

18. Find the volume of a hollow sphere of outer radius 9 cm and inner radius 6 cm.
(a) 342π cm^3 (b) 684π cm^3
(c) 36π cm^3 (d) 128π cm^3

19. A hollow hemispherical bowl of thickness 1 cm has an inner radius of 4.5 cm. Find the curved surface area of the bowl.
(a) 106π cm^2 (b) 108π cm^2
(c) 101π cm^2 (d) 102π cm^2

20. If the length of each edge of a tetrahedron is 18 cm, then the volume of the tetrahedron is ______.
(a) $482\sqrt{2}$ cm^3 (b) $480\sqrt{2}$ cm^3
(c) $484\sqrt{2}$ cm^3 (d) $486\sqrt{2}$ cm^3

21. Find the total surface area of a regular octahedron, each edge of which is 10 cm.
(a) $100\sqrt{3}$ cm^2 (b) $200\sqrt{3}$ cm^2
(c) $300\sqrt{3}$ cm^2 (d) $400\sqrt{3}$ cm^2

22. The number of edges in a pyramid whose base has 20 edges is ______.
(a) 10 (b) 20
(c) 30 (d) 40

23. A copper cable, 32 cm long, having a diameter 6 cm, is melted to form a sphere. Find the radius of the sphere.
(a) 6 cm (b) 8 cm
(c) 10 cm (d) 12 cm

24. The number of diagonals of a regular polygon in which each interior angle is 156°, is ______.
(a) 24 (b) 54
(c) 90 (d) 45

25. *ABCDEF* is a regular hexagon. If *AB* is 6 cm long, then what is the area of triangle *ABD*?
(a) $8\sqrt{3}$ cm^2 (b) $12\sqrt{3}$ cm^2
(c) $15\sqrt{3}$ cm^2 (d) $18\sqrt{3}$ cm^2

26. The area and the radius of a sector are 6.93 sq. cm and 4.2 cm, respectively. Find the length of the arc of the sector.
(a) 1.72 cm (b) 0.86 cm
(c) 3.3 cm (d) 6.6 cm

27. A large sphere of radius 3.5 cm is carved from a cubical solid. Find the difference between their surface areas.
(a) 224 cm^2 (b) 140 cm^2
(c) 176 cm^2 (d) 80.5 cm^2

28. If one of the edges of a regular octahedron is $4\sqrt{3}$ cm, then find its height.
(a) $2\sqrt{3}$ cm (b) $4\sqrt{6}$ cm
(c) $6\sqrt{3}$ cm (d) $2\sqrt{6}$ cm

29. The dimensions of a cuboidal container are 12 cm × 10 cm × 8 cm. How many bottles of syrup can be poured into the container, if each bottle contains 20 cm^3 of syrup?
(a) 46 (b) 54
(c) 48 (d) 58

Level 2: Review Your Concepts

30. A circle of radius 2 cm is inscribed in an equilateral triangle. Find the area of the triangle in cm^2.
(a) $12\sqrt{3}$ (b) $4\sqrt{3}$
(c) $6\sqrt{3}$ (d) $24\sqrt{3}$

31. The circum-radius of a right triangle is 10 cm and one of the two perpendicular sides is 12 cm. Find the area of the triangle in sq. cm.
(a) 96 (b) 128
(c) 48 (d) 64

32. A parallelogram has two of its adjacent sides measuring 13 each. Find the sum of the squares of its diagonals.
(a) 169 (b) 338
(c) 676 (d) 507

33. A classroom is 5 m long, 2.5 m broad and 3.6 m high. If each student is given 0.5 m^2 of the floor area, then how many cubic metres of air would each student get?
(a) 1.4 (b) 1.8
(c) 1.2 (d) 1.6

34. If the volume of a right equilateral triangular prism is $8500\sqrt{3}$ dm^3 whose height is 50 cm, then find the side of its base.
(a) $10\sqrt{17}$ cm (b) $10\sqrt{17}$ dm
(c) $20\sqrt{17}$ dm (d) $20\sqrt{17}$ cm

35. How many cubes, each of total surface area 54 sq.dm, can be made from a cube of edge 1.2 meter.
(a) 64 (b) 81
(c) 125 (d) 25

36. Four times the sum of the areas of the two circular faces of a cylinder is equal to the twice its curved surface area. Find the diameter of the cylinder if its height is 8 cm.

(a) 4 cm (b) 8 cm
(c) 2 cm (d) 6 cm

37. If the base of a right pyramid is a square of side 4 cm and its height is 18 cm, then the volume of the pyramid is _______.

(a) 90 cm^3 (b) 104 cm^3
(c) 100 cm^3 (d) 96 cm^3

38. A right circular conical tent is such that the angle at its vertex is 60° and its base radius is 14 m. Find the cost of the canvas required to make the tent at the rate of ₹25 per m^2.

(a) ₹15,400 (b) ₹30,800
(c) ₹16,400 (d) ₹32,800

39. A goat is tied to a corner of a rectangular plot of dimensions 14 m × 7 m with a 21 m long rope. It cannot graze inside the plot, but can graze outside it as far as it is permitted by the rope. Find the area it can graze (in m^2). (Take $\pi = \frac{22}{7}$)

(a) 240 (b) 1560.5
(c) 1543.5 (d) 1232

40. If the breadth of a rectangle is increased by 5 cm, its area increases by 25 cm^2. If its length is increased by 5 cm, its area increases by 20 cm^2. Find the area of the rectangle (in cm^2).

(a) 20 (b) 25
(c) 30 (d) 35

41. A cylinder-shaped tank is surmounted by a cone of equal radius. The height of the cone is 6 m and the total height of the tank is 18 m. Find the volume of the tank if the base radius of the cylinder is 5 m.

(a) 1650 m^3 (b) 1244 m^3
(c) 1100 m^3 (d) 2200 m^3

42. The radius of the cross-section of an inflated cycle tyre is 7 cm. The distance of the centre of the cross-section from the axle is 20 cm. Find the volume of air in the tyre.

(a) 19,360 cm^3 (b) 1760 cm^3
(c) 6160 cm^3 (d) 880 cm^3

43. If h is the length of the perpendicular drawn from a vertex of a regular tetrahedron to the opposite face and each edge is of length s, then s^2 is equal to _______.

(a) $\frac{3h^2}{8}$ (b) $\frac{3h^2}{2}$
(c) h^2 (d) $\frac{8h^2}{3}$

44. The radii of the ends of a frustum of a cone are 28 cm and 7 cm. The height of the cone is 40 cm. Find its volume.

(a) 32,340 cm^3 (b) 43,120 cm^3
(c) 10,780 cm^3 (d) None of these

45. The diagonal of a cube is $8\sqrt{3}$ cm. Find its total surface area.

The following are the steps involved in solving the above problem. Arrange them in sequential order.

(A) Then the diagonal of cube = $a\sqrt{3}$ cm.

(B) ∴ Total surface area = $6a^2 = 6(8)^2 = 384$ cm^2.

(C) Let the side of cube be a cm.

(D) From the given data, $a\sqrt{3} = 8\sqrt{3} \Rightarrow a = 8$ cm.

(a) ACBD (b) CADB
(c) ABCD (d) CBAD

46. The length of the diagonals of a rhombus are 10 cm and 24 cm. Find its side. (in cm)

(a) 10 (b) 13
(d) 12 (d) 11

47. Area of a right-angled triangle is 6 cm^2 and its perimeter is 12 cm. Find its hypotenuse. (in cm)

(a) 5 (b) 6
(c) 7 (d) 8

48. A largest possible right-circular cylinder is cut out from a wooden cube of edge 7 cm. Find the volume of the wood left over after cutting the cylinder. (in cu cm)

(a) 73.5 (b) 82.5
(c) 76 (d) 92

49. A solid sphere of radius 4 cm is melted and recast into 'n' solid hemispheres of radius 2 cm each. Find n.

(a) 32 (b) 16
(c) 8 (d) 4

50. Three small metallic cubes whose edges are in the ratio 3 : 4 : 5 are melted to form a big cube. If the diagonal

of the cube so formed is 18 cm, then find the total surface area of the smallest cube. (in cm^2)

(a) 154 (b) 184

(c) 216 (d) 162

51. A solid hemisphere of radius 8 cm is melted and recast into x spheres of radius 2 cm each. Find x.

(a) 4 (b) 8

(c) 16 (d) 32

Level 3: Assess Your Concepts

52. In the following figure, $ABCD$ is a rectangle with $AB = 9$ cm and $BC = 6$ cm. O is the centre of the circle. Find the area of the shaded region. (in cm^2)

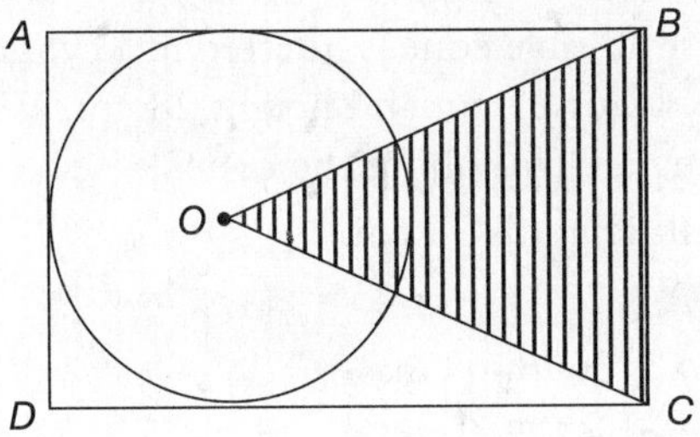

(a) 18 (b) 24

(c) 27 (d) 15

53. A circus tent is cylindrical upto a height of 8 m and conical above it. If its base diameter is 70 m and the slant height of the conical part is 50 m, the area of the canvas required to make the tent is ______ m^2.

(a) 6380 (b) 7260

(c) 6850 (d) 7460

54. A water tank of dimensions 11 m × 6 m × 5 m is full of water. The tank is emptied through a pipe of cross-section 33 cm^2 in 20 hours. Find the rate of flow of water. (in kmph)

(a) 2 (b) 5

(c) 6 (d) 10

55. P and Q are two cylinders having equal total surface areas. The radius of each cylinder is equal to the height of the other. The sum of the volumes of both the cylinders is 250π cm^3. Find the sum of their curved surface areas. (in cm^2)

(a) 80π (b) 100π

(c) 60π (d) 120π

56. In a triangle, the average of any two sides is 6 cm more than half of the third side. Find area of the triangle. (in sq. cm)

(a) $64\sqrt{3}$ (b) $48\sqrt{3}$

(c) $72\sqrt{3}$ (d) $36\sqrt{3}$

57. The lengths of the diagonals of a rhombus are 9 cm and 12 cm. Find the distance between any two parallel sides of the rhombus.

(a) 7.2 cm (b) 8 cm

(c) 7.5 cm (d) 6.9 cm

58. In a triangle, the sum of any two sides exceed the third side by 6 cm. Find its area (in sq. cm).

(a) $12\sqrt{3}$ (b) $9\sqrt{3}$

(c) $15\sqrt{3}$ (d) $18\sqrt{3}$

59. From each corner of a square sheet of side 8 cm, a square of side y cm is cut. The remaining sheet is folded into a cuboid. The minimum possible volume of the cuboid formed is M cubic cm. If y is an integer, then find M.

(a) 32 (b) 18

(c) 36 (d) 12

60. In the given figure, QPR is quadra circle and $ABCD$ is a square, whose side is $\sqrt{10}$ cm. If A and B are equidistant from the centre O, then find the radius of the circle.

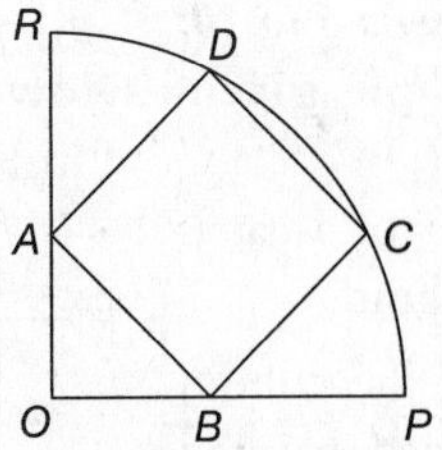

(a) 2 (b) 3

(c) 5 (d) 7

AT

PRACTICE QUESTIONS JEE SPECIAL WING

Multiple-Answer Type Questions

Directions for questions 1 to 5:
Each question has FOUR options (a), (b), (c), and (d). ONE OR MORE THAN ONE of these four option(s) is/are the correct answer(s).

1. The sides of a rectangle are integers in cm. If the area of the rectangle is 200 sq cm, which of the following can be the perimeter of the rectangle?
(a) 402 cm (b) 204 cm
(c) 80 cm (d) 60 cm

2. The base radius and the height of a cylinder are integers in cm. If the volume of the cylinder is 1078 sq cm, which of the following can be the radius of the cylinder?
(a) 1 cm (b) 3.5 cm
(c) 7 cm (d) 10.5 cm

3. From each corner of a square sheet of side x cm, a square of side y cm is cut. The remaining sheet is folded into a cuboid of volume 100 cubic cm. Here both x and y are positive integers. Which of the following can be a value of $x + y$?
(a) 13 (b) 17
(c) 77 (d) 301

4. A largest possible cone is inserted in a cylindrical vessel of base radius 21 cm and height 28 cm. Which of the following are true about the cone?
(a) Slant height is 35 cm.
(b) CSA is 2310 sq cm.
(c) TSA is 3696 sq cm.
(d) Volume is 12369 cu cm.

5. The areas of three mutually adjacent faces of a cuboid are 30 sq cm, 20 sq cm and 24 sq cm. Which of the following is/are true for the cuboid?
(a) TSA is 148 sq cm
(b) The volume is 120 cu cm
(c) The longest needle that can be placed in the cuboid is 9 cm.
(d) The volume of the largest possible cube carved out of the cuboid is 64 cu cm.

Match The Column

Directions for questions 6 to 10:
Read the paragraph given below and answer the questions.

The *AC* compressor of a car is in the shape of a cuboid.

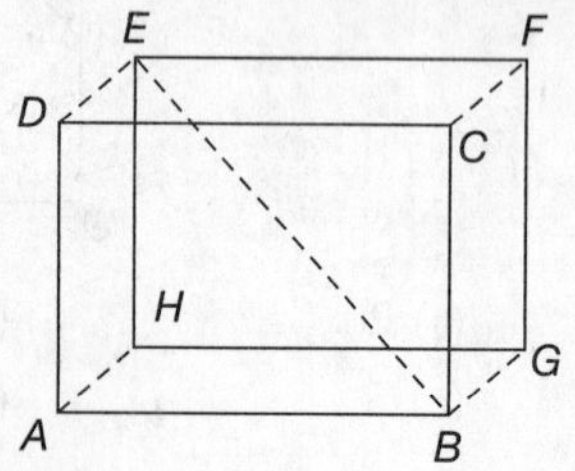

The side walls of the cuboid (compressor) has been painted and the cuboid (compressor) has been filled with a gas called R134a refrigerant.

Further information is as follows:

ABCDEFGH is a cuboidal compressor.

ABGH is a face of the compressor which is fixed on a surface of the car.

$AB = 12$ cm

$BC = 4$ cm

$CF = 3$ cm

Match the values in Column A with those in Column B.

Column A	Column B (cm/sq cm/cu cm/\$)
6. The body diagonal	(a) 4
7. The shortest face diagonal	(b) 5
8. The area of one of the faces	(c) 8
9. The cost of painting outside the side walls at \$1 for 8 sq cm.	(d) 12
10. The cost of filling the gas in the compressor at \$1 for 18 cu cm.	(e) 13
	(f) 15
	(g) 18

Comprehension-Based Questions

Directions for questions 11 to 15:

Read the paragraph given below and answer the questions.

Mihira is very good at maths and sciences. She makes very interesting models with clay. She teaches maths to her sister, Kyra using models. One day she made a regular octahedron of edge 9 cm. The same is shown in the diagram. She asked her sister to answer the following questions.

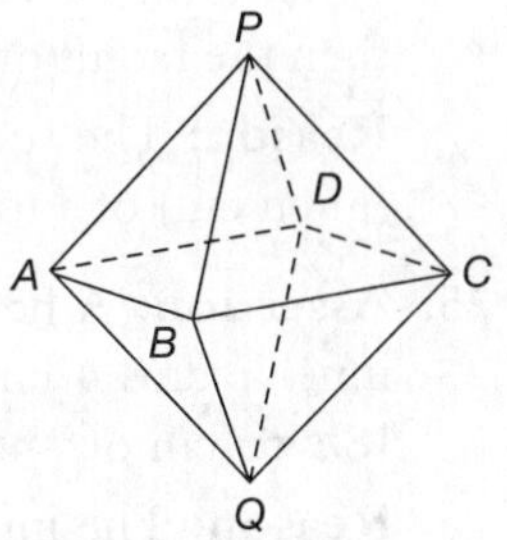

11. What is the length of the octahedron?
(a) $9\sqrt{2}$ cm (b) $8\sqrt{2}$ cm
(c) $6\sqrt{2}$ cm (d) $3\sqrt{2}$ cm

12. What is the total surface area of the octahedron?
(a) $126\sqrt{3}$ sq cm (b) $162\sqrt{3}$ sq cm
(c) $171\sqrt{3}$ sq cm (d) $198\sqrt{3}$ sq cm

13. What is the volume of the octahedron ?
(a) $729\sqrt{2}$ cu cm (b) $243\sqrt{2}$ cu cm
(c) $81\sqrt{2}$ cu cm (d) $27\sqrt{2}$ cu cm

14. If the octahedron is melted and recast into x regular tetrahedrons of edge 3 cm, what will be the value of x?
(a) 18 (b) 36
(c) 54 (d) 108

15. If the octahedron is cut vertically by a plane from P to Q, what is the cross-sectional area?
(a) $67.5\sqrt{2}$ sq cm (b) $50.4\sqrt{2}$ sq cm
(c) $40.5\sqrt{2}$ sq cm (d) $37.8\sqrt{2}$ sq cm

Directions for questions 16 to 20:

Read the paragraph given below and answer the questions.

Sanju made a conical bucket with a lid using a thin iron sheet. The curved surface area of the bucket considering $\pi = \frac{22}{7}$, is 110 sq cm.

r is the radius of the base R is the radius of the top.

l is the slant height of the bucket.

h is the height of the bucket.

Also, R, r, and l are three consecutive integers.

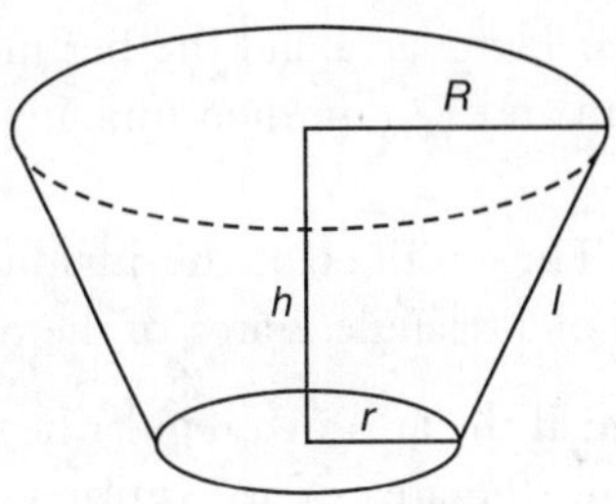

16. What is the measure of the height of the bucket?
(a) $2\sqrt{2}$ cu cm (b) $2\sqrt{3}$ cu cm
(c) $2\sqrt{6}$ cu cm (d) $3\sqrt{2}$ cu cm

17. What is the area of the sheet to make the bucket with lid (Consider $\pi = 3.14$)?
(a) 0 (b) 1
(c) 2 (d) 188.5 sq cm

18. What is the quantity of water that the bucket can hold? (Consider $\pi = 3.14$ and $\sqrt{6} = 2.45$)
(a) 569.28 ml (b) 576.42 ml
(c) 598.26 ml (d) 545.44 ml

19. What is the approximate weight of the metal used if the weight of the metal is 5.31 grams per 1 sq cm (Consider $\pi = 3.14$)?
(a) 0.9 kg (b) 1 kg
(c) 1.1 kg (d) 1.2 kg

20. If the inner surface of the bucket is painted, what is the cost of painting at ₹5 for10 sq cm (Consider $\pi = 3.14$)?
(a) ₹94.25 (b) ₹95.5
(c) ₹96.75 (d) ₹97.5

Assertion and Reason Type Questions

Directions for questions 21 to 25:

Read the options given below and answer the questions.

(a) Both assertion (A) and reason (R) are true, and the reason (R) is the correct explanation of the assertion (A).

(b) Both assertion (A) and reason (R) are true, and the reason (R) is not the correct explanation of the assertion (A).

(c) Assertion (A) is true, but reason (R) is false.

(d) Assertion (A) is false, and reason (R) is true.

21. **Assertion:** If the sum and the difference of the radii of two concentric circles are 7 cm and 1 cm respectively, then the area of the bigger circle which is not a part of the smaller circle is 22 cm.

    Reason: The area of a circular ring is given by $\pi\left(R^2 - r^2\right)$.

22. **Assertion:** If the area and the perimeter of a triangle are 6 sq cm and 12 cm, then inradius of the triangle is 2 cm.

    Reason: The product of the inradius and the semi-perimeter of a triangle is area of the triangle.

23. **Assertion:** If the area of a regular hexagon of side x is 1296 sq cm, the area of an equilateral triangle of side x cm is 216 sq cm.

    Reason: The diagonals joining exactly opposite vertices of a regular polygon divide it in to six equilateral triangles.

24. **Assertion:** If the surface area (in sq cm) and the volume (in cu cm) of a torus are numerically equal, then the radius of the cross section of the torus is 2 cm.

    Reason: The surface area (in sq cm) and the volume (in cu cm) of a torus are $2\pi^2ra$ and π^2r^2a.

25. **Assertion:** A hemispherical bowl of outer radius and inner radius 4 cm and 3 cm can hold a maximum of 18π cu cm of water.

    Reason: The inner curved surface area a hemispherical bowl is given by $2\pi r^2$, where r is the inner radius of the bowl.

ANSWER KEYS

Crossword

Across

4. Torus
6. Polyhedron
8. Volume
9. Tetrahedron
10. Octahedron
12. Cube

Down

1. Cone
2. Solid
3. Parallelogram
5. Sphere
7. Sixty
11. Area

Classroom Wing

Very Short Answer Type Questions

1. 60 cm^2
2. 6
3. 6
4. 16 π sq. cm
5. parallelogram, 13 cm^2
6. $\sqrt{4r^2 + h^2}$
7. $\frac{\sqrt{3}}{12}a^2 \times h$
8. 3 : 2
9. 4 : 9
10. 4 : 9
11. 3
12. $\frac{1}{3}\text{ cm}^2$
13. 72.8%
14. Sphere
15. $\frac{2}{3}\pi x^3 - \frac{2}{3}\pi(x-y)^3$
16. 4.5 units
17. 1944 cm^3
18. $3 \times 3 \times 3 = 27\text{ cm}^3$
19. (i) 256 cm^2 (ii) $8\sqrt{3}$ cm
20. 9

Short Answer Type Questions

21. 6.56 cm
22. 33 cm
23. $18\pi\text{ m}^2$
24. 8 cm^2
25. 216 cm^2
26. $\sqrt{2}(a+b)$ units
27. $\frac{49}{11}\text{ cm}^2$
28. 3360 cm^3
29. 148 cm^2
30. 6 : π
31. 605 cm^2
32. $49\pi\text{ cm}^2$
33. $216\sqrt{3}\text{ cm}^3$
34. 36 cm^2
35. 282.6 m^2

Essay Type Questions

36. ₹20,096
37. $1\frac{3}{7}$ ft
38. 38720 cm^2
39. 157 m^2
40. 3.5 cm
41. $8\sqrt{3}$
42. $\frac{594}{7}$

Competition Wing

Level 1: Apply Your Concepts

1. 50
2. 2
3. 6
4. 6
5. (c)
6. (a)
7. (a)
8. (c)
9. (b)
10. (b)
11. (b)
12. (b)
13. (a)
14. (b)
15. (d)
16. (a)
17. (b)
18. (b)
19. (c)
20. (d)

21. (b)	22. (d)	23. (a)	24. (c)	25. (d)
26. (c)	27. (b)	28. (b)	29. (c)	

Level 2: Review Your Concepts

30. (a)	31. (a)	32. (c)	33. (b)	34. (c)
35. (a)	36. (b)	37. (d)	38. (b)	39. (d)
40. (a)	41. (c)	42. (a)	43. (b)	44. (a)
45. (b)	46. (b)	47. (a)	48. (a)	49. (b)
50. (d)	51. (d)			

Level 3: Assess Your Concepts

52. (a)	53. (b)	54. (b)	55. (b)	56. (d)
57. (a)	58. (b)	59. (d)	60. (c)	

JEE Special Wing

Multiple-Answer Type Questions

1. (a, b, d)	2. (a, c)	3. (a, b, c, d)	4. (a, b, c)	5. (a, b, d)

Match The Column

6. (e)	7. (b)	8. (d)	9. (f)	10. (c)

Comprehension-Based Questions

11. (a)	12. (b)	13. (b)	14. (d)	15. (c)
16. (c)	17. (d)	18. (a)	19. (b)	20. (b)

Assertion and Reason Type Questions

21. (a)	22. (d)	23. (a)	24. (c)	25. (b)

Hints and Explanations

Classroom Wing

Very Short Answer Type Questions

1. $8^2 + 15^2 = 17^2$

   $\therefore$ Then the triangle is right-angled.

   Required area $= \frac{1}{2} \times 15 \times 8 = 60$ cm^2.

2. $n + 1 = 5 + 1 = 6$

3. Tetrahedron is a triangular pyramid.

   $\therefore$ Number of edges $= 2x = 2(3) = 6$.

4. 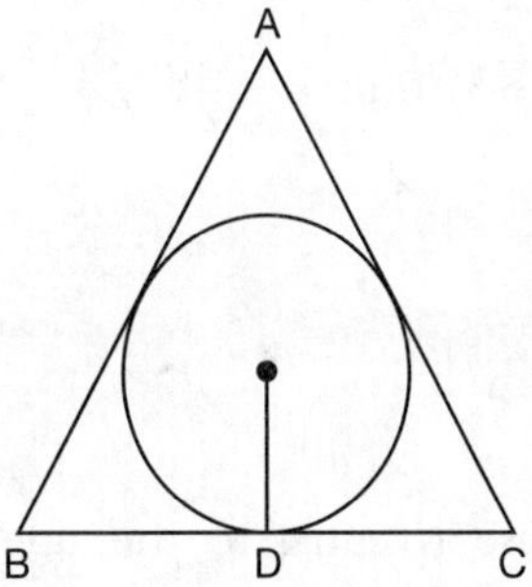

   Given, inradius of an equilateral triangle = 2 cm

   $\therefore$ circum-radius = 2(2 cm) = 4 cm

   Area of the circle circumscribing the triangle ABC = $\pi(4)^2 = 16\pi$ sq. cm

5. Area of the parallelogram inside a quadrilateral

   $= \frac{1}{2} \times$ Area of quadrilateral

   $= \frac{1}{2} \times 26$

   $= 13$ cm^2

6. The longest needle that can be placed in a cylinder of volume $\pi r^2 h$, is

   Longest needle $= \sqrt{4r^2 + h^2}$

7. Volume of pyramid $= \frac{1}{3} \times \frac{\sqrt{3}}{4} \times a^2 \times h$

   $= \frac{\sqrt{3}}{12} a^2 \times h$

8. The height of two cylinders are equal and their radii are in the ratio of 3:2. The ratio of their curved surface area is:

   $$\frac{\text{CSA of cylinder 1}}{\text{CSA of cylinder 2}} = \frac{2\pi(3x)h}{2\pi(2x)h} = 3:2$$

9. $= \dfrac{\frac{1}{3}\pi(R_1)^2 h}{\frac{1}{3}\pi(R_2)^2 h} = \dfrac{R_1^2}{R_2^2}$

10. 4 : 9 $\quad \dfrac{4\pi(2)^2}{4\pi(3)^2} = \dfrac{4}{9} = 4:9$

11. **3**

12. $\frac{1}{3}$ C.C $= \frac{1}{3} \times (2+\sqrt{3})(2-\sqrt{3})$

    $= \frac{1}{3}(4-3) = \frac{1}{3}$ cm^2

13. 72.8%

    Let the side of the cube is 1m.

    Volume $= 1^3 = 1$cm^3

    20% of 1 m = 0.2m

    Side of cube = 1 + 0.2 = 1.2

    Hence cube volume = 1.728 = 172.8%

    Increase in volume = 72.8%

14. Sphere

15. $\frac{2}{3}\pi x^3 - \frac{2}{3}\pi(x-y)^3$

16. 4.5 units

    $\frac{2}{3}\pi R^3 = 3\pi R^2$

    $R = 4.5$ units

17. Volume of Prism = area of hexagonal × height of prism

    $= \frac{3\sqrt{3}}{2} \times 36 \times 12\sqrt{3} = 1944$ cm^3

18. $3 \times 3 \times 3 = 27\text{cm}^3$

19. Lateral surface area

$= 4 \times s^2 = 4 \times (8)^2 = 4 \times 64 = 256\ \text{cm}^2$

Length of diagonal $= 8\sqrt{3}\ \text{cm} = \sqrt{3} \times 8 = 8\sqrt{3}$

20. 9

No. of Soaps $= \dfrac{\not{6} \times 3 \times \not{15}}{\not{2} \times \not{3} \times \not{5}}$ (with 3 written above the cancelled factors)

$= 9$

Short Answer Type Questions

21. $x^2 = (2.6)^2 + \left(\dfrac{6.4}{2}\right)^2$

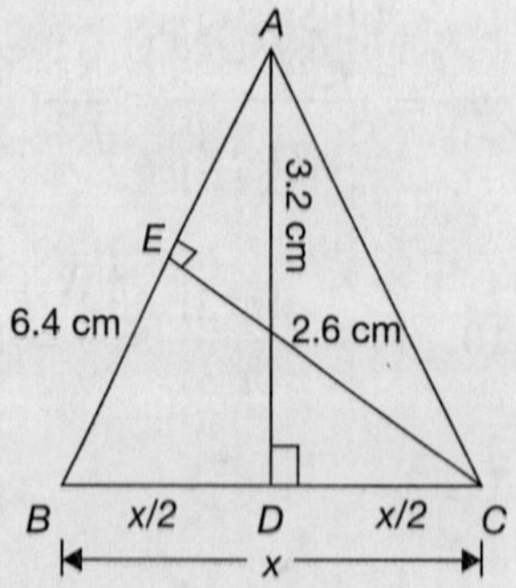

$x^2 = 17$

$x = 4.1$ cm

Area of the triangle

$= \dfrac{1}{2} \times 4.1 \times 3.2 = 4.1 \times 1.6$

$= 6.56\ \text{cm}^2$

22. Length of Major arc $= 2\pi r \times \dfrac{\text{angle}}{360}$

Angle of Major arc $= 360 - 90$

$= 270°$

$\not{2} \times \dfrac{\overset{11}{\not{22}}}{\not{7}} \times \not{7} \times \dfrac{3}{\not{4}} = 33$ cm

23. $\dfrac{1}{\not{2}} \times \not{2}r \times r = 18$

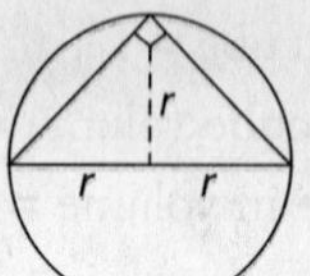

$r^2 = 18 \Rightarrow \sqrt{18} = r$

$\pi r^2 = 18\pi\ \text{cm}^2$

24. $2(x + y) = 10x + y$

$2x + 2y = 10x + y$

$y = 8x$

$l = 1$

$b = 8$

So, Area $= 1 \times 8 = 8\ \text{cm}^2$

25. $A = \dfrac{\sqrt{3}}{4} a^2$

$a^2 = \dfrac{36 \times 4}{\sqrt{3}} = \dfrac{3 \times 4 \times 12}{\sqrt{3}} = 48\sqrt{3}$

$a = \sqrt{48\sqrt{3}}$

Area of hexagon $= A = \dfrac{3\sqrt{3}}{2} a$

$= \dfrac{3\sqrt{3}}{2}\left(\sqrt{48\sqrt{3}}\right)$

$= \dfrac{3 \times 3 \times 48}{2}$

$= 216\ \text{cm}^2$

26. $(a + b)^2 + (a - b)^2 = x^2$

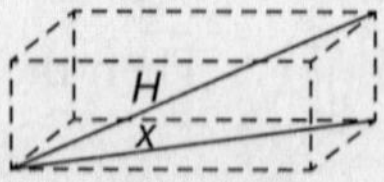

$x = \sqrt{(a + b)^2 + (a - b)^2}$

$((a + b)^2 + (a - b)^2 + 4ab) = H^2$

$H = \sqrt{a^2 + b^2 + a^2 + b^2 - 2ab + 2ab + 4ab}$

$H = \sqrt{2(a^2 + b^2) + 4ab}$

$H = \sqrt{2(a + b)^2} = \sqrt{2}(a + b)$ units

27. $2\pi r = 28$

$\pi r = 14$

$r = \dfrac{14}{\pi}$

(circumference of the base is equal to the side the square we can find r be it)

$\pi r^2 = \pi \times \dfrac{14}{\pi^2} = \dfrac{14}{\frac{22}{7}} = \dfrac{14 \times 7}{22}$

$\dfrac{98}{22} = \dfrac{49}{11}\ \text{cm}^2$

28. For finding the base of the cuboid.

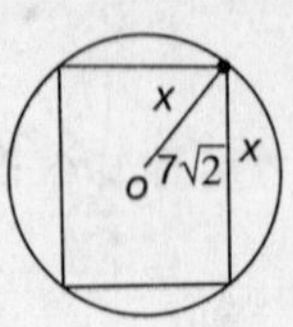

$(7\sqrt{2})^2 + (7\sqrt{2})^2 = x^2$

$49 \times 2 \times 49 \times 2 = x^2$

$\sqrt{49(4)} = x$

$x = 7 \times 2$

$x = 14$

waste $= L(\pi r^2 - x^2)$

$= 30\left(\dfrac{22}{7} \times \left(7\sqrt{2}\right)^2 - (14)^2\right)$

$= 30(22 \times 14 - 14 \times 14)$

$= 30(14(22 - 14))$

$= 3360\ \text{cm}^3$

29. 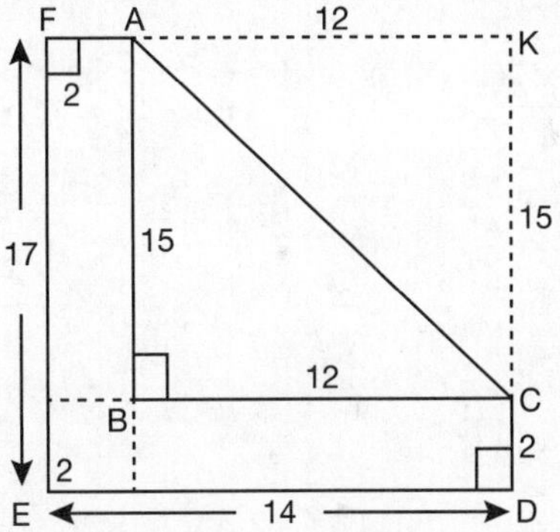

Let $\overline{FA}$ and $\overline{DC}$ extended meet at K.

Area of rectangle FEDK = 14 × 17 = 98 cm²

Area of ΔAKC = $\frac{1}{2}$ × 15 × 12 = 90 cm²

∴ required area = 238 – 90 = 148 cm².

30. 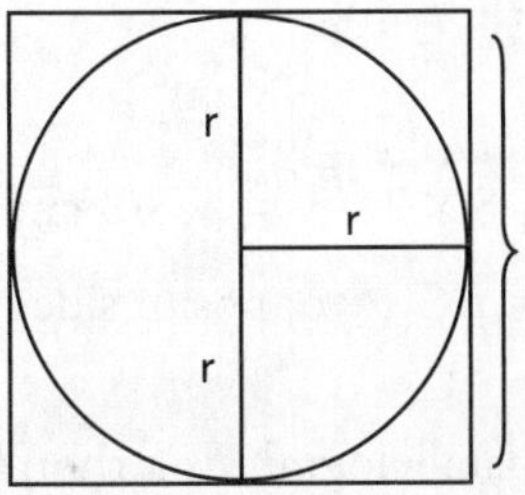

Let 'r' be the radius of the sphere.

Edge of the cube = 2r.

Required ratio = Volume of the cube: Volume of the sphere.

$= (2r)^3 : \frac{4}{3}\pi r^3 = 8r^3 : \frac{4}{3}\pi r^3 = 6 : \pi$

31. 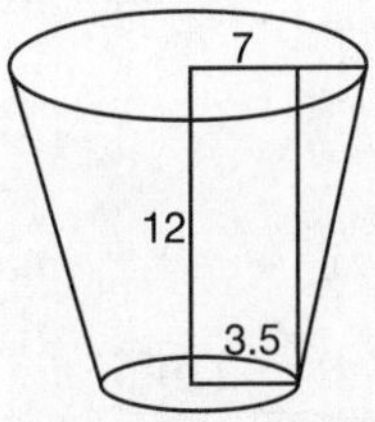

Let 'R' and 'r' be the radii of the top and bottom circular ends of the bucket. Let 'ℓ' be the slant height of the bucket.

$R = \frac{14}{2} = 7$ cm and $r = \frac{7}{2} = 3.5$ cm

Given height (h) = 12 cm

Slant height (ℓ) = $\sqrt{(R-r)^2 + h^2}$

$= \sqrt{(7-3.5)^2 + 12^2} = 12.5$cm

Total surface area of the bucket = $\pi\ell(R + r) + \pi r^2 + \pi R^2$

$= \pi\,[(12.5)(7 + 3.5) + 3.5^2 + 7^2]$

$= \frac{22}{7}\,[192.5] = 605$ cm²

32. 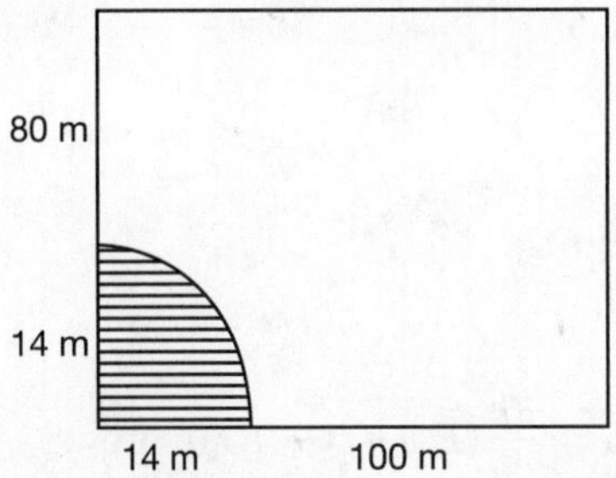

Given, the cow is tied by a rope of length 14 m to the pole at a corner of the field of length 100 m and breadth 80 m.

Required area = $\frac{90°}{360°} \times \pi \times 14^2 = \frac{1}{4} \times 196 = 49\pi$ cm².

33. Given: Height (h) = 12 cm

Perimeter of the base of the right pyramid(6a) = 36 cm

∴ side of the base (a) = 6 cm

Area of the base = $6 \times \frac{\sqrt{3}}{4} \times a^2 = 6 \times \frac{\sqrt{3}}{4} \times 6 \times 6$

$= 54\sqrt{3}$ cm²

Volume of the pyramid = $\frac{1}{3}$ × area of the base × height

$= \frac{1}{3} \times 54\sqrt{3} \times 12 = 216\sqrt{3}$ cm³

34. $\frac{\sqrt{3}}{4} \times a^2 = 16\sqrt{3}$

$a^2 = 64$

$\boldsymbol{a = 8}$

Lateral area $= 3 \times \frac{1}{2} \times 8 \times 3$

$= 9 \times 4 = 36$

35. Total circumference

$2 \times \pi \times 750 = 4710$

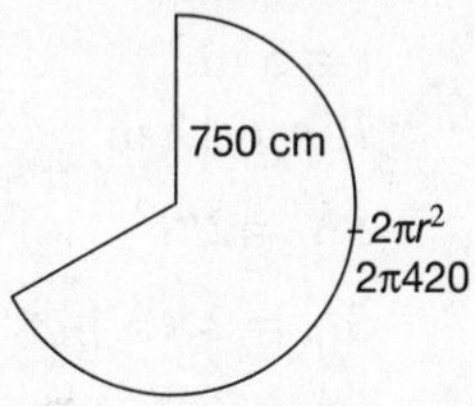

$\frac{x}{360} = \frac{753.6}{4710}$

$x° = 57.6°$

Total area required for 10 test

$= 10 \times \pi \times 750^2 \times \frac{57.6}{360}$

$= 2826000$ cm²

$= 282.6$ m²

Essay Type Questions

36. Lateral area

$= \pi(8) \times (10)$

$= 80\ \pi m^2$

$= 251.2\ m^2$

$= 25120/100\ cm^2$

$\text{cost} = 0.8 \times 25120$

$= ₹20,096$

37. $\text{Volume of frustum} = \frac{\pi h}{3}(R^2 + r^2 + Rr)$

$= \frac{5\pi}{3}((20)^2 + (14)^2 + (20 \times 14))$

$= \frac{1460 \times 22}{7}$

$= \frac{32120}{7}$

$73 \times 44 \times x = \frac{32120}{7}$

$x = \frac{32120}{73 \times 44 \times 7} = \frac{32170}{22484}$

$x = 1.43$ ft

$= 1\frac{3}{7}$ ft

38. $\text{Surface area} = 4\pi^2 ra$

$r = 28$

$a = 63 - 28 = 35$

$= 4 \times \pi^2 \times 35 \times 28$

$= 4 \times \frac{(22)^2}{(7)^2} \times \overset{5}{\cancel{35}} \times \overset{4}{\cancel{28}}$

$= 4 \times 22 \times 22 \times 4 \times 5$

$= 38720\ cm^2$

39. $\text{SA} = 3\pi R^2 + \pi r^2$

$r = 5$ m,

$R = 6.12$ m

$\text{SA} = 2\pi r^2$

$\text{SA} = 2 \times 3.14 \times 25$

$= 157\ m^2$

40. $2\pi r^2 = 77$

$r = \frac{77}{\frac{2 \times 22}{7}} = \frac{\overset{7}{\cancel{77}} \times 7}{\underset{4}{\cancel{44}}}$

$= \sqrt{\frac{49}{4}} = \frac{7}{2}$

$2\pi R^2 = 308$

$R = \sqrt{\frac{308 \times 7}{2 \times 22}}$

$= \sqrt{49} = 7$

Thickness $= R - r = 7 - 3.5 = 3.5$ cm

41.

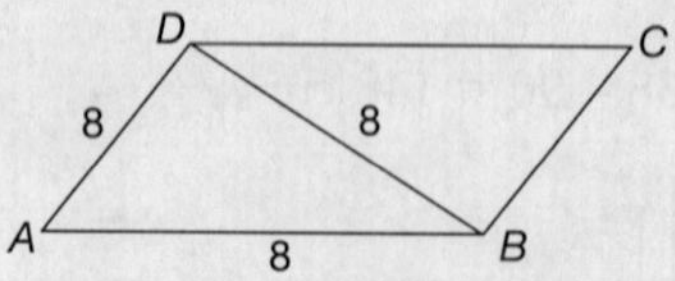

Area of the parallelogram $= 8 \times 4\sqrt{3} = 32\sqrt{3}\ cm^2$

Clearly, $AB = CD = AD = BC$ ($\because$ opposite sides of a parallelogram are equal)

Since $AD = AB$ the given parallelogram is a rhombus.

Area of the rhombus $= \frac{1}{2} d_1 d_2 = 32\sqrt{3}\ cm^2$

$d_2 = \frac{32\sqrt{3} \times 2}{8}$

$d_2 = 8\sqrt{3}$ cm.

42.

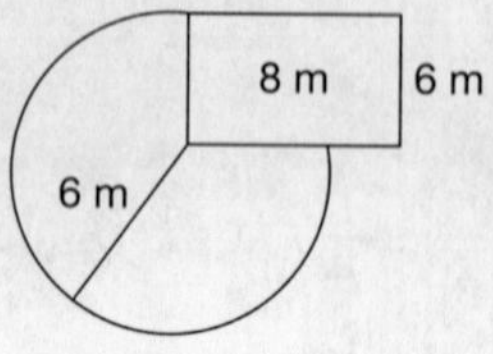

$\therefore$ Area of the field that the can graze $= \frac{270°}{360°} \times p \times (6)^2$

$= 3/4 \times 36\pi$

$= 27\pi = 27 \times \frac{22}{7} = \frac{594}{7}$ sq m.

Competition Wing

Level 1: Apply Your Concepts

1. The diagonal of a square is 10 cm.

$$\text{Area} = \frac{(\text{diagonal})^2}{2}$$

$$= \frac{(10)^2}{2} = \frac{100}{2} = 50 \text{ cm}^2$$

2. If the circumference of a circle is numerically equal to its area,

Circumference = $2\pi r$

radius = πr^2

$2\pi r = \pi r^2$

$2 = r$

$\therefore$ Radius = 2 units

3. A solid object has 8 vertices and 12 edges it has 6 faces

4. 6

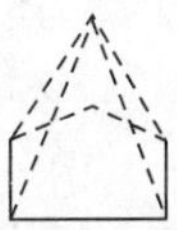

5. Use Pythagoras theorem.

6.

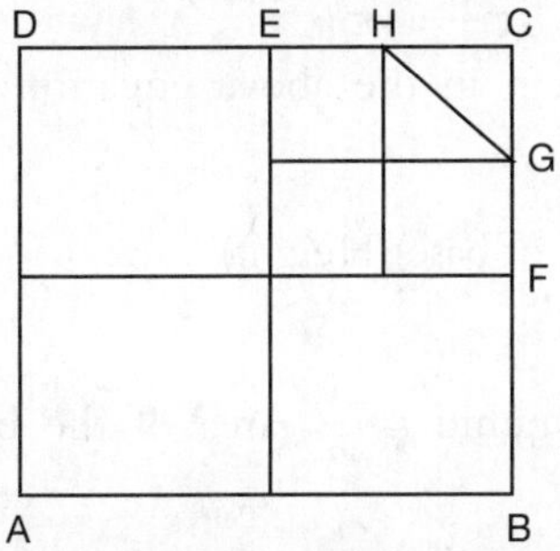

Given : ABCD is a rectangle DE = EC, CF = FB, EH = HC and CG = GF

$$HC = \frac{DC}{4} \text{ and } CG = .\frac{CB}{4}$$

$$\therefore \text{Area of } \Delta\, HCG\ \frac{1}{2}\ (HC)\ (CG)= \frac{1}{2}\left(\frac{DC}{4}\right)\left(\frac{BC}{4}\right)$$

$$= \frac{1}{32}\ (DC)(BC)$$

$$= \frac{1}{32} \times 96 = 3 \text{ cm}^2.$$

7.

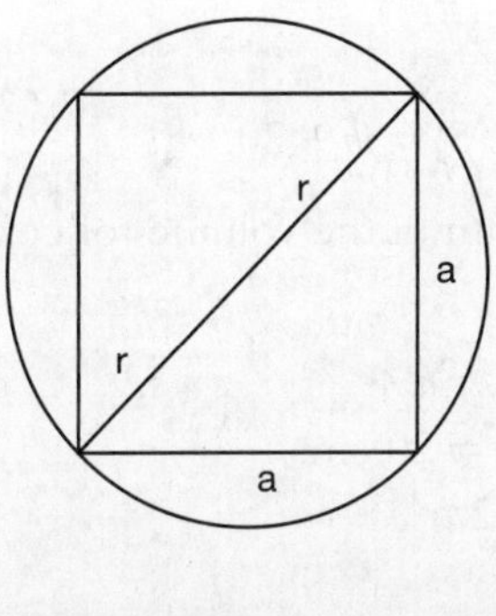

Let 'r' be the radius of the sphere and 'a' be the edge of the cube.

Here, the diameter of the sphere = The diagonal of the cube.

i.e, $2r = \sqrt{3}\ a \Rightarrow a = \dfrac{2r}{\sqrt{3}}$ r

$$\text{Required ratio} = 4\,\pi\, r^2 : 6\left(\frac{2r}{\sqrt{3}}\right)^2 = 4\,\pi\, r^2 : 6 \times \frac{4}{3}\ r^2$$

$= \pi : 2$

8.

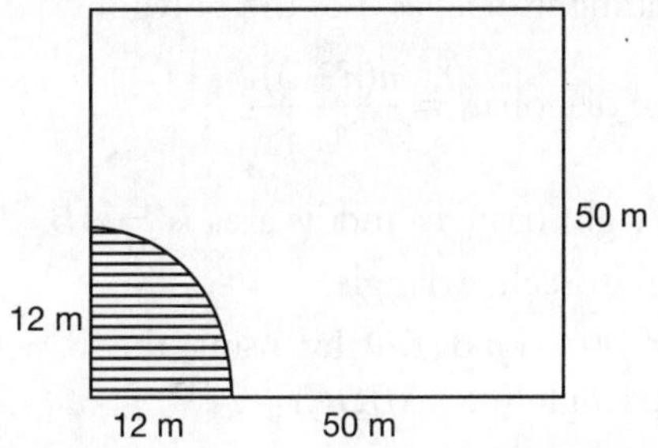

$$\text{Required area} = \frac{90°}{360°} \times \pi \times 12^2 = \frac{1}{4} \times \pi \times 144 = 36\,\pi$$

9. Let 'a' be the edge of the regular tetrahedron.

Given: a = $4\sqrt{3}$ cm

$$\text{Slant height of the tetrahedron} = \frac{\sqrt{3}}{2}\ a = \frac{\sqrt{3}}{2} \times 4\sqrt{3}$$

= 6 cm

10. Use the formula to find volume of the cone.

11. Find the side of the square.

12. Find height of the cone.

13. Find $\dfrac{r_1}{r_2}$.

14. Find r by using the formula of volume of a sphere.

15. Use Euler's formula.

16. Volume of the cylinder = Volume of 15 spheres.

17. Percentage increase in volume =

$$\frac{\text{Increase in volume}}{\text{Original volume}} \times 100.$$

18. Volume of hollow sphere $= \dfrac{4}{3}\pi(R^3 - r^3)$.

19. CSA of hollow hemisphere $= 2\pi(R^2 + r^2)$.

20. Volume of tetrahedron $= \frac{1}{3}$ (Area of base) × Height, where height of the tetrahedron $= \sqrt{\frac{2}{3}} \times$ Length of the edge.

21. TSA of the octahedron = 8 × Area of each face.

22. The number of the side of the base = The number of lateral edges.

23. Volume of the sphere = Volume of the cylinder.

24. (i) Find the number of sides n of the polygon.
(ii) Number of diagonals $= \frac{n(n-3)}{2}$.

25. (i) ABD is a right triangle and its area is $\frac{1}{2} AB \cdot BD$.
(ii) BCD is an isosceles triangle.
(iii) $\angle ABD = 90°$. Find BD by using the basics of isosceles triangle (i.e., ΔBDC).

26. (i) $l = \frac{2A}{r}$.
(ii) Use the formula, $A = \frac{(lr)}{2}$.

27. (i) Edge of the cube = Diameter of the sphere.
(ii) Radius of sphere is 3.5 cm, edge of the cube is 2(3.5 cm), i.e., 7 cm.
(iii) Difference between their surface areas $= 4\pi r^2 - 6s^2$.

28. (i) Height of regular octahedron = 2(Height of regular tetrahedron).
(ii) Height of the octahedron $(h) = \sqrt{2}\,a$.

29. Number of bottles $= \frac{\text{Volume of container}}{\text{Volume of each bottle}}$.

Level 2: Review Your Concepts

30. (i) Radius of the circle is one-third of the median of the triangle.
(ii) Inradius is 2 cm.
(iii) Height of the equilateral triangle = 3(2 cm) = 6 cm.
(iv) Area of an equilateral triangle $= \frac{h^2}{\sqrt{3}}$.

31. (i) Circum-radius is half of the hypotenuse. Use Pythagoras's theorem.
(ii) Circum-radius is 10 cm, so hypotenuse is 2(10 cm).
(iii) Use Pythagoras's theorem and get the length of the other perpendicular side and find the area.

32. (i) Given parallelogram is a rhombus.
(ii) As adjacent sides are equal, parallelogram becomes rhombus.
(iii) Sum of the squares of diagonals is equal to four times the square of the side.

33. (i) Find the number of students.
(ii) Number of students $= \frac{\text{Area of the floor}}{0.5}$.
(iii) The amount of air each student would get $= \frac{\text{Volume of the room}}{\text{Number of students}}$.

34. (i) Volume of prism = (Area of the base)(Height).
(ii) Area of equilateral triangle $= \frac{\sqrt{3}a^2}{4}$.
(iii) 1 dm = 10 cm.

35. (i) Edge (a) of small cube is to be found by using $6a^2 = 54$.
(ii) Number of small cubes $= \frac{\text{Volume of the big cube}}{\text{Volume of each small cube}}$.

36. (i) Use relevant formula.
(ii) Given condition is $8\pi r^2 = 4\pi rh$.
(iii) Substitute $h = 8$ cm in the above equation and solve for r.

37. (i) Volume $= \frac{1}{3}$ (Area of base)(Height).
(ii) Area of square $= s^2$.
(iii) Volume of the pyramid $= \frac{1}{3}$ (Area of the base) (height).

38. (i) Base radius, vertical height, and slant height form a right triangle with angles 30°, 60°, and 90°.
(ii) Base radius (14 cm) is opposite to 30°.
(iii) Cost of canvas = LSA × Cost/m^2.

39. (i) Draw the figure and proceed.
(ii) The required area is equal to the sum of the areas of a sector of an angle 270° and radius 21 m, a sector of an angle 90° and radius 7 m and a sector of an angle 90° and radius 14 m.
(iii) Area of sector $= \frac{\theta}{360°}(\pi r^2)$.

40. $l(b + 5) = lb + 25$ and $b(l + 5) = lb + 20$.

41. Required volume is the sum of the volumes of conical part and cylindrical part.

42. (i) Volume of torus $= 27\pi r^2 a$.
(ii) Given, $r = 7$ cm and $a = 20$ cm.
(iii) Volume of the tyre $= 2\pi r^2 a$.

43. (i) Height of the regular tetrahedron, $h = \sqrt{\frac{2}{3}}s$.

(ii) Square the above equation and get s^2.

44. (i) Volume of frustum $= \frac{1}{3}\pi h(R^2 + r^2 + Rr)$.

(ii) Volume of cone frustum $= \frac{\pi h}{3}(R^2 + Rr + r^2)$.

45. CADB is the required sequential order.

46. Let $ABCD$ be a rhombus.

Let CE be the height of the rhombus.

Given $AC = 10$ cm and $BD = 24$ cm.

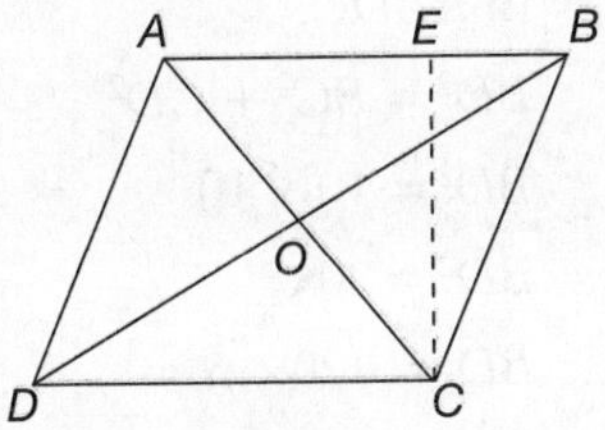

$BC = \sqrt{OC^2 + OB^2} = \sqrt{5^2 + 12^2} = 13$ cm.

47. Let the sides of the triangle (in cm) be a, b, and c, where $a < b < c$.

$\therefore$ c is the hypotenuse and a and b are the perpendicular sides.

Given, $a + b + c = 12$ (1)

$\frac{1}{2}(a)(b) = 6$ (2)

From Eq. (1) $\Rightarrow a + b = 12 - c$

Squaring both sides,

$a^2 + b^2 + 2ab = 12^2 - 24c + c^2$

$= a^2 + b^2 + 4\left(\frac{1}{2}ab\right) = 12^2 - 24c + c^2$

$\Rightarrow c^2 + 4(6) = 12^2 - 24c + c^2$

$c = 5$.

48. Diameter of the cylinder = 7 cm.

$\therefore$ Radius of the cylinder = 3.5 cm.

Height of the cylinder = 7 cm.

Volume of cube $= 7^3 = 343$ cm^3.

Volume of the cylinder $\Rightarrow \pi r^2 h = \frac{22}{7} \times 3.5 \times 3.5 \times 7$

$= 269.5\,\text{cm}^3$

$\therefore$ The required volume $= 343 - 269.5 = 73.5$ cm^3.

49. Given that, $n \times \frac{2}{3}\pi(2)^3 = \frac{4}{3}\pi(4)^3 \Rightarrow n = 16$.

50. Let the edges of the cubes be $3x$, $4x$, and $5x$, respectively.

Volume of the cube formed = Sum of the volumes of the small cubes $= (3x)^3 + (4x)^3 + (5x)^3 = 216x^3$.

$\therefore$ Edges of the cube formed $= 6x$.

Diagonal of the cube formed $= \sqrt{3}(6x) \Rightarrow 6\sqrt{3}x = 18 \Rightarrow x = \sqrt{3}$.

$\therefore$ TSA of smallest cube $= 6a^2 = 6(3\sqrt{3})^2$

$= 162$ cm^2.

51. Given that, $x \times \frac{4}{3}\pi(2)^3 = \frac{2}{3}\pi(8)^3 \Rightarrow x = 32$.

Level 3: Assess Your Concepts

56. Let the sides of the triangle be a, b, and l.

Given, $\frac{a+b}{2} = 6 + \frac{c}{2}, \frac{a+c}{2} = 6 + \frac{b}{2}$ and $\frac{b+c}{2}$

$= 6 + \frac{a}{2}$.

$\Rightarrow a + b = 12 + c$ (1)

$b + c = 12 + a$ (2)

$c + a = 12 + b$ (3)

By solving, we get:

$a = b = c = 12$

$\Rightarrow$ Area of $\Delta ABC = \frac{\sqrt{3}}{2} \times 12^2$

$= 36\sqrt{3}$ sq. cm.

57.

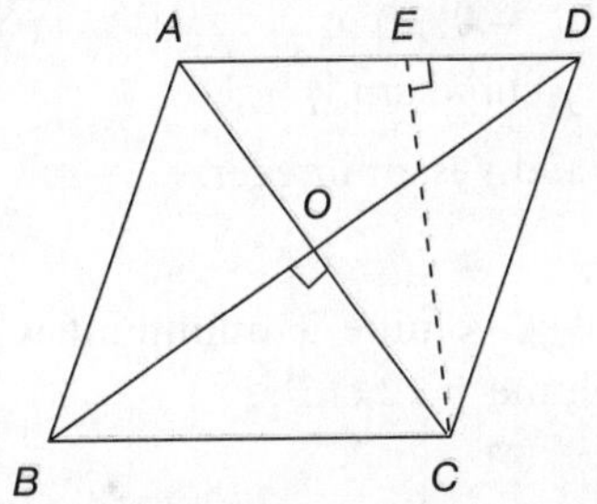

In ΔBOC, $BO^2 + OC^2 = BC^2$

$\Rightarrow 6^2 + (4.5)^2 = BC^2 \Rightarrow BC = 7.5$ cm.

Let CE be the required distance.

Area of rhombus $= \frac{12 \times 9}{2} = 54$ sq. cm

$\Rightarrow \frac{CE}{2}(AB + CD) = 54$ (Area of parallelogram)

$\Rightarrow CE = \frac{108}{15} = 7.2$ cm.

58. Let the sides of the triangle be a cam, b cm, and c cm.

$a + b - c = a + c - b = b + c - a = 6$

$\Rightarrow a + b - c + a + c - b + b + c - a = 18$

$a + b + c = 18$.

Area of the triangle =

$$\sqrt{\left(\frac{a+b+c}{2}\right)\left(\frac{a+b+c}{2}-a\right)\left(\frac{a+b+c}{2}-b\right)\left(\frac{a+b+c}{2}-c\right)}$$

$$=\sqrt{\left(\frac{a+b+c}{2}\right)\left(\frac{b+c-a}{2}\right)\left(\frac{a+c-b}{2}\right)\left(\frac{a+b-c}{2}\right)}$$

$$=\frac{1}{4}\sqrt{(18)(6)(6)(6)} = 9\sqrt{3}\text{ cm}^2.$$

59. 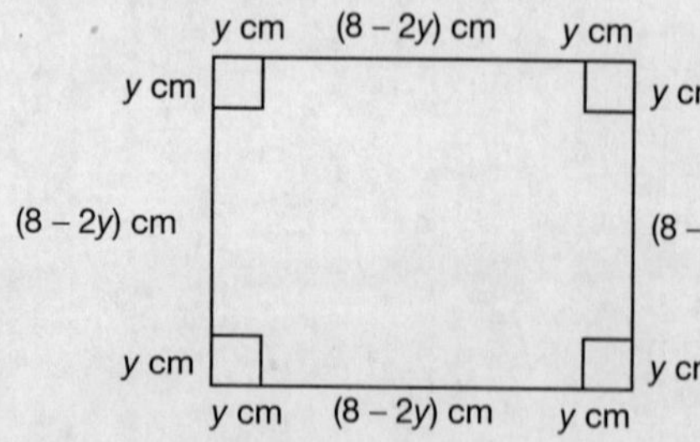

Length = Breadth = $(8 - 2y)$ cm and height = y cm.

Its volume = $(8 - 2y)(8 - 2y)y$

$= (8 - 2y)^2\, y$ cubic cm.

$8 - 2y > 0$, i.e., $y < 4$ and y is an integer.

$\therefore\ y = 1$ or 2 or 3.

Among these values of y, volume is minimum when $y = 3$. When $y = 3$, volume = 12 cm^3.

$\therefore\ M = 12.$

60. Given, $BC = \sqrt{10}$ cm

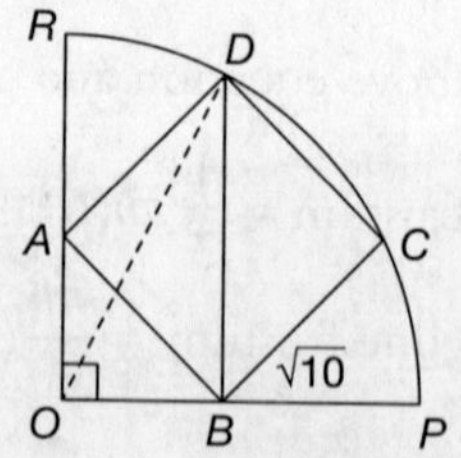

In ΔBDC,

$BD^2 = BC^2 + CD^2$

$BD^2 = 10 + 10$

$BD^2 = 20$

$BD = \sqrt{20}$ cm

In ΔOAB, $OB^2 + OA^2 = AB^2$

$2(OB^2) = 10\ (\because OB = OA)$

$OB^2 = 5$

$OB = \sqrt{5}$ cm.

In ΔOBD,

$OD^2 = OB^2 + BD^2$

$OD^2 = 5 + 20$

$OD = \sqrt{25}$

$OD = 5$ cm

$\therefore$ Required radius is 5 cm.

JEE Special Wing

Multiple-Answer Type Questions

1. Given that the sides of a rectangle are integers in cm. Let the length and breadth of the rectangle be l and b. Also, given that the area of the rectangle is 20 sq cm.
$\Rightarrow l \times b = 200$, where l and b are integers.

$l \times b$	$l + b$	$2(l + b)$
200×1	201	402
100×2	102	204
50×4	54	108
25×8	33	66
20×10	30	60

So, the perimeter $\left[2(l+b)\right]$ of the rectangle can be 402 cm, 204 cm, 108 cm, 66 cm or 60 cm.
Hence, choice (a), choice (b) and choice (d) are follows.

2. Given that the base radius and height of a cylinder are integers in cm.
Let the base radius and height of a cylinder be r and h respectively.
Also, given that the volume of the cylinder are 1078 sq cm.
$\Rightarrow \pi r^2 h = 1078$, where r and h are integers.

$$\Rightarrow \frac{22}{7} r^2 h = 1078$$

$$\Rightarrow r^2 h = 1078 \times \frac{7}{22}$$

$$\Rightarrow r^2 h = 7^2 \times 7 = 1^2 \times 343$$

$$\Rightarrow r = 7 \text{ cm or } r = 1 \text{ cm.}$$

Hence, choice (a) and choice (c) are follows.

3. 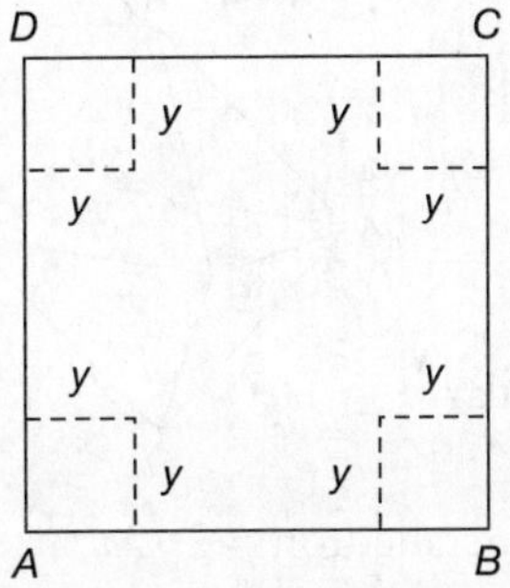

Given that $ABCD$ is a square sheet of side x cm.
A square of side y cm is cut from each corner of the sheet.
The remaining sheet is folded into a cuboid.

Length of the cuboid $= (x - 2y)$ cm
Breadth of the cuboid $= (x - 2y)$ cm
Height of the cuboid $= y$ cm.
Volume of the cuboid = 100 cubic cm (Given)

$$\Rightarrow (x-2y)(x-2y)y = 100$$

$\Rightarrow (x-2y)^2 y = 100$, where x and y are positive integers.

$$\Rightarrow (x-2y)^2 y = (10)^2 1 = (12-2)^2 1$$

$$\Rightarrow x + y = 12 + 1 = 13$$

$$\Rightarrow (x-2y)^2 y = (5)^2 4 = (13-8)^2 4$$

$$\Rightarrow x + y = 13 + 4 = 17$$

$$\Rightarrow (x-2y)^2 y = (2)^2 25 = (52-50)^2 25$$

$$\Rightarrow x + y = 52 + 25 = 77$$

$$\Rightarrow (x-2y)^2 y = (1)^2 100 = (201-200)^2 100$$

$$\Rightarrow x + y = 201 + 100 = 301$$

Hence, choice (a), choice (b), choice (c) and choice (d) are follows.

4. Given that a largest possible cone is inserted in a cylindrical vessel of base radius 21 cm and height 28 cm.

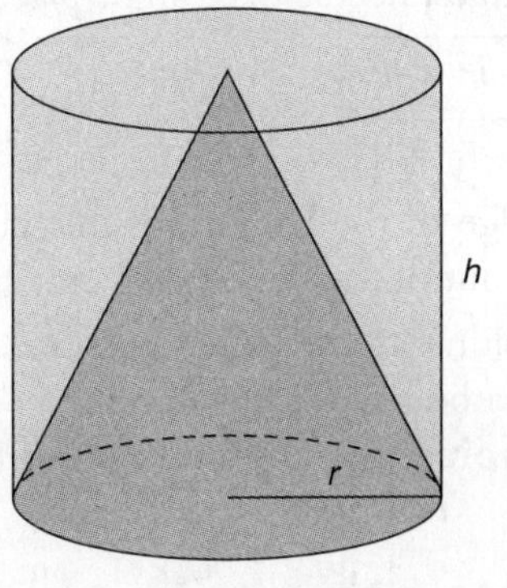

Base radius of the cone = base radius of the cylinder (r) = 21 cm.
Height of the cone = height of the cylinder (h) = 28 cm.

(a) Slant height of the cone $(l) = \sqrt{r^2 + h^2}$.

$$= \sqrt{(21)^2 + (28)^2}$$

$$= \sqrt{(7)^2\left[(3)^2 + (4)^2\right]}$$

$$= \sqrt{(7)^2 (5)^2} = 35 \text{ cm.}$$

(b) CSA of the cone $= \pi r l$

$$= \frac{22}{7} \times 21 \times 35 = 2310 \text{ sq cm.}$$

(c) TSA of the cone = CSA + Base area

$= 2310 + \pi r^2$

$= 2310 + \frac{22}{7}\times(21)^2$

$= 3696$ sq cm.

(d) Volume of the cone $= \frac{1}{3}\pi r^2 h$

$= \frac{1}{3}\times\frac{22}{7}\times(21)^2\times 28 = 12936$ cu cm.

Hence, choice (a), choice (b) and choice (c) are follows.

5. Let the dimensions of the cuboid be l, b and h.

The areas of three mutually adjacent faces of the cuboid are lb, bh and lh.

Given that the three mutually adjacent faces of the cuboid are 30 sq cm, 20 sq cm and 24 sq cm.

(a) TSA of the cuboid $= 2(lb + bh + lh)$

$= 2(30 + 20 + 24) = 148$ sq cm.

(b) Now, $lb \times bh \times lh = 30 \times 20 \times 24$

$lb \times bh \times lh = 6\times5\times5\times4\times4\times6$

$l^2 \times b^2 \times h^2 = 6^2 \times 5^2 \times 4^2$

$(lbh)^2 = (6\times5\times4)^2$

$lbh = 6\times5\times4 = 120$ cu cm.

(c) The longest needle that can be placed in the cuboid

$= \sqrt{l^2+b^2+h^2}$

$= \sqrt{6^2+5^2+4^2} = \sqrt{77}$ cm.

(d) The edge of the largest possible cube that can be carved out of the cuboid is 4 cm.

The volume of the largest possible cube carved out of the cuboid $= 4^3 = 64$ cu cm.

Hence, choice (a), choice (b) and choice (d) are follows.

Match The Column

Common Solutions for questions 6 to 10:

ABCDEFGH is a cuboidal cylinder.

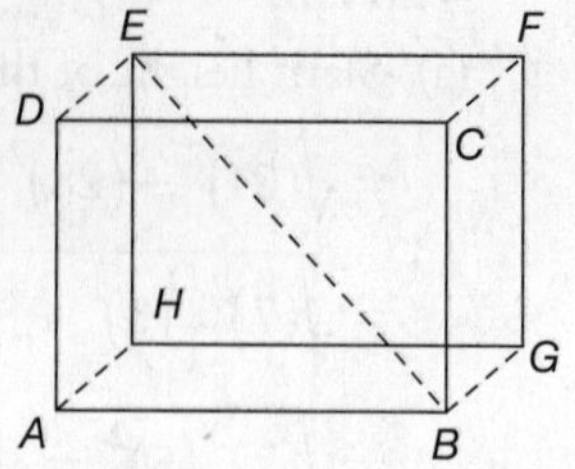

ABGH is a face of the cylinder which is fixed on a surface of the car.

$AB = 12$ cm = Length of the cuboid (l)

$BC = 4$ cm = Height of the cuboid (h)

$CF = 3$ cm = Breadth of the cuboid (b)

6. The body diagonal $= \sqrt{l^2+b^2+h^2}$

$= \sqrt{(12)^2+3^2+4^2}$

$= \sqrt{144+9+16}$

$= \sqrt{169} = 13$ cm.

Hence, the correct option is (e).

7. The shortest face diagonal $= \sqrt{b^2+h^2}$

$= \sqrt{3^2+4^2}$

$= \sqrt{9+16}$

$= \sqrt{25} = 5$ cm.

Hence, the correct option is (b).

8. The areas of three distinct faces are lb, bh, and lh

That is: 12×4, 12×3 and 4×3

That is: 48 sq cm, 36 sq cm, and 12 sq cm.

The area of one of the faces is 12 sq cm.

Hence, the correct option is (d).

9. The LSA of the cuboid $= 2h(l+b)$

$= 2\times4(12+3) = 120$ sq cm.

The cost of painting outside the side walls at \$1 for 8 sq cm $= \frac{120}{8}\times\$1 = \$15$.

Hence, the correct option is (f).

10. The volume the cuboid $= lbh$

$= 12\times3\times4 = 144$ cu cm.

The cost of filling the gas in the cylinder at \$1 for 18 cu cm $= \frac{144}{18}\times\$1 = \$8$.

Hence, the correct option is (c).

Comprehension-Based Questions

Common Solutions for questions 11 to 15:

We know that all the edges of a regular octahedron are equal.

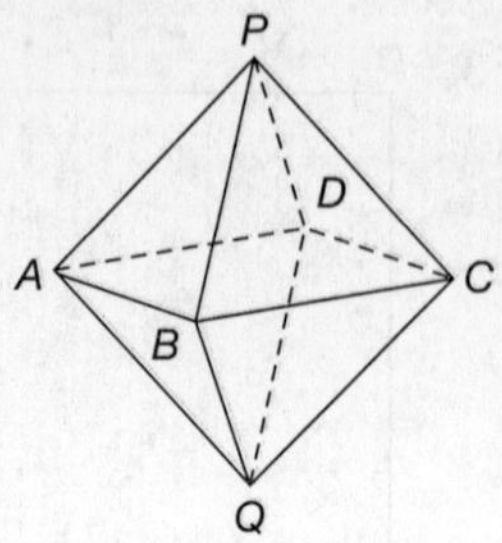

The measure of each edge (a) = 9 cm.

We know that:

The length of the regular octahedron $= \sqrt{2}a$.

The surface area of a regular octahedron $= 2\sqrt{3}a^2$

The volume of a regular octahedron $= \frac{\sqrt{2}}{3}a^3$

11. The length of the regular octahedron (PQ) $= \sqrt{2}a$

$= 9\sqrt{2}$ cm.

Hence, the correct option is (a).

12. The total surface area of the regular octahedron
$= 2\sqrt{3}(9)^2$
$= 162\sqrt{3}$ sq cm.
Hence, the correct option is (b).

13. The volume of the regular octahedron $= \dfrac{\sqrt{2}}{3}a^3$
$= \dfrac{\sqrt{2}}{3} \times 9^3 = 243\sqrt{2}$ cu cm.
Hence, the correct option is (b).

14. Let A be the edge of each regular tetrahedron, where $A = 3\sqrt{3}$ cm.
$x = \dfrac{\text{The volume of the regular octahedron}}{\text{The volume of the regular tetrahedron}}$
$= \dfrac{\frac{\sqrt{2}}{3}a^3}{\frac{A^3}{6\sqrt{2}}}$
$= \dfrac{\sqrt{2}}{3}a^3 \times \dfrac{6\sqrt{2}}{A^3}$
$= 243\sqrt{2} \times \dfrac{6\sqrt{2}}{3\times3\times3} = 108.$
Hence, the correct option is (d).

15. As shown in the figure the required cross section is in the shape of a rhombus.
Here, $PQ = 9\sqrt{2}$ cm.
MN = Edge of the octahedron
= 9 cm.
The area of the cross section
$= \dfrac{PQ \times MN}{2}$
$= \dfrac{9\sqrt{2}\times 9}{2} = 40.5\sqrt{2}$ sq cm.

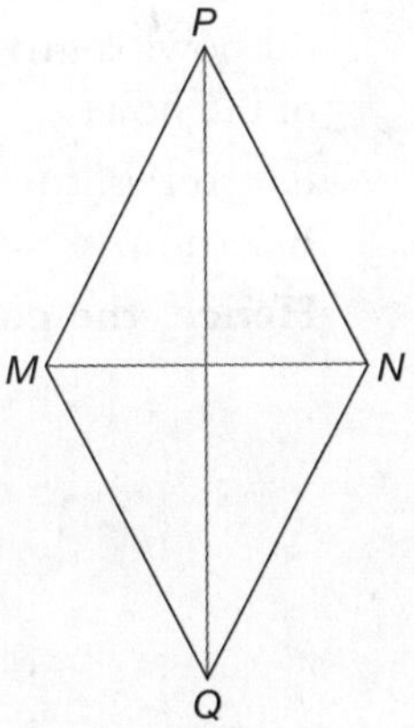

Hence, the correct option is (c).

Common Solutions for questions 16 to 20:

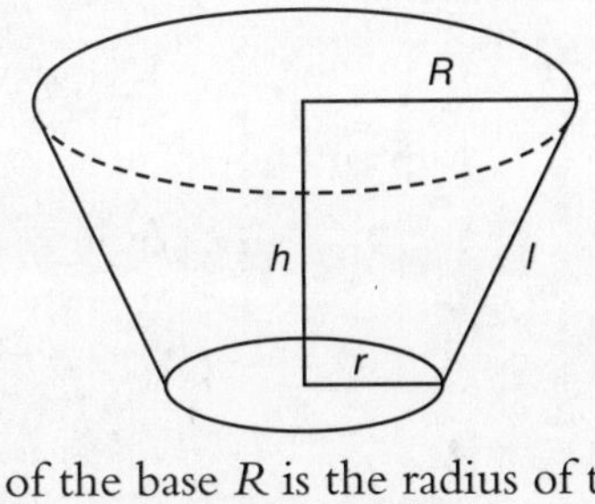

r is the radius of the base R is the radius of the top.
l is the slant height of the bucket.
h is the height of the bucket.
Also, R, r, and l are three consecutive integers.
The curved surface area of the bucket is 110 sq cm.
$\Rightarrow \pi(r+R)l = 110$
$\Rightarrow \dfrac{22}{7}\times(r+R)l = 110$
$\Rightarrow (r+R)l = 7\times5$
$\Rightarrow (r+R)l = (3+4)\times5$
$\Rightarrow r = 3, R = 4$ and $l = 5$ (in cm)

16. We have $l^2 = (R-r)^2 + h^2$
$\Rightarrow 5^2 = (4-3)^2 + h^2$
$\Rightarrow h^2 = 24$
$\Rightarrow h = 2\sqrt{6}$ cm.
Hence, the correct option is (c).

17. The required area of the sheet to make the bucket with lid = CSA + Area of the base + Area of the lid
$= 110 + \pi r^2 + \pi R^2$
$= 110 + \pi(r^2 + R^2)$
$= 110 + 3.14(3^2 + 4^2)$
$= 110 + 3.14(25)$
$= 188.5$ sq cm.
Hence, the correct option is (d).

18. The quantity of water that the bucket can hold
$= \pi(r^2 + R^2 + Rr)h$
$= 3.14(3^2 + 4^2 + 3\times4)2\sqrt{6}$
$= 3.14(9+16+12)2\times2.45$
$= 3.14\times37\times4.9$
$= 569.282 \sim 569.28$ cu cm $= 569.28$ ml.
Hence, the correct option is (a).

19. The weight of the metal used $= 188.5 \times 5.31$ grams
$= 1000.935$ grams ~ 1 kg.
Hence, the correct option is (b).

20. The cost of painting $= 188.5 \times \dfrac{₹5}{10}$
$= ₹94.25$
Hence, the correct option is (b).

Assertion and Reason Type Questions

21. **Assertion:** Given that $R + r = 7$ cm and $R - r = 1$ cm. The area of the bigger circle which is not a part of the smaller circle is the area of the ring $= \pi(R^2 - r^2)$
$= \pi(R+r)(R-r)$

$= \frac{22}{7}(4+3)(4-3) = 22$ cm.

So, Assertion is true.

Reason: The area of a circular ring is given by $\pi(R^2 - r^2)$.

Reason is true and is the correct explanation to Assertion.

Hence, the correct option is (a).

22. **Assertion:** Given that the area of a triangle = 6 sq cm.
The perimeter of the triangle = 12 cm.
The inradius of a triangle

$$= \frac{\text{Area of the triangle}}{\text{Semi} - \text{perimeter of the triangle}}$$

$$= \frac{6}{\frac{12}{2}} \text{ is 1 cm.}$$

So, Assertion is false.

Reason: The product of the inradius and the semi-perimeter of a triangle is area of the triangle.

Reason is true.

Hence, the correct option is (d).

23. **Assertion:** The area of a regular hexagon of side $x = \frac{3\sqrt{3}a^2}{2}$

$$= 6\left(\frac{\sqrt{3}a^2}{4}\right)$$

= 6(the area of an equilateral triangle of side x cm)
Also, 1296 sq cm = 6(216) sq cm.

So, Assertion is true.

Reason: The diagonals joining exactly opposite vertices of a regular polygon divide it in to six equilateral triangles.

Reason is true and is the correct explanation to Assertion.

Hence, the correct option is (a).

24. **Assertion:** Given that the surface area (in sq cm)If the surface area (in sq cm) and the volume (in cu cm) of a torus are numerically equal.

$\Rightarrow 4\pi^2 ra = 2\pi^2 r^2 a$

$\Rightarrow r = 2$

So, Assertion is true.

Reason: The surface area (in sq cm) and the volume (in cu cm) of a torus are $4\pi^2 ra$ and $2\pi^2 r^2 a$.

So, Reason is false.

Hence, the correct option is (c).

25. **Assertion:** If r is the inner radius of a hemispherical bowl, the capacity of the bowl $= \frac{2}{3}\pi r^3$

$= \frac{2}{3}\pi(3)^3 = 18\pi$ cu cm.

So, Assertion is true.

Reason: The inner curved surface area a hemispherical bowl is given by $2\pi r^2$, where r is the inner radius of the bowl.

Reason is true but not the correct explanation to Assertion.

Hence, the correct option is (b).

CHAPTER

11

Coordinate Geometry

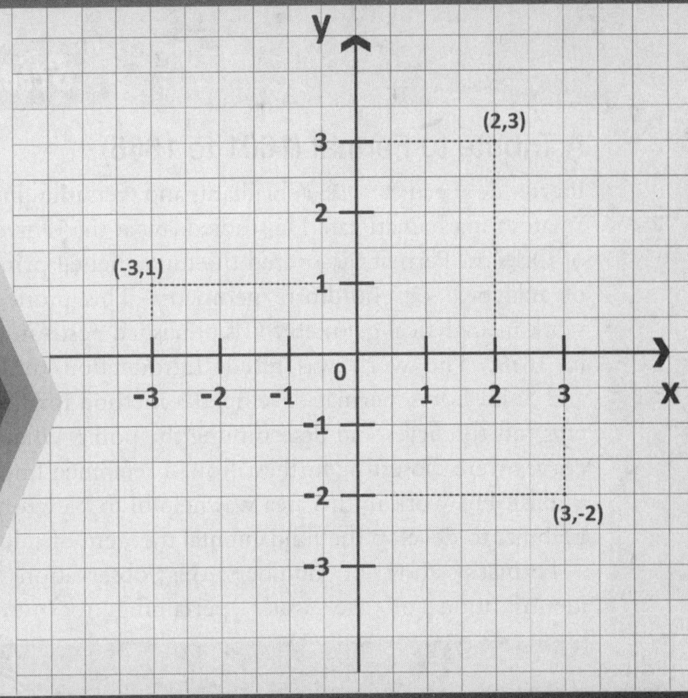

Remember

Before beginning this chapter, you should be able to:

- Know planes, lines and angles.
- Remember different types of triangles and polygons.

Key Ideas

After completing this chapter, you should be able to:

- Find the coordinates of a point and conversion of signs.
- Study about points on a plane and the distance between points.
- Know the applications of distance formula, mid-point of a line segment and centroid of a triangle.
- Learn about equation of some standard lines.

Scientific Crypt

A Tribute to Fermat (1601 to 1665)

Pierre de Fermat was a brilliant and versatile French amateur mathematician. He studied law at the University of Orleans. Fermat discovered the fundamental principle of analytical or coordinate geometry. This pioneering work in analytical geometry was published posthumously in 1679. The work was titled 'Introduction to Plane and Solid Loci'. Fermat developed a method for finding tangents to curves and determining the points where the curves were closest or furthest from a reference line (the x-axis). His work in this area was helpful to Newton and Leibniz, to develop the fundamental theorem of calculus.

Fermat's study of numbers, his observations and identification of the issues pertaining to numbers subsequently shaped number theory. He discovered what is now known as Fermat's Little Theorem and invented a factorization method, known after his name, He is perhaps most widely known for the theorem known as Fermat's Last Theorem. This theorem states that no three positive integers a, b and c can satisfy the equation $a^n + b^n = c^n$, for any integral value of n greater than two. This theorem remained a conjecture for nearly three hundred and fifty years until it was proved by the English mathematician Andrew Wiles, who built on the work of several 20th century mathematicians to complete the proof.

FUN TIME

CROSSWORD

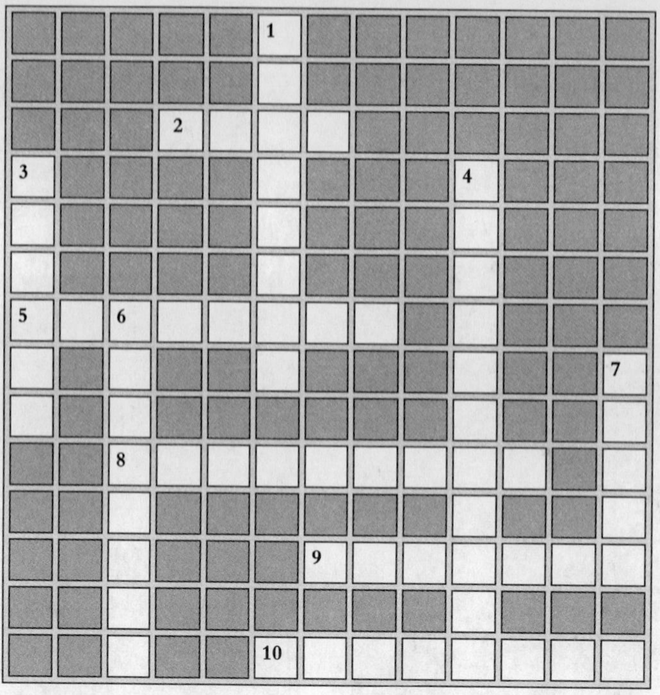

Across

2. The slope of any horizontal line.
5. It is the form of an equation which passes through the origin.
8. (2, 2000), (3, 3000), (4, 4000)
9. This line is neither parallel to the x-axis nor parallel to the y-axis.
10. y-coordinate

Down

1. The slopes of these lines are equal.
3. The intersection of the coordinate axes.
4. The angle made by a straight line with a positive direction of the x-axis.
6. x-coordinate
7. It is the tangent value of the inclination of a line.

INTRODUCTION

Let $X'OX$ and YOY' be two mutually perpendicular lines intersecting at point O in a plane. These two lines are called reference lines or coordinate axes. The horizontal reference line $X'OX$ is called X-axis and the vertical reference line YOY' is called Y-axis. The point of intersection of these two axes, i.e., O is called the origin. The plane containing the coordinate axes is called coordinate plane or XY-plane.

Coordinates of a Point

Let P be a point in the XY-plane. Draw perpendiculars PL and PM to X-axis and Y-axis, respectively (see Fig. 11.1).

Let $PL = y$ and $PM = x$. The point P is taken as (x, y). Here, x and y are called the rectangular Cartesian coordinates or coordinates of the point P. x is called x-coordinate or abscissa and y is called y-coordinate or ordinate of the point P.

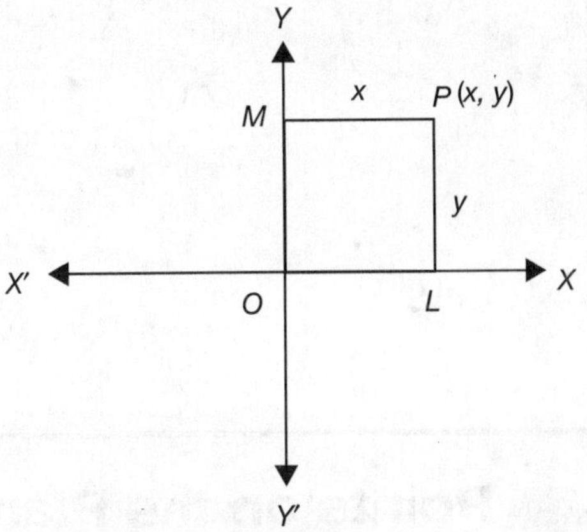

Figure 11.1

Convention of Signs

1. Towards the right side of the Y-axis, x-coordinate of any point on the graph paper is taken positive and towards the left side of the Y-axis, x-coordinate is taken negative.
2. Above the X-axis, the y-coordinate of any point on the graph paper is taken positive and below the X-axis, y-coordinate is taken negative.

If (x, y) is a point in the plane and Q_1, Q_2, Q_3, and Q_4 are the four quadrants of rectangular coordinate system, then:

1. If $x > 0$ and $y > 0$, then $(x, y) \in Q_1$.
2. If $x < 0$ and $y > 0$, then $(x, y) \in Q_2$.
3. If $x < 0$ and $y < 0$, then $(x, y) \in Q_3$.
4. If $x > 0$ and $y < 0$, then $(x, y) \in Q_4$.

EXAMPLE 11.1 If the point $(-x, -y) \in Q2$, then $(-x, y)$ belongs to ______.

(a) Q1 (b) Q2 (c) Q3 (d) Q4

SOLUTION

Given $(-x, -y) \in Q2$

$\Rightarrow x > 0, y < 0$

$\therefore (-x, y) \in Q3$.

EXAMPLE 11.2 The slope of the line joining the points $(-x, x)$ and $(0, x + x\sqrt{3})$ is ______.

(a) $\sqrt{3}$ (b) $\frac{1}{\sqrt{3}}$ (c) $2x$ (d) 0

SOLUTION

Given points are $(-x, x)$, $(0, x + x\sqrt{3})$

Let $(x_1, y_1) = (-x, x)$, $(x_2, y_2) = (0, x + x\sqrt{3})$

Slope $(m) = \frac{y_2 - y_1}{x_2 - x_1}$

$= \frac{x + x\sqrt{3} - x}{0 - (-x)}$

$= \frac{x\sqrt{3}}{x}$

$= \sqrt{3}$.

EXAMPLE 11.3 Plot the points $A(2, 3)$, $B(-1, 2)$, $C(-3, -2)$, and $D(4, -2)$ in the XY-plane.

SOLUTION

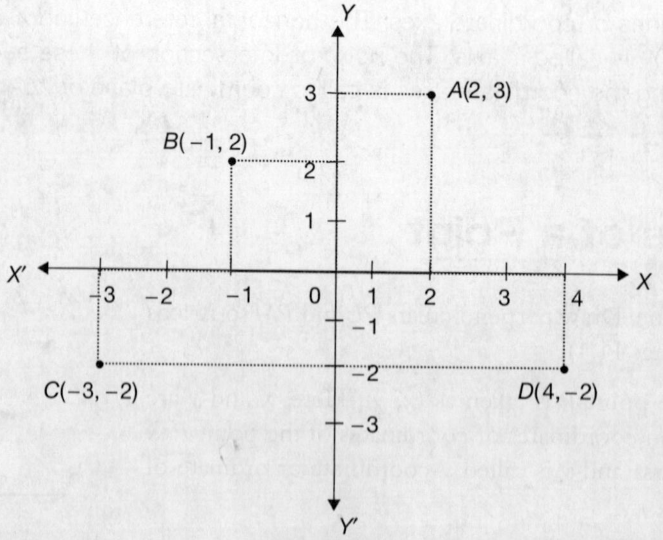

Figure 11.2

Points on the Plane

Point on X-axis and Y-axis

Let P be a point on X-axis, so that its distance from X-axis is zero. Hence, point P can be taken as $(x, 0)$.

Let P' be a point on Y-axis, so that its distance from Y-axis is zero. Hence, point P' can be taken as $(0, y)$ (see Fig. 11.3).

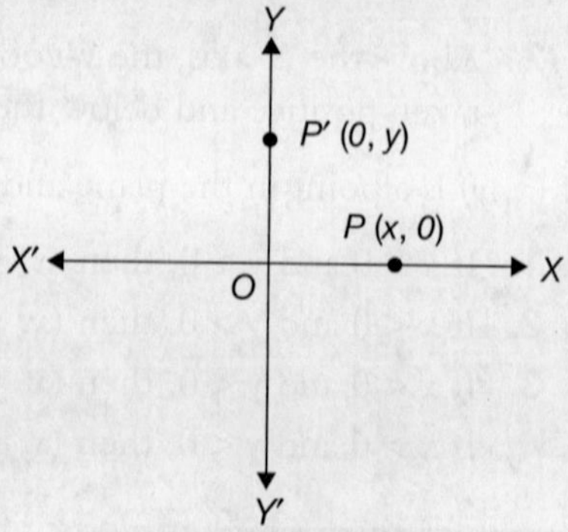

Figure 11.3

Distance Between Two Points

Consider two points $A(x_1, y_1)$ and $B(x_2, y_2)$. Draw perpendiculars AL and BM from A and B to X-axis. AN is the perpendicular drawn from A on to BM (see Fig. 11.4).

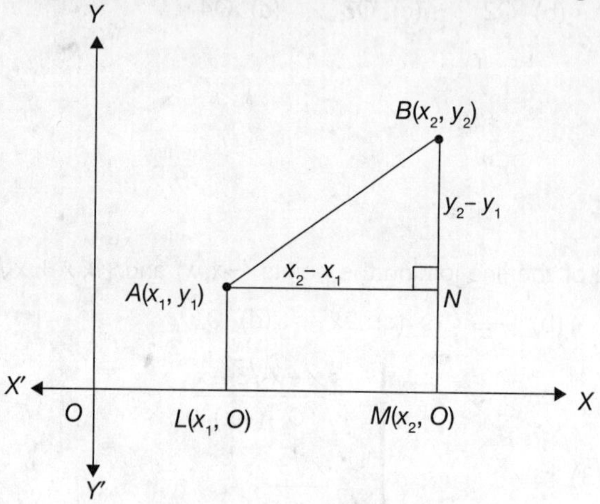

Figure 11.4

Info Bytes!

The distance of a point $A(x_1, y_1)$ from origin $O(0, 0)$ is $OA = \sqrt{x_1^2 + y_1^2}$.

From right triangle ABN, $AB = \sqrt{AN^2 + BN^2}$, (we have $AB^2 = AN^2 + BN^2$).

Here, $AN = x_2 - x_1$ and $BN = y_2 - y_1$.

$$AB = \sqrt{(x_2 - x_1)^2 + (y_2 - y_1)^2}.$$

Hence, the distance between two points $A(x_1, y_1)$ and $B(x_2, y_2)$ is:

$$AB = \sqrt{(x_2 - x_1)^2 + (y_2 - y_1)^2} \text{ units.}$$

EXAMPLE 11.4 Find the distance between points (–4, 5) and (2, –3).

SOLUTION

Let the given points be $A(-4, 5)$ and $B(2, -3)$

$AB = \sqrt{(2-(-4))^2 + (-3-5)^2}$

$= \sqrt{36+64} = 10$ units.

EXAMPLE 11.5 Find a, if the distance between points $A(8, -7)$ and $B(-4, a)$ is 13 units.

SOLUTION

Given, $AB = 13$

$\Rightarrow \sqrt{(-4-8)^2 + (a+7)^2} = 13$

Taking squares on both sides, we get,

$(a + 7)^2 = 169 - 144 = 25$

$a + 7 = \sqrt{25}$

$a + 7 = \pm 5$

$\therefore a = -2$ or -12.

EXAMPLE 11.6 Find the coordinates of a point on Y-axis which is equidistant from points (13, 2) and (12, –3).

SOLUTION

Let $P(0, y)$ be the required point and the given points be $A(12, -3)$ and $B(13, 2)$.

Then, $PA = PB$ (given)

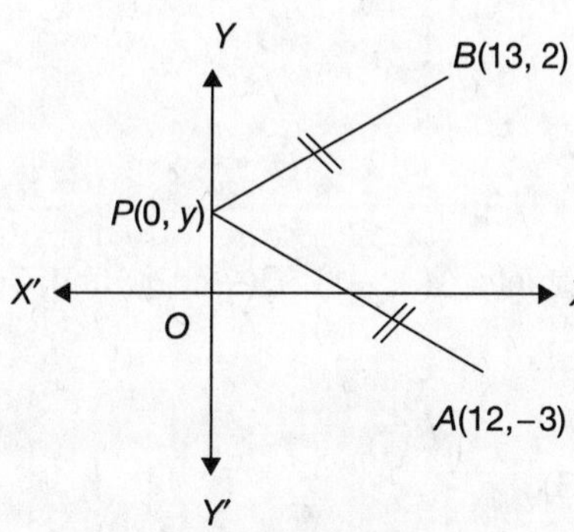

Figure 11.5

$$\sqrt{(12-0)^2+(-3-y)^2}=\sqrt{(13-0)^2+(2-y)^2}$$

$$\Rightarrow \sqrt{144+(y+3)^2}=\sqrt{169+(2-y)^2}$$

Taking squares on both sides, we get,

$169 + 4 + y^2 - 4y = 144 + 9 + y^2 + 6y$

$\Rightarrow 10y = 20 \Rightarrow y = 2$

$\therefore$ The required point on Y-axis is (0, 2).

Collinearity of Three Points

Let A, B, and C be three given points. The distances AB, BC, and CA can be calculated using distance formula. If the sum of any two of these distances is found to be equal to the third distance, then points A, B, and C are said to be collinear.

By Notes (1), (2), and (3), we can find the position of the points in collinearity.

Konnect

1. If $AB + BC = AC$, then points A, B, and C are collinear.

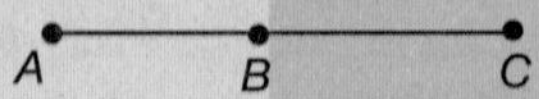

2. If $AC + CB = AB$, then points A, C, and B are collinear.

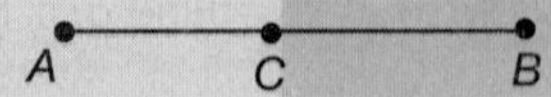

3. $BA + AC = BC$, then points B, A, and C are collinear.

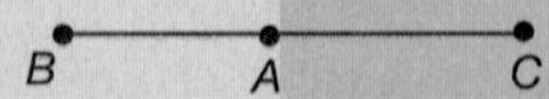

Distance Formula

Given the two points (x_1, y_1) and (x_2, y_2), the distance d between these points is given by the foumula:

$$d=\sqrt{(x_2-x_1)^2+(y_2-y_1)^2}$$

EXAMPLE 11.7 Show that points $P(5, 6)$, $Q(4, 5)$, and $R(3, 4)$ are collinear.

SOLUTION

Given, $P = (5, 6)$, $Q = (4, 5)$ and $R = (3, 4)$.

$PQ = \sqrt{(4-5)^2+(5-6)^2} = \sqrt{2}$ units.

$QR = \sqrt{(3-4)^2+(4-5)^2} = \sqrt{2}$ units.

$PR = \sqrt{(3-5)^2+(4-6)^2} = \sqrt{8} = 2\sqrt{2}$ units.

Now, $PQ + QR = \sqrt{2} + \sqrt{2} = 2\sqrt{2} = PR$.

That is, $PQ + QR = PR$.

Hence, points P, Q, and R are collinear.

EXAMPLE 11.8 Show that points $A(3, -1)$, $B(-1, 2)$, and $C(6, 3)$ form an isosceles right-angled triangle when joined.

SOLUTION

Given, $A = (3, -1)$, $B = (-1, 2)$, and $C = (6, 3)$.

$AB = \sqrt{(-1-3)^2+(2+1)^2} = 5$ units

$BC = \sqrt{(6-(-1))^2+(3-2)^2} = \sqrt{50}$ units

$AC = \sqrt{(6-3)^2 + (3-(-1))^2} = 5$ units

Clearly,

$BC^2 = AB^2 + AC^2$.

Also, $AB = AC$.

Hence, the given points form the vertices of a right-angled isosceles triangle.

EXAMPLE 11.9 Show that points $(2-\sqrt{3}, \sqrt{3}+1)$, $(1, 0)$, and $(3, 2)$ form an equilateral triangle.

SOLUTION

Let $A(2-\sqrt{3}, \sqrt{3}+1)$, $B(1, 0)$, and $C(3, 2)$ be the given points.

$AB = \sqrt{(1-2+\sqrt{3})^2 + \left(0-(\sqrt{3}+1)\right)^2}$

$= \sqrt{(\sqrt{3}-1)^2 + (-1-\sqrt{3})^2}$.

$AB = \sqrt{8}$ units.

$BC = \sqrt{(3-1)^2 + (2-0)^2} = \sqrt{8}$ units

$AC = \sqrt{\left(3-(2-\sqrt{3})\right)^2 + \left(2-(\sqrt{3}+1)\right)^2}$

$= \sqrt{(1+\sqrt{3})^2 + (1-\sqrt{3})^2} = \sqrt{8}$ units.

$\therefore AB = BC = AC = \sqrt{8}$ units.

Hence, the given points form an equilateral triangle.

EXAMPLE 11.10 Show that points $A(-1, 0)$, $B(-2, 1)$, $C(1, 3)$, and $D(2, 2)$ form a parallelogram.

SOLUTION

Given, $A(-1, 0)$, $B(-2, 1)$, $C(1, 3)$ and $D(2, 2)$.

$AB = \sqrt{(-2+1)^2 + (1-0)^2} = \sqrt{2}$ units

$BC = \sqrt{(1-(-2))^2 + (3-1)^2} = \sqrt{13}$ units

$CD = \sqrt{(2-1)^2 + (2-3)^2} = \sqrt{2}$ units

$DA = \sqrt{(2-(-1))^2 + (2-0)^2} = \sqrt{13}$ units

$AC = \sqrt{(1-(-1))^2 + (3-0)^2} = \sqrt{13}$ units

$BD = \sqrt{(2-(-2))^2 + (2-1)^2} = \sqrt{17}$ units

Clearly,

$AB = CD$, $BC = DA$ and $AC \neq BD$.

That is, the opposite sides of the quadrilateral are equal and diagonals are not equal.

Hence, the given points form a parallelogram.

EXAMPLE 11.11 Find the circum-centre and the circum-radius of a triangle ABC formed by the vertices $A(2, -2)$, $B(-1, 1)$, and $C(3, 1)$.

SOLUTION

Let $S(x, y)$ be the circum-centre of ΔABC.

$\therefore SA^2 = SB^2 = SC^2$

Consider, $SA^2 = SB^2$

$\Rightarrow (x-2)^2 + (y+2)^2 = (x+1)^2 + (y-1)^2$

$x^2 - 4x + 4 + y^2 + 4y + 4 = x^2 + 2x + 1 + y^2 - 2y + 1$

$-4x + 4y + 8 = 2x - 2y + 2$

$6x - 6y - 6 = 0$

$x - y - 1 = 0$ (1)

$SB^2 = SC^2$

$\Rightarrow (x+1)^2 + (y-1)^2 = (x-3)^2 + (y-1)^2$

$x^2 + 2x + 1 + y^2 - 2y + 1 = x^2 - 6x + 9 + y^2 - 2y + 1$

$2x - 2y + 2 = -6x - 2y + 10$

$8x - 8 = 0$

$\Rightarrow x = 1.$

Substituting $x = 1$ in Eq. (1), we get $y = 0$.

$\therefore$ The required circum-centre of ΔABC is $(1, 0)$.

Circum-radius, $SA = \sqrt{(2-1)^2 + (-2-0)^2} = \sqrt{5}$ units.

EXAMPLE 11.12 Find the area of the circle whose centre is $(-1, -2)$ and $(3, 4)$ is a point on the circle.

SOLUTION

Let the centre of the circle be $A(-1, -2)$, and the point on the circumference be $B(3, 4)$.

Radius of circle $= AB$

$= \sqrt{(3-(-1))^2 + (4-(-2))^2} = \sqrt{52}$ units.

$\therefore$ The area of the circle $= \pi r^2$

$= \pi(\sqrt{52})^2 = 52\pi$ sq. units.

EXAMPLE 11.13 Find the area of the square whose one pair of opposite vertices are $(2, -3)$ and $(4, 5)$.

SOLUTION

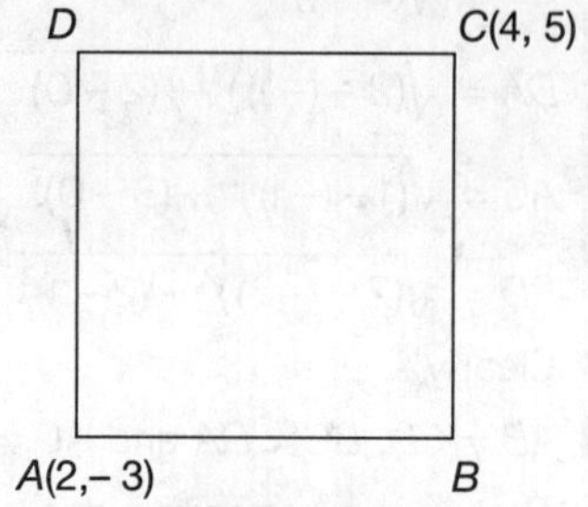

Figure 11.6

Let the given vertices be $A(2, -3)$ and $C(4, 5)$.

Length of $AC = \sqrt{(4-2)^2 + (5+3)^2}$

$= \sqrt{68}$ units.

$\therefore$ Area of the square $= \dfrac{AC^2}{2} = \dfrac{(\sqrt{68})^2}{2} = 34$ sq. units.

Straight Lines

Inclination of a Line

The angle made by a straight line with positive direction of X-axis in the anti-clockwise direction is called its inclination.

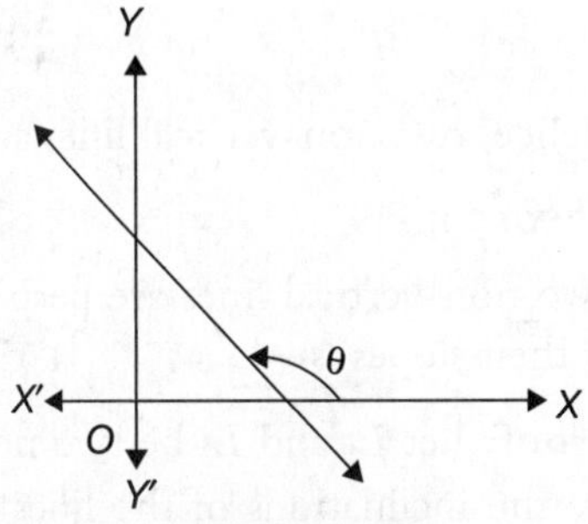

Figure 11.7

Slope or Gradient of a Line

If θ is the inclination of a line L, then its slope is denoted by m and is given by $m = \tan\theta$ (see Fig. 11.7).

Example: The inclination of the line l in adjacent Fig. 11.8 is 45°.

$\therefore$ The slope of the line is $m = \tan 45° = 1$.

Example: The line L in Fig. 11.9 makes an angle of 45° in clockwise direction with X-axis. So, the inclination of the line L is 180° – 45° = 135°.

$\therefore$ The slope of the line L is $m = \tan 135° = -1$.

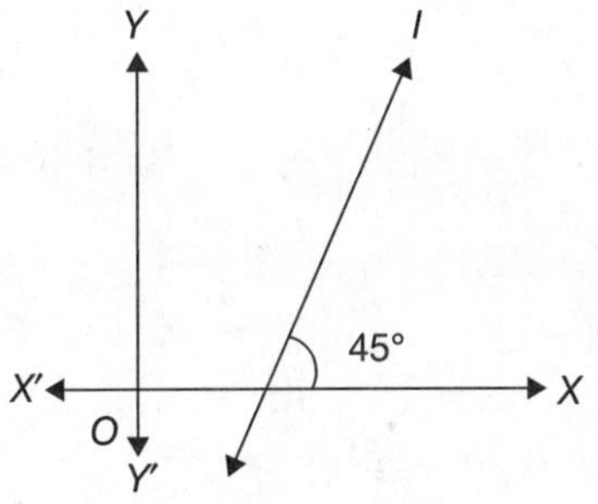

Figure 11.8

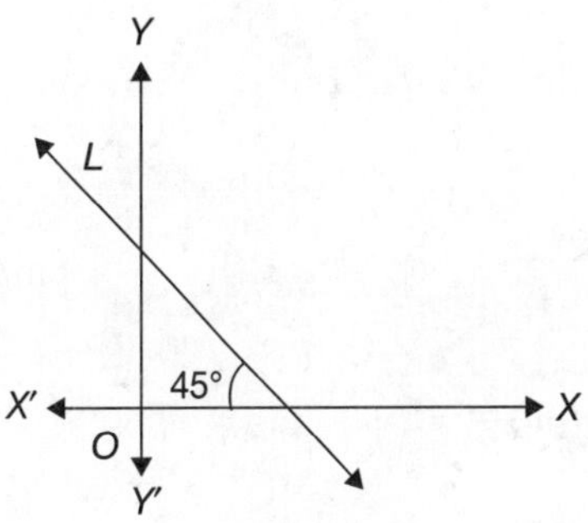

Figure 11.9

Some Results on the Slope of a Line

1. The slope of a horizontal line is zero. Hence,
   (i) Slope of X-axis is zero.
   (ii) Slope of any line parallel to X-axis is also zero.
2. The slope of a vertical line is not defined. Hence,
   (i) Slope of Y-axis is undefined.
   (ii) Slope of any line parallel to Y-axis is also undefined.

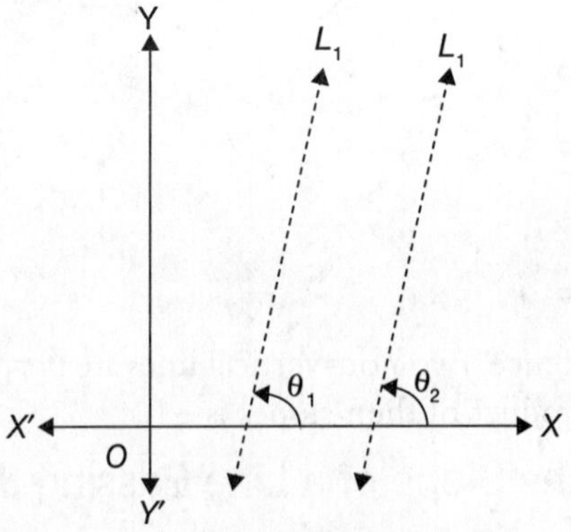

Figure 11.10

Theorem 1

Two non-vertical lines are parallel, if and only if, their slopes are equal.

Proof: Let L_1 and L_2 be two non-vertical lines with slopes m_1 and m_2, respectively.
If θ_1 and θ_2 are the inclinations of the lines, L_1 and L_2, respectively, then $m_1 = \tan\theta_1$ and $m_2 = \tan\theta_2$, since $L_1 \,||\, L_2$ .Then, $\theta_1 = \theta_2$ (see Fig. 11.10).

($\because$ They form a pair of corresponding angles)

$\Rightarrow$ $$\tan\theta_1 = \tan\theta_2$$

$\Rightarrow$ $$m_1 = m_2$$

Conversely: Let $m_1 = m_2$

$\Rightarrow$ $$\tan\theta_1 = \tan\theta_2$$

$$\Rightarrow \qquad \theta_1 = \theta_2$$

$$\Rightarrow \qquad L_1 \parallel L_2$$

($\because$ θ_1 and θ_2 form a pair of corresponding angles.)

Hence, two non-vertical lines are parallel, if and only if, their slopes are equal.

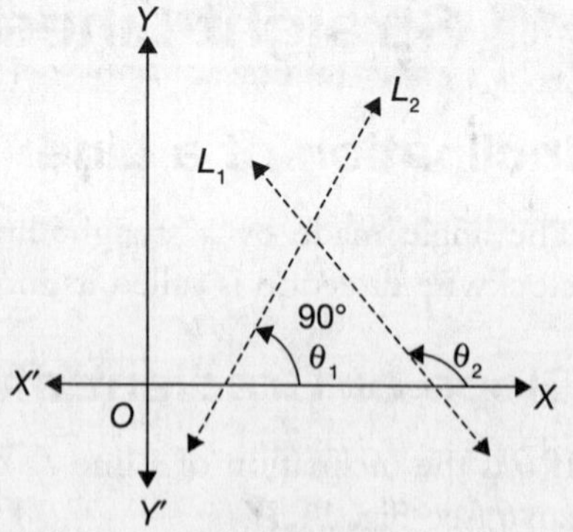

Figure 11.11

Theorem 2

Two non-vertical lines are perpendicular to each other, if and only if, the product of their slopes is −1.

Proof: Let L_1 and L_2 be two non-vertical lines with slopes m_1 and m_2. If θ_1 and θ_2 are the inclinations of the lines L_1 and L_2, respectively, then $m_1 = \tan\theta_1$ and $m_2 = \tan\theta_2$ (see Fig. 11.11).

If $L_1 \perp L_2$, then

$$\theta_2 = 90° + \theta_1$$

($\because$ The exterior angle of a triangle is equal to the sum of two opposite interior angles.)

$$\Rightarrow \qquad \tan\theta_2 = \tan(90° + \theta_1)$$

$$\Rightarrow \qquad \tan\theta_2 = -\cot\theta_1$$

$$\Rightarrow \qquad \tan\theta_2 = \frac{-1}{\tan\theta_1} \qquad [\because \theta_1 \neq 0]$$

$$\Rightarrow \qquad \tan\theta_1 \times \tan\theta_2 = -1$$

$$\therefore \qquad m_1 m_2 = -1.$$

Conversely: Let $m_1 m_2 = -1$

$$\Rightarrow \qquad \tan\theta_1 \tan\theta_2 = -1$$

$$\Rightarrow \qquad \tan\theta_2 = \frac{-1}{\tan\theta_1} \qquad [\because \theta_1 \neq 0]$$

$$\Rightarrow \qquad \tan\theta_2 = -\cot\theta_1$$

$$\Rightarrow \qquad \tan\theta_2 = \tan(90° + \theta_1)$$

$$\Rightarrow \qquad \theta_2 = 90° + \theta_1$$

$$\Rightarrow \qquad L_1 \perp L_2$$

Hence, two non-vertical lines are perpendicular to each other, if and only if, the product of their slopes is −1.

The Slope of a Line Passing through Points (x_1, y_1) and (x_2, y_2)

Let $A(x_1, y_1)$ and $B(x_2, y_2)$ be two given points.

Let AB be the straight line passing through points A and B.

Let θ be the inclination of line $\overleftrightarrow{AB}$.

Draw perpendiculars AL and BM on to X-axis from A and B, respectively. Also, draw $AN \perp BM$ (see Fig. 11.12).

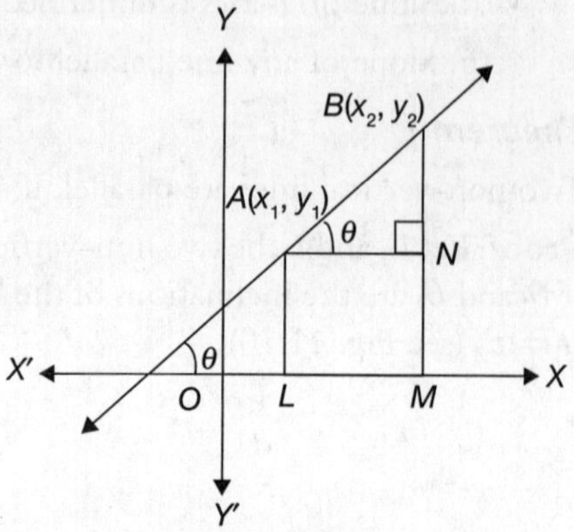

Figure 11.12

Then, let $\angle NAB = \theta$.

Here, $BN = BM - MN = BM - AL = y_2 - y_1$

$AN = LM = OM - OL = x_2 - x_1$

∴ The slope of the line L is

$$m = \tan\theta = \frac{BN}{AN} = \frac{y_2 - y_1}{x_2 - x_1}.$$

Hence, the slope of a line passing through points (x_1, y_1) and (x_2, y_2) is $m = \dfrac{y_2 - y_1}{x_2 - x_1}$.

The following table gives inclination (θ) of the line and its corresponding slope (m) for some particular values of θ.

θ	0°	30°	45°	60°	90°	120°	135°	150°
$m = \tan\theta$	0	$\frac{1}{\sqrt{3}}$	1	$\sqrt{3}$	∞	$-\sqrt{3}$	−1	$-\frac{1}{\sqrt{3}}$

Konnect

If points A, B, and C are collinear, then the slope (m_1) of AB = the slope (m_2) of BC.

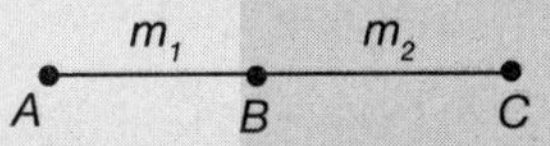

EXAMPLE 11.14

Find the slope of the line joining points (3, 8) and (−9, 6).

SOLUTION

Let $A(3, 8)$ and $B(-9, 6)$ be the given points.

Then, the slope of $\overleftrightarrow{AB} = \dfrac{y_2 - y_1}{x_2 - x_1}$

$$= \frac{6-8}{-9-3} = \frac{1}{6}.$$

EXAMPLE 11.15

Find the value of p if the slope of the line joining points $(5, -p)$ and $(2, -3)$ is $\dfrac{-1}{3}$.

SOLUTION

Let the given points be $A(5, -p)$ and $B(2, -3)$.

Given, the slope of $\overleftrightarrow{AB} = \dfrac{-1}{3}$.

That is, $\dfrac{-3-(-p)}{2-5} = \dfrac{-1}{3}$

$\Rightarrow \dfrac{p-3}{-3} = \dfrac{-1}{3}$

$\Rightarrow p - 3 = 1$

$\Rightarrow p = 4.$

EXAMPLE 11.16

Find the value of k, if lines AB and CD are perpendicular, where $A = (4, 5)$, $B = (k + 2, -3)$, $C = (-3, 2)$, and $D = (2, 4)$.

SOLUTION

The slope of $\overleftrightarrow{AB}$ $(m_1) = \dfrac{y_2 - y_1}{x_2 - x_1}$

$$= \frac{-3-5}{(k+2)-4} = \frac{-8}{k-2}.$$

Slope of $\overleftrightarrow{CD}$ $(m_2) = \dfrac{4-2}{2-(-3)} = \dfrac{2}{5}.$

Since, $AB \perp PQ \Rightarrow m_1 m_2 = -1$

That is, $\dfrac{-8}{k-2} \times \left(\dfrac{2}{5}\right) = -1$

$\Rightarrow \dfrac{16}{5k-10} = 1$

$\Rightarrow 16 = -10 + 5k$

$\Rightarrow k = \dfrac{26}{5}.$

EXAMPLE 11.17

Find the value of k, if points $(-2, -4)$, $(k, -2)$, and $(3, 4)$ are collinear.

SOLUTION

Let the given points be $A(-2, -4)$, $B(k, -2)$, and $C(3, 4)$.

The slope of $AB = \dfrac{-2+4}{k+2} = \dfrac{2}{k+2}.$

The slope of $BC = \dfrac{4+2}{3-k} = \dfrac{6}{3-k}.$

Since the points A, B, and C are collinear,

The slope of $\overleftrightarrow{AB}$ = the slope of $\overleftrightarrow{BC}$

$\Rightarrow \dfrac{2}{k+2} = \dfrac{6}{3-k}$

$\Rightarrow 2(3-k) = 6(k+2)$

$\Rightarrow 3 - k = 3k + 6$

$\Rightarrow 4k = -3$

$\Rightarrow k = \dfrac{-3}{4}.$

EXAMPLE 11.18

The orthocentre of a triangle formed by the vertices (7, 8), (8, 7) and (11, 10) is ______.

SOLUTION

Let A = (7,8), B = (8,7) and C = (11,10)

The slope of AB = $\dfrac{7-8}{8-7} = -1$

The slope of BC = = $\dfrac{10-7}{11-8} = 1$

The slope of AC = $\frac{10-8}{11-7} = \frac{1}{2}$

As the product of the slope of AB and BC is −1,

$\angle B = 90°$.

∴ The orthocentre lies at B (8, 7).

Intercepts of a Straight Line

Say a straight line *L* meets *X*-axis in *A* and *Y*-axis in *B*.

Then, *OA* is called the *x*-intercept and *OB* is called the *y*-intercept (see Fig. 11.13).

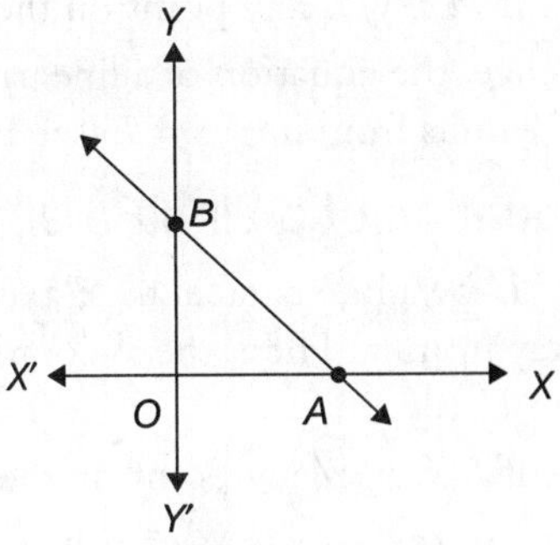

Figure 11.13

Info Bytes!

OA and *OB* are taken as positive or negative, based on whether the line meets positive or negative axes.

EXAMPLE 11.19 The line *l* in Fig. 11.14 meets *X*-axis at *A*(−5, 0) and *Y*-axis at *B*(0, −3).

SOLUTION

Hence, *x*-intercept = −5 and *y*-intercept = −3.

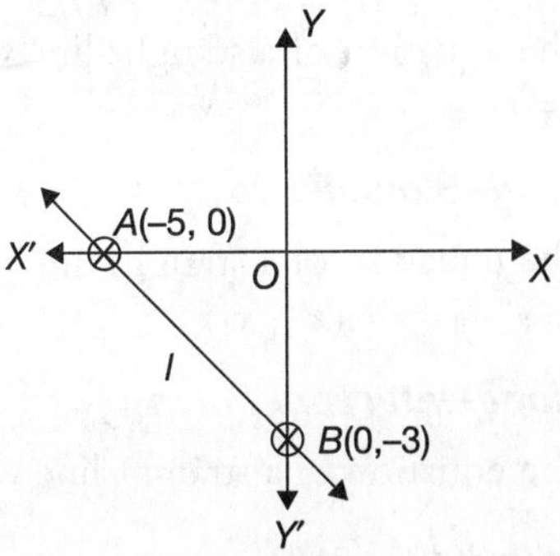

Figure 11.14

Equation of a Line in General Form

An equation of the form, $ax + by + c = 0$ (where $|a| + |b| \neq 0$, i.e., *a* and *b* are not simultaneously equal to zero), which is satisfied by every point on a line is called the equation of a line.

Equations of Some Standard Lines

Equation of *X*-axis

We know that the *y*-coordinate of every point on *X*-axis is zero. So, if *P*(*x*, *y*) is any point on *X*-axis, then $y = 0$.

Hence, the equation of *X*-axis is $y = 0$.

Equation of *Y*-axis

We know that the *x*-coordinate of every point on *Y*-axis is zero. So, if $P(x, y)$ is any point on *Y*-axis, then $x = 0$. Hence, the equation of *Y*-axis is $x = 0$.

Equation of a Line Parallel to *X*-axis

Let *L* be a line parallel to *X*-axis and at a distance of *k* units away from *X*-axis.

Then the *y*-coordinate of every point on the line *L* is *k*.

So, if $P(x, y)$ is any point on the line *L*, then $y = k$.

Hence, the equation of a line parallel to *X*-axis at a distance of *k* units from it, is $y = k$ (see Fig. 11.15).

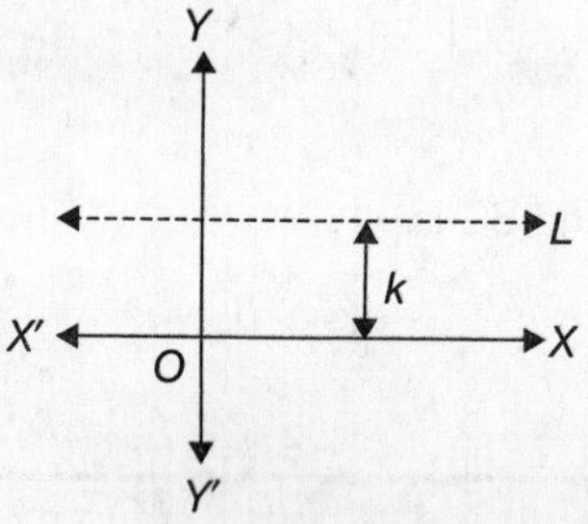

Figure 11.15

Konnect

For the lines lying below *X*-axis, *k* is taken as negative.

Equation of a Line Parallel to *Y*-axis

Let *L*′ be a line parallel to *Y*-axis and at a distance of *k* units away from it. Then, the *x*-coordinate of every point on the line *L*′ is *k*.

So, if $P(x, y)$ is any point on the line *L*′, then $x = k$.

Hence, the equation of a line parallel to *Y*-axis and at a distance of *k* units from it, is $x = k$ (see Fig. 11.16).

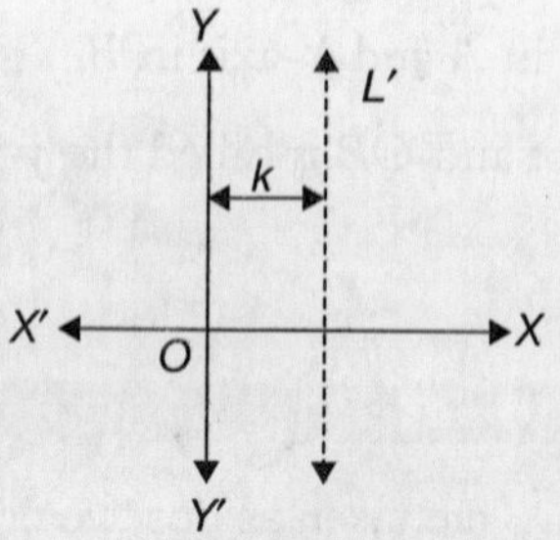

Figure 11.16

Info Bytes!

For the lines lying on the left side of *Y*-axis, *k* is taken as negative.

Oblique Line

A straight line which is neither parallel to *X*-axis nor parallel to *Y*-axis is called an oblique line or an inclined line.

Different Forms of Equations of Oblique Lines

Gradient Form (or) Slope Form

The equation of a straight line with slope *m* and passing through the origin is given by $y = mx$.

Info Bytes!

Area of triangle formed by the line $y = mx + c$ is $\frac{1}{2}\left|\frac{c^2}{m}\right|$ sq. units.

Point–Slope Form

The equation of a straight line passing through point (x_1, y_1) and with slope *m* is given by $y - y_1 = m(x - x_1)$.

Slope–Intercept Form

The equation of a straight line with slope *m* and having *y*-intercept as *c* is given by $y = mx + c$.

Two-point Form

The equation of a straight line passing through points (x_1, y_1) and (x_2, y_2) is given by:

$$y - y_1 = \frac{y_2 - y_1}{x_2 - x_1}(x - x_1) \quad \text{or} \quad \frac{y - y_1}{y_2 - y_1} = \frac{x - x_1}{x_2 - x_1}.$$

Intercept Form

The equation of a straight line with *x*-intercept as *a* and *y*-intercept as *b* is given by $\frac{x}{a} + \frac{y}{b} = 1$.

Konnect

Area of triangle formed by line $\frac{x}{a} + \frac{y}{b} = 1$ with the coordinate axes is $\frac{1}{2}|ab|$ sq. units.

EXAMPLE 11.20 Find the equation of the line parallel to Y-axis and passing though point (5, −7).

SOLUTION

The equation of a line parallel to Y-axis is $x = k$.

Given, the line passes through point (5, −7)

$\Rightarrow k = 5$.

Hence, the equation of the required line is $x = 5$.

That is, $x - 5 = 0$.

EXAMPLE 11.21 Find the equation of the line passing through (3, 4) and having a slope $\frac{4}{5}$.

SOLUTION

The equation of the line passing through (x_1, y_1) and having slope m is given by $y - y_1 = m(x - x_1)$.

Hence, the equation of the required line is:

$y - 4 = \frac{4}{5}(x - 3)$

$5y - 20 = 4x - 12$

$4x - 5y + 8 = 0$.

EXAMPLE 11.22 Find the equation of a line making intercepts 4 and 5 on the coordinate axes.

SOLUTION

Given, x-intercept $(a) = 4$ and y-intercept $(b) = 5$.

∴ The equation of the required line is $\frac{x}{a} + \frac{y}{b} = 1$.

That is, $\frac{x}{4} + \frac{y}{5} = 1$

$\Rightarrow 5x + 4y - 20 = 0$.

Equation of a Line Parallel or Perpendicular to the Given Line

Let $ax + by + c = 0$ be the equation of a straight line, then:

1. The equation of a line passing through point (x_1, y_1) and parallel to the given line:

   The slope of the required line (m) = The slope of $ax + by + c = 0$

   $= \frac{-a}{b}$ (Since the lines are parallel)

   ∴ The required line is

$$y - y_1 = m(x - x_1)$$

$$\Rightarrow y - y_1 = \frac{-a}{b}(x - x_1)$$

$$\Rightarrow b(y - y_1) = -a(x - x_1)$$

$$\Rightarrow a(x - x_1) + b(y - y_1) = 0.$$

2. The equation of a line passing through point (x_1, y_1) and perpendicular to the given line:

The slope of $ax + by + c = 0$ is $\frac{-a}{b}$.

$\therefore$ The slope of the required line is $\frac{b}{a}$. (Since the line are perpendicular.)

$\therefore$ The required line is

$$(y - y_1) = m(x - x_1)$$
$$\Rightarrow (y - y_1) = \frac{b}{a}(x - x_1)$$
$$\Rightarrow b(x - x_1) - a(y - y_1) = 0.$$

EXAMPLE 11.23 Find the equation of a line passing through the point $P(-3, 2)$ and parallel to line $4x - 3y - 7 = 0$.

SOLUTION

Here, $(x_1, y_1) = (-3, 2)$, $a = 4$ and $b = -3$.

$\therefore$ Equation of the line passing through $P(-3, 2)$ and parallel to $4x - 3y - 7 = 0$.

$a(x - x_1) + b(y - y_1) = 0$

$\Rightarrow 4(x + 3) - 3(y - 2) = 0$

$\Rightarrow 4x - 3y + 18 = 0$.

Hence, the equation of the required line is $4x - 3y + 18 = 0$.

EXAMPLE 11.24 Find the equation of a line passing through point $(-2, 3)$ and perpendicular to $7x + 2y + 3 = 0$.

SOLUTION

Here, $(x_1, y_1) = (-2, 3)$, $a = 7$ and $b = 2$.

$\therefore$ Equation of the line perpendicular to $7x + 2y + 3 = 0$ and passing through $(-2, 3)$ is $b(x - x_1) - a(y - y_1) = 0$.

That is, $2(x + 2) - 7(y - 3) = 0$

$\Rightarrow 2x - 7y + 25 = 0$.

Hence, the required equation of the line is $2x - 7y + 25 = 0$.

EXAMPLE 11.25 The line $(8x + 3y - 15) + \lambda(3x - 8y + 2) = 0$ is parallel to X-axis. Find λ.

SOLUTION

The given line is $(8x + 3y - 15) + \lambda(3x - 8y + 2) = 0$.

That is, $x(8 + 3\lambda) + y(3 - 8\lambda) + (2\lambda - 15) = 0$.

Since the given line is parallel to X-axis, its slope = 0.

$$\frac{-(8+3\lambda)}{3-8\lambda} = 0$$

$\Rightarrow 8 + 3\lambda = 0$

Hence, $\lambda = \frac{-8}{3}$.

EXAMPLE 11.26 The equation of the line passing through the point of intersection of lines $2x - y + 3 = 0$ and $3x + y + 7 = 0$ and perpendicular to $2x - 3y + 4 = 0$, is ______.

(a) $3x + 2y - 7 = 0$ (b) $3x + 2y + 8 = 0$
(c) $3x + 2y - 8 = 0$ (d) $3x - 2y + 1 = 0$

SOLUTION

(i) Find m and the intersection point. Then use slope-point form.
(ii) Find the common point (x_1, y_1) of first two equations.
(iii) Find the slope (m) of third line.
(iv) Find the equation of the line passing through (x_1, y_1) and having slope $\left(-\frac{1}{m}\right)$.

EXAMPLE 11.27 The area of the figure formed by $|x| + |y| = 2$ is ______. (in sq. units)

(a) 2 (b) 4 (c) 6 (d) 8

SOLUTION

(i) Plot the figure.
(ii) Find the intercepts made by given line.
(iii) If the intercepts are a and b, then the area of the triangle is $\frac{|ab|}{2}$.

EXAMPLE 11.28 The sum of the reciprocals of the intercepts of a line is $\frac{1}{2}$, then the line passes through the point is______.

(a) (1, 1) (b) (2, 1) (c) $\left(\frac{1}{4}, \frac{1}{4}\right)$ (d) (2, 2)

SOLUTION

(i) Use $\frac{x}{a} + \frac{y}{b} = 1$.

(ii) Solve, $\frac{1}{a} + \frac{1}{b} = \frac{1}{2}$ and get the relation between a and b.

(iii) Use the formula $\frac{x}{a} + \frac{y}{b} = 1$.

Section Formula

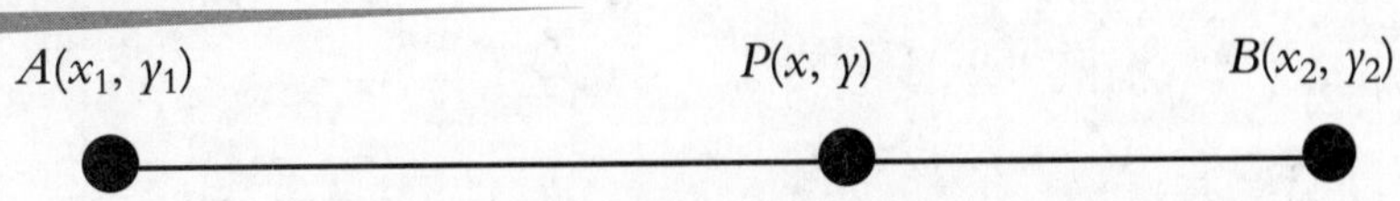

If Point $P(x, y)$ lies on line segment $\overline{AB}$ (between points A and B) and satisfies $AP : PB = m : n$, then we say that P divides $\overline{AB}$ internally in the ratio $m : n$. The point of division has the coordinates:

$$P = \left(\frac{mx_2 + nx_1}{m+n}, \frac{my_2 + ny_1}{m+n}\right).$$

Mid-point

Let $A(x_1, y_1)$ and $B(x_2, y_2)$ be two given points and M be the mid-point of AB.

Then, $M = \left(\frac{x_1 + x_2}{2}, \frac{y_1 + y_2}{2}\right)$.

Hence, the coordinates of the mid-point of the line segment joining the points (x_1, y_1) and (x_2, y_2) are given by $\left(\frac{x_1+x_2}{2}, \frac{y_1+y_2}{2}\right)$.

EXAMPLE 11.29 Find the mid-point of the line segment joining the points (2, −6) and (6, −4).

SOLUTION

Let $A(2, -6)$ and $B(6, -4)$ be the given points and M be the mid-point of AB.

Then,

$$M = \left(\frac{x_1+x_2}{2}, \frac{y_1+y_2}{2}\right)$$

$$= \left(\frac{2+6}{2}, \frac{-6+(-4)}{2}\right) = (4, -5).$$

Hence, the mid-point of AB is (4, −5).

Centroid

Let $A(x_1, y_1)$, $B(x_2, y_2)$, and $C(x_3, y_3)$ be the vertices of ΔABC, and G be its centroid. Then, the coordinates of G are given by, $G = \left(\frac{x_1+x_2+x_3}{2}, \frac{y_1+y_2+y_3}{2}\right)$.

EXAMPLE 11.30 Find the centroid of ΔABC whose vertices are $A(2, -3)$, $B(4, 2)$, and $C(-3, -2)$.

SOLUTION

Given, $A(2, -3)$, $B(4, 2)$, and $C(-3, -2)$.

So, centroid of ΔABC

$$\left(\frac{x_1+x_2+x_3}{2}, \frac{y_1+y_2+y_3}{2}\right) = \left(\frac{2+4-3}{3}, \frac{-3+2-2}{3}\right) = (1, -1).$$

Hence, (1, −1) is the centroid of ΔABC.

EXAMPLE 11.31 Find the third vertex of ΔABC, if two of its vertices are $A(-2, 3)$, $B(4, 5)$, and its centroid is $G(1, 2)$.

SOLUTION

Let $C(x, y)$ be the third vertex.

Given, centroid of $\Delta ABC = (1, 2)$

$$\Rightarrow \left(\frac{-2+4+x}{3}, \frac{3+5+y}{3}\right) = (1, 2)$$

$$\Rightarrow \left(\frac{x+2}{3}, \frac{y+8}{3}\right) = (1, 2)$$

$$\Rightarrow \frac{x+2}{3} = 1, \frac{y+8}{3} = 2$$

$\Rightarrow x = 1$, $y = -2$.

∴ The third vertex is (1, −2).

Konnect

1. If the mid-points of the sides BC, AC, and AB of ΔABC, respectively, are $P(x_1, y_1)$, $Q(x_2, y_2)$, and $R(x_3, y_3)$, then its vertices are $A(-x_1 + x_2 + x_3, -y_1 + y_2 + y_3)$, $B(x_1 - x_2 + x_3, y_1 - y_2 + y_3)$, and $C(x_1 + x_2 - x_3, y_1 + y_2 - y_3)$.
2. The fourth vertex of a parallelogram whose three consecutive vertices are (x_1, y_1), (x_2, y_2), and (x_3, y_3) when taken in order is $(x_1 - x_2 + x_3, y_1 - y_2 + y_3)$.

EXAMPLE 11.32 Find the fourth vertex of the parallelogram whose three consecutive vertices are (8, 8), (6, 1), and (–1, 1).

SOLUTION

Let the three vertices of the parallelogram be $A(8, 8)$, $B(6, 1)$, and $C(-1, 1)$, then fourth vertex $D(x, y)$ is given by

$$D(x, y) = (x_1 - x_2 + x_3, y_1 - y_2 + y_3)$$
$$= (8 - 6 - 1, 8 - 1 + 1)$$
$$= (1, 8).$$

Hence, the fourth vertex is $D(1, 8)$.

EXAMPLE 11.33 If the centroid of a triangle is (6, 6) and its ortho-centre is (0, 0), then find its circum-centre.

(a) (3, 3) (b) (6, 6) (c) (9, 9) (d) (12, 12)

SOLUTION

Ortho-centre, centroid, and circum-centre are collinear.

We know that centroid divides the line segment joining the ortho-centre, centroid, and circum-centre ($\overline{OGS}$) in the ratio 2 : 1 from the ortho-centre (O).

Let $S(x, y)$, $G(6, 6)$, and $O(0, 0)$

$$(6, 6) = \left(\frac{2x \times 1 \times 0}{2+1}, \frac{2 \times y \times 0}{2+1}\right)$$

$$(6, 6) = \left(\frac{2x}{3}, \frac{2y}{3}\right)$$

$$\Rightarrow \frac{2x}{3} = 6, \frac{2y}{3} = 6$$

$$\Rightarrow x = 9 \text{ and } y = 9.$$

$\therefore$ The circum-centre is (9, 9).

EXAMPLE 11.34 $C(3, 0)$ and $D(3, 1)$ are the points of trisection of a line segment AB. Find the respective coordinates of A and B.

(a) (3, 2), (3, 0) (b) (3, −1), (3, 2)

(c) (−3, 1), (3, 2) (d) None of these

SOLUTION

Let A and B be (a_1, b_1) and (a_2, b_2). Given, $C(3, 0)$ and $D(3, 1)$ are the points of trisection of AB.

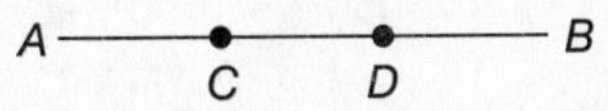

$\Rightarrow$ C is the mid-points of AD and D is the mid-points of CB.

$\Rightarrow (3, 0) = \left(\frac{a_1+3}{2}, \frac{b_1+1}{2}\right)$

$\Rightarrow a_1 = 3$ and $b_1 = -1$.

Also, $(3, 1) = \left(\frac{3+a_2}{2}, \frac{0+b_2}{2}\right)$

$\Rightarrow a_2 = 3$ and $b_2 = 2$.

$\therefore$ The coordinates of A and B are $(3, -1)$ and $(3, 2)$.

POINTS TO REMEMBER

- ✔ The distance between two points $A(x_1, y_1)$ and $B(x_1, y_1)$ is:
  $AB = \sqrt{(x_2 - x_1)^2 + (y_2 - y_1)^2}$ units.
- ✔ Given the two points (x_1, y_1) and (x_2, y_2), the distance d between these points is given by the foumula:
  $$d = \sqrt{(x_2 - x_1)^2 + (y_2 - y_1)^2}$$
- ✔ Two non-vertical lines are parallel, if and only if, their slopes are equal.
- ✔ Two non-vertical lines are perpendicular to each other, if and only if, the product of their slopes is -1.
- ✔ The slope of a line passing through points (x_1, y_1) and (x_2, y_2) is $m = \frac{y_2 - y_1}{x_2 - x_1}$.
- ✔ Area of triangle formed by line $\frac{x}{a} + \frac{y}{b} = 1$ with the coordinate axes is $\frac{1}{2}|ab|$ sq. units.
- ✔ The point of division has the coordinates:
  $$P = \left(\frac{mx_2 + nx_1}{m+n}, \frac{my_2 + ny_1}{m+n}\right).$$
- ✔ Let $A(x_1, y_1)$, $B(x_2, y_2)$, and $C(x_3, y_3)$ be the vertices of ΔABC, and G be its centroid. Then, the coordinates of G are given by, G = $\left(\frac{x_1 + x_2 + x_3}{2}, \frac{y_1 + y_2 + y_3}{2}\right)$.

DW

PRACTICE QUESTIONS CLASSROOM WING

Very Short Answer Type Questions

Directions of questions from 1 to 20:
Fill in the blanks.

1. The perimeter of a triangle formed by the points A(0, 0), B(4, 0) and C(0, 3) is ______ units.
2. The slope of the line joining $(x, x + 3)$ and $(x - 2, 2x + 3)$ is _______. (where $x > 0$)
3. The graph of $5x + 6y - 30 = 0$ does not lie in _______.
4. The slope of the line joining $(2x + 3, 3x - 3)$ and $(5x + 3, 3x - 3)$ is ______.
5. The slope of altitude from A to BC of triangle $A(2, 3)$, $B(-3, 2)$, and $C(3, 5)$ is ______.
6. If the line $\frac{x}{a}+\frac{y}{b}= m$ passes through origin, then the value of m is _______.
7. The slope-intercept form of the line $2x + 3y + 5 = 0$ is ______.
8. The lines $3x + 2y + 7 = 0$ and $6x + 4y + 9 = 0$ are ________to each other.
9. The points $(p, q + r)$, $(q, r + p)$ and $(r, q + p)$ are ______.
10. The points (2, 3), (−1, 5) and $(x, -2)$ form a straight line, then x is _____.
11. If the point (x, y) lies in the second quadrant, then x is ______ and y is ______.
12. The angle between lines $x = 5$ and $x = 7$ is ______.
13. The point of intersection of X-axis and $3x + 2y - 5 = 0$ is ______.
14. If $a = 0$, then the line $ax + by + c = 0$ is parallel to ______.
15. The point of intersection of X-axis and Y-axis is ______.
16. A, B, and C are three points such that $AB = AC + CB$, then A, B, and C are _______.
17. If slope of a line (l) is $\tan\theta$, then slope of a line perpendicular to (l) is ______.
18. The lines $x = 2$ and $y = -3$ intersect in ______ quadrant.
19. The slope of a line which is parallel to the line making an inclination of 45° with positive X-axis is _____.
20. If the slope of two lines are equal, then the lines are ______.

Short Answer Type Questions

21. Find the equation of a line passing through points $A(-2, 3)$ and $B(4, 7)$.
22. Find the area of the circle passing through (−2, 3) with centre (5, 2).
23. Let $A(-3, 2)$, $B(4, 1)$ and $C(-2, k)$ be three points such that $AC = BC$. Find the value of k.
24. Find the distance between points (2, −3) and (4, 6).
25. If the line $2x - ky + 6 = 0$ passes through the point (2, −8), then find the value of k.
26. Find the area of square, whose diagonally opposite vertices are (−2, 3) and (4, 5).
27. If $A(a + b, a - b)$ and $B(-a + b, -a - b)$, then find the distance AB.
28. Find the intercepts made by the line $3x - 2y - 6 = 0$ on the coordinate axes.
29. Find the inclination of the line $\sqrt{3}x - 3y + 6 = 0$.
30. Find the circum-centre of the triangle whose vertices are $A(-3, -1)$, $B(1, 2)$ and $C(0, -4)$.
31. Find the equation of a line having inclination 60° and making an intercept of $\frac{-1}{3}$ on Y-axis.
32. Find the point on X-axis, which is equidistant from $A(6, 3)$ and $B(-1, 4)$.
33. Show that the points (−1, −1), (6, 1), (8, 8), and (1, 6), when joined in the given order form a rhombus.

34. Find the equation of a line, whose y-intercept is -5 and passes through point $A(-3, 2)$.

Essay Type Questions

35. If a straight line passes through the point $(-3, 5)$ and has equal intercepts, then the sum of the intercepts of the line is ________.

36. ABCD is a rhombus. The equation of AC is $2x + 3y = 12$ and B = $(2, -3)$. The equation of BD is ________.

37. Find the equation of the line passing through $(-5, 11)$ and making equal intercepts, but opposite in magnitude on the coordinate axes.

38. Find the equations of a line which forms area 5 sq. units with the coordinate axes and having sum of intercepts is 7.

39. If points $A(1, 6)$, $B(5, 2)$, and $C(12, 9)$ are three consecutive vertices of a parallelogram, then find the equation of the diagonal BD.

PRACTICE QUESTIONS COMPETITION WING

Level 1: Apply Your Concepts

Directions of questions from 1 to 4:
Fill in the blanks.

1. If $x > 0$ and $y < 0$, then the point $(x, -y)$ lies in ______ quadrant.
2. Which point among (2, 3), (–3, –4) and (1, –7) is nearest to the origin?
3. The lines $2y + 3 = 0$ and $x = 3$ intersect at ______.
4. The points (0, 0), (0, 4), and (4, 0) form a/an ______ triangle.

Directions of questions from 5 to 60:
Select the correct alternative from the given choices.

5. If (1, –3), (–2, –3), and (–2, 2) are the three vertices of a parallelogram taken in that order, then the fourth vertex is ______.
   (a) (–1, –2) (b) (1, 2)
   (c) (–1, 2) (d) (1, –2)
6. Find the coordinates of the point on the x – axis which is at equidistant from (2, 4) and (3, 2).
   (a) $\left(\frac{5}{2}, 0\right)$ (b) $\left(\frac{-5}{2}, 0\right)$
   (c) $\left(\frac{7}{2}, 0\right)$ (d) $\left(\frac{-7}{2}, 0\right)$
7. If the point $(x, y) \in Q_2$, then $(-x, y)$ belongs to ______.
   (a) Q_1 (b) Q_2
   (c) Q_3 (d) Q_4
8. Find the coordinates of the point on the y – axis which is at equidistant from (2, 4) and (3, 5)
   (a) $\left(0, \frac{7}{2}\right)$ (b) $\left(0, \frac{-7}{2}\right)$
   (c) (0, 7) (d) (0, –7)
9. Which of the following represents a pair of parallel lines?
   (a) $y = 3;\ x = 3$ (b) $y = 8;\ x = 4$
   (c) $x = 0,\ y = 0$ (d) $y = 8,\ y = 4$
10. If O(0, 0) and A(4, 0) are the two vertices of a right isosceles triangle OAB, then the number of posible non negative coordinates for the third vertex B is ______.
    (a) two (b) three
    (c) six (d) infinite
11. The centroid of the triangle formed by the lines $x = 0$, $y = 0$ and $x + y = 9$ is ______.
    (a) (9, 9) (b) $\left(\frac{9}{2}, \frac{9}{2}\right)$
    (c) (2, 2) (d) (3, 3)
12. The endpoints of the longest chord of a circle are (–4, 2) and (–6, –8). Find its centre.
    (a) $\left(-\frac{10}{3}, -2\right)$ (b) (–5, –2)
    (c) (–5, –4) (d) (–5, –3)
13. The slope of the line $x - \sqrt{3}\,y + 3 = 0$ is ______.
    (a) $\frac{1}{\sqrt{3}}$ (b) $\frac{-1}{\sqrt{3}}$
    (c) $\sqrt{3}$ (d) $-\sqrt{3}$
14. If the line $2x + 3y = 6$ cuts the x and y axes at P, Q respectively, then PQ = ______.
    (a) $\sqrt{18}$ (b) $\sqrt{13}$
    (c) $\sqrt{7}$ (d) $\sqrt{6}$
15. If the slope and the y-intercept of a line are the roots of the equation $x^2 - 7x - 18 = 0$, then the equation of the line can be ______.
    (a) $2x + y - 9 = 0$ (b) $2x - y + 9 = 0$
    (c) $9x + y + 2 = 0$ (d) $9x + 2y - 2 = 0$
16. If the points $(k, k-1)$, $(k+2, k+1)$, and $(k, k+3)$ are three consecutive vertices of a square, then its area (in square units) is ______.
    (a) 2 (b) 4
    (c) 8 (d) 6
17. The equation of the line making intercepts of equal magnitude and opposite signs, and passing through the point (–3, –5) is ______.
    (a) $x - y = 2$ (b) $2x + y = -4$
    (c) $3x + 3y = 6$ (d) $x - y = -10$
18. If the endpoints of the diameter of a circle are (–2, 3) and (6, –3), then the area of the circle (in square units) is ______.

(a) $\frac{550}{3}$ (b) $\frac{540}{7}$

(c) $\frac{560}{7}$ (d) $\frac{550}{7}$

19. The inclination of the line $\sqrt{3}x - y + 3 = 0$ with the positive X-axis is ______.
(a) 30° (b) 45°
(c) 60° (d) 90°

20. The two lines $3x + 4y - 6 = 0$ and $6x + ky - 7 = 0$ are such that any line which is perpendicular to the first line is also perpendicular to the second line. Then, $k =$ ______.
(a) –8 (b) –6
(c) 6 (d) 8

21. Find the area in square units, of the rhombus with vertices (2, 1), (–5, 2), (–4, –5), and (3, –6), taken in that order.
(a) 24 (b) 48
(c) 36 (d) 50

22. The radius of a circle with centre (–2, 3) is 5 units, then the point (2, 5) lies ______.
(a) On the circle (b) Inside the circle
(c) Outside the circle (d) None of the above

23. One end of the diameter of a circle with the centre as origin is (–2, 10). Find the other end of the diameter.
(a) (–2, –10) (b) (0, 0)
(c) (2, –10) (d) (2, 10)

24. If the roots of the quadratic equation $x^2 - 7x + 12 = 0$ are intercepts of a line, then the equation of the line can be ______.
(a) $2x + 3y = 6$ (b) $4x + 3y = 12$
(c) $4x + 3y = 6$ (d) $3x + 4y = 6$

25. Find the value of λ, if the line $x - 3y + 4 + \lambda(8x - 3y + 2) = 0$ is parallel to the X-axis.
(a) $\frac{1}{5}$ (b) $\frac{5}{8}$
(c) $-\frac{3}{8}$ (d) $-\frac{1}{8}$

26. The slope of the line joining the points (2, $k - 3$) and (4, –7) is 3. Find k.
(a) –10 (b) –6
(c) –2 (d) 10

27. The angle between the lines $x = 10$ and $y = 10$ is ______.
(a) 0° (b) 90°
(c) 180° (d) None of these

28. The two lines $5x + 3y + 7 = 0$ and $kx - 4y + 3 = 0$ are perpendicular to the same line. Find the value of k.
(a) $-\frac{20}{7}$ (b) $-\frac{20}{3}$
(c) $\frac{20}{9}$ (d) $\frac{12}{5}$

29. The lines $x - 2y + 3 = 0$, $3x - y = 1$ and $kx - y + 1 = 0$ are concurrent. Find k.
(a) 1 (b) $\frac{1}{2}$
(c) $\frac{3}{2}$ (d) $\frac{5}{2}$

30. The circum-centre of the triangle formed by points $O(0, 0)$, $A(6, 0)$, and $B(0, 6)$ is ______.
(a) (3, 3) (b) (2, 2)
(c) (1, 1) (d) (0, 0)

31. The lines $3x - y + 2 = 0$ and $x + 3y + 4 = 0$ intersect each other in the ______.
(a) 1st quadrant (b) 4th quadrant
(c) 3rd quadrant (d) 2nd quadrant

32. Centre of the circle is (a, b). If (0, 3) and (2, 0) are two points on a circle, then find the relation between a and b.
(a) $4a - 6b - 5 = 0$ (b) $4a + 6b - 5 = 0$
(c) $-4a + 5 = 0$ (d) $4a - 6b + 5 = 0$

Level 2: Review Your Concepts

33. For which of the following lines the angle between them is 90°?
(a) $2x + 3y + 5 = 0$, $2x + 3y - 5 = 0$ (b) $2x - 3y + 7 = 0$, $3x - 2y + 9 = 0$
(c) $2x + 3y - 7 = 0$, $3x - 2y + 6 = 0$ (d) $3x - 2y + 8 = 0$, $2x - 3y - 8 = 0$

34. PQRS is a square. The equation of QS is $5x - 7y = 16$. Which of the following can be the equation of PR?
(a) $5x + 7y = 14$ (b) $7x + 5y = 13$
(c) $5x - 7y = 8$ (d) $7x - 5y = 10$

35. PQR is a triangle, whose sides are $x = 0$, $y = 0$ and $x - y + 5 = 0$. Which of the following are the angles of the triangle?

(A) 30° (B) 45°
(C) 60° (D) 90°
(a) (A) and (B) (b) (B) and (C)
(c) (B) and (D) (d) (A), (C) and (D)

36. The graph of $x - y = 0$ lies in ______.
(a) Q_1 and Q_2 (b) Q_2 and Q_4
(c) Q_1 and Q_3 (d) Q_2 and Q_3

37. If A = (–4, 5), B = (4, 5), C = (3, –2) and D = (–3, –2), then ABCD forms a/an ______.
(a) rectangle (b) square
(c) isosceles trapezium (d) rhombus

38. The line joining the points $(2m + 2, 2m)$ and $(2m + 1, 3)$ passes through $(m + 1, 1)$, if the values of m are ______.
(a) $5, -\frac{1}{5}$ (b) 1, –1
(c) $2, -\frac{1}{2}$ (d) $3, -\frac{1}{3}$

39. The length (in units) of the line joining the points (4, 3) and (–4, 9) intercepted between the coordinate axes is ______.
(a) 10 (b) 8
(c) 6 (d) 4

40. The equation of a line parallel to $8x - 3y + 15 = 0$ and passing through the point (–1, 4) is ______.
(a) $8x - 3y - 4 = 0$ (b) $8x - 3y - 20 = 0$
(c) $8x - 3y + 4 = 0$ (d) $8x - 3y + 20 = 0$

41. $(0, 0), (3, \sqrt{3})$ and $(0, 2\sqrt{3})$ are the three vertices of a triangle. The distance between the ortho-centre and the cirum-centre of the triangle is ______. (in units)
(a) $\sqrt{3}$ (b) $\sqrt{5}$
(c) $\sqrt{6}$ (d) 0

42. If the roots of the quadratic equation $3x^2 - 2x - 1 = 0$ are the intercepts of a line, then the line can be ______.
(a) $x - 3y - 1 = 0$ (b) $3x - y + 1 = 0$
(c) Either (a) or (b) (d) None of these

43. The length (in units) of a line segment intercepted between the coordinate axes by the line joining the points (1, 2) and (3, 4) is ______.
(a) 4 (b) 6
(c) 8 (d) $\sqrt{2}$

44. Find the product of intercepts made by the line $7x - 2y - 14 = 0$ with coordinate axes.
(a) –7 (b) 2
(c) 14 (d) –14

45. Find the value of k, if points (–2, 5), (–5, –10) and $(k, -13)$ are collinear.
(a) $\frac{5}{28}$ (b) $\frac{-28}{5}$
(c) 28 (d) 5

46. The inclination of the line $\sqrt{3}y - x + 24 = 0$, is ______.
(a) 60° (b) 30°
(c) 45° (d) 135°

47. Find the product of intercepts of the line $3x + 8y - 24 = 0$.
(a) 8 (b) 24
(c) 3 (d) 12

48. The equation of a line whose x-intercept is –3 and which is parallel to $5x + 8y - 7 = 0$ is ______.
(a) $5x + 8y + 15 = 0$ (b) $5x + 8y - 15 = 0$
(c) $5x + 8y - 17 = 0$ (d) $5x - 8y - 18 = 0$

Level 3: Assess Your Concepts

49. The area of a square with one of its vertices as (5, –2) and the mid-point of the diagonals as (3, 2), is ______. (in sq. units)
(a) 40 (b) 20
(c) 60 (d) 70

50. The equation of the line perpendicular to the line inclined equally to the coordinate axes and passing through (2, –3) is ______.
(a) $x + y + 1 = 0$ (b) $x - y - 2 = 0$
(c) $x + y + 2 = 0$ (d) $2x + y - 1 = 0$

51. A triangle is formed by points (6, 0), (0, 0) and (0, 6). How many points with the integer coordinates are in the interior of the triangle?
(a) 7 (b) 6
(c) 8 (d) 10

52. The equation of one of the diagonals of a square is $3x - 8y + 4 = 0$. Find the equation of the other diagonal passing through the vertex (4, –6).

(a) $8x + 3y - 15 = 0$ (b) $3x - 8y - 11 = 0$
(c) $8x + 3y - 14 = 0$ (d) $8x + 3y + 15 = 0$

53. The lines $2x + 3y - 6 = 0$ and $2x + 3y - 12 = 0$ are represented on the graph. The difference between the areas of triangles formed by the lines with the coordinate axes is ______. (in sq. units)

(a) 12 (b) 9
(c) 6 (d) 3

54. The equation of a line whose x-intercept is 11 and perpendicular to $3x - 8y + 4 = 0$, is ______.

(a) $7x + 3y - 77 = 0$ (b) $8x + 3y - 88 = 0$
(c) $5x + 3y - 55 = 0$ (d) $3x + 8y - 88 = 0$

55. $A(-11, 7)$ and $B(-10, 6)$ are the points of trisection of a line segment PQ. Find the coordinates of P and Q.

(a) (–12, 8); (–9, 5) (b) (–12, –8); (–9, 5)
(c) (12, 0); (9, –5) (d) (12, –8); (9, –5)

56. If one of the diagonals of a rhombus is $3x - 4y + 10 = 0$, then find the equation of the other diagonal which passes through point (–2, –3).

(a) $4x + 3y + 17 = 0$ (b) $3x - 4y + 15 = 0$
(c) $4x + 3y - 15 = 0$ (d) $3x - 4y - 11 = 0$

57. The equation of the diagonal AC of a square $ABCD$ is $3x + 4y + 12 = 0$. Find the equation of BD, where D is (2, –3).

(a) $4x - 3y - 8 = 0$ (b) $4x - 3y - 17 = 0$
(c) $4x - 3y + 17 = 0$ (d) $4x + 3y - 17 = 0$

58. Find the area of the triangle formed by the lines $y = 4$, $\frac{x}{5} + \frac{y}{4} = 1$, and $\frac{x}{5} - \frac{y}{8} = 1$.

(a) 10 (b) 12
(c) 15 (d) 18

59. Find the perimeter of the triangle formed by $y = 3$, $x = 5$ and $y = x$.

(a) $3(4 + \sqrt{2})$ (b) $2\sqrt{2}$
(c) $(2 + \sqrt{2})$ (d) $2(2 + \sqrt{2})$

60. Find the equation of a line passing through the point of intersection of the lines $2x - 3y = 5$ and $4x + 5y = 10$ with slope $\frac{-2}{3}$.

(a) $2x + 3y = 5$ (b) $x + 3y = 7$
(c) $2x + 3y = 9$ (d) $x + y = 5$

AT

PRACTICE QUESTIONS JEE SPECIAL WING

Multiple-Answer Type Questions

Directions for questions 1 to 5:
Each question has FOUR options (a), (b), (c), and (d). ONE OR MORE THAN ONE of these four option(s) is/are the correct answer(s).

1. The area of the triangle formed by $px + qy = 10$ with the coordinate axes is 5 square units, where neither p nor q is 1 and -1. If p and q are integers, then which of the following can be the value of $p + q$?
   (a) -11 (b) -9
   (c) -7 (d) -3

2. If $(-3, 4)$ is the midpoint of a line segment PQ, which of the following can be the possible coordinates of P and Q?
   (a) $P = (6, 8)$ and $Q = (-12, 0)$
   (b) $P = (-4, -3)$ and $Q = (-2, 11)$
   (c) $P = (14, -11)$ and $Q = (-20, 17)$
   (d) $P = (21, 15)$ and $Q = (-27, -7)$

3. If a line $ax + by = c$ makes 45° with the x-axis in the positive direction, then which of the following statements is/are true?
   (a) $ab = -1$ (b) $\frac{b}{a} = -1$
   (c) $a - b = 0$ (d) $a + b = 0$

4. The orthocentre of a triangle formed by the vertices $A(3, 7)$, $B(x, y)$ and $C(6, 5)$ is $B(x, y)$. Which of the following can be (x, y)?
   (a) (6, 7) (b) (3, 5)
   (c) (5, 7) (d) (3, 6)

5. $ABCD$ is a parallelogram. Which of the following can be the vertices of the parallelogram?
   (a) $A = (-2, 3)$, $B = (-3, 6)$, $C = (-6, 6)$, and $D = (-5, 3)$.
   (b) $A = (-3, 4)$, $B = (-1, 8)$, $C = (-4, 8)$, and $D = (-6, 4)$.
   (c) $A = (0, 5)$, $B = (-2, 7)$, $C = (-3, 7)$, and $D = (-1, 5)$.
   (d) $A = (-4, 1)$, $B = (0, 10)$, $C = (-4, 10)$, and $D = (-8, 1)$.

Match The Column

Directions for questions 6 to 10:
Read the paragraph given below and answer the questions.

A math teacher gave coordinates of four points to five students. They need to plot the points and name the figures formed by joining the points.

The following table shows the details of the points which are received by the students:

Name of the Student	Points in Order
Aahana	$A(5, 5)$, $B(-1, 5)$, $C(-1, -2)$, $D(5, -2)$
Brinda	$P(-1, 5)$, $Q(5, 5)$, $R(7, -2)$, $S(1, -2)$
Chavvi	$E(5, -2)$, $F(1, -2)$, $G(-3, 2)$, $H(6, 2)$
Dipta	$U(3, 1)$, $V(5, 5)$, $W(7, 1)$, $X(5, -3)$
Ekiya	$K(7, -3)$, $L(7, 1)$, $M(3, 1)$, $M(3, -3)$

Match the values in Column A with those in Column B.

Column A	Column B
6. Aahana	(a) Only a pair of opposite sides are parallel.
7. Brinda	(b) Only two pairs of adjacent sides are equal.
8. Chavvi	(c) Diagonals bisect each other but are not equal and are not perpendicular.
9. Dipta	(d) Diagonals perpendicularly bisect each other but are not equal.
10. Ekiya	(e) Diagonals are equal and bisect each other but are not perpendicular.
	(f) Diagonals are equal and perpendicularly bisect to each other.

Comprehension-Based Questions

Directions for questions 11 to 15:

Read the paragraph given below and answer the questions.

Osha is an enthusiastic students and she loves to create puzzles. She has created a puzzle on coordinate points. The puzzle is in the form of the following data and the questions that follow.

P is point on the coordinate plane.

If x is positve, then y is negative.

If y is positve, then x is also positive.

If x is negative, then y is the additve inverse of x.

If y is negative, then x is 0.

11. If $x > 0$, then $P(x, y)$ lies in the ____ .

(a) Q_1 (b) Q_2
(c) Q_3 (d) Q_4

12. If $y > 0$, then $P(x + y, x - y)$ lies in/on the ____ .

(a) Q_1 (b) Q_2
(c) positive x-axis (d) Cannot say

13. If $x < 0$, then $P(x, y + x)$ lies in/on the ____ .

(a) Q_2 (b) Q_3
(c) negative x-axis (d) negative y-axis

14. If $y < 0$, then $P(x, x - y)$ lies in/on the ____ .

(a) positive x-axis (b) positive y-axis
(c) negative x-axis (d) negative y-axis

15. If $x < 0$, then $P(y, y - x)$ lies in/on the ____ .

(a) Q_1 (b) Q_2
(c) Q_3 (d) Q_4

Assertion and Reason Type Questions

Directions for questions 16 to 20:

Read the options given below and answer the questions.

(a) Both assertion (A) and reason (R) are true, and the reason (R) is the correct explanation of the assertion (A).
(b) Both assertion (A) and reason (R) are true, and the reason (R) is not the correct explanation of the assertion (A).
(c) Assertion (A) is true, but reason (R) is false.
(d) Assertion (A) is false, and reason (R) is true.

16. Assertion: $A(8, 7)$ is equidistant from $P(11, 3)$ and $Q(4, 10)$.

Reason: The distance between (x_1, y_1) and (x_2, y_2) is given by $\sqrt{(x_2 - x_1)^2 + (y_2 - y_1)^2}$.

17. Assertion: If $x = y$, the distance between $(2, x)$ and $(5, y)$ is 3 units.

Reason: The distance between (x_1, a) and (x_2, a) is $|x_2 - x_1|$.

18. Assertion: If the centroid of the triangle formed by $A(9, -3)$, $B(-7, 3)$ and C is $(1, 1)$, then C is $(1, 0)$.

Reason: The centroid of the triangle formed by (x_1, y_1), (x_2, y_2) and (x_3, y_3) is $\left(\frac{x_1 + x_2 + x_3}{3}, \frac{y_1 + y_2 + y_3}{3}\right)$.

19. Assertion: The area of the triangle formed by $5x + 4y = 20$ with the coordinate axes is 10 square units.

Reason: The area of the triangle formed by $ax + by = c$ with the coordinate axes is $\frac{c}{2}$ square units.

20. Assertion: The lines $6x - 9y = 21$ and $8x - 12y = 27$ represent a pair of parallel lines.

Reason: The *x-axis* and the *y-axis* are represented by $y = 0$ and $x = 0$ respectively.

ANSWER KEYS

Crossword

Across

2. Zero
5. Gradient
8. Collinear
9. Oblique
10. Ordinate

Down

1. Parallel
3. Origin
4. Inclination
6. Abscissa
7. Slope

Classroom Wing

Very Short Answer Type Questions

1. 12 units
2. $\frac{-x}{2}$
3. 3rd Quadrant
4. 0
5. –2
6. 0
7. $y=\frac{-2}{3}x-\frac{5}{3}$
8. Parallel
9. Collinear
10. $x=\frac{19}{2}$
11. (–ve, +ve)
12. 0°
13. $\left(\frac{5}{3}, 0\right)$
14. *X*-axis
15. Origin (or) (0, 0)
16. Collinear
17. $-\cot\theta$
18. Fourth
19. 1
20. Parallel

Short Answer Type Questions

21. $3y - 2x - 13 = 0$ or $2x - 3y + 13 = 0$
22. 50π
23. $k = -16$
24. $\sqrt{85}$ units
25. $k = \frac{-5}{4}$
26. 20 sq. units
27. $2\sqrt{2}a$
28. $x = 2, y = -3$
29. 30°
30. $\left[\frac{1}{14}, \frac{-13}{14}\right]$
31. $3\sqrt{3}x - 3y - 1 = 0$
32. (2, 0)
33. *ABCD* is a rhombus
34. $7x + 3y + 15 = 0$

Essay Type Questions

35. 4
36. 12
37. 0
38. 1
39. 0

Competition Wing

Level 1: Apply Your Concepts

1. First
2. (2, 3)
3. $\left[3, -\frac{3}{2}\right]$
4. Right-angled isosceles triangle
5. (b)
6. (d)
7. (a)
8. (c)
9. (d)
10. (b)
11. (d)
12. (d)
13. (a)
14. (b)
15. (a)
16. (c)
17. (a)
18. (d)
19. (c)

20. (d)	21. (b)	22. (b)	23. (c)	24. (b)
25. (d)	26. (a)	27. (b)	28. (b)	29. (a)
30. (a)	31. (c)	32. (d)		

Level 2: Review Your Concepts

33. (c)	34. (b)	35. (c)	36. (c)	37. (c)
38. (c)	39. (a)	40. (d)	41. (d)	42. (c)
43. (d)	44. (d)	45. (b)	46. (b)	47. (b)
48. (a)				

Level 3: Assess Your Concepts

49. (a)	50. (a)	51. (d)	52. (c)	53. (b)
54. (b)	55. (a)	56. (a)	57. (b)	58. (c)
59. (d)	60. (a)			

JEE Special Wing

Multiple-Answer Type Questions

1. (c, d)	2. (a, b, d)	3. (b, d)	4. (a, b)	5. (a, b, c, d)

Match The Column

6. (e)	7. (c)	8. (a)	9. (d)	10. (f)

Comprehension-Based Questions

11. (d)	12. (d)	13. (c)	14. (b)	15. (a)

Assertion and Reason Type Questions

16. (a)	17. (a)	18. (d)	19. (c)	20. (b)

Hints and Explanations

Classroom Wing

Very Short Answer Type Questions

1. A = (0, 0), B = (4, 0) and C = (0, 3)

   $AB = 4 - 0 = 4$; $BC = \sqrt{4^2 + 3^2} = 5$; $AC = 3 - 0 = 3$

   ∴ The perimeter of $\Delta ABC = 4 + 5 + 3 = 12$ units.

2. Slope $= \dfrac{2x+3-x-3}{x-2-x} = \dfrac{-x}{2}$ which is negative. ($\because x > 0$)

3. As $5x + 6y = 30$ which is positive, $(x, y) \notin Q_3$.

4. Slope $\dfrac{3x-3-3x+3}{5x+3-2x-3} = \dfrac{0}{3x} = 0$

5. Since, altitude is always perpendicular to the base

   Therefore, slope (altitude) × slope (BC) = −1

   $\left(\dfrac{y_2 - y_1}{x_2 - x_1}\right) = -1$

   Slope (altitude) × $\left(\dfrac{5-2}{3+3}\right) = -1$

   ⇒ Slope (altitude) = −2

6. If $\dfrac{x}{a} + \dfrac{y}{b} = m$ passes through origin then it will satisfy (0, 0)

   $\Rightarrow \dfrac{0}{a} + \dfrac{0}{b} = m$

   $\Rightarrow m = 0$

7. $2x + 3y + 5 = 0$

   $\Rightarrow 2x + 3y = -5$

   $\Rightarrow \dfrac{-2x}{5} + \dfrac{-3y}{5} = 1$

   $\Rightarrow y = \dfrac{-2}{3}x - \dfrac{5}{3}$

8. Line 1: $3x + 2y + 7 = 0$

   $m_1 = \dfrac{-3}{2}$

   Line 2: $6x + 4y + 9 = 0$

   $m_2 = \dfrac{-6}{4} = \dfrac{-3}{2}$

   Since $m_1 = m_2$

   ⇒ lines are parallel.

9. Slope between points $(p, q + r)$, $(q, r + p)$

   $= \dfrac{(r+p)-(q+r)}{q-p} = \dfrac{p-q}{q-p} = -1$

   Slope between points $(q, r + p)(r, q + p)$

   $= \dfrac{(q+p)-(r+p)}{r-q} = \dfrac{q-r}{r-q} = -1$

   ⇒ These points are collinear.

10. If (2, 3), (−1, 5), and (x, −2) form a straight line then,

    $\Rightarrow \dfrac{5-3}{-1-2} = \dfrac{-2-5}{x-(-1)}$

    $\Rightarrow \dfrac{2}{-3} = \dfrac{-7}{x+1}$

    $\Rightarrow 2x + 2 = 21$

    $x = \dfrac{19}{2}$

11. If (x, y) lies in 2nd quadrant then $x < 0$ and $y > 0$

    ⇒ (x, y) = (−ve, +ve)

12. Line $x = 5$ and $x = 7$ are equations of the lines parallel to y-axis.

    Hence line $x = 5$ is parallel to line $x = 7$

    ∴ angle between $x = 5$ and $x = 7 = 0°$

13. Equation of x-axis: $y = 0$ (1)

    Let point of intersection between x-axis and $3x + 2y - 5 = 0$ be (a, b) (2)

    ⇒ (a, b) will satisfy both equations:

    ⇒ $b = 0$ (from eqn (1))

    $3a + 2b - 5 = 0$ (from eqn (2))

    $3a - 5 = 0$

    $a = \dfrac{5}{3}$

    Hence, point of intersection is $\left(\dfrac{5}{3}, 0\right)$

14. $ax + by + c = 0$

    If $a = 0$

    then $by + c = 0$

    $y = \dfrac{-c}{b}$

    ⇒ It is the equation of line parallel of x-axis.

15. Point of intersection of (x-axis) and (y-axis) is origin (0, 0).

16. If A, B, C are 3 points, such that $AB = AC + BC$
$\Rightarrow A, B, C$ are collinear

17. If $m_1 = \tan\theta$, then slope of line perpendicular to m_1 will be:

$m_1 \times m_2 = -1$

$\tan\theta \times m_2 = -1$

$m_2 = \dfrac{-1}{\tan\theta} = -\cot\theta$

$m_2 = -\cot\theta$

18. Lines ($x = 2$) and ($y = 3$) intersect at point (2, –3)
Hence, it will intersect in 4th quadrant.

19. Line making an angle of 45° has slope
$m = \tan\theta$
$\Rightarrow m = \tan 45° = 1$
Now, line parallel to this will also have equal slope
Hence $m = 1$.

20. If slopes of 2 lines are equal, then lines are parallel.

Short Answer Type Questions

21. Line passes through $A(-2, 3)$ and $B(4, 7)$ using 2 points form of line:

$$(y - y_1) = \left(\frac{y_2 - y_1}{x_2 - x_1}\right)(x - x_1)$$

Substituting the value of (x_1, y_1) and (x_2, y_2),

$$(y - 3) = \left(\frac{7-3}{4+2}\right)(x+2)$$

$$y - 3 = \frac{4}{6}(x+2)$$

$3y - 9 = 2x + 4$

$3y - 2x - 13 = 0$ or $2x - 3y + 13 = 0$

22. Centre = (5, 2)
Point of circumference = (–2, 3)
Radius = distance between (5, 2) and (–2, 3)

$$\text{Radius} = \sqrt{(5+2)^2 + (2-3)^2} = \sqrt{50} = 5\sqrt{2} \text{ units}$$

$$\text{Area of circle} = \pi r^2 = \left(5\sqrt{2}\right)^2 \pi \text{ sq units.}$$

$$= 50\pi \text{ sq units}$$

23. $AC = BC$ using distance formula

$$\sqrt{(-2+3)^2 + (k-2)^2} = \sqrt{(4+2)^2 + (1-k)^2}$$

Squaring on both sides:
$1 + (k - 2)^2 = 36 + (1 - k)^2$

$1 + \cancel{k^2} + 4 - 4k = 36 + 1 + \cancel{k^2} - 2k$

$-2k = 32$

$k = -16$

24. Using distance formula:

$$\text{Distance} = \sqrt{(4-2)^2 + (6+3)^2}$$

$$= \sqrt{4+81} = \sqrt{85} \text{ units.}$$

25. If line $2x - ky + 6 = 0$ passes through (2, –8), then (2, –8) will satisfy the equation:
$2(2) - k(-8) + 6 = 0$
$4 + 8k + 6 = 0$
$8k = -10$

$k = \dfrac{-5}{4}$

26. Length of diagonal:

$$\sqrt{(4+2)^2 + (5-3)^2} = \sqrt{36+4} = \sqrt{40} \text{ units}$$

Also,
Diagonal = $\sqrt{2} \times$ (side of square)

$$\Rightarrow \text{Side of square} = \frac{\text{diagonal}}{\sqrt{2}}$$

$$= \frac{\sqrt{40}}{\sqrt{2}} = \sqrt{20} \text{ units}$$

Hence, area of square = (sides)^2

$$= \left(\sqrt{20}\right)^2 \text{ sq units}$$

area = 20 sq. units.

27. $$\overline{AB} = \sqrt{\left(-a + \cancel{b} - a - \cancel{b}\right)^2 + \left(-a - \cancel{b} - a + \cancel{b}\right)^2}$$

$$= \sqrt{4a^2 + 4a^2} = 2\sqrt{2}a \text{ sq. units}$$

$\overline{AB} = 2\sqrt{2}a$ sq. units

28. $3x - 2y - 6 = 0$
$\Rightarrow 3x - 2y = 6$

$$\Rightarrow \frac{3x}{6} - \frac{2y}{6} = 1$$

$$\Rightarrow \frac{x}{2} + \frac{y}{(-3)} = 1$$

Hence,
x-intercept = 2
y-intercept = –3

29. $\sqrt{3}x - 3y + 6 = 0$

Slope $m = \dfrac{-(\text{coefficient of } x)}{(\text{coefficient of } y)}$

$m = \dfrac{-\sqrt{3}}{-3} = \dfrac{1}{\sqrt{3}} = \tan\theta$

$\tan\theta = \dfrac{1}{\sqrt{3}}$

$\Rightarrow \tan\theta = \tan 30°$

$\Rightarrow \theta = 30°$

30. Let $D(p, q)$ be the circum-centre of the triangle ABC

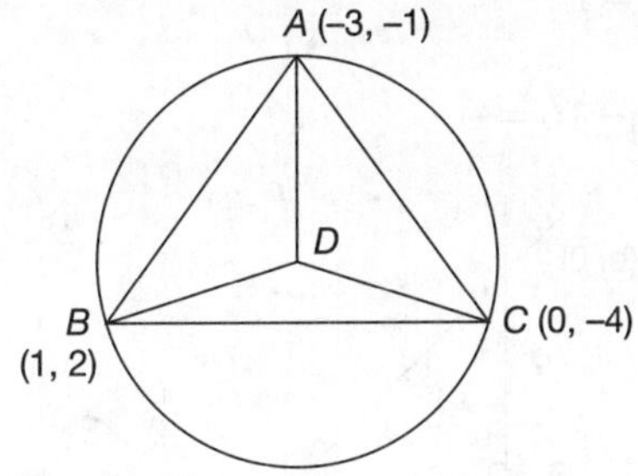

Now, $A\Delta = B\Delta = \Delta C$ (all 3 are radius)

$A\Delta = C\Delta$ (1)

$B\Delta = \Delta C$ (2)

Using distance formula in equation (1) and (2)

For equation (1),

$\sqrt{(-3-p)^2 + (-1-q)^2} = \sqrt{(0-p)^2 + (-4-q)^2}$

$(-3-p)^2 + (-1-q)^2 = p^2 + (-4-q)^2$

$9 + \not{p^2} + 6p + 1 + \not{q^2} + 2q = \not{p^2} + 16 + \not{q^2} + 8q$

$6p + 2q + 10 = 8q + 16$

$6p - 6q = 6$

$p - q = 1$ (*)

For equation (2),

$\sqrt{(1-p)^2 + (2-q)^2} = \sqrt{(0-p)^2 + (-4-q)^2}$

$(1-p)^2 + (2-q)^2 = p^2 + (-4-q)^2$

$1 + \not{p^2} - 2p + 4 + \not{q^2} - 4q = \not{p^2} + 16 + \not{q^2} + 8q$

$5 - 2p - 4q = 16 + 8q$

$-2p - 12q = 11$ (**)

On solving equation (*) and (**)

Simultaneously, we get:

$p = \dfrac{1}{14}, q = \dfrac{-13}{14}$

So, circumcentre is $\left[\dfrac{1}{14}, \dfrac{-13}{14}\right]$

31. Let equation of the line be $y = mx + c$

Now, $m = \tan\theta$

Here, $\theta = 60°$

$\therefore m = \tan 60° = \sqrt{3}$

and $c = \dfrac{-1}{3}$ (intercept on y-axis)

$\Rightarrow y = \sqrt{3}x - \dfrac{1}{3}$

$3y = 3\sqrt{3}x - 1$

$\Rightarrow 3\sqrt{3}x - 3y - 1 = 0$

32. Let the point on x-axis be $p(a, 0)$ since it is equidistant then

$|AP| = |PB|$

Using distance formula

$\sqrt{(6-a)^2 + (3-0)^2} = \sqrt{(-1-a)^2 + (4-0)^2}$

Squaring on both sides:

$(6-a)^2 + 9 = (a+1)^2 + 16$

$36 + \not{a^2} - 12a + 9 = \not{a^2} + 1 + 2a + 16$

$28 = 14a$

$\Rightarrow a = 2 \Rightarrow p = (2, 0)$

33. $A = (-1, -1)$; $B = (6, 1)$; $C = (8, 8)$; $D = (1, 6)$ for $ABCD$ to be rhombus

$AB = BC = CD = DA$ (all sides should be equal)

and $AB \,||\, CD$ and $BC \,||$

Now $|AB| = \sqrt{(6+1)^2 + (1+1)^2} = \sqrt{53}$

$|BC| = \sqrt{(8-6)^2 + (8-1)^2} = \sqrt{53}$

$|CD| = \sqrt{(8-1)^2 + (8-6)^2} = \sqrt{53}$

$|AD| = \sqrt{(1+1)^2 + (6+1)^2} = \sqrt{53}$

$\Rightarrow |AB| = |BC| = |CD| = |AD|$

Hence all sides are equal.

Now, slope(AB) = slope(CD) and slope(BC) = slope(AD).

Slope of $AB = \dfrac{1+1}{6+1} = \dfrac{2}{7} = m_1$

Slope of $CD = \dfrac{6-8}{1-8} = \dfrac{2}{7} = m_2$

Slope of $BC = \dfrac{8-1}{8-6} = \dfrac{7}{2} = m_3$

Slope of $AD = \dfrac{-1-6}{-1-1} = \dfrac{7}{2} = m_4$

Now, $m_1 = m_2$ and, $m_3 = m_4$
Hence $AB || CD$ and $BC || AD$
$\Rightarrow ABCD$ is a rhombus

34. Let the equation of line be $\frac{x}{a}+\frac{y}{b}=1$
Where $b = y$-intercept $= -5$
Since, it passes through $A(-3, 2)$, it will satisfy above equation:

$$\frac{-3}{a}+\frac{2}{-5}=1$$

$$\Rightarrow \frac{-3}{a}=1+\frac{2}{5} \Rightarrow \frac{-3}{a}=\frac{7}{5}$$

$$\Rightarrow a=\frac{-15}{7}$$

Now, equation will be

$$\frac{x}{\left(\frac{-15}{7}\right)}+\frac{y}{(-5)}=1$$

$$\Rightarrow \frac{-7x}{15}-\frac{y}{5}=1$$

$$-7x-3y=15$$

$$\Rightarrow 7x+3y+15=0$$

Essay Type Questions

35. We have $\frac{x}{a}+\frac{y}{b}=1$

$$\Rightarrow \frac{x}{a}+\frac{y}{a}=1 \text{ (given that } a=b)$$

It passes through the point (–3, 5).

$$\Rightarrow \frac{-3}{a}+\frac{5}{a}=1$$

$$\Rightarrow \frac{2}{a}=1$$

$$\Rightarrow a=2$$

Now $a + b = 2a = 4$

36. ABCD is a rhombus. The equation of AC: $2x + 3y = 12$.
Let the equation of BD be $3x - 2y = k$, since $\overline{AC} \perp \overline{BD}$.
And also given that $3x - 2y = k$ passes through the point (2, –3).
$3(2) - 2(-3) = k$
$k = 12$
$\therefore$ The equation of BD is $3x - 2y = 12$.

37. Let the equation of the line be $\frac{x}{a}+\frac{y}{b}=1$ and let the intercept be a and $-a$ since, it passes through (–5, 11).

$$\frac{-5}{a}-\frac{11}{a}=1$$

$$-5-11=a$$

$$\Rightarrow a=-16$$

Hence, the equation of line is:

$$\frac{x}{16}-\frac{y}{16}=1$$

$$\Rightarrow x-y-16=0$$

38.

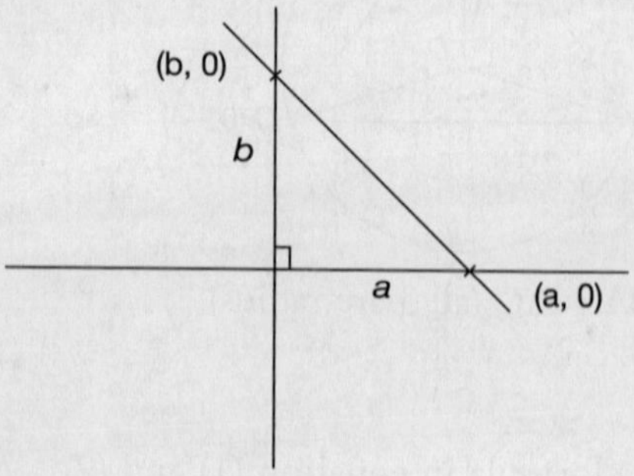

A.T.Q.

$a + b = 7$ (1)

and $\frac{1}{2}ab = 5$ sq units

$$\Rightarrow ab = 10$$

$$b=\frac{10}{a}$$

Using this value of b in (1) we get,

$$a+\frac{10}{a}=7$$

$$a^2+10=7a$$

$$a^2-5a-2a+10=0$$

$$a(a-5)-2(a-5)=0$$

$$(a-5)(a-2)=0$$

$a = 5, 2$

If $a = 5$ then $b = 2$

Equation of line

$$\frac{x}{5}+\frac{y}{2}=1$$

If $a = 2$ then $b = 5$

Equation of line

$$\frac{x}{2}+\frac{y}{5}=1$$

39.

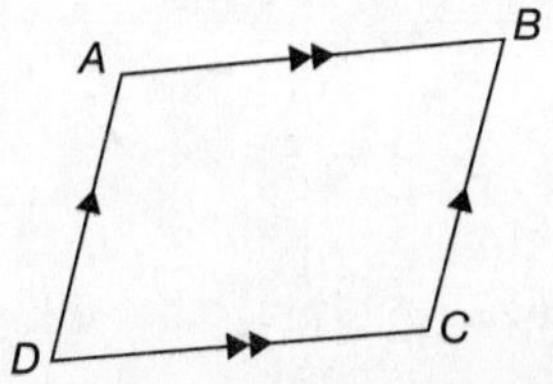

Let the variable of D be (p, q)

Since, $ABCD$ is a parallelogram

$\Rightarrow AB || CD$ and $AD || BC$

$\Rightarrow$ Slope $AB =$ Slope CD and Slope $(AD) =$ Slope (BC)

$$\frac{2-6}{5-1} = \frac{q-9}{p-12} \text{ and } \frac{q-6}{p-1} = \frac{9-2}{12-5}$$

$$-1 = \frac{q-9}{p-12} \text{ and } \frac{q-6}{p-1} = 1$$

$12 - p = q - 9$ and $p - 1 = q - 6$

$p + q = 21$ and $p - q = -5$

On solving these simultaneously we get,

$p = 8,\ q = 13$

$\Rightarrow$ coordinates of D are $(8, 13)$

Now, Equation of diagonal BD

$$(y-2) = \frac{13-2}{8-5}(x-5)$$

$\Rightarrow 3y - 6 = 11x - 55$

$\Rightarrow 11x - 3y - 49 = 0$

Competition Wing

Level 1: Apply Your Concepts

1. If $x > 0$ and $y < 0$
Then (x, y) lies in
First Quadrant

2.

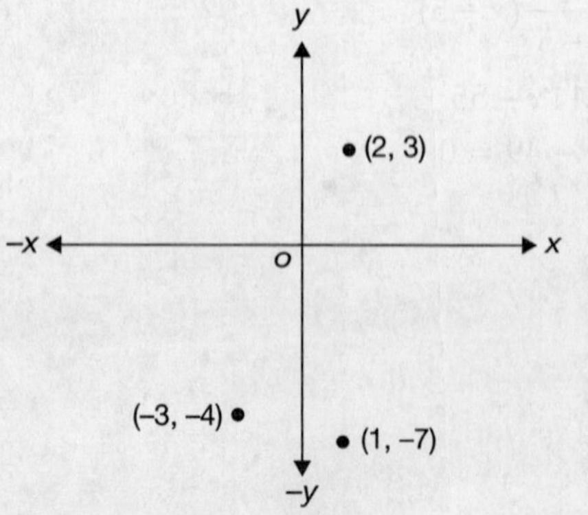

Nearest to the origin is (2, 3)

3. $2y + 3 = 0$ and $x = 3$
Let the intersecting point be (a, b)
then, (a, b) will satisfy both equations.
Hence, $a = 3$ and $2b + 3 = 0$

$b = \frac{-3}{2}$

$\Rightarrow (a, b) = \left(3, \frac{-3}{2}\right)$

4.

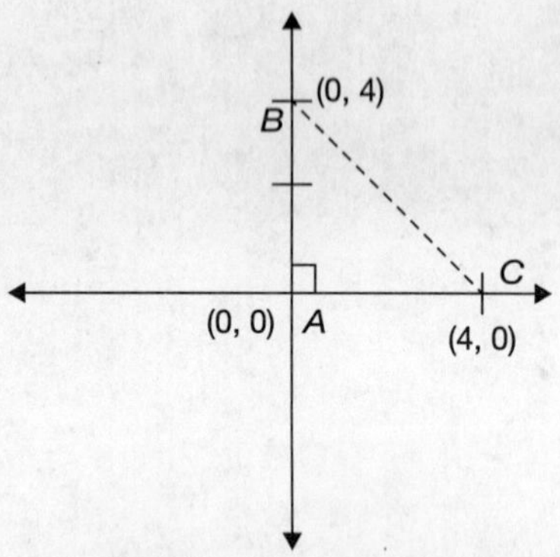

Let $A = (0, 0)$
$B = (0, 4)$
$C = (4, 0)$
then $\angle A = 90°$ and $AB = AC$
Hence, ΔABC is a right-angled isosceles triangle.

5. Fourth vertex of a parallelogram is $(x_1 + x_3 - x_2, y_1 + y_3 - y_2)$.

6. Let C$(x, 0)$ be the point on x – axis.
Let A(2, 4) and B (3, 2)
Given, AC = BC
$AC^2 = BC^2$
$(x - 2)^2 + (0 - 4)^2 = (x - 3)^2 + (2 - 0)^2$
$x^2 + 4 - 4x + 16 = x^2 + 9 - 6x + 4$
$2x = -7$
$x = \frac{-7}{2}$
$\therefore$ required point $= (x, 0) = \left(\frac{-7}{2}, 0\right)$.

7. Given $(x, y) \in Q_2$
$\Rightarrow x < 0, y > 0$
$\therefore (-x, y) \in Q_1$.

8. Let C$(0, y)$ be the point on y – axis
Let A(2, 4) and B(3, 5)
Given AC = BC
$\Rightarrow AC^2 = BC^2$
$(0 - 2)^2 + (y - 4)^2 = (0 - 3)^2 + (y - 5)^2$
$4 + y^2 + 16 - 8xy = 9 + y^2 + 25 - 10y$
$2y = 14$
$y = 7$
$\therefore$ required point, $(0, y) = (0, 7)$.

9. $y = 8$ and $y = 4$ are parallel to each other.

10. There are 3 possibilities to get the third vertex B.

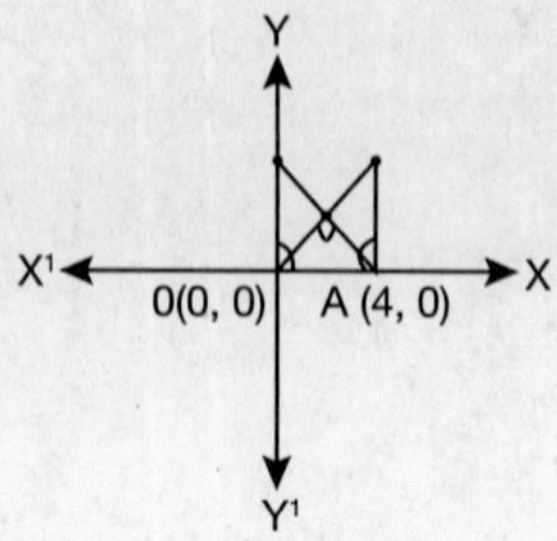

11. Equation of the sides are $x = 0$, $y = 0$, $x + y = 9$
$\therefore x + y = 9$
$\therefore \frac{x}{9} + \frac{y}{9} = 1$
X – intercept = 9
$\therefore$ Point on X-axis is (9, 0)
Y – intercept = 9.
$\therefore$ Point on Y-axis is (0, 9)
$x = 0$ is equation of the y-axis.
$y = 0$ is equation of the y-axis.
Intersecting point of the coordinate axis is (0, 0).
Vertices of the triangle are (0, 0), (9, 0), (0, 9)

Centroid $= \left(\dfrac{0+9+0}{3}, \dfrac{0+0+9}{3}\right)$

$= (3, 3)$.

12. The centre of a circle is the mid-point of the diameter.

13. The slope of the line $= \dfrac{-a}{b} = \dfrac{-1}{-\sqrt{3}} = \dfrac{1}{3}$

14. The line $2x + 3y = 6$

$\therefore \dfrac{2x+3y}{6} = \dfrac{6}{6}$

$\dfrac{x}{3} + \dfrac{y}{2} = 1$

x – intercept = 3

$\therefore$ Point on X-axis P = (3, 0)

y – intercept = 2

$\therefore$ Point on Y-axis, Q = (0, 2)

Distance of PQ $= \sqrt{(0-3)^2 + (2-0)^2} = \sqrt{9+4} = \sqrt{13}$.

15. Find the roots, and then use slope-intercept form of line.

16. Area of square = (side)^2.

17. Use $\dfrac{x}{a} + \dfrac{y}{b} = 1$ and $a = -b$.

18. (i) Find the diameter of the circle then find its area.

(ii) The distance between (–2, 3) and (6, –3) is the length of the diameter of the circle.

(iii) Area of circle $= \dfrac{\pi d^2}{4}$, where d is the length of the diameter.

19. Use $m = \tan\theta$.

20. If two lines are perpendicular to the same line, then they are parallel to each other.

21. Find lengths of the diagonals, then area of rhombus $= \dfrac{1}{2} \times d_1 \times d_2$.

22. Find the distance between the given two points and compare that distance with the radius given.

23. The mid-point of the diameter is the centre of a circle.

24. Find the roots of the given equation, then use intercepts form of line.

25. (i) Equation of a line parallel to X-axis is of the form y = constant.

(ii) Slope of a line parallel to X-axis is zero.

(iii) Slope of a line $= \dfrac{-(x\text{-coefficient})}{(y\text{-coeffcient})}$.

26. The slope of the line joining two points is $\dfrac{y_2 - y_1}{x_2 - x_1}$.

27. The first line is parallel to the Y-axis. The second line is parallel to the X-axis.

28. Two lines, which are perpendicular to the same line, must be parallel to each other.

29. Solve the first two equations and substitute (x, y) in the third equation and evaluate k.

30. The circum-centre of a right-angled triangle is the mid-point of its hypotenuse.

31. Find the coordinates of the point of intersection.

32. The distance from centre of the circle to any point on the circle is its radius.

Level 2: Review Your Concepts

33. The perpendicular lines are in the form of $ax + by + c = 0$ and $bx - ay + k = 0$.

34. PQRS is a square. The equation of QS : $5x - 7y = 16$

$\therefore$ The equation of PR will be in the form of $7x + 5y = k$. Hence, choice (b) follows

35. $x = 0$, $y = 0$ and $x - y + 5 = 0$ form a right isosceles triangle.

$\therefore$ The angles of the triangle are 45°, 45° and 90°.

36. $\Rightarrow x = y$

$\Rightarrow (x, y) \in Q_1$ and Q_3.

37. Method -1:

If we plot A = (–4, 5), B = (4, 5), C = (3, –2) and D = (–3, –2),

we will get an isosceles trapezium.

Method -2:

AB is parallel to x - axis ($\because$ y - coordinates are equal)

CD is also parallel to x - axis ($\because$ y - coordinates are equal)

$\Rightarrow \overline{AB} \,||\, \overline{CD} \,||\, x$ axis BC is not parallel to y - axis.

But AD = BC.

Hence ABCD is an isosceles trapezium.

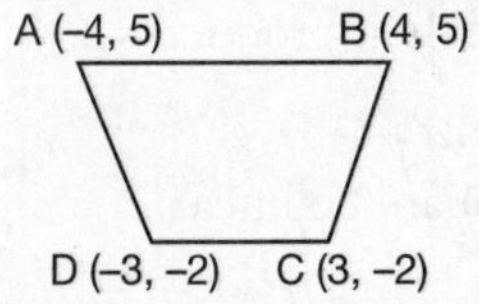

38. (i) The three points are collinear.
(ii) Given points A, B, and C are collinear.
(iii) Use, slope of AB = slope of AC and find m.

39. (i) Find the intercepts, then find the distance between them.
(ii) Find the equation of the line joining the given points.
(iii) Find the intercepts (a and b) made by the above line with coordinate axes.
(iv) The distance between $(a, 0)$ and $(0, b)$.

40. (i) Use the formula $a(x - x_1) + b(y - y_1) = 0$.
(ii) Slopes of parallel lines are equal.
(iii) Use, point-slope form, i.e., $(y - y_1) = m(x - x_1)$ and find the equation of the line.

41. (i) The given vertices form an equilateral triangle.
(ii) Given points are the vertices of an equilateral triangle.
(iii) In any equilateral triangle, geometric centres (except ex-centre) coincide.

42. (i) Find the roots, then use $\frac{x}{a} + \frac{y}{b} = 1$.
(ii) Roots of $3x^2 - 2x - 1 = 0$ are $\frac{-1}{3}$ and 1.
(iii) x-intercept is either $\frac{-1}{3}$ or 1.
y-intercept is either 1 or $\frac{-1}{3}$.
(iv) The required equation of the line is $\frac{x}{a} + \frac{y}{b} = 1$.

43. (i) Find the intercepts, then find the distance between the intercepted points.
(ii) Find the equation of the line joining points (1, 2) and (3, 4).
(iii) Find the intercepts (a and b) of the line by putting $x = 0$ and $y = 0$.
(iv) Length of the required line is $\sqrt{a^2 + b^2}$.

44. $7x - 2y - 14 = 0 \Rightarrow 7x - 2y = 14$

$\Rightarrow \frac{x}{2} - \frac{y}{7} = 1 \Rightarrow \frac{x}{2} + \frac{y}{(-7)} = 1.$

$\therefore$ Intercepts are 2 and -7, and their product $= 2 \times (-7) = -14$.

45. $(-2, 5)$, $(-5, -10)$ and $(k, -13)$ are collinear

$\Rightarrow \frac{-10-5}{-5+2} = \frac{-13+10}{k+5}$

$\Rightarrow \frac{-15}{-3} = \frac{-3}{k+5}$

$\Rightarrow 5(k+5) = -3$

$\Rightarrow k+5 = \frac{-3}{5}$

$\Rightarrow k = \frac{-3}{5} - 5 = \frac{-28}{5}$

$\therefore k = \frac{-28}{5}$.

46. $\sqrt{3}y - x + 24 = 0 \Rightarrow m = \frac{1}{\sqrt{3}}$.

$\therefore m = \tan\theta = \frac{1}{\sqrt{3}}$

$\Rightarrow \tan\theta = \frac{1}{\sqrt{3}}$

$\Rightarrow \theta = 30°$. $\left(\because \tan 30° = \frac{1}{\sqrt{3}}\right)$

47. $3x + 8y = 24$

$\Rightarrow \frac{x}{8} + \frac{y}{3} = 1$

$\Rightarrow$ Intercepts are 8 and 3 and their product is $8 \times 3 = 24$.

48. $y = \left(-\frac{5}{8}\right)x + \frac{7}{8}$

where $m = \left(-\frac{5}{8}\right)$

$\Rightarrow c = -\frac{15}{8}$

$\Rightarrow y = \left(-\frac{5}{8}\right)x + \frac{15}{8}$

Level 3: Assess Your Concepts

49. Slope of the line parallel to $5x + 8y - 7 = 0$ is $\frac{-5}{8}$.

Given that the x-intercept of the required line is -3.
$\therefore$ It passes through $(-3, 0)$. Hence, the required line is

$-\frac{5}{8} = \frac{y-0}{x-(-3)}$

$y = \frac{-5}{8}(x+3)$

$\Rightarrow 8y = -5x - 15 \Rightarrow 5x + 8y + 15 = 0.$

50. (i) Required line is perpendicular to $x = y$ and passes through $(2, -3)$.
(ii) Find m, then use the slope–point form.

51. Draw the triangle and list the possible points.

52. (i) In a square, the diagonals are perpendicular to each other.
(ii) Find the slope of the second diagonal and use the slope–point form.

53. (i) Find the intercepts made by the lines on the coordinate axes by writing the equations in the intercept form.
(ii) If the intercepts made are a and b, then the area of the triangle formed is $\frac{ab}{2}$.

54. Slope of the line perpendicular to $3x - 8y + 4 = 0$ is

$$\frac{-1}{\text{Slope of } 3x - 8y + 4 = 0} = \frac{-1}{\frac{3}{8}} = -\frac{8}{3}.$$

Given that, x-intercept of the required line is 11.
$\therefore$ It passes through $(11, 0)$.

Hence, the required line is $-\frac{8}{3} = \frac{y-0}{x-11}$.

That is, $y - 0 = -\frac{8}{3}(x - 11)$

$\Rightarrow 8x + 3y - 88 = 0.$

55. Let $P = (a_1, b_1)$, and $Q = (a_2, b_2)$. Given, $A = (-11, 7)$ and $B = (-10, 6)$.

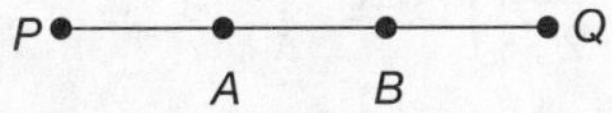

$\Rightarrow A$ is the mid-point of the line segment PB.

$$\therefore A = \left(\frac{a_1 - 10}{2}, \frac{b_1 + 6}{2}\right)$$

$$(-11, 7) = \left(\frac{a_1 - 10}{2}, \frac{b_1 + 6}{2}\right)$$

$\Rightarrow a_1 = -12$ and $b_1 = 8$

$\Rightarrow P = (-12, 8)$. Similarly, $Q = (-9, 5)$.

56. One diagonal of the rhombus is $3x - 4y + 10 = 0$.

Slope of $3x - 4y + 10 = 0$ is $\frac{3}{4}$.

In a rhombus, diagonals bisect each other perpendicularly.

$\therefore$ The slope of the other diagonal

$$= \frac{-1}{\frac{3}{4}} = -\frac{4}{3}.$$

The required equation is $-\frac{4}{3} = \frac{y-(-3)}{x-(-2)}$

$\Rightarrow y + 3 = -\frac{4}{3}(x + 2)$

$\Rightarrow 4x + 3y + 17 = 0.$

57. The equation of diagonal AC is $3x + 4y + 12 = 0$.

Its slope $= -\frac{3}{4}$.

Slope of the other diagonal BD $\frac{1}{\frac{-3}{4}} = \frac{4}{3}$.

BD passes through $(2, -3)$

$$\therefore \frac{4}{3} = \frac{y-(-3)}{x-2}$$

$$\therefore y + 3 = \frac{4}{3}(x - 2)$$

$4x - 3y - 17 = 0.$

58. Given $\frac{x}{5} + \frac{y}{4} = 1$ $\frac{x}{5} - \frac{y}{8} = 1$, and $y = 4$

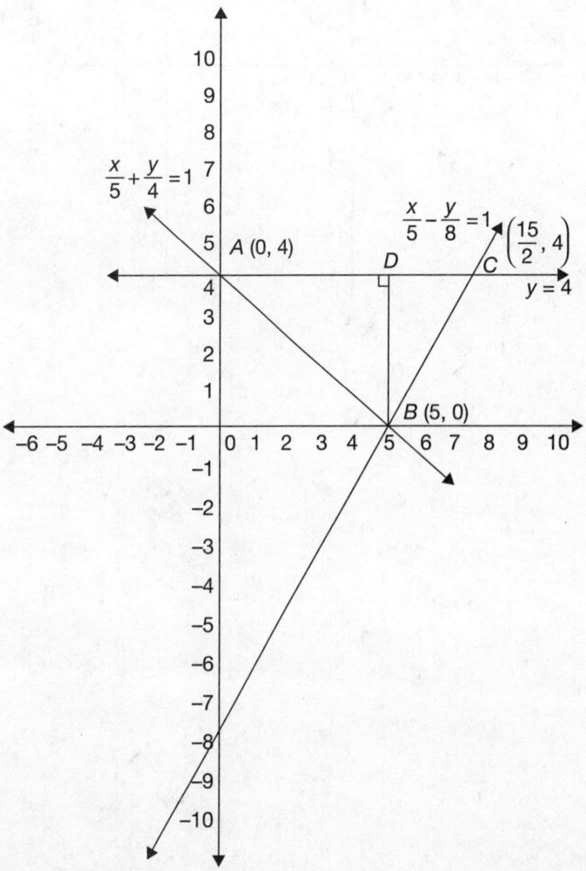

The intersecting point of $y = 4$ and $\frac{x}{5} - \frac{y}{8} = 1$

$$\frac{x}{5} - \frac{4}{8} = 1 \Rightarrow \frac{x}{5} = 1 + \frac{1}{2} \Rightarrow \frac{x}{5} = \frac{3}{2}$$

$$x = \frac{15}{2} \Rightarrow (x, y) = \left(\frac{15}{2}, 4\right)$$

The vertices of the triangle formed are A (0, 4), B(5, 0) and $C\left(\frac{15}{2}, 4\right)$.

$$AC = \frac{15}{2} - 0 = \frac{15}{2}$$

$BD = 4$

$$\text{Area of the triangle } ABC = \frac{AC \times BD}{2}$$

$$= \frac{1}{2} \times \frac{15}{2} \times 4 = 15 \text{ sq units}$$

59. Let A, B and C be the vertices of the triangle.

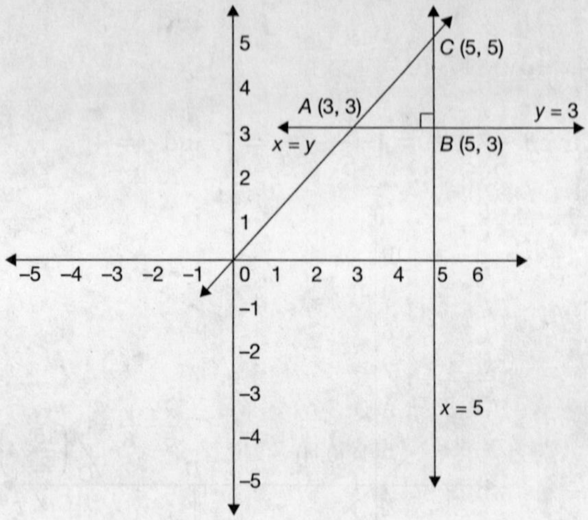

$A(3, 3)$, $B(5, 3)$ and $C(5, 5)$.

$AB = 5 - 3 = 2$ units

$BC = 5 - 3 = 2$ units

$$CA = \sqrt{(5-3)^2 + (5-3)^2}$$

$$= 2\sqrt{2} \text{ units}$$

$$\text{Perimeter} = 2 + 2 + 2\sqrt{2} \text{ units}$$

$$= \left(4 + 2\sqrt{2}\right) \text{ units}$$

$$= 2\left(2 + \sqrt{2}\right) \text{ units.}$$

60. $2x - 3y = 5$ ...(1)

$4x + 5y = 10$ ...(2)

Equation (1) × 2 – equation (2)

$$\begin{array}{r} 4x - 6y = 10 \\ 4x + 5y = 10 \\ \hline -11y = 0 \end{array}$$

$y = 0$

Substitute in $y = 0$ in $2x - 3y = 5$, we get

$2x - 3(0) = 5$

$2x = 5$

$$x = \frac{5}{2}$$

$$\text{Slope } (m) = \frac{-2}{3}.$$

Point slope form of a line is $y - y_1 = m(x - x_1)$

$$y - 0 = \frac{-2}{3}\left(x - \frac{5}{2}\right)$$

$$y = \frac{-2}{3}\left(\frac{2x - 5}{2}\right)$$

$3y = -2x + 5$

$2x + 3y = 5.$

JEE Special Wing

Multiple-Answer Type Questions

1. Given that the area of the triangle formed by $px + qy = 10$ with the coordinate axes is 5 square units where neither p nor q is 1 and -1.

(i) Let us put $y = 0$.

$px = 10 \Rightarrow x = \frac{10}{p} \Rightarrow x\text{-intercept}(a) = \frac{10}{p}$.

(ii) Let us put $y = 0$.

$qy = 10 \Rightarrow y = \frac{10}{q} \Rightarrow y\text{-intercept}(b) = \frac{10}{q}$.

The area of a triangle formed by a straight line with the coordinate axes is $\frac{|ab|}{2}$ sq units.

Given that $\frac{|ab|}{2} = 5$.

$$\Rightarrow \frac{\left|\frac{10}{p} \times \frac{10}{q}\right|}{2} = 5$$

$$\Rightarrow \left|\frac{10}{p} \times \frac{10}{q}\right| = 10$$

$\Rightarrow |pq| = 10$

$\Rightarrow pq = \pm 10$, where none of p and q is 1 and -1. Also, p and q are integers.

$\Rightarrow p \times q = 2 \times 5$ (or) -2×-5 (or) -2×5 (or) 2×-5.

$\Rightarrow p + q = 7$ (or) -7 (or) 3 (or) -3.

Hence, choice (c) and choice (d) follow.

2. The midpoint of the line segment $PQ = (-3, 4)$.

The midpoint of the line segment joining (x_1, y_1) and (x_2, y_2) is $\left(\frac{x_1 + x_2}{2}, \frac{y_1 + y_2}{2}\right)$.

Going by options:

(a) $P = (6, 8)$ and $Q = (-12, 0)$

$$\text{Midpoint} = \left(\frac{6 - 12}{2}, \frac{8 + 0}{2}\right) = \left(\frac{-6}{2}, \frac{8}{2}\right) = (-3, 4).$$

(b) $P = (-4, -3)$ and $Q = (-2, 11)$

$$\text{Midpoint} = \left(\frac{-4 - 2}{2}, \frac{-3 + 11}{2}\right) = \left(\frac{-6}{2}, \frac{8}{2}\right) = (-3, 4).$$

(c) $P = (14, -11)$ and $Q = (-20, 17)$

$$\text{Midpoint} = \left(\frac{14 - 20}{2}, \frac{-11 + 17}{2}\right) = \left(\frac{-6}{2}, \frac{6}{2}\right) = (-3, 3).$$

(d) $P = (21, 15)$ and $Q = (-27, -7)$

$$\text{Midpoint} = \left(\frac{21 - 27}{2}, \frac{15 - 7}{2}\right) = \left(\frac{-6}{2}, \frac{8}{2}\right) = (-3, 4)$$

Hence, choice (a), choice (b) and choice (d) follow.

3. Given that $ax + by = c$.

Angle of inclination = 45°.

We have $\tan 45° = \frac{-a}{b}$.

$\Rightarrow 1 = \frac{-a}{b}$

$\Rightarrow \frac{a}{b} = -1$

$\Rightarrow \frac{b}{a} = -1$

$\Rightarrow b = -a \Rightarrow a + b = 0$

Hence, choice (b) and choice (d) follow.

4. Given that the orthocentre of a triangle formed by the vertices $A(3, 7)$, $B(x, y)$ and $C(6, 5)$ is $B(x, y)$.

As orthocentre is one of the vertices B, $\angle ABC = 90°$.

That is $AB \perp BC$.

Going by options:

(a) $A(3, 7)$, $B(6, 7)$ and $C(6, 5)$:

A and B lie on the line $y = 7$, B and C lie on the line $x = 6$.

We know that $y = 7$ and $x = 6$ are perpendicular.

So, $A(3, 7)$, $B(6, 7)$ and $C(6, 5)$ form a right triangle right angled at B.

(b) $A(3, 7)$, $B(3, 5)$and $C(6, 5)$:

A and B lie on the line $x = 3$, B and C lie on the line $y = 5$.

We know that $x = 3$ and $y = 5$ are perpendicular.

So, $A(3, 7)$, $B(3, 5)$ and $C(6, 5)$ form a right triangle right angled at B.

(c) $A(3, 7)$, $B(5, 7)$ and $C(6, 5)$:

A and B lie on the line $y = 7$, but B and C do not lie on its perpendicular line of the form $x = k$.

So, $A(3, 7)$, $B(5, 7)$ and $C(6, 5)$ cannot form a right triangle.

(d) $A(3, 7)$, $B(3, 6)$ and $C(6, 5)$:

A and B lie on the line $x = 3$, but B and C does not lie on its perpendicular line of the form $y = k$.

So, $A(3, 7)$, $B(3, 6)$ and $C(6, 5)$ cannot form a right triangle.

Hence, choice (a) and choice (b) follow.

5. Given that $ABCD$ is a parallelogram.
If $A(x_1, y_1)$, $B(x_2, y_2)$ and $C(x_3, y_3)$ are the three vertices of a parallelogram $ABCD$, then the fourth vertex, $D = (x_1 - x_2 + x_3, y_1 - y_2 + y_3)$.
Going by options:
(a) $A = (-2, 3)$, $B = (-3, 6)$, $C = (-6, 6)$
The fourth vertex, $D = (-2 + 3 - 6, 3 - 6 + 6)$ $= (-5, 3)$.
(b) $A = (-3, 4)$, $B = (-1, 8)$, $C = (-4, 8)$
The fourth vertex, $D = (-3 + 1 - 4, 4 - 8 + 8)$ $= (-6, 4)$.
(c) $A = (0, 5)$, $B = (-2, 7)$, $C = (-3, 7)$
The fourth vertex, $D = (0 + 2 - 3, 5 - 7 + 7) = (-1, 5)$.
(d) $A = (-4, 1)$, $B = (0, 10)$, $C = (-4, 10)$, and D
The fourth vertex, $D = (-4 - 0 - 4, 1 - 10 + 10)$ $= (-8, 1)$.
Hence, choice (a), choice (b), choice (c) and choice (d) follow.

Match The Column

Common Solutions for questions 6 to 10:

Name of the Student	Points in Order
Aahana	$A(5, 5)$, $B(-1, 5)$, $C(-1, -2)$, $D(5, -2)$
Brinda	$P(-1, 5)$, $Q(5, 5)$, $R(7, -2)$, $S(1, -2)$
Chavvi	$E(5, -2)$, $F(1, -2)$, $G(-3, 2)$, $H(6, 2)$
Dipta	$U(3, 1)$, $V(5, 5)$, $W(7, 1)$, $X(5, -3)$
Ekiya	$K(7, -3)$, $L(7, 1)$, $M(3, 1)$, $M(3, -3)$

6. Given that $A(5, 5)$, $B(-1, 5)$, $C(-1, -2)$, $D(5, -2)$.
A and B lie on the line $y = 5$.
C and D lie on the line $y = -2$.
So, AB is parallel to CD (1)
C and B lie on the line $x = -1$.
A and D lie on the line $x = 5$.
So, BC is parallel to AD (2)
As $y = -2$ and $x = -1$ are perpendicular to each other, $AB \perp BC$ (3)
From (1), (2) and (3), $ABCD$ is a rectangle or square.
Now $AB = 5 - (-1) = 6$ units.
$BC = 5 - (-2) = 7$ units.
As $AB \neq BC$, $ABCD$ is a rectangle.
So, diagonals are equal and bisect to each other, but not perpendicular.
Hence, the correct option is (e).

7. Given that $P(-1, 5)$, $Q(5, 5)$, $R(7, -2)$, $S(1, -2)$.
P and Q lie on the line $y = 5$.
R and S lie on the line $y = -2$.
So, PQ is parallel to RS (1)
$PQ = 5 - (-1) = 6$ units.
$RS = 7 - 1 = 6$ units.
So, $PQ = RS$ (2)
From (1) and (2), $PQRS$ is a parallelogram.
P and Q lie on the line $y = 5$, but Q and R do not lie on its perpendicular line of the form $x = k$.
As PQ is not perpendicular to QR, $PQRS$ is a parallelogram but not rectangle.
We know that the distance between (x_1, y_1) and (x_2, y_2) is given by $\sqrt{(x_2 - x_1)^2 + (y_2 - y_1)^2}$.
$QR = \sqrt{(7-5)^2 + (-2-5)^2} = \sqrt{4+49} = \sqrt{53}$ units.
As $PQ \neq QR$, $PQRS$ is a parallelogram but not a rhombus.
Hence, $PQRS$ is a parallelogram but not a rectangle or rhombus.
So, in $PQRS$, diagonals bisect each other, but are not equal and not perpendicular.
Hence, the correct option is (c).

8. Given that $E(5, -2)$, $F(1, -2)$, $G(-3, 2)$, $H(6, 2)$.
E and F lie on the line $y = -2$.
G and H lie on the line $y = 2$.
So, EF is parallel to GH (1)
We know that the slope of the line joining (x_1, y_1) and (x_2, y_2) is $\frac{y_2 - y_1}{x_2 - x_1}$.
The slope of $FG = \frac{2+2}{-3-1} = -1$.
The slope of $EH = \frac{2+2}{6-1} = 4$.
As the slopes of FG and EH are not equal, they are not parallel.
So, in $EFGH$, only a pair of opposite sides are parallel.
Hence, the correct option is (a).

9. Given that $U(3, 1)$, $V(5, 5)$, $W(7, 1)$, $X(5, -3)$.
U and W lie on the line $y = 1$.
V and X lie on the line $x = 5$.
So, UW is perpendicular to VX.
We know that the midpoint of the line segment joining (x_1, y_1) and (x_2, y_2) is $\left(\frac{x_1 + x_2}{2}, \frac{y_1 + y_2}{2}\right)$.
The midpoint of $UW = \left(\frac{3+7}{2}, \frac{1+1}{2}\right) = (5, 1)$.

The midpoint of $VX = \left(\frac{5+5}{2}, \frac{5-3}{2}\right) = (5,1)$.

So, UW and VX are perpendicularly bisect to each other.

Now $UW = 7 - 3 = 4$ units.

$VX = 5 - (-3) = 8$ units.

So, $UW \neq VX$.

Hence, in $UVWX$, diagonals perpendicularly bisect each other, but not equal.

Hence, the correct option is (d).

10. Given that $K(7, -3)$, $L(7, 1)$, $M(3, 1)$, $N(3, -3)$.

$KL = 1 - (-3) = 4$ units.

$LM = 7 - 3 = 4$ units.

$MN = 1 - (-3) = 4$ units.

$KN = 7 - 3 = 4$ units.

$KL = LM = MN = KN$ (1)

We know that the distance between (x_1, y_1) and (x_2, y_2) is given by $\sqrt{(x_2 - x_1)^2 + (y_2 - y_1)^2}$.

$KM = \sqrt{(7-3)^2 + (-3-1)^2} = \sqrt{16+16} = 4\sqrt{2}$ units.

$LN = \sqrt{(7-3)^2 + (1+3)^2} = \sqrt{16+16} = 4\sqrt{2}$ units.

$KM = LN$ (2)

From (1) and (2), $KLMN$ is a square.

Hence, in $KLMN$, diagonals are equal and perpendicularly bisect each other.

Hence, the correct option is (f).

Comprehension-Based Questions

Common Solution 11 to 15:

Given that:

P is point on the coordinate plane.

If x is positve, then y is negative.

If y is positve, then x is also positive.

If x is negative, then y is additve inverse of x.

If y is negative, then x is 0.

11. Given that $x > 0$.

So, $y < 0$.

Hence, $P(x, y)$ lies in the Q_4.

Hence, the correct option is (d).

12. Given that $y > 0$.

So, $x > 0$.

Now, $x + y > 0$.

But $x - y$ can be positive, negative or zero.

Hence, the correct option is (d).

13. Given that $x < 0$.

So, y is additive inverse of x.

That is y is positive or $-x$.

$\Rightarrow y + x = 0$.

Hence, $P(x, y + x)$ i.e., $P(-ve, 0)$ lies on the negative axis.

Hence, the correct option is (c).

14. Given that $y < 0$.

So, $x = 0$.

Hence, $P(x, x - y)$ i.e., $P(0, 0 - y)$

i.e., $P(0, +ve)$ lies on the positive *y-axis*.

Hence, the correct option is (b).

15. Given that $x < 0$.

So, y is additive inverse of x.

That is y is positive or $-x$.

Hence, $P(y, y - x)$ i.e., $P(+ve, +ve)$ lies in the Q_1.

Hence, the correct option is (a).

Assertion and Reason Type Questions

Solutions for questions 16 to 20:

16. **Assertion:** Given that $A(8, 7)$, $(11, 3)$ and $(4, 10)$.

We know that the distance between (x_1, y_1) and (x_2, y_2) is given by $\sqrt{(x_2 - x_1)^2 + (y_2 - y_1)^2}$.

$AP = \sqrt{(11-8)^2 + (3-7)^2} = \sqrt{9+16} = 5$ units.

$AQ = \sqrt{(4-8)^2 + (10-7)^2} = \sqrt{16+9} = 5$ units.

$\Rightarrow AP = AQ$

So, Assertion is true.

Reason: The distance between (x_1, y_1) and (x_2, y_2) is given by $q\sqrt{(x_2 - x_1)^2 + (y_2 - y_1)^2}$.

Reason is true, and is the correct explanation to Assertion.

Hence, the correct option is (a).

17. **Assertion:** Given that $x = y$.

$(2, x)$ and $(5, y)$

We know that the distance between (x_1, y_1) and (x_2, y_2) is given by $\sqrt{(x_2 - x_1)^2 + (y_2 - y_1)^2}$.

$= \sqrt{(5-2)^2 + (x-y)^2}$

$= \sqrt{9} = 3$.

Reason: The distance between (x_1, a) and (x_2, a) is $|x_2 - x_1|$.

Reason is true and is the correct explanation to Assertion.

Hence, the correct option is (a).

18. **Assertion:** Given that the centroid of the triangle formed by $A(9, -3)$, $B(-7, 3)$ and C is $(1, 1)$.

We know that the centroid of the triangle formed by $(x_1, y_1), (x_2, y_2)$ and (x_3, y_3) is $\left(\frac{x_1+x_2+x_3}{3}, \frac{y_1+y_2+y_3}{3}\right)$.

Now, $\left(\frac{9-7+x_3}{3}, \frac{-3+3+y_3}{3}\right) = (1, 1)$.

$x_3 = 1$ and $y_3 = 3$.

$\therefore$ C is $(1, 3)$.

So, Assertion is false.

Reason: The centroid of the triangle formed by (x_1, y_1), (x_2, y_2) and (x_3, y_3) is $\left(\frac{x_1+x_2+x_3}{3}, \frac{y_1+y_2+y_3}{3}\right)$.

Reason is true.

Hence, the correct option is (d).

19. **Assertion:** Given that $5x + 4y = 10$.

(i) Let us put $y = 0$.

$5x = 20 \Rightarrow x = \frac{20}{5} \Rightarrow x\text{-intercept}\,(a) = 4.$

(ii) Let us put $y = 0$.

$4y = 20 \Rightarrow y = \frac{20}{4} \Rightarrow y\text{-intercept}\,(b) = 5.$

The area of a triangle formed by a straight line with the coordinate axes is $\frac{|ab|}{2}$ sq units.

$= \frac{|4 \times 5|}{2} = 10$ sq units.

Assertion is true.

Reason: Given that $ax + by = c$.

$$\frac{ax}{c} + \frac{by}{c} = 1$$

$$\frac{x}{\frac{c}{a}} + \frac{y}{\frac{c}{b}} = 1$$

The area of a triangle formed by a straight line with the coordinate axes is $\frac{\left|\frac{c}{a} \times \frac{c}{b}\right|}{2}$ sq units.

That is $\frac{\left|\frac{c^2}{ab}\right|}{2}$ sq units, but not $\frac{c}{2}$ square units.

So, Reason is false.

Hence, the correct option is (c).

20. **Assertion:** Given that $6x - 9y = 21$ and $8x - 12y = 27$.

The slope of $6x - 9y = 21$ is $\frac{-6}{-9} = \frac{2}{3}$.

The slope of $8x - 12y = 27$ is $\frac{-8}{-12} = \frac{2}{3}$.

So, the given pair of equations represents a pair of parallel lines.

So, Assertion is true.

Reason: The x-*axis* and the y-*axis* are represented by $y = 0$ and $x = 0$ respectively.

Reason is true but not the correct explanation to Assertion.

Hence, the correct option is (b).

CHAPTER

12

Trigonometry

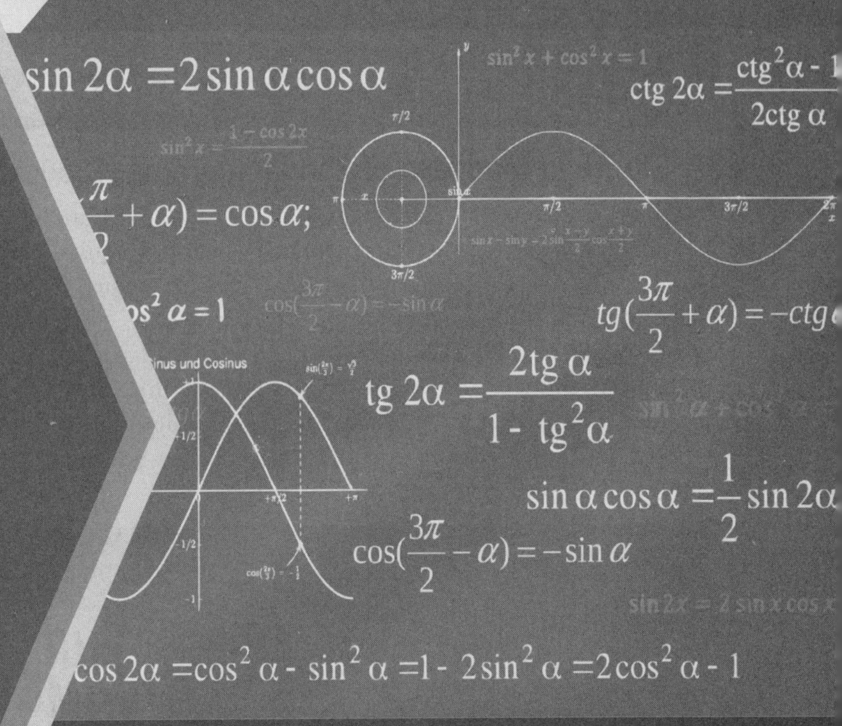

Remember

Before beginning this chapter, you should be able to:

- Know the different types of angles and their values
- Understand the definitions of triangles and their types

Key Ideas

After completing this chapter, you should be able to:

- Know the systems of measurement of angle and their inter-relations
- Understand trigonometric ratios and identities
- Learn the trigonometric ratios of compound angles

Scientific Crypt

A Tribute to Madhava of Sangamagrama (1350 AD to 1425 AD)

Madhava of Sangamagrama was an Indian Mathematician and astronomer from Irinnalakkutla near Cochin, Kerala. He was the first mathematician to express trigonometric functions as infinite power series. This was a major development, as until then mathematicians were using finite expressions to compute these functions. Besides trigonometry, Madhava also made significant contributions to algebra, calculus, geometry and the theory of infinite series.

Some historians of mathematics have maintained that Madhava's work was transmitted to the West through missionaries and traders who visited Kochi, which was then a hub of commercial and academic activity. This had an influence on later developments in Europe in analysis and calculus.

FUN TIME

CROSSWORD

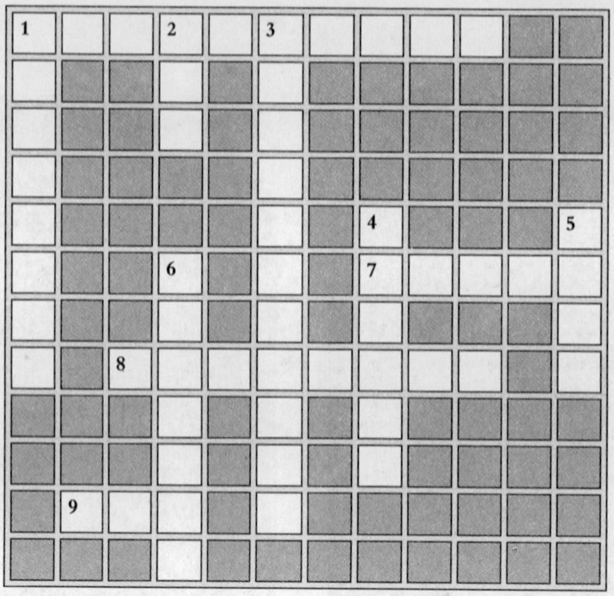

Across

1. The system in which an angle is measured in grades
7. The measure formed between two rays
8. The secant of 90 degrees
9. The tangent of 45 degrees

Down

1. The system in which an angle is measured in radians
2. The cosecant of 30 degrees
3. The system in which an angle is measured in degrees
4. The angle subtended by an arc of length equal to the radius of a circle at its centre.
5. The cosine of 90 degrees
6. $100(\sin^2 100° + \cos^2 100°)$

INTRODUCTION

The word trigonometry is originated from the Greek word 'tri' means three, 'gonia' means angle and 'metron' means measure. Hence, the word trigonometry means three angle measure, i.e., it is the study of geometrical figures which have three angles, i.e., triangles.

The great Greek mathematician Hipapachus of 140 BC gave relation between the angles and sides of a triangle. Further trigonometry is developed by Indian (Hindu) mathematicians. This was migrated to Europe via Arabs. Trigonometry plays an important role in the study of Astronomy, Surveying, Navigation, and Engineering. Now a days it is used to predict stock market trends.

Angle

A measure formed between two rays having a common initial point is called an angle. The two rays are called the arms or sides of the angle and the common initial point is called the vertex of the angle.

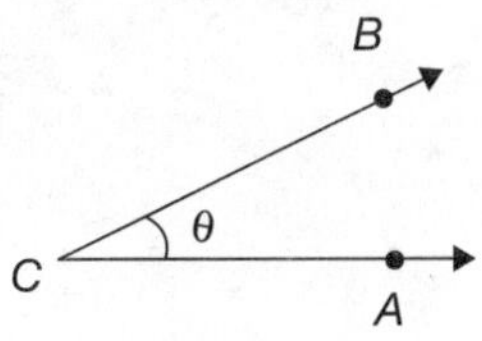

Figure 12.1

In the Fig. 12.1, OA is said to be the initial side and the other ray OB is said to be the terminal side of the angle.

The angle is taken positive when measured in anti-clockwise direction and is taken negative when measured in clockwise direction (see Fig. 12.2).

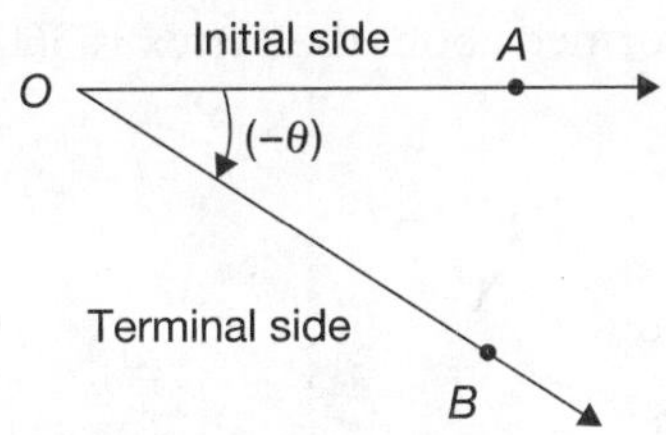

Figure 12.2

Info Bytes!

Angles can be measured in several different systems, with degrees and radians being the most common. There are 360 degrees in a circle, but only 2π (approximately 6.28318) radians. This means that 180 degrees is equivalent to π radians.

Systems of Measurement of Angle

We have the following systems of the measurement of angle.

Sexagesimal System

In this system, the angle is measured in degrees (°).

Degree When the initial ray is rotated through $\left(\frac{1}{360}\right)$ of one revolution, we say that an angle of one degree (1°) is formed at the initial point. A degree is divided into 60 equal parts and each part is called one minute (1 m).

Further, a minute is divided into 60 equal parts called seconds (″).

So, 1 right angle = 90°

1° = 60′ (minutes) and

1′ = 60″ (seconds)

Info Bytes!

This system is also called the British system.

Centesimal system

In this system, the angle is measured in grades.

Grade When the initial ray is rotated through $\left(\frac{1}{400}\right)$ of one revolution, an angle of one grade is said to be formed at the initial point. It is written as 1^g.

Further one grade is divided into 100 equal parts called minutes and one minute is further divided into 100 equal parts called seconds.

So, 1 right angle = 100^g
$1^g = 100'$ (minutes) and
$1' = 100''$ (seconds)

Konnect

This system is also called the French system.

Circular System

In this system, the angle is measured in radians.

Radian The angle subtended by an arc of length equal to the radius of a circle at its centre is said to have a measure of one radian (see Fig. 12.3). It is written as 1^c.

Info Bytes!

This measure is also known as radian measure.

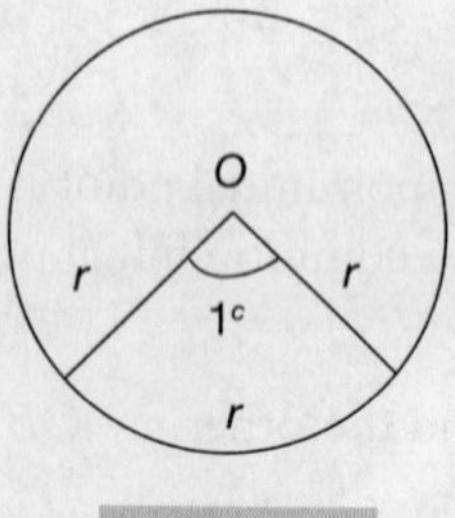

Figure 12.3

Relation Between the Units of the Three Systems

When a rotating ray completes one revolution, the measure of angle formed about the vertex is $360°$ or 400^g or $2\pi^c$.

So,

$$360° = 400^g = 2\pi^c$$

(or)

$$90° = 100^g = \frac{\pi^c}{2}.$$

For convenience, the above relation can be written as,

$$\frac{D}{90} = \frac{G}{100} = \frac{R}{\frac{\pi}{2}}.$$

Where, D denotes degrees, G grades, and R radians.

Remember

1. $1° = \frac{\pi}{180}$ radians = 0.0175 radians (approximately).
2. $1^c = \frac{180}{\pi}$ degrees = $57°17'44''$ (approximately).

Konnect

1. The measure of an angle is a real number.
2. If no unit of measurement is indicated for any angle, it is considered as radian measure.

EXAMPLE 12.1 Convert 60° into circular measure.

SOLUTION

Given, $D = 60°$

We have, $\frac{D}{90} = \frac{R}{\frac{\pi}{2}}$

So, $\frac{60}{90} = \frac{R}{\frac{\pi}{2}}$

$\frac{2}{3} \times \frac{\pi}{2} = R$

$R = \frac{\pi}{3}$.

Hence, 60° in circular measure is $\frac{\pi}{3}$.

EXAMPLE 12.2 Convert 180*g* into sexagesimal measure.

SOLUTION

Given, $G = 180g$

We have, $\frac{D}{90} = \frac{G}{100}$

So, $\frac{D}{90} = \frac{180}{100}$

$D = \frac{9}{5} \times 90 = 162.$

Hence, sexagesimal measure of 180*g* is 162°.

EXAMPLE 12.3 The angle measuring $\frac{\pi}{4}$ when expressed in sexagesimal measure is ________.

SOLUTION

Given, $R = \frac{\pi}{4}$.

We have, $\frac{D}{90} = \frac{R}{\frac{\pi}{2}}$.

So, $\frac{D}{90} = \frac{\frac{\pi}{4}}{\frac{\pi}{2}}$

$D = \frac{2}{4} \times 90 = 45°$

Hence, the sexagesimal measure of $\frac{\pi^c}{4}$ is 45°.

Trigonometric Ratios

Let *AOB* be a right triangle with $\angle AOB$ as 90°. Let $\angle OAB$ be θ. Notice that $0° < \theta < 90°$. That is, θ is an acute angle (see Fig. 12.4).

We can define six possible ratios among the three sides of the triangle *AOB*, known as trigonometric ratios. They are defined as follows.

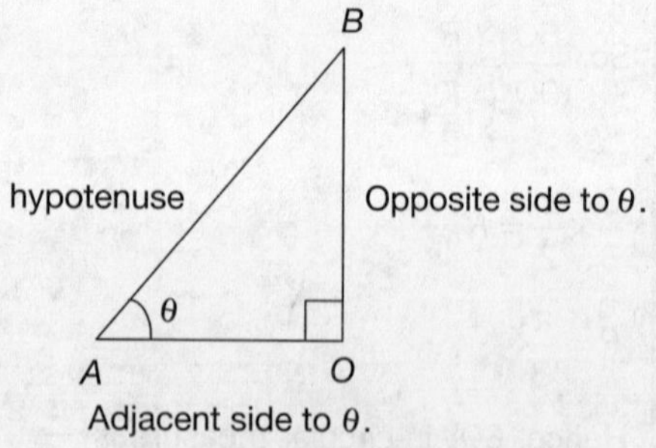

Figure 12.4

1. Sine of the angle θ or simply $\sin\theta$:

$$\sin\theta = \frac{\text{Side opposite to angle } \theta}{\text{Hypotenuse}} = \frac{OB}{AB}.$$

2. Cosine of the angle θ or simply $\cos\theta$:

$$\cos\theta = \frac{\text{Side adjacent to angle } \theta}{\text{Hypotenuse}} = \frac{OA}{AB}.$$

3. Tangent of the angle θ or simply $\tan\theta$:

$$\tan\theta = \frac{\text{Side opposite to } \theta}{\text{Side adjacent to } \theta} = \frac{OB}{OA}.$$

4. Cotangent of the angle θ or simply $\cot\theta$:

$$\cot\theta = \frac{\text{Side adjacent to } \theta}{\text{Side opposite to } \theta} = \frac{OA}{OB}.$$

5. Cosecant of the angle θ or simply $\operatorname{cosec}\theta$:

$$\operatorname{cosec}\theta = \frac{\text{Hypotenuse}}{\text{Side opposite to } \theta} = \frac{AB}{OB}.$$

6. Secant of the angle θ or simply $\sec\theta$:

$$\sec\theta = \frac{\text{Hypotenuse}}{\text{Side adjacent to } \theta} = \frac{AB}{OA}.$$

Observe that,

1. $\operatorname{cosec}\theta = \dfrac{1}{\sin\theta}$, $\sec\theta = \dfrac{1}{\cos\theta}$ and $\cot\theta = \dfrac{1}{\tan\theta}$.
2. $\tan\theta = \dfrac{\sin\theta}{\cos\theta}$ and $\cot\theta = \dfrac{1}{\tan\theta} = \dfrac{\cos\theta}{\sin\theta}$.

EXAMPLE 12.4 If $\cos\theta = \frac{3}{5}$, then find the values of $\tan\theta$, $\operatorname{cosec}\theta$.

SOLUTION

Given, $\cos\theta = \frac{3}{5}$

Let *PQR* be the right triangle such that $\angle QPR = \theta$ (see Fig. 12.5)

Assume that $PQ = 3$ and $PR = 5$.

Then, $QR = \sqrt{PR^2 - PQ^2} = \sqrt{25-9} = 4$.

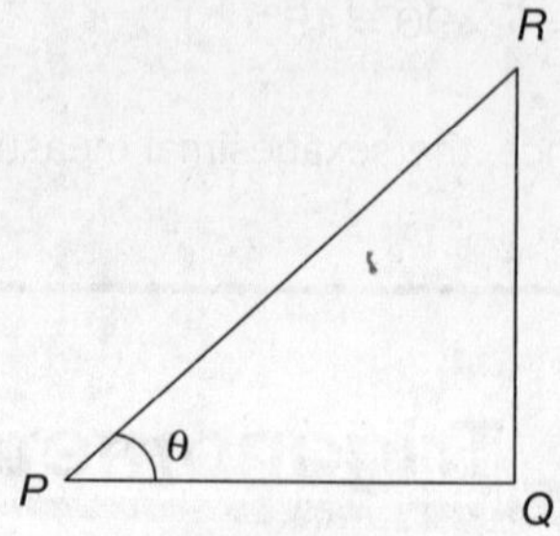

Figure 12.5

So, $\tan\theta = \dfrac{\text{Opposite side}}{\text{Adjacent side}} = \dfrac{QR}{PQ} = \dfrac{4}{3}$ and $\operatorname{cosec}\theta = \dfrac{\text{Hypotenuse}}{\text{Opposite side}} = \dfrac{PR}{QR} = \dfrac{5}{4}$.

Pythagorean Triplets

1. 3, 4, 5
2. 5, 12, 13
3. 8, 15, 17
4. 7, 24, 25
5. 9, 40, 41

Trigonometric Identities

1. $\sin^2\theta + \cos^2\theta = 1$
2. $\sec^2\theta - \tan^2\theta = 1$
3. $\text{cosec}^2\theta - \cot^2\theta = 1$

Values of Trigonometric Ratios for Specific Angles

	Angle				
Trigonometric Ratios	0°	30°	45°	60°	90°
$\sin\theta$	0	$\frac{1}{2}$	$\frac{1}{\sqrt{2}}$	$\frac{\sqrt{3}}{2}$	1
$\cos\theta$	1	$\frac{\sqrt{3}}{2}$	$\frac{1}{\sqrt{2}}$	$\frac{1}{2}$	0
$\tan\theta$	0	$\frac{1}{\sqrt{3}}$	1	$\sqrt{3}$	∞
$\text{cosec}\,\theta$	∞	2	$\sqrt{2}$	$\frac{2}{\sqrt{3}}$	1
$\sec\theta$	1	$\frac{2}{\sqrt{3}}$	$\sqrt{2}$	2	∞
$\cot\theta$	∞	$\sqrt{3}$	1	$\frac{1}{\sqrt{3}}$	0

From the above table, we observe that

1. $\sin\theta = \cos\theta$, $\tan\theta = \cot\theta$ and $\sec\theta = \text{cosec}\,\theta$, if $\theta = 45°$.
2. $\sin\theta$ and $\tan\theta$ are increasing functions in $0° \leq \theta \leq 90°$.
3. $\cos\theta$ is a decreasing function in $0° \leq \theta \leq 90°$.

Trigonometric Ratios of Complementary Angles

Two angles are said to be complementary if their sum is equal to 90°.

In the right angle triangle, α and β are complementary angles.

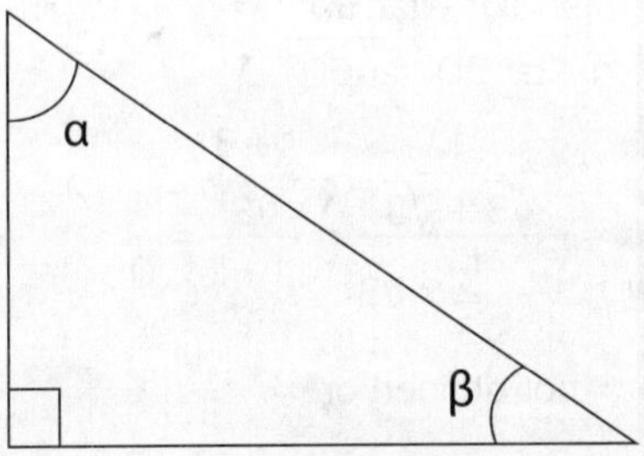

$\alpha + \beta + 90° = 180°$ (Sum of all the three angles of a triangle is 180°)

$\Rightarrow \alpha + \beta = 90°$

$\Rightarrow \alpha$ and β are complementary angles. We represent the complementary angle as follows:

The trigonometric ratios of complementary angles θ and (90°– θ) are:

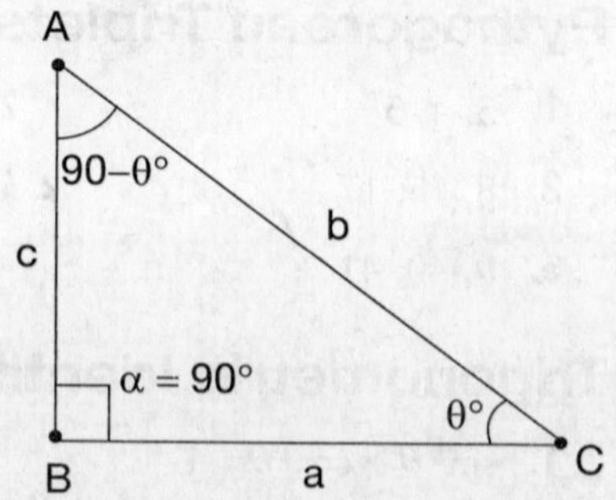

$\sin(90° - \theta) = \cos\theta$

$\cos(90° - \theta) = \sin\theta$

$\tan(90° - \theta) = \cot\theta$

$\text{cosec}(90° - \theta) = \sec\theta$

$\sec(90° - \theta) = \text{cosec}\,\theta$

$\cot(90° - \theta) = \tan\theta$

EXAMPLE 12.5 Find the value of $\sin 60° + 2\tan 45° - \cos 30°$.

SOLUTION

$\sin 60° + 2\tan 45° - \cos 30°$

$$= \frac{\sqrt{3}}{2} + 2(1) - \frac{\sqrt{3}}{2} = 2$$

$\therefore \sin 60° + 2\tan 45° - \cos 30° = 2.$

EXAMPLE 12.6 Using the trigonometric table and evaluate
(a) $\sin^2 45° + \cos^2 45°$ **(b)** $\sec^2 30° - \tan^2 30°$

SOLUTION

(a) $\sin^2 45° + \cos^2 45°$

$$= \left(\frac{1}{\sqrt{2}}\right)^2 + \left(\frac{1}{\sqrt{2}}\right)^2$$

$$= \frac{1}{2} + \frac{1}{2} = 1.$$

Hence, $\sin^2 45° + \cos^2 45° = 1.$

(b) $\sec^2 30° - \tan^2 30°$

$$= \left(\frac{2}{\sqrt{3}}\right)^2 - \left(\frac{1}{\sqrt{3}}\right)^2$$

$$= \frac{4}{3} - \frac{1}{3} = \frac{3}{3} = 1.$$

Hence, $\sec^2 30° - \tan^2 30° = 1.$

EXAMPLE 12.7 Find the values of $\dfrac{\tan 30° + \tan 60°}{1 - \tan 30° \tan 60°}$ and tan 90°. What do you observe?

SOLUTION

$$\frac{\tan 30° + \tan 60°}{1 - \tan 30° \tan 60°}$$

$$= \frac{\frac{1}{\sqrt{3}} + \sqrt{3}}{1 - \frac{1}{\sqrt{3}} \times \sqrt{3}} = \frac{\frac{1+3}{\sqrt{3}}}{1-1} = \frac{4}{0}$$

= not defined or ∞.

$= \tan 90°$

Hence, $\dfrac{\tan 30° + \tan 60°}{1 - \tan 30° \tan 60°} = \tan 90°$.

Trigonometric Ratios of Compound Angles

1. $\sin(A + B) = \sin A \cos B + \cos A \sin B$ and
   $\sin(A - B) = \sin A \cos B - \cos A \sin B$.
2. $\cos(A + B) = \cos A \cos B - \sin A \sin B$ and
   $\cos(A - B) = \cos A \cos B + \sin A \sin B$.
3. $\tan(A+B) = \dfrac{\tan A + \tan B}{1 - \tan A \tan B}$ and
   $\tan(A-B) = \dfrac{\tan A - \tan B}{1 + \tan A \tan B}$.

Also, by taking $A = B$ in the above relations, we get,

1. $\sin 2A = 2\sin A \cos A$.
2. $\cos 2A = \cos^2 A - \sin^2 A = 2\cos^2 A - 1 = 1 - 2\sin^2 A$.
3. $\tan 2A = \dfrac{2\tan A}{1 - \tan^2 A}$.

EXAMPLE 12.8 Find the value of $\sin 15°$.

SOLUTION

We have, $\sin 15° = \sin(45° - 30°)$

$= \sin 45° \cos 30° - \cos 45° \sin 30°$

$= \dfrac{1}{\sqrt{2}} \times \dfrac{\sqrt{3}}{2} - \dfrac{1}{\sqrt{2}} \times \dfrac{1}{2} = \dfrac{\sqrt{3}-1}{2\sqrt{2}}$

$\therefore \sin 15° = \dfrac{\sqrt{3}-1}{2\sqrt{2}}$.

EXAMPLE 12.9 Find the value of $\tan 75°$.

SOLUTION

We have, $\tan 75° = \tan(45° + 30°)$

$\dfrac{\tan 45° + \tan 30°}{1 - \tan 45° \cdot \tan 30°}$

$= \dfrac{1 + \frac{1}{\sqrt{3}}}{1 - 1 \times \frac{1}{\sqrt{3}}} = \dfrac{\sqrt{3}+1}{\sqrt{3}-1}$.

$= \left(\dfrac{\sqrt{3}+1}{\sqrt{3}-1}\right)\left(\dfrac{\sqrt{3}+1}{\sqrt{3}+1}\right) = \dfrac{3+1+2\sqrt{3}}{2} = 2 + \sqrt{3}$

$\therefore \tan 75° = \dfrac{\sqrt{3}+1}{\sqrt{3}-1}$ or $2 + \sqrt{3}$.

EXAMPLE 12.10 Eliminate θ from the equations $a = x \sec\theta$ and $b = y \tan\theta$.

SOLUTION

We know that trigonometric ratios are meaningful when they are associated with some θ, i.e., we cannot imagine any trigonometric ratio without θ. Eliminate θ means, eliminating the trigonometric ratios by using suitable identity.

Given, $a = x \sec\theta$ and $b = y \tan\theta$

$$\frac{a}{x} = \sec\theta \text{ and } \frac{b}{y} = \tan\theta.$$

We know that, $\sec^2\theta - \tan^2\theta = 1$.

$$\text{So, } \left(\frac{a}{x}\right)^2 - \left(\frac{b}{y}\right)^2 = 1$$

$$\frac{a^2}{x^2} - \frac{b^2}{y^2} = 1.$$

Hence, the required equation is $\frac{a^2}{x^2} - \frac{b^2}{y^2} = 1$.

EXAMPLE 12.11 Find the length of the chord PQ subtending an angle of 120° of the center of the circle whose radius is 12 cm.

SOLUTION

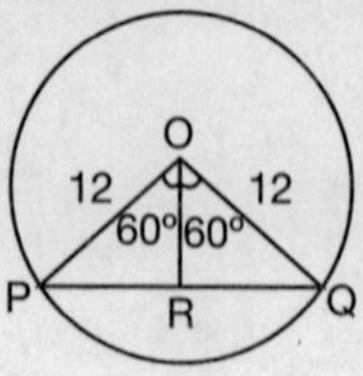

Let the chord be PQ and 'O' be the centre of the circle.

Given, ∠POQ = 120° and OP = OQ = 12 cm

'OR' be the shortest distance from O to PQ

$\Delta POR \cong \Delta QOR$.

$$\Delta POR, \sin 60° = \frac{PR}{OP}$$

$$\therefore \frac{\sqrt{3}}{2} = \frac{PR}{12}$$

$$PR = 6\sqrt{3}$$

$$PQ = 2PR = 12\sqrt{3} \text{ cm}$$

EXAMPLE 12.12 Eliminate θ from the equations $p = a \operatorname{cosec}\theta$ and $q = a \cot\theta$.

SOLUTION

Given, $p = a \operatorname{cosec}\theta$ and $q = a \cot\theta$

$$\frac{P}{a} = \operatorname{cosec}\theta \text{ and } \frac{Q}{a} = \cot\theta.$$

We know that, $\operatorname{cosec}^2\theta - \cot^2\theta = 1$

$$\left(\frac{P}{a}\right)^2 - \left(\frac{Q}{a}\right)^2 = 1$$

$$p^2 - q^2 = a^2.$$

Hence, the required relation is $p^2 - q^2 = a^2$.

EXAMPLE 12.13 Eliminate θ from the equations $s = \sin\theta + \text{cosec}\,\theta$ and $r = \sin\theta - \text{cosec}\,\theta$.

SOLUTION

Given, $s = \sin\theta + \text{cosec}\,\theta$ (1)

$r = \sin\theta - \text{cosec}\,\theta$ (2)

Adding Eqs. (1) and (2), we get,

$s + r = 2\sin\theta$

$$\sin\theta = \frac{s+r}{2}. \quad (3)$$

Subtracting Eq. (2) from Eq. (1), we get,

$s - r = 2\,\text{cosec}\,\theta$

$$\text{cosec}\,\theta = \frac{s-r}{2}. \quad (4)$$

Multiplying Eqs. (3) and (4), we get,

$$\sin\theta \cdot \text{cosec}\theta = \left(\frac{s+r}{2}\right)\left(\frac{s-r}{2}\right)$$

$$\sin\theta \cdot \frac{1}{\sin\theta} = \frac{s^2 - r^2}{4}$$

$$1 = \frac{s^2 - r^2}{4} \quad \text{(or)} \quad s^2 - r^2 = 4.$$

Hence, by eliminating θ, we obtain the relation $s^2 - r^2 = 4$.

EXAMPLE 12.14 If $\cos(A + B) = 0$ and $\cos B = \frac{\sqrt{3}}{2}$, then what is the value of A?

SOLUTION

$\cos(A + B) = 0 \Rightarrow \cos(A + B) = \cos 90°$

$A + B = 90$ ——— (1)

$\cos B = \frac{\sqrt{3}}{2} \Rightarrow \cos B = \cos 30°$

$B = 30°$ ——— (2)

$(1) \Rightarrow A = 60°$

EXAMPLE 12.15 Find the length of the chord which subtends an angle of 90° at the centre '*O*' and which is at a distance of 6 cm from the centre.

SOLUTION

Let the chord be *PQ* and *OR* be the distance of chord from the centre of circle (see Fig. 12.6).

Given $\angle POQ = 90°$ and $OR = 6$ cm.

Clearly, $\Delta POR \cong \Delta QOR$, by SSS axiom of congruency.

$$\angle POR = \angle QOR = \frac{1}{2}\angle POQ = 45°.$$

In ΔPOR, $\tan 45° = \frac{PR}{OR}$.

$$1 = \frac{PR}{6}$$

$PR = 6$ cm.

$\therefore$ The length of the chord $PQ = 2\,PR = 12$ cm.

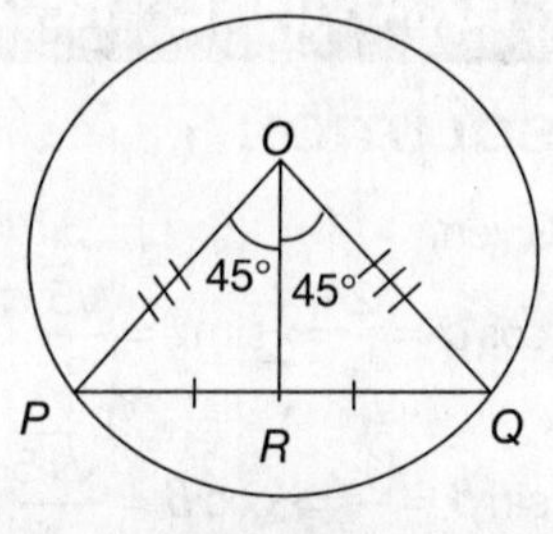

Figure 12.6

EXAMPLE 12.16

Which of the following is equal to $\sqrt{\dfrac{\operatorname{cosec} x-\cot x}{\cot x+\operatorname{cosec} x}}$?

(a) $\dfrac{1-\cos x}{\sin x}$ (b) -1 (3) $\dfrac{1+\cos x}{\sin x}$ (4) $\dfrac{\cos x-1}{\sin x}$

SOLUTION

$$\sqrt{\frac{\operatorname{cosec} x-\cot x}{\cot x+\operatorname{cosec} x}}=\sqrt{\frac{(\operatorname{cosec} x-\cot x)^2}{\operatorname{cosec}^2 x-\cot^2 x}}$$

$$=\frac{\operatorname{cosec} x-\cot x}{1}$$

$$=\operatorname{cosec}x-\cot x=\frac{1}{\sin x}-\frac{\cos x}{\sin x}=\frac{1-\cos x}{\sin x}$$

EXAMPLE 12.17

If sin α and cos α are the roots of the equation $ax^2 - bx - 1 = 0$, then find the relation between a and b.

SOLUTION

The given equation is $ax^2 - bx - 1 = 0$.

Here, $a = a$, $b = -b$ and $c = -1$.

$$\sin\alpha+\cos\alpha=\frac{-b}{a}=\frac{-(-b)}{a}=\frac{b}{a}$$

$$\sin\alpha\cdot\cos\alpha=\frac{c}{a}=\frac{-1}{a}.$$

Consider,

$$\sin\alpha+\cos\alpha=\frac{-b}{a}$$

Squaring on both sides,

$$(\sin\alpha+\cos\alpha)^2=\left(\frac{-b}{a}\right)^2$$

$$=1+2\left(\frac{-1}{a}\right)=\frac{b^2}{a^2}$$

$$=1-\frac{b^2}{a^2}=\frac{2}{a}$$

$$\therefore\ a^2-b^2=2a.$$

EXAMPLE 12.18

If $\cos\alpha=\dfrac{2}{3}$ and $\sin\beta=\dfrac{1}{4}$, then find $\cos(\alpha-\beta)$.

SOLUTION

Given,

$$\cos\alpha=\frac{2}{3}\Rightarrow\sin\alpha=\frac{\sqrt{5}}{3}$$

$$\sin\beta=\frac{1}{4}\Rightarrow\cos\beta=\frac{\sqrt{15}}{4}$$

$$\cos(\alpha-\beta)=\cos\alpha\cdot\cos\beta+\sin\alpha\cdot\sin\beta=\frac{2}{3}\times\frac{\sqrt{15}}{4}+\frac{\sqrt{5}}{3}\times\frac{1}{4}$$

$$\cos(\alpha-\beta)=\frac{2\sqrt{15}+\sqrt{5}}{12}.$$

EXAMPLE 12.19 Express the following as a single trigonometric ratio:

(a) $\sqrt{3}\cos\theta - \sin\theta$ **(b)** $\sin\theta - \cos\theta$

SOLUTION

(a) Here,

$\sqrt{3}\cos\theta - \sin\theta$

$= 2\left(\frac{\sqrt{3}}{2}\cos\theta - \frac{1}{2}\sin\theta\right)$

$= 2(\cos\theta \cdot \cos 30° - \sin\theta \cdot \sin 30°)$

$= 2(\cos(\theta + 30°))$

$\Rightarrow \sqrt{3}\cos\theta - \sin\theta = 2\cos(\theta + 30°)$.

(b) Here,

$\sin\theta - \cos\theta$

$= \sqrt{2}\left(\frac{\sin\theta - \cos\theta}{\sqrt{2}}\right)$

$= \sqrt{2}\left(\frac{1}{\sqrt{2}}\sin\theta - \frac{1}{\sqrt{2}}\cos\theta\right)$

$= \sqrt{2}\left[\sin\theta\cos\left(\frac{\pi}{4}\right) - \cos\theta\sin\left(\frac{\pi}{4}\right)\right]$

$= \sqrt{2}\sin\left(\theta - \frac{\pi}{4}\right)$. $(\because \sin(A - B) = \sin A\cos B - \cos A\sin B)$

POINTS TO REMEMBER

- ✔ A measure formed between two rays having a common initial point is called an angle.
- ✔ The two rays are called the arms or sides of the angle and the common initial point is called the vertex of the angle.
- ✔ When the initial ray is rotated through $\left(\frac{1}{360}\right)$ of one revolution, we say that an angle of one degree (1°) is formed at the initial point. A degree is divided into 60 equal parts and each part is called one minute (1 m).
- ✔ When the initial ray is rotated through $\left(\frac{1}{400}\right)$ of one revolution, an angle of one grade is said to be formed at the initial point. It is written as 1^g.
- ✔ The angle subtended by an arc of length equal to the radius of a circle at its centre is said to have a measure of one radian. It is written as 1^c.
- ✔ Two angles are said to be complementary if their sum is equal to 90°.
- ✔ $\sin(A + B) = \sin A\cos B + \cos A\sin B$ and $\sin(A - B) = \sin A\cos B - \cos A\sin B$.
- ✔ $\cos(A + B) = \cos A\cos B - \sin A\sin B$ and $\cos(A - B) = \cos A\cos B + \sin A\sin B$.
- ✔ $\tan(A+B) = \frac{\tan A + \tan B}{1 - \tan A\tan B}$ and $\tan(A-B) = \frac{\tan A - \tan B}{1 + \tan A\tan B}$.
- ✔ $\sin 2A = 2\sin A\cos A$.
  $\cos 2A = \cos^2 A - \sin^2 A = 2\cos^2 A - 1 = 1 - 2\sin^2 A$.
  $\tan 2A = \frac{2\tan A}{1 - \tan^2 A}$.

PRACTICE QUESTIONS CLASSROOM WING

Very Short Answer Type Questions

Directions of questions from 1 to 12:
Fill in the blanks.

1. If cos (90° – 3θ) = sin (12θ – 90°), then tan 3θ = ______.

2. If $\operatorname{cosec}\theta - \cot\theta = x$, then $\operatorname{cosec}\theta + \cot\theta =$ ______.

3. The value of $\dfrac{\sin 20^\circ \cos 70^\circ + \cos 20^\circ \sin 70^\circ}{\sin 23^\circ \operatorname{coses} 23^\circ + \cos 23^\circ \sec 23^\circ}$ is ______.

4. If cotα = 4 and cotβ = $\dfrac{5}{3}$, then the value of α + β is ______.

5. If $\tan\theta = \dfrac{5}{6}$ and $\tan\phi = \dfrac{1}{11}$, then $\theta + \phi =$ ______.

6. If $A - B = 45^\circ$ and $\tan A - \tan B = \sqrt{3}$, then $\tan A \cdot \tan B =$ ______.

7. If α and β are complementary angles and α = 2β, then $\cos^2\alpha + \sin^2\beta$ = ______.

8. cot1° × cot2° × cot3° × .... × cot90° = ______.

9. If sec (25° + 7θ) = cosec (15° + 3θ), then cot 9θ = ______.

10. $\tan(A+B) = \sqrt{3}$ and $\sin A = \dfrac{1}{\sqrt{2}}$, then the value of B in radians is ______.

11. If sin A = cos B, where A and B are acute angles, then $A + B =$ ______.

12. ABC is a right isosceles triangle, right angled at B. Then $\sin^2 A + \cos^2 C =$ ______.

Directions of questions from 13 to 20:
Answer the following questions.

13. Evaluate: $\sin^2 60^\circ \cos^2 45^\circ \cos^2 60^\circ \operatorname{cosec}^2 90^\circ$.

14. If $\sin\theta = \dfrac{3}{5}$ and θ is acute, then find the value of $\dfrac{\tan\theta - 2\cos\theta}{3\sin\theta + \sec\theta}$.

15. Find the values of the cos 15°.

16. Convert $\dfrac{\pi^c}{15}$ into the other two systems.

17. Simplify and express $\sec^4\alpha - \tan^4\alpha$ in their least exponents.

18. Convert $\left(\dfrac{200}{3}\right)^g$ into other two systems.

19. Convert 270° into other two systems.

20. Evaluate: $\cos 0^\circ + \sqrt{2}\sec 45^\circ - \sqrt{3}\tan 30^\circ$.

Short Answer Type Questions

21. In the adjoining figure, find the value of sin C.

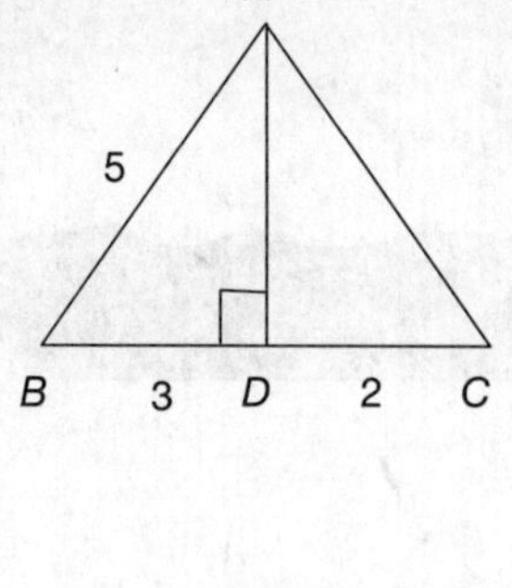

22. If sin (A – B) = $\dfrac{1}{2}$ and cos (A + B) = $\dfrac{1}{2}$, then A = ?

23. If $\sin^2\alpha + \sin\alpha = 1$, then what is the value of $7\cos^2\alpha + 7\cos^4\alpha + 3$?

24. Find the value of tan 75°.

25. If $\sec^2\alpha + \cos^2\alpha = 2$, then find the value of $\sec\alpha + \cos\alpha$.

26. Eliminate θ from the equations, $a = x \sin\theta - y \cos\theta$ and $b = x \cos\theta + y \sin\theta$.

27. If $\cos\alpha = \frac{12}{13}$ and $\sin\beta = \frac{4}{5}$, then find $\sin(\alpha + \beta)$.

28. Express $\sin\theta$ in terms of $\cot\theta$.

29. If $\sin\alpha = \frac{4}{5}$, then find the value of $\sin 2\alpha$.

30. Find the value of $\sin 2\alpha$, if $\sin\alpha + \cos\alpha = \frac{1}{3}$.

31. The length of the minutes hand of a wall clock is 36 cm. Find the distance covered by its tip in 35 minutes.

32. If $\tan 2\alpha = \frac{3}{4}$, then find $\tan\alpha$.

33. If $A + B = 45°$, then find the value of $\tan A + \tan B + \tan A \tan B$.

34. If θ is an acute angle and $\frac{\cos\theta}{1-\sin\theta} + \frac{\cos\theta}{1+\sin\theta} = 4$, then find the value of θ.

35. If $\frac{1+\cos\theta}{1-\cos\theta} = 4$, then find the value of $\frac{\sin\theta + \cos\theta}{\sin\theta - \cos\theta}$.

Essay Type Questions

36. If the length of a chord of a circle is $4\sqrt{3}$ cm and the chord making an angle 120° at the center, then the value of radius of the circle (in cm)?

37. If $\cos^2\alpha + \cos\alpha = 1$, then find the value of $4\sin^2\alpha + 4\sin^4\alpha + 2$.

38. Obtain the relation by eliminating θ from the equations, $x = a + r\cos\theta$ and $y = b + r\sin\theta$.

39. One of the angles of a rhombus is 60° and the length of the diagonal opposite to it is 6 cm. Find the area of the rhombus (in sq.cm).

40. If $\alpha + \beta + \gamma = 90°$, then $\tan\alpha + \tan\beta + \tan\alpha \tan\beta \cot\gamma$ is ______.

PRACTICE QUESTIONS COMPETITION WING

Level 1: Apply Your Concepts

Directions of questions from 1 to 4:
Fill in the blanks.

1. The value of sin 30° · sin 45° · cosec 45° · cos 30° = _______.

2. If $\dfrac{1-\tan^2 60°}{1+\tan^2 60} = \cos X$, then the value of X is _______.

3. The value of log [(sec θ + tan θ) (sec θ – tan θ)] is _______.

4. If $\dfrac{\cos 13° + \sin 13°}{\cos 13° - \sin 13°} = \tan A$, then A = _______.

Directions of questions from 5 to 63:
Select the correct alternative from the given choices.

5. The length of the minutes hand of a wall clock is 6 cm. Find the distance covered by the tip of the minutes hand in 25 minutes.
   (a) $\dfrac{270}{7}$ cm (b) 110 cm
   (c) $\dfrac{88}{7}$ cm (d) $\dfrac{110}{7}$ cm

6. The value of tan 10° · tan 20° · tan 45° · tan 70° · tan 80° =
   (a) 1 (b) $\dfrac{1}{\sqrt{3}}$
   (c) 0 (d) 8

7. The value of sin θ in terms of tan θ is _______.
   (a) $\dfrac{\tan\theta}{\sqrt{1-\tan^2\theta}}$ (b) $\dfrac{\tan^2\theta}{\sqrt{1+\tan^2\theta}}$
   (c) $\dfrac{\tan^2\theta}{\sqrt{1-\tan^2\theta}}$ (d) $\dfrac{\tan\theta}{\sqrt{1+\tan^2\theta}}$

8. The value of $\sin^2 60° + \cos^2 30° - \sin^2 45°$ is _______.
   (a) 1 (b) sin 90°
   (c) $\dfrac{1}{2}$ (d) Both (a) and (b)

9. The simplified value of $\text{cosec}^2\alpha\left(1+\dfrac{1}{\sec\alpha}\right)\left(1-\dfrac{1}{\sec\alpha}\right)$ is _______.
   (a) 1 (b) 0
   (c) 2 (d) –1

10. Which of the following is equal to $\dfrac{\sqrt{1+\cot^2\theta}}{\cot\theta}$?
    (a) cosecθ (b) secθ
    (c) cosθ (d) sinθ

11. Which of the following is equal to $\sqrt{\dfrac{\sec x + \tan x}{\sec x - \tan x}}$?
    (a) $\dfrac{1-\sin x}{\cos x}$ (b) $\dfrac{1-\cos x}{\sin x}$
    (c) $\dfrac{1+\sin x}{\cos x}$ (d) $\dfrac{1+\cos x}{\sin x}$

12. Which of the following is equal to $\left[\dfrac{1+\sin\theta}{\cos\theta}+\dfrac{\cos\theta}{1+\sin\theta}\right]$ cotθ? (Where 0° < θ < 90°)
    (a) 2 secθ (b) 2 cosecθ
    (c) 2 sinθ (d) 2 cosθ

13. Which of the following is equal to $\dfrac{\cos^4 A - \sin^4 A}{\sin^2 A - \cos^2 A}$?
    (a) –1 (b) 0
    (c) 1 (d) $1 - 2\sin^2 A$

14. Which of the following is equal to tanθ?
    (a) $\dfrac{\sqrt{\sec^2\theta - 1}}{\sec\theta}$ (b) $\dfrac{\sec\theta}{\sqrt{\sec^2\theta-1}}$
    (c) $\dfrac{1}{\sqrt{\sec^2\theta-1}}$ (d) $\sqrt{\sec^2\theta-1}$

15. The value of $\log_{\sec\theta}(1-\sin^2\theta)$ is _______.
    (a) 2 (b) –2
    (c) 0 (d) 1

16. If $a = \sin^4\theta$ and $b = \cot^4\theta$ where 0° < θ < 90°, then which of the following is true?

(a) $\frac{1}{\sqrt{a}} + \sqrt{b} = 1$ (b) $\sqrt{a} + \sqrt{b} = 1$

(c) $\sqrt{a} - \sqrt{b} = 1$ (d) $\frac{1}{\sqrt{a}} - \sqrt{b} = 1$

17. If $\sin\alpha = \frac{3}{5}$, then which of the following is the value of $\sec\alpha$?

(a) $\frac{7}{5}$ (b) 0

(c) $\frac{4}{5}$ (d) $\frac{5}{4}$

18. If $\sec^2\alpha + \sec\alpha = 1$, then which of the following is the value of $5\tan^2\alpha - 5\tan^4\alpha + 6$?

(a) 1 (b) 0

(c) 6 (d) –1

19. Which of the following is equal to $\frac{\sec^8 A - \tan^8 A}{\sec^4 A + \tan^4 A}$?

(a) 1 (b) $2\tan^2 A - 1$

(c) $2\sec^2 A - 1$ (d) –1

20. The distance covered by the tip of a minute hand in 35 minutes is 33 cm. What is the length of the minute hand?

(a) 6 cm (b) 9 cm

(c) 10 cm (d) 12 cm

21. If $\sin\alpha = \frac{4}{5}$, where $(0° \le \alpha \le 90°)$, then find $\sin 2\alpha$.

(a) $\frac{12}{25}$ (b) $-\frac{24}{25}$

(c) $\frac{25}{24}$ (d) $\frac{24}{25}$

22. In a ΔABC, $\cos\left(\frac{A+B}{2}\right) =$ _____.

(a) $\cos\frac{C}{2}$ (b) $-\sin\frac{C}{2}$

(c) $\cos\left(\frac{A-B}{2}\right)$ (d) $\sin\frac{C}{2}$

23. $\sin^4\theta - \cos^4\theta =$

(a) –1 (b) $\cos 2\theta$

(c) $2\sin^2\theta - 1$ (d) $\sin 2\theta$

24. If $P : Q = \tan 2A : \cos A$ and $Q : R = \cos 2A : \sin 2A$, then $P : R$ is _________.

(a) $\tan 2A$ (b) $2\sin A$

(c) 1 (d) $\sec A$

25. If $\cot(A - B) = 1$ and $\cos(A + B) = \frac{1}{2}$, then find B.

(a) $42\frac{1°}{2}$ (b) $7\frac{1°}{2}$

(c) $15\frac{1°}{2}$ (d) 60°

26. Find the measure of angle A, if $(2\sin A + 1)(2\sin A - 1) = 0$.

(a) 75° (b) 60°

(c) 45° (d) 30°

27. The value of $\cos 2\theta$ in terms of $\cot\theta$ is _______.

(a) $\frac{\cot^2\theta + 1}{\cot^2\theta - 1}$ (b) $-\frac{1+\cot^2\theta}{\cot^2\theta - 1}$

(c) $\frac{\cot^2\theta - 1}{\cot^2\theta + 1}$ (d) $\frac{1-\cot^2\theta}{1+\cot^2\theta}$

28. The simplified value of $\sin^4\alpha + \cos^4\alpha + \frac{1}{2}\sin^2 2\alpha$ is:

(a) –1 (b) $\sin\alpha + \cos\alpha$

(c) 0 (d) 1

29. If A and B are complementary angles, then the value of $\frac{\sin^2 A + \sin^2 B}{\text{cosec}^2 A - \tan^2 B}$ is _______.

(a) 0 (b) 1

(c) –1 (d) 2

30. Find the value of $4(\sin^4 30° + \cos^4 30°) - 3(\cos^2 45° + \sin^2 90°)$.

(a) $-\frac{1}{2}$ (b) –2

(c) 2 (d) $\frac{1}{2}$

31. If $\sec\theta + \tan\theta = \frac{4}{3}$, then $\sec\theta\tan\theta =$

(a) $\frac{175}{24}$ (b) $\frac{25}{576}$

(c) $\frac{27}{576}$ (d) $\frac{175}{576}$

Level 2: Review Your Concepts

32. If $\sin\alpha + \cos\alpha = n$, then $\sin^6\alpha + \cos^6\alpha$ in terms of n is ______.
(a) $4 + 3(n-1)^2$ (b) $\frac{4+3(n^2-1)}{4}$
(c) $\frac{4-3(n^2-1)^2}{4}$ (d) None of these

33. Find the value of $\frac{\sin 25°}{\cos 35°} - \frac{\cos 25°}{\sin 35°}$.
(a) cosec 70° (b) sin 70°
(c) –sin 70° (d) –cosec 70°

34. The value of $\frac{3\tan 30° - \tan^3 30°}{1 - 3\tan^2 30°}$ is ______.
(a) tan 90° (b) tan 60°
(c) tan 45° (d) tan 30°

35. If $\cot^4 x - \cot^2 x = 1$, then the value of $\cos^4 x + \cos^2 x$ is ______.
(a) –1 (b) 0
(c) 2 (d) 1

36. If $\frac{\cos(A-B)}{\cos(A+B)} = \frac{8}{3}$, then $\tan A \cdot \tan B$ is ______.
(a) $\frac{5}{11}$ (b) $\frac{7}{13}$
(c) $\frac{8}{5}$ (d) $\frac{11}{5}$

37. If $\cot\theta + \tan\theta = 2$, then the value of $\tan^2\theta - \cot^2\theta$ is ______.
(a) 1 (b) 0
(c) –1 (d) 2

38. The value of $\cot 5° \cdot \cot 15° \cdot \cot 25° \cdot \cot 35° \cdot \cot 45° \cdot \cot 55° \cdot \cot 65° \cdot \cot 75° \cdot \cot 85°$ is ______.
(a) 0 (b) –1
(c) –2 (d) 1

39. The simplified form of $\sqrt{1+\sin\left(\frac{x}{8}\right)}$ is ______.
(a) $\sin\left(\frac{x}{8}\right) + \cos\left(\frac{x}{8}\right)$
(b) $\sin\left(\frac{x}{16}\right) + \cos\left(\frac{x}{16}\right)$
(c) $\sin\left(\frac{x}{4}\right) + \cos\left(\frac{x}{4}\right)$
(d) None of these

40. $\sin^4\theta + \cos^4\theta$ in terms of $\sin\theta$ is ______.
(a) $2\sin^4\theta - 2\sin^2\theta - 1$ (b) $2\sin^4\theta - 2\sin^2\theta + 1$
(c) $2\sin^4\theta + 2\sin^2\theta - 1$ (d) $2\sin^4\theta - 2\sin^2\theta$

41. If $\sin\beta + \cos\beta = \frac{5}{4}$, then find the value of $\sin\beta \cdot \cos\beta$.
(a) $\frac{1}{4}$ (b) $\frac{9}{32}$
(c) $\frac{5}{16}$ (d) $\frac{11}{32}$

42. If $\sin^2\alpha + \sin\alpha = 1$, then the value of $\cos^4\alpha + \cos^2\alpha$ is ______.
(a) 0 (b) –1
(c) 1 (d) 2

43. If $\tan P + \cot P = 2$, then the value of $\tan^n P + \cot^n P$ is ______.
(a) 2 (b) 2^n
(c) 2^{n-1} (d) 2^{n+1}

44. The value of $\sqrt{3}\tan 10° + \sqrt{3}\tan 20° + \tan 10° \cdot \tan 20°$ is ______.
(a) –1 (b) 0
(c) 1 (d) 2

45. If $\cos(A-B) = \frac{1}{2}$ and $\sin(A+B) = \frac{\sqrt{3}}{2}$, then find A and B.

The following are the steps involved in solving the following problem. Arrange them in sequential order.
(A) $2A = 120° \Rightarrow A = 60°$.
(B) $\therefore A = 60°, B = 0°$.
(C) $\cos(A-B) = \frac{1}{2} \Rightarrow \cos(A-B) = \cos 60°$ and $\sin(A+B) = \frac{\sqrt{3}}{2} \Rightarrow \sin(A+B) = \sin 60°$.
(D) $A + B = 60°$ and $A - B = 60°$.
(a) DCAB (b) CADB
(c) DCBA (d) CDAB

46. If $\sin\alpha + \sin\beta + \sin\gamma = 3$, then $\sin^3\alpha + \sin^3\beta + \sin^3\gamma$ = ______.
(a) 0 (b) 2
(c) 3 (d) 1

47. $\sec^4\theta - \sec^2\theta =$ ______.

(a) $\tan^2\theta\sec^2\theta$ (b) $\dfrac{\tan^2\theta}{\sec^2\theta}$

(c) $\text{cosec}^2\theta\cot^2\theta$ (d) $\dfrac{\cot^2\theta}{\text{cosec}^2\theta}$

48. $\sin\theta + \cos\theta = \sqrt{2}$, then $\sin^{16}\theta =$ ______.

(a) $\dfrac{\cos^{16}\theta}{2^{16}}$ (b) $\dfrac{\sec^{16}\theta}{2^8}$

(c) $\dfrac{1}{2\sec^{16}\theta}$ (d) $\dfrac{1}{2^{16}\cos^{16}\theta}$

Level 3: Assess Your Concepts

49. If $\dfrac{\sin(x-y)}{\sin(x+y)} = \dfrac{3}{5}$, then $\tan x \cdot \cot y$ is ______.

(a) 1 (b) 2

(c) 3 (d) 4

50. $\sqrt{\sqrt{16\sin^4\theta + \text{cosec}^4\theta + 8} - 4} =$

(a) $2\sin\theta - \text{cosec}\,\theta$ (b) $2\sin\theta + \text{cosec}\,\theta$

(c) $2\text{cosec}\,\theta + \cos\theta$ (d) $2\text{cosec}\,\theta + \sin\theta$

51. If $\sin\alpha - \cos\alpha = m$, then the value of $\sin^6\alpha + \cos^6\alpha$ in terms of m is ______.

(a) $1 + \dfrac{3}{4}(1+m^2)^2$ (b) $1 - \dfrac{4}{3}(m^2-1)^2$

(c) $1 - \dfrac{3}{4}(1-m^2)^2$ (d) $1 - \dfrac{3}{4}(1+m^2)^2$

52. The value of $\dfrac{8\sec^4\theta - 8\tan^4\theta}{4 + 8\tan^2\theta} - \dfrac{2\cos^6\theta + 2\sin^6\theta}{1 - 3\sin^2\theta\cos^2\theta}$ is ______.

(a) 0 (b) 1

(c) –1 (d) 3

53. If $\dfrac{1+\tan\theta}{1-\tan\theta} = \sqrt{3}$, then find the value of θ.

(a) 30° (b) 25°

(c) 15° (d) 45°

54. If $A \times B = 1$, $A + B = \text{cosec}\,\theta \cdot \sec\theta$ then $\dfrac{A}{B}$ can be ______.

(a) $\tan^2\theta$ (b) $\sec^2\theta$

(c) $\sin^2\theta\cos^2\theta$ (d) $\text{cosec}^2\theta\sec^2\theta$

55. If $7\sin^2\theta + 3\cos^2\theta = 4$, then find $\tan\theta$.

(a) $\dfrac{1}{\sqrt{3}}$ (b) $\dfrac{2}{\sqrt{3}}$

(c) $\sqrt{3}$ (d) 1

56. If $\sin(A+B) = \dfrac{\sqrt{3}+1}{2\sqrt{2}}$ and $\sec A = 2$, then the value of B in circular measure is ______.

(a) $\dfrac{\pi}{12}$ (b) $\dfrac{3\pi}{5}$

(c) $\dfrac{7\pi}{5}$ (d) $\dfrac{5\pi}{12}$

57. If $\tan\theta - \cot\theta = 7$, then the value of $\tan^3\theta - \cot^3\theta$ is:

(a) 250 (b) 354

(c) 343 (d) 364

58. If $x^n = a^m\cos^4\theta$ and $y^n = b^m\sin^4\theta$, then:

(a) $\dfrac{x^{n/2}}{a^{m/2}} + \dfrac{y^{n/2}}{b^{m/2}} = 1$ (b) $\dfrac{x^n}{a^m} + \dfrac{y^n}{b^m} = 1$

(c) $\dfrac{x^{n/2}}{y^{n/2}} + \dfrac{a^{m/2}}{b^{m/2}} = 1$ (d) None of these

59. If $\sin^2\theta + 2\cos^2\theta + 3\sin^2\theta + 4\cos^2\theta + \cdots +$ 40 terms = 405 where θ is acute, then find the value of $\tan\theta$.

(a) $\dfrac{1}{\sqrt{3}}$ (b) $\sqrt{3}$

(c) 1 (d) ∞

60. If $\sin\alpha + \sin\beta = 2$, then find the value of $\cos^2\alpha + \cos^2\beta$.

(a) 0 (b) 1

(c) 2 (d) 3

61. If $\cos^2\theta + 2\sin^2\theta + 3\cos^2\theta + 4\sin^2\theta + \cdots$ (200 terms) = 10025, where θ is acute, then the value of $\sin\theta - \cos\theta$ is:

(a) $\dfrac{1-\sqrt{3}}{2}$ (b) $\dfrac{1+\sqrt{3}}{2}$

(c) $\dfrac{\sqrt{3}-1}{2}$ (d) 0

62. If $a\sin\theta - b\cos\theta = 0$ and $a\sin^3\theta + b\cos^3\theta = \sin 2\theta$, then find the value of $a^2 + b^2$.

(a) 2 (b) 3 (c) 4 (d) 5

63. If $\cos^2\theta + \cos\theta = 1$, then find the value of $\sin^6\theta + \cos^6\theta + 3\sin^8\theta + 3\cos^5\theta + 3$.

(a) 0 (b) 1 (c) 2 (d) 4

PRACTICE QUESTIONS JEE SPECIAL WING

Multiple-Answer Type Questions

Directions for questions 1 to 5:

Each question has FOUR options (a), (b), (c), and (d). ONE OR MORE THAN ONE of these four option(s) is/are the correct answer(s).

1. Which of the following statements are equivalent to 1?
   (a) $\sin 30° + \cos 60°$ (b) $\sec^2 29° - \tan^2 29°$
   (c) $\text{cosec}^2 21° - \cot^2 21°$ (d) $\sec 30° - \sec 0°$

2. Which of the following is equivalent to $\frac{\text{cosec} 20°}{\sec 20°}$?
   (a) $\frac{\cos 20°}{\sin 20°}$ (b) $\cot 20°$
   (c) $\tan 20°$ (d) $\cos 20°$

3. Which of the following is/are equivalent to $\cos 30°$?
   (a) $2\cos^2 15° - 1$ (b) $1 - \cos^2 15°$
   (c) $1 - 2\sin^2 15°$ (d) $\sin^2 15° - 1$

4. Which of the following is equivalent to $\cot\theta$?
   (a) $\sqrt{\frac{1+\cot^2\theta}{1+\tan^2\theta}}$ (b) $\sqrt{\frac{1+\tan^2\theta}{1+\cot^2\theta}}$
   (c) $\frac{\cot\theta - 1}{1-\tan\theta}$ (d) $(\tan\theta + \cot\theta)\cos^2\theta$

5. If $\sin\theta = \frac{x-y}{x+y}$, then which of the following are true?
   (a) $\sec\theta = \frac{x+y}{2\sqrt{xy}}$ (b) $\tan\theta = \frac{x-y}{2\sqrt{xy}}$
   (c) $\cos\theta = \frac{2\sqrt{xy}}{x+y}$ (d) $\text{cosec}\theta = \frac{x+y}{x-y}$

Match The Column

Directions for questions 6 to 10:

Read the paragraph given below and answer the questions.

$\sin(A+B) = \sin A\cos B + \sin B\cos A$

$\sin(A-B) = \sin A\cos B - \sin B\cos A$

$\cos(A+B) = \cos A\cos B - \sin A\sin B$

$\cos(A-B) = \cos A\cos B + \sin A\sin B$

$\tan(A+B) = \frac{\tan A + \tan B}{1-\tan A\tan B}$

$\tan(A-B) = \frac{\tan A - \tan B}{1+\tan A\tan B}$

Using the above information, match the values in Column A with those in Column B.

Column A	Column B
6. $\sin 75° \times \tan 15°$	(a) 4
7. $\sec 75° + \cot 15°$	(b) 8
8. $\text{cosec} 15° \times \sec 15°$	(c) 12
9. $(\tan 75° - \cot 75°)^2$	(d) $\frac{\sqrt{6}-\sqrt{2}}{4}$
10. $\text{cosec} 75° - \cos 15°$	(e) $2+\sqrt{6}+\sqrt{3}+\sqrt{2}$
	(f) $\frac{2\sqrt{6}-5\sqrt{2}+\sqrt{6}}{4}$

Comprehension-Based Questions

Directions for questions 11 to 15:

Read the paragraph given below and answer the questions.

A person travels at a constant speed. He starts from point P and travels towards a tower AB. He observes the top of the tower from points P and Q with angles of 30° and 60° respectively. The person then travels away from the tower and reaches point R, where he observes the top of the tower with an angle of 45°.

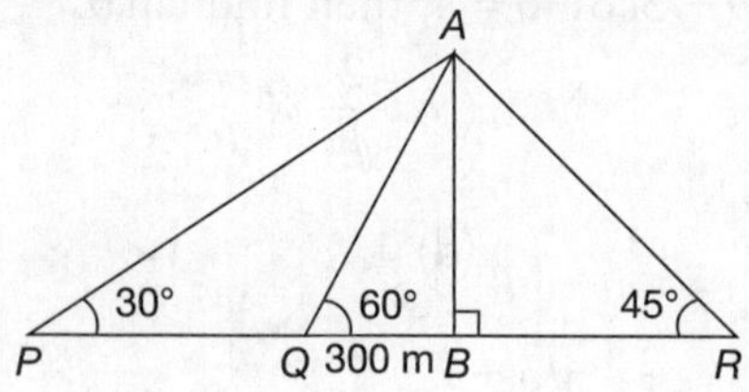

The distance Q and B is 300 m.

$\angle APB = 30°$

$\angle AQB = 60°$

$\angle ARB = 45°$

11. What is the height of the tower?

(a) $150\sqrt{3}$ m (b) $300\sqrt{3}$ m

(c) $450\sqrt{3}$ m (d) $600\sqrt{3}$ m

12. What is the distance between points *P* and *Q*?

(a) 900 m (b) 750 m

(c) 600 m (d) 450 m

13. What is the distance between points *P* and *R*?

(a) $150(3+\sqrt{3})$ m (b) $100(3+\sqrt{3})$ m

(c) $450(3+\sqrt{3})$ m (d) $300(3+\sqrt{3})$ m

14. If the person takes 2.5 minutes to travel from *Q* to *B*, then what is the time taken by him to travel from *P* to reach the tower?

(a) 5 minutes (b) 6 minutes

(c) 7.5 minutes (d) 9.5 minutes

15. If the person travels at 5 m/s, then what is the time taken by him to travel from point *P* to reach point *R*?

(a) $3+\sqrt{3}$ minutes (b) $6-\sqrt{3}$ minutes

(c) $4.5+\sqrt{3}$ minutes (d) $4.5-\sqrt{3}$ minutes

Assertion and Reason Type Questions

Directions for questions 16 to 20:

Read the options given below and answer the questions.

(a) Both assertion (A) and reason (R) are true, and the reason (R) is the correct explanation of the assertion (A).

(b) Both assertion (A) and reason (R) are true, and the reason (R) is not the correct explanation of the assertion (A).

(c) Assertion (A) is true, but reason (R) is false.

(d) Assertion (A) is false, and reason (R) is true.

16. Assertion: $\sin 75° = \dfrac{\sqrt{3}+1}{2\sqrt{2}}$

Reason: $\sin(A+B) = \sin A\cos B + \sin B\cos A$.

17. Assertion: $\sec^4\theta - \tan^4\theta = \sec^2\theta + \tan^2\theta$.

Reason: $\sin^2\theta + \cos^2\theta = 1$.

18. Assertion: If $\sin\theta + \cos\theta = 1$, then $\sin 2\theta = 0$.

Reason: $\sin^2\theta + \cos^2\theta = 1$ and $\sin 2\theta = 2\sin\theta\cos\theta$.

19. Assertion: If $\tan(A+B) = \dfrac{\tan A + \tan B}{1-\tan A\tan B}$, then

$\cot(A+B) = \dfrac{\cot A + \cot B}{\cot A\cot B - 1}$

Reason: $\tan A \times \cot A = 1$.

20. Assertion: If $\tan A = \dfrac{1}{11}$ and $\tan B = \dfrac{5}{6}$, then

$A + B = 45°$

Reason: $\tan(A+B) = \dfrac{\tan A - \tan B}{1+\tan A\tan B}$.

ANSWER KEYS

Crossword

Across

1. Centesimal 7. Angle 8. Infinite 9. One

Down

1. Circular 2. Two 3. Sexagesimal 4. Radian 5. Zero
6. Hundred

Classroom Wing

Very Short Answer Type Questions

1. $\frac{1}{\sqrt{3}}$ 2. $\frac{1}{x}$ 3. $\frac{1}{2}$ 4. $45° = \frac{\pi^c}{4}$ 5. 45°
6. $\sqrt{3}-1$ 7. $\frac{1}{2}$ 8. 0 9. 1 10. $\frac{\pi}{12}$
11. $A + B = 90°$ 12. $1 (A = 45°, C = 45°)$ 13. $\frac{3}{32}$ 14. $\frac{-17}{11}$ 15. $\frac{\sqrt{3}+1}{2\sqrt{2}}$
16. $\frac{40^g}{3}$, 12° 17. $\sec^2\alpha + \tan^2\alpha$ 18. $60°, \frac{\pi}{3}$ 19. $300^g, \frac{3\pi^c}{2}$ 20. 2

Short Answer Type Questions

21. $\frac{2\sqrt{5}}{5}$ 22. $\frac{\pi^c}{4}$ 23. 10 24. $2+\sqrt{3}$ 25. ±2
26. $x^2 + y^2 = a^2 + b^2$ 27. $\frac{63}{65}$ 28. $\sqrt{\frac{1}{1+\cot^2\theta}}$ 29. $\frac{24}{25}$ 30. $-\frac{8}{9}$
31. 132 cm 32. $\frac{1}{3}$ or −3 33. 1 34. 60° 35. 7

Essay Type Questions

36. 4 cm 37. 6 38. $(x-a)^2 + (y-b)^2 = r^2$ 39. $18\sqrt{3}$
40. $\cot y$

Competition Wing

Level 1: Apply Your Concepts

1. $\frac{\sqrt{3}}{4}$ 2. 120° 3. 0 4. 58° 5. (d)
6. (a) 7. (d) 8. (d) 9. (a) 10. (b)
11. (c) 12. (b) 13. (a) 14. (d) 15. (b)
16. (d) 17. (d) 18. (a) 19. (c) 20. (b)
21. (d) 22. (d) 23. (c) 24. (d) 25. (b)

26. (d)	27. (c)	28. (d)	29. (b)	30. (b)
31. (d)				

Level 2: Review Your Concepts

32. (c)	33. (d)	34. (a)	35. (d)	36. (a)
37. (b)	38. (d)	39. (b)	40. (b)	41. (b)
42. (c)	43. (a)	44. (c)	45. (d)	46. (c)
47. (a)	48. (d)			

Level 3: Assess Your Concepts

49. (d)	50. (c)	51. (c)	52. (a)	53. (c)
54. (a)	55. (a)	56. (a)	57. (d)	58. (a)
59. (b)	60. (a)	61. (a)	62. (c)	63. (d)

JEE Special Wing

Multiple-Answer Type Questions

1. (a, b, c, d)	2. (a, b)	3. (a, c)	4. (a, b, d)	5. (a, b, c, d)

Match The Column

6. (d)	7. (e)	8. (a)	9. (c)	10. (f)

Comprehension-Based Questions

11. (b)	12. (c)	13. (d)	14. (c)	15. (a)

Assertion and Reason Type Questions

16. (a)	17. (b)	18. (a)	19. (d)	20. (c)

Hints and Explanations

Classroom Wing

Very Short Answer Type Questions

1. Given,

$\cos(90° - 3\theta) = \sin(12\theta - 90°)$

$\Rightarrow (90° - 3\theta) + (12\theta - 90°) = 90°$

$\Rightarrow 9\theta = 90° \Rightarrow \theta = 10°$

$\tan 3\theta = \tan 30° = \dfrac{1}{\sqrt{3}}$

2. We know that,

$1 + \cot^2\theta = \text{cosec}^2\theta$

$1 = \text{cosec}^2\theta - \cot^2\theta$

$\Rightarrow (\text{cosec}\,\theta + \cot\theta)(\text{cosec}\,\theta - \cot 0) = 1$

$\Rightarrow x(\text{cosec}\,\theta + \cot\theta) = 1$

$\Rightarrow \text{cosec}\,\theta + \cot\theta = \dfrac{1}{x}$

3. $\dfrac{\sin 20\cos 70 + \cos 20\sin 70}{\sin 23°\,\text{cosec}\,23° + \cos 23°\sec 23°}$

Since, $\sin(A + B) = \sin A\cos B + \cos A\sin B$ using this equation in numerator, we get:

$$\frac{\sin(20+70)}{\frac{\sin 23°}{\sin 23°} + \frac{\cos 23°}{\sec 23°}} = \frac{\sin 90}{2} = \frac{1}{2}$$

4. Given that, $\cot\alpha = 4$ and $\cot\beta = \dfrac{5}{3}$

$\cot\alpha = 4 \Rightarrow \tan\alpha = \dfrac{1}{4}$

$\cot\beta = \dfrac{5}{3} \Rightarrow \tan\beta = \dfrac{3}{5}$

$$\tan(\alpha+\beta) = \frac{\tan\alpha + \tan\beta}{1 - \tan\alpha\tan\beta} = \frac{\frac{1}{4} + \frac{3}{5}}{1 - \frac{1}{4}\times\frac{3}{5}}$$

$$\tan(\alpha+\beta) = \frac{\frac{17}{20}}{\frac{17}{20}}$$

$\tan(\alpha + \beta) = 1$

$\tan(\alpha + \beta) = \tan 45°$

$\alpha + \beta = 45°$

$45° = \dfrac{\pi^c}{4}$

5. $\tan\theta = \dfrac{5}{6}, \tan\phi = \dfrac{1}{11}$

$$\tan(\theta+\phi) = \frac{\tan\theta + \tan\phi}{1 - \tan\theta\cdot\tan\phi} = \frac{\frac{5}{6} + \frac{1}{11}}{1 - \frac{5}{66}}$$

$$\tan(\theta+\phi) = \frac{\frac{55+6}{66}}{\frac{66-5}{66}} = \frac{61}{61} = 1$$

$\tan(\theta+\phi) = 1 = \tan 45°$

$\Rightarrow \theta + \phi = 45°$

6. $A - B = 45°$, $\tan A - \tan B = \sqrt{3}$, $\tan(A - B) = \tan 45°$

$\dfrac{\tan A - \tan B}{1 + \tan A\cdot\tan B} = 1 \Rightarrow \sqrt{3} = 1 + \tan A\cdot\tan B$

$\tan A \cdot \tan B = \sqrt{3} - 1$

7. Given that, $\alpha + \beta = 90°$ and $\alpha = 2\beta$

$2\beta + \beta = 90°$

$\beta = 30°$

$\alpha = 60°$

$\therefore \cos^2\alpha + \sin^2\beta = \cos^2 60° + \sin^2 30°$

$= \left(\dfrac{1}{2}\right)^2 + \left(\dfrac{1}{2}\right)^2$

$= \dfrac{1}{4} + \dfrac{1}{4}$

$= \dfrac{1}{2}$

8. $(\cot 1°) \times (\cot 2°) + (\cot 3°) \times \ldots \times (\cot 90°)$

$= 0\ (\because \cot 90° = 0)$

9. Given,

$\sec(25° + 7\theta) = \text{cosec}(15° + 3\theta)$

$\Rightarrow (25° + 7\theta) + (15° + 3\theta) = 90°$

$10\theta + 40° = 90°$

$10\theta = 50°$

$\Rightarrow \theta = 5°$

$\cot 9\theta$

$\Rightarrow = \cot 45° = 1$

10. $\tan(A+B)=\sqrt{3}$ *and* $\sin A = \dfrac{1}{\sqrt{2}}$

$\tan(A+B) = \tan 60°$ and $\sin A = \sin 45°$

$A + B = 60°$ and $A = 45°$

$\Rightarrow B = 15° = 15 \times \dfrac{\pi}{180} = \dfrac{\pi}{12}$

12

$B = \dfrac{\pi}{12}$

11. If $\sin A = \cos B$, where $0° \le A, B \le 90°$

$\Rightarrow A = 90 - B$

$\Rightarrow A + B = 90°$

12.

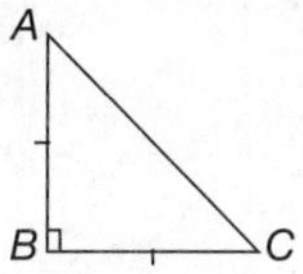

$AC^2 = AB^2 + BC^2$

since $AB = BC$

$\therefore \quad AC^2 = 2\,BC^2$ (1)

now $\sin A = \dfrac{BC}{AC} \Rightarrow \sin^2 A = \dfrac{BC^2}{AC^2}$

$\cos C = \dfrac{BC}{AC} \Rightarrow \cos^2 C = \dfrac{BC^2}{AC^2}$

$\sin 2A + \cos 2C = \dfrac{2BC^2}{AC^2} = \dfrac{2BC^2}{2BC^2} = 1$

$\sin^2 A + \cos^2 C = 1$ where A, $C = 45°$

13. $(\sin 60 \cdot \cos 45 \cdot \cos 60 \cdot \text{cosec } 90)^2$

$= \left(\dfrac{\sqrt{3}}{2} \cdot \dfrac{1}{\sqrt{2}} \cdot \dfrac{1}{2} \cdot 1\right)^2 = \dfrac{3}{32}$

14. $\sin\theta = \dfrac{3}{5}$

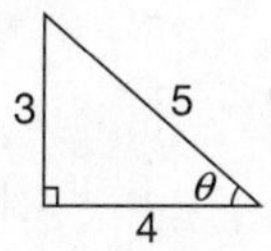

$\tan\theta = \dfrac{3}{4}$,

$\cos\theta = \dfrac{4}{5}$, $\sec\theta = \dfrac{5}{4}$.

$\dfrac{\tan\theta - 2\cos\theta}{3\sin\theta + \sec\theta} = \dfrac{\dfrac{3}{4} - \dfrac{8}{5}}{\dfrac{9}{5} + \dfrac{5}{4}} = \dfrac{15-32}{36+20} = \dfrac{-17}{11}$

15. $\cos 15° = \cos(45 - 30°)$

$= \cos 45 \cdot \cos 30 + \sin 45 \cdot \sin 30°$

$= \dfrac{1}{\sqrt{2}} \cdot \dfrac{\sqrt{3}}{2} + \dfrac{1}{\sqrt{2}} \cdot \dfrac{1}{2}$

$\cos 15° = \dfrac{1+\sqrt{3}}{2\sqrt{2}}$

16. $\dfrac{\pi}{15} = \dfrac{\pi}{15} \times \dfrac{180°}{\pi} = 12°$

also $= \left(\dfrac{40}{3}\text{ rad}\right)$

17. $\sec^4\alpha - \tan^4\alpha$

$= (\sec^2\alpha - \tan^2\alpha)(\sec^2\alpha + \tan^2\alpha)$ (1)

Since $\sec^2\alpha = 1 + \tan^2\alpha$

Therefore, $\sec^2\alpha - \tan^2\alpha = 1$

Using this in equation (1) we get,

$= 1 \cdot (\sec^2\alpha + \tan^2\alpha)$

$= \sec^2\alpha + \tan^2\alpha$

18. $\left(\dfrac{200}{3}\right)^R = 300° \cdot \dfrac{3\pi}{100 \cdot 2} \cdot \dfrac{200}{3} \times \dfrac{180}{200} = 60° = \dfrac{\pi}{3}$

19. $270° = 270 \times \dfrac{200}{180} = 300R$

(cancellation marks: 3 over 270, 2 under 180)

$270° = 270 \times \dfrac{\pi}{180} = \dfrac{3\pi}{2}$

(cancellation marks: 3 over 270, 2 under 180)

20. $\cos 0° + \sqrt{2}\sec 45° - \sqrt{3}\tan 30°$

$= 1 + \sqrt{2} \times \sqrt{2} - \sqrt{3} \times \dfrac{1}{\sqrt{3}}$

$= 1 + 2 - 1 = 2$

Short Answer Type Questions

21.

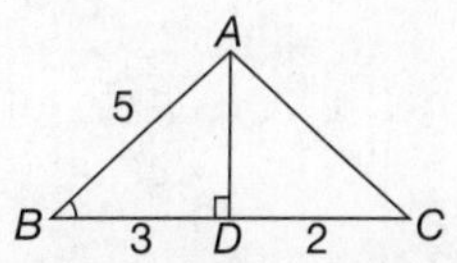

$AD^2 + BD^2 = AB^2$

$\Rightarrow AD^2 = 25 - 9 = 16$

$AD = 4$

also, $AD^2 + CD^2 = AC^2$

$AC^2 = 16 + 4 = 20$

$\Rightarrow AC = 2\sqrt{5}$

Since $= \dfrac{AD}{AC} = \dfrac{4}{2\sqrt{5}} = \dfrac{2\sqrt{5}}{5}$

22. $\sin(A - B) = \dfrac{1}{2} \Rightarrow \sin(A - B) = \sin 30°$

$A - B = 30°$ -------- (1)

$\cos(A + B) = \cos 60°$

$A + B = 60°$ -------- (2)

From (1) and (2)

$A + B = 60°$

$A - B = 30°$

$2A = 90°$

$A = 45°$

$= \dfrac{\pi^c}{4}$

23. $\sin^2\alpha + \sin\alpha = 1 \Rightarrow \sin\alpha = 1 - \sin^2\alpha = \cos^2 x$

$7\cos^2\alpha + 7(\cos^2\alpha)^2 + 3 = 7\cos^2\alpha + 7\sin^2\alpha + 3$

$= 7(\cos^2\alpha + \sin^2\alpha) + 3$

$= 7(1) + 3 = 10$

24. $\tan 75° = \tan(45 + 30°)$

$$\tan(45° + 30°) = \frac{\tan 45° + \tan 30°}{1 - \tan 45° \cdot \tan 30°}$$

$$= \frac{1 + \dfrac{1}{\sqrt{3}}}{1 - \dfrac{1}{\sqrt{3}}} = \frac{\sqrt{3}+1}{\sqrt{3}-1} = 2 + \sqrt{3}$$

25. $\sec^2\alpha + \cos^2\alpha = 2$

$\dfrac{1}{\cos^2\alpha} + \cos^2\alpha = 2$

$1 + \cos^4\alpha = 2\cos^2\alpha$

$\Rightarrow \cos^4\alpha - 2\cos^2\alpha + 1 = 0$

$\Rightarrow (\cos^2\alpha - 1)^2 = 0$

$\Rightarrow \cos^2\alpha = 1$

$\Rightarrow \cos\alpha = \pm 1$

$\Rightarrow \sec\alpha = \dfrac{1}{\cos\alpha} = \pm 1$

$\therefore \mathbf{\sec\alpha \pm \cos\alpha = \pm 2}$

26. $a = x\sin\theta - y\cos\theta$, $b = x\cos\theta + y\sin\theta$

square and add both equations:

$a^2 + b^2 = x^2(\sin^2\theta + \cos^2\theta) + y^2(\cos^2\theta + \sin^2\theta)$

$a^2 + b^2 = x^2 + y^2$

27. $\cos\alpha = \dfrac{12}{13}$ and $\sin\beta = \dfrac{4}{5}$

$\sin(\alpha + \beta) = ?$

of $\cos\alpha = \dfrac{12}{13}$, then $\sin\alpha = \dfrac{5}{13}$

$\sin\beta = \dfrac{4}{5}$ then $\cos\beta = \dfrac{3}{5}$

$\sin(\alpha + \beta) = \sin\alpha\cos\beta + \cos\alpha\sin\beta$

$= \dfrac{5}{13} \times \dfrac{3}{5} + \dfrac{12}{13} \times \dfrac{4}{5}$

$= \dfrac{15}{65} + \dfrac{48}{65} = \dfrac{63}{65}$

28. $\operatorname{cosec}^2\theta = 1 + \cot^2\theta$

$\Rightarrow \dfrac{1}{\sin^2\theta} = 1 + \cot^2\theta$

$\Rightarrow \sin^2\theta = \dfrac{1}{1 + \cot^2\theta}$

$\Rightarrow \mathbf{\sin\theta = \sqrt{\dfrac{1}{1 + \cot^2\theta}}}$

29. If $\sin\alpha = \dfrac{4}{5}$ then $\cos\alpha = \dfrac{3}{5}$

$\sin^2\alpha = 2\sin\alpha\cos\alpha = 2 \cdot \dfrac{4}{5} \cdot \dfrac{3}{5} = \dfrac{24}{25}$

30. $\sin\alpha + \cos\alpha = \dfrac{1}{3}$

Squaring both sides:

$\sin^2\alpha + \cos^2\alpha + 2\sin\alpha\cos\alpha = \dfrac{1}{9}$

$2\sin\alpha\cos\alpha = \dfrac{1}{9} - 1$

$\Rightarrow \sin 2\alpha = \dfrac{-8}{9}$

31. Length covered by tip in 1 min $= 2\pi r$

$\therefore$ Length covered in 35 min $= \dfrac{35}{60} \times 2\pi r$

$= \dfrac{\overset{5}{\cancel{35}}}{60} \times 2 \times 36 \times \dfrac{22}{\cancel{7}}$

$22 \times 6 = 132$

32. $\tan 2\alpha = \frac{3}{4}$

$$\Rightarrow \frac{2\tan\alpha}{1-\tan^2\alpha} = \frac{3}{4}$$

$8\tan\alpha = 3 - 3\tan^2\alpha$

$3\tan^2\alpha + 8\tan\alpha - 3 = 0$

$3\tan^2\alpha + 9\tan\alpha - \tan\alpha - 3 = 0$

$3\tan\alpha(\tan\alpha + 3) - 1(\tan\alpha + 3) = 0$

$(\tan\alpha + 3)(3\tan\alpha - 1) = 0$

$\Rightarrow \tan\alpha = \frac{1}{3}, -3$

33. $A + B = 45°$

$\tan(A + B) = \tan 45°$

$$\frac{\tan A + \tan B}{1 - \tan A \tan B} = 1$$

$\tan A + \tan B = 1 - \tan A \tan B$

$\tan A + \tan B + \tan A \cdot \tan B = 1$

34. $\frac{\cos\theta}{1-\sin\theta} + \frac{\cos\theta}{1+\sin\theta} = 4$

$$\cos\theta\left[\frac{1}{1-\sin\theta} + \frac{1}{1+\sin\theta}\right] = 4$$

$$\cos\theta\left[\frac{1+\sin\theta+1-\sin\theta}{(1-\sin\theta)(1+\sin\theta)}\right] = 4$$

$$\cos\theta\left[\frac{2}{1-\sin^2\theta}\right] = 4$$

$$\cos\theta\left(\frac{1}{\cos^2\theta}\right) = 2$$

$\sec\theta = 2$

$\sec\theta = \sec 60°$

$\theta = 60°$

35. Given, $\frac{1+\cos\theta}{1-\cos\theta} = \frac{4}{1}$

By Componendo and Dividendo

$$\frac{1+\cos\theta+1-\cos\theta}{1+\cos\theta-1+\cos\theta} = \frac{4+1}{4-1}$$

$$\frac{2}{2\cos\theta} = \frac{5}{3}$$

$\cos\theta = \frac{3}{5} \Rightarrow \sin\theta = \frac{4}{5}$

$$\frac{\sin\theta + \cos\theta}{\sin\theta - \cos\theta} = \frac{\left(\frac{4}{5}\right)+\left(\frac{3}{5}\right)}{\left(\frac{4}{3}\right)-\left(\frac{3}{5}\right)} = \frac{\left(\frac{7}{5}\right)}{\left(\frac{1}{5}\right)} = 7$$

Essay Type Questions

36.

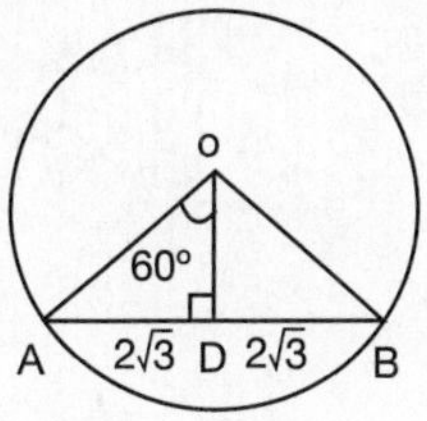

Let the chord be AB and 'O' be the centre of the circle.

Given, $\angle AOB = 120°$ and $AB = 4\sqrt{3}$ cm

OD is the shortest distance from O to AB

$\Delta AOD \cong \Delta BOD$

$\therefore AD = DB = 2\sqrt{3}$ ($\because$ CPCT)

In ΔAOD,

$$\sin 60° = \frac{AD}{AO}$$

$$\frac{\sqrt{3}}{2} = \frac{2\sqrt{3}}{AO}$$

$$AO = \frac{4\sqrt{3}}{\sqrt{3}}$$

AO = 4 cm

$\therefore$ Radius of the circle is 4 cm

37. $\cos^2\alpha + \cos\alpha = 1$

$\cos^2\alpha = 1 - \cos\alpha$

$\cos^4\alpha = 1 + \cos^2\alpha - 2\cos\alpha$

$\cos^4\alpha - \cos^2\alpha = 1 - 2(1 - \cos^2\alpha)$

$(1 - \sin\alpha)^2 - (1 - \sin^2\alpha) = (1 - 2\sin^2\alpha)$

$\cancel{1} + \sin^4\alpha - \cancel{2\sin^2\alpha} - \cancel{1} + \sin^2\alpha = 1 - \cancel{2\sin^2\alpha}$

$\sin^4\alpha + \sin^2\alpha = 1$

$4\sin^4\alpha + 4\sin^2\alpha = 4$

$4\sin^4\alpha + 4\sin^2\alpha + 2 = 4 + 2 = 6$

$4\sin^4\alpha + 4\sin^2\alpha + 2 = 6$

38. $x = a + r\cos\theta \Rightarrow r\cos\theta = x - a$ (1)

$y = b + r\sin\theta \Rightarrow r\sin\theta = y - b$ (2)

Squaring and adding (1) and (2),

$r^2(\cos^2\theta + \sin^2\theta) = (x - a)^2 + (y - b)^2$

$r^2 = (x - a)^2 + (y - b)^2$

39.

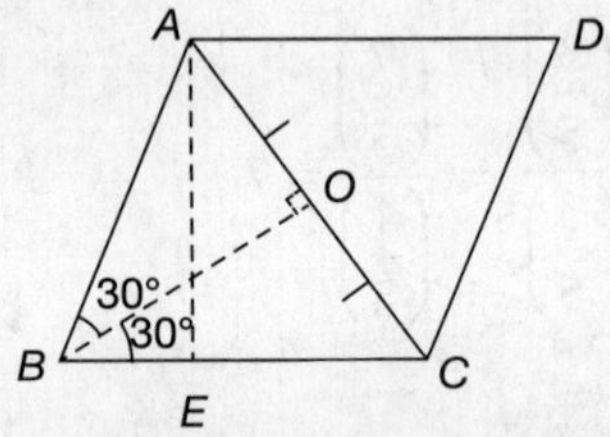

In rhombus $ABCD$,

$\angle B = 60°$, $AC = 6$ cm

$\Rightarrow OC = 3\text{cm}$

In BOC,

$$\sin 30° = \frac{OC}{BC} = \frac{1}{2}$$

$\Rightarrow BC = 2 \times OC = 2 \times 3 = 6$ cm.

In ΔABE,

$$\sin 60° = \frac{AE}{AB} = \frac{\sqrt{3}}{2} \Rightarrow AE = 3\sqrt{3}\text{cm}$$

Area of Rhombus = AE × BC

$= 6 \times 3\sqrt{3} = 18\sqrt{3}$ cm

40. $\alpha + \beta + \gamma = 90°$

$\alpha + \beta = 90° - \gamma$

$\tan(\alpha + \beta) = \tan(90 - \gamma)$

$\tan(\alpha + \beta) = \cot \gamma$

$$\frac{\tan \alpha + \tan \beta}{1 - \tan \alpha \tan \beta} = \cot \gamma$$

$\tan \alpha + \tan \beta = \cot \gamma - \tan \alpha \tan \beta \cot \gamma$

$\tan \alpha + \tan \beta + \tan \alpha \tan \beta \cot \gamma = \cot \gamma$

Competition Wing

Level 1: Apply Your Concepts

1. sin 30 · sin 45 · cosec 45° · cos 30°

$$= \frac{1}{2} \times \frac{1}{\sqrt{2}} \times \sqrt{2} \times \frac{\sqrt{3}}{2} = \frac{\sqrt{3}}{4}$$

2. $\frac{1-(\tan 60)^2}{1+(\tan 60)^2} = \cos X$

$$\Rightarrow \cos X = \cos X = \frac{1-(\sqrt{3})^2}{1+(\sqrt{3})^2} = \frac{-2}{4} = \frac{-1}{2} = \cos 120^o$$

$\Rightarrow X = 120°$

3. $\log[(\sec\theta + \tan\theta)(\sec\theta - \tan\theta)]$

$\log[\sec^2\theta - \tan^2\theta$

Since $\tan^2\theta = 1 + \sec^2 6$

$\therefore \log[\sec^2\theta - \tan^2\theta] = \log[1] = 0$

4. $\frac{\cos 13° + \sin 13°}{\cos 13° - \sin 13°} = \tan A$

$$\frac{\cos(58° - 45°) + \sin(58° - 45°)}{\cos(58° - 45°) - \sin(58° - 45°)} = \tan A$$

$$= \frac{\cos 58° \cos 45° + \sin 58° \sin 45° + \sin 58° \cos 45° - \cos 58° \sin 45°}{\cos 58° \cos 45° + \sin 58° \sin 45° - \sin 58° \cos 45° + \cos 58° \sin 45°}$$

$$= \frac{\frac{\cos 58°}{\sqrt{2}} + \frac{\sin 58°}{\sqrt{2}} + \frac{\sin 58°}{\sqrt{2}} - \frac{\cos 58°}{\sqrt{2}}}{\frac{\cos 58°}{\sqrt{2}} + \frac{\sin 58°}{\sqrt{2}} - \frac{\sin 58°}{\sqrt{2}} + \frac{\cos 58°}{\sqrt{2}}}$$

$$= \frac{\frac{2}{\sqrt{2}}\sin 58°}{\frac{2}{\sqrt{2}}\cos 58°} = \tan 58° = \tan A$$

$\Rightarrow A = 58°$

5. (i) The minutes hand covers an angle of 6° per minute.

(ii) Use $l = r \times \theta$.

6. Use $\tan\theta \cdot \tan(90 - \theta) = 1$.

7. Use $\sec^2\theta - \tan^2\theta = 1$.

8. Take the values of trigonometric ratios from the table.

9. Use $(a + b)(a - b) = a^2 - b^2$ and $\cos^2\theta + \sin^2\theta = 1$.

10. $= \frac{\sqrt{1+\cot^2\theta}}{\cot\theta}$

$$= \frac{\sqrt{\text{cosec}^2\theta}}{\cot\theta} = \frac{\text{cosec}\theta}{\cot\theta} = \sec\theta$$

11. $\sqrt{\frac{\sec x + \tan x}{\sec x - \tan x}}$

$$= \sqrt{\frac{(\sec x + \tan x)^2}{\sec^2 x - \tan^2 x}}$$

$= \sec x + \tan x$

$$= \frac{1}{\cos x} + \frac{\sin x}{\cos x}$$

$$= \frac{1+\sin x}{\cos x}$$

12. Given, $\left[\frac{1+\sin\theta}{\cos\theta} + \frac{\cos\theta}{1+\sin\theta}\right] \cot\theta$

$$= \left[\frac{1+\sin\theta}{\cos\theta} + \frac{\cos\theta(1-\sin\theta)}{1^2 - \sin^2\theta}\right] \cot\theta$$

$$= \left[\frac{1-\sin\theta}{\cos\theta} + \frac{\cos\theta(1-\sin\theta)}{\cos^2\theta}\right] \cot\theta$$

$$= \left[\frac{2}{\cos\theta}\right]\left[\frac{\cos\theta}{\sin\theta}\right] = \frac{2}{\sin\theta} = 2\,\text{cosec}\,\theta.$$

13. $\frac{\cos^4 A - \sin^4 A}{\sin^2 A - \cos^2 A} = \frac{(\cos^2 A - \sin^2 A)(\cos^2 A + \sin^2 A)}{\sin^2 A - \cos^2 A}$

$= -(\cos^2 A + \sin^2 A) = -1$

14. We know that $\sec^2\theta - \tan^2\theta = 1$

$\sec^2\theta - 1 = \tan^2\theta$

$\tan\theta = \sqrt{\sec^2\theta - 1}$

15. Use $\cos^2\theta + \sin^2\theta = 1$.

16. Given that, $a = \sin^4\theta$ and $b = \cot^4\theta$

$$\frac{1}{\sqrt{a}} = \frac{1}{\sin^2\theta} \text{ and } \sqrt{b} = \cot^2\theta$$

$$\frac{1}{\sqrt{a}} = \text{cosec}^2\theta$$

$$\text{Now } \frac{1}{\sqrt{a}} - \sqrt{b} = \text{cosec}^2\theta - \cot^2 = 1$$

17. Given, $\sin\alpha = \frac{3}{5}$

$\sec\alpha = \frac{5}{4}$

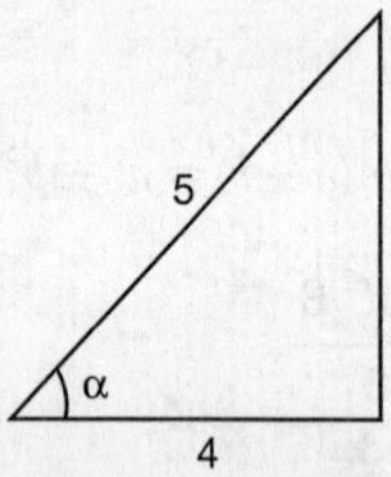

18. $\sec^2\alpha - \sec\alpha = 1 \Rightarrow \sec\alpha = \sec^2\alpha - 1 = \tan^2\alpha$

$\therefore 5\tan^2\alpha - 5(\tan^2\alpha)^2 + 6 = 5\tan^2\alpha - 5\sec^2\alpha + 6$

$= 5(\tan^2\alpha - \sec^2\alpha) + 6$

$= -5 + 6 = 1$

19. $\frac{\sec^8 A - \tan^8 A}{\sec^4 A + \tan^4 A} = \frac{(\sec^4 A - \tan^4 A)(\sec^4 A + \tan^4 A)}{(\sec^4 A + \tan^4 A)}$

$= \sec^4 A - \tan^4 A$

$= (\sec^2 A + \tan^2 A)(\sec^2 A - \tan^2 A)$

$= \sec^2 A + \tan^2 A$

$= 2\sec^2 A - 1$

20. (i) Minutes hand moves 6° in one minute.

(ii) Use $l = r \times \theta$.

21. Use $\sin 2\alpha = 2\sin\alpha\cos\alpha$.

22. In triangle ABC, $\frac{A+B}{2} = \frac{180 - C}{2}$.

23. Apply $a^2 - b^2 = (a + b)(a - b)$.

25. Use $\tan 45° = 1$ and $\sin 60° = \frac{\sqrt{3}}{2}$.

26. Use $(a + b)(a - b) = a^2 - b^2$ and solve.

27. Use $\cos 2\theta = \frac{1 - \tan^2\theta}{1 + \tan^2\theta}$.

28. Use $a^2 + b^2 = (a + b)^2 - 2ab$.

29. (i) $\sin^2 A = \sin^2(90 - B)$. If A and B complementary angles.

(ii) If $A + B = 90°$, then $\sin A = \cos B$ and $\tan B = \cot A$.

30. Use trigonometric ratios values from table.

31. Squaring both sides of given equation.

Level 2: Review Your Concepts

32. (i) $\sin^6\alpha + \cos^6\alpha = (\sin^2\alpha)^3 + (\cos^2\alpha)^3$. Use the formula $a^3 + b^3 = (a + b)^3 - 3ab(a + b)$.

(ii) Find $\sin\alpha \cdot \cos\alpha$ by substituting $\sin\alpha + \cos\alpha = n$ in the above equation.

33. (i) Use $\cos A \cos B - \sin A \sin B = \cos(A + B)$ and $\sin 2A = 2\sin A \cos A$.

(ii) Find the LCM of denominators and simplify.

(iii) Use the formula $\cos(A + B) = \cos A \cos B - \sin A \sin B$.

34. (i) Use $\tan 30° = \frac{1}{\sqrt{3}}$.

(ii) Substitute the value of $\tan 30°$ and simplify.

(iii) Then check from the options.

35. Use $\operatorname{cosec}^2 x = 1 + \cot^2 x$ and $\sin^2 x + \cos^2 x = 1$.

36. (i) Use componendo and dividendo theorem, i.e., $\frac{a}{b} = \frac{a+b}{a-b}$.

(ii) Use the formula $\cos(A - B)$ and $\cos(A + B)$.

(iii) Take cross multiplication and find $\tan A + \tan B$.

37. (i) Put $\theta = 45°$.

(ii) If $\tan\theta + \cot\theta = 2$, then $\theta = 45°$.

38. Use $\cot A \cdot \cot(90 - A) = 1$.

39. (i) Apply $\sqrt{1 + \sin 2A} = \sin A + \cos A$.

(ii) $\sin\frac{x}{8} = \sin 2\left(\frac{x}{16}\right)$ and $\sin 2\theta = 2\sin\theta\cos\theta$.

(iii) Use the identity $1 = \sin^2\theta + \cos^2\theta$.

40. (i) Use $(a + b)^2 = a^2 + b^2 + 2ab$ and $\cos^2\theta = 1 - \sin^2\theta$.

(ii) Take $\cos^4\theta$ as $(1 - \sin^2\theta)^2$ and simplify.

41. (i) By squaring on both the sides of the given equation we can obtain.

(ii) Square on both sides of $\sin\beta + \cos\beta = \frac{5}{4}$.

42. (i) Use $\sin^2 x + \cot^2 x = 1$.

(ii) $\cos^4\alpha = (1 - \sin^2\alpha)^2$.

(iii) $\cos^2\alpha = (1 - \sin^2\alpha)$.

(iv) Substitute the above values in the given expression.

43. If $x + \frac{1}{x} = 2$, then $x^n + \frac{1}{x^n} = 2$.

44. (i) Use $\tan(A + B) = \frac{\tan A + \tan B}{1 - \tan A \tan B}$.

(ii) Take $\tan(10° + 20°) = \tan 30°$, i.e.,

$\frac{\tan 10° + \tan 20°}{1 - \tan 10° \cdot \tan 20°} = \frac{1}{\sqrt{3}}$ and simplify.

45. CDAB is the required sequential order.

46. Given, $\sin\alpha + \sin\beta + \sin\gamma = 3$.

This is possible only if $\sin\alpha = \sin\beta = \sin\gamma = 1$, i.e., if $\alpha = \beta = \gamma = 90°$.

$\therefore \sin^3\alpha + \sin^3\beta + \sin^3\gamma = 1^3 + 1^3 + 1^3 = 3.$

47. $\sec^4\theta - \sec^2\theta = \sec^2\theta(\sec^2\theta - 1) = \sec^2\theta\tan^2\theta.$

48. $\sin\theta + \cos\theta = \sqrt{2}$

$\sin^2\theta + \cos^2\theta + 2\sin\theta\cos\theta = 2$

$\Rightarrow 2\sin\theta\cos\theta = 1$

$\sin\theta\cos\theta = \frac{1}{2}$

$\sin^{16}\theta = \frac{1}{2^{16}\cos^{16}\theta}.$

Level 3: Assess Your Concepts

49. (i) Apply componendo and dividendo rule, i.e., $\frac{a}{b} = \frac{a+b}{a-b}$.

(ii) Use the formula $\sin(x - y)$ and $\sin(x + y)$.

(iii) And then apply cross multiplication.

50. Use $a^2 + b^2 + 2ab = (a + b)^2$ and $\sin\theta \cdot \operatorname{cosec}\theta = 1$.

51. (i) Use the identity $a^3 + b^3 = (a + b)^3 - 3ab(a + b)$.

(ii) Find the value of $\sin\alpha\cos\alpha$ by squaring $\sin\alpha - \cos\alpha = m$.

52. (i) Put $\theta = 0$ and simplify.

(ii) $\sec^4\theta - \tan^4\theta = \sec^2\theta + \tan^2\theta$.

(iii) $a^3 + b^3 = (a + b)^3 - 3ab(a + b)$.

53. $\frac{1+\tan\theta}{1-\tan\theta} = \sqrt{3}$

$\frac{\tan 45 + \tan\theta}{1 - \tan 45 \cdot \tan\theta} = \sqrt{3}$

$\tan(45° + \theta) = \tan 60°$

$\Rightarrow 45° + \theta = 60°$

$\theta = 60° - 45° = 15°.$

54. $AB = 1 \Rightarrow A = \frac{1}{B}$

$A + B = \frac{1}{\sin\theta}\frac{1}{\cos\theta} = \frac{1}{\sin\theta\cos\theta}$

$= \frac{\sin^2\theta + \cos^2\theta}{\sin\theta\cos\theta}$

$A + B = \frac{\sin\theta}{\cos\theta} + \frac{\cos\theta}{\sin\theta}$

$A + B = \tan\theta + \cot\theta.$

Since, $\tan\theta \times \cot\theta = 1 = AB.$

$\therefore A = \tan\theta,\ B = \cot\theta.$

$\frac{A}{B} = \frac{\tan\theta}{\cot\theta} = \tan\theta \cdot \tan\theta = \tan^2\theta.$

$A = \cot\theta, B = \tan\theta, \frac{A}{B} = \cot^2\theta.$

55. $3\sin^2\theta + 4\sin^2\theta + 3\cos^2\theta = 4$

$3 + 4\sin^2\theta = 4$

$4\sin^2\theta = 1$

$\sin\theta = \frac{1}{\sqrt{4}} = \frac{1}{2}$

$\theta = 30°.$

$\therefore \tan\theta = \frac{1}{\sqrt{3}}.$

56. $\sin(A + B) = \frac{\sqrt{3}+1}{2\sqrt{2}}$

$\sin(A + B) = \sin 75°$

$A + B = 75°.$ (1)

$\sec A = 2$

$\sec A = \sec 60°$

$A = 60°.$

Substitute the value of A in Eq. (1),

$60° + B = 75°$

$B = 15°.$

In circular measure,

$B = 150° \times \frac{\pi}{180°} = \frac{\pi^c}{12}.$

57. Given, $\tan\theta - \cot\theta = 7.$

We know that,

$a^3 - b^3 = (a - b)^3 + 3ab\,(a - b)$

$\tan^3\theta - \cot^3\theta = (\tan\theta - \cot\theta)^3 + 3\tan\theta\cot\theta(\tan\theta - \cot\theta)$

$= 7^3 + 3(7) = 343 + 21 = 364.$

58. $x^n = a^m\cos^4\theta$, and $y^n = b^m \sin^4\theta$

$\Rightarrow \cos^4\theta = \dfrac{x^n}{a^m}$ and $\sin^4\theta = \dfrac{y^n}{b^m}$

$\Rightarrow \cos^2\theta = \dfrac{x^{n/2}}{a^{m/2}}, \sin^2\theta = \dfrac{y^{n/2}}{b^{m/2}}.$

But, $\sin^2\theta + \cos^2\theta = 1$

$\therefore \dfrac{x^{n/2}}{a^{m/2}} + \dfrac{y^{n/2}}{b^{m/2}} = 1.$

59. Given,

$\sin^2\theta + 2\cos^2\theta + 3\sin^2\theta + \ldots$ 40 terms = 405

$\Rightarrow (\sin^2\theta + 3\sin^2\theta + \ldots$ 20 terms) + $(2\cos^2\theta + 4\cos^2\theta$ + … 20 terms) = 405

$\Rightarrow 20^2\sin^2\theta + (20^2 + 20)\cos^2\theta = 405$

$\Rightarrow 400(\sin^2\theta + \cos^2\theta) + 20\cos^2\theta = 405$

$\Rightarrow 400 + 20\cos^2\theta = 405 \Rightarrow 20\cos^2\theta = 5$

$\Rightarrow \cos^2\theta = \dfrac{1}{4}$

$\Rightarrow \cos\theta = \dfrac{1}{2}$ ($\because \theta$ is acute)

$\Rightarrow \theta = 60°.$

$\therefore \tan 60° = \sqrt{3}.$

60. Given, $\sin\alpha + \sin\beta = 2$

$\alpha = \beta = 90°.$

$\therefore \cos^2\alpha + \cos^2\beta = \cos^2 90° + \cos^2 90° = 0.$

61. Given,

$\cos^2\theta + 2\sin^2\theta + 3\cos^2\theta + 4\sin^2\theta + \cdots + 200$ terms = 10025

$\Rightarrow (\cos^2\theta + 3\cos^2\theta + 5\cos^2\theta + \cdots$ 100 terms) + $(\sin^2\theta$ + $2\sin^2\theta + \cdots$ + 100 terms) = 10025

$\Rightarrow 100^2\cos^2\theta + (100^2 + 100)\sin^2\theta = 10025$

$\Rightarrow 10000(\cos^2\theta + \sin^2\theta) + 100\sin^2\theta = 10025$

$\Rightarrow 100\sin^2\theta = 25$

$\Rightarrow \sin^2\theta = \dfrac{1}{4}$

$\Rightarrow \sin\theta = \dfrac{1}{2}$ ($\because \theta$ is acute)

$\Rightarrow \theta = 30°.$

$\therefore \sin\theta - \cos\theta = \sin 30° - \cos 30°$

$= \dfrac{1}{2} - \dfrac{\sqrt{3}}{2} = \dfrac{1-\sqrt{3}}{2}.$

62. Given, $a\sin\theta - b\cos\theta = 0$

$a\sin\theta = b\cos\theta$ …(1)

$a\sin^3\theta + b\cos^3\theta = \sin 2\theta$

$a\sin\theta\sin^2\theta + b\cos\theta\cos^2\theta = 2\sin\theta\cos\theta$

$b\cos\theta\sin^2\theta + b\cos\theta\cos^2\theta = 2\sin\theta\cos\theta$

$b\cos\theta[\sin^2\theta + \cos^2\theta) = 2\sin\theta\cos\theta$

$b\cos\theta = 2\sin\theta\cos\theta$

$b = 2\sin\theta$ …(2)

(1) $\Rightarrow a\sin\theta = 2\sin\theta\cos\theta$

$a = 2\cos\theta$

$a^2 + b^2 = (2\cos\theta)^2 + (2\sin\theta)^2$

$= 4\cos^2\theta + 4\sin^2\theta$

$= 4(\cos^2\theta + \sin^2\theta) = 4$

63. Given, $\cos^2\theta + \cos\theta = 1$

$\cos\theta = 1 - \cos^2\theta$

$\cos\theta = \sin^2\theta$

$\sin^6\theta + \cos^6\theta + 3\sin^8\theta + 3\cos^5\theta + 3$

$= (\sin^2\theta)^3 + (\cos^2\theta)^3 + 3(\sin^2\theta)^2\sin^4\theta + 3\cos\theta\cos^4\theta + 3$

$= (\sin^2\theta)^3 + (\cos^2\theta)^3 + 3(\sin^2\theta)^2\cos^2\theta + 3\sin^2\theta(\cos^2\theta)^2 + 3$

$= (\sin^2\theta + \cos^2\theta)^3 + 3$

$= 1 + 3$

$= 4$

JEE Special Wing

Multiple-Answer Type Questions

1. (a) $\sin 30° + \cos 60° = \frac{1}{2} + \frac{1}{2} = 1.$

(b) $\sec^2 29° - \tan^2 29° = 1.$ $(\because \sec^2\theta - \tan^2\theta = 1)$

(c) $\operatorname{cosec}^2 21° - \cot^2 21° = 1.$ $(\because \operatorname{cosec}^2\theta - \cot^2\theta = 1)$

(d) $\sec 30° - \sec 0° = 2 - 1 = 1.$

Hence, choice (a), choice (b), choice (c) and choice (d) follow.

2. $\frac{\operatorname{cosec} 20°}{\sec 20°} = \frac{\frac{1}{\sin 20°}}{\frac{1}{\cos 20°}}$

$= \frac{\cos 20°}{\sin 20°}$

$= \cot 20°.$

Hence, choice (a) and choice (b) follow.

3. $\cos 30° = \cos(2 \times 15°)$

$= \cos^2 15° - \sin^2 15°$ $(\because \cos 2\theta = \cos^2\theta - \sin^2\theta)$

$= (1 - \sin^2 15°) - \sin^2 15°$ $(\because \sin^2\theta + \cos^2\theta = 1)$

$= 1 - 2\sin^2 15°$

$= 1 - 2(1 - \cos^2 15°)$

$= 1 - 2 + 2\cos^2 15°$

$= 2\cos^2 15° - 1.$

Hence, choice (a) and choice (c) follow.

4. Going by options:

(a) $\sqrt{\frac{1+\cot^2\theta}{1+\tan^2\theta}} = \sqrt{\frac{1+\frac{\cos^2\theta}{\sin^2\theta}}{1+\frac{\sin^2\theta}{\cos^2\theta}}}$

$= \sqrt{\frac{\frac{\sin^2\theta+\cos^2\theta}{\sin^2\theta}}{\frac{\sin^2\theta+\cos^2\theta}{\cos^2\theta}}}$

$= \sqrt{\frac{\frac{1}{\sin^2\theta}}{\frac{1}{\cos^2\theta}}}$

$= \sqrt{\frac{\cos^2\theta}{\sin^2\theta}}$

$= \sqrt{\cot^2\theta} = \cot\theta.$

(b) Now, $\sqrt{\frac{1+\tan^2\theta}{1+\cot^2\theta}} = \frac{1}{\cot\theta} = \tan\theta.$

(c) $\frac{\cot\theta - 1}{1 - \tan\theta} = \frac{\frac{\cos\theta}{\sin\theta} - 1}{1 - \frac{\sin\theta}{\cos\theta}}$

$= \frac{\frac{\cos\theta - \sin\theta}{\sin\theta}}{\frac{\cos\theta - \sin\theta}{\cos\theta}}$

$= \frac{\frac{1}{\sin\theta}}{\frac{1}{\cos\theta}}$

$= \frac{\cos\theta}{\sin\theta} = \cot\theta.$

(d) $(\tan\theta + \cot\theta)\cos^2\theta = \left(\frac{\sin\theta}{\cos\theta} + \frac{\cos\theta}{\sin\theta}\right)\cos^2\theta$

$= \left(\frac{\sin^2\theta + \cos^2\theta}{\cos\theta\sin\theta}\right)\cos^2\theta$

$= \left(\frac{1}{\sin\theta}\right)\cos\theta = \cot\theta.$

Hence, choice (a), choice (b), and choice (d) follow.

5. 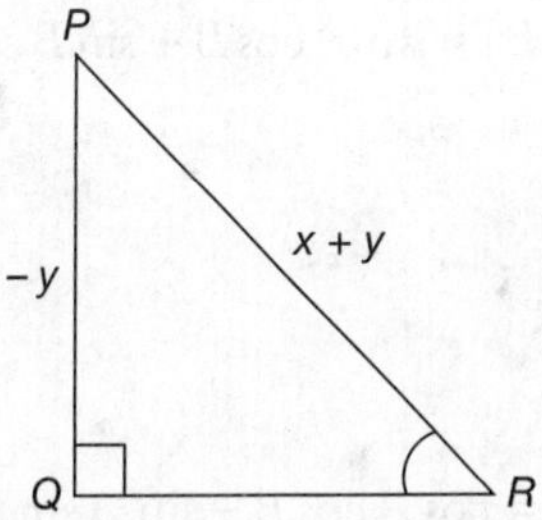

Given that $\sin\theta = \frac{x-y}{x+y}.$

We have $\sin\theta = \frac{\text{Opposite to } \theta}{\text{Hypotenuse}}$

If $PQ = x - y$, then $PR = x + y$.

Now $QR = \sqrt{(PR)^2 - (PQ)^2}$

$= \sqrt{(x+y)^2 - (x-y)^2}$

$= \sqrt{4xy} = 2\sqrt{xy}$

(a) $\sec\theta = \frac{PR}{QR} = \frac{x+y}{2\sqrt{xy}}$

(b) $\tan\theta = \frac{PQ}{QR} = \frac{x-y}{2\sqrt{xy}}$

(c) $\cos\theta = \frac{QR}{PR} = \frac{2\sqrt{xy}}{x+y}$

(d) $\operatorname{cosec}\theta = \frac{PR}{PQ} = \frac{x+y}{x-y}$

Hence, choice (a), choice (b), choice (c) and choice (d) follow.

Match The Column

Common Solutions for questions 6 to 10:

We know that $\sin(A+B) = \sin A\cos B + \sin B\cos A$

$$\sin(75°) = \sin(45°+30°) = \sin 45°\cos 30° + \sin 30°\cos 45°$$

$$= \frac{1}{\sqrt{2}}\times\frac{\sqrt{3}}{2} + \frac{1}{2}\times\frac{1}{\sqrt{2}}$$

$$(\because \sin(A+B) = \sin A\cos B + \sin B\cos A)$$

$$= \frac{\sqrt{3}}{2\sqrt{2}} + \frac{1}{2\sqrt{2}}$$

$$\sin(75°) = \frac{\sqrt{3}+1}{2\sqrt{2}}$$

We know that $\sin(A-B) = \sin A\cos B - \sin B\cos A$

$$\sin(15°) = \sin(45°-30°) = \sin 45°\cos 30° - \sin 30°\cos 45°$$

$$= \frac{1}{\sqrt{2}}\times\frac{\sqrt{3}}{2} - \frac{1}{2}\times\frac{1}{\sqrt{2}}$$

$$(\because \sin(A+B) = \sin A\cos B + \sin B\cos A)$$

$$= \frac{\sqrt{3}}{2\sqrt{2}} - \frac{1}{2\sqrt{2}}$$

$$\sin(15°) = \frac{\sqrt{3}-1}{2\sqrt{2}}$$

We know that $\cos(A+B) = \cos A\cos B - \sin A\sin B$.

$$\cos(75°) = \cos(45°+30°) = \cos 45°\cos 30° - \sin 45°\sin 30°$$

$$= \frac{1}{\sqrt{2}}\times\frac{\sqrt{3}}{2} - \frac{1}{\sqrt{2}}\times\frac{1}{2}$$

$$= \frac{\sqrt{3}}{2\sqrt{2}} - \frac{1}{2\sqrt{2}}$$

$$\cos(75°) = \frac{\sqrt{3}-1}{2\sqrt{2}}$$

$$\cos(A-B) = \cos A\cos B + \sin A\sin B$$

$$\cos(15°) = \cos(45°-30°) = \cos 45°\cos 30° + \sin 45°\sin 30°$$

$$= \frac{1}{\sqrt{2}}\times\frac{\sqrt{3}}{2} + \frac{1}{\sqrt{2}}\times\frac{1}{2}$$

$$= \frac{\sqrt{3}}{2\sqrt{2}} + \frac{1}{2\sqrt{2}}$$

$$\cos(15°) = \frac{\sqrt{3}+1}{2\sqrt{2}}$$

We know that $\tan(A+B) = \frac{\tan A + \tan B}{1-\tan A\tan B}$.

$$\tan(75°) = \tan(45°+30°) = \frac{\tan 45° + \tan 30°}{1-\tan 45°\times\tan 30°}$$

$$= \frac{1+\frac{1}{\sqrt{3}}}{1-1\times\frac{1}{\sqrt{3}}}$$

$$= \frac{\frac{\sqrt{3}+1}{\sqrt{3}}}{\frac{\sqrt{3}-1}{\sqrt{3}}} = \frac{\sqrt{3}+1}{\sqrt{3}-1}$$

$$\tan(75°) = \frac{\sqrt{3}+1}{\sqrt{3}-1} = \frac{(\sqrt{3}+1)^2}{(\sqrt{3}-1)(\sqrt{3}+1)}$$

$$= \frac{3+1+2\sqrt{3}}{3-1} = \frac{4+2\sqrt{3}}{2} = 2+\sqrt{3}$$

We know that $\tan(A-B) = \frac{\tan A - \tan B}{1+\tan A\tan B}$.

$$\tan(15°) = \tan(45°-30°) = \frac{\tan 45° - \tan 30°}{1+\tan 45°\times\tan 30°}$$

$$= \frac{1-\frac{1}{\sqrt{3}}}{1+1\times\frac{1}{\sqrt{3}}}$$

$$= \frac{\frac{\sqrt{3}-1}{\sqrt{3}}}{\frac{\sqrt{3}+1}{\sqrt{3}}} = \frac{\sqrt{3}-1}{\sqrt{3}+1}$$

$$\tan(15°) = \frac{\sqrt{3}-1}{\sqrt{3}+1} = 2-\sqrt{3}$$

6. $\sin 75°\times\tan 15° = \frac{\sqrt{3}+1}{2\sqrt{2}}\times\frac{\sqrt{3}-1}{\sqrt{3}+1}$

$$= \frac{\sqrt{3}-1}{2\sqrt{2}}$$

$$=\frac{(\sqrt{3}-1)\times\sqrt{2}}{2\sqrt{2}\times\sqrt{2}}=\frac{\sqrt{6}-\sqrt{2}}{4}$$

Hence, the correct option is (d).

7. $\sec 75° + \cot 15° = \frac{1}{\cos 75°} + \frac{1}{\tan 15°}$

$$=\frac{1}{\frac{\sqrt{3}-1}{2\sqrt{2}}}+\frac{1}{\frac{\sqrt{3}-1}{\sqrt{3}+1}}$$

$$=\frac{2\sqrt{2}}{\sqrt{3}-1}+\frac{\sqrt{3}+1}{\sqrt{3}-1}$$

$$=\frac{2\sqrt{2}+\sqrt{3}+1}{\sqrt{3}-1}$$

$$=\frac{(2\sqrt{2}+\sqrt{3}+1)(\sqrt{3}+1)}{(\sqrt{3}-1)(\sqrt{3}+1)}$$

$$=\frac{2\sqrt{6}+2\sqrt{2}+3+\sqrt{3}+\sqrt{3}+1}{3-1}$$

$$=\frac{4+2\sqrt{6}+2\sqrt{3}+2\sqrt{2}}{2}=2+\sqrt{6}+\sqrt{3}+\sqrt{2}.$$

Hence, the correct option is (e).

8. $\operatorname{cosec} 15° \times \sec 15° = \frac{1}{\sin 15°}\times\frac{1}{\cos 15°}$

$$=\frac{1}{\frac{\sqrt{3}-1}{2\sqrt{2}}}\times\frac{1}{\frac{\sqrt{3}+1}{2\sqrt{2}}}$$

$$=\frac{2\sqrt{2}}{\sqrt{3}-1}\times\frac{2\sqrt{2}}{\sqrt{3}+1}=\frac{8}{2}=4.$$

Hence, the correct option is (a).

9. $(\tan 75° - \cot 75°)^2 = \left(\tan 75° - \frac{1}{\tan 75°}\right)^2$

$$=\left(2+\sqrt{3}-\frac{1}{2+\sqrt{3}}\right)^2$$

$$=\left(2+\sqrt{3}-(2-\sqrt{3})\right)^2$$

$$=\left(2\sqrt{3}\right)^2=12.$$

Hence, the correct option is (c).

10. $\operatorname{cosec} 75° - \cos 15° = \frac{1}{\sin 75°} - \cos 15°$

$$=\frac{1}{\frac{\sqrt{3}+1}{2\sqrt{2}}}-\frac{\sqrt{3}+1}{2\sqrt{2}}$$

$$=\frac{2\sqrt{2}}{\sqrt{3}+1}-\frac{\sqrt{3}+1}{2\sqrt{2}}$$

$$=\frac{2\sqrt{2}\times2\sqrt{2}-(\sqrt{3}+1)\times(\sqrt{3}+1)}{(\sqrt{3}+1)\times2\sqrt{2}}$$

$$=\frac{8-(4+2\sqrt{3})}{(\sqrt{3}+1)\times2\sqrt{2}}$$

$$=\frac{4-2\sqrt{3}}{(\sqrt{3}+1)\times2\sqrt{2}}$$

$$=\frac{2-\sqrt{3}}{(\sqrt{6}+\sqrt{2})}$$

$$=\frac{(2-\sqrt{3})(\sqrt{6}-\sqrt{2})}{(\sqrt{6}+\sqrt{2})(\sqrt{6}-\sqrt{2})}$$

$$=\frac{2\sqrt{6}-2\sqrt{2}-3\sqrt{2}+\sqrt{6}}{6-2}$$

$$=\frac{2\sqrt{6}-5\sqrt{2}+\sqrt{6}}{4}.$$

Hence, the correct option is (f).

Comprehension-Based Questions

Common Solution 11 to 15:

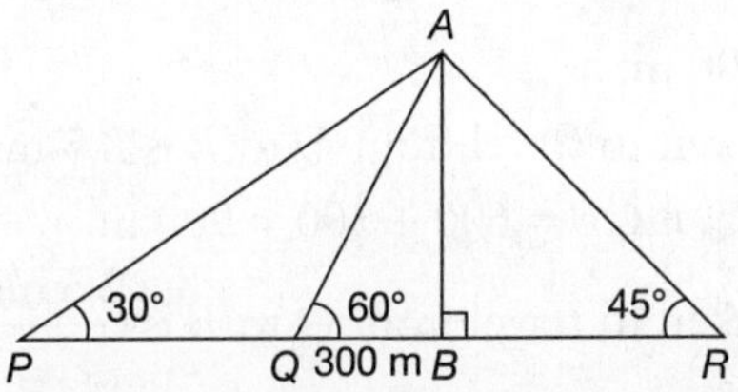

The distance Q and B is 300 m.

$\angle APB = 30°$

$\angle AQB = 60°$

$\angle ARB = 45°$

11. In $\Delta AQB, \angle AQB = 60°$ and $\angle ABQ = 90°$.

$$\tan 60° = \frac{AB}{BQ}$$

$$\sqrt{3}=\frac{AB}{300}$$

$AB = 300\sqrt{3}$ m.

The height of the tower $= 300\sqrt{3}$ m.

Hence, the correct option is (b).

12. In $\Delta APB, \angle APB = 30°$ and $\angle ABP = 90°$.

$$\tan 30° = \frac{AB}{PB}$$

$$\frac{1}{\sqrt{3}} = \frac{300\sqrt{3}}{PQ + QB}$$

$$\frac{1}{\sqrt{3}} = \frac{300\sqrt{3}}{PQ + 300}$$

$$PQ + 300 = 300\sqrt{3} \times \sqrt{3}$$
$$PQ + 300 = 900$$
$$PQ = 600$$

The distance between points P and $Q = 600$ m.

Hence, the correct option is (c).

13. In $\Delta ABR, \angle ARB = 45°$ and $\angle ABR = 90°$.

$$\tan 45° = \frac{AB}{BR}$$

$$1 = \frac{300\sqrt{3}}{BR}$$

$BR = 300\sqrt{3}$ m.

The distance between points P and R

$= PQ + QB + BR$

$= 600 + 300 + 300\sqrt{3}$

$= 900 + 300\sqrt{3}$

$= 300\left(3 + \sqrt{3}\right)$ m.

Hence, the correct option is (d).

14. $QB = 300$ m.

Time taken to travel from Q to B is 2.5 minutes.

$PB = PQ + QB = 600 + 300 = 900$ m.

Time taken to travel from Q to B is $\frac{2.5 \text{ minutes}}{300} \times 900$

$= 7.5$ minutes.

Hence, the correct option is (c).

15. The speed of the person = 5 m/s.

$PR = 300\left(3 + \sqrt{3}\right)$ m.

$$\text{Time taken} = \frac{\text{Distance}}{\text{Speed}}$$

$= \frac{300\left(3 + \sqrt{3}\right)}{5}$ seconds

$= 60\left(3 + \sqrt{3}\right)$ seconds

$= \left(3 + \sqrt{3}\right)$ minutes.

Hence, the correct option is (a).

Assertion and Reason Type Questions

16. Assertion: $\sin 75° = \sin\left(45° + 30°\right)$

$= \sin 45° \cos 30° + \sin 30° \cos 45°$

$= \frac{1}{\sqrt{2}} \times \frac{\sqrt{3}}{2} + \frac{1}{2} \times \frac{1}{\sqrt{2}}$

$\left(\because \sin\left(A + B\right) = \sin A \cos B + \sin B \cos A\right)$

$= \frac{\sqrt{3}}{2\sqrt{2}} + \frac{1}{2\sqrt{2}}$

$= \frac{\sqrt{3} + 1}{2\sqrt{2}}$

So, Assertion is true.

Reason: $\sin\left(A + B\right) = \sin A \cos B + \sin B \cos A$.

Reason is true and is the correct explanation to Assertion.

Hence, the correct option is (a).

17. Assertion: $\sec^4\theta - \tan^4\theta = \left(\sec^2\theta\right)^2 - \left(\tan^2\theta\right)^2$

$= \left(\sec^2\theta + \tan^2\theta\right)\left(\sec^2\theta - \tan^2\theta\right)$

$= \sec^2\theta + \tan^2\theta \quad \left(\because \sec^2\theta - \tan^2\theta = 1\right)$

So, Assertion is true.

Reason: $\sin^2\theta + \cos^2\theta = 1$.

Reason is true but not the correct explanation to Assertion.

Hence, the correct option is (b).

18. Assertion: Given that $\sin\theta + \cos\theta = 1$.

$\left(\sin\theta + \cos\theta\right)^2 = 1^2$

$\sin^2\theta + \cos^2\theta + 2\sin\theta\cos\theta = 1$

$1 + \sin 2\theta = 1$

$\sin 2\theta = 0$.

So, Assertion is false.

Reason: $\sin^2\theta + \cos^2\theta = 1$ and $\sin 2\theta = 2\sin\theta\cos\theta$.

Reason is true and is the correct explanation to Assertion.

Hence, the correct option is (a).

19. Assertion: Given that $\tan\left(A + B\right) = \frac{\tan A + \tan B}{1 - \tan A \tan B}$.

$$\frac{1}{\cot\left(A + B\right)} = \frac{\frac{1}{\cot A} + \frac{1}{\cot B}}{1 - \frac{1}{\cot A} \times \frac{1}{\cot B}}$$

$$\frac{1}{\cot\left(A + B\right)} = \frac{\frac{\cot B + \cot A}{\cot A \times \cot B}}{\frac{\cot A \times \cot B - 1}{\cot A \times \cot B}}$$

$$\frac{1}{\cot(A+B)} = \frac{\cot A + \cot B}{\cot A \times \cot B - 1}$$

$$\cot(A+B) = \frac{\cot A \times \cot B - 1}{\cot A + \cot B}$$

So, Assertion is false.

Reason: $\tan A \times \cot A = 1$.

Reason is true.

Hence, the correct option is (d).

20. Assertion: Given that $\tan A = \frac{1}{11}$ and $\tan B = \frac{5}{6}$.

$$\tan(A+B) = \frac{\tan A + \tan B}{1 - \tan A \tan B}$$

$$\tan(A+B) = \frac{\frac{1}{11} + \frac{5}{6}}{1 - \frac{1}{11} \times \frac{5}{6}}$$

$$\tan(A+B) = \frac{\frac{6+55}{66}}{\frac{66-5}{66}}$$

$$\tan(A+B) = \frac{61}{61}$$

$$\tan(A+B) = 1 = \tan(45°)$$

$$A + B = 45°$$

So, Assertion is true.

Reason: $\tan(A+B) = \frac{\tan A + \tan B}{1 - \tan A \tan B}$

So, Reason is false.

Hence, the correct option is (c).

CHAPTER 13

Statistics

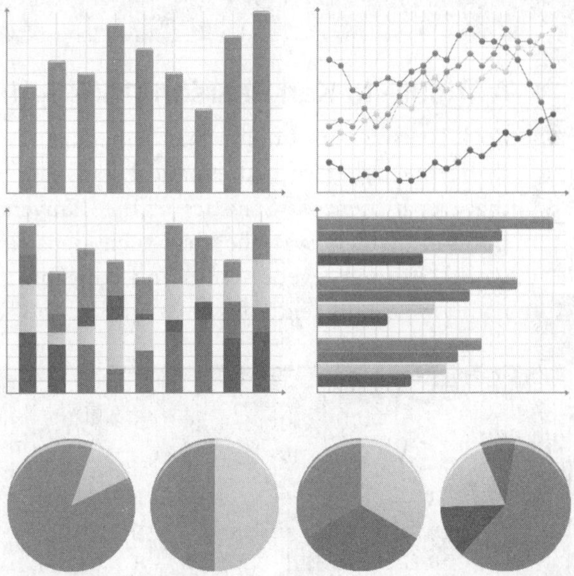

Remember

Before beginning this chapter, you should be able to:

- Know basic terms like data and information
- Understand the presentation of data in daily life

Key Ideas

After completing this chapter, you should be able to:

- Study about data, types of data, tabulation of data, and statistical graphs
- Understand the measures of central tendencies for grouped and ungrouped data such as mean, median, and mode
- Study range, quartiles, and estimation of median and quartiles from ogives
- Find mean deviation

Scientific Crypt

A Tribute to Karl Pearson (1857 – 1936)

Karl Pearson, an English mathematician is considered to be the father of mathematical statistics. He founded the Department of Statistics at the University College London, which was the first such department in the world. Among several results and concepts that bear his name appear in textbooks of statistics, the most widely known is the Pearson Correlation Coefficient, a measure of the closeness of the relation between two variables. His interests extended in every direction – much beyond statistics. His book *'The Grammar of Science'* had a deep impact on Einstein and other scientists.

FUN TIME

CROSSWORD

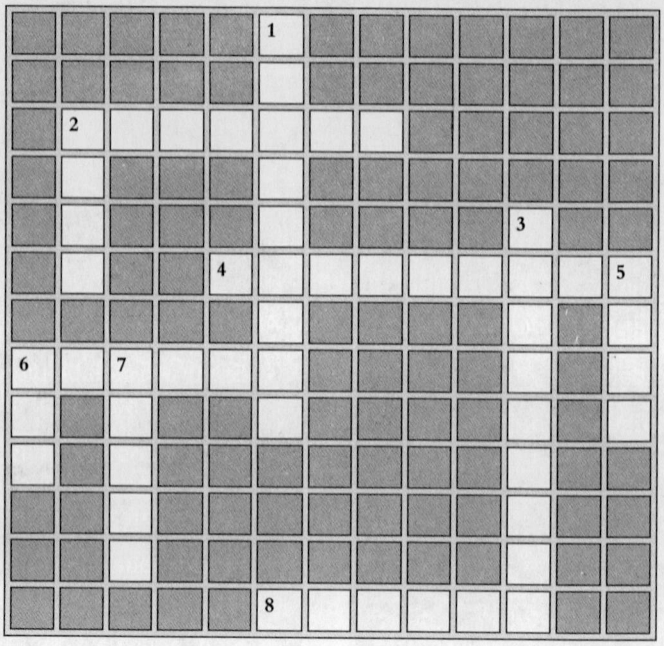

Across

2. In quartiles, Q_2 gives
4. This graph is drawn for classified frequency distribution.
6. The median of the first 10 prime numbers.
8. Range of the scores 32, 12, 29, 19, 42, 36

Down

1. The observations that divide the given set of observations into four equal parts.
2. It can be calculated graphically
3. The number of times an observation occurs
5. It can't be calculated graphically
6. Mean of first 19 natural numbers
7. For symmetric distribution mean, median and mode are

INTRODUCTION

The word 'statistics' is derived from the Latin word 'status' which means political state. Political states had to collect information about their citizens to facilitate Governance and plan for the development. Then, in course of time, statistics came to mean a branch of mathematics which deals with the collection, classification, and analysis of numerical data.

In this chapter, we shall learn about the classification of data, *viz.*, grouped and ungrouped, measures of central tendencies, and their properties.

Data

The word 'data' means information in the form of numerical figures or a set of given facts. For example, the percentage of marks scored by 10 pupils of a class in a test are:

36, 80, 65, 75, 94, 48, 12, 64, 88 and 98.

The set of these figures is the data related to the marks obtained by 10 pupils in a class test.

Types of Data

Statistics is basically the study of numerical data. It includes methods of collection, classification, presentation, analysis of data, and inferences from data. Data as such can be qualitative or quantitative in nature. If one speaks of honesty, beauty, color, etc., the data is qualitative while height, weight, distance, marks, etc., are quantitative. Data can also be classified as raw data and grouped data.

Raw Data

Data obtained from direct observation is called raw data. The marks obtained by 10 students in a monthly test is an example of raw data or ungrouped data.

In fact, very little can be inferred from this data. So, to make this data clearer and more meaningful, we group it into ordered intervals.

Grouped Data

To present the data in a more meaningful way, we condense the data into convenient number of classes or groups, generally not exceeding 10 and not less than 5. This helps us in perceiving, at a glance, certain salient features of data.

Some Basic Definitions

Before getting into the details of tabular representation of data, let us review some basic definitions:

Observation

Each numerical figure in a data is called an observation.

Frequency

The number of times a particular observation occurs is called its frequency.

Tabulation or Presentation of Data

A systematical arrangement of the data in a tabular form is called tabulation or presentation of the data. This grouping results in a table called the frequency table which indicates the number of scores within each group. Many conclusions about the characteristics of the data, the behavior of variables etc., can be drawn from this table.

The quantitative data that is to be analyzed statistically, can be divided into three categories:

1. Individual series
2. Discrete series
3. Continuous series

Individual Series

Any raw data that is collected form is an individual series.

Examples:

1. Runs scored by 6 batsmen in a test match:

   13, 89, 56, 24, 48 and 17

2. Number of students in different classes in a school:

   54, 46, 52, 38, 45, 50, 29, 60, 35, 56

Discrete Series

A discrete series is formulated from the raw data by taking the frequency of the observations into consideration.

Example: Given below is the data showing the number of children in 10 families of a locality:

1, 1, 2, 2, 3, 1, 2, 3, 2, 2

Arranging the data in the ascending order, we get 1, 1, 1, 2, 2, 2, 2, 2, 3, 3.

To count, we can use tally marks. We record tally marks in bunches of five, the fifth one crossing the other four diagonally, i.e., ~~||||~~ .

Thus, we may prepare a frequency table as below:

Number of Children	Tally Marks	Number of Families (Frequency)
1	|||	3
2	~~||||~~	5
3	||	2

Continuous Series

Continuous series formulates where frequencies are given along with the value of the variable in the form of class intervals. When the data contains large number of observations, we put them into different groups, called class intervals such as, 1–10, 11–20, 21–30, etc.

Here, 1–10 means data whose values lie between 1 and 10, including both 1 and 10.

This form is known as an **inclusive form**. Also, 1 is called the **lower limit** and 10 is called the **upper limit**.

EXAMPLE 13.1 Given below are the ages of 40 people in a colony:

33	8	7	28	30	25	6	50	24	44
56	32	27	21	17	62	58	16	14	19
24	31	27	5	12	46	15	42	67	34
4	21	10	40	20	50	48	63	9	21

Taking class intervals 1–10, 11–20, 21–30, 31–40, 41–50, 51–60 and 61–70, we construct a frequency distribution table for the above data.

SOLUTION

First, we write the ages in the ascending order as:

4	5	6	7	8	9	10	12	14	15
16	17	19	20	21	21	21	24	24	25
27	27	28	30	31	32	33	34	40	42
44	46	48	50	50	56	58	62	63	67

Now, we can prepare the frequency distribution table as below:

Class Interval	Tally Marks	Frequency
1–10	~~IIII~~ II	7
11–20	~~IIII~~ II	7
21–30	~~IIII~~ ~~IIII~~	10
31–40	~~IIII~~	5
41–50	~~IIII~~ I	6
51–60	II	2
61–70	III	3

Class Interval

A group into which the raw data is condensed is called a class interval.

Each class is bounded by two figures, which are called the class limits. The figure on the LHS is called the lower limit and the figure on the RHS is called the upper limit of the class. Thus, 0–10 is a class with lower limit being 0 and the upper limit being 10.

Class Boundaries

In an exclusive form, the lower and upper limits are known as class boundaries or true lower limit and true upper limit of the class, respectively.

Thus, the boundaries of 15–25 which is in exclusive form are 15 and 25.

The boundaries in an inclusive form are obtained by subtracting 0.5 to the lower limit and adding 0.5 to the upper limit, if the difference between upper limit of a class and lower limit or the succeeding class is 1.

Thus, the boundaries of 15–25, which is in inclusive form are 14.5–25.5.

Class Size

The difference between the true upper limit and the true lower limit is called the class size. Hence, in the above example, the class size = 25 – 15 = 10.

Class Mark or Mid-value

Class mark = $\frac{1}{2}$(upper limit + lower limit).

Thus, the class mark of 15–25 is $\frac{1}{2}(25+15)=20$.

Statistical Graphs

The information provided by a numerical frequency distribution is easily understood when represented by diagrams or graphs. The diagrams act as visual aids and leave a lasting impression on the mind. This enables the investigator to make quick conclusions about the distribution.

There are different types of graphs or diagrams to represent statistical data. Some of them are:

1. Bar chart or bar graph (for unclassified frequency distribution)
2. Histogram (for classified frequency distribution)
3. Frequency polygon (for classified frequency distribution)
4. Frequency curve (for classified frequency distribution)
5. Cumulative frequency curves (for classified frequency distribution)
   - **(i)** Less than cumulative frequency curve
   - **(ii)** Greater than cumulative frequency curve

Info Bytes!

- The earliest known statistical graph was invented by William Playfair in 1786. It was a time series plot.
- Bar graphs, pie charts, and histograms are some of the most common types of statistical graphs used to represent data visually.

Bar Graph

The important features of bar graphs are:

1. Bar graphs are used to represent unclassified frequency distributions.
2. Frequency of a value of a variable is represented by a bar (rectangle), whose length (i.e., height) is equal (or proportional) to the frequency.
3. The breadth of the bar is arbitrary and the breadth of all the bars are equal. The bars may or may not touch each other.

EXAMPLE 13.2 Represent the following frequency distribution by bar graph:

Value of Variable	3	6	9	12	15
Frequency	6	10	4	3	8

SOLUTION

Either of the following bar graphs [Fig. 13.1 (a) or Fig. 13.2 (b)] may be used to represent the above frequency distribution. The first graph takes value of the variable along the *X*-axis and the frequency along the *Y*-axis, whereas the second one takes the frequency along the *X*-axis and the value of the variable on the *Y*-axis.

All the rectangles (bars) should be of same width and uniform spaces should be left between any two consecutive bars.

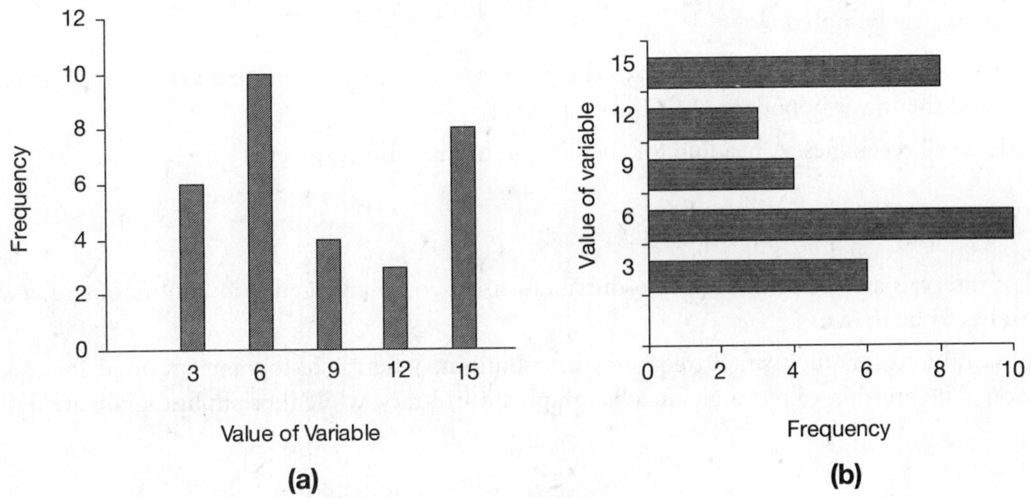

Figure 13.1

Histograms

Classified or grouped data is represented graphically by histograms. A histogram consists of rectangles each of which has its breadth proportional to the size of concerned class interval and its height proportional to the corresponding frequency. In a histogram, two consecutive rectangles have a common side.

Hence, in a histogram, we do the following:

1. We represent class boundaries along the *X*-axis.
2. We represent class frequencies along the *Y*-axis.
3. We construct rectangles with bases along the *X*-axis and heights along the *Y*-axis.

EXAMPLE 13.3 Construct a histogram for the frequency distribution below:

Class Interval	10–20	20–30	30–40	40–50	50–60
Frequency	6	3	8	4	7

SOLUTION

Here, the class intervals are continuous. The following histogram is drawn according to the method described in Fig 13.2.

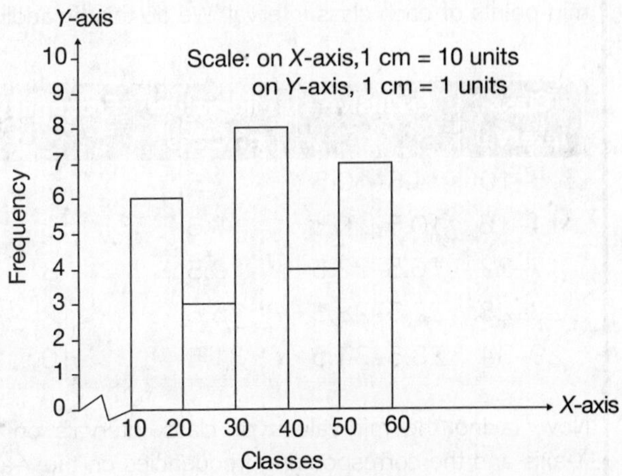

Figure 13.2

Remarks

The following points may be noted:

1. A link mark (∿) made on the horizontal axis, between the vertical axis and first vertical rectangle, if there is a gap between 0 and the lower boundary of first class interval.
2. We may shade all rectangles. A heading for the histogram may also be given.

Important Observations

1. If the class intervals are discontinuous, the distribution has to be changed into continuous intervals and then the histogram has to be drawn.
2. Bar graphs are used for unclassified frequency distributions, whereas histograms are used for classified frequency distribution. The breadths of rectangles in a bar graph are arbitrary, while those in histogram are determined by class size.

Frequency Polygon

Frequency polygons are used to represent classified or grouped data graphically. It is a polygon whose vertices are the mid-points of the top sides of the rectangles, forming the histogram of the frequency distribution.

To draw a frequency polygon for a given frequency distribution, the mid values of the class intervals are taken on *X*-axis and the corresponding frequencies on *Y*-axis and the points are plotted on a graph sheet. These points are joined by straight line segments which form the frequency polygon.

EXAMPLE 13.4 Construct a frequency polygon for the following data:

Class Interval	5–10	11–16	17–22	23–28	29–34	Total
Frequency	7	13	8	12	10	50

SOLUTION

Here, the class intervals are discontinuous. Hence, first we convert the class intervals to continuous class intervals and then find mid-points of each class interval. We do this by adding 0.5 to each upper limit and subtracting 0.5 from each lower limit.

Class Interval	Exclusive	Mid-value of Class	Frequency
5–10	4.5–10.5	7.5	7
11–16	10.5–16.5	13.5	13
17–22	16.5–22.5	19.5	8
23–28	22.5–28.5	25.5	12
29–34	28.5–34.5	31.5	10

Now, taking the mid-values of class intervals on the *X*-axis and the corresponding frequencies on the *Y*-axis, we draw a frequency polygon as shown in the Fig. 13.3.

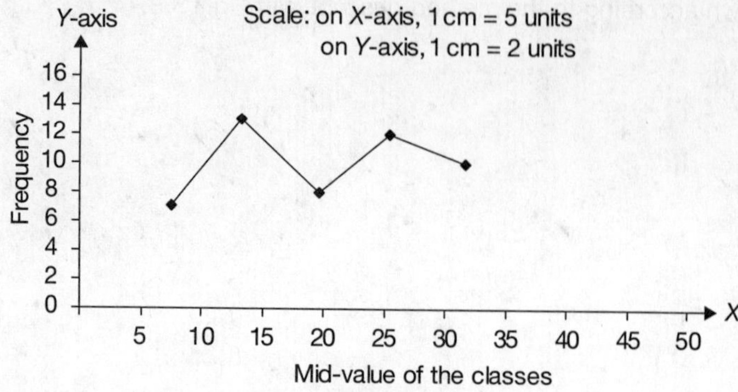

Figure 13.3

Frequency Curve

Frequency curves are used to represent classified or grouped data graphically. As the class-interval in a frequency distribution decreases, the points of the frequency polygon become closer and closer and then the frequency polygon tends to become a frequency curve. So, when the number of scores in the data is sufficiently large and the class intervals become smaller (ultimately tending to zero), the limiting form of frequency polygon becomes frequency curve.

EXAMPLE 13.5 Draw a frequency curve for the data given below:

Class Interval	0–10	10–20	20–30	30–40	40–50	50–60	60–70
Frequency	3	2	4	6	9	7	10

SOLUTION

Following table shows the mid-values of classes and corresponding frequencies for the given data:

Class Interval	Mid-value	Frequency
0–10	5	3
10–20	15	2
20–30	25	4
30–40	35	6
40–50	45	9
50–60	55	7
60–70	65	10

Now, taking the mid-values of the classes along the *X*-axis and the corresponding frequencies along the *Y*-axis, we mark the points obtained from the above table in a graph sheet and join them with a smooth curve, which gives the frequency curve as shown in the Fig. 13.4.

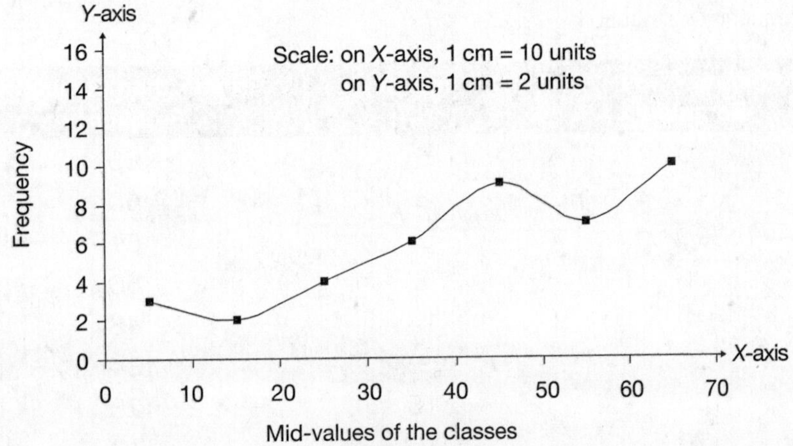

Figure 13.4

Cumulative Frequency Curves

The curves drawn for cumulative frequencies, less than or more than the true limits of the classes of a frequency distribution are called cumulative frequency curves. The curve drawn for the 'less than cumulative frequency distribution' is called the 'less than cumulative frequency curve' and the curve drawn for the 'greater than cumulative frequency distribution' is called the 'greater than cumulative frequency curve'.

From these curves, we can find the total frequency above or below a particular value of the variable.

EXAMPLE 13.6 For the given distribution, draw the less than and greater than cumulative frequency curves.

Class Interval	0–10	10–20	20–30	30–40	40–50	50–60	60–70	70–80
Frequency	5	3	7	2	14	9	15	10

SOLUTION

Less than cumulative frequency distribution:

Upper Class Boundary	Frequency	Less than Cumulative Frequency
10	5	5
20	3	8
30	7	15
40	2	17
50	14	31
60	9	40
70	15	55
80	10	65

Greater than cumulative frequency distribution:

Lower Class Boundary	Frequency	Greater than Cumulative Frequency
0	5	65
10	3	60
20	7	57
30	2	50
40	14	48
50	9	34
60	15	25
70	10	10

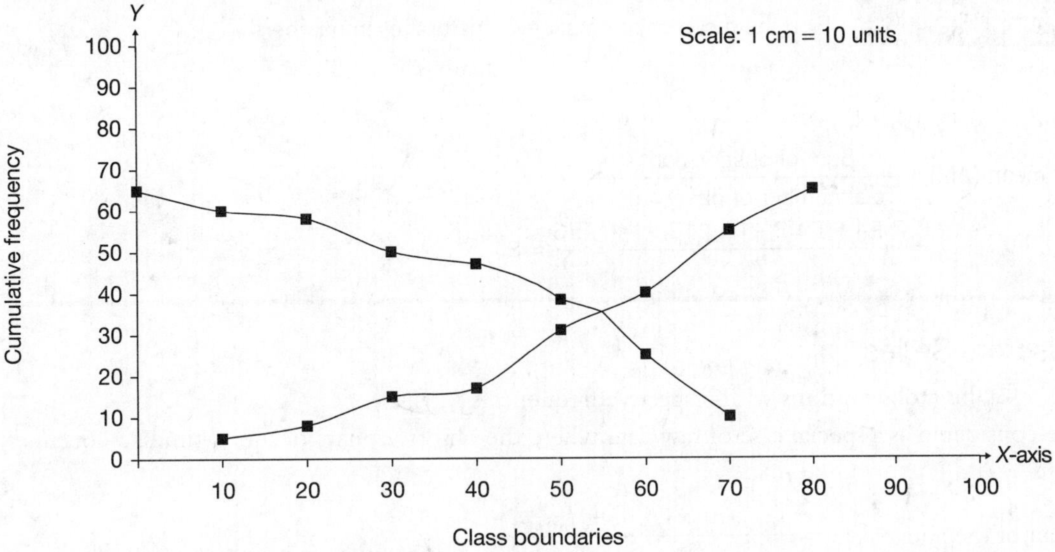

Figure 13.5

Measures of Central Tendencies For Ungrouped Data

Till now, we have seen that the data collected in statistical enquiry or investigation is in the form of raw data. If the data is very large, the user cannot get much information from such data. For this reason, the data is grouped together to obtain some conclusions.

The measure of central tendency is a value which represents the total data, i.e., it is the value in a data around which the values of all the other observations tend to concentrate.

The most commonly used measures of central tendencies are:

1. Arithmetic mean
2. Median
3. Mode

These measures give an idea about how the data is clustered or concentrated.

Arithmetic Mean or Mean (AM)

The arithmetic mean (or simply the mean) is the most commonly used measure of central tendency.

Arithmetic Mean for Raw Data

Definition The arithmetic mean of a statistical data is defined as the quotient obtained when the sum of all the observations or entries is divided by the total number of items.

If $x_1, x_2, \ldots, x_n$ are the n items, then

$$\text{AM} = \frac{x_1 + x_2 + \cdots + x_n}{n} = \frac{\sum_{i=1}^{n} x_i}{n} \quad \text{or briefly} \quad \frac{\sum x}{n}.$$

AM is usually denoted by $\bar{x}$.

EXAMPLE 13.7 Find the mean of the first seven natural even numbers.

SOLUTION

Given data is 2, 4, 6, 8, 10, 12, 14.

$$\therefore \text{Arithmetic mean (AM)} = \frac{\text{Sum of observations}}{\text{Total number of observations}}$$

$$= \frac{2+4+6+8+10+12+14}{7} = \frac{56}{7} = 8.$$

Mean of Discrete Series

Let $x_1, x_2, x_3 \ldots, x_n$ be n observations with respective frequencies $f_1, f_2, \ldots, f_n$.

This can be considered as a special case of raw data where the observation x_1 occurs f_1 times, x_2 occurs f_2 times, and so on.

$$\therefore \text{The mean of the above data} = \frac{f_1x_1 + f_2x_2 + \cdots + f_nx_n}{f_1 + f_2 + \cdots + f_n}.$$

It can also be represented by $\bar{x} = \dfrac{\sum_{i=1}^{n} f_i x_i}{\sum_{i=1}^{n} f_i}$.

Weighted Arithmetic Mean

When the variables $x_1, x_2, \ldots, x_n$ do not have same importance, and the weights $w_1, w_2, \ldots, w_n$ are given to each of the variables, the weighted arithmetic is given by $\bar{x}_w = \dfrac{\sum x_i w_i}{\sum w_i}$.

EXAMPLE 13.8 The population of 50 villages in a state is given below:

Population	Number of Villages
6000	8
7000	10
9000	12
10000	5
11000	7
13000	6
15000	2
Total	50

Find the mean population of the villages of the state.

SOLUTION

The mean $\bar{x}$ is given by

$$\bar{x} = \frac{(6000 \times 8) + (7000 \times 10) + (9000 \times 12) + (10000 \times 5) + (11000 \times 7) + (13000 \times 6) + (15000 \times 2)}{8+10+12+5+7+6+2}$$

$$= \frac{461000}{50}$$

$$\bar{x} = 9220.$$

That is, the mean population of the villages is 9220.

Some Important Results about AM

1. The algebraic sum of deviations taken about the mean is zero, i.e., $\sum_{i=1}^{n}(x_i - \overline{x}) = 0$.
2. The value of the mean depends on all the observations.
3. The AM of two numbers a and b is $\dfrac{a+b}{2}$.
4. Combined mean: If $\overline{x}_1$ and $\overline{x}_2$ are the arithmetic means of two series with n_1 and n_2 observations respectively, then the combined mean is:

$$\overline{x}_c = \frac{n_1\overline{x}_1 + n_2\overline{x}_2}{n_1 + n_2}$$

   The above result can be extended to any number of groups of data.
5. If $\overline{x}$ is the mean of $x_1, x_2, \ldots, x_n$, then the mean of $x_1 + a$, $x_2 + a$, $x_3 + a$, …, $x_n + a$ is $\overline{x} + a$, for all values of a.
6. If $\overline{x}$ is the mean of $x_1, x_2, \ldots, x_n$, then the mean of $ax_1, ax_2, \ldots, ax_n$ is $a\overline{x}$ and that of $\dfrac{x_1}{a}, \dfrac{x_2}{a}, \ldots, \dfrac{x_n}{a}$ is $\dfrac{\overline{x}}{a}$.
7. The mean of the first n natural numbers is $\left(\dfrac{x+1}{2}\right)$.
8. The mean of the squares of the first n natural numbers $= \dfrac{(n+1)(2n+1)}{6}$.
9. The mean of the cubes of the first n natural numbers $= \dfrac{n(n+1)^2}{4}$.

Median

Another measure of the central tendency of a given data is the median.

Definition

If the values x_i in the raw data are arranged either in the increasing or decreasing order of their magnitude, then the middle-most value in this arrangement is called the median.

Thus, for the raw (ungrouped) data, the median is computed as follows:

1. The values of the observations are arranged in the order of magnitude.
2. The middle-most value is taken as the median. Hence, depending on the number of observations (odd or even), we determine median as follows.

   (i) When the number of observations (n) is odd, then the median is the value of $\left(\dfrac{n+1}{2}\right)$thobservation.

   (ii) If the number of observations (n) is even, then the median is the mean of $\left(\dfrac{n}{2}\right)$th and $\left(\dfrac{n}{2}+1\right)$th observations.

EXAMPLE 13.9 Find the median of the following data:
1, 12, 5, 3, 7, 13, 9, 23, 17, 11 and 6

SOLUTION

Arranging the given numbers in the ascending order, we have 1, 3, 5, 6, 7, 9, 11, 12, 13, 17, 23.

Here, the middle term is 9

∴ Median = 9.

EXAMPLE 13.10 The median of a data consists an odd number of observations is 30. If two observations 10 and 40 removed from the data, then the median of the new data is _______.

SOLUTION

Given, the median of the data is 30.
From the data 10 and 40 are removed, those two observations are either side of 30.
Therefore, the median never changes.

Some Important Facts about Median

1. The median does not take all the items into consideration.
2. The sum of absolute deviations taken about the median is the least.
3. The median can be calculated graphically while the mean cannot be.
4. The median is not effected by extreme values.
5. The sum of deviations taken about median is less than the sum of absolute deviations taken from any other observation in the data.

Mode

The third measure of central tendency of a data is the mode.

Definition

The most frequently found value in the data is called the mode. This is the measure which can be identified in the simplest way.

EXAMPLE 13.11 Find the mode of 1, 0, 2, 1, 0, 2, 3, 1, 3, 1, 0, 4, 2, 4, 1 and 2.

SOLUTION

Among the observations given, the most frequently found observation is 1. It occurs 5 times.
∴ Mode = 1.

Some Important Facts about Mode

1. For a given data, the mode may or may not exist. In a series of observations, if no item occurs more than once, then the mode is said to be ill-defined.
2. If the mode exists for a given data, it may or may not be unique.
3. Data having unique mode is uni-modal while data having two modes is bi-modal.

Properties of Mode

1. It can be calculated graphically.
2. It is not effected by extreme values.
3. It can be used for open-ended distribution and qualitative data.

Empirical Relationship among Mean, Median, and Mode

For a moderately symmetric data, the above three measures of central tendency can be related by the formula,

$$\text{Mode} = 3\ \text{Median} - 2\ \text{Mean}.$$

EXAMPLE 13.12 If the difference of the median and the mean of a data is 20, then the difference of the mode and the median is _____.

SOLUTION

Given, Median – Mean = 20
We know that Mode = 3 Median – 2 Mean
Mode – Median = 2 (Median – Mean)
Mode – Median = 40

Observations

1. For a symmetric distribution,

   Mean = Median = Mode.

2. Given any two of the mean, median, and mode the third can be calculated.
3. This formula is to be applied in the absence of sufficient data.

Measure of Central Tendencies For Grouped Data

We studied the measure of central tendencies of ungrouped or raw data. Now we study the measures of central tendencies (mean, median, and mode) for grouped data.

Mean of Grouped Data

If the frequency distribution of 'n' observations of a variable x has k classes, x_i is the mid-value and f_i is the frequency of ith class, then the mean $\overline{x}$ of grouped data is defined as:

$$\overline{x} = \frac{f_1x_1 + f_2x_2 + \cdots + f_kx_k}{f_1 + f_2 + \cdots + f_k} = \frac{\sum_{i=1}^{k} f_ix_i}{\sum_{i=1}^{k} f_i}$$

(or) simply,

$$\overline{x} = \frac{\sum f_ix_i}{N} \text{ where } N = \sum_{i=1}^{k} f_i.$$

In grouped data, it is assumed that the frequency of each class is concentrated at its mid-value.

EXAMPLE 13.13 The mean of the following data is 29. Find 'm'.

Class	1–9	10–18	19–27	28–36	37–45	46–54
Frequency	9	11	8	m	3	11

SOLUTION

Class	Frequency (fi)	Midvalues of Adjusted class (xi)	fi xi
1 – 9	9	5	45
10 – 18	11	14	154
19 – 27	8	23	184
28 – 36	M	32	32m
37 – 45	3	41	123
46 – 54	11	50	550
	Σfi = 42 +m		Σfi xi = 1056 +32m

$$Mean = \frac{\sum fixi}{\sum fi}$$

$$29 = \frac{1056 + 32m}{42 + m}$$

$\Rightarrow 1056 + 32m = 29\ (42 + m)$

$\Rightarrow 1056 + 32m = 1218 + 29\ m$

$\Rightarrow 3m = 162 \Rightarrow m = 54$

Short-cut Method for Finding the Mean of Grouped Data (Deviation Method)

Sometimes, when the frequencies are large in number, the calculation of mean using above formula is cumbersome. This can be simplified if the class interval of each class of grouped data is the same. Under the assumption of equal class intervals, we get the following formula for the mean of grouped data:

$$\overline{x} = A + \frac{1}{N}\left(\sum_{i=1}^{k} f_i u_i\right) \times c.$$

Where, A = assumed mean value from among mid-values

c = length of class interval

k = number of classes of the frequency distribution

N = Sum of frequencies = $\sum_{i=1}^{k} f_i$

$u_i = \dfrac{x_i - A}{C}$, $i = 1, 2, 3, \ldots, k$

x_i = mid-value of the ith class

u_i is called the deviation or difference of the mid-value of the ith class from the assumed value, divided by the class interval.

Using this method, the previous example can be worked out as follows:

Short-cut Method for the Above Example

Salaries of Employees	Number of Employees (f_i)	Mid-values (x_i)	Deviation $u_i = \dfrac{x_i - A}{C}$	$f_i u_i$
0–10	4	5	−3	−12
10–20	13	15	−2	−26
20–30	8	25	−1	−8
30–40	9	35(A)	0	0
40–50	6	45	1	6
	$N = 40$			$\Sigma f_i u_i = -40$

Here, $A = 35$, $N = 40$, $c = 10$, $\Sigma f_i u_i = -40$

$$\therefore \text{AM} = A + \frac{1}{N}(\Sigma f_i u_i) \times C$$

$$= 35 + \frac{1}{40}(-40) \times 10 = 25.$$

Median of Grouped Data

Before finding out how to obtain the median of grouped data, we first review what a median class is.

If n is the number of observations, then from the cumulative frequency distribution, the class in which $\left(\frac{n}{2}\right)$th observation lies is called the median class.

Formula for calculating median:

$$\text{Median } (M) = L + \frac{\frac{N}{2} - F}{f}(C)$$

Where, L = Lower boundary of the median class, i.e., class in which $\left(\frac{n}{2}\right)$th observation lies

N = Sum of frequencies

F = cumulative frequency of the class just preceding the median class

f = frequency of the median class

C = length of class interval

EXAMPLE 13.14 Given below is the data showing heights of 50 students in a class. Find its median.

Height (in cm)	162	164	166	167	168	170	173	175	177	180
Number of Students	6	4	5	12	8	3	7	2	2	1

SOLUTION

To find median, we prepare less than cumulative frequency table as given below:

Height (in cm)	Number of Students	Cumulative Frequency (f)
162	6	6
164	4	10
166	5	15
167	12	27
168	8	35
170	3	38
173	7	45
175	2	47
177	2	49
180	1	50

Here $N = 50$, which is even.

$\therefore$ Median = $\frac{N}{2}$ value $\frac{50}{2}$ or 25th observation.

From the column of cumulative frequency, the value of 25th observation is 167.

$\therefore$ Median = 167 cm.

Konnect

In the above example, we do not have any class interval. As there is no class interval, we cannot use the formula.

EXAMPLE 13.15 Find the median of the following data:

Class Interval	0–10	10–20	20–30	30–40	40–50
Frequency	6	8	5	4	7

SOLUTION

To find the median, we prepare the following table:

Class Interval	Frequency	Cumulative Frequency
0–10	6	6
10–20	8	14(F)
20–30	5(f)	19
30–40	4	23
40–50	7	30
Total	$N = 30$	

Here $N = 30 \Rightarrow \frac{N}{2} = 15.$

This value appears in the class 20–30.

L = Lower boundary of the median class 20–30 = 20

$F = 14, f = 5, C = 10$ (class length)

$$\text{Median} = L + \frac{\left(\frac{N}{2} - F\right)}{f} \times C$$

$$\therefore \text{Median} = 20 + \frac{(15 - 14)}{5} \times 10 = 22.$$

Mode of Grouped Data

The formula for determining the mode of grouped data is $L_1 + \frac{\Delta_1 C}{\Delta_1 + \Delta_2}$.

Where, L_1 = lower boundary of the modal class (class with highest frequency)

$\Delta_1 = f - f_1$ and $\Delta_2 = f - f_2$ where f is the frequency of modal class

f_1 = frequency of previous class of the modal class

f_2 = frequency of next class of the modal class

Rewriting the formula,

$$\text{Mode} = L_1 + \frac{(f - f_1)C}{(f - f_1) + (f - f_2)}$$

$$\text{Mode} = L_1 + \frac{(f - f_1)C}{2f - (f_1 + f_2)}.$$

EXAMPLE 13.16 The mode of the following data is 36.25. Find x.

Class	0 – 10	10 – 20	20 – 30	30 – 40	40 – 50	50 – 60
Frequency	2	7	x	23	20	10

SOLUTION

Class	Frequency	
0 – 10	2	
10 – 20	7	
20 – 30	$x(f_1)$	
30 – 40	23(f)	⟶ Modal class
40 – 50	$20(f_2)$	
50 – 60	10	

Given, mode = 36.25, it is lies between 30–40.

∴ 30–40 is the modal class.

$\Rightarrow f = 23, f_1 = x$ and $f_2 = 20$

L = 30 and C = 10

$$\text{Mode} = L + \frac{(f - f_1) \times c}{2f - (f_1 + f_2)}$$

$$36.25 = 30 + \frac{(23 - x) \times 10}{2 \times 23 - (x + 20)}$$

$$\Rightarrow \frac{(23 - x) \times 10}{46 - x - 20} = 36.25 - 30$$

$$= \frac{(23 - x) \times 10}{26 - x} = 6.25$$

$\Rightarrow 230 - 10x = 162.5 - 6.25x$

$\Rightarrow 10x - 6.25x = 230 - 162.5$

$\Rightarrow 3.75x = 67.5$

$$\Rightarrow x = \frac{67.5}{3.75} \text{ or } x = 18.$$

Range

The difference between the maximum and the minimum values of the given observations is called the range of the data.

Given $x_1, x_2, \ldots, x_n$ (n individual observations)

$$\text{Range} = (\text{Maximum value}) - (\text{Minimum Value}).$$

EXAMPLE 13.17 The range of the scores 26, 19, 32, 23 and x where $x < 19$ is x, then x is ____ .

SOLUTION

Given, 26, 19, 32, 23 and x.

Range = Maximum value – Minimum value

$x = 32 - x$

$\Rightarrow 2x = 32$

$\Rightarrow x = 16.$

Info Bytes!

The range of the class interval is the difference of the actual limits of the class.

Quartiles

In a given data, the observations that divide the given set of observations into four equal parts are called quartiles.

First Quartile or Lower Quartile

When the given observations are arranged in ascending order, the observation which lies midway between the lower extreme and the median is called the first quartile or the lower quartile and is denoted as Q_1.

Third Quartile or Upper Quartile

Of the data when the given observations are arranged in ascending order, the observation that lies in midway between the median and the upper extreme observation is called the third quartile or the upper quartile and is denoted by Q_3.

We can find Q_1 and Q_3 for an ungrouped data containing n observations as follows.

Rearrange the given n observations or items in the ascending order then, lower or first quartile, Q_1 is $\left(\frac{n}{4}\right)$th item or observation if n is even and $\left(\frac{n+1}{4}\right)$th item or observation, when n is odd.

EXAMPLE 13.18 Find Q_1 for the data 23, 7, 11, 9, 15, 12, 20, and 18.

SOLUTION

Arranging the given observations in ascending order, we have 7, 9, 11, 12, 15, 18, 20, 23.

Here $n = 8$ (n is even)

$\therefore$ first quartile,

$Q_1 = \left(\frac{n}{4}\right)$th item $= \left(\frac{8}{4}\right)$th item

= second observation of the data, i.e., 9

$\therefore Q_1 = 9.$

EXAMPLE 13.19 Find Q_1 of 2, 4, 9, 13, 23, 29 and 32.

SOLUTION

Given, 2, 4, 9, 13, 23, 29 and 32.

N = 7

$Q_1 = \left(\frac{N+1}{4}\right)^{th} = 2^{nd}$ term = 4

EXAMPLE 13.20 The ages of 10 employees in an organization are 26, 23, 27, 33, 39, 43, 41, 36, 42, 25. Find Q_1.

SOLUTION

The given observations when arranged in ascending order, we get 23, 25, 26, 27, 33, 36, 39, 41, 42, 43.

Here $n = 10$ (even)

$\therefore Q_1 = \left(\frac{n}{4}\right)$th observation

$= \left(2\frac{1}{2}\right)$th observation of the data

$\therefore Q_1 =$ 2nd observation $+ \frac{1}{2}$(3rd – 2nd) observation

$= 25 + \frac{1}{2}(26 - 25) = 25.5$

$\therefore Q_1 = 25.5.$

Third Quartile

$$Q_3 = \left(\frac{3n}{4}\right)\text{th item, when } n \text{ is even.}$$

$$= 3\left(\frac{n+1}{4}\right)\text{th item, when } n \text{ is odd.}$$

EXAMPLE 13.21 Find Q_3 of 2, 4, 9, 13, 23, 29 and 32.

SOLUTION

Given, 2, 4, 9, 13, 23, 29 and 32.

N = 7

$Q_3 = 3\left(\frac{N+1}{4}\right)^{th}$ term $= 3\left(\frac{7+1}{4}\right)^{th}$ term $= 6^{th}$ term = 29.

Semi-inter Quartile Range or Quartile Deviation (QD)

Quartile deviation, $QD = \frac{Q_3 - Q_1}{2}$.

EXAMPLE 13.22 Find the quartile deviation of the following data 6, 10, 12, 13, 14, 18, 22, 26.

SOLUTION

6, 10, 12, 13, 14, 18, 22, 26

N = 8

$Q_3 = 3\left(\frac{N}{4}\right)^{th}$ term = 6th term = 18

$Q_1 = \left(\frac{N}{4}\right)^{th}$ term = 2nd term = 10

Quartile deviation (Q. D) = $\frac{Q_3 - Q_1}{2} = \frac{18-10}{2} = \frac{8}{2} = 4$

Estimation of Median and Quartiles from Ogive

1. Prepare the cumulative frequency table with the given data.
2. Draw an ogive graph.
3. Let the total number of observations = sum of all frequencies = N.
4. Mark the points A, B and C on Y-axis, corresponding to $\frac{N}{4}, \frac{N}{2}$, and $\frac{3N}{4}$, respectively.
5. Mark three points (P, Q and R) on ogive corresponding to $\frac{3N}{4}, \frac{N}{2}$, and $\frac{N}{4}$, respectively.
6. Draw vertical lines from the points R, Q and P to meet X-axis Q_1, M and Q_3, respectively.
7. Then, the abscissas of Q_1, M and Q_3 gives lower quartile, median, and upper quartile, respectively.

Konnect

For an individual data, the second quartile Q_2 coincides with median.

$\Rightarrow Q_2$ = Median of the data.

EXAMPLE 13.23 The following table shows the distribution of the percentage of marks of a group of students:

Percentage of Marks	30–40	40–50	50–60	60–70	70–80	80–90
Number of Students	4	11	3	7	5	2

SOLUTION

Class Interval	Number of Students (f)	Cumulative Frequency
30–40	4	4
40–50	11	15
50–60	3	18
60–70	7	25
70–80	5	30
80–90	2	32
	$N = 32$	

$N = 32$, $\frac{N}{2} = 16$ and $\frac{3N}{4} = 24$.

From the graph,

Lower quartile (Q_1) = 44

Upper quartile (Q_3) = 69

Median (M) = 53

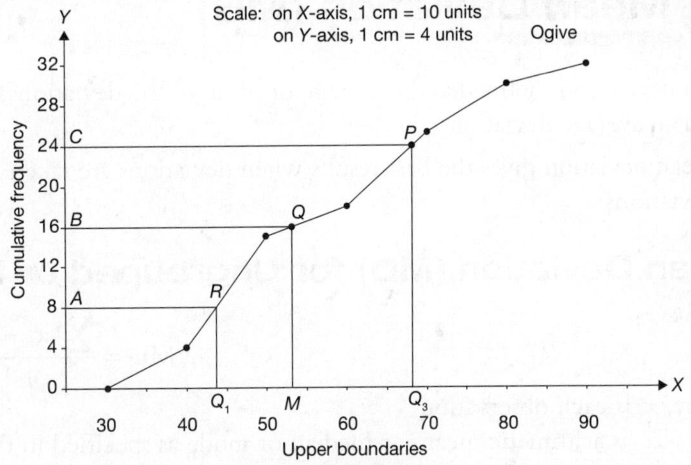

Figure 13.6

Estimation of Mode from Histogram

1. Draw a histogram to represent the given data.
2. From the upper corners of the highest rectangle, draw the line segments to meet the opposite corners of adjacent rectangles, diagonally as shown in the given example. Mark the intersecting point as P.
3. Draw PM perpendicular to X-axis, to meet X-axis at M.
4. Abscissa of M gives the mode of the data.

EXAMPLE 13.24 Estimate the mode of the following data from the histogram.

Class Interval	0–10	10–20	20–30	30–40	40–50	50–60	60–70	70–80
Frequency	8	10	15	16	20	13	14	12

From the graph, Mode (M) = 44.

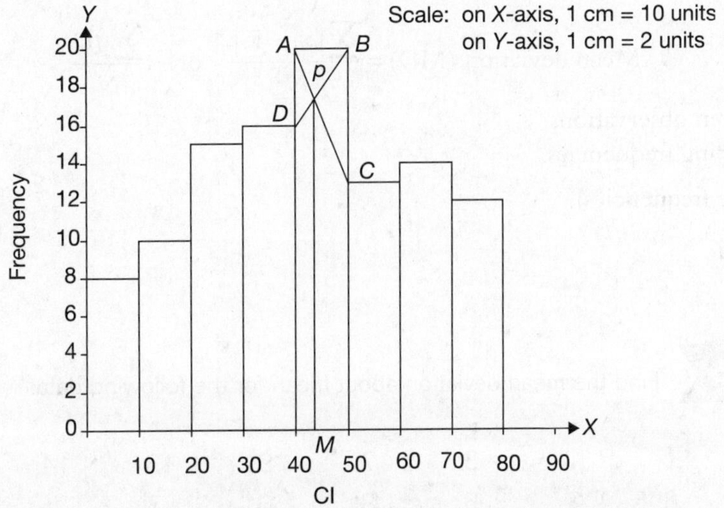

Figure 13.7

Mean Deviation (MD)

Mean deviation is defined as the average or mean of the deviations taken about mean or median or mode. Hence, it is also called an average deviation.

Mean deviation gives the best results when deviations are taken about median. We should take only the positive values of deviations.

Mean Deviation (MD) for Ungrouped or Raw Data

$$\text{MD} = \frac{\sum |x_i - \bar{x}|}{n}$$

Where, x_i is each observation

$\bar{x}$ is arithmetic mean, or median or mode as specified in the problem

n is the number of observations.

Info Bytes!

Mean deviation is also called the "'mean absolute deviation"' in some textbooks, emphasizing that negative deviations don't decrease the overall deviation.

EXAMPLE 13.25 The mean deviation of 2, 6, 5, 10, 14, 8 and 17 about the median is ____.

SOLUTION

Given data, 2, 6, 5, 10, 14, 8 and 17.

Arrange the data in ascending order:

2, 5, 6, 8, 10, 14, 17

$\therefore$ N = 7

$\Rightarrow$ Median = 8

$$\text{Mean deviation} = \frac{|2-8|+|5-8|+|6-8|+|8-8|+|10-8|+|14-8|+|17-8|}{7}$$

$$= \frac{6+3+2+0+2+6+9}{7} = \frac{28}{7} = 4$$

Mean Deviation for Discrete Data

$$\text{Mean deviation (MD)} = \frac{\sum |x_i - \bar{x}|}{N} \quad \text{or} \quad \frac{\sum fD}{N}.$$

Where, x_i is each of the given observations

f_i is their corresponding frequencies.

$N = \Sigma f_i$ (sum of the frequencies).

$D = |x_i - \bar{x}|$.

EXAMPLE 13.26 Find the mean deviation about mean for the following data:

x	1	3	7	9	13	14
f	2	5	8	6	3	1

SOLUTION

x_i	f_i	f_ix_i	$D = \|x_i - \overline{x}\|$	f_iD
1	2	2	6.2	12.4
3	5	15	4.2	21.0
7	8	56	0.2	1.6
9	6	54	1.8	10.8
13	3	39	5.8	17.4
14	1	14	6.8	6.8
	$N = \Sigma f = 25$	$\Sigma fx = 180$		$\Sigma fD = 70$

$$\overline{x} = \text{AM} = \frac{\sum fx}{\sum f} \Rightarrow \overline{x} = \frac{180}{25} = 7.2$$

$$\therefore \text{MD} = \frac{\sum fD}{N} = \frac{70}{25} = 2.8.$$

Mean Deviation for Grouped Data

$$\text{MD} = \frac{\sum f_i \,|\, x_i - \overline{x} \,|}{N} \quad \text{or} \quad \frac{\sum fD}{N}$$

Where, x_i is mid-value of each class
f_i is the corresponding frequency
$\overline{x}$ is mean or median or mode
N is sum of frequencies
$D = |\, x_i - \overline{x} \,|$.

Info Bytes!

The formula for discrete data and grouped data is same except for one change, i.e., x_i is to be replaced by mid values of the classes for grouped data.

EXAMPLE 13.27 Find mean deviation for the following data about median:

Class Interval	5–9	10–14	15–19	20–24	25–29
f	5	9	12	8	6

SOLUTION

Class Interval	f	x	Cumulative Frequency	$D = \|x - \overline{x}\|$	fD
5–9	5	7	5	10	50
10–14	9	12	14(F)	5	45
15–19	12(f)	17	26	0	0
20–24	8	22	34	5	40
25–29	6	27	40	10	60
					$\Sigma fD = 195$

$\frac{N}{2} = \frac{40}{2} = 20, L = 14.5, F = 14, f = 12, C = 5$

$$\text{Median} = L + \frac{\frac{N}{2} - F}{f} \times C$$

$$= 14.5 + \frac{20 - 14}{12} \times 5$$

$$= 14.5 + 2.5 = 17$$

$$\therefore \text{MD} = \frac{\sum f\,|x - \bar{x}|}{N} \text{ or } \frac{\sum fD}{N}$$

$$= \frac{195}{40} = 4.875.$$

Some Important Results Based on MD

1. MD depends on all observations.
2. By default, MD is to be computed about mean.
3. MD about median is the least.
4. MD of two numbers a and b is $\frac{|a - b|}{2}$.

POINTS TO REMEMBER

- ✔ The word 'data' means information in the form of numerical figures or a set of given facts.
- ✔ Data obtained from direct observation is called raw data.
- ✔ Any raw data that is collected form is an individual series.
- ✔ A discrete series is formulated from the raw data by taking the frequency of the observations into consideration.
- ✔ A group into which the raw data is condensed is called a class interval.
- ✔ In an exclusive form, the lower and upper limits are known as class boundaries or true lower limit and true upper limit of the class respectively
- ✔ A histogram consists of rectangles each of which has its breadth proportional to the size of concerned class interval and its height proportional to the corresponding frequency.
- ✔ Polygon whose vertices are the mid-points of the top sides of the rectangles, forming the histogram of the frequency distribution.
- ✔ The arithmetic mean of a statistical data is defined as the quotient obtained when the sum of all the observations or entries is divided by the total number of items.
- ✔ The AM of two numbers a and b is $a + b/ 2$
- ✔ The mean of the first n natural numbers is (x + 1/ 2)
- ✔ The mean of the squares of the first n natural numbers = $\dfrac{(n+1)(2n+1)}{6}$.
- ✔ The mean of the cubes of the first n natural numbers = $\dfrac{n(n+1)^2}{4}$.
- ✔ Another measure of the central tendency of a given data is the median.
- ✔ The observations that divide the given set of observations into four equal parts are called quartiles.
- ✔ The observation which lies midway between the lower extreme and the median is called the first quartile or the lower quartile and is denoted as Q1.
- ✔ The observation that lies in midway between the median and the upper extreme observation is called the third quartile or the upper quartile and is denoted by Q3.
- ✔ Mean deviation is defined as the average or mean of the deviations taken about mean or median or mode. Hence, it is also called an average deviation.

PRACTICE QUESTIONS CLASSROOM WING

Very Short Answer Type Questions

Directions of questions from 1 to 12:
Fill in the blanks.

1. If the median of the scores 1, 2, x, 4 and 5 (where $1 < 2 < x < 4 < 5$) is 3, then the mean of the scores is ______.
2. Mode of the scores 2, 3, 2, 4, 3, 2, 4, 6 is ______.
3. If median of the scores $\frac{x}{2}, \frac{x}{3}, \frac{x}{4}, \frac{x}{5}$, and $\frac{x}{6}$ (where $x > 0$) is 6 then $\frac{x}{6}$ is ______.
4. The coefficient of range of the scores 1, 2, 3, 4, and 5 is ______.
5. If sum of the 20 deviations from the mean is 100, then the mean deviation is ______.
6. If lower and upper quartiles of the data are x and y respectively, then quartile deviation is ______.
7. If mode and median of the certain scores are 2 and 2, then mean is ______.
8. If the mean of the scores x_1, x_2, x_3, x_4, x_5, and x_6 is x, then mean of $5x_1$, $5x_2$, $5x_3$, $5x_4$, $5x_5$, and $5x_6$ is ______.
9. If the mean of a, b, and c is b, then $a + c$ in terms of b is ______.
10. If lower and upper quartiles of the data are 23 and 25, respectively, then coefficient of quartile deviation is ______.
11. Mode of certain scores is x. If each score is decreased by 3, then the mode of the new series is ______.
12. If the mean of 2, 4, 6, 8, x and y is 5, then $x + y$ is ______.

Directions of questions from 13 to 22:
Answer the following questions.

13. Find the mean of the following:

$$10\frac{1}{4}, 9, 4\frac{3}{4}, 8, 2\frac{2}{3}, 12, \text{ and } 2\frac{1}{3}$$

14. Find the median of the following data:

2.0025, 2.0205, −2.06, −2.206, and −2.006

15. Find the median of the following data:

23, 92, 43, 34, 54, 48, 82, 14, 62, and 46

16. If the strengths of 10 classes in a school are given as 28, 42, 25, 30, 45, 22, 25, 34, 26 and 36, then find the median strength.
17. The mean of 8 observations was found to be 20. Later it was detected that one of the observations was misread as 62. What is the correct observation, if the correct mean is 15.5?
18. Find the coefficient of range of the scores 25, 30, 22, 34, 50, 56 and 67.
19. If the median of 33, 28, 20, 25, 34, and x is 29, then find the maximum possible value of x.
20. If the mode of the scores 3, 4, 3, 5, 4, 6, 6, and x is 4, then find the value of x.
21. If the heights of five students in a class are 132 cm, 158 cm, 150 cm, 145 cm, and 155 cm, then find their mean height.
22. Following are the runs scored by 11 members of a cricket team in a test innings. Calculate the quartile deviation of the data.

20, 22, 30, 32, 39, 41, 42, 60, 62, 65 and 80

Short Answer Type Questions

23. If the mean weight of 10 students is 25 kg and the mean weight of another 10 students is 35 kg, then the mean weight of 20 students is ______.
24. Given below are the number of students in 30 class rooms in a school. Construct a frequency distribution table for this data with a class interval of 4.

25 30 24 18 20 24 32 35 22 20
22 32 40 28 30 25 26 29 34 15
38 28 19 16 15 20 24 30 26 18

25. The average marks of 50 students of a class is 76. If the average marks of all boys is 70 and that of all girls is 80 in that class, then find the number of boys in the class.

26. The mean of 30 observations is 25. If two observations 30 and 60 are misread as 20 and 40, then find the correct mean.

27. The mean expenditure of a person from Monday to Wednesday is ₹250, and the mean expenditure from Wednesday to Friday is ₹400. If he spend ₹300 on Wednesday, find the mean expenditure of the person from Monday to Friday.

28. The sum of deviations of *n* observations about 25 is 25 and sum of deviations of the same *n* observations about 35 is –25. Find the mean of the observations.

29. If the sum of mode and mean of certain observations is 129 and the median of the observations is 63, then find mode and mean.

30. The height (in cms) of 20 children of class 9 is given, find the mean.

Height (in cm)	Number of Children
120	2
121	4
122	3
123	2
124	5
125	4

31. Find the median of the following distribution:

x	*f*		*x*	*f*
10	2		30	4
20	3		40	5
50	6		80	3
60	5		90	3
70	4		100	1

32. Find the quartile deviation of the following data:

x	*f*		*x*	*f*
2	4		13	2
3	6		17	4
5	8		19	6
7	9		23	6
11	10			

33. Calculate the mean deviation for the following data about median.

15, 20, 16, 13, 10, 11, 18

34. Draw a histogram for the following data:

Class Interval	*f*
0–5	2
5–10	10
10–15	8
15–20	6
20–25	4

35. Draw the frequency polygon for the following data by drawing a histogram:

Class Interval	*f*
0–5	10
5–10	20
10–15	15
15–20	30
20–25	32
25–30	44

36. (A) Draw the less than cumulative frequency curve for the following data:

Class Interval	*f*
10–14	10
15–19	8
20–24	15
25–29	20
30–34	25

(B) The average height a certain group of students is 148 cm. A boy of height 136 cm joins the group, the average height of new group decreases by 2 cm. Find the number of students initially.

37. (A) If the mean of the following data is 26, then find the missing frequency x.

Class Interval	f
0–10	4
10–20	x
20–30	9
30–40	5
40–50	6

(B) Find the quartile deviation of the following discrete series.

x	6	10	14	18	22	26
f	3	6	8	7	5	2

Essay Type Questions

38. Find the AM of the following data by short-cut method.

Class Interval	f
1–5	5
6–10	10
11–15	15
16–20	10
21–25	5

39. Find the quartile deviation for the following grouped data.

Class Interval	f
0–4	1
5–9	3
10–14	2
15–19	4
20–24	5
25–29	3
30–34	2
35–39	4
40–44	3
45–49	3

40. Find the mode of the following distribution given below.

Class Interval	f
0–19	12
20–39	20
40–59	23
60–79	22
80–99	13

41. Calculate the mean deviation about mean for the following data.

Class Interval	f
10–14	5
15–19	6
20–24	3
25–29	10
30–34	4
35–39	8
40–44	15
45–49	10

42. Draw the frequency curve for the following data.

Class Interval	f
2–5	12
5–8	7
8–11	8
11–14	6
14–17	10
17–20	9

43. There are two sections A and B in 9th class of Meridian school. The average marks in Maths exam of section A, section B and both the sections together are 80, 90 and 87 respectively. Which of the following cannot be the total number of students?

(a) 40 (b) 45

(c) 50 (d) 60

PRACTICE QUESTIONS COMPETITION WING

Level 1: Apply Your Concepts

Directions of questions from 1 to 5:
Fill in the blanks.

1. If 1–10, 11–20, 21–30, 31–40, …, are the classes of a frequency distribution, then the upper boundary of the class 31–40 is ______.

2. If 1–5, 6–10, 11–15, …, are classes of a frequency distribution, then the mid-value of the class 11–15 is ______.

3. In a class, seven students got 90 marks each, the frequency of the observation 90 is ______.

4. If the lower boundary of a class is 35 and length of the class is 5, then the upper boundary is ______.

5. Range of the scores 27, 35, 47, 36, 25 and x is 23, where $x < 25$, then x is ______.

Directions of questions from 6 to 64:
Select the correct alternative from the given choices.

6. The mean of first n natural numbers is $\frac{5n}{9}$. Find n.
(a) 5 (b) 4
(c) 9 (d) None of these

7. If the difference of mode and median of a data is 24, then the difference of median and mean is:
(a) 12 (b) 24
(c) 8 (d) 36

8. The mode of the observations $2x + 3$, $3x - 2$, $4x + 3$, $x - 1$, $3x - 1$, $5x + 2$ (x is a positive integer) can be
(a) 3 (b) 5
(c) 7 (d) 9

9. The median of 21 observations is 18. If two observations 15 and 24 are included to the observations, then the median of the new series is:
(a) 15 (b) 18
(c) 24 (d) 16

10. If the quartile deviation of a set of observations is 10 and the third quartile is 35, then the first quartile is
(a) 24 (b) 30 (c) 17 (d) 15

11. The upper class limit of inclusive type class interval 10–20 is ______.
(a) 10.5 (b) 20 (c) 20.5 (d) 17.5

12. The semi-inter quartile range of the observations 9, 12, 14, 6, 23, 36, 20, 7, 42, and 32 is
(a) 12.75 (b) 12.5
(c) 9.75 (d) 9.5

13. Find the mode of the following discrete series.

x	f	x	f
1	5	6	8
3	7	12	6
5	3	15	5

(a) 3 (b) 12
(c) 8 (d) 6

14. The mean deviation of $a^3 + b^3$ and $a^3 - b^3$ (where a and $b > 0$) is ______.
(a) a^3 (b) b^3
(c) $2a^3$ (d) $2b^3$

15. If the arithmetic mean of the observations $x_1, x_2, x_3, \ldots, x_n$ is 1, then the arithmetic mean of $\frac{x_1}{k}, \frac{x_2}{k}, \frac{x_3}{k}, \ldots, \frac{x_n}{k}$ $(k > 0)$ is
(a) greater than 1. (b) less than 1.
(c) equal to 1. (d) None of these

16. Range of 14, 12, 17, 18, 16 and x is 20. Find x ($x > 0$).
(a) 2 (b) 28
(c) 32 (d) Cannot be determined

17. The mean of a set of observation is a. If each observation is multiplied by b and each product is decreased by c, then the mean of new set of observations is ______.
(a) $\frac{a}{b} + c$ (b) $ab - c$
(c) $\frac{a}{b} - c$ (d) $ab + c$

18. The mean deviation of first 8 composite numbers is ______.
(a) 2.9375 (b) 4.83
(c) 5.315 (d) 3.5625

19. Find the mode of the following discrete series.

x	f	x	f
1	5	5	12
2	4	6	3
3	6	7	9
4	8	8	10

(a) 4 (b) 8
(c) 5 (d) 7

20. The the highest score of certain data exceeds its lowest score by 16 and coefficient of range is $\frac{1}{3}$. Find the sum of the highest score and the lowest score.
(a) 36 (b) 48
(c) 24 (d) 18

21. Find the mean deviation (approximately) about the mode for the following ungrouped data: 20, 25, 30, 18, 15, 40.
(a) 6.71 (b) 4.52
(c) 7.61 (d) 5.33

22. The mean of first n odd natural numbers is $\frac{n^2}{81}$. Find n.
(a) 9 (b) 81
(c) 27 (d) None of these

23. The arithmetic mean of 12 observations is 15. If two observations 20 and 25 are removed then the arithmetic mean of remaining observations is
(a) 14.5 (b) 13.5
(c) 12.5 (d) 13

24. The arithmetic mean and mode of a data is 24 and 12, respectively, then the median of the data is _______.
(a) 20 (b) 18
(c) 20 (d) 22

25. The inter-quartile range of the observations 3, 5, 9, 11, 13, 18, 23, 25, 32, and 39 is
(a) 24 (b) 17
(c) 31 (d) 8

26. The mean of the following distribution is 5, then find the value of b.

x	f
3	2
5	a
7	5
4	b

(a) 10 (b) 6
(c) 8 (d) None of these

27. The mean deviation of $\frac{a+b}{2}$ and $\frac{a-b}{2}$ (where a and $b > 0$) is _______.
(a) $\frac{b}{2}$ (b) $\frac{a}{2}$
(c) a (d) b

28. If the mean of $x + 2$, $2x + 3$, $3x + 4$ and $4x + 5$ is $x + 2$, then find the value of x.
(a) 0 (b) 1
(c) −1 (d) 2

29. The range of 15, 14, x, 25, 30, 35, is 23. Find the least possible value of x.
(a) 14 (b) 12
(c) 13 (d) 11

30. Find the median of the following data.

Class Interval	f
0–10	12
10–20	13
20–30	25
30–40	20
40–50	10

(a) 25 (b) 23
(c) 24 (d) 26

31. In the following table, pass percentage of three schools from the year 2001 to the year 2006 are given. Which school students' performance is more consistent?

	2001	2002	2003	2004	2005	2006
School X	80	89	79	83	84	65
School Y	92	94	76	75	80	63
School Z	93	97	67	63	70	85

(a) X (b) Y
(c) Z (d) X and Y

32. Which of the following does not change for the observations 23, 50, 27, $2x$, 48, 59, 72, 89, $5x$, 100, 120, when x lies between 15 and 20?
(a) Arithmetic mean
(b) Range
(c) Median
(d) Quartile deviation

Level 2: Review Your Concepts

33. If the ratio of mean and median of a certain data is 2 : 3, then find the ratio of its mode and mean.

(a) 4 : 3 (b) 7 : 6
(c) 7 : 8 (d) 5 : 2

34. If mean of the following distribution is 13, then the value of *p* is:

x	5	10	12	17	16	20
f	9	3	*p*	8	7	5

(a) 6 (b) 7
(c) 10 (d) 4

35. If the ratio of mode and median of a certain data is 6 : 5, then find the ratio of its mean and median.

(a) 8 : 9 (b) 9 : 10
(c) 9 : 7 (d) 8 : 11

36. If the arithmetic mean of the following distribution is 8.2, then find the value of *p*.

x	1	3	5	9	11	13
f	3	2	7	*p*	4	8

(a) 5 (b) 6
(c) 9 (d) None of these

37. The median of the series 8, 12, 15, 7, *x*, 19, and 22 lies in the interval.

(a) [12, 15] (b) [7, 15]
(c) [15, 17] (d) [9, 12]

38. The mean of the following data is:

Class Interval	*f*
10–15	5
15–20	7
20–25	3
25–30	4
30–35	8

(a) 22 (b) 23.05
(c) 24.05 (d) 27.05

39. The median of the following frequency distribution is:

Class Interval	*f*
0–10	5
10–20	8
20–30	7
30–40	10
40–50	20

(a) 35 (b) 30
(c) 40 (d) 45

Direction for questions 40 and 47:
These questions are based on the following data (figure).

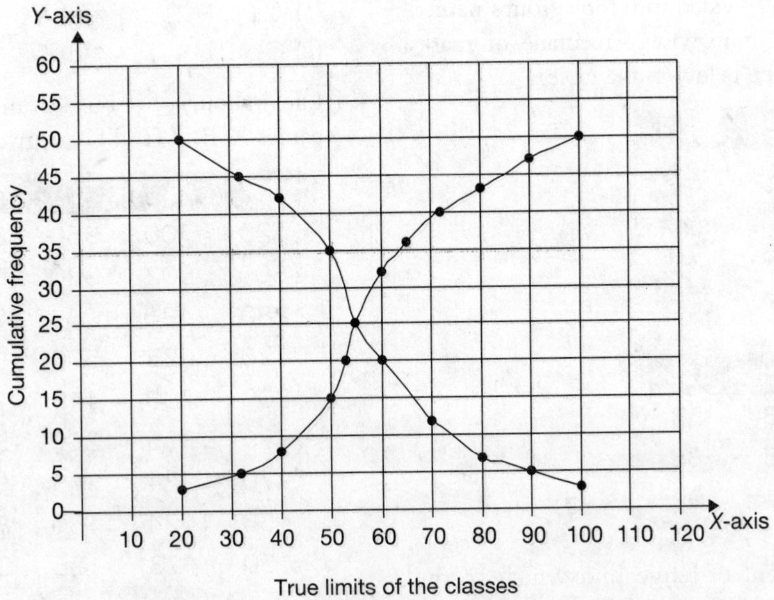

The given figure represents the percentage of marks on *X*-axis and the number of students on *Y*-axis.

40. Find the number of students who scored less than or equal to 50% of marks.
(a) 35 (b) 15
(c) 20 (d) 30

41. Find the number of students who scored greater than or equal to 90% of marks.
(a) 47 (b) 45
(c) 5 (d) 10

42. In a class of 15 students, on an average, each student got 12 books. If exactly two students received same number of books, and the average of books received by remaining students be an integer, then which of the following could be the number of books received by each of the two students who received same number of books?
(a) 11 (b) 15
(c) 20 (d) 25

43.

Weight (in kg)	Number of Students
20	8
22	4
24	3
25	7
30	5

Find the mean deviation (approximately) about the median for the above data.
(a) 2.5 (b) 1.5
(c) 3 (d) 0.5

44. Find the mean deviation (approximately) about the mean for the following.

Class Interval	*f*
0–5	3
5–0	4
10–15	8
15–20	10
20–25	5

(a) 5 (b) 4
(c) 6 (d) 3

45. If $p < q < 2p$; the median and mean of p, q, and $2p$ are 36 and 31, respectively, then find the mean of p and q.
(a) 21.5 (b) 23
(c) 27.5 (d) 24

46. If $x < y < 2x$; the median and the mean of x, y, and $2x$ are 27 and 33, respectively, then find the mean of x and y.
(a) 23.5 (b) 24
(c) 23 (d) 25.5

47. The mean of a set of 12 observations is 10 and another set of 8 observations is 12. The mean of combined set is ______.
(a) 11 (b) 10.8
(c) 11.2 (d) 0.6

Level 3: Assess Your Concepts

48. A class of 40 students is divided into four groups named as A, B, C, and D. Group-wise percentage of marks scored by them are given below in the table.

A	B	C	D
20	42	10	21
30	51	25	69
40	45	85	70
25	58	73	86

A	B	C	D
22	53	98	53
45	64	43	68
65	72	64	99

By using the coefficient of range find which of the group has shown good performance.
(a) A (b) B
(c) C (d) D

49. Life (in hour) of 10 bulbs from each of four different companies A, B, C, and D are given below in the table.

A	B	C	D
120	700	950	530
1600	502	330	650
280	1430	1200	720
420	625	500	550
800	780	445	748
770	335	1260	570
270	224	375	635
455	1124	1130	804
150	473	185	500

By using the coefficient of range find which company has shown the best consistency in its quality?

(a) A (b) B
(c) C (d) D

50. If the mode of the observations 5, 4, 4, 3, 5, x, 3, 4, 3, 5, 4, 3, and 5 is 3, then find the median of the observations.

(a) 3 (b) 4
(c) 5 (d) 3.5

51. In a colony, the average age of the boys is 14 years and the average age of the girls is 17 years. If the average age of the children in the colony is 15 years, find the ratio of number of boys to that of girls.

(a) 1 : 2 (b) 2 : 1
(c) 2 : 3 (d) 3 : 2

52. Find the median of the following data.

Class Interval	f
0–4	3
4–8	6
8–12	6
12–16	6
16–20	8

(a) 13 (b) 12
(c) 11 (d) 10

53. In a class of 20 students, 10 boys brought 11 books each, and 6 girls brought 13 books each. Remaining students brought atleast one book each and no two students brought the same number of books. If the average number of books brought in the class is a positive integer, then what could be the total number of books brought by the remaining students?

(a) 12 (b) 16
(c) 14 (d) 8

54. The mean of a set of 20 observations is 8 and another set of 30 observations is 10. The mean of combined set is ______.

(a) 9.2 (b) 10.8
(c) 11.2 (d) 9.8

55. Find the approximate value of mean deviation about the mode of the following data.

Class Interval	f
0–10	4
10–20	6
20–30	3
30–40	9
40–50	5

(a) 11.5 (b) 12.5
(c) 13.5 (d) 14.5

56. The mean of the following distribution is 4. Find the value of q.

x	2	3	4	5	7
f	4	4	2	3	q

(a) 2 (b) 3
(c) 0 (d) 4

57. If the ratio of mean and median of a certain data is 5 : 7, then find the ratio of its mode and mean.

(a) 2 : 5 (b) 11 : 5
(c) 6 : 5 (d) 2 : 3

58. Find the mode of the following discrete series.

x	1	2	3	4	5	6	7	8	9
f	3	8	15	1	9	12	14	5	7

(a) 7 (b) 5
(c) 2 (d) 3

59. Find the mean deviation about the median for the following data.

x	1	2	3	4	5	6
f	3	7	5	8	2	5

(a) 1 (b) $0.\overline{7}$
(c) 3 (d) $1.\overline{3}$

60. Find the arithmetic mean of the observations $x + 5$, $x + 6$, $x + 10$, $x + 11$, $x + 14$, $x + 20$ (where x is any real number).

(a) $x + 11$ (b) $x + 5$
(c) $x + 13$ (d) $x + 7$

61. Find the mean of the following continuous distribution.

Class Interval	f
0–10	8
10–20	4
20–30	6
30–40	3
40–50	4

(a) 20.8 (b) 21.4
(c) 21.8 (d) 22.2

62. Which of the following is not changed for the observations 31, 48, 50, 60, 25, 8, $3x$, 26, 32? (where x lies between 10 and 15).

(a) Arithmetic mean (b) Range
(c) Median (d) Quartile deviation

63. If the mean of following distribution is 8, then the value of k is

x	3	5	7	9	11
f	2	5	6	7	k

(a) 7 (b) 8
(c) 9 (d) 10

64. If the mean of the following table is 56.25, but the frequencies f_1 and f_2 are missing, then find the missing frequencies.

CI	0-15	15-30	30-45	45-60	60-75	75-90	Total
f	5	10	f_1	25	f_2	20	100

(a) 7,19 (b) 8,27
(c) 9,30 (d) 10,30

AT

PRACTICE QUESTIONS JEE SPECIAL WING

Multiple-Answer Type Questions

Directions for questions 1 to 5:

Each question has FOUR options (a), (b), (c), and (d). ONE OR MORE THAN ONE of these four option(s) is/are the correct answer(s).

1. Which of the following statements is/are true about a bar graph?
   (a) Bar graphs are used to represent unclassified frequency distribution.
   (b) Bar graphs are used to represent classified frequency distribution.
   (c) The length of a bar is proportional to the frequency of the corresponding variable.
   (d) The breadths of all the bars are equal.

2. Which of the following statements is/are true about cumulative frequency curves?
   (a) Cumulative frequency curves are used to represent unclassified frequency distribution.
   (b) Cumulative frequency curves are used to represent classified frequency distribution.
   (c) There are two types of cumulative frequency curves - less than cumulative frequency (**lcf**) curve and greater than cumulative frequency (**gcf**) curve.
   (d) The value of the corresponding class boundary of the point of intersections of **lcf** and **gcf** curves is the arithmetic mean of the data.

3. Which of the following statements is/are true about the first five perfect squares?
   (a) The mean is 11. (b) The median is 12.5.
   (c) The mode is ill defined. (d) The range is 4.

4. A country consists of 20 cities.

Number of People (in lakhs)	No. of Cities
0 – 10	4
10 – 20	10
20 – 30	6

Which of the following is/are equivalent to 16 lakhs?
   (a) Mean (b) Median
   (c) Mode (d) Mean Deviation

5. For a given data, if the ratio of the mean and median is 5 : 4, then which of the following statements is/are true?
   (a) The ratio of the mean and mode is 5 : 2.
   (b) The ratio of the mode and median is 1 : 2.
   (c) The ratio of the range and mode is 5 :1.
   (d) The ratio of the lower and upper quartiles is 1 : 3.

Match The Column

Directions for questions 6 to 10:

Read the paragraph given below and answer the questions.

A joint family lives together under one roof, share the same kitchen, and the economic expenses. Thus means a joint family is usually an expanded family where the parents live with their children and their spouses. Often there are more members in a joint family that might include grandparents, uncles, aunts, and even more. But the system of joint family is in the mode of disintegration.

Let us consider a joint family that consists of ten persons. Ramana and Mola are the heads of the family, and their ages (in years) are 67 and 69. Their children are Mourya and Mrunal of ages (in years) 40 and 36. Their daughters-in-law are Mila and Alia of ages (in years) 36 and 34. The grandchildren are Likhitha, Geetha, Etash and Mouni of ages (in years) 8, 9, 10, and 11.

Using the above information, match the values in Column A with those in Column B.

Column A	Column B (in years)
6. Median age	(a) 13
7. Quartile deviation	(b) 14.25
8. Mean deviation about mean	(c) 17.6
9. Mean deviation about mode	(d) 18
10. The average age of the eldest and the youngest persons in the family	(e) 22.5
	(f) 35
	(g) 38.5

Comprehension-Based Questions

Directions for questions 11 to 15:

Read the paragraph given below and answer the questions.

Class 9 of a school consists of 19 students. The average weight of the class is 40 kg. The average weight of the first ten lightest students is 38.6 kg and the average weight of the first ten heaviest students is 41 kg. The average weight of all the girls is 38 kg and that of all the boys is 47.5 kg. If we include their math teacher in the group, the average weight of the class including the teacher will increase by 1 kg. If we exclude Rama from the class, the average weight of the remaining class will decrease by 0.5 kg.

11. What is the weight of the Math teacher?
(a) 55 kg (b) 60 kg
(c) 65 kg (d) 70 kg

12. What is the weight of Rama?
(a) 41 kg (b) 43 kg
(c) 47 kg (d) 49 kg

13. What is the difference between the number of boys and the number of girls?
(a) 12 (b) 11
(c) 7 (d) 4

14. What is the weight of the 10th heaviest student?
(a) 34 kg (b) 36 kg
(c) 44 kg (d) 46 kg

15. If a certain number of students of average weight 30 kg were absent on a day, then the average of the remaining students would be 49 kg. What would be the number of absentees on that particular day?
(a) 9 (b) 7
(c) 11 (d) 6

Assertion and Reason Type Questions

Directions for questions 16 to 20:

Read the options given below and answer the questions.

(a) Both assertion (A) and reason (R) are true, and the reason (R) is the correct explanation of the assertion (A).
(b) Both assertion (A) and reason (R) are true, and the reason (R) is not the correct explanation of the assertion (A).
(c) Assertion (A) is true, but reason (R) is false.
(d) Assertion (A) is false, and reason (R) is true.

16. **Assertion:** The mean of 1, 3, 5, 7, 9, 11, 13, … 191 is 96.
Reason: The mean of the terms, where there is the same difference for any two consecutive terms, is the average of the first and the last terms.

17. **Assertion:** 11, 12, 12, 11, 14, 15, 11, 14, 15, 14 is a bi-modal data.
Reason: A data which consists of two modes is a bi-model data.

18. **Assertion:** If the median of 101, 102, 103, 104 … 200 is 150.5, then the 110, 111, 112, 113, 114 … 209 is 159.5.
Reason: If $x_1 < x_2 < x_3 < x_4 < \ldots < x_n$, the median of $x_1, x_2, x_3, x_4 \ldots x_n$ is $\frac{x_1 + x_n}{2}$.

19. **Assertion:** The mean of 1, 2, 3, 4 … 99 is 50. The sum of the deviations of the data taken about 50 is zero.
Reason: The mean of a data is given by the ratio of the sum of the observations and the number of observations of the data.

20. **Assertion:** The range of the first 50 odd natural numbers is 48.
Reason: In a data, the range of the scores is the difference between the highest score and the lowest score.

ANSWER KEYS

Crossword

Across

2. Median 4. Histogram 6. Twelve 8. Thirty

Down

1. Quartiles 2. Mode 3. Frequency 5. Mean 6. Ten 7. Equal

Classroom Wing

Very Short Answer Type Questions

1. 3 2. 2 3. 4 4. $\frac{2}{3}$ 5. 5
6. $\frac{y-x}{2}$ 7. 2 8. $5x$ 9. $a+c=2b$ 10. $\frac{1}{24}$
11. $(x-3)$ 12. 10 13. 7 14. −2.006 15. 46
16. 28 17. 26 18. $\frac{45}{89}$ 19. 30 20. 4
21. 148 cm 22. 16

Short Answer Type Questions

23. 30 kg 25. 10 26. 26 27. ₹330 28. 30
29. 69 30. 122.8 cm 31. 50 32. 6 33. 15, 2.9
36. (B) 5 37. (A) 6 (B) 4

Essay Type Questions

38. 13 39. 10.625 40. 54.5 41. 9.9 (approx) 43. (b)

Competition Wing

Level 1: Apply Your Concepts

1. 40.5 2. 13 3. 7 4. 40 5. 24
6. (c) 7. (a) 8. (c) 9. (b) 10. (d)
11. (b) 12. (c) 13. (d) 14. (b) 15. (d)
16. (c) 17. (b) 18. (a) 19. (c) 20. (b)
21. (c) 22. (b) 23. (b) 24. (c) 25. (b)
26. (b) 27. (a) 28. (c) 29. (b) 30. (d)
31. (a) 32. (b)

Level 2: Review Your Concepts

33. (d) 34. (b) 35. (b) 36. (b) 37. (a)
38. (b) 39. (a) 40. (b) 41. (c) 42. (d)
43. (d) 44. (a) 45. (c) 46. (d) 47. (b)

Level 3: Assess Your Concepts

48. (b)	49. (d)	50. (b)	51. (b)	52. (c)
53. (a)	54. (a)	55. (b)	56. (b)	57. (b)
58. (d)	59. (d)	60. (a)	61. (b)	62. (b)
63. (b)	64. (d)			

JEE Special Wing

Multiple-Answer Type Questions

1. (a, c, d)	2. (b, c, d)	3. (a, b, c, d)	4. (a, b, c)	5. (a, b)

Match The Column

6. (f)	7. (b)	8. (d)	9. (c)	10. (g)

Comprehension-Based Questions

11. (b)	12. (d)	13. (b)	14. (a)	15. (a)

Assertion and Reason Type Questions

16. (a)	17. (a)	18. (c)	19. (b)	20. (d)

Hints and Explanations

Classroom Wing

Very Short Answer Type Questions

1. $n = 5$(odd)

$\Rightarrow$ median = $(n + \frac{1}{2})$th term = 3rd term

$\Rightarrow x = 3$

Mean = $\left(\frac{1+2+3+4+5}{5}\right) = 3$

2. Mode of the score 2, 3, 2, 4, 3, 2, 4, 6 is

Class	2	3	4	6
Frequency	3	2	2	1

Mode = 2

3. If medium of scores $\frac{x}{2}, \frac{x}{3}, \frac{x}{4}, \frac{x}{5}, \frac{x}{6}$ is 6 then $\frac{x}{6}$ is 4

4. Coefficient of range of scores 1, 2, 3, 4, and 5, is $\frac{2}{3}$.

5. If sum of 20 deviations from mean is 100, mean duration is 5.

6. If lower and upper quartiles of data are x and y. Then quartile deviations is $\frac{y-x}{2}$.

7. If mode and median of certain scores are 2 and 2, then mean is

Mean – mode = 3 (Mean – Median)

Mean – 2 = 3 (Mean – 2)

Mean – 2 = 3 Mean – 6

2 Mean = 4

Mean = 2.

8. If mean of score x_1, x_2, x_3, x_4, x_5, and x_n, is x, then mean of $5x_1$, $5x_2$, $5x_3$, $5x_4$, $5x_5$, $5x_6$ is $5x$.

9. If mean of a, b, and c, is b then $a + c$ in terms of b is

$\frac{a+b+c}{3} = b$

$\Rightarrow a + c = 3b - b$

$\Rightarrow a + c = 2b$

10. $\frac{24-23}{24} = \frac{1}{24}$

11. The New Mode of new series is $x - 3$.

12. $\frac{2+4+6+8+x+y}{6} = 5$

$20 + x + y = 30$

$x + y = 30 - 20$

$x + y = 10$

13. $\frac{41}{4}, 9, \frac{19}{4}, 8, \frac{8}{3}, 12, \frac{7}{3}$

$$\frac{\frac{41}{4}+9+\frac{19}{4}+8+\frac{8}{3}+12+\frac{7}{3}}{7}$$

$$= \frac{\frac{\cancel{60}^{15}}{\cancel{4}}+\frac{\cancel{15}^{5}}{\cancel{3}}+29}{7} = \frac{15+5+29}{7} = \frac{49}{7} = 7$$

14. 2.0025, 20205, –2.06, –2.206, –2.006

2.0205 > 2.0025 > –2.006 > –2.06 > –2.006

Median = –2.006.

15. 23, 92, 43, 34, 54, 48, 82, 14, 62

92 > 82 > 62 > 54 > 48 > 46 > 43 > 34 > 23 > 14

Median = 46.

16. 28, 42, 25, 30, 45, 22, 25, 34, 26, 36

45 < 42 < 36 < 34 < 30 < 28 < 26 < 25 < 25 < 22

Median = $\left(\frac{10}{2}\right)^{th}$ =5th term= 28

17. $\frac{(x_1+x_2+x_3+x_4+x_5+x_6+x_7)+62}{8} = 20$

If the correct observation is 'a'

$(x_1+x_2+x_3+x_4+x_5+x_6+x_7) = 160 - 62 = 98.$

$\frac{98+a}{8} = 15.5$

$98 + a = 124$

$a = 26.$

18. 25, 30, 22, 34, 50, 56, 67

22, 25, 30, 34, 50, 56, 67

$$\text{Coefficient of range} = \frac{67-22}{67+22}$$
$$= \frac{45}{89}$$

19. 33, 28, 20, 25, 34 and x is 29

20 25 28 ↓ 33 34
x

$$\frac{28+x}{2} = 29$$
$28 + x = 58$
$x = 30$

20. 3, 4, 3, 5, 4, 6, 6, x
If mode = 4 the count of '4' should be Maximum
Value of x should be '4' for Mode to be '4'

21. $$\frac{132+158+150+145+155}{5}$$
$$\frac{740}{5} = 148 \text{ cm}$$

22. 20, 22, 30, 32, 39, 41, 42, 60, 62, 65, 80

$$Q_1 = \frac{11+1}{4} = \frac{12}{4} = 3^{rd}$$
$$Q_3 = \frac{3(11+1)}{4} = 9^{th}$$
$$\frac{Q_3 - Q_1}{2} = \frac{62-30}{2} = \frac{32}{2} = 16$$

Short Answer Type Question

23. $$\frac{25+35}{2} = \frac{60}{2} = 30\text{kg}$$
30 kg is the mean of 20 students.

24.

Marks Interval	Number of students (fg)
15 – 19	6
20 – 24	8
25 – 29	7
30 – 34	6
35 – 39	2
40 – 44	1
	30

25. $b + g = 50$
$x + y = a = 50 \times 76$
$$\frac{a}{b+g} = 76$$

$$\frac{x}{b} = 70 \quad \frac{y}{g} = 80$$
$b + g = 50$
$70b + 80g = 76 \times 50$
$-\cancel{70b} - 70g = -70 \times 50$
$\cancel{70b} + 80g = 3900$
$10g = 3900 - 3500$
$$g = \frac{40\cancel{0}}{1\cancel{0}} = 40$$
Boys = 10 and Girls = 40

26. $$\frac{x_1 + x_2 \ldots. x_{30}}{30} = 25$$
$$\frac{x_1 + x_2 \ldots. x_{30} + 30}{30} = \text{Real Mean}$$
$$\frac{30 \times 25 + 30}{30} = \frac{750+30}{3}$$
$$\frac{780}{30} = \frac{26\cancel{0}}{1\cancel{0}} = 26$$

27. Sum of expenditures from Monday to Wednesday $= 250 \times 3 =$ Rs 750
Sum of expenditures from Wednesday to Friday $= 400 \times 3 =$ Rs 1200
Total sum of expenditures from Monday to Friday = Rs (1200 + 750) – Rs 300 = Rs 1650
So, the mean expenditure from Monday to Friday is
$$= \frac{1650}{5}$$
= ₹330

28. Let 'n' be the required number of observations.
Therefore,
$\Sigma(x_i - 25) = 25$
$\Sigma x_i - 25n = 25$ (i)
Similarly,
$\Sigma(x_i - 35) = -25$
$\Sigma x_i - 35n = -25$ (ii)
On substituting both
$\Sigma x_i - 25n = 25$
$\Sigma x_i - 35n = -25$
$10n = 50$
$n = 5$
Putting $n = 5$ in equation (i)
We get,

$\Sigma_0 Fx_i - 25(5) = 25$

$\Sigma x_i - 125 = 25$

$\Sigma Fx_i = 150$

Now,

Mean is given by

$$x = \Sigma \frac{x_i}{n} = \frac{150}{5} = 30$$

29. Given Data

Mode + Mean = 129 (i)

Median = 63 (ii)

We know that,

Mode = 3 Median – 2 Mean (iii)

Substituting Equation (i) and Equation (iii), we get,

129 – Mean = 3 Median – 2 Mean

∴ Mean = 3 × 63 – 129 (From Equation (ii), Median = 63)

Mean = 189 – 124

Mean = 60

∴ Mode = 3 Median – 2 Mean

Mode = 3 × 63 – 2 × 60

Mode = 189 – 120

Mode = 69

∴ Mean = 60, Median = 63, Mode = 69

30.

Height (in cm) (x_i)	Number of children (f_i)	f_ix_i
120	2	240
121	4	484
122	3	366
123	2	246
124	5	620
125	4	500
	$\Sigma f_i = 20$	$\Sigma f_ix_i = 2456$

$$\text{Mean} = \frac{\Sigma f_ix_i}{\Sigma f_i} = \frac{2456}{20} = 122.8$$

∴ Mean is obtained to be 122.8.

31.

x	f	Cumulative frequency
10	2	2
20	3	(2 + 3) = 5
30	4	(5 + 4) = 9
40	5	14
50	6	20
60	5	25
70	4	29
80	3	32
90	3	35
100	1	36

∴ Total number of observation, is 36 (even)

$$\text{Median (even)} = \frac{\left(\frac{n}{2}\right)^{\text{th}} \text{observation} + \left(\frac{n}{2}+1\right)^{\text{th}} \text{observation}}{2}$$

$$= \frac{18^{\text{th}} \text{ observation} + 19^{\text{th}} \text{ observation}}{2}$$

∵ The above table shows that the corresponding value of 18th and 19th observation on cumulative frequency table is 20, i.e $x = 50$

$$\therefore \text{Median (Even)} = \frac{50+50}{2} = 50$$

∴ Median (Even) = 50

32.

x	f	cf (Cumulative frequency)
2	4	4
3	6	10
5	8	18
7	9	27
11	10	37
13	2	39
17	4	43
19	6	49
23	6	55

We know that,

$$\text{Quartile Deviation} = \frac{Q_3 - Q_1}{2}$$

Q_1 is the size of $\frac{N+1}{4}$

$$= \frac{55+1}{4} = \frac{56}{4} = 14^{th} \text{ item}$$

The above table shows the corresponding values of 14th observation is 18th observation i.e., $x_i = 5$.

$\therefore$ $Q_1 = 5$

$$Q_3 \text{ is the size of } 3\left(\frac{N+1}{4}\right) = 3\left(\frac{55+1}{4}\right) = 42^{th} \text{ item}$$

$\therefore$ $Q_3 = 43^{th}$ observation = 17

$Q_3 = 17$

$$\therefore \text{Quartile Deviation} = \frac{Q_3 - Q_1}{2}$$

$$= \frac{17-5}{2} = 6$$

33. 15, 20, 16, 13, 10, 11, 18

Arranging the data in ascending order

10, 11, 13, 15, 16, 18, 20

Here number of observation = n = 7 (odd)

$$\therefore \text{Median (odd)} = \left(\frac{n+1}{2}\right)^{th} \text{ observation}$$

$M = 4^{th}$ observation

Median = 15

Now, calculating mean deviation about median,

$$\text{Mean deviation about median} = \frac{\Sigma|x_i - m|}{n}$$

$$\text{M.D (M)} = \frac{\left(\begin{array}{l}|10-15|+|11-15|+|13-15|+|15-15|+\\|16-15|+|18-15|+|20-15|\end{array}\right)}{7}$$

$$= \frac{5+4+2+0+1+3+5}{7}$$

$$= \frac{20}{7} = 2.9$$

$\therefore$ Median = 15

M.D (M) = 2.9

34.

Class Interval	f
0-5	2
5-10	10
10-15	8
15-20	6
20-25	4

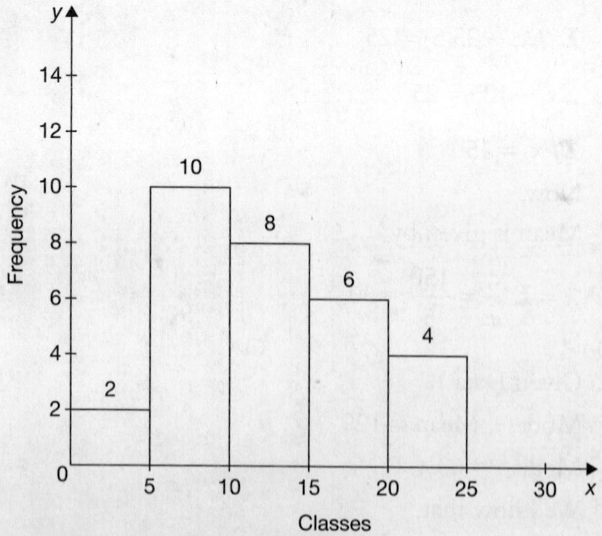

35.

Class Interval	f
0-5	10
5-10	20
10-15	15

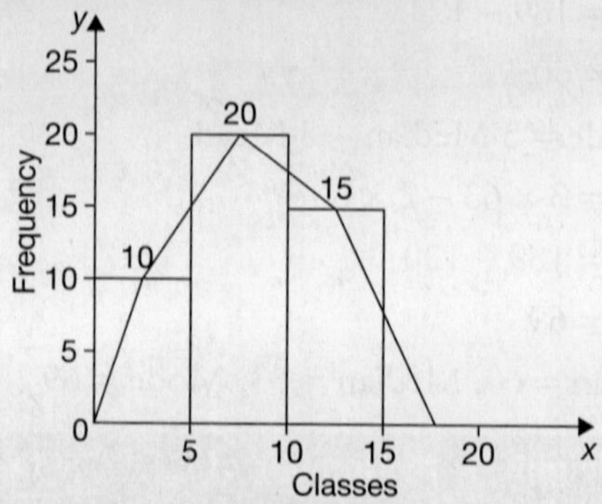

36. (A)

	F	CF
10 – 14	10	10
15 – 19	8	18
20 – 24	15	33
25 – 29	20	53
30 – 34	25	78

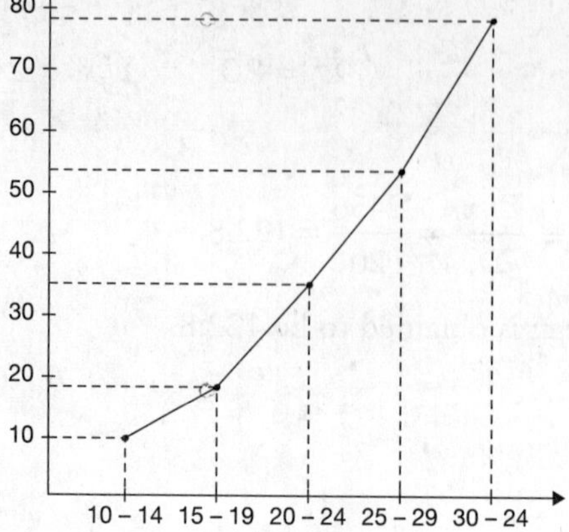

(B) Let the number of students initially be x

Average height = 148 cm

Given that

$$\frac{148x + 136}{x+1} = 146$$

$\Rightarrow 148x + 136 = 146x + 146$

$\Rightarrow 2x = 10$

$\Rightarrow x = 5$

37. (A)

Class Interval	f_i	$\left(\frac{x_i}{2}\right)$	$f_i x_i$
0-10	4	5	20
10-20	x	15	15x
20-30	9	25	225
30-40	5	35	175
40-50	6	45	270
	$\Sigma f_i = 24 + x$		$\Sigma f_i x_i = 690 + 15x$

Given that,

$(\overline{x})$ = Mean = 26

We know that,

$$\overline{x} = \frac{\Sigma f_i x_i}{\Sigma f_i}$$

$$26 = \frac{690 + 15x}{24 + x}$$

$26(24 + x) = 690 + 15x$

$624 + 26x = 690 + 15x$

$11x = 66$

$x = 6$

∴ The missing frequency $x = 6$.

(B)

x	f	cmf
6	3	3
10	6	9
14	8	17
18	7	24
22	5	29
26	2	31

Q_1 = size of $\left(\frac{N+1}{4}\right)$th item = 8th item = 10

Q_3 = size of $3\left(\frac{N+1}{4}\right)$ th item = 24th item = 18

$$\text{Q.D} = \frac{Q_3 - Q_1}{2} = \frac{18 - 10}{2} = \frac{8}{2} = 4$$

Essay Type Questions

38.

Class Interval	f	$x_i \left(\frac{\text{C.I}}{2}\right)$	$d = x - A$	fd
1-5	5	3	–10	–50
6-10	10	8	–5	–5
11-15	15	13 A	0	0
16-20	10	18	5	50
21-25	5	23	10	50
				0

By shortcut method,

$$\text{Mean} = A + \frac{\Sigma fd}{n}$$

$= 13 + 0 = 13$

Mean = 13

39.

Class Interval	f	Cumulative frequency	Lower boundary
0-4	1	1	–0.5
5-9	3	4	4.5
10-14	2	6	9.5
15-19	4	10	14.5
20-24	5	15	19.5
25-29	3	18	24.5
30-34	2	20	29.5
35-39	4	24	34.5
40-44	3	27	39.5
45-49	3	30	44.5

$$Q \cdot D = \frac{Q_3 - Q_1}{2}$$

$$= Q_1 = \left(\frac{N}{4}\right)^{\text{th}} \text{ item}$$

$$= \left(\frac{30}{4}\right)^{\text{th}} \text{ item} = 7.5^{\text{th}} \text{ item}$$

From the tables, bigger value of 7.5th item is 10th item,

∴ First quartile class, lower boundary is 14.5

$$Q_1 = l + \frac{\left(\frac{N}{4} - c\right)}{f} \times \lambda$$

$$= 14.5 + \frac{(1.5)}{4} \times 5$$

$= 16.375$

$Q_3 = 3\left(\frac{N}{4}\right)^{\text{th}}$ item

$= 3\ (7.5) = 22.5^{\text{th}}$ item $\rightarrow 24^{\text{th}}$ item from table

$$Q_3 = l + \frac{3\left(\frac{N}{4} - C\right)}{f} \times \lambda$$

$$= 34.5 + \frac{(22.5 - 20)}{4} \times 5$$

$Q_3 = 37.625$

$Q \cdot D = \frac{Q_3 - Q_1}{2} = 10.625$

$Q \cdot D = 10.625$

40.

Class interval	f	Class boundary
0-19	12	–0.5-14.5
20-39	20	19.5-39.5
40-59	23	39.5-59.5
60-79	22	59.5-79.5
80-99	13	79.5-99.5

Class 39.5-59.5 is having the highest frequency, therefore it is one mode class

$$\text{Mode} = l + \lambda\left(\frac{f_m - f_1}{2f_m - f_1 - f_2}\right)$$

$$= 39.5 + 20\left(\frac{23 - 20}{46 - 42}\right)$$

$$= 39.5 + 20\left(\frac{3}{4}\right)$$

Mode = 54.5

$\therefore$ Mode = 54.5

41.

Class interval	f	Class boundaries	x_i	f_ix_i
10-14	5	9.5-14.5	12	60
15-19	6	14.5-19.5	17	102
20-24	3	19.5-24.5	22	66
25-29	10	24.5-29.5	27	270
30-34	4	29.5-34.5	32	128
35-39	8	34.5-39.5	37	296
40-44	15	39.5-44.5	42	630
45-49	10	44.5-49.5	47	470
	$\Sigma f_i = 61$			$\Sigma f_ix_i = 2022$

$$(\bar{x})\text{Mean} = \frac{\Sigma f_i x_i}{\Sigma f_i}$$

$$= \frac{2022}{61}$$

$= 33.15$

$$d_x = \frac{\Sigma f(Q_x)}{\Sigma f}$$

$$= \frac{604.25}{61}$$

$= 9.9$

$\therefore$ Mean derivation from mean of group data = 9.9

42.

Class Interval	f
2-5	12
5-8	7
8-11	8
11-14	6
14-17	10
17-20	9

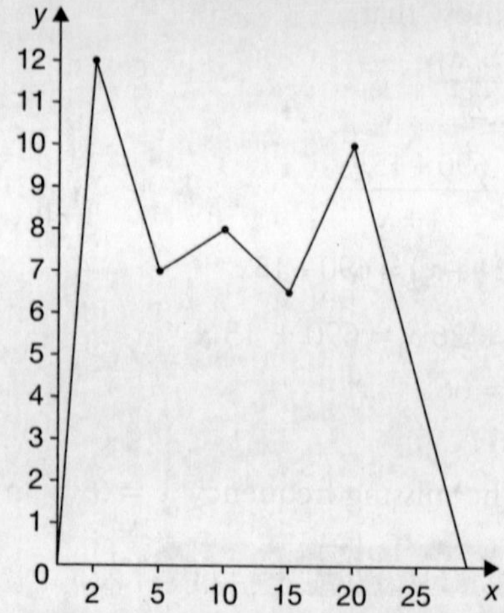

43.

Section	Number of students	Average marks	Total marks
A	x	80	80x
B	y	90	90y
A & B together	x + y	87	87(x + y)

$\Rightarrow 80x + 90y = 87(x + y)$

$\Rightarrow 7x = 3y$

$\Rightarrow \frac{x}{y} = \frac{3}{7}$

$\therefore$ Total number of students must be a multiple of $(3 + 7)$ i.e, 10

Choice (b)

Competition Wing

Level 1: Apply Your Concepts

1. If 1 – 10, 11 – 20, 21 – 30, 31 – 40 are the classes of a frequency distribution, then the upper boundary of the class 31 – 40 is 40.5.
2. If 1 – 5, 6 – 10, 11 – 15, … are classes of a frequency distribution, then the mid value of class 11 – 15 is 13.
3. In a class, seven students got 90 marks each, the frequency of observation 90 is 7.
4. If the lower boundary of a class is 35 and length of the class is 5, then the upper boundary is 40.
5. Range of scores 27, 35, 47, 36, 25, and x is 23, where $x < 25$, then x is 24.
6. Sum of the first n natural numbers is $\dfrac{n(n+1)}{2}$.
7. Use empirical formula.
8. Substitute $x = 1$.
9. Observe median after including new observations.
10. Recall the formula for quartile deviation.
11. For inclusive type class, given values are the limits.
12. Semi-quartile range is the quartile deviation.
13. The 'x' value of the highest frequency class is the mode.
14. Mean deviation of x and y is $\dfrac{|x-y|}{2}$.
15. Mean depends on the value of k.
16. Range = Maximum value – Minimum value.
17. Use the properties of mean.
18. Mean deviation $= \dfrac{\Sigma|x_i - A|}{n}$, where A = Arithmetic mean.
19. The 'x' value of the highest frequency class is the mode.
20. Use the formula for coefficient of range.
21. Find the mode by using mean and median then find mean deviation.
22. Mean $= \dfrac{\text{Sum of the observations}}{\text{Total number of observations}}$.
23. AM $= \dfrac{\text{Sum of all observation}}{\text{Total number of observations}}$.
24. Mode = 3 median – 2 mean.
25. Inter-quartile range $= \dfrac{Q_3 - Q_1}{2}$

    $Q_3 = \dfrac{3(n+1)}{4}$ th observation

    $Q_1 = \dfrac{(n+1)}{4}$ th observation.
26. (i) $\dfrac{\sum fx}{N} = 5$.

    (ii) Find the value of Σfx and Σf.

    (iii) Mean $= \dfrac{\sum fx}{\sum f}$.
27. Mean deviation of x and y is $\dfrac{|x-y|}{2}$.
28. (i) Find the sum of observations.

    (ii) Use, $x + 2 = \dfrac{\text{Sum of observations}}{\text{Number of observations}}$.
29. (i) Consider x as the least value.

    (ii) Use, Range = Highest score – Lowest score and find x.
30. (i) Write the cumulative frequencies of each class.

    (ii) Trace the median class, i.e., the class corresponding the commutative frequency equal to $\left(\dfrac{N}{2}\right)$.

    (iii) Evaluate median, by using median $= L + \left(\dfrac{\frac{N}{2} - F}{f}\right) \times C$.
31. (i) Find the average (mean) pass percentage of all the schools.

    (ii) The school with the maximum pass percentage is more consistent.
32. (i) Recall the properties of central tendencies.

    (ii) For different values of x, AM, Median, and QD will be changed.

    (iii) The maximum and minimum values are not changed in the given interval of x.

Level 2: Review Your Concepts

33. (i) Substitute, median $= \frac{3}{2}$ mean in empirical relation.

(ii) Mode = 3 Median – 2 Mean.

(iii) Express median in terms of mean according to the given data.

(iv) Now write the ratio of the mode and mean using the relation in (i).

34. (i) $\frac{\sum fx}{N} = 13.$

(ii) Find $\sum fx$ and $\sum f$.

(iii) Mean $= \frac{\sum fx}{\sum f}$, where $\sum f = N$.

35. (i) Mode = 3 Median – 2 Mean.

(ii) Divide the above equation by median.

(iii) Substitute, $\frac{\text{Mode}}{\text{Median}} = \frac{6}{5}$ and obtain the required ratio.

36. (i) $\frac{\sum fx}{N} = 8.2.$

(ii) Find $\sum fx$ and $\sum f$.

(iii) Mean $= \frac{\sum fx}{\sum f}$.

37. (i) Recall the properties of central tendencies.

(ii) Arrange the given observations (except x) in ascending order.

(iii) Find the median for different values of x.

(iv) Write median interval for all values of x.

38. (i) Use deviation method.

(ii) Find the mid values of the class intervals.

(iii) Find $\sum fx$ and $\sum f$.

(iv) Mean $= \frac{\sum fx}{\sum f}$.

39. (i) Median $= l + \frac{\frac{N}{2} - m}{f} \times C.$

(ii) Find the cumulative frequency.

(iii) Find $\frac{N}{2}$, F, f and c.

(iv) Find the median by the formula,

$$\text{Median} = l + \frac{\frac{N}{2} - m}{f} \times C.$$

40. (i) Inferences from the graph.

(ii) Use less than cumulative frequency curve.

(iii) Identify the cumulative frequency corresponding to 50.

41. (i) Inferences from the graph.

(ii) Use greater than cumulative frequency curve and identify the frequency corresponding to 90.

42. (i) Use mean concept.

(ii) Let the two students received x number of books each.

(iii) According to the data $2x + 13p = 180$.

(iv) From the options choose x such that p must be an integer.

43. (i) Find median and then mean deviation.

(ii) Calculate the median of the given discrete data.

(iii) Evaluate mean deviation by using $\frac{\sum |x_i - A| f}{\sum f}$.

44. (i) Find mean and then mean deviation.

(ii) Find the mid-values of the series.

(iii) Find the mean.

(iv) Find the mean deviation using the formula,

$$\text{MD} = \sqrt{\sum \frac{(x_i - A) f}{\sum f}}$$

45. As p, q and $2p$ are in descending order, their median is 36.

$\therefore \quad q = 36$

$$\frac{p + q + 2p}{3} = 31$$

$\Rightarrow 3p + 36 = 93 \Rightarrow p = 19.$

$\therefore \quad$ Mean of 19 and 36 $= \frac{19 + 36}{2} = 27.5.$

46. As x, y and $2x$ are in ascending order, median is y.

$y = 27.$

$$\text{Mean} = \frac{x+y+2x}{3} = 33$$

$$\Rightarrow \frac{3x+27}{3} = 33 \Rightarrow x = 24.$$

$$\therefore \text{Mean of } x \text{ and } y = \frac{x+y}{2} \Rightarrow \frac{24+27}{2} = 25.5.$$

47. The mean of set of 12 observations is 10.
Sum of the observations = 12 × 10 = 120
The mean of another set of 8 observations is 12
Sum of the observations = 12 × 8 = 96
Total number of observations = 12 + 8 = 20
Total sum of observations = 216

$$\text{Combined mean } = \frac{216}{20} = 10.8.$$

Level 3: Assess Your Concepts

48. (i) Find the coefficient of range of A, B, C, and D and compare.

(ii) Coefficient of range =

$$\frac{\text{Maximum value} - \text{Minimum value}}{\text{Maximum value} + \text{Minimum value}}.$$

(iii) Find the coefficient of range of A, B, C, and D.

(iv) The least coefficient of range implies good performance.

49. (i) Find the coefficient of range of A, B, C, and D and compare.

(ii) Coefficient of range =

$$\frac{\text{Maximum value} - \text{Minimum value}}{\text{Maximum value} + \text{Minimum value}}.$$

(iii) Find the coefficient of range of A, B, C, and D.

(iv) The least coefficient of range implies good performance.

50. Given, Mode = 3

$\therefore x = 3$

Now, arrange the given data in ascending order,

3, 3, 3, 3, 3, 4, 4, 4, 4, 5, 5, 5, 5

∴ Median = 4

Hence, option (b) is correct.

51. Given,

Avg. age of boys = 14 years

Avg. age of girls = 17 years

Avg. age of children in society = 15 years

Let no. of boys be x, and

No. of girls be y

⇒ Sum of boys = 14 × no. of boys

Sum of girls = 17 × no. of girls

Sum of children = 15 × (no. of boys + no. of girls)

$\Rightarrow 14 \times \text{no. of boys} + 17 \times \text{no. of girls} = 15 \times (x + y)$

$\Rightarrow 14x + 17y = 15x + 15y$

$\Rightarrow x - 2y = 0$

$\Rightarrow x = 2y$

$\therefore x : y = 2 : 1$

Hence, option (b) is correct.

52.

Class Interval	f	Cumulative Frequency
0–4	3	3
4–8	5	8 m
8–12	6	14
12–16	3	17
16–20	8	25

Here, $N = 25$

$$\frac{N}{2} = \frac{25}{2} = 12.5.$$

∴ The median class = 8 – 12

$\therefore l = 8, f = 6, m = 8, c = 4.$

$$\text{Median} = l + \frac{\frac{N}{2} - m}{f} \times c = 8 + \frac{12.5-8}{6} \times 4$$

$$= 8 + \frac{4.5}{3} \times 2 = 8 + 1.5 \times 2 = 8 + 3 = 11.$$

53. 10 boys brought 11 books each. Therefore, total number of books brought by 10 boys = 110. Six girls brought 13 books each. Therefore, total number of books brought by 6 girls = 78.

Remaining number of students are 4 and the total number of books brought by 4 students = x.

Given that $\frac{x + 78 + 110}{20}$ is a positive integer.

If $x = 12$ then the above value is an integer.

54. The mean of set of 20 observations is 8.
Sum of the observations = 20 × 8 = 160
The mean of another set of 30 observations is 10
Sum of the observations = 30 × 10 = 300
Total number of observations = 20 + 30 = 50
Total sum of observations = 460

Combined mean = = $\frac{460}{50} = 9.2$.

55.

Class Interval	f	x	|dx| = |x − x|	fD
0–10	4	5	31	124
10–20	6	15	21	126
20–30	3	25	11	33
30–40	9	35	1	9
40–50	5	45	9	45

$$\text{Mode} = L + \frac{\Delta_1}{\Delta_1 + \Delta_2} \times c.$$

Here, maximum frequency is 9.

∴ Model class is 30–40

∴ $L = 10$

$\Delta_1 = f - f_1$ and $\Delta_2 = f - f_2$

$\Delta_1 = 9 - 3$, $\Delta_2 = 9 - 5 = 4$ and $C = 10$

$$\text{Mode} = 30 + \frac{6}{6+4} \times 10 = 30 + \frac{6}{10} \times 10$$

$= 30 + 6 = 36.$

$\sum fD = 337, N = 27$

$$\therefore \text{MD} = \frac{\sum f \cdot d}{N} = \frac{337}{27} \sim 12.5.$$

56.

x	f	fx
2	4	8
3	4	12
4	2	8
5	3	15
7	q	7q

Here $\sum fx = 43 + 7q$

$\sum f = 13 + q$

We know that, $\text{AM} = \frac{\sum fx}{\sum f}$

$$4 = \frac{43 + 7q}{13 + q}$$

$52 + 4q = 43 + 7q \Rightarrow 3q = 9 \Rightarrow q = 3.$

57. Given that, $\frac{\text{Mean}}{\text{Median}} = \frac{5}{7}$

We know that, Mode = 3 Median − 2 Mean.

$$\text{Mode} = \text{Mean}\left(\frac{3\,\text{Median}}{\text{Mean}} - 2\right)$$

$$\frac{\text{Mode}}{\text{Mean}} = \left(3 \cdot \frac{7}{5} - 2\right) = \frac{21 - 10}{5} = \frac{11}{5}.$$

58. Mode = 3
∴ Since the frequency of 3 is maximum.

59.

x_i	f_i	Cumulative Frequency	$D = x_i - A$	$f_i\|D\|$
1	3	3	−2	6
2	7	10	−1	7
3	5	15	0	0
4	8	23	1	8
5	2	25	2	4
6	5	30	3	15
				40

Here $N = 30$

$\frac{N}{2} = 15$, which falls in the class with $x = 3$.

∴ Median = 3, $\Sigma f\,|D| = 40$

$$\text{Mean deviation} = \frac{\sum f|D|}{N} = \frac{40}{30} = 1.33.$$

60. $\text{AM} = \frac{\text{Sum of all observations}}{\text{Total number of observations}}$

$$= \frac{x + 5 + x + 6 + x + 10 + x + 11 + x + 14 + x + 20}{6}$$

$$= \frac{6x + 66}{6} = \frac{6(x + 11)}{6} = x + 11.$$

61.

Class Interval	D	x	fx
0–10	8	5	40
10–20	4	15	60
20–30	6	25	150
30–40	3	35	105
40–50	4	45	180

Here $\Sigma fx = 535$

$\Sigma f = 25$

$$\text{Mean} = \frac{\Sigma fx}{\Sigma f} = \frac{535}{25} = 21.4.$$

62. If we take x value between 10 and 15. There is no change in maximum value and the minimum value.

$\therefore$ Range will not change.

63.

x	f	fx
3	2	6
5	5	25
7	6	45
9	7	63
11	k	$11k$
	$\Sigma f = 20 + k,$	$\Sigma fx = 136 + 11k$

$$AM = \frac{\sum fx}{\sum f}$$

$$8 = \frac{136 + 11k}{20 + k}$$

$160 + 8k = 136 + 11k$

$24 = 3k \Rightarrow 8 = k$

64. $\Sigma f = 100$

$\therefore f_1 + f_2 = 40$ (1)

Mid values of class are 7.5, 22.5, 37.5, 52.5, 67.5 and 82.5

$\therefore$ Mean $= \Sigma fx / \Sigma f$

$[(7.5)(5)+(22.5)(10)+(37.5)(f_1)+(52.5)(25)+(67.5)f_2+(82.5)20]/100$

$= 56.25$

$\therefore 3225 + 37.5 f_1 + 67.5 f_2 = 5625$

$\Rightarrow 37.5 f_1 + 67.5 f_2 = 2400$ (2)

Solving (1) and (2), we get $f_1 = 10$ and $f_2 = 30$

JEE Special Wing

Multiple-Answer Type Questions

1. The following statements are true regarding bar graphs:
   (a) Bar graphs are used to represent unclassified frequency distribution.
   (c) The length of a bar is proportional to the frequency of the corresponding variable
   (d) The breadths of all the bars are equal.

   Hence, choice (a), choice (c) and choice (d) follow.

2. The following statements are true regarding bar graphs:
   (b) Cumulative frequency curves are used to represent classified frequency distribution.
   (c) There are two types of cumulative frequency curves - less than cumulative frequency (**lcf**) curve and greater than cumulative frequency (**gcf**) curve.
   (d) The value of the corresponding class boundary of the point of intersections of **lcf** and **gcf** curves is the arithmetic mean of the data.

   Hence, choice (b), choice (c) and choice (d) follow.

3. Let us consider the first five perfect squares:
   1, 4, 9, 16, 25

   $$\text{Mean} = \frac{1+4+9+16+25}{5} = \frac{55}{5} = 11.$$

   $$\text{Median} = \frac{9+16}{2} = \frac{25}{2} = 12.5$$

   As there is no observation which is repeated, the mode is ill defined.

   Range = Highest score – Least Score = 25 – 1 = 24.

   Hence, choice (a), choice (b), choice (c) and choice (d) follow.

4. (a)

Number of People (in lakhs)	No. of Cities (f_i)	Mid-values (x_i) (in lakhs)	$f_i \times x_i$ (in lakhs)
0 – 10	4	5	20
10 – 20	10	15	150
20 – 30	6	25	150
Total	$n = \sum f_i = 20$		$\sum f_i \times x_i = 320$

$$\text{Mean } \textbf{(in lakhs)} = \frac{\sum f_i \times x_i}{\sum f_i}$$

$$= \frac{320}{20} = 16$$

(b)

Number of People (in lakhs)	No. of Cities (f_i)	LCF
0 – 10	4	$4\,(F)$
10 – 20	$10\,(f)$	14
20 – 30	6	20
Total	$n = \sum f_i = 20$	

$$\frac{n}{2} = \frac{20}{2} = 10.$$

Median class is 10 – 20.

The lower boundary (L) of the median class is 10.

Width of each class (C) = 10

$$\text{Median (in lakhs)} = L + \frac{\frac{n}{2} - F}{f} \times C$$

$$= 10 + \frac{10-4}{10} \times 10 = 16.$$

(c)

Number of People (in lakhs)	No. of Cities (f_i)
0 – 10	$4\,(f_1)$
10 – 20	$10\,(f)$
20 – 30	$6\,(f_2)$

Modal class is 10 – 20

(The class which has the highest frequency)

The lower boundary (L) of the modal class is 10.

Width of each class (C) = 10

$$\text{Mode (in lakhs)} = L + \frac{f - f_1}{2f - f_1 - f_2} \times C$$

$$= 10 + \frac{10-4}{20-4-6} \times 10 = 16.$$

(d) $\bar{x} = 10$ = Mean (or) Median (or) Mode

Number of People (in lakhs)	No. of Cities (f_i)	Mid-values (x_i) (in lakhs)	$D_i = \lvert x_i - \bar{x}\rvert$ (in lakhs)	$f_i \times D_i$ (in lakhs)
0 – 10	4	5	5	20
10 – 20	10	15	5	50
20 – 30	6	25	15	90
Total	$n = \sum f_i = 20$			$\sum f_i \times D_i = 160$

$$\text{Mean Deviation (in lakhs)} = \frac{\sum f_i \times D_i}{\sum f_i} = \frac{160}{20} = 8.$$

Hence, choice (a), choice (b) and choice (c) follow.

5. Given that the ratio of the mean and median of a data is 5 : 4.

Let the mean and median of a data be $5x$ and $4x$ respectively.

We know that mode = 3 median − 2mean

$\text{Mode} = 3(4x) - 2(5x) = 2x.$

(a) The ratio of the mean and mode is $5x : 2x = 5 : 2$.

(b) The ratio of the mode and median is $2x : 4x = 1 : 2$.

There is no sufficient data to find the range and the quartiles.

So, we cannot comment on the statements (c) and (d).

Hence, choice (a) and choice (b) follow.

Match The Column

Common Solutions for questions 6 to 10:

The ages of ten family members in years are as follows:

8, 9, 10, 11, 34, 36, 36, 40, 67, 69

The number of observations $(n) = 10$.

$$\text{Mean} = \frac{8+9+10+11+34+36+36+40+67+69}{10} = 32.$$

$$\text{Median} = \frac{34+36}{2} = 35.$$

Mode = 36 (It has the highest frequency)

6. Median age = 35 years.

Hence, the correct option is (f).

7. $Q_1 = \left(\frac{n}{4}\right)^{th}$ observation $= (2.5)^{th}$ observation

$= \frac{9+10}{2} = 9.5$

$Q_3 = 3\left(\frac{n}{4}\right)^{th}$ observation $= (7.5)^{th}$ observation

$= \frac{36+40}{2} = 38$

$$\text{Quartile deviation} = \frac{38-9.5}{2} = 14.25 \text{ years.}$$

Hence, the correct option is (b).

8. **Given Data:** 8, 9, 10, 11, 34, 36, 36, 40, 67, 69.

Mean $(\overline{x}) = 32$.

$$\text{Mean deviation about mean} = \frac{\sum |x_i - \overline{x}|}{\sum f_i}$$

$$= \frac{24+23+22+21+2+4+4+8+35+37}{10} = 18.$$

Hence, the correct option is (d).

9. **Given Data:** 8, 9, 10, 11, 34, 36, 36, 40, 67, 69.

Mode $(\overline{x}) = 36$.

$$\text{Mean deviation about mode} = \frac{\sum |x_i - \overline{x}|}{\sum f_i}$$

$$= \frac{28+27+26+25+2+0+0+4+31+33}{10} = 17.6.$$

Hence, the correct option is (c).

10. **Given Data:** 8, 9, 10, 11, 34, 36, 36, 40, 67, 69.

The average age of the eldest and the youngest persons in the family

$= \frac{8+69}{2} = 38.5$ years.

Hence, the correct option is (g).

Comprehension-Based Questions

Common Solutions for questions 11 to 15:

The number of students = 19.

The average weight of the class is 40 kg.

The sum of the weights of all the students = 19 × 40 kg = 760 kg.

The average weight of the first ten lightest students is 38.6 kg.

The average weight of the first ten heaviest students is 41 kg.

The average weight of all the girls is 38 kg and that of all the boys is 47.5 kg.

11. Let the weight of the Math teacher be x kg.

Given that $760 + x = 20 \times 41$

$x = 820 - 760 = 60$.

The weight of the Math teacher = 60 kg.

Hence, the correct option is (b).

12. Let the weight of Rama be y kg.

Given that $760 - y = 18 \times 39.5$

$y = 760 - 711 = 49$.

The weight of Rama = 49 kg.

Hence, the correct option is (d).

13. Given that the average weight of all the girls is 38 kg and that of all the boys is 47.5 kg.

Let the number of boys and girls respectively be a and b.

Given that $a + b = 19$ (1)

Also, $47.5a + 38b = 760$.

$95a + 76b = 1520$.

$5a + 4b = 80$ (2)

Equation (2) – 4 × Equation (1):

$a = 4$.

Now $b = 19 - 4 = 15$

The required difference = 15 – 4 = 11.

Hence, the correct option is (b).

14. The average weight of the first ten lightest students is 38.6 kg.

The average weight of the first ten heaviest students is 41 kg.

The weight of 10th heaviest student = 10(41) – 10(38.6) = 410 – 386 = 34 kg.

Hence, the correct option is (a).

15. Let the number of absentees be c.

The average weight of c students = 30 Kg.

The average of the remaining $19 - c$ students is 49 kg.

Now $30c + (19 - c)49 = 760$.

$30c - 49c + 931 = 760$.

$19c = 171$

$c = 9$.

The number of absentees = 9.

Hence, the correct option is (a).

Assertion and Reason Type Questions

Solutions for questions 16 to 20:

16. **Assertion:** The mean of 1, 3, 5 is $= \frac{1+3+5}{3} = 3$

= The mean of 1 and 5.

The mean of 1, 3, 5, 7 is $= \frac{1+3+5+7}{4} = 4 =$ The mean of 1 and 7.

The mean of 1, 3, 5, 7, 9 is $= \frac{1+3+5+7+9}{5} = 5 =$ The mean of 1 and 9.

Similarly, the mean of 1, 3, 5, 7, 9, 11, 13, ... 191 is the mean of 1 and 191.

That is $\frac{1+191}{3} = 96$.

So, Assertion is true.

Reason: The mean of the terms, where there is the same difference for any two consecutive terms, is the average of the first and the last terms.

Reason is true and is the correct explanation to Assertion.

Hence, the correct option is (a).

17. **Assertion:** Given Data: 11, 12, 12, 11, 14, 15, 11, 14, 15, 14.

Observation	Frequency
11	3
12	2
14	3
15	2

The frequencies of 11 and 14 have equal frequencies and that is the highest frequency. It is a bi-modal data.

So, Assertion is true.

Reason: A data which consists of two modes is a bi-model data.

Reason is true and is the correct explanation to Assertion.

Hence, the correct option is (a).

18. **Assertion:** Given that the median of 101, 102, 103, 104 ... 200 is 150.5.

If each observation of the above data increases by 9, then we will get 110, 111, 112, 113, 114 ... 209.

If each observation of the above data increases by 9, then the median also increases by 9. The required median is 150.5 + 9 = 159.5.

So, Assertion is true.

Reason: If $x_1 < x_2 < x_3 < x_4 < \ldots < x_n$, the median of $x_1, x_2, x_3, x_4 \ldots x_n$ is $\frac{x_1 + x_n}{2}$.

It may not be true in some cases. For example, the median of 12, 14, 17 is 14, but it is not equal to $\frac{12+17}{2}$.

So, Reason is false.

Hence, the correct option is (c).

19. **Assertion:** Given that the mean of 1, 2, 3, 4 ... 99 is 50.

$(1-50)+(2-50)+(3-50)+\ldots+(50-50)+$
$(51-50)+(52-50)+(53-50)+\ldots+(99-50)$
$= -49 - 48 - 47 + \ldots + 0 + 1 + 2 + 3 + \ldots + 49 = 0$.

So, Assertion is true.

Reason: The mean of a data is given by the ratio of the sum of the observations and the number of observations of the data.

Reason is true but not the correct explanation to Assertion.

Hence, the correct option is (b).

20. **Assertion:** The first 50 odd natural numbers are: 1, 3, 5 … 99.

Range = 99 – 1 = 98.

So, Assertion is false.

Reason: In a data, the range of the scores is the difference between the highest score and the lowest score.

Reason is true.

Hence, the correct option is (d).

CHAPTER

14

Probability

Remember

Before beginning this chapter, you should be able to:

- Understand the basic concepts of probability
- Compute basic probability in daily life

Key Ideas

After completing this chapter, you should be able to:

- Learn the concepts related to probability
- Find probability of happening of any event
- Apply the concept of probability in daily life and solve problems

Scientific Crypt

A Tribute to Blaise Pascal

Blaise Pascal, born in 1623 in Clermont-Ferrand, France, was a versatile French polymath who excelled in mathematics, science, philosophy, and theology. His profound insights, experiments and writings played a pivotal role in refining our understanding of the physical world.

Pascal's early mathematical brilliance led to contributions like Pascal's Theorem at age 16 and his significant role in advancing probability theory through correspondence with Fermat. Pascal also pioneered mechanical calculators, known as Pascalines, establishing himself as an early inventor in this field. Beyond mathematics, he challenged conventional views on atmospheric. pressure and the vacuum, advocating for the scientific method.

In 1654, Pascal's life took a transformative turn with a profound religious experience, leading to his philosophical and theological writings. During this period, he authored notable works such as the 'Lettres Provinciales' and the 'Pensées,' which contains his famous 'Pascal's Wager' argument for the existence of God.

Despite enduring chronic health issues and religious crises that influenced his writings, Pascal's brilliance and determination allowed him to make substantial contributions to mathematics, science, and philosophy in his relatively short life. He passed away at the age of 39.

Pascal's legacy extends far beyond his time, with numerous honours and recognitions, including the naming of educational institutions in France and the dedication of an apostolic letter by Pope Francis in 2023, marking the fourth centenary of his birth. Additionally, the SI unit of pressure, Pascal, bears his name, solidifying his enduring impact across multiple domains.

FUN TIME

CROSSWORD

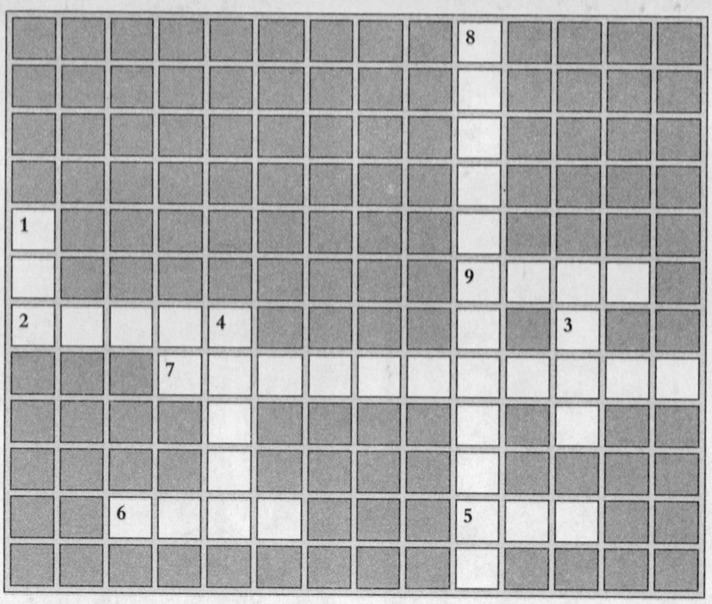

Across

2. Every result of rolling a pair of dice.
5. Total outcomes in tossing a coin.
6. The possibility that you will get a tail in a coin toss.
7. What is the theory of uncertainty called ________.
9. One of the results of flipping a coin.

Down

1. The total of all the experiments potential exclusive event probability.
3. How many possible outcomes there are when you roll a die.
4. Tossing of a coin.
8. When discussing __________, terms like "chances" and "doubt" are used.

INTRODUCTION

In this chapter, probability is a numerical description of how likely an event is to occur or how likely it is that a proposition is true. Probability is a number between 0 and 1, where, roughly speaking, 0 indicates impossibility and 1 indicates certainty.

Probability

In our daily life, we frequently use some statements like the following:

1. I will probably get a scholarship for my performance.
2. I doubt that I will catch the train.
3. The chances of the prices of all commodities going up are very high.
4. There is a fifty-fifty chance of Sania winning the match.
5. I will most probably return from my official tour in three days.
6. The chances of Sachin making a century in his next match are very few.

In the above statements the words probably, chances, doubt, and most probably involve an uncertainty.

In statement (1), I will probably get a scholarship means he may get a scholarship or he may not get a scholarship. Here we are predicting a scholarship based on his performance. Similar predictions are also made in statements (2) to (6). In this chapter, we are going to learn how to measure the uncertainty (i.e., probability) numerically by using probability in many cases. Actually probability started with gambling but it has been used extensively in all fields like biological sciences, medical sciences, weather forecasting, commerce, etc.

Example: Take any ₹1 coin and toss it 5 times, 10 times, 15 times, 20 times, etc., and record your observations in three columns as shown below:

Number of Times Coin Tossed	Number of Times Head Shows up	Number of Times Tail Shows up
5	3	2
10	6	4
15	6	9
20	8	12
:	:	:
:	:	:

Now find the values in each of the following case:

1. $\dfrac{\text{Number of times head shows up}}{\text{Total number of times the coin is tossed}}$

2. $\dfrac{\text{Number of times a tail shows up}}{\text{Total number of times the coin is tossed}}$

Observations

1. As the number of times a head/a tail shows up is less than the total number of times the coin is tossed, the values of the above two fractions are proper fractions.
2. The values of the above two fractions are positive but less than one.

3. We observe that, when the number of times the coin tossed becomes larger and larger, then the value of the above two fractions approaches $\frac{1}{2}$ or 0.5.

Example: A six-faced (well-balanced) cube with its six faces marked with numbers 1 to 6 is called a dice.

Roll a dice 30 times and record the faces showing up with numbers 1 to 6 in each case as shown below:

Number of Times a Dice is Rolled	Number of Times Each Face with the Following Values Shows up					
	1	2	3	4	5	6
30	8	5	4	6	5	2

Find the values of the following:

1. $\frac{\text{Number of times 1 turned up}}{\text{Total number of times the dice is rolled}}$

2. $\frac{\text{Number of times 2 turned up}}{\text{Total number of times the dice is rolled}}$

3. $\frac{\text{Number of times 3 turned up}}{\text{Total number of times the dice is rolled}}$

4. $\frac{\text{Number of times 4 turned up}}{\text{Total number of times the dice is rolled}}$

5. $\frac{\text{Number of times 5 turned up}}{\text{Total number of times the dice is rolled}}$

6. $\frac{\text{Number of times 6 turned up}}{\text{Total number of times the dice is rolled}}$

Info Bytes!

Our brain often tricks us into seeing patterns even where none exist. This phenomenon is called 'apophenia'. It's one of the reasons people see 'streaks' in casino games, leading them to make irrational bets.

By repeating the above 20, 40, or 50 times, we observe the following:

1. The value of each fraction is a proper fraction and the value of it lies between 0 and 1.

2. The value of each fraction approaches $\frac{1}{6}$.

In the above examples each toss of a coin or each roll of a dice is called a trial.

When a coin is tossed, the possible outcome is a head or a tail.

Getting a head or tail in a particular throw is called an event with outcome head or tail.

When a dice is rolled, the possible outcome is 1, 2, 3, 4, 5, or 6. Getting a particular numbered face will be an event. Getting an odd number is also an event and this event consists of three outcomes 1, 3, and 5. Getting a prime number is also an event and consists of three outcomes 2, 3, and 5. Getting a multiple of 3 is an event which consists of two outcomes 3 and 6.

An event can be defined as the collection of some outcomes of a trial, or we can say an event is a subset of a set of all the outcomes of a trial.

The probability of happening of any event (E) of a trial is denoted by $P(E)$ and is defined as:

$$P(E) = \frac{\text{Number of favourable cases for the event to happen}}{\text{Total number of trials}}.$$

EXAMPLE 14.1

A coin is tossed 1200 times whereby head occurred in 745 cases and in the remaining tail occurred. Find the probability of each event.

SOLUTION

Given that the coin is tossed 1200 times.

Total number of trials = 1200

Let the event of getting a head be H, and getting a tail be T.

The number of times the event H occurred = 745

$$\text{Probability of event } H\text{, i.e., } P(H) = \frac{\text{Number of times head occured}}{\text{Total number of trials}} = \frac{745}{1200} = \frac{149}{240}$$

Number of times tail, i.e., event T occurred = 1200 − 745 = 455.

$$\therefore \text{Probability of event } T\text{, i.e., } P(T) = \frac{\text{number of times tail occured}}{\text{total number of trials}}$$

$$= \frac{455}{1200} = \frac{91}{240}$$

Konnect

1. The number of possible outcomes in each of the above trial is two (H and T).
2. $P(H) + P(T) = \frac{149}{240} + \frac{91}{240} = \frac{240}{240} = 1.$

EXAMPLE 14.2

When three coins are tossed, find the number of outcomes for getting at least 2 heads.

SOLUTION

Total possible outcomes = {HHH, HHT, HTH, THH, HTT, THT, TTH, TTT}

Favourable cases of getting atleast two heads = {HHT, HTH, THH, HHH}

Number of favourable cases = 4.

Info Bytes!

1. The possible outcomes in each trial are 1, 2, 3, 4, 5, and 6.
2. Sum of the probabilities, $P(E_1) + P(E_2) + P(E_3) + P(E_4) + P(E_5) + P(E_6) = 1.$

EXAMPLE 14.3

Three biased coins were tossed 600 times simultaneously. The outcomes are given in the table below.

Outcomes	No head	One heads	Two heads
Frequency	x	250	50

The occurrence of no heads was two third that of all the three heads. Find x.

SOLUTION

Let 'y' be the occurrence of all the three heads

Given, occurrence of no head was two third that of all the three heads.

i.e, $x = \frac{2}{3}(y) \Rightarrow y = \frac{3x}{2}$

Outcomes	No head	One heads	Two heads	Three heads
Frequency	x	250	50	$\frac{3x}{2}$

$\therefore$ Total frequency = 600

$$x + 250 + 50 + \frac{3x}{2} = 600$$

$$\frac{5x}{2} = 300$$

$\therefore$ x = 120.

EXAMPLE 14.4 The percentage of monthly targets achieved in producing a certain type of bolts in a company for different months is given in the following table:

Month	Jan	Feb	Mar	April	May	June
Target Achieved (in percent)	55	87	73	82	74	80

Find the probability that the company achieved 80% of the monthly target in producing the bolts.

SOLUTION

The total number of months for which target is fixed = 6.

The number of months the company achieved 80% of the target fixed = 3.

$\therefore$ P(achieving 80% of the target in producing bolts) $= \frac{3}{6} = \frac{1}{2} = 0.5.$

EXAMPLE 14.5 A pack has 90 cards. Each card was marked with a different number among 110 to 199. A card was selected at random. Find the probability that the number on it is not a perfect square.

(a) $\frac{37}{45}$ (b) $\frac{13}{15}$ (c) $\frac{41}{45}$ (d) $\frac{43}{45}$

SOLUTION

Among 110 to 199, the perfect squares are 121, 144, 169 and 196. Let the number on the card be x.

Probability (x being a perfect square) $= \frac{4}{90} = \frac{2}{45}.$

$\therefore$ Required probability $= 1 - \frac{2}{45} = \frac{43}{45}.$

EXAMPLE 14.6 A number was chosen at random from the first 300 three digits natural numbers. Find the probability of it ending with a zero.

(a) $\frac{1}{15}$ (b) $\frac{1}{25}$ (c) $\frac{1}{10}$ (d) $\frac{1}{20}$

SOLUTION

Let the number be x, $100 \le x \le 399$.
A number ending with a 0 is divisible by 10.
Least value of x, divisible by $10 = 100 = 10(10)$
Greatest value of x, divisible by $10 = 390 = 10(39)$
Number of values of x divisible by 10 = number of numbers from 10 to 39 = 30

$\therefore$ Required probability $= \frac{30}{300} = \frac{1}{10}$.

POINTS TO REMEMBER

- ✔ Probability of event H, i.e., $P(H) = \frac{\text{Number of times head occured}}{\text{Total number of trials}}$
- ✔ The possible outcomes in each trial are 1, 2, 3, 4, 5, and 6.
- ✔ Sum of the probabilities, $P(E_1) + P(E_2) + P(E_3) + P(E_4) + P(E_5) + P(E_6) = 1$.

DW

PRACTICE QUESTIONS CLASSROOM WING

Very Short Answer Type Questions

Directions of questions from 1 to 8:
Answer the following questions.

1. When two coins are tossed simultaneously, list out the possible outcomes.
2. When a dice is rolled, what are all the possible outcomes?
3. Two coins are tossed. Find the number of outcomes of getting one head.
4. What is the sum of all the probabilities of trials of an experiment?
5. When a dice is rolled, then what is the number of possible outcomes of obtaining an even number?
6. Let n be the number of trials that an event E occurred and m be the total number of trials, then find the probability of the event E.
7. A dice is rolled. Find the number of outcomes of getting a composite number.
8. A coin is tossed 20 times and head occurred 12 times. How many times did tail occur?

Short Answer Type Questions

9. A coin is tossed 500 times. Head occurs 343 times and tail occurs 157 times. Find the probability of each event.
10. A day is selected in a week, find the probability that the day is Monday.
11. In a monthly test, 10 students were awarded marks in a Mathematics examination as follows:

    23, 25, 18, 15, 20, 17, 10, 24, 15, 19

    If a student is selected at random, what is the probability that he gets more than 18 marks?
12. (A) In a cricket match, Dhoni hits a six 4 times from 24 balls he plays. Find the probability of hitting a six.
    (B) A number is chosen from {1, 3, 6, 9, 15, 20, 16, 18}. Find the probability that it satisfies the equation $(x - 3)(x - 10)(x - 9) = 0$.
13. Three coins are tossed 100 times, and three heads occurred 25 times, two heads occurred 38 times, one head occurred 14 times and head did not occur 23 times. Find the probability of getting more than one head.

Essay Type Questions

14. A dice is rolled 250 times, and the outcomes 1, 2, 3, 4, 5 and 6 occurred as given in the following table:

Outcome	1	2	3	4	5	6
Frequency	56	78	46	27	19	24

Find the probability of getting an odd number.

15. A Class IX English book contains 200 pages. A page is selected at random. What is the probability that the number on the page is divisible by 10?
16. In a colony there are 75 families and each family has two children. The number of male children of the families is as follows:

Male Child	2	1	0
Number of Families	27	38	10

If a family is selected at random, what is the probability that the family has only one male child?

17. The percentage of marks obtained by a student in a monthly test is as follows:

Test	I	II	III	IV
Marks	78%	63%	82%	65%

What is the probability that the student gets more than 75% marks in a test?

18. A box contains 50 tickets. Each ticket is numbered from 1 to 50. One ticket is selected at random, find the probability that the number on the ticket is not a perfect square.

19. A circle is inscribed in a square of side 7 cm. If we mark a point inside the square at random, then what is the probability that the point does not lie in the interior of the circle?

PRACTICE QUESTIONS COMPETITION WING

Level 1: Apply Your Concepts

Directions of questions from 1 and 2:
Fill in the blanks.

1. Probability of occurring of an event always lies between ______.

2. When a dice is rolled the probability that the number on the face showing up is greater than 6 is ______.

Directions of questions from 3 to 32:
Select the correct alternative from the given choices.

3. If a month is selected at random in a year, then find the probability that the month is either March or September.

   (a) $\frac{1}{12}$ (b) $\frac{1}{6}$
   (c) $\frac{3}{4}$ (d) None of these

4. A coin is tossed 1000 times. Head occurred 625 times. Find the probability of getting a tail.

   (a) $\frac{5}{8}$ (b) $\frac{7}{8}$
   (c) $\frac{1}{8}$ (d) $\frac{3}{8}$

5. A dice is rolled 600 times and the occurrence of the outcomes 1, 2, 3, 4, 5 and 6 are given below in the table:

Outcome	1	2	3	4	5	6
Frequency	200	30	120	100	50	100

   Find the probability of getting a prime number.

   (a) $\frac{1}{3}$ (b) $\frac{2}{3}$
   (c) $\frac{49}{60}$ (d) $\frac{39}{125}$

6. A bag contains 50 coins and each coin is marked from 51 to 100. One coin is picked at random. What is the probability that the number on the coin is not a prime number?

   (a) $\frac{1}{5}$ (b) $\frac{3}{5}$
   (c) $\frac{2}{5}$ (d) $\frac{4}{5}$

7. From the letters of the word 'MOBILE', if a letter is selected, what is the probability that the letter is a vowel?

   (a) $\frac{1}{3}$ (b) $\frac{4}{7}$
   (c) $\frac{3}{7}$ (d) $\frac{1}{2}$

8. The percentage of attendance of different classes in a year, in a school is given below:

Class	X	IX	VIII	VII	VI	V
Attendance	30	62	85	92	76	55

   What is the probability that the class attendance is more than 75%?

   (a) $\frac{1}{6}$ (b) $\frac{1}{3}$
   (c) $\frac{5}{6}$ (d) $\frac{1}{2}$

9. In a book, the frequency of units digit of a number on the pages is given below:

Units Digits	Frequency
0	50
1	40
2	10
3	25
4	15
5	80
6	90
7	110
8	120
9	60

   Find the probability of getting 8 in the units place on the pages.

   (a) $\frac{1}{5}$ (b) $\frac{1}{10}$
   (c) $\frac{1}{4}$ (d) $\frac{1}{60}$

10. 10 bags of rice, each bag marked 10 kg, actually contained the following weights of rice (in kgs). 10.03, 10.09, 9.97, 9.98, 10.01, 9.94, 10.05, 9.99, 9.95, 10.02. Find the probability that the bag chosen at random contains more than 10 kg.

(a) $\frac{1}{2}$ (b) $\frac{3}{5}$

(c) $\frac{5}{8}$ (d) $\frac{2}{5}$

11. If a three digit number is chosen at random, what is the probability that the chosen number is a multiple of 2?

(a) $\frac{499}{900}$ (b) $\frac{5}{9}$

(c) $\frac{1}{2}$ (d) $\frac{500}{899}$

12. If a two-digit number is chosen at random, what is the probability that the number chosen is a multiple of 3?

(a) $\frac{3}{10}$ (b) $\frac{29}{100}$

(c) $\frac{1}{3}$ (d) $\frac{7}{25}$

Level 2: Review Your Concepts

13. A mathematics book contains 250 pages. A page is selected at random. What is the probability that the number on the page selected is a perfect square?

(a) $\frac{3}{25}$ (b) $\frac{7}{50}$

(c) $\frac{3}{50}$ (d) $\frac{7}{125}$

14. The runs scored by Sachin Tendulkar in different years is given below:

Year	Score
1996–97	1000
1997–98	3000
1999–2000	1000
2000–01	5000
2001–02	3000
2002–03	8000
2003–04	4000

What is the probability that in a year Sachin scored more than 3000 runs?

(a) $\frac{3}{7}$ (b) $\frac{1}{4}$

(c) $\frac{3}{4}$ (d) $\frac{5}{8}$

15. To know the opinion of people about the political leaders, a survey on 1000 members was conducted. The data recorded is shown in the following table:

Option	Number of People
Like	200
Dislike	500
No opinion	300

Find the probability that a person chosen at random is with no opinion on political leaders.

(a) $\frac{1}{2}$ (b) $\frac{3}{10}$

(c) $\frac{1}{5}$ (d) None of these

16. A bag contains 12 pencils, 3 sharpeners and 7 pens. What is the probability of drawing a pencil from the bag?

(a) $\frac{6}{11}$ (b) $\frac{3}{22}$

(c) $\frac{7}{22}$ (d) $\frac{15}{22}$

17. In a football match, Ronaldo scores 4 goals from 10 penalty kicks. Find the probability of converting a penalty kick into a goal by Ronaldo.

(a) $\frac{1}{4}$ (b) $\frac{1}{6}$

(c) $\frac{1}{3}$ (d) $\frac{2}{5}$

18. From the month of August, whose first day is Tuesday, a day is selected at random. Find the probability that the day selected is not a Tuesday.

(a) $\frac{5}{6}$ (b) $\frac{26}{31}$

(c) $\frac{6}{31}$ (d) $\frac{27}{31}$

19. In a cricket match, Warne took three wickets in every 27 balls that he bowled. Find the probability of a batsman not getting out by Warne's bowling.

(a) $\frac{1}{9}$ (b) $\frac{4}{9}$

(c) $\frac{8}{9}$ (d) $\frac{5}{9}$

20. A day is selected at random from April, whose first day is Monday. Find the probability that the day selected is a Monday.

(a) $\frac{1}{7}$ (b) $\frac{1}{5}$

(c) $\frac{1}{6}$ (d) $\frac{2}{5}$

21. A month is selected at random in a year. Find the probability that it is either January or June.

(a) $\frac{1}{4}$ (b) $\frac{1}{3}$

(c) $\frac{1}{6}$ (d) $\frac{1}{2}$

22. A two-digit number is chosen at random. Find the probability that it is a multiple of 7.

(a) $\frac{11}{90}$ (b) $\frac{13}{90}$

(c) $\frac{7}{45}$ (d) $\frac{8}{45}$

23. In City X, there were 900 residents. A survey was conducted in it regarding the favorite beverages of the residents. The results of the survey are partially conveyed in the table below.

Beverages	Number of Residents Liking it/them
Only tea	350
Only coffee	250
Both tea and coffee	200

Find the probability that a resident chosen at random likes only tea or only coffee.

(a) $\frac{2}{3}$ (b) $\frac{5}{9}$

(c) $\frac{7}{9}$ (d) $\frac{4}{9}$

Level 3: Assess Your Concepts

24. Find the probability that a non-leap year contains exactly 53 Mondays.

(a) $\frac{6}{7}$ (b) $\frac{1}{7}$

(c) $\frac{52}{365}$ (d) None of these

25. Two dice were rolled simultaneously. Find the probability that the sum of the numbers on them was a two digits prime number.

(a) $\frac{1}{9}$ (b) $\frac{1}{18}$

(c) $\frac{1}{12}$ (d) $\frac{1}{6}$

26. Three biased coins were tossed 800 times simultaneously. The outcomes are given in the table below partially.

Outcome	No head	One head	Two heads
Frequency	120	280	x

If the occurrence of two heads was thrice that of all heads. Find x.

(a) 150 (b) 240

(c) 300 (d) 360

27. In the Question 27, find the probability that the sum of the numbers on the dice was a perfect cube.

(a) $\frac{5}{36}$ (b) $\frac{7}{36}$

(c) $\frac{2}{9}$ (d) $\frac{1}{6}$

28. A three-digit number was chosen at random. Find the probability that it's hundreds digit, tens digit and units digit are consecutive integers in descending order.

(a) $\frac{1}{75}$ (b) $\frac{4}{225}$

(c) $\frac{2}{225}$ (d) $\frac{1}{45}$

29. x = ABCDEFGHIJ...Z. Find the probability of a letter selected from those in odd positions of x being a vowel.

(a) $\frac{5}{13}$ (b) $\frac{6}{13}$

(c) $\frac{7}{13}$ (d) $\frac{8}{13}$

30. In a bag, there are 2 red balls, 3 green balls and 4 brown balls. Find the probability of drawing a ball at random being red or green.

(a) $\frac{5}{9}$ (b) $\frac{1}{4}$

(c) $\frac{1}{5}$ (d) $\frac{4}{9}$

31. Year X is not a leap year. Find the probability of X containing exactly 53 Sundays.

(a) $\frac{1}{7}$ (b) $\frac{2}{7}$

(c) $\frac{3}{7}$ (d) $\frac{1}{14}$

32. A three-digit number was chosen at random. Find the probability that it is divisible by both 2 and 3.

(a) $\frac{1}{12}$ (b) $\frac{1}{6}$

(c) $\frac{1}{9}$ (d) $\frac{1}{8}$

AT

PRACTICE QUESTIONS JEE SPECIAL WING

Multiple-Answer Type Questions

Directions for questions 1 to 5:

Each question has FOUR options (a), (b), (c), and (d). ONE OR MORE THAN ONE of these four option(s) is/are the correct answer(s).

1. Three coins are tossed for 100 times. The results are as follows.

Event	Three heads	Two heads	One head
No. of times	28	24	26

If three coins are tossed, the probability of getting ______.

(a) three tails is $\frac{11}{50}$ (b) two tails is $\frac{13}{50}$

(c) one tail is $\frac{6}{25}$ (d) no tails is $\frac{7}{25}$

2. A dice is rolled for 140 times. The results are as follows.

Score	1	2	3	4	5	6
Occurrences	x	$\frac{x}{2}$	$\frac{x}{3}$	$\frac{x}{4}$	$\frac{x}{6}$	$\frac{x}{12}$

If a dice is rolled, the probability of getting a number which is______.

(a) neither prime nor composite is $\frac{3}{14}$

(b) a prime is $\frac{3}{7}$

(c) a composite is $\frac{1}{7}$

(d) a perfect square is $\frac{15}{28}$

3. A bag consists of balls of different colours. The details are as follows:

Colour	Azure	Coral	Lavender	Olive
No. of balls	75	85	95	105

If a ball is selected at random, the probability of getting _____.

(a) a ball which is neither Azure nor Coral is $\frac{5}{9}$.

(b) a ball which is either Lavender or Coral is $\frac{1}{3}$.

(c) an Azure coloured ball is $\frac{5}{24}$.

(d) a ball which is not Olive $\frac{17}{24}$.

4. In an apartment, there are 150 flats where each flat is inhabited by a family. The following table shows the number of family members in each family.

No. of Family Members	2	3	4	5	6
No. of flats	10	20	30	40	50

If a flat is selected at random, the probability of finding _____.

(a) a family which consists of even number of members is $\frac{2}{5}$.

(b) a family which consists of odd number of members is $\frac{3}{5}$.

(c) a family which consists of more than 3 members is $\frac{4}{5}$.

(d) a family which consists not more than 4 members is $\frac{1}{5}$.

5. An unbiased dice is rolled. Which of the following statements is/are true?

(a) The probability of getting an odd number is equal to that of getting an even number.

(b) The probability of getting a composite number is less than that of getting a prime number.

(c) The probability of getting a number which has only one factor is 0.

(d) The probability of getting a perfect square is equal to that of a perfect cube.

Match The Column

Directions for questions 6 to 10:

Read the paragraph given below and answer the questions.

Each stage of life is vital, and it is difficult to determine which is the most important. The experiences and lessons learned in childhood, adolescence, adulthood, middle age, and old age all contribute to moulding an individual's personality, values, and worldview.

In a colony there are 1000 residents. Some of the details of the residents are as follows:

Stages	Age (in years)	No. of Persons
Infancy	0 – 2	100
Childhood	3 – 12	120
Adolescence	13 – 19	180
Adulthood	20 – 40	250
Middle Age	41 – 60	200
Old Age	60 above	150

If a person is selected at random, the probability getting a required event is x.

Using the above information, match the values in Column A with those in Column B.

Column A (Event)	Column B (x)
6. A person whose age is more than 40 years	(a) $\frac{3}{20}$
7. A person whose age is less than 20 years	(b) $\frac{11}{50}$
8. A person whose is not in adulthood	(c) $\frac{3}{10}$
9. A person whose is in old age	(d) $\frac{7}{20}$
10. A person who belongs to childhood or adolescence	(e) $\frac{2}{5}$
	(f) $\frac{3}{4}$
	(g) $\frac{3}{5}$

Comprehension-Based Questions

Directions for questions 11 to 15:

Read the paragraph given below and answer the questions.

Leap years are necessary for our calendar year to coincide with the solar year, which is the duration of Earth's orbit around the Sun. It might not seem like a big problem to take 5 hours, 46 minutes, and 48 seconds out of a year. However, if you deduct approximately 6 hours a year for several years, things can get quite problematic.

Let's take an example where you reside in a pleasant, summery place like July. All those hours lost would accumulate into days, weeks, and possibly months if leap years had never been. After a few centuries, July would truly fall during the chilly winter months.

Let us consider a leap year 2000 and the year started with Saturday. An employee availed leave on all the Saturdays and Sundays in addition to 9 festival days which do not fell either on Saturday or Sunday.

11. If a day of the week is selected at random from year 2000, what is the probability that it occurred exactly 52 times?

(a) $\frac{2}{7}$ (b) $\frac{3}{7}$

(c) $\frac{5}{7}$ (d) $\frac{6}{7}$

12. If a day of the week is selected at random from year 2000, what is the probability that the employee availed leave?

(a) $\frac{115}{366}$ (b) $\frac{113}{366}$

(c) $\frac{106}{366}$ (d) $\frac{104}{366}$

13. If a month is selected at random from year 2000, what is the probability that it has three days of the week occur five times?

(a) 0 (b) $\frac{5}{12}$

(c) $\frac{6}{12}$ (d) $\frac{7}{12}$

14. If a month is selected at random from year 2000, what is the probability that each day of the week occurs exactly four times?

(a) 0 (b) $\frac{1}{12}$

(c) $\frac{5}{12}$ (d) $\frac{7}{12}$

15. If a year is selected from 2000 to 2004 at random, what is the probability of it being a leap year?

(a) $\frac{1}{2}$ (b) $\frac{2}{5}$ (c) $\frac{1}{4}$ (d) $\frac{1}{5}$

Assertion and Reason Type Questions

Directions for questions 16 to 20:

Read the options given below and answer the questions.

(a) Both assertion (A) and reason (R) are true, and the reason (R) is the correct explanation of the assertion (A).
(b) Both assertion (A) and reason (R) are true, and the reason (R) is not the correct explanation of the assertion (A).
(c) Assertion (A) is true, but reason (R) is false.
(d) Assertion (A) is false, and reason (R) is true.

16. Assertion: If a card is selected at random from cards numbered from integers, 1 to 100, the probability of getting an even-numbered card is $\frac{1}{2}$.

Reason: If a number is selected at random from integers, 1 to 50, the probability of getting an even number is $\frac{1}{2}$.

17. Assertion: If a number is chosen at random from even numbers below 202, the probability of getting a number which has exactly one factor is 0.

Reason: The probability of getting an impossible event is more than 0 and less than 1.

18. Assertion: In a school the number of boys, girls, teachers and non-teaching staff (including principal and vice principal) are 175, 200, 75 and 50 respectively. If a person is selected at random, the probabilty of a teacher getting selected is $\frac{3}{25}$.

Reason: In an experiment, the probability of getting an event is $\frac{\text{The number of favourable cases to the desired event}}{\text{The total number of cases}}$

19. Assertion: If a number is chosen at random from the set of the first ten natural numbers, the probability of getting a composite number is $\frac{1}{2}$.

Reason: If a number is chosen at random from the set of the first ten natural numbers, the probability of getting an even number is equal to that of an odd number.

20. Assertion: A month is selected at random from a calendar year, the probability that the month consists of exactly 30 days is $\frac{1}{3}$.

Reason: In an experiment, the probability of occurrence of an event is $\frac{\text{The number of favourable cases to the desired event}}{\text{The total number of cases}}$

ANSWER KEYS

Crossword

Across

2. Event
5. Two
6. Half
7. Probability
9. Tail

Down

1. One
3. Six
4. Trial
8. Uncertainity

Classroom Wing

Very Short Answer Type Questions

1. HH, HT, TH, or TT
2. 1, 2, 3, 4, 5, or 6
3. HT and TH
4. 1
5. 3
6. $\frac{n}{m}$
7. 2
8. 8

Short Answer Type Questions

9. $\frac{343}{500}, \frac{157}{500}$
10. $\frac{1}{7}$
11. $\frac{1}{2}$
12. (A) $\frac{1}{6}$ (B) $\frac{1}{4}$
13. $\frac{63}{100}$

Essay Type Questions

14. $\frac{121}{250}$
15. $\frac{1}{10}$
16. $\frac{38}{75}$
17. $\frac{1}{2}$
18. $\frac{43}{50}$
19. $\frac{3}{14}$

Competition Wing

Level 1: Apply Your Concepts

1. 0 and 1
2. 0
3. (b)
4. (d)
5. (a)
6. (d)
7. (d)
8. (d)
9. (a)
10. (a)
11. (c)
12. (c)

Level 2: Review Your Concepts

13. (c)
14. (a)
15. (b)
16. (a)
17. (d)
18. (b)
19. (c)
20. (c)
21. (c)
22. (b)
23. (a)

Level 3: Assess Your Concepts

24. (b)
25. (b)
26. (c)
27. (a)
28. (c)
29. (a)
30. (a)
31. (a)
32. (b)

JEE Special Wing

Multiple-Answer Type Questions

1. (a, b, c, d)
2. (b, c, d)
3. (a, c, d)
4. (c, d)
5. (a, b)

Match The Column

6. (d)
7. (e)
8. (f)
9. (a)
10. (c)

Comprehension-Based Questions

11. (c)
12. (a)
13. (d)
14. (a)
15. (b)

Assertion and Reason Type Questions

16. (b)
17. (c)
18. (d)
19. (b)
20. (a)

Hints and Explanations

Classroom Wing

Very Short Answer Type Questions

1. Heads = H Tails = T
   {HH, HT, TH, TT}
2. Dice has 6 sides
   {1, 2, 3, 4, 5, 6}
3. Heads = H Tails = T
   {HT, TH}
4. 1
5. Possible outcomes = {1, 2, 3, 4, 5, 6}
   Even number outcomes = {2, 4, 6}
   3
6. We know P (Any event)
   $= \frac{\text{Number of favourable cases for the event to happen}}{\text{Total number of trails.}}$
   $\therefore$ P (E) = $\frac{n}{m}$
7. Probable outcomes when dice is rolled = {1, 2, 3, 4, 5, 6}
   1 is neither prime nor composite
   only 4 and 6 are composite number
   $\therefore$ Only 2
8. P(E) = 20, P(H) = 12, P(T) = ?
   P(E) = P(H) + P(T)
   20 = 12+P(T)
   P(T) = 8

Short Answer Type Questions

9. P(Heads) = $\frac{343}{500}$ P(Tails) = $\frac{157}{500}$
   Because P(Event) =
   $\frac{\text{Number of favorable cases for the event to happen}}{\text{Total number of trails}}$
10. P(E) = {Sunday, Monday, Tuesday, Wednesday, Thursday, Friday, Saturday}
    P(E) = 7
    Probability of the day being Monday is 1.
    $\therefore$ P(M) = $\frac{1}{7}$
11. In a monthly test, 10 students were awarded marks in a mathematics examination as follows: 23, 25, 18, 15, 20, 17, 10, 24, 15, 19.
    Total awarded marks = {23, 25, 15, 15, 20, 17, 10, 24, 15, 19}
    More than 18 marks = {23, 25, 20, 24, 19}
    P(18 <) = 5
    P(E) = $\frac{5}{10} = \frac{1}{2}$
12. (A) In a cricket match, Dhoni hits a six 4 times from 24 balls he plays.
    P(T) = total number of balls = 24
    P(S) = total number of sixes = 4
    P(E) = $\frac{4}{24} = \frac{1}{6}$
    (B) Given set *S* is {1, 3, 6, 9, 15, 20, 16, 18}
    One number can be selected from set '*S*' in 8 ways.
    $n(S) = 8$.
    3 and 9 satisfying the equation $(x - 3)(x - 10)(x - 9) = 0$
    $\therefore$ favourable cases = 2
    $\therefore$ The required probability = $\frac{2}{8} = \frac{1}{4}$.
13. P(T) = 100; P(3H) = 25; P(2H) = 38; P(1H) = 14; P(0H) = 23
    P(E) = $\frac{25}{100} + \frac{38}{100}$
    $= \frac{63}{100}$

Essay Type Questions

14. A dice is rolled 250 times and the outcomes 1, 2, 3, 4, 5 occurred as given in the following table:

Outcome	1	2	3	4	5	6
Frequency	56	78	46	27	19	24

P(1) = 56; P(3) = 46; P(5) = 19; P(T) = 250

P(E) = $\frac{56}{250} + \frac{46}{250} + \frac{19}{250} = \frac{121}{250}$

15. Total number of pages = P(T) = 200

Divisible by 10 = P(10) = {10, 20, 30, 40, 50, 60, 70, 80, 90, 100, 110, 120, 130, 140, 150, 160, 170, 180, 190, 200} = 20

$$P(E) = \frac{20}{200} = \frac{1}{10}$$

16. In a colony there are 75 families and each family has two children. The number of male children of the families is as follows:

Male child	2	1	0
Number of families	27	38	10

only one male child = P(1) = 38

Total number of families = P(T) = 75

$$P(E) = \frac{38}{75}$$

17. The % of marks obtained by a students in a monthly test is as follows:

Test	I	II	III	IV
Marks	78%	63%	82%	65%

Total number of tests = P(T) = 4

Obtained more than 75% = P(75) = {78%, 82%} = 2

$$P(E) = \frac{2}{4} = \frac{1}{2}$$

18. Perfect square between 1 to 50 = {1, 4, 9, 16, 25, 36, 49} = 7

∴ not a perfect square = 50 – 7 = 43

Total number of tickets = 50

$$P(E) = \frac{\text{Not a perfect square}}{\text{Total number of tickets}} = \frac{43}{50}$$

19. The length of the side of the square = 7 cm

∴ Area of the square = 7^2 cm^2

The radius of the circle (r) = $\frac{7}{2}$ cm

Area of the circle = πr^2

$$= \frac{22}{7}\left(\frac{7}{2}\right)^2 = \frac{11(7)}{2}$$

The required probability

$$= \frac{\text{Area of the square} - \text{Area of circle}}{\text{Area of the square}} = \frac{7^2 - \frac{11(7)}{2}}{7^2}$$

$$= \frac{\left[7 - \frac{11}{2}\right]}{7} = \frac{3}{14}$$

Competition Wing

Level 1: Apply Your Concepts

1. 0 and 1

2. 0 because dice has numbers from 1 to 6 hence no number can show up greater than 6.

3. P(March or September)

$$= \frac{2}{\text{Total number of months in a year}}.$$

4. $P(\text{getting a tail}) = \frac{\text{Number of times tail occured}}{\text{Number of times coin tossed}}.$

5. P(getting a prime number)

$$= \frac{\text{Sum of frequences of getting prime numbers}}{\text{Total number of times dice rolled}}.$$

6. P(getting a number which is not a prime)

$$= \frac{\text{Number of numbers which are not prime from 51 to 100}}{\text{Total numbers from 51 to 100}}.$$

7. (i) Probability of selecting a vowel

$$= \frac{\text{Number of vowels}}{\text{Total number of letters}}.$$

(ii) The word contains 3 vowels, *viz.*, O, I, E.

(iii) The total number of letters in the word are 6.

8. P(the attendance of the class more than 75%)

$$= \frac{\text{Number of classes with more than 75\% attendance}}{\text{Total number of classes}}.$$

9. $P(\text{units place is 8}) = \frac{\text{Frequency of 8}}{\text{Sum of frequencies}}.$

10. P(a bag chosen is with > 10 kg rice)

$$= \frac{\text{Number of bags with weight} > 10 \text{ kg}}{\text{Total number of bags}}.$$

11. (i) Total number of three digits numbers = 900. Total number of three digits even numbers = 450.

(ii) The first and the last three digits numbers, which are multiplies of 2 are 100 and 998.

(iii) Count the numbers in the above case.

(iv) The total number of three digits numbers are 900.

(v) Apply the formula to find the required probability.

12. P(choosing a multiple of 3)

$$= \frac{\text{Number of two digit numbers divisible by 3}}{\text{Total number of two digit numbers}}.$$

Level 2: Review Your Concepts

14. (i) Total years = 7

(ii) Favourable years = 3

(iii) In the years 2000–01, 2002–03, and 2003–04, he scored more than 3000 runs.

15. P(a person chosen with no opinion on political lead-ers) $= \frac{\text{Number of persons with no opinion}}{\text{Total number of persons surveyed}}.$

16. (i) Probability of drawing a pencil

$$= \frac{\text{Number of pencils}}{\text{Total number of items in the bag}}.$$

(ii) The bag contains a total of 22 articles.

17. $P(\text{converting into a goal}) = \frac{4}{10} = \frac{2}{5}.$

18. If August starts with Tuesday it will have 5 Tuesdays out of 31 days.

$\therefore P(\text{not a Tuesday}) = \frac{26}{31}.$

19. $P(\text{batsman getting out}) = \frac{3}{27} = \frac{1}{9}.$

$\therefore P(\text{batsman not getting out}) = 1 - \frac{1}{9} = \frac{8}{9}.$

20. $P(\text{Monday}) = \frac{5}{30} = \frac{1}{6}.$

21. Required Probability = Probability (it being January) + Probability (it being June)

$$= \frac{1}{12} + \frac{1}{12} = \frac{1}{6}.$$

22. The two-digit multiples of 7 are 14, 21, 28, ..., 98.

Number of such numbers = 14 – 1 = 13. (first 14 mul-tiplies except 7)

There are 90 two digits numbers.

$\therefore$ Required probability $= \frac{13}{90}.$

23. Required probability = Probability (resident liking only tea) + probability (resident liking only coffee)

$$= \frac{350}{900} + \frac{250}{900} = \frac{600}{900} = \frac{2}{3}.$$

Level 3: Assess Your Concepts

24. (i) On a non-leap year, every day repeats 52 times with one day left.

(ii) A non-leap year has 365 days, i.e., (52 weeks + 1 day).

(iii) The extra one day should be Monday.

25. Let the numbers on the dice be a and b, a, $b \le 6$.

If $a + b$ was a two digits prime number, it must be 11.

In this case, $(a, b) = (5, 6)$ or $(6, 5)$

$\therefore$ Required probability $= 2\left(\frac{1}{6}\right)\left(\frac{1}{6}\right) = \frac{1}{18}$.

26. Let the frequency of all heads be y.

$\frac{x}{800} = 3\left(\frac{y}{800}\right)$, i.e., $x = 3y$ (1)

$120 + 280 + x + y = 800$, i.e., $x + y = 400$

From Eq. (1) $\Rightarrow x + \frac{x}{3} = 400$

$x = 300$.

27. In the solution of Question 27, $1 \le a$, $b \le 6$.

$2 \le a + b \le 12$.

If $a + b$ was a perfect cube, $a + b$ must be 8.

$\therefore$ $(a, b) = (2, 6)$ or $(3, 5)$ or $(5, 3)$ or $(4, 4)$ or $(6, 2)$.

$\therefore$ Required probability $= 5\left(\frac{1}{6}\right)\left(\frac{1}{6}\right) = \frac{5}{36}$.

28. Let the number be xyz.

If x, y, and z are consecutive integers in descending order, $xyz = 987$ or 876 or 765 or 654 or 543 or 432 or 321 or 210.

Required probability $= \frac{8}{900} = \frac{2}{225}$.

29. The vowels are A, E, I, O, and U. In x, the positions of A, E, I, O, and U are 1, 5, 9, 15 and 21, respectively. A total of 13 odd positions are present in x, of which 5 are occupied by vowels.

$\therefore$ Required probability $= \frac{5}{13}$.

30. There are 2 red balls and 3 green balls. The number of possible outcomes $= 2 + 3 = 5$.

The total number of cases $= 2 + 3 + 4 = 9$

The required probability $= \frac{5}{9}$.

31. A non-leap year has 365 days, i.e., 52 weeks and 1 day. In the first 52 weeks of that year, there will be 52 Sundays. The 1st day of the 53rd week would be the last day of that year. The day of the week on this day would be the same as the day of the week on the 1st day of that year. If the first day of a non-leap year is a Sunday, that year will have 53 Sundays. Otherwise it will have 52 Sundays.

Required probability (first day of a week being a Sunday) $= \frac{1}{7}$.

32. Let the number be x, $100 \le x \le 999$. (There are 900 three digits numbers)

A number divisible by both 2 and 3 must be divisible by the LCM of $(2, 3) = 6$.

Least value of x divisible by $6 = 102 = 6(17)$

Greatest value of x divisible by $6 = 996 = 6(166)$

There are 150 values of x divisible by 6.

Required probability $= \frac{150}{900} = \frac{1}{6}$.

JEE Special Wing

Multiple-Answer Type Questions

1. Three coins are tossed for 100 times. The results are as follows.

Event	Three heads = No tails	Two heads = One tail	One head = Two tails	No heads = Three tails	Total
No. of times	28	24	26	100 – 78 = 22	100

(a) If three coins are tossed, the probability of getting three tails is $\frac{22}{100} = \frac{11}{50}$.

(b) If three coins are tossed, the probability of getting two tails is $\frac{26}{100} = \frac{13}{50}$.

(c) If three coins are tossed, the probability of getting one tail is $\frac{24}{100} = \frac{6}{25}$.

(d) If three coins are tossed, the probability of getting no tails is $\frac{28}{100} = \frac{7}{25}$.

Hence, choice (a), choice (b), choice (c) and choice (d) follow.

2. A dice is rolled for 140 times. The results are as follows.

Score	1	2	3	4	5	6
Occurrences	x	$\frac{x}{2}$	$\frac{x}{3}$	$\frac{x}{4}$	$\frac{x}{6}$	$\frac{x}{12}$

$$x + \frac{x}{2} + \frac{x}{3} + \frac{x}{4} + \frac{x}{6} + \frac{x}{12} = 140$$

$$\frac{12x + 6x + 4x + 3x + 2x + x}{12} = 140$$

$$\frac{28x}{12} = 140$$

$$x = 60.$$

Now the results are as follows.

Score	1	2	3	4	5	6
Occurrences	60	30	20	15	10	5

(a) If a dice is rolled, the probability of getting a number which is neither prime nor composite is $\frac{60}{140} = \frac{3}{7}$.

(b) Events which are prime are 2, 3, and 5.
If a dice is rolled, the probability of getting a number which is a prime is $\frac{30 + 20 + 10}{140} = \frac{3}{7}$.

(c) Events which are composite are 4 and 6.
If a dice is rolled, the probability of getting a number which is a composite is $\frac{20}{140} = \frac{1}{7}$.

(d) Events which are perfect squares are 1 and 4.
If a dice is rolled, the probability of getting a number which is a perfect square is $\frac{60 + 15}{140} = \frac{75}{140} = \frac{15}{28}$.

Hence, choice (b), choice (c) and choice (d) follow.

3. A bag consists of different colours of balls. The details are as follows:

Colour	Azure	Coral	Lavender	Olive	Total
No. of balls	75	85	95	105	360

(a) If a ball is selected at random, the probability of getting a ball which is neither Azure nor Coral is $\frac{360 - 75 - 85}{360} = \frac{200}{360} = \frac{5}{9}$.

(b) If a ball is selected at random, the probability of getting a ball which is either Lavender or Coral is $\frac{95 + 85}{360} = \frac{180}{360} = \frac{1}{2}$.

(c) If a ball is selected at random, the probability of getting an Azure coloured ball is $\frac{75}{360} = \frac{5}{24}$.

(d) If a ball is selected at random, the probability of getting a ball which is not Olive is $\frac{360 - 105}{360} = \frac{255}{360} = \frac{17}{24}$.

Hence, choice (a), choice (c) and choice (d) follow.

4. In an apartment, there are 150 flats where each flat is occupied by a family. The following table shows the number of family members in each family.

No. of Family Members	2	3	4	5	6	Total
No. of flats	10	20	30	40	50	150

(a) If a flat is selected at random, the probability of getting a family which consists of even number of members (2 or4 or 6) is $\frac{10+30+50}{150} = \frac{90}{150} = \frac{3}{5}$.

(b) If a flat is selected at random, the probability of getting a family which consists of odd number of members (3 or 5) is $\frac{20+40}{150} = \frac{60}{150} = \frac{2}{5}$.

(c) If a flat is selected at random, the probability of getting a family which consists of more than 3 members (4 or 5 or 6) is $\frac{30+40+50}{150} = \frac{120}{150} = \frac{4}{5}$.

(d) If a flat is selected at random, the probability of getting a family which consists not more than 3 (2 or 3)is $\frac{10+20}{150} = \frac{30}{150} = \frac{1}{5}$.

Hence, choice (c) and choice (d) follow.

5. An unbiased dice is rolled.

(a) Odd numbers: 1, 3, 5

Even numbers: 2, 4, 6

The probability of getting an odd number $= \frac{3}{6} = \frac{1}{2}$.

The probability of getting an even number $= \frac{3}{6} = \frac{1}{2}$.

So, the probability of getting an odd number is equal to that of getting an even number. So, (b) is true.

(b) Composite numbers: 4, 6

Prime numbers: 2, 3, 5

The probability of getting a composite number $= \frac{2}{6} = \frac{1}{3}$.

The probability of getting a prime number $= \frac{3}{6} = \frac{1}{2}$.

So, the probability of getting a composite number is less than that of getting a prime number. So, (b) is true.

(c) The number which has only one factor is 1.

So, the probability of getting a number which has only one factor is $= \frac{1}{6}$.

So, (c) is false.

(d) A dice is rolled.

(a) Perfect squares: 1, 4

Perfect cubes: 1

The probability of getting a perfect square $= \frac{2}{6} = \frac{1}{3}$.

The probability of getting a perfect cube $= \frac{1}{6}$.

So, the probability of getting a perfect square is more than that of getting a perfect cube. So, (d) is false.

Hence, choice (a) and choice (b) follow.

Match The Column

Common Solutions for questions 6 to 10:

Stages	Age (in years)	No. of Persons
Infancy	0 – 2	100
Childhood	3 – 12	120
Adolescence	13 – 19	180
Adulthood	20 – 40	250
Middle Age	41 – 60	200
Old Age	60 above	150
Total		1000

If a person is selected at random, the probability getting required event is x.

6. The number of persons of age more than 40 years $= 200 + 150 = 350$.

The probability of a person of age more than 40 years $= \frac{350}{1000} = \frac{7}{20}$.

Hence, the correct option is (d).

7. The number of persons of age less than 20 years $= 100 + 120 + 180 = 400$.

The probability of a person of age less than 20 years $= \frac{400}{1000} = \frac{2}{5}$.

Hence, the correct option is (e).

8. The number of persons who are not in adulthood $= 1000 - 250 = 750$.

The probability getting a person who is not in adulthood $= \frac{750}{1000} = \frac{3}{4}$.

Hence, the correct option is (f).

9. The number of persons who are in old age = 150.
The probability getting a person who is in old age $= \frac{150}{1000} = \frac{3}{20}$.
Hence, the correct option is (a).

10. The number of persons who belongs to childhood or adolescence = 120 + 180 = 300.
The probability getting a person who belongs to childhood or adolescence $= \frac{300}{1000} = \frac{3}{10}$.
Hence, the correct option is (c).

Comprehension-Based Questions

Common Solutions for questions 11 to 15:

A year 2000 is a leap year and the year started with Saturday. An employee availed leave on all the Saturdays and Sundays in addition to 9 festival days which do not fell either on Saturday or Sunday.

Every leap year has 366 days, that is 52 weeks + 2 days.

As the year started with Saturday, the year consists of 52 Mondays, 52 Tuesdays, 52 Wednesdays, 52 Thursdays, 52 Fridays, 53 Saturdays and 53 Sundays.

11. The probability of getting a day which occurs exactly 52 times in the year $= \frac{5}{7}$.
Hence, the correct option is (c).

12. The number of leaves that he availed in the year 2000 is 53 + 53 + 9 = 115.
The probability of getting a day on which the employee availed leave $= \frac{115}{366}$.
Hence, the correct option is (a).

13. As a month of 31 days is nothing but $7(7\times4)+3$ days, three days of the week repeat five times in the month.
The months which have 31 days are January, March, May, July, August, October, and December that is seven months.
The probability of getting a month in in which three days of the week occur five times $= \frac{7}{12}$.
Hence, the correct option is (d).

14. A month should consist of only 28 days to satisfy the given condition. In a leap year, there are no such months.
The probability of getting a month in which each day of the week occurs only four times $= \frac{0}{12} = 0$.
Hence, the correct option is (a).

15. The given years are 2000, 2001, 2002, 2003, and 2004. Among these years 2000 and 2004 are leap years.
The probability of getting a leap year $= \frac{2}{5}$.
Hence, the correct option is (b).

Assertion and Reason Type Questions

Solutions for questions 16 to 20:

16. **Assertion:** card is selected at random from cards numbered from integers 1 to 100. From 1 to 100, there are 50 even numbers and 50 odd numbers.
The probability of getting an even number $= \frac{50}{100} = \frac{1}{2}$.
So, Assertion is true.
Reason: A number is selected at random from integers,1 to 50.
From 1 to 50, there are 25 even numbers and 25 odd numbers.
The probability of getting an even number $= \frac{25}{50} = \frac{1}{2}$.
Reason is true but not the correct explanation to Assertion.
Hence, the correct option is (b).

17. **Assertion:** In the set of even numbers, there are no numbers which have exactly one factor. So, the required event is an impossible event. Hence, the probability of getting a number which has exactly one factor been 0.
So, Assertion is true.
Reason: The probability of getting an impossible event is 0.
So, Reason is false.
Hence, the correct option is (c).

18. **Assertion:** In a school the number of boys, girls, teachers and non-teaching staff (including principal and vice principal) are 175, 200, 75 and 50 respectively. If a person is selected at random, the probabilty of a teacher getting selected is $\frac{75}{500} = \frac{3}{20}$.
So, Assertion is false.
Reason: In an experiment, the probability occurrence of an event is $\frac{\text{The number of favourable cases to the desired event}}{\text{The total number of cases}}$.
Reason is true.
Hence, the correct option is (d).

19. **Assertion:** The composite numbers in the set of the first ten natural numbers are 4, 6, 8, 9, and 10.

The probability of getting a composite number is $\frac{5}{10} = \frac{1}{2}$.

So, Assertion is true.

Reason: The even numbers in the set of the first ten natural numbers are 2, 4, 6, 8, and 10.

The probability of getting an even number is $\frac{5}{10} = \frac{1}{2}$.

The odd numbers in the set of the first ten natural numbers are 1, 3, 5, 7, and 9.

The probability of getting an odd number is $\frac{5}{10} = \frac{1}{2}$.

So, Reason is true but not the correct explanation to Assertion.

Hence, the correct option is (b).

20. **Assertion:** In a calendar year, the months which have exactly 30 days are April, June, September, and November.

The probability of that the month consists of exactly 30 days is $\frac{4}{12} = \frac{1}{3}$.

So, Assertion is true.

Reason: In an experiment, the probability of occurrence of an event is $\frac{\text{The number of favourable cases to the desired event}}{\text{The total number of cases}}$.

Reason is true and is the correct explanation to Assertion.

Hence, the correct option is (a).